About The
Gardens

Welcome to The Y
to the nearly 3,80
just waiting to be

The National Gardens Scheme has been opening gardens to raise money for nursing and caring charities since 1927. So by visiting an NGS garden this year you will be following in a great British tradition and making a vital contribution to the charities the NGS supports.

Funds are donated to our beneficiaries annually. How much we are able to give away is driven by the number of visitors that go to the gardens. So by visiting a garden that opens on behalf of the National Gardens Scheme you can really make a difference and help raise much needed money.

Thanks to the generosity and hard work of garden owners, volunteers and visitors, in 2013 the NGS gave away £2.2 million to our beneficiaries. You can find out more about them on Page 7.

Most of the gardens that open for the National Gardens Scheme are privately owned and offer visitors a unique opportunity to enjoy the garden owners' individual creations. The variety is breathtaking: from village openings to roof gardens; tiny cottage gardens to rolling acres; allotments to barges; you will find gardens to inform and inspire. Your donation, as well as the tea you drink, the cake you eat and the plants you buy, will make a real difference to the life of someone who needs care or support at a critical time in their life.

Enjoy your garden visiting in 2014.

Thank you.
Your visit to a garden really counts.

Image: Bluebell Cottage Gardens, Cheshire, by Joe Wainwright

Volunteering and community activity are increasingly relevant and important parts of life in Britain. As Patron of the National Gardens Scheme, I am constantly struck by the outstanding model that the Scheme provides for such forms of selfless service, and how they lie at the heart of the National Gardens Scheme's continuing health and success.

During 2012, when the weather conspired against garden-opening at almost every turn, National Gardens Scheme volunteers and garden owners did not flinch and visitors turned out against the odds. In 2013, when the weather was far more generous, they celebrated by producing the most successful year ever, enabling the Scheme to announce record donations to beneficiary charities.

There could be no better example of volunteer commitment than Penny Snell, who will stand down as the National Gardens Scheme's Chairman later this year. She first joined the National Gardens Scheme in 1980 as the county organizer for London, which she continues to manage, and she has devoted a large part of her life to the Scheme. I am sure that in her last few months as Chairman she will lead the National Gardens Scheme through a happy and successful season, and I would like to thank all those who give their time so generously to this important project which has resulted in yet another year of outstanding donations to very worthy causes.

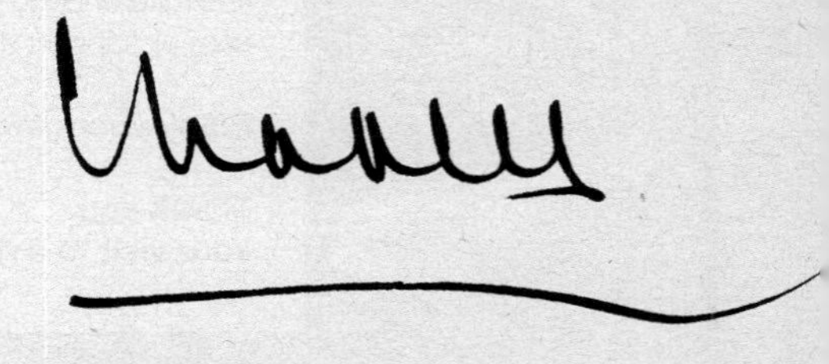

Contents

ngs gardens open for charity

The National Gardens Scheme
A company limited by guarantee. Registered in England & Wales.
Charity No. 1112664. Company No. 5631421

Registered & Head Office: Hatchlands Park, East Clandon, Guildford, Surrey, GU4 7RT

T 01483 211535
Web www.ngs.org.uk

Published by Constable, an imprint of Constable & Robinson Ltd, 55-56 Russell Square, London WC1B 4HP
CONSTABLE
Independent Thinking Since 1895
www.constablerobinson.com

Front cover image: Legsheath Farm, East Sussex
Photographer: Leigh Clapp

Who's who in the National Gardens Scheme

Image: Shorelands Wildlife Gardens, Norfolk

Chairman's Message

2013 was a special year for The National Gardens Scheme in many ways. In June we launched our first ever Festival Weekend. In spite of rather dismal weather in some regions, the festival was a great success gaining as it did extensive new publicity for the NGS and raising awareness of our charitable status. £420,000 was raised in one weekend, an amazing result on a weekend when the sun didn't do much to help us.

Following the Festival, summer arrived bringing out record numbers of visitors to see the gardens. Nothing is more disappointing for owners who work so hard to make their gardens perfect for The Day than having a cold wet day – although many of you intrepid gardeners do still visit whatever the weather. As always we are enormously grateful to our owners for sharing their gardens, helping us raise a record sum for the charities we support, warmly welcoming visitors and often providing teas.

More good news is that Joe Swift has agreed to be our President for a further three years. Joe's commitment and energetic support is enormously valuable to us and I would like to take this opportunity to thank him.

This year there are some 600 new gardens opening for the first time and some 300 returning after taking a year or more off. A special message of welcome to our new gardens and a message of 'welcome back' to the others. These 900 contribute to the total of 3800 gardens opening this year in England and Wales. Thank you for buying this book which will guide you to all the gardens you choose to visit. I urge you to keep an eye on our website too – **www.ngs.org.uk** – as last minute extra openings are always posted there.

To you all, our visitors, our volunteer teams, our garden owners and our staff at Hatchlands Park, my personal thanks for helping to make The National Gardens Scheme the success that it is.

Penny Snell

Above: Penny Snell in her garden.
Image: Nicola Stocken Tomkins

Below: Penny Snell and Joe Swift.
Image: Richard Raworth

Our Charitable Heritage

The National Gardens Scheme is one of the most significant charitable funders of nursing and caring in the UK. It was founded in 1927 by the Queen's Nursing Institute to raise funds to support district nurses, for whom the QNI was responsible until the introduction of the National Health Service in 1948. At that time the Scheme had become so successful and popular that the QNI continued it as an annual fundraising project. In 1980 the QNI created an independent charity with the foundation of the National Gardens Scheme Charitable Trust and this charitable body has continued ever since.

Since our foundation we have donated over £40 million to nominated beneficiaries (see opposite). Our continuing support means that for all of our beneficiaries we are the largest cumulative donor in their histories; this is the case with our founder the QNI, and with our two largest beneficiaries, Macmillan and Marie Curie.

Above: Joe Swift promoting the 2013 Festival Weekend with Marie Curie nurses. Image: Karen Hatch

The physical and mental health benefits of visiting gardens and, indeed, of actual gardening are very real and form an increasingly significant link between the National Gardens Scheme and its beneficiaries (see page 16). In a sense it is integral to our charitable heritage and the element that we are actively developing in partnership with our beneficiaries.

The Trustees of The National Gardens Scheme regularly review the charity's beneficiary policy and in addition to annual donations to major beneficiaries they oversee other donations. The Elspeth Thompson Bursary Fund is a partnership with the Royal Horticultural Society with the NGS providing the funds and the RHS administering the bursaries.

The NGS continues to support the National Trust's careership scheme for training future head gardeners and currently provides an annual bursary for a trainee at the Garden Museum in London.

Since 2010 a different 'guest' charity has been chosen from recommendations from NGS volunteers for a special donation. In 2013 the decision was taken to extend the period of support for a guest charity from one to two or three years and the current guest charity is Parkinson's UK.

The National Gardens Scheme's commitment to nursing and caring remains constant and we are working increasingly closely with our beneficiaries to maximise the amounts we are able to give and the effect that the funds have. Every visitor to an NGS garden is making an essential contribution to the care of others, in particular care at home and for those with chronic or life-threatening illness.

Our Beneficiaries

WE ARE MACMILLAN. CANCER SUPPORT

The NGS has been a partner of Macmillan Cancer Support since 1985 and is proud to be the charity's largest single donor. Raising in excess of £14.2 million, the NGS has funded over 147 vital Macmillan services for people affected by cancer including; clinical nursing specialists, financial advisors, dieticians, physiotherapists and counsellors, helping Macmillan to ensure that no one has to face cancer alone.

The NGS has supported Marie Curie Cancer Care since 1996, raising a staggering £6 million during this time. This money enables the charity to continue to provide high quality nursing, totally free, to give people with terminal cancer and other illnesses the choice of dying at home, supported by their families.

Help the Hospices

Help the Hospices is the UK's leading charity for hospice care, supporting over 200 hospices. The NGS has supported us since 1996, raising over £2.6 million for hospice care. Over the years, their generous funding has supported a variety of programmes. Help the Hospices also manages the UK edition of ehospice, a global news website and free app that brings you all the latest news on hospice and end of life care. www.ehospice.com/uk.

Carers Trust works to improve support, services and recognition for anyone living with the challenges of caring, unpaid, for a family member or friend who is ill, frail, disabled or has mental health or addiction problems. Ongoing support from the NGS has meant so much to carers over the years, and countless individuals have benefited as a direct result of its donations.

The Queen's Nursing Institute

The Queen's Nursing Institute campaigns for the best possible nursing care for patients in their own homes. Our community of Queen's Nurses leads by example, and we support practical projects in the community to improve patient care. We believe that skilled, professional and dedicated nursing should be available to everyone, where and when they need it.

PERENNIAL
Gardeners' Royal Benevolent Society
Helping Horticulturists In Need Since 1839

Through Perennial, the NGS helps horticulturists who are facing difficulties. The NGS donation is invaluable to the charity's on-going work to help individuals and families. The annual donation to Perennial for gardeners' children also enables on-going support for families when one or both parents have died, and for children who are disadvantaged by other circumstances.

Guest charity

PARKINSON'S UK
CHANGE ATTITUDES.
FIND A CURE.
JOIN US.

Parkinson's UK is the research and support charity for anyone affected by the condition. We are privileged to be the first guest charity to be supported for two years by the NGS, who are helping to fund specialist Parkinson's nurses. Not everyone with Parkinson's in the UK has access to this vital service so, together with the NGS, we're working to ensure that no one faces Parkinson's alone.

In short, every visitor to an NGS garden is helping to make an essential contribution to someone's life, and especially those who really need care or support through times of personal crisis or chronic and life threatening illness. Thank you!

Competition Winners

In 2013 NGS gardens won two of the most prestigious national competitions for gardens. Here their owners tell their gardening stories.

Fran Wakefield from the Tithe Barn in Berkshire – winner of the Gardener's Garden Competition promoted by *The English Garden* magazine

I hadn't intended to become a gardener and knew nothing about the National Gardens Scheme beyond imagining fanatical horticulturists opening their prize plots for charity. How things change.

Seven years ago the period property adjacent to me was demolished along with a boundary line. This resulted in my shady, secluded and partly walled garden being exposed to full view. In order to compensate me, the developer agreed to build me a beautiful wall using period bricks from the bulldozed manor house. The plot was transformed into a sunny walled garden. The possibilities were endless. I was off to the races!

First task was to level the site and then put in the hard landscaping. I knew I wanted a classical walled garden with straight paths and box hedged borders and yew. In my mind I saw it filled with roses, lavender, clematis, delphiniums, hostas and agapanthus – absolutely gorgeous. In addition I wanted to stay in keeping with my house, an eighteenth century converted Tithe Barn. So only reclaimed materials were used. The terrace was laid using York stone and Victorian brick pavers edge up all the paths.

As my garden progressed so too did my enthusiasm. The bug had well and truly bitten. I found myself absorbed with this amazing pastime – being a gardener. One day, head down in the flower beds as usual, I glanced up and saw for the first time the beauty of my garden. It occurred to me that, just maybe, it might be good enough for acceptance in the Yellow Book – the holy grail for gardeners. The thought was thrilling. When subsequently Heather Skinner, the NGS County Organiser paid me a visit, I thought that with a bit of luck I might join with other local gardens to share an open day. So imagine my delight when she suggested that my garden should open on its own. I admit I was a little bit scared.

What had I let myself in for? If I was off to the races before I was now in the starting stalls ready to actually take part in the race.

Having spent all my time developing the walled garden at the back of my house I was now forced to cast a critical eye over the front; I decided I could not possibly welcome fellow gardeners through my gates without giving it some serious attention. To say I was frazzled when I opened on June 6th would be an understatement but the joy I had from sharing my garden with fellow enthusiasts was something I had not imagined. It was beautiful sunny weather and the one hundred and twenty visitors made it one of the most enjoyable days I have had. It is always good to receive compliments for all your efforts but to be able to it to raise money for good causes makes it so much more worthwhile.

My garden continues to develop and improve as does my passion for it. I have to admit that during the winter months I look out and wonder where will I find the enthusiasm for the next season but I only have to see a snowdrop peeping through and it all comes flooding back.

This year Heather contacted me to let me know that *The English Garden* magazine were launching the 'Gardener's Garden' Competition, generously sponsored by Henton & Chattell. The magazine is a favourite read of mine so I didn't need much persuasion to enter. After a fairly long wait, which convinced me I was not in the running, imagine my delight to get a phone call telling me I was in the final three. Another seemingly long wait had me busy in the garden keeping it in tip top condition and fretting about the heat wave – wonderful to enjoy but not always great for the garden. I finally got the phone call I had been hoping for – I had won. Not only had I won but the prize was my choice of garden machinery worth £1000. The leaf blower and hedge cutter will make my work this autumn a lot easier and my choice of a lawn scarifier will put me back on the starting blocks next spring. I absolutely can't wait.

Left: Fran Wakefield in the garden she has created at Tithe Barn. Image: Nicola Stocken Tomkins.

Below: A view of immaculate borders, lawn and clipped hedges that typifies the garden. Image: Nicola Stocken Tomkins.

John and Corinnne Layton from One Brook Hall Cottages, Essex – winners of the Daily Mail's National Garden Competition

Our garden is bordered by farmland and situated between the rivers Blackwater and Crouch and the North Sea in a very beautiful and windswept part of the county. It is small, just a quarter of an acre with an improved clay soil with low rainfall. We are motivated by our care and concern for wildlife, my love of growing plants and John's talent for woodwork and building. All of the garden, which is triangular, lies behind the cottage and is sheltered by native hedges. The garden can be described as a contemporary cottage garden and is managed without the use of chemicals. We grow from seed and cuttings many nectar rich plants which are grown in a naturalistic style – a sort of organised wildness. I am very particular about colour, preferring subtle combinations of purple, black and grey, taking into account texture and form.

Our friends sent us details of the competition – we were not really sure and we missed the original closing date for entries. They were very disappointed, but as the closing date had been delayed because of the late spring we sent off our entry. The competition rules required photographs and a plan of the garden and a couple of weeks later we were informed that from over 2,000 entries our garden had been included in the last 11.

Two charming judges came to look at the garden on a beautiful day in early July. I walked around with them discussing various aspects of the design and planting. Everything was very late because of the cold spring but this helped in some ways because it showed off the structure and shape of the garden. I remarked to John when he came home from work that I was very pleased with their comments – they really did seem to enjoy being in the garden.

The last four gardens were chosen and an article with photographs of four finalists was published. The gardens were very different but all lovely – ours was described as a 'subtle organic masterpiece.'

In August we were visited for a second time – the two charming judges returned with a third who was a garden designer.

August is one of the months in which we open so we had been having a final push to get the garden ready for our NGS visitors – and praying that the agapanthus and dahlias would finally open! The visit went well, they asked me questions and made comments on the parts of the garden they thought interesting, appealing and worth copying!

We were thrilled to win, received a blue plaque and we were pictured in the garden supplement in our 'stunning Essex garden'.

Next year will be our 7th year in the National Gardens Scheme and we will use some of the £2000 prize money to make a circular route around the garden which we hope our visitors will enjoy.

Left: John and Corinne at One Brook Hall Cottages. Image: Mike Lawn.

Below: A view confirming Corinne and John's combination of planting and ornamental skills. Image: Nicola Stocken Tomkins

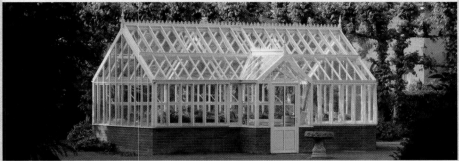

Gardens are **good for you**

George Plumptre, outlines how the NGS is working with its beneficiary partners to champion the benefits of gardens for everyone's health and wellbeing

Above: the (very new) garden of the Marie Curie Hospice in Solihull

At the National Gardens Scheme annual Conference towards the end of last year, Lord Howard of Lympne was one of the guest speakers in his capacity as Chairman of Help the Hospices. He began with a quote from Roger Ulrich's ground-breaking study of 1984, *Health Benefits of Gardens in Hospitals*;

'The fact that there is limited but growing scientific evidence that viewing gardens can measurably reduce patient stress and improve health outcomes has been a key factor in the major resurgence in interest internationally in providing gardens in hospitals and other healthcare facilities.'

The National Gardens Scheme has spent more than eighty years promoting gardens as places to visit, for enjoyment and education and as a means to raise funds for charity. Now, in partnership with our major beneficiary charities, we are working in a variety of ways to emphasise the extent to which just being in gardens, having access whether physical or visual, is of substantial benefit to everyone. A few weeks ago I contributed an article to a special feature for Carers Trust that was published by *The Times* as a supplement with the newspaper, called *The Carer*. In the article I said,

'Carers in particular have a very stressful life looking after perhaps mum, a child or a friend. So if they can get time off to go and sit in a garden we know from first hand that they find this beneficial and recuperative in a way few other things can match.'

As suggested by Michael Howard's earlier quote, our beneficiaries have long realised the benefits of gardens for both hospitals and hospices – indeed for the latter the garden is usually a major priority in the overall design and layout the buildings. Jane Collins, Chief Executive of Marie Curie Cancer Care confirmed this following visits that she made in 2013 to Marie Curie hospices in Liverpool and Belfast;

'In both cities there was sunshine so perhaps for that reason I looked even more closely at the beautiful hospice gardens... Research has shown that the natural environment improves our sense of wellbeing. This applies whether we are patients, families, staff or volunteers. The sight of greenery has been shown to prompt a relaxation response in our brains and spending time in the garden can reduce tension, blood pressure and help us manage stress. So our gardens at Marie Curie are important for literally all of us.'

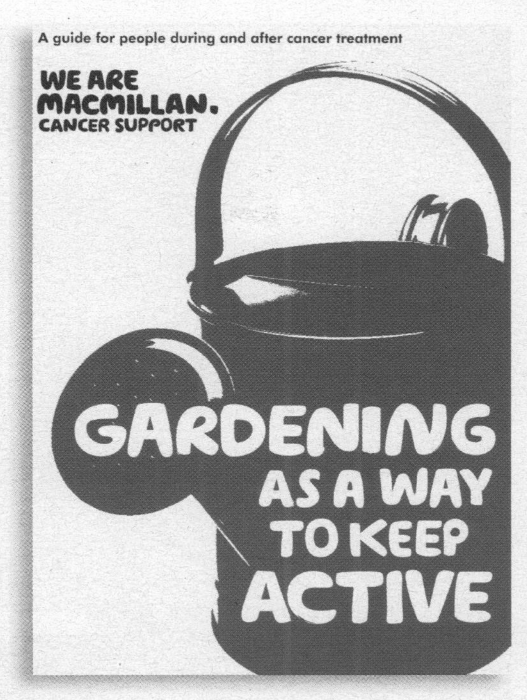

A guide for people during and after cancer treatment
WE ARE
MACMILLAN.
CANCER SUPPORT
GARDENING
AS A WAY
TO KEEP
ACTIVE

Above: The front cover of a joint Macmillan/NGS Leaflet

Left: Jane Cummings, Chief Nursing Officer for England, addressing the NGS 2013 Conference.
Image: Karen Hatch

But beyond the care of hospitals and hospices and the healing, restorative benefits which gardens add to their environments, we all increasingly appreciate the degree to which gardens per se are a major and vital source of sustenance and revival for people's health and wellbeing generally. There will not be a single person amongst the thousands opening their gardens in support of the NGS this year who would not agree that being in their garden, whether working or relaxing, makes them feel better.

Since 2012 we have developed an exciting partnership with Macmillan Cancer Support, actively contributing to their landmark work in promoting the considerable benefits to cancer sufferers of physical exercise, being in gardens and active gardening; especially for those who have survived cancer.

Above: Gardens are places for contemplation and restoration

Ciaran Devane, Chief Executive of Macmillan summed the partnership up when he said,

'Over the last few years our partnership has developed to include more strategic elements including contributing to Macmillan's cancer toolkit for schools and our Physical Activity project through the Move More campaign. We've continued this campaign by developing a 'Gardening for Health' leaflet and exercise DVD in conjunction with the NGS, both of which illustrate the health benefits of gardening in treatment, wellbeing and survivorship.'

With our unrivalled community of gardeners and their dazzling array of gardens large and small all over the country, we are in a unique position to take the lead in efforts to get the message across that 'Gardens are good for you.' As a substantial funder to our group of nursing caring charities, we make a major annual contribution to each of them as highlighted by Jane Cummings, the Chief Nursing Officer for England, when she also addressed the NGS 2013 Conference;

'I have greatly enjoyed meeting so many people who are actively involved in supporting so many charities in their work to provide excellent nursing care to patients across the country.'

Equally important, this gives us the basis for leading a partnership with all our beneficiary charities to demonstrate the myriad ways that gardens are good for you and as a result to make a growing contribution to public and individual health and wellbeing.

Festival Weekend 2014

Last year the NGS launched the first Festival Weekend, on 15-16 June. The aim was to create a focus in the year's calendar of garden openings when the NGS would follow the pattern of many charities and have an annual 'hurrah' to attract extra publicity and raise awareness of its activities.

In particular, this meant aspiring to raise awareness of the charitable activities, how much money is raised annually at NGS garden openings and where the money goes. People are amazed when they hear that an organisation whose core activity is opening gardens to visitors is one of the largest charitable funders of nursing and caring in England and Wales, having donated a total of over £40 million to its major beneficiaries who receive annual donations.

The concept of the Festival Weekend got fantastic support in the media and this alone was one of the key objectives. Anneka Rice and Clare Balding both encouraged people to take part in the Festival on their early morning weekend Radio 2 programmes and Anneka went the extra mile, taking to a helicopter generously donated and piloted by Jono Baker and dropped in to visit five different gardens around the country. The garden belonging to Formula One legend, Frank Williams, was featured on BBC Gardener's World on the Friday evening and up and down the country local press and radio came out in support of the event.

A clear sign of increased activity was the fact that the NGS website was strained throughout the two days by enormous extra quantities of traffic. Similarly, social media activity promoting and discussing the NGS and specific garden openings mushroomed to an all-time record.

The weekend also proved a huge success in activating the NGS's partnership with its beneficiary charities. All of them gave the Festival amazing support in the lead-up to the weekend and then turned out in numbers to visit themselves and get first-hand experience of how our annual donations are raised by hard working garden owners.

Top: Anneka Rice and friends at the 2013 Festival Weekend. Image: Fred Fratter

Above: A suitably festive NGS tea. Image: Karen Hatch

So not surprisingly we are going to repeat the Festival Weekend in 2014, on 7 and 8 June. We know that our loyal audience of keen gardening visitors will come out in support as they always do, but we hope to build on last year's effort to widen awareness of the NGS and its gardens so that we continue to attract new visitors.

So we look forward to seeing you join in the Festival Weekend celebrations and helping to boost the amounts of money we are able to raise and donate to our beneficiaries in nursing and caring.

Festival
Weekend
7– 8 June 2014
ngs
gardens open
for charity
Take part in our
Festival Weekend

On 7-8 June 2014 hundreds of gardens up and down the country will be welcoming visitors to help increase the amounts raised by the NGS for charity

To find gardens open near you, visit **www.ngs.org.uk** or look out for the yellow arrows.

Yellow Book on the Move

Find details of nearly 3,800 gardens to visit with our free iOS and Android apps

The app features these shiny features:

- See what's on and share garden opening details with friends via Facebook and Twitter
- Search for and find nearly 3,800 NGS gardens close to your current location or postcode
- View galleries of spectacular images of these gardens
- Latest opening times, prices, contact details and directions
- Save your favourite places – where you've been and where you'd like to go
- Send your friends email invites to visit gardens with you
- Sign up to receive weekly suggestions of gardens to visit

Our mobile app is suitable for iPhone, iPod Touch, iPad, and Android devices. Requires iOS 4.0 or later. Screen shot representative of product.

To find out more scan the QR Code.

Also follow The National Gardens Scheme on Twitter  and Facebook 

Our supporters

We are very grateful for the ongoing partnerships we will have in 2014 with Griffin Glasshouses, Dobies of Devon, Woodmansterne Cards and Brightwater Holidays. All four offer items for sale from the proceeds of which they donate a percentage to the NGS.

Griffin Glasshouses

Griffin Glasshouses is proud to support The National Gardens Scheme as its partner. Griffin Glasshouses creates beautiful bespoke glasshouses, greenhouses and orangeries for discerning gardeners, featuring The National Gardens Scheme (NGS) Collection. This exclusive collection includes five popular designs which can be personalised with a range of accessories and finished in any colour. Griffin's glasshouses are individually designed to be perfect for you, offering many gardener-friendly features, virtually no maintenance and with a lifetime structural guarantee.

Dobies of Devon

New for 2014 – discover the NGS Online Garden Centre! Find all the best value seeds, plants and gardening equipment in one convenient website, whilst raising valuable funds for the charities the NGS supports. Plus, don't forget to claim your £2 off any NGS plant collection today at www.ngsdobies.co.uk.

Dobies of Devon, alongside our customers, are proud to support The National Gardens Scheme by raising funds through our gardening catalogues and the new NGS Online Garden Centre, and hope to do so for many years to come.

Buy a Woodmansterne greeting card and spread the word

Woodmansterne's greeting cards have been bringing awareness of the NGS brand to the High Street since 2006 and helping to contribute to the wonderful work of the charities the NGS supports.

Look out for the ever-changing photography being added every year (around 25 designs across different shapes and sizes this year alone). Ever popular are favourite themes such as making fun in the garden, relaxing, admiring flowers and cheeky garden animals. A range of small square cards are the latest innovation.

Cards are available from all good independent card and gift shops, garden centres and WHSmith, Waitrose, and John Lewis.

Woodmansterne

Top-notch British greeting cards for thoughts that count

Quality Garden Tours

Brightwater Holidays are delighted to continue partnering with the National Gardens Scheme to offer exclusive holidays based on stunning NGS gardens. For each place booked on these tours Brightwater Holidays will make a donation from the total booking cost to the NGS.

In 2014 we have four wonderful garden tours especially created with the help of the NGS county organisers to ensure that our short holidays visit the most interesting gardens in their respective areas.

Experienced tour leaders will lead the four tours in 2014 to Somerset's Secret Gardens – 27 June, High Summer in Hampshire – 11 July, Historic Gardens of Norfolk and Cambridgeshire – 4 September and a special tour for The NGS Festival Weekend – 6 June.

For full details contact Brightwater Holidays 01334 657155 or ngs@brightwaterholidays.com

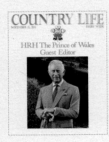

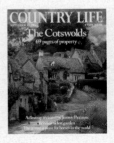

How to use your Yellow Book

This book lists all gardens opening for the NGS between January 2014 and early 2015. It is divided up into county sections, each including a calendar of opening dates and details of each garden, listed alphabetically.

There are three simple ways to find gardens to visit:

1 **If you are looking for a specific garden**, you can look it up in the index at the back, or if you know which county it is in, you can go straight to the relevant county section.

2 **If you want to find out more about gardens near you or in a specific location**, go to the relevant county map (at the front of each section) and look for the numbered markers. Use those numbers to look up further information in the county listings.

3 **If you are looking to see what is open near you on a specific date**, go straight to the relevant county. There is a calendar of opening dates after each county map.

Images and longer descriptions of the 3,800 gardens that will open this year on behalf of the National Gardens Scheme can be found by visiting: **www.ngs.org.uk**

County name
Gardens in England are listed first, followed by gardens in Wales.

Group opening information
Showing gardens that open together on the same day or days.

Description
A short description of each garden covers the main features. This is written by the garden owner.

Directions
A simple set of directions to each garden. Most gardens also list postcodes for use with computer or satellite navigation systems.

Admission price
The admission price applies to all visitors unless exceptions are noted e.g. child free.

364 LONDON

GROUP OPENING

ELM COURT GARDENS, EN4
Oakhurst Avenue, East Barnet EN4 8HA, 020 8361 2642. *200 yds from Oakleigh Pk Stn on rail line to Welwyn Garden City. M25 J24, then A111 to Cockfosters & A110 down Cat Hill to East Barnet Village.* Home-made teas. **Combined adm £4.50, chd free.** Sun 13 July (2-6).

3 ELM COURT
Mike & Alyne Lidgley
Visitors also welcome by appt July to Aug. No min, max 20 visitors.
020 8361 2642

4 ELM COURT
Simon Moor & Jayne Evans

Many contrasts in these two quite different gardens, both larger than average. Front gardens - one a formal parterre, one natural, with gravel, grasses, conifers and reclaimed materials. Back gardens: one with hot annuals, perennials, shrubs, hanging baskets, water feature, two topiary beds, pink, blue, 'spiky' and heuchera beds, a 'ball' bed, greenhouse, garden and potting sheds, 2 rockeries, alpine troughs, and much more. The other is long and shady, with curving lawns, a gravel area with containers full of colour, a white bed, a rockery and the whole emphasis is on attracting pollinators - blue, pink, purple and yellow shrubs and perennials. Jayne is a successful artist and has her studio in the garden. A developing garden, still evolving and hungrily devouring cuttings, contributions and advice from all sources and gradually triumphing over poor soil, overhanging trees and lack of water. Plant crèche: plants purchased delivered locally after the event, free of charge. Raffle. 3 Elm Court featured in Garden News.

ELM TREE COTTAGE
85 Croham Road, South Croydon CR2 7HJ. Wendy Witherick & Michael Wilkinson, 020 8681 8622, elmtreecottage@sky.com. *2m S of Croydon. Off B275 from Croydon, off A2022 from Selsdon, bus 64. Station: East or South Croydon.* **Adm £3, chd free.** Sun 4 May, Sun 15 June, Sun 10 Aug (1-4). **Visitors also welcome by appt May to Sept.**
Picture this! Come through the gate of our c1855 flint cottage and welcome to the Mediterranean! Meander up the sloping brick path to the sound of running water, see lemon trees, olives, palms and other drought-tolerant plants. Look inside the glasshouse and you will find agaves, cacti and succulents. Rest before you carry on your journey, past lavender, rosemary and much much more! Steep garden, unsuitable for those unsteady on their feet. Regret no dogs or children.

S

11 ERNLE ROAD, SW20
Wimbledon, London SW20 0HH. Theresa-Mary Morton. *¼ m from Wimbledon Village, 200yds from Crooked Billet PH. Exit A3 at A238 to Wimbledon, turning L at Copse Hill. Mainline: Wimbledon or Raynes Park. Tube: Wimbledon; Bus: 200 to Christchurch then 100yds walk.* Home-made teas. **Adm £3.50, chd free.** Sat 3, Sun 4 May (2.30-6). **Also open 9a Calonne Road, Sun 4 May.**
Established suburban garden of ¼ acre on sandy acid soil, spatially organised into separate sections: oak pergola framing the main vista, hidden parterre, woodland, pool, winter iris border, flower garden and summerhouse. Featured in Country Life. Beaten gravel paths, one step up to main garden.

48 ERSKINE HILL, NW11
Hampstead Garden Suburb, London NW11 6HG. Marjorie & David Harris, 020 8455 6507. *1m N of Golders Green. Nr A406 & A1. Tube: Golders Green. H2 Hail & Ride bus from Golders Green to garden, or 82, 460, 102 buses to Temple Fortune (10 mins walk).* Light refreshments. **Adm £3.50, chd free.** Sun 8 June (2-6). **Visitors also welcome by appt May to Sept.**
Bird-friendly garden, wrapped around Arts and Crafts artisan's cottage, featuring perennials, shrubs, roses, clematis, old apple tree and flowering cherry. Terrace with well-planted containers. Intriguing brick-paved area with four raised beds. Greenhouse. London Gardens Society 'highly recommended back garden' visited by LGS patron, HRH Prince Edward, June 2013. Nest boxes, miniature long grass areas, organic and pesticide-free. Featured in Ham & High (Royal visit) and Suburb News. Some single steps and narrow paths. Rail to lawn.

65 FARM WAY
Worcester Park KT4 8SB. Mr & Mrs A Rutherford. *Stn: Worcester Park. Bus: 213.* Cream teas. **Adm £3, chd free.** Sun 29 June (1-5).
Plant lover's 6yr-old garden with wide mixed borders bursting with colour and plants of different textures and interest, incl shrubs, roses and perennials. Assorted pots of vegetables, raised beds. Paving and decking, plenty of seating areas.

◆ FENTON HOUSE, NW3
Hampstead Grove, Hampstead, London NW3 6SP. National Trust, www.nationaltrust.org.uk. *300yds from Hampstead tube. Entrances: Top of Holly Hill & Hampstead Grove.* **For NGS: Tue 8 Apr (6.30-8.30). Pre booking essential for Special Evening Tour, £10 with wine & light refreshments. Please phone 01932 864532. Please note: Payment by cheque only. For other opening times and information, please see garden website.**
Join the Gardener-in-Charge for a special evening tour. Andrew Darragh who brings over 10 yrs' experience from Kew to Fenton House will explore this timeless 1½ -acre walled garden. Laid out over 3 levels, and featuring formal walks and areas, a small sunken rose garden, a 300yr-old orchard and a kitchen garden, Andrew will present the garden and his plans for its future development.

54 FERNDOWN
Northwood Hills HA6 1PH. David Bryson & Ros Preston, 020 8866 3792, davidbryson@sky.com. *Tube: Northwood Hills 5 mins walk. R out of stn, R down Briarwood Dr then 1st R.* Cream teas. **Adm £3, chd free.**

Symbols explained

NEW Gardens opening for the first time this year or re-opening after a long break.

◆ Garden also opens on non-NGS days. (Gardens which carry this symbol contribute to the NGS either by opening on a specific day(s) and/or by giving a guaranteed contribution.)

Wheelchair access to at least the main features of the garden.

Dogs on short leads welcome.

Plants usually for sale.

NCH Plant Heritage National Collection Holder.

Gardens that offer accommodation.

Refreshments are available, normally at a charge.

D Garden designed by a Fellow, Member or Pre-registered Member of The Society of Garden Designers.

Garden accessible to coaches. Coach sizes vary so please contact garden owner or County Organiser in advance to check details.

Group Visits Group Organisers may contact the County Organiser or a garden owner direct to organise a group visit to a particular county or garden. See the end of each county section for County Organiser contact details, or visit www.ngs.org.uk

Children must be accompanied by an adult

Photography is at the discretion of the garden owner; please check first. Photographs must not be used for sale or reproduction without prior permission of the owner.

Share To indicates that a proportion of the money collected will be given to the nominated charity.

Toilets are not usually available at private gardens

If you cannot find the information you require from a garden or County Organiser, call the NGS office on 01483 211535

Geographical area map

The areas shown on this map are specific to the organisation of The National Gardens Scheme. The Gardens of Wales, listed by area, follow the Gardens of England.

Discover wonderful gardens near you

In 2014 there will be nearly 3,800 gardens across England and Wales opening on behalf of The National Gardens Scheme. In the last 10 years the NGS has donated more than £26 million to nursing, caring and gardening charities.

How you can help support the NGS:

Visit a garden – All our gardens offer something special, and with so many uniquely different gardens to visit you could be spoilt for choice. A visit typically offers the chance to meet the garden owner, with tea and home-made cake in lovely surroundings. Go home inspired with ideas and perhaps a plant from the plant stall - then spread the word to your family and friends!

Open your garden – Joe Swift says: 'It's the sense of community, sharing and fun which makes the gardens which open for the NGS so special'. Opening your garden is a rewarding way to share your passion and hard work while raising money for charity. Size is not critical; many NGS gardens are no larger than typical back gardens. Visitors are looking for interesting design, a good range of plants and gardens which have been tended with love and care. Why not talk to our friendly County Volunteers (details at the end of each county)?

Volunteer – **Lend a hand** and join your local team! The NGS is run by volunteers based in each county and over 350 people share the fun and work involved in organising thousands of open garden events. A range of roles is available, so you don't need to be a gardening expert, but should enjoy being part of a team and working with and meeting new people.

Make a donation – support this wonderful tradition by making a donation online at **www.justgiving.com/ngs/donate**

To find out more
or to receive
our newsletter
please visit
www.ngs.org.uk
or phone
01483 211535

Image: Manor Farm, Norfolk, by Val Corbett

BEDFORDSHIRE

Opening Dates

All entries subject to change. For latest information check www.ngs.org.uk

January

Sunday 26
8 King's Arms Garden

March

Sunday 30
14 The Old Vicarage

April

Sunday 27
5 NEW 4 George Street

May

Saturday 3
5 NEW 4 George Street

Sunday 11
4 Flaxbourne Farm

Sunday 25
16 Park End Thatch

Saturday 31
23 NEW Whitsundoles Farm

June

Sunday 1
13 NEW The Old Rectory
17 Southill Park

Saturday 14
2 22 Elmsdale Road
7 The Hyde Walled Garden

Sunday 15
2 22 Elmsdale Road

Friday 20
12 The Manor House, Stevington (Evening)

Saturday 21
1 NEW Dragons Glen

Sunday 22
1 NEW Dragons Glen
11 The Manor House, Barton-le-Clay
16 Park End Thatch
22 Wayside Cottage

Sunday 29
14 The Old Vicarage
15 NEW Old Warden Village Gardens

July

Sunday 13
6 How End Cottage
7 The Hyde Walled Garden
10 Luton Hoo Walled Garden

Saturday 19
21 Walnut Cottage

Sunday 20
21 Walnut Cottage

Sunday 27
9 Luton Hoo Hotel Golf & Spa

August

Sunday 10
20 NEW 1 Tyrells End

Sunday 17
4 Flaxbourne Farm

September

Sunday 14
1 NEW Dragons Glen

Sunday 21
18 Swiss Garden

October

Sunday 26
8 King's Arms Garden

January 2015

Sunday 25
8 King's Arms Garden

Gardens open to the public

8 King's Arms Garden
10 Luton Hoo Walled Garden
12 The Manor House, Stevington

By appointment only

3 The Firs
19 Treize

Also open by appointment

2 22 Elmsdale Road
4 Flaxbourne Farm
5 4 George Street
6 How End Cottage
14 The Old Vicarage
16 Park End Thatch
20 1 Tyrells End
21 Walnut Cottage

The Gardens

1 NEW DRAGONS GLEN

17 Great Lane, Clophill, Bedford MK45 4BQ. Kate Gardner. *Clophill is situated approx midway between Bedford & Luton on the A6.* Home-made teas (June) will be served in St Mary's church as part of the village open gardens weekend. **Adm £3.50, chd free. Sat 21 June (12-6); Sun 22 June (12-5); Sun 14 Sept (2-5.30).**

This contemporary garden takes full advantage of the sloped landscape and dry conditions of its Greensand Ridge location to great effect. Dry woodland, herbaceous borders, waterfall and wildlife pond create distinct spaces that are linked together by the Oriental influences that run throughout the garden. Limited wheelchair access due to the steep slopes and steps around the garden.

2 22 ELMSDALE ROAD

Wootton, Bedford MK43 9JN. Roy & Dianne Richards, 07733 222495, roy.richards60@ntlworld.com. *4m from J13 M1. Join old A421 towards Bedford, follow signs to Wootton. Turn R at The Cock PH follow rd to Elmsdale Rd on R.* Home-made teas. **Adm £3.50, chd free. Sat 14, Sun 15 June (1-5). Visitors also welcome by appt Apr to Sept, groups 8+.**

Topiary garden greets visitors before they enter a genuine Japanese Feng Shui garden incl bonsais, every plant is strictly Japanese, large Koi pond with bamboo bridge and Tea House. The garden was created from scratch by the owners and has many interesting features.

3 THE FIRS

33 Bedford Road, Sandy SG19 1EP. Mr & Mrs D Sutton, 01767 227589, d.sutton7@ntlworld.com. *7m E of Bedford. On B1042 between Sandy town centre & A1. On-road parking.* **Adm £3.50, chd free. Visitors welcome by appt, refreshments can be arranged.**

1/4 -acre town garden with many garden features reflecting the different conditions from full sun to shade. Designed and created from scratch since 2000 this garden is productive in fruit, flowers, vegetables and wildlife. Run organically, this garden has everything from shrubs, trees, alpines, perennials, to water features and railway memorabilia. Some gravel paths.

Oriental influences that run throughout the garden . . .

The Old Vicarage

4 FLAXBOURNE FARM

Salford Road, Aspley Guise MK17 8HZ. Geoff & Davina Barrett, 01908 585329, geoffanddean@gmail.com. *5m W of Ampthill. 1m S of J13 of M1. Turn R in village centre, 1m over railway line.* Home-made teas. **Adm £5, chd free. Suns 11 May; 17 Aug (2-6). Visitors also welcome by appt Apr to Sept.**
Beautiful and entertaining fun garden of 3 acres, lovingly developed with numerous water features, windmill, modern arches and bridges, small moated castle, lily pond, herbaceous borders, Greek temple ruin. Recently established three way bridge, planted up with Japanese acers, tree ferns, echiums, bananas and zinnia creating a tropical full of the Wow Factor! New for 2011 Japanese garden with flyover walkway, inspirational woodland setting. Crow's nest, crocodiles, tree house with zip wire for children. Huge Roman stone arched gateway as featured in ITV's This Morning programme and BBC One Show. An ideal garden for coach tours lasting at least 3 hours, if teas and conducted tour requested. Wheelchair access is available to all the main parts of the garden.

5 NEW 4 GEORGE STREET

Clapham, Bedford MK41 6AZ. Graham Bolton, 07746 864247, bolton_graham@hotmail.com. *3m N of Bedford (not the bypass). Clapham village High St. R into Mount Pleasant Rd then L into George St. 1st white Bungalow on R.* Tea available on request. **Adm £2, chd free. Sun 27 Apr; Sat 3 May (2-5.30). Visitors also welcome by appt Apr to May.**
Alpine lovers can see a wide variety of alpines in two small scree gardens, front and back of bungalow plus pans, tubs with dwarf salix, rhododendron, daphne's. Dwarf acers, conifers, pines, hellebores and epimediums. Two small mixed borders of herbaceous salvias and lavenders potentillas. Two small greenhouses and cold frames with plants for sale. Limited wheelchair access. No access at the rear of property due to narrow gravel paths but garden can be viewed from the patio.

6 HOW END COTTAGE

How End Road, Houghton Conquest MK45 3JT. Jeremy & Gill Smith, 01515 404121, smith201@btinternet.com. *1m N of Ampthill. Turn R 1m from Ampthill off B530 towards Houghton Conquest. How End Rd 300yds on RH-side. Garden at end of rd, approx 1/2 m.* Home-made teas. **Adm £4, chd free. Sun 13 July (2.30-5.30). Visitors also welcome by appt Mar to Sept.**
Approx 1 acre garden with 2 ponds, large vegetable garden, greenhouse and orchard. Large lawn gives an uninterrupted view of Houghton House. The garden contains mature trees and beds with many types of slow growing fir trees. Flower beds contain home grown bedding plants and roses. 3 acres of paddocks, wood and further pond. Many spring bulbs.

7 THE HYDE WALLED GARDEN

East Hyde, Luton LU2 9PS. D J J Hambro Will Trust. *2m S of Luton. M1 exitJ10/10a.* Home-made teas. **Adm £4, chd free. Sat 14 June; Sun 13 July (2-5).**
Walled garden adjoins the grounds of The Hyde (not open). Extends to approx 1 acre and features rose garden, seasonal beds and herbaceous borders, imaginatively interspersed with hidden areas of formal lawn. An interesting group of Victorian greenhouses, coldframes and cucumber house are serviced from the potting shed in the adjoining vegetable garden. Gravel paths.

8 ◆ KING'S ARMS GARDEN

1 Brinsmade Road, Ampthill MK45 2PP. Ampthill Town Council, 01525 755648, bryden.k@ntlworld.com. *8m S of Bedford. Free parking in town centre. Entrance opp old Market Place, down King's Arms Yard*. Light refreshments in the Garden or in the town centre. **Adm £2, chd free. For NGS: Sun 26 Jan (2-4); Sun 26 Oct (2.30-5); Sun 25 Jan 2015. For other opening times and information, please phone or email garden.**

Small woodland garden of about 1½ acres created by plantsman the late William Nourish. Trees, shrubs, bulbs and many interesting collections throughout the yr. Maintained since 1987 by 'The Friends of the Garden' on behalf of Ampthill Town Council. Wheelchair access to most of the garden.

9 LUTON HOO HOTEL GOLF & SPA

The Mansion House, Luton Hoo, Luton LU1 3TQ. Luton Hoo Hotel Golf & Spa, www.lutonhoo.co.uk. *Approx 1m from J10 M1, take London Rd A1081 signed Harpenden for approx ½ m - entrance on L for Luton Hoo*. Light refreshments. **Adm £5, chd free. Sun 27 July (11-4).**

The gardens and parkland designed by Capability Brown are of national historic significance and lie in a conservation area. Main features - lakes, woodland and pleasure grounds, Victorian grass tennis court and late C19 sunken rockery. Italianate garden with herbaceous borders and topiary garden. Gravel paths.

10 ◆ LUTON HOO WALLED GARDEN

Luton Hoo Estate, Luton LU1 4LF. Exors of N H Phillips, 01582 879089, www.lhwg.org.uk. *Luton Hoo Estate. Take A1081. Turn at sign for Newmill End. After approx. 100 metres turn L through black gates. Follow red signs to Walled Garden*. Home-made teas. **Adm £3, chd free. For NGS: Sun 13 July (11-4). For other opening times and information, please phone or see garden website.**

The 5 acre Luton Hoo Walled Garden was designed by Capability Brown and established by Lord Bute in the late 1760s. Successive owners of the estate adapted the garden to match changing horticultural fashions, only for it to fall into decline in the 1980s. The garden is now being restored. Exhibition of research material on the history of the garden. Guided tours. Illustrated talks. Exhibition of old tools. Disabled parking next to Walled Garden Entrance. A hard path goes through and around the garden.

An evening of music, roses, floral canapés and wine . . .

11 THE MANOR HOUSE, BARTON-LE-CLAY

87 Manor Road, Barton-le-Clay MK45 4NR. Mrs Veronica Pilcher. *Off A6 between Bedford & Luton. Take old A6 (Bedford Rd) through Barton-le-Clay Village (not the by-pass) and Manor Rd is off Bedford Rd. Parking in paddock*. Home-made teas. **Combined adm £4, chd free with Wayside Cottage. Sun 22 June (2-5).**

The garden was beautifully landscaped during the 1930s and much interest is created by picturesque stream which incorporates a series of waterfalls. Colourful streamside planting incl an abundance of arum lilies. Sunken garden with lily pond and a magnificent wisteria thrives at the rear of the house. Children under supervision as there is a water hazard. Partial wheelchair access, 2ft wide bridges.

12 ◆ THE MANOR HOUSE, STEVINGTON

Church Road, Stevington, nr Bedford MK43 7QB. Kathy Brown, 01234 822064, www.kathybrownsgarden.com. *5m NW of Bedford. Off A428 through Bromham*. Light refreshments. **For NGS: Evening Opening adm £4.50, chd free, wine, Fri 20 June (6-9). For other opening times and information, please phone or see garden website.**

An evening of music, roses, floral canapés and wine will provide a beautiful combination to savour against the backdrop of a modern 4-acre country garden, designed and cared for by owners Simon and Kathy Brown. Roses and other climbers abound on the house walls, over the pergolas and high up into the trees. Formal parterres and herbaceous borders, a wild flower meadow, major container displays, an edible flower border plus extensive naturalistic planting schemes offer further delights. Coaches by arrangement only. Disabled WC. Partial wheelchair access.

13 NEW THE OLD RECTORY

Church Lane, Wrestlingworth, Sandy SG19 2EU. Mrs Josephine Hoy. *5m E of Sandy, 5m NE of Biggleswade. Wrestlingworth is situated on B1042. Behind church to E of village*. Home-made teas. **Adm £4, chd free. Sun 1 June (2-6).**

4-acre extensive gardens, alliums, tulips, peonies. Mixed borders, wild flower meadows, woodland garden, natural pond and box parterres. Many mature trees and orchard. Gravel and terrace gardens. Wheelchair access may be limited on grass paths.

14 THE OLD VICARAGE

Church Road, Westoning MK45 5JW. Ann & Colin Davies, 01525 712721, ann@no1colin.plus.com. *2m S of Flitwick. Off A5120, 2m N of M1 J12. ¼ m up Church Rd, next to church*. Cream teas at C14 church next door. **Adm £3.50, chd free. Suns 30 Mar; 29 June (2-5.30). Visitors also welcome by appt Mar to July, no parking for coaches. Refreshments incl.**

A traditional 2-acre vicarage garden with box and laurel hedges, formal lawn, large magnolia grandiflora and many other mature shrubs and trees. More recent additions include many colour co-ordinated herbaceous beds, a romantic cornfield meadow, an English rose garden, a pond, a rockery and a small vegetable plot. A good show of hellebores and daffodils in spring. First open days for three years. Wheelchair access generally good.

GROUP OPENING

15 NEW OLD WARDEN VILLAGE GARDENS
Old Warden, Biggleswade SG18 9HB. *3m W of Biggleswade. Parking in the village hall car park, opposite the Hare & Hounds PH. Seven gardens in the centre of the village of Old Warden.* Home-made teas in village hall. **Combined adm £4, chd free. Sun 29 June (2-5).**

NEW THE VICARAGE
Michael & Sue Scott

ORCHARD GRANGE
Mrs Victoria Diggle.
In Old Warden village, just NE of entrance to Shuttleworth College. Parking in garden, or adjacent village hall car park

NEW SWISS COTTAGE
Mr Paul Quenby

NEW 28 THE VILLAGE
Mr Bob Parr

NEW 30 THE VILLAGE
Mrs Shirley Benjamin

NEW 31 THE VILLAGE
Mr & Mrs Prior

NEW 49 THE VILLAGE
49-50 The Village. Mr & Mrs Les Long

Old Warden, with its picturesque thatched cottages, medieval church, neat holly hedges and charming pub, is one of the prettiest villages in Bedfordshire. Many of the houses were built by the 3rd Lord Ongley (1803-1877) in the early C19 in the cottage-ornée style then in vogue. Further attractive buildings were added by the Shuttleworth family. This year 7 gardens will be opening. The largest is that at Orchard Grange which has a walled kitchen garden, formal areas, and a wildflower orchard. The Old Vicarage has an established garden planted for year-round interest. There are plenty of seats from which to enjoy the clipped box and the soft colours and perfume of climbing roses, clematis, perennials and container planting; the whole set off by manicured lawns in a woodland setting. Swiss Cottage and the other village gardens all have wonderful cottage planting with some lovely topiary, elaborate bedding schemes and other surprises. Most gardens are accessible to wheelchairs but there are some steps, banks and gravel paths.

16 PARK END THATCH
58 Park Road, Stevington, Bedford MK43 7QG. Susan Young, 01234 826430, susankyoung@btconnect.com, www.skygardeninganddesign.com. *5m NW of Bedford. Off A428, through Bromham.* Light refreshments. **Adm £4, chd free. Suns 25 May; 22 June (12-5). Visitors also welcome by appt May to July, please phone for information.**
½ -acre cottage garden set within old orchard and designed by the owner, a member of The Professional Gardeners' Guild. View of Stevington windmill. Sunny borders of flowering shrubs with herbaceous planting. Fragrant roses and climber covered pergola. Winding grass paths shaded by trees. Trellis border featuring colour and texture groupings. Fruit production and herbs. Garden cultivated to be drought tolerant. Wildlife friendly. Small plant nursery. Outside WC for use by visitors but cannot be accessed by wheelchair. Featured in Garden News - Garden of The Week. Main path is gravel on a slight slope, grass paths. Most of the garden is accessible by wheelchair.

17 SOUTHILL PARK
Southill, nr Biggleswade SG18 9LL. Mr & Mrs Charles Whitbread. *3m W of Biggleswade. In the village of Southill. 3m from A1 junction at Biggleswade.* **Adm £3.50, chd free. Sun 1 June (2-5).**
Large garden, with mature trees and flowering shrubs, herbaceous borders, rose garden and wild garden. Large conservatory with tropical plants. The parkland was designed by Lancelot 'Capability' Brown in 1777.

18 SWISS GARDEN
Old Warden Park, Old Warden, Biggleswade SG18 9ER. Shuttleworth Trust in Partnership with Central Beds Council, www.shuttleworth.org. *2m W of Biggleswade. Signed from A1 & A600.* Light refreshments. **Adm £6, chd free. Sun 21 Sept (9.30-5).**
This Swiss picturesque garden was created for the 3rd Lord Ongley in the early C19 and re-opens in summer 2014 after a major restoration project. Winding paths lead to contrived vistas, many of which focus on the thatched Swiss Cottage. The pulhamite, ironwork, ponds and garden buildings (incl the Cottage and the Grotto and Fernery), have been given a new lease of life by this landmark restoration. Gravel paths, some steep slopes, bridges and lawns.

19 TREIZE
Cranfield Road, Wootton Green, Bedford MK43 9EA. Roger & Anna Skipper, 01234 768640, roger.skipper@btinternet.com. *5m SW of Bedford. 10m NE of Milton Keynes.. C70 road Kempston to Cranfield rd, ½ m SW of Wootton, immed on R at Wootton Green hamlet sign, 150 metres on R up private lane.* Light refreshments. **Adm £5, chd free. Visitors welcome by appt 1 Mar to 14 May; Sept and Oct, guided tour of the garden by garden owners.**
1-acre plantsman's garden set out for yr-round interest on heavy clay. Hidden gardens and established herbaceous borders, formal pond, rockery, gravel beds and containers. Around 50 species of established and younger trees, conifers, shrubs, vast collection of perennials, incl over 100 varieties and species of penstemon. The garden continues to evolve. Large pond, summerhouse, and interesting trees. Featured in Garden News - 5 page article and photographs by Melissa Mabbitt. Wheelchair access to majority of garden.

20 NEW 1 TYRELLS END

Eversholt, Milton Keynes MK17 9DS. Mike & Gwinith Cox, 01525 280849. *East Woburn. 3m S of J13 M1, at Woburn turn L through Woburn Abbey Park, 1m on R in centre of Eversholt Village.* Home-made teas. **Adm £3.50, chd free. Sun 10 Aug (1-5). Visitors also welcome by appt July to Sept.**

A delightful country village garden, with a very large collection of hydrangeas, giving an outstanding array of absolutely gorgeous blooms throughout the whole of the August period. Mike was formally head gardener at Woburn Abbey Estates, now retired and with dedicated help from his wife Gwinith he has built up this huge collection of mainly hydrangea.

21 WALNUT COTTAGE

8 Great North Road, Chawston MK44 3BD. D G Parker, 0778 4792975. *2m S of St Neots. Between Wyboston & Blackcat r'about on S-bound lane of A1. Turn off at McDonalds, at end of filling station forecourt turn L. Off rd parking.* Home-made teas. **Adm £4, chd free. Sat 19, Sun 20 July (2-6). Visitors also welcome by appt Feb to Nov.**

Once a land settlement. 4-acre Ass. smallholding. 1 acre cottage garden. Over 2000 species give year round interest. Bulbs, herbaceous, water, bog plants, ferns, grasses, shrubs, trees, coppiced paulownias. Rare, exotic and unusual plants abound. Large pond, level grass paths. 1-acre young trees and shrubs. 2500sq metre glasshouse growing Chinese vegetable. 1½ -acre picnic and party zone. Level grass paths.

Flaxbourne Farm

22 WAYSIDE COTTAGE

74 Manor Road, Barton-le-Clay MK45 4NR. Nigel Barrett. *1m off A6. Take old A6 (Bedford Rd) through Barton-le-Clay Village (not the by-pass), Manor Rd is off Bedford Rd. Parking in paddock at the Manor House.* **Combined adm £4, chd free with The Manor House, Barton le Clay. Sun 22 June (2-5).**

The garden is sited on a ½ -acre plot. Developed over 50yrs it has mature trees, shrubs and flower borders. A well-stocked pond with fountain and waterfalls. A variety of attractive outbuildings nestle within the old walled garden for a tranquil scene with plenty of hidden corners.

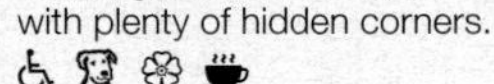

23 NEW WHITSUNDOLES FARM

Broughton Road, Salford, Milton Keynes MK17 8BU. Mr & Mrs Nick & Wendy Hall. *½ m past Salford village on Broughton Rd. J13 of M1 follow sign for Salford & Cranfield. Straight through Hulcote & Salford. ½ m W turn R at Whitsundoles sign.* Home-made teas. **Adm £4, chd free. Sat 31 May (2-5.30).**

A maturing garden of 4 acres, ⅓ of which is a lake, all recently created from a gravel pit. Wildlife orientated with many seating areas where you are welcome to contemplate the serenity of this countryside garden. Surrounded by thousands of recently planted deciduous trees are numerous herbaceous and perennial beds.

Bedfordshire County Volunteers

County Organiser

Judy Stewart, The Old Vicarage, Melchbourne MK44 1BQ, 01234 708629, jug.stewart@gmail.com

County Treasurer

Colin Davies, The Old Vicarage, Church Road, Westoning MK45 5JW, 01525 712721, colin.davies@which.net

Publicity

Gill Smith, How End Cottage, How End Road, Houghton Conquest, Bedford MK45 3JT, 01525 404121, smith201@btinternet.com

Assistant County Organisers

Geoff & Davina Barrett, Flaxbourne Farm, Aspley Guise, Milton Keynes MK17 8HZ, 01908 585329, geoffanddean@gmail.com
Victoria Coubrough, Riverstone House, Westfield Road, Oakley MK43 7SU, 01234 822371, victoria@coubrough.co.uk
Victoria Diggle, Orchard Grange, Old Warden, Biggleswade SG18 9HB, 01767 627247, victoria@diggledesign.com

BERKSHIRE

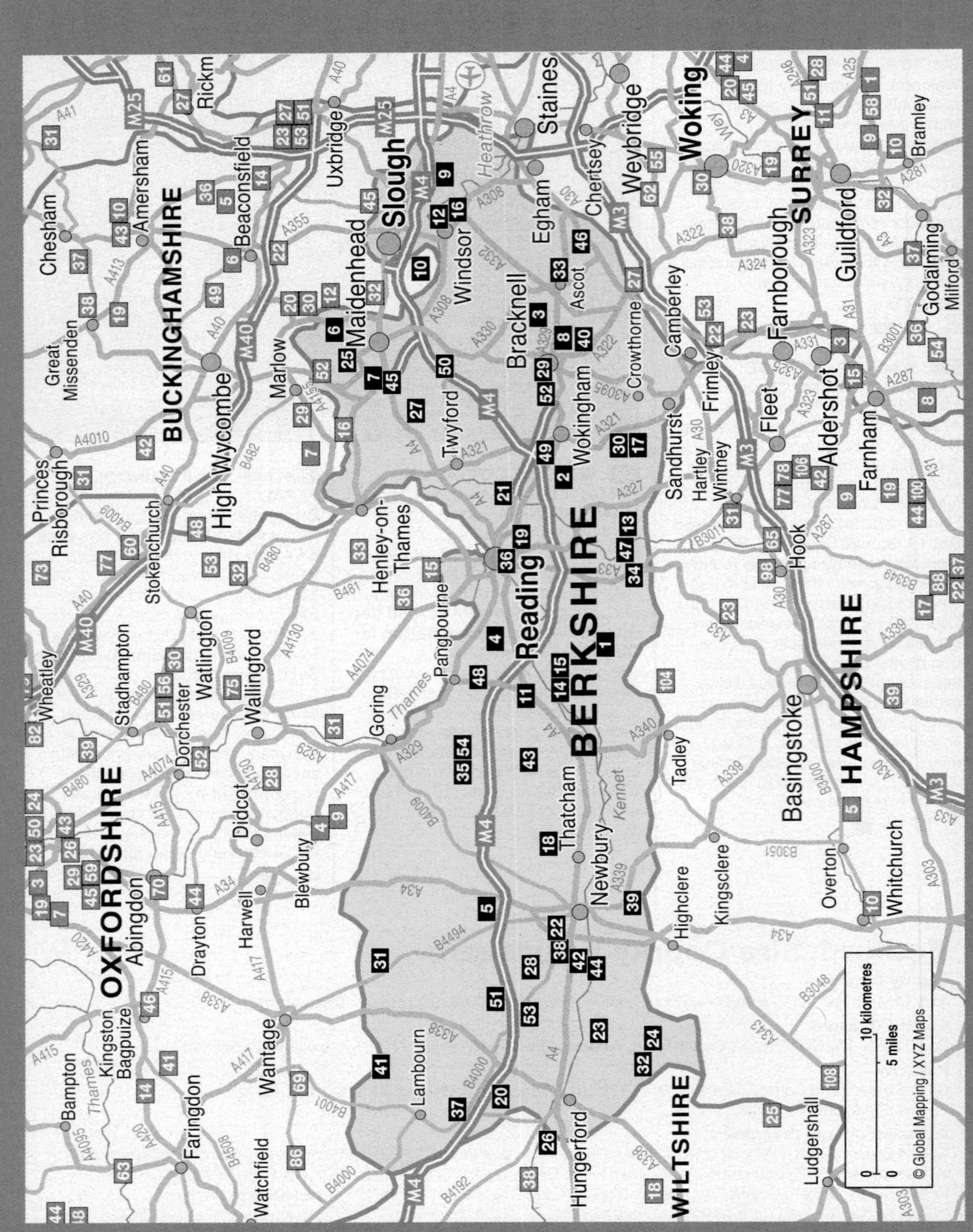
BERKSHIRE
OXFORDSHIRE
BUCKINGHAMSHIRE
SURREY
HAMPSHIRE
WILTSHIRE
Reading
Slough
Maidenhead
Windsor
Bracknell
Wokingham
Newbury
Thatcham
Hungerford
Lambourn
Twyford
Ascot
Crowthorne
Sandhurst
Pangbourne
Goring
Henley-on-Thames
Marlow
High Wycombe
Beaconsfield
Amersham
Chesham
Great Missenden
Princes Risborough
Stokenchurch
Watlington
Wallingford
Didcot
Abingdon
Wantage
Faringdon
Staines
Egham
Chertsey
Weybridge
Woking
Camberley
Farnborough
Guildford
Godalming
Milford
Aldershot
Farnham
Fleet
Basingstoke
Tadley
Kingsclere
Highclere
Overton
Whitchurch
Ludgershall
Heathrow
Uxbridge
Rickm
Wheatley
Stadhampton
Dorchester
Blewbury
Harwell
Drayton
Kingston Bagpuize
Bampton
Watchfield
Hook
Hartley Wintney
Frimley
Bramley
Thames
Kennet
Wey
10 kilometres
5 miles
© Global Mapping / XYZ Maps

Opening Dates

All entries subject to change. For latest information check www.ngs.org.uk

February

Sunday 23
30 Oak Cottage

April

Saturday 5
45 Stubbings House

Sunday 6
45 Stubbings House

Sunday 13
31 The Old Rectory Farnborough

Sunday 27
9 Ditton Manor

Wednesday 30
20 Inholmes
37 Rooksnest
44 Stockcross House

A little oasis with lots of ideas for the keen gardener . . .

May

Saturday 3
45 Stubbings House

Sunday 4
17 Glenmere
30 Oak Cottage
45 Stubbings House

Monday 5
45 Stubbings House

Saturday 10
36 The RISC Roof Garden, Reading

Sunday 11
13 Farley Hill Place Gardens
25 Little Harwood
31 The Old Rectory Farnborough

Monday 12
25 Little Harwood

Wednesday 14
44 Stockcross House

Sunday 18
2 Bearwood College

Sunday 25
38 Rookwood Farm House
42 Springfield Cottage

Monday 26
46 Sunningdale Park

Wednesday 28
44 Stockcross House

Saturday 31
6 Cookham Gardens

June

Tuesday 3
16 Frogmore House Garden

Festival Weekend

Saturday 7
10 Dorney Court Kitchen Garden

Sunday 8
4 NEW 80 Chapel Hill
19 The Harris Garden
20 Inholmes
48 The Tithe Barn
52 Whitehouse Farm Cottage

Wednesday 11
44 Stockcross House

Saturday 14
12 Eton College Gardens
26 Littlecote House Hotel

Sunday 15
5 Chieveley Manor
22 NEW Jannaways
31 The Old Rectory Farnborough
53 NEW Wickham House

Sunday 22
24 Kirby House
32 NEW The Old Rectory Inkpen
43 Stanford Dingley Gardens

Wednesday 25
20 Inholmes
37 Rooksnest

Saturday 28
26 Littlecote House Hotel
35 Pyt House
54 Willow Tree Cottage

Sunday 29
7 NEW Deepwood Stud Farm
23 Kintbury Gardens
35 Pyt House
38 Rookwood Farm House
41 Sheepdrove Organic Farm
42 Springfield Cottage
47 Swallowfield Horticultural Society
49 Twigs
54 Willow Tree Cottage

Monday 30
7 NEW Deepwood Stud Farm

July

Saturday 12
26 Littlecote House Hotel
36 The RISC Roof Garden, Reading

Sunday 20
27 Lower Lovetts Farm

Sunday 27
3 NEW Brockdale Cottage

August

Saturday 9
36 The RISC Roof Garden, Reading

Sunday 10
9 Ditton Manor

Sunday 24
33 Old Waterfield

Sunday 31
18 Greenlands

Gardens open to the public

11 Englefield House

By appointment only

1 NEW Barnwood
8 Devonia
14 Field Farm Cottage
21 Ivydene
28 The Mill House, Boxford
29 Moor Close Gardens
34 The Priory
39 Sandleford Place
40 10 Shaftesbury Close
50 Waltham Place Gardens
51 Welford Park

Also open by appointment

2 Bearwood College
5 Chieveley Manor
7 Deepwood Stud Farm
13 Farley Hill Place Gardens
17 Glenmere
18 Greenlands
20 Inholmes
27 Lower Lovetts Farm
37 Rooksnest
44 Stockcross House
45 Stubbings House

The Gardens

1 NEW BARNWOOD

Burghfield Common RG7 3DS. Mrs Wanda Ayres, 01189 831274, wanda.ayres@gmail.com. *6m SW of Reading. Directions available by email or phone.* Home-made teas. **Adm £3.50, chd free. Visitors welcome by appt May to July for groups of 4-12.**

½ -acre terraced plantswoman's garden. This natural garden has a lovely woodland backdrop and consists of many interesting perennials, shrubs, spring bulbs and annuals. With areas of sun and shade the garden combines multiple environments for all year round interest. Includes greenhouse, fruit cage and raised vegetable beds. Particularly pretty in late spring, early summer.

2 BEARWOOD COLLEGE
Winnersh RG41 5BG. Richard Ryall, 01189 748300, rpr@bearwoodcollege.co.uk. *5m SE of Reading. Off B3030, 1m S of A329/B3030 intersection at Winnersh, midway between Reading & Wokingham. Look for Bearwood Rd & college sign*. Cream teas. **Adm £4, chd free. Sun 18 May (2-5). Visitors also welcome by appt May to June. As this is a school, appointments are restricted.**
Late C19 mansion and parkland once owned by the last private owner of The Times newspaper, now an independent school. Azaleas, rhododendrons, walks through mature woodland. Pinetum, lake, natural margins, and ice house. Extensive hidden Pulham rock and water garden under restoration. Visits incl access to some of the mansion rooms. Specialist plants, charcoal making (subject to weather).

3 NEW BROCKDALE COTTAGE
Cricketers Lane, Warfield, Nr Bracknell RG42 6JR. Mr & Mrs Mark & Tam Cowell. *2m NE of Bracknell. From Bracknell College r'about take A3095 Warfield Rd. After 1m turn R along B3034 Forest Rd. After 1m follow NGS signs for car parking*. Light refreshments. **Adm £4, chd free. Sun 27 July (11-3).**
A 6-acre garden creatively designed and developed with emphasis on pollinating plants to attract insects and support working beehives. Lots of interest including a stylish contemporary double-pond garden, productive walled kitchen garden and greenhouse, traditional lawn and shrubs, woodland and young orchard, pilot brewery, rare breed pigs and also seasonal honey for sale. Limited wheelchair access.

4 NEW 80 CHAPEL HILL
Tilehurst, Reading RG31 5DQ. Mrs Iris Geater. *4m S of Reading. M4 J12, exit A4 to Reading. Go over 2 r'abouts, then L at T-lights up Langley Hill onto Park Lane, 1m over 2 r'abouts. At 3rd r'about turn L into Chapel Hill*. Home-made teas at Tithe Barn, Tidmarsh. **Adm £2.50, chd free. Sun 8 June (2-5). Also open - The Tithe Barn,Tidmarsh (2.5 miles west).**
This may be a small town garden, but it is a little oasis with lots of ideas for the keen gardener. Both front and back areas have colour for yr-round interest. The back garden has been creatively developed with lush deep borders, ferns, acers, roses, heucheras and many shrubs. Winner of Reading in Bloom 2010, 2011, 2012 and 2013.

5 CHIEVELEY MANOR
Chieveley, nr Newbury RG20 8UT. Mr & Mrs CJ Spence, 01635 248208, spence@chieveleymanor.fsworld.co.uk. *5m N of Newbury. Take A34 N, pass under M4, then L to Chieveley. After ½ m L up Manor Lane*. Home-made teas. **Adm £4, chd free (share to St Mary's Church, Chieveley). Sun 15 June (2-5). Visitors also welcome by appt June to July for groups of 20 max.**
Large garden surrounding listed house (not open) in the heart of Chieveley village. Attractive setting with fine views over stud farm. Walled garden containing lovely borders, shrubs and rose garden, evolving every year. Box parterre, filled with alliums, white geraniums and lavender. Many viticella clematis growing through shrubs. Featured in Amateur Gardening and on BBC Radio Berkshire.

GROUP OPENING

6 COOKHAM GARDENS
Cookham SL6 9QD. *3½ m N of Maidenhead. Along B4447 in Cookham. Car parking can be tricky. Please use NT car park at Cookham Moor, street parking, or around railway station. Tickets & map for all 3 gardens available at any garden, follow NGS signs*. Home-made teas at Hunters Lodge. **Combined adm £5, chd free. Sat 31 May (2-5).**

2 BELLE VUE COTTAGES
Liz & William Wells

HUNTERS LODGE
Daphne Wardell-Yerburgh

2 VICARAGE CLOSE D
Sue Yerburgh

Three contrasting gardens in the beautiful Thameside village of Cookham, all within ½ m walk and close to the Stanley Spencer Gallery. Two showcase innovative use of limited spaces. A small stunning modern garden, **2 Bellevue Cottages** has a curving walkway that weaves through arbours bordered by lush, exotic and evergreen planting, punctuated by dabs of intense colour. Sorry not suitable for children.
2 Vicarage Close is a small, contemporary water garden with simplistic planting surrounding a straight sided deep pool with cascading water. An overhanging deck with 'floating' steps over to a small grass area. The third, **Hunters Lodge** is a country style garden with a series of rooms leading to a Victorian summer house. Filled with herbaceous and climbing plants, lawned areas and set behind Victorian house in heart of village, it is a lovely place to enjoy afternoon tea.

Designed and developed with emphasis on pollinating plants to attract insects and support working beehives . . .

7 NEW DEEPWOOD STUD FARM
Henley Road, Stubbings, Nr Maidenhead SL6 6QW. Mr & Mrs E Goodwin, 01628 822684, deepwood@dsl.pipex.com. *2m W of Maidenhead. M4 J 8/9 take A404M N. 2nd exit for A4 to Maidenhead. L at 1st r'about on A4130 Henley, 0.9m on R*. Tea served on the lawn or in the conservatory. **Adm £3.50, chd free. Sun 29, Mon 30 June (2-5). Visitors also welcome by appt May to Aug for groups 10-20.**
4-acres of formal and informal gardens within a stud farm - so great roses! Small lake with Monet-style bridge and 3 further water features. Several neo-classical follies and statues. Walled garden with windows cut in to admire the views and horses. Woodland walk and enough hanging baskets to decorate a pub! Limited wheelchair access.

Jannaways

8 DEVONIA
Broad Lane, Bracknell RG12 9BH. Andrew Radgick, 01344 862683, aradgick@btinternet.com. *1m S of Bracknell. From A322 Horse & Groom r'about take exit into Broad Lane, over 2 r'abouts. 3rd house on L after railway bridge. Parking in nearby side roads*. Light refreshments by arrangement. **Adm £3, chd free.** **Visitors welcome by appt June to Aug for groups of 4+.**
1/3 -acre plantsman and plantaholic's garden designed for all seasons and planted to require minimal watering. Divided into several areas to provide appropriate conditions for over 1300 different shrubs, climbers, perennials, bulbs and alpines, incl many rare and unusual. Hot and dry front garden, shady and sheltered corners to the rear. Also a recently developed garden of coloured foliage.

9 DITTON MANOR
Riding Court Road, Datchet, Slough SL3 9LL. CA Technologies. *J5 of M4. Leave M4 J5, follow signs for Langley. At T-lights (Marriott Hotel is on the L) turn L. Cross over r'about then next turning on the R*. Home-made teas. **Adm £3.50, chd free.** **Suns 27 Apr, 10 Aug (11-5).**
Ditton Manor sits on a 14-acre moated island at the centre of a fine 208-acre estate created in the traditional English landscape style, originally designed by Lancelot 'Capability' Brown. The Manor enjoys fine views over parkland, woodland and lakes. Formal lawns, walled garden, kitchen garden and cutting garden.

10 DORNEY COURT KITCHEN GARDEN
Court Lane, Dorney, Windsor SL4 6QP. Ryan & Stretch, www.dckg.co.uk. *5m W of Slough. From M4 J7, take A4 W through T-lights then L at r'about to B3026 Lake End Rd. Approx 1½ m into Dorney, past Pineapple PH, then R into Court Lane*. Light refreshments. **Adm £3, chd free.** **Sat 7 June (9-5.30).**
Inspirational and educational walled kitchen garden, adjacent to plant nursery, in historic village of Dorney. Sunken garden, water features, herbs, fruit, vegetables, children's tree house and play area. Family-friendly Open Day for the NGS including BBQ. Steps down to sunken garden, otherwise full wheelchair access.

11 ◆ ENGLEFIELD HOUSE
Englefield, Reading RG7 5EN. Mr & Mrs Richard Benyon, 01189 302504, www.englefieldestate.co.uk. *6m W of Reading. M4 J12. Take A4 towards Theale. 2nd r'about take A340 to Pangbourne. After 0.6m entrance on L.* **For opening times and information, please phone or see garden website.**
The 12-acre garden descends dramatically from the hill above the house through woodland where mature native trees mix with Victorian conifers. Drifts of daffodils then spring and summer bulbs are followed by striking autumn colour. Stone balustrades enclose the lower terrace, with wide lawns, roses, mixed borders and topiary. Open every Mon throughout yr (10-6). Group bookings only: Tues-Thur from 4 March - 30 October. A children's garden with hidden jets of water provides fun for younger visitors.

12 ETON COLLEGE GARDENS
Eton SL4 6DB. Eton College. *½ m N of Windsor. Parking signed off B3022 entering Eton. Walk across fields to entry. Cars with Disabled badges will be directed closer. Tickets & map at entrance to Head Master's garden*. Home-made teas. **Adm £5, chd free.** **Sat 14 June (2-5).**
A rare chance to visit a group of central College gardens surrounded by historic school buildings, incl Luxmoore's garden on an island in the Thames, reached across an attractive bridge. Also an opportunity to explore the fascinating Eton College Natural History Museum. Wheelchair access limited to 3 central gardens and over grass to Luxmoores, with no access to the Museum or further gardens in Eton town.

13 FARLEY HILL PLACE GARDENS

Farley Hill, Reading RG7 1TZ. Mr & Mrs Tony & Margaret Finch, 01189 762544, tony.finch7@btinternet.com. *From M4 J11, take A33 S to Basingstoke. At T-lights turn L for Spencers Wood, B3349. Go 2m turn L, on through Swallowfield towards Farley Hill. Garden ½ m on R.* Home-made teas. **Adm £4, chd free. Sun 11 May (2-5). Visitors also welcome by appt Mar to Sept for groups of 15+. Please mention NGS.**

A 4-acre, C18 cottage garden. 1½-acre walled garden with spring colour for open day and all year round interest for by appt visits. Well stocked herbaceous borders, vegetable and wild areas, cutting garden and orchard.

14 FIELD FARM COTTAGE

Sulhamstead Hill, Sulhamstead RG7 4DA. Mrs Anne Froom, 01189 302735, www.bandbwestberkshire.co.uk. *From A4 take lane by The Spring Inn for 1m. Garden on L 150yds past 2 LH turns.* Home-made teas. **Adm £3, chd free. Visitors welcome by appt May to Sept for groups of 10+.**

A pretty cottage garden in ¾ -acre planted with a wide variety of herbaceous perennials, set in a series of garden rooms. Lovely borders spill over the lawn and there is a large pond which is fed by a natural spring. Wild garden, small white garden and a variety of trees planted by the owner. Small vegetable garden and greenhouse.

15 FOLLY FARM

Sulhamstead Hill, Sulhamstead RG7 4DG. *7m SW of Reading. From A4 between Reading & Newbury (2m W of M4 J12) take road marked Sulhamstead at The Spring Inn. Restricted car parking.* Home-made teas. **Adm £25. Private tour for groups of 10-12 only on Weds 7, 14 May, 4 June, 2 July, 6, 13 Aug (2-4.30). Pre-booking essential due to limited availability by phoning 01483 211535 or visit www.ngs.org.uk.**

Gardens laid out in 1912 by Sir Edwin Lutyens and Gertrude Jekyll. Garden designs evolved during culmination of their partnership and considered one of their most complex. Extensively restored and re-planted by current owners assisted by Dan Pearson. Recently re-opened for private group visits which include 1½ hour guided tour and refreshments. Paths are uneven and there are many sets of steps between areas of the garden.

16 ◆ FROGMORE HOUSE GARDEN

Windsor SL4 1LB. Her Majesty The Queen. *1m SE of Windsor. Entrance via Park St gate into Long Walk.* Light refreshments available and picnics welcome. **For NGS: Tues 3 June. For advance tickets, please phone 01483 211535 or visit www.ngs.org.uk.**

The private royal garden at Frogmore House on the Crown Estate at Windsor. This landscaped garden set in 30-acres with notable trees, lawns, flowering shrubs and C18 lake, is rich in history. It is largely the creation of Queen Charlotte, who in the 1790s introduced over 4,000 trees and shrubs to create a model 'picturesque' landscape. The historic plantings, including tulip trees and redwoods, along with Queen Victoria's Tea House, remain key features of the garden today. Please note the Royal Mausoleum is closed due to long term restoration.

17 GLENMERE

246 Nine Mile Ride, Finchampstead RG40 3PA. Heather Bradly & John Kenney, 01189 733274. *2½m S of Wokingham. On B3430, 0.4m E of California Crossroads r'about.* Home-made teas at Oak Cottage. **Adm £3.50, chd free. Sun 4 May (2-5). Combined adm £4.50, chd free with Oak Cottage on 4 May only. Visitors also welcome by appt Apr to Aug for 12 max, with teas by arrangement.**

Japanese style garden with waiting arbour, raked gravel area, tea house, Torii gate, dry stream bed with bridge and pond. Vegetable garden, greenhouse and soft fruit area.

18 GREENLANDS

Collaroy Road, Cold Ash, Thatcham RG18 9PE. Barbara & Stephen Stroud, 07887 694414. *1m N of Thatcham. A4 from Theale to Thatcham, turn R at signs for Cold Ash. Up Cold Ash Hill, 2nd R into Collaroy Rd. Entrance in Gladstone Lane.* Home-made teas. **Adm £3.50, chd free. Sun 31 Aug (12-6). Visitors also welcome by appt May to Sept for groups of 10+.**

Recently developed 2-acre plantswoman's garden, ornamental pond with large bog area and lots of exotic tropical plants. Grass border, herbaceous borders, box, parterre, rose arbours, woodland area, orchard, kitchen garden and a courtyard filled with a profusion of colourful and unusual plants.

Many hidden gems provide visitors with a rich panoply of vistas round every corner . . .

19 THE HARRIS GARDEN

Whiteknights, Reading RG6 6UR. The University of Reading, www.friendsoftheharrisgarden.org.uk. *1½ m S of Reading. Off A327, Shinfield Rd. Turn R just inside Pepper Lane entrance to campus.* Home-made teas. **Adm £3, chd free. Sun 8 June (2-5).**

12-acre amenity, research and teaching garden. Floral meadows, herbaceous borders, stream garden and pond, notable trees and shrubs, some very rare. Plant Heritage Digitalis collection.

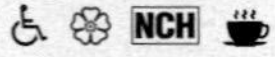

20 INHOLMES

Woodlands St Mary RG17 7SY, 07811 381211. *3m SE Lambourn. M4 J14, take A338 N (Wantage Rd), then 1st L onto B4000 towards Lambourn. After 1.6m, Inholmes signed on L.* **Adm £4.50, chd free. Wed 30 Apr (11-4); Sun 8 June (12-4); Wed 25 June (11-4). Also**

open with Rooksnest Weds 30 Apr, 25 June. Combined adm £6.50. Visitors also welcome by appt Apr to July for groups of 10-30.
Set in 10-acres with views over parkland. Lots to enjoy with large walled garden, rose beds, cutting and sunken garden. Individual touches incl brightly painted gates and benches and spooky wood. Walks to lake and meadow. Beautiful display of bulbs and bluebell wood in spring, then in summer the inspirational borders burst with colour. Featured on BBC Gardener's World.

21 IVYDENE

283 Loddon Bridge Road, Woodley, Reading RG5 4BE. Janet & Bill Bonney, 01189 697591, janetbonney2003@aol.com. *3½ m E of Reading. Loddon Bridge Rd is main road through Woodley. Garden approx 100yds S of Just Tiles r'about. Parking in adjacent roads.* Home-made teas. **Adm £3.50, chd free. Visitors welcome by appt June to Aug (max 30). Please mention NGS.**
Small urban gardeners' garden, with mature tree fern walkway and many unusual hostas, ornamental grasses and plants. Overflowing herbaceous borders and rose bed, using mainly patio roses. NEW for 2014 is the vertical garden. The garden also features stained glass and ceramic art to complete the picture. Owner is a previous BBC Gardener of the Year finalist. Featured in Garden News - Garden of the Week.

22 NEW JANNAWAYS

Bagnor, Newbury RG20 8AH. Mr & Mrs Sharples. *3m W of Newbury. From M4 J15, S on A34. Take A4 exit towards Newbury. 1st L to Station Rd. Turn L to Lambourn Rd. 1st R to Bagnor then follow NGS signs.* Light refreshments. **Adm £4, chd free. Sun 15 June (2-5.30).**
This 5-acre garden encompasses a lake naturally fed by springs. A circular walk from formal beds near the house leads along a woodland path, crossing a weir to wild flowers and specimen trees. A pitch perfect lawn, fishpond, pagodas and many hidden gems provide visitors with a rich panoply of vistas round every corner.

GROUP OPENING

23 KINTBURY GARDENS

Kintbury, Hungerford RG17 9TR. *From A4 between Hungerford to Newbury, take road signed Kintbury. Go 1m to village centre. Please park with consideration in village. Follow NGS signs.* Home-made teas available at both gardens. **Combined adm £5, chd free. Sun 29 June (12-5).**

MIDSUMMER HOUSE
Mr & Mrs Neil & Martine Newport

THE OLD VICARAGE

Two very different gardens, which are approx ½ m apart in the village of Kintbury. Beyond the garden at **Midsummer House** is a small arboretum planted with a lovely selection of specimen trees. Enjoy identifying them as you follow the tree trail. The picturesque grounds of **The Old Vicarage** extend for 350yds along the Kennet & Avon Canal. They incl terraces, lawns, flower beds, pasture land, herb garden, extensive vegetable garden, rose arch walkway, shrubs and mature trees, including a c200 yr-old beech.

24 KIRBY HOUSE

Upper Green, Inkpen RG17 9ED. Mr & Mrs R Astor. *5m SE of Hungerford. A4 to Kintbury. L at Xrds for Inkpen. After 2m turn L at Crown & Garter PH, L at junction, house at bottom of hill on R.* **Adm £4, chd free. Sun 22 June (2-5). Also open with The Old Rectory, Inkpen (2 miles). Combined adm £5.00.**
7-acres in beautiful setting with views of S Berkshire Downs and historical Combe Gibbet, across lawn with ha-ha and parkland. C18 Queen Anne House (not open). Formal rose borders, double herbaceous border, colour themed border between yew buttress hedges, lily pond garden by Harold Peto, reflecting pond with fountain, lake, walled garden and contemporary sculptures. Featured in Country Life magazine. Some uneven paths.

25 LITTLE HARWOOD

Choke Lane, Pinkneys Green SL6 6PL. Mr & Mrs David Harrold. *2½ m NW of Maidenhead. A308 at Pinkneys Green turn R into Winter Hill Rd. When road forks, continue R on main road now Choke Lane. 500yds on, Z bend & SLOW sign. Garden on L.* Light refreshments. **Adm £4, chd free. Sun 11 May (12-4); Mon 12 May (11-4).**
2-acre mature, well-labelled plantsman's garden. Formal and informal, terraced gardens with stunning views; incl water garden, rock garden, herbaceous border, lawn, herb bed, and contemporary garden buildings. Large specimen trees and clipped yew and hawthorn hedges. 16-acre bluebell woodland walk and wild flower meadow. Some steps.

26 LITTLECOTE HOUSE HOTEL

Hungerford RG17 0SU. Warner Leisure Hotels, 01488 682509, www.warnerleisurehotels.co.uk. *2m W of Hungerford. From A4 turn R onto B4192 signed Swindon. After 1½ m exit L & follow signs.* Light refreshments. **Adm £4. Sats 14, 28 June, 12 July (11-4).**
Beautiful setting around Grade I listed house with views of the Kennet Valley over lawns and parkland. Formal areas incl herbaceous borders, rose and herb garden, clipped yew, box hedging, and fruit trees. Don't miss the stumpery and the courtyard with large planters. Attractive selection of hanging baskets. Sorry, no children. Plants and garden gifts for sale in Potting Shed Shop. Gravel paths, some slopes.

Ditton Manor

27 LOWER LOVETTS FARM

Knowl Hill Common, Knowl Hill RG10 9YE. Mr Richard Sandford, info@lowerlovettsfarm.com, www.lowerlovettsfarm.com. *Off A4 at Knowl Hill into Knowl Hill Common. Past PH and across common to T-junction. Turn L down dead end lane.* Home-made teas. **Adm £4, chd free. Sun 20 July (1-5). Visitors also welcome by appt 21-26 July for groups of 8+ (no teas for by appt visits). Lane not suitable for coaches.**

A fascinating large modern organic kitchen garden (60m x 30m). Wide variety of vegetables and fruit grown for home consumption and nutritional value. Flowers grown for eating or herbal teas. Produce is also dried or bottled for yr-round use. Lots of interesting growing techniques and tips. See garden website for more information. Featured in national press and on BBC Gardener's World.

28 THE MILL HOUSE, BOXFORD

Boxford, Newbury RG20 8DP. Mrs Heather Luff, 01488 608385. *5m W of Newbury. Take B4000 to Stockcross. 2m on, turn R to Boxford. At T-junction turn R and then L. Over bridge, The Mill House is first on L.* Teas by arrangement. **Adm £4, chd free. Visitors welcome by appt Apr to Oct for groups of 4+.**

Very attractive large mature garden surrounding Grade II listed Mill House with R Lambourn running through. Herbaceous borders, rose garden, espalier fruit trees, lawns and vegetables. Good spring colour with daffodils, tulips and alliums. New tulip planting for spring 2014. Riverside walk overlooking water meadows. Lovely autumn garden with sedum, echinacea and clipped box. Featured in 'Country Homes & Interiors' and 'Period Living'.

29 MOOR CLOSE GARDENS

Popeswood Road, Binfield RG42 4AH. Newbold College, 01344 452424, avtm96@ntlworld.com. *2m W of Bracknell. M4 J10, A329M S to Bracknell. Take 1st exit, then L on B3408 to Bracknell. At 2nd T-lights, L into St Marks Rd, go 1/3 m to entrance at Popeswood Rd.* Refreshments by arrangement. **Adm £2.50, chd free. Visitors welcome by appt for 25 max.**

Small Grade II* listed garden designed 1911-13 by Oliver Hill and a rare example of his early work. Lavender garden, water parterre, remains of Italianate garden. Undergoing long-term restoration, it currently offers most interest in its historical architecture rather than planting. We hope you enjoy learning about its history from tours with our knowledgable volunteers.

30 OAK COTTAGE

99B Kiln Ride, Finchampstead, Wokingham RG40 3PD. Ms Liz Ince, www.facebook.com/oakcottagegarden. *2 1/2 m S of Wokingham. Off B3430 Nine Mile Ride between A321 Sandhurst Rd & B3016 Finchampstead Rd.* Light refreshments (Feb). Home-made teas (May). **Adm £3.50, chd free. Sun 23 Feb (2-4.30); Sun 4 May (2-5). Combined adm £4.50, chd free with Glenmere on 4 May only.**

1/4 -acre garden with woodland feel. Mature trees underplanted with snowdrops and other spring flowering bulbs. Several unusual winter flowering plants including an Edgeworthia chrysantha, Chrysosplenium macrophyllum and many Hellebores. Pine pergola with various climbers, greenhouse, island beds and eclectic planting. Small vegetable patch with fruit trees. Main paths offer wheelchair access, but others are gravel and bark and unsuitable.

THE OLD MILL
See Wiltshire

31 THE OLD RECTORY FARNBOROUGH

Wantage, Oxon OX12 8NX. Mr & Mrs Michael Todhunter. *4m SE of Wantage. Take B4494 Wantage-Newbury Rd, after 4m turn E at sign for Farnborough. Approx 1m to village, Old Rectory on L.* Home-made teas. **Adm £5, chd free (share to Farnborough PCC). Suns 13 Apr, 11 May, 15 June (2-5.30).**

In a series of immaculately tended garden rooms, incl herbaceous borders, arboretum, boules, rose, pool and vegetables. There is an explosion of rare and interesting plants, beautifully combined for colour and texture. With stunning views across the countryside, it is the perfect setting for the 1749 rectory (not open), once home of John Betjeman, in memory of whom John

Piper created a window in the local church. Awarded Finest Parsonage in England by Country Life and the Rectory Society. Featured in 'Country Life' magazine. Some steep slopes and gravel paths.

32 NEW THE OLD RECTORY INKPEN
Lower Green, Inkpen RG17 9DS. Mrs C McKeon. *4m SE of Hungerford. Off Spray Rd, opposite St Michael's Church.* Home-made teas. **Adm £3.50, chd free. Sun 22 June (2-5). Also open with Kirby House, Inkpen (2 miles). Combined adm £5.00.**
On a gentle hillside with lovely countryside views, the Old Rectory offers a peaceful setting for this pretty 2-acre garden. Enjoy strolling through the formal and walled gardens, herbaceous borders, pleached lime walk and wild flower meadow (some slopes).

33 OLD WATERFIELD
Winkfield Road, Ascot SL5 7LJ. Hugh & Catherine Stevenson. *6m SW of Windsor to E of Ascot Racecourse. On A330 midway between A329 & A332. Parking by kind permission of Royal Ascot Golf Club. Access by gate near entrance to Golf Club.* Home-made teas. **Adm £4, chd free. Sun 24 Aug (2-5).**
Set in 4-acres between Ascot Heath and Windsor Great Park, the original cottage garden has been developed and extended over the past few years. Herbaceous borders, meadow with specimen trees, large productive vegetable garden, orchard, mixed hedging. Plants and dried flowers for sale including unusual varieties grown from seed. Home-made jams and chutneys also for sale.

34 THE PRIORY
Beech Hill RG7 2BJ. Mr & Mrs C Carter, 01189 883146, tita@getcarter.org.uk. *5m S of Reading. M4 J11, A33 S to Basingstoke. At T-lights, L to Spencers Wood. After 1.5m turn R for Beech Hill. After 1.6m, L into Wood Lane, R down Priory Drive.* Home-made teas. **Adm £4, chd free. Visitors welcome by appt June to Aug for groups of 6-30.**
Extensive gardens in grounds of former C12 Benedictine Priory (not open), rebuilt 1648. The mature gardens are in an attractive setting beside the R Loddon. Large formal walled garden with espalier fruit trees, lawns, mixed and replanted herbaceous borders, vegetables and roses. Woodland, fine trees, lake and Italian style water garden.

35 PYT HOUSE
Ashampstead RG8 8RA. Hans & Virginia von Celsing. *4m W of Pangbourne. From Yattendon head towards Reading. Rd forks L into a beech wood towards Ashampstead. Keep L & join lower rd. 1/2 m turn L just before houses.* Home-made teas. **Combined adm £5, chd free with Willow Tree Cottage. Sat 28, Sun 29 June (2-5).**
A 4-acre garden planted over the last 8yrs by designer owner, around C18 house (not open). Mature trees, yew, hornbeam and beech hedges, pleached limes, modern perennial borders, pond, orchard and vegetable garden. New iris beds. Broadly organic, a haven for bees and butterflies. Chickens.

D

Small edible roof forest garden developed to demonstrate sustainability and our dependence on plants . . .

36 THE RISC ROOF GARDEN, READING
35-39 London Street, Reading RG1 4PS. Reading International Solidarity Centre, www.risc.org.uk/garden. *Central Reading. 5 mins walk from Oracle Shopping Centre. 10 mins from station. Park in Queens Rd or Oracle car parks or top car park only at back of RISC building.* Light refreshments at RISC Global Cafe. **Adm £3, chd free (share to RISC). Sats 10 May, 12 July, 9 Aug (12-4).**
Small edible roof forest garden developed to demonstrate sustainability and our dependence on plants. All plants in the garden have an economic use for food, clothing, medicine etc, and come from all over the world. Demonstration of renewable energy, water harvesting and irrigation systems. Garden accessed by external staircase. Regular tours of garden. Featured in My Cool Allotment by Lia Leendertz.

37 ROOKSNEST
Ermin Street, Lambourn Woodlands RG17 7SB. Dame Theresa Sackler, 01488 71678, garden@rooksnest.net. *2m S of Lambourn on B4000. From M4 J14, take A338 Wantage Rd, turn 1st L onto B4000 (Ermin St) to Lambourn. Rooksnest signposted after 3m.* Home-made teas. **Adm £4.50, chd free. Weds 30 Apr, 25 June (11-4). Also open with Inholmes Weds 30 Apr, 25 June only. Combined adm £6.50. Visitors also welcome by appt Apr to July for groups of 10+.**
Approx 10-acre exceptionally fine traditional English garden. Rose and herbaceous garden, newly re-designed and planted pond area, herb garden, vegetables and glasshouses. Many specimen trees and fine shrubs, orchard and terraces renovated and recently replanted. Garden mostly designed by Arabella Lennox-Boyd since 1980. Please note Plants Sale - June only. Mostly grass and hard patio, some gravel. Happy to provide assistance to wheelchair users.

D

38 ROOKWOOD FARM HOUSE
Stockcross RG20 8JX. The Hon Rupert & Charlotte Digby, www.rookwoodfarmhouse.co.uk. *3m W of Newbury. M4 J13, A34(S). After 3m exit for A4(W) to Hungerford. At 2nd r'about take B4000 towards Stockcross, after 0.7m R then L into Rookwood.* Home-made teas. **Combined adm £5.00, chd free with Springfield Cottage. Suns 25 May, 29 June (2-5).**
This exciting valley garden - a work in progress - has elements all visitors can enjoy. A rose covered pergola, fabulous tulips, giant alliums, a kitchen garden featuring a parterre of raised beds, as well as bog gardens and colour-themed herbaceous planting, all make Rookwood well worth a visit. Please see website for B&B details. Gravel paths, some steep slopes.

Brockdale Cottage

39 SANDLEFORD PLACE
Newtown, Newbury RG20 9AY. Mel Gatward, 01635 40726, melgatward@btinternet.com. *1½ m S of Newbury on A339. House on NW-side of Swan r'about at Newtown.* Light refreshments available upon request. **Adm £7.50, chd free. Visitors welcome by appt Feb to Oct.**
A plantswoman's 5-acres, more exuberant than manicured with R Enborne flowing through. Various areas of shrub and mixed borders create a romantic, naturalistic effect. Wonderful old walled garden. Long herbaceous border flanks wild flower meadow. Yr-round interest from early carpets of snowdrops, crocus-covered lawn and large areas of daffodils, to autumn berries and leaf colour. Partial wheelchair access. Guide dogs only.

40 10 SHAFTESBURY CLOSE
Bracknell RG12 9PX. Gill Cheetham, 01344 423440, gillcheetham@btopenworld.com. *At Bracknell A322 Sports Centre r'about, exit for Harmanswater. At 2nd mini-r'about, R on Harmanswater Rd. 2nd L to Nightingale Crescent, L to Shaftesbury Close.* Home-made teas. **Adm £2.50, chd free. Visitors welcome by appt Mar to May.**
Pine woodland garden, with many different ericaceous shrubs and plants. Good spring colour with underplanted trees. Walled garden. New Zealand border, pond, scree and alpine. Colour themed herbaceous borders planned for all-year colour. Many rare and unusual plants in realistic settings. Visit to nearby allotment can be arranged. Limited street parking. Beautiful spring-time garden.

41 SHEEPDROVE ORGANIC FARM
Sheepdrove Road, Lambourn RG17 7UU. Mr & Mrs Peter Kindersley, www.sheepdrove.com. *2m N Lambourn. Do not use SatNav - input Sheepdrove Road. At Xrds in Lambourn, N towards Wantage. After ½ m, turn R up Sheepdrove Rd. After 2m, over wheelwash, follow road past red barn on L, then follow NGS signs.* Home-made teas at Eco-Conference Centre Barn. **Adm £4, chd free. Sun 29 June (11-3).**
Four fascinating gardens at the heart of Sheepdrove Farm, home to owners of Neal's Yard Remedies. Juliet's garden at the Farmhouse has a potager and gravel garden with herbs, vegetables and flowers. Walled organic vegetable garden with glasshouses nearby. Delightful physic garden designed by Jekka McVicar. Neal's Yard Remedies garden for supplying some of their herbs.

42 SPRINGFIELD COTTAGE
Stockcross RG20 8LJ. Anne & Ron Cummings. *3m W of Newbury. M4 J13, A34(S). After 3m exit for A4(W) to Hungerford. At 2nd r'about take B4000 towards Stockcross, after 0.7m first cottage on L.* Home-made teas at Rookwood Farm House. **Combined adm £5.00, chd free with Rookwood Farm House. Suns 25 May, 29 June (2-5).**
Pretty cottage garden attached to a C16 listed thatched property and terraced on three levels. Lovingly designed and created by the owner

over the last eight years with mixed shrub and herbaceous borders, rose garden and lawns with seating areas, small pond and laburnum arbour.

GROUP OPENING

43 STANFORD DINGLEY GARDENS

Stanford Dingley RG7 6LS. *5m SW of Pangbourne. M4 J12 to Newbury, at 2nd r'about R to Pangbourne. 1st L to Bradfield, over at College Xrds. 1st L, on for 2m. Car parking in field.* Home-made teas at Fairholme Farm or village hall depending on weather. **Combined adm £5, chd free.** **Sun 22 June (2-6).**

BRIDGE COTTAGE
Mrs Marilyn Mansefield

NEW **FAIRHOLME FARM**
Mrs Min Vaughan -Fowler

JENNETTS HILL HOUSE
Mr & Mrs Hugh Priestley

NEW **KING'S COPSE HOUSE**
Mr & Mrs Caroline & John Wyatt

THE SPRING
Mr & Mrs Mark Hawkesworth

Stanford Dingley is a pretty village within the Pang Valley. These 5 gardens offer interest in a variety of styles and sizes, and most have lovely vistas. Bridge Cottage, The Spring and Fairholme Farm are within walking distance of each other but transport is required for Jennett's Hill House and King's Copse House. Map provided with tickets.

44 STOCKCROSS HOUSE

Church Road, Stockcross, Nr Newbury RG20 8LP. Susan & Edward Vandyk, 07765 674863, dragonflygardens@btinternet.com. *3m W of Newbury. M4 J13, A34 (S). After 3m exit for A4 (W) to Hungerford. At 2nd r'about take B4000, 1m to Stockcross, 2nd L into Church Rd.* Home-made teas. **Adm £4, chd free. Weds 30 Apr; 14, 28 May; 11 June (11-4). Visitors also welcome by appt May to June for groups of 10-30. Refreshments by arrangement.**
A 2-acre garden with an emphasis on plant partnerships, colour combinations and naturalistic planting. Long wisteria and clematis covered pergola, reflecting pool with folly, cascade with pond and duck house, rich variety of roses, vegetable and cutting garden. Sculptural elements by local artists.

45 STUBBINGS HOUSE

Henley Road, Maidenhead SL6 6QL. Mr & Mrs D Good, 01628 825454, www.stubbingsnursery.co.uk. *2m W of Maidenhead. From A4130 Henley Rd follow private access road (signed) opp Stubbings Church. See website for further directions.* Lunches & refreshments in the Nursery Cafe. **Adm £3.50, chd free. Sat 5, Sun 6 Apr, Sat 3, Sun 4, Mon 5 May (10.30-4). Visitors also welcome by appt Mar to Oct for groups of 10+.**
Parkland garden accessed via adjacent retail nursery. Set around C18 house (not open), home to Queen Wilhelmina of Netherlands in WW2. Large lawn with ha-ha and woodland walks. Notable trees incl historic cedars and araucaria. March brings an abundance of daffodils, then bluebells in April, and in May a 60m wall of wisteria. C18 ice house. Access to adjacent NT woodland. A level site with firm, gravel paths.

46 SUNNINGDALE PARK

Larch Avenue, Ascot SL5 0QE. De Vere Group, 01344 634000. *6m S of Windsor. On A30 at Sunningdale take Broomhall Lane. After ½ m, R into Larch Ave. From A329 turn into Silwood Rd towards Sunningdale.* Home-made teas. **Adm £4, chd free. Mon 26 May (2-5).**
Over 20-acres of beautifully landscaped gardens in Capability Brown style. Terrace garden and Victorian rockery designed by Pulham incl cave and water features. Lake area with paved walks, extensive lawns with specimen trees and flower beds, and early rhododendrons. Lovely 1m woodland walk. Grade II listed building (not open). Free garden history tour at 3.30pm. There are steps down to the lake.

GROUP OPENING

47 SWALLOWFIELD HORTICULTURAL SOCIETY

Swallowfield RG7 1QX. *5m S of Reading. M4 J11 & A33/B3349 signed 'Swallowfield NGS Opening'. Tickets from Doctors Surgery car park, The Street RG7 1QY.* Light refreshments. **Combined adm £6, chd free. Sun 29 June (11-5).**

THE ALLOTMENTS
Pam Wright

APRIL COTTAGE
Linda & Bill Kirkpatrick

5 BEEHIVE COTTAGES
Ray Tormey

BORDER COTTAGE
David & Caroline Cotton

BRAMBLES
Sarah & Martyn Dadds

5 CURLYS WAY
Mr & Mrs Carolyn & Gary Clark

NORKETT COTTAGE
Jenny Spencer

PRIMROSE COTTAGE
Mr & Mrs Hilda & Eddie Phillips

THREE GABLES
Sue & Keith Steptoe

WESSEX HOUSE
Val Payne

WOLSELEY COTTAGE
Christine Tainton

Swallowfield - a real village enhanced by a C12 church, nestled amongst rural countryside, by the Whitewater, Blackwater and Loddon rivers, creating an abundance of wildlife and lovely views. We are proud to offer a variety of beautiful well stocked gardens of all shapes and sizes, including a model train at Wessex House. Most gardens are within walking distance of each other, but transport is required for outlying gardens.

48 THE TITHE BARN
Tidmarsh RG8 8ER. Fran Wakefield. *1m S of Pangbourne, off A340. In Tidmarsh, turn by side of Greyhound PH, over bridge, R into Mill Corner field for car park. Short walk over field to garden.* Home-made teas adjacent to Norman church. **Adm £3.50, chd free. Sun 8 June (2-5). Also open - 80 Chapel Hill (2.5 miles east).**
This is a delightful village garden (1/4 -acre) within high brick walls around The Tithe Barn dating from 1760. Formally laid out with parterres of box and yew. There are roses, hostas, topiary and a little fernery as well as interesting vintage pots and containers. Working beehives. Winner of the English Garden magazine 'Gardener's Garden' competition.

49 TWIGS
Old Forest Road, Winnersh, Wokingham RG41 1JA. Jenny & Gerry Winterbourne, www.pbase.com/gerrywinterbourne/garden_intro. *1 1/2 m NW of Wokingham. From Winnersh A329/B3030 junction (Sainsburys) S for 0.7m towards Wokingham. Turn L into Old Forest Rd, over bridge, 0.3m on L.* Home-made teas. **Adm £3, chd free. Sun 29 June (2-5.30).**
A 1/2 -acre semi-formal garden with two lily ponds at the top, a small vegetable garden to one side and gravel paths that lead down to a more natural woodland area. Planting is mainly trees and shrubs, under-planted with drifts of bulbs and perennials. There are no lawns, the whole garden is given over to plants.

50 ◆ WALTHAM PLACE GARDENS
Church Hill, White Waltham SL6 3JH. Mr & Mrs N Oppenheimer, 01628 825517, www.walthamplace.com. *3 1/2 m W of Maidenhead. From M4 J8/9 take A404. Follow signs to White Waltham. Pass airfield on R. Turn L to Windsor/Paley St. Up hill 550 metres, entrance on L by post box.* Home-made cakes, organic soup and salads made from produce from the garden available in our tea-room. **Adm £5, chd £1. For NGS: Visitors welcome by appt for tours with a gardener every Weds from 21 May to 24 Sept. Please phone to book.**
Influenced by Henk Gerritsen, who collaborated with Strilli Oppenheimer to embrace a naturalistic philosophy combining forces with nature. A haven for insects, animals, fungi and indigenous flora. Naturalistic planting, woodland and meadows. Organic and bio-dynamic kitchen garden and farm.

Naturalistic planting, woodland and meadows. Organic and bio-dynamic kitchen garden and farm . . .

51 ◆ WELFORD PARK
Welford RG20 8HU. Mrs J H Puxley, 01488 608203, dpuxley@welfordpark.co.uk. *6m NW of Newbury. M4 J13, A34 (S). After 3m exit for A4 (W) to Hungerford. At 2nd r'about take B4000, after 4m turn R signed Welford. Entrance on Newbury-Lambourn Rd.* Refreshments by arrangement. **Adm £5, chd free. For NGS: Visitors welcome by appt from March for groups of 6-40. Please phone or email to book.**
An NGS 1927 pioneer garden with attractive parkland for walks. Emphasis on wildlife habitat and wild flowers. Formal garden with peony border, rose pergola and large wisteria on south side of Queen Anne House. Naturalistic and healing planting for calm atmosphere and delicious scents.

52 WHITEHOUSE FARM COTTAGE
Murrell Hill Lane, Binfield RG42 4BY. Louise Lusby, 01344 423688, garden.cottages@ntlworld.com. *Between Bracknell & Wokingham. Please do not use Sat Nav. From A329 take B3408. At 2nd set of T-lights turn L into St Marks Rd, 2nd L (opp Roebuck PH) into Foxley Lane. L into Murrell Hill Lane.* Home-made teas. **Adm £3.50, chd free (share to Sam Beare Hospice). Sun 8 June (11-5).**
Atmospheric cottage garden of 'rooms' with brick, china and decorative pebble areas - riotously planted with roses, herbs, ferns and other favourites. The courtyard with pot and lily ponds leads to terrace with circular domed seating area. Pond garden contains a pretty summer house and glasshouse. Featured in The English Garden Magazine and on ITV's Love Your Garden.

53 NEW WICKHAM HOUSE
Wickham, Newbury RG20 8HD. Mr & Mrs James D'Arcy. *7m NW of Newbury or 6m NE of Hungerford. From M4 J14, take A338(N) signed Wantage. 0.7m turn R onto B4000 for Wickham & Shefford Woodlands. Through Wickham village, entrance 100yds on R.* Home-made teas and light refreshments.
Adm £4.50, chd free. Sun 15 June (11-5).
In a beautiful country house setting, this exceptional 1/2 -acre walled garden was created from scratch 5-yrs-ago. Designed by Robin Templar-Williams, the different rooms have distinct themes and colour schemes. Delightful arched clematis and rose walkway. Wide variety of trees, planting, pots brimming with colour and places to sit and enjoy the views. Separate cutting and vegetable garden. Gravel paths.

D

54 WILLOW TREE COTTAGE
Ashampstead RG8 8RA. Katy & David Weston. *4m W of Pangbourne. From Yattendon head towards Reading. L fork in beech wood to Ashampstead, keep L, join lower rd, 1/2 m turn L before houses.* Home-made teas at Pyt House.
Combined adm £5, chd free with Pyt House. Sat 28, Sun 29 June (2-5).
Small pretty cottage garden surrounding the house that was originally built for the gardener of Pyt House. Substantially redesigned and replanted in recent years. Perennial borders, vegetable garden, pond with ducks and chickens.

Rooksnest

Berkshire County Volunteers

County Organiser
Heather Skinner, 5 Liddell Close, Finchampstead, Wokingham RG40 4NS, 01189 737197, heatheraskinner@aol.com

County Treasurer
Hugh Priestley, Jennetts Hill House, Stanford Dingley, Reading RG7 6JP, 01189 744349, priestleyc1@aol.com

Assistant County Organisers
Angela O'Connell, 22 The Hatches, Frimley Green GU21 6HE, 01252 668645, angela.oconnell@icloud.com
Nikki Sketch, Newlands, Courtlands Hill, Pangbourne RG8 7BE, 07768 934030, nikki@sketch.cc

BUCKINGHAMSHIRE

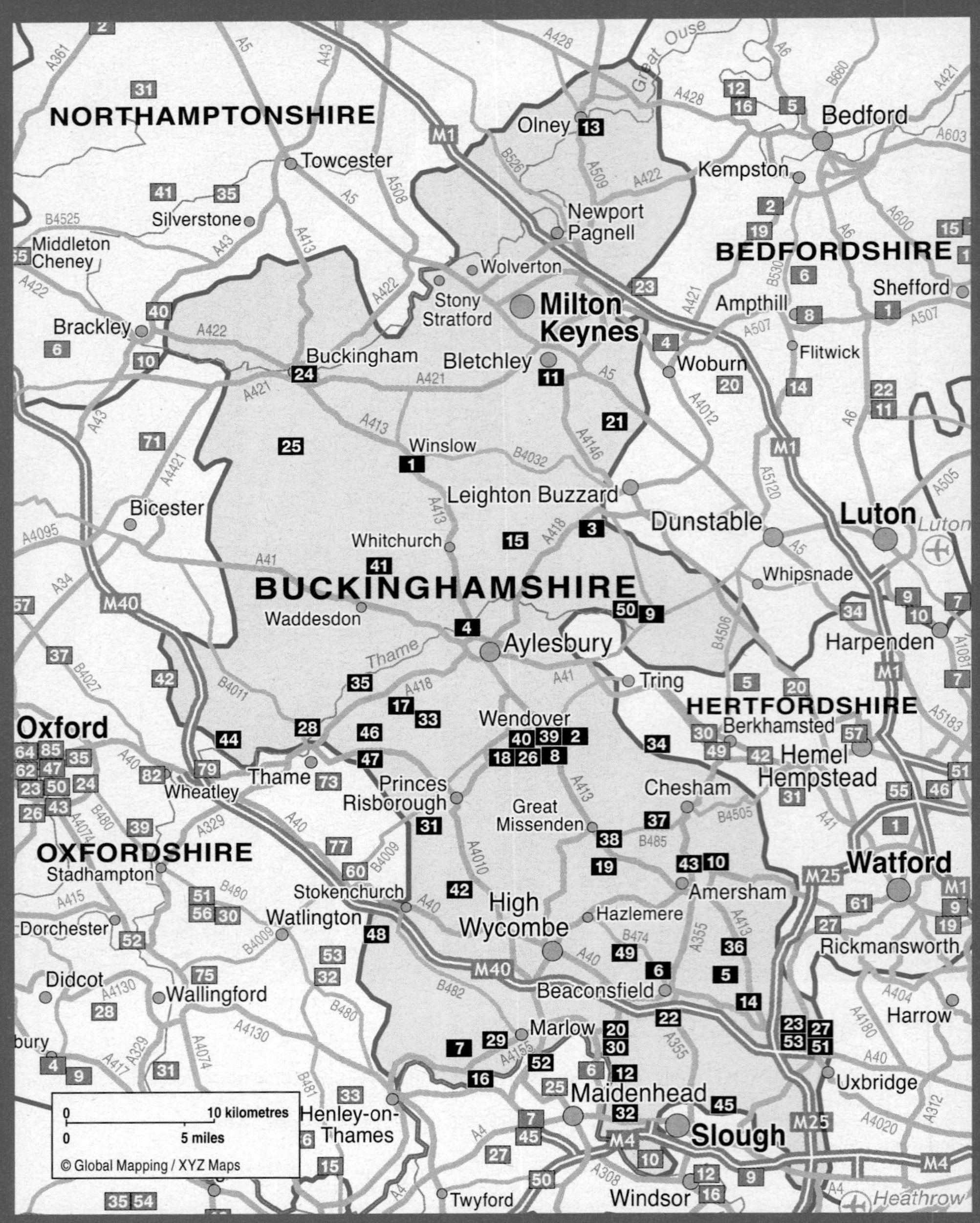

Opening Dates

All entries subject to change. For latest information check www.ngs.org.uk

February

Sunday 23
41 Quainton Gardens

March

Sunday 2
30 Magnolia House

Sunday 16
53 Wind in the Willows

Sunday 30
10 Chesham Bois House

A harmonious arrangement of arcs and circles introduces a rhythm that leads through the garden . . .

April

Sunday 20
38 Overstroud Cottage

Monday 21
43 Rivendell
50 Westend House

Saturday 26
12 Cliveden

Sunday 27
28 Long Crendon Gardens
45 Stoke Poges Memorial Gardens
52 Whitewalls

May

Sunday 4
31 The Manor House

Monday 5
3 Ascott
35 Nether Winchendon House
46 Turn End

Sunday 11
10 Chesham Bois House
38 Overstroud Cottage
40 The Plough

Sunday 18
5 Beech House
19 Fressingwood
45 Stoke Poges Memorial Gardens

Saturday 24
32 Maryfield

Sunday 25
23 Higher Denham Gardens
32 Maryfield

Monday 26
35 Nether Winchendon House
37 The Old Sun House
40 The Plough

June

Sunday 1
1 Abbots House
38 Overstroud Cottage

Festival Weekend

Saturday 7
13 Cowper & Newton Museum Gardens

Sunday 8
13 Cowper & Newton Museum Gardens
15 Cublington Gardens

Sunday 15
6 18 Brownswood Road
25 Hillesden House
31 The Manor House
41 Quainton Gardens

Thursday 19
29 Lords Wood

Saturday 21
2 Acer Corner
21 Great Brickhill Gardens
39 11 The Paddocks

Sunday 22
2 Acer Corner
7 Burrow Farm
11 126 Church Green Road
17 Dinton Village Gardens
20 Grange Drive Wooburn
39 11 The Paddocks
51 The White House

Tuesday 24
11 126 Church Green Road

Wednesday 25
20 Grange Drive Wooburn

Friday 27
39 11 The Paddocks (Evening)

Sunday 29
4 Aylesbury Gardens
9 Cheddington Gardens
24 Hill House, Buckingham
38 Overstroud Cottage
43 Rivendell

July

Saturday 5
21 Great Brickhill Gardens
39 11 The Paddocks

Sunday 6
18 Ellesborough Village Gardens
39 11 The Paddocks
47 Tythrop Park

Sunday 13
7 Burrow Farm
10 Chesham Bois House

Saturday 19
48 The Walled Garden

Sunday 20
52 Whitewalls

August

Sunday 3
50 Westend House

Tuesday 5
16 Danesfield House

Thursday 7
16 Danesfield House

Sunday 10
26 Homelands

Tuesday 12
16 Danesfield House

Thursday 14
16 Danesfield House

Monday 25
3 Ascott
35 Nether Winchendon House

September

Sunday 7
52 Whitewalls

Thursday 11
29 Lords Wood

October

Saturday 18
2 Acer Corner

Sunday 19
2 Acer Corner

February 2015

Sunday 22
41 Quainton Gardens

Gardens open to the public

3 Ascott
12 Cliveden
13 Cowper & Newton Museum Gardens
35 Nether Winchendon House
45 Stoke Poges Memorial Gardens

By appointment only

8 Cedar House
14 Craiglea House
22 Hall Barn
27 Kayalami

- 33 Moat Farm
- 34 Montana
- 36 North Down
- 42 Red Kites
- 44 Rose Tree Cottage
- 49 Watercroft

Also open by appointment

- 1 Abbots House
- 2 Acer Corner
- 4 Tolverne, Aylesbury Gardens
- 6 18 Brownswood Road
- 7 Burrow Farm
- 9 Bridge Cottage, Cheddington Gardens
- 10 Chesham Bois House
- 15 Larkspur House, Cublington Gardens
- 24 Hill House, Buckingham
- 25 Hillesden House
- 26 Homelands
- 30 Magnolia House
- 32 Maryfield
- 38 Overstroud Cottage
- 39 11 The Paddocks
- 41 Thorngumbald, Quainton Gardens
- 41 The Vine, Quainton Gardens
- 50 Westend House
- 52 Whitewalls
- 53 Wind in the Willows

Designer's garden with Japanese influence and large collection of maples . . .

The Gardens

1 ABBOTS HOUSE

10 Church Street, Winslow MK18 3AN. Mrs Jane Rennie, 01296 712326, jane@renniemail.com. *9m N of Aylesbury. A413 into Winslow. From town centre take Horn St & R into Church St, L fork at top. Entrance 20m on L. Parking in town centre & adjacent streets.* Home-made teas. **Adm £3, chd free. Sun 1 June (2-5.30). Visitors also welcome by appt Apr to Aug for groups of 20 max.**

Garden on different levels divided into 4. Courtyard near house with arbour, new pond and pots, woodland garden with rose arbour, swimming pool garden with grasses. Walled Victorian kitchen garden with glass houses, potager, fruit pergola, wall trained fruit, many Mediterranean plants and recent meadow planting. Limited wheelchair access.

2 ACER CORNER

10 Manor Road, Wendover HP22 6HQ. Jo Naiman, 07958 319234, jo@acercorner.com. *3m S of Aylesbury. Follow A413 into Wendover. L at clock tower r'about into Aylesbury Rd. R at next r'about into Wharf Rd, continue past schools on L, garden on R.* Home-made teas. **Adm £2.50, chd free (share to South Bucks Jewish Community Charity). Sat 21, Sun 22 June, Sat 18, Sun 19 Oct (2-5). Visitors also welcome by appt May to Oct.**

Garden designer's garden with Japanese influence and large collection of Japanese maples. The enclosed front garden is Japanese in style. Back garden is divided into 3 areas: patio area surrounded by roses; densely planted area with many acers and roses; and the corner which incl a productive greenhouse and interesting planting. Amateur Gardening October 2011.

3 ◆ ASCOTT

Ascott, Wing, Leighton Buzzard LU7 0PR. Sir Evelyn de Rothschild, National Trust, 01296 688242, www.nationaltrust.org.uk/ascott. *2m SW of Leighton Buzzard, 8m NE of Aylesbury. Via A418. Buses: 150 Aylesbury - Milton Keynes, 100 Aylesbury & Milton Keynes.* **Adm £5, chd £2.50 (NT members are required to pay to enter the gardens on NGS days). For NGS: Mon 5 May, Mon 25 Aug (2-6). For other opening times and information, please phone or see garden website.**

Combining Victorian formality with early C20 natural style and recent plantings to lead it into the C21, with a recently completed garden designed by Jacques and Peter Wirtz who designed the gardens at Alnwick Castle, and also a Richard Long Sculpture. Terraced lawns with specimen and ornamental trees, panoramic views to the Chilterns. Naturalised bulbs, mirror-image herbaceous borders, impressive topiary incl box and yew sundial. Entry in to Ascott House is free to NT members, non-members will be required to pay. Outdoor wheelchairs available from car park. Indoor wheelchairs are available in the house. Prior booking advised for both.

GROUP OPENING

4 AYLESBURY GARDENS

Aylesbury HP21 7LR. *3/4 m SE of Aylesbury Centre. SE of town centre (3 gardens off A413, 1 garden off A41).* Home-made teas at 2 Spenser Road. **Combined adm £4, chd free. Sun 29 June (2-6).**

16 MILTON ROAD
Roger & Frances King

2 SPENSER ROAD
Graham & Rosemary Brown

TOLVERNE
Bill Nuttycombe & Julian Oaten-Wareham
Visitors also welcome by appt May to Aug on Sats only (11-2). aylesbury-guy@hotmail.co.uk

7 WENDOVER WAY
Ms Jackie Bennett OBE

Four mature town gardens within walking distance of each other showing a wide range of ideas and designs. Each garden displays the individuality of its owners and their passions, including tender perennials, herbaceous borders, many hostas and ponds. Other features are a rare Victorian greenhouse with cast-iron features, raised vegetable beds, a broad selection of garden trees and colourful cottage style planting.

5 BEECH HOUSE

Long Wood Drive, Jordans, Beaconsfield HP9 2SS. Sue & Ray Edwards. *From A40 follow signs to Seer Green & Jordans for approx 1m.* **Adm £3, chd free. Sun 18 May (2-5.30).**

2-acre plantsman's garden built up over the last 25yrs, with a wide range of plants aimed at providing yr-round interest. Many shrubs, roses, grasses, ferns and trees planted for their ornamental bark and autumnal foliage. A particular feature is the meadow in the back garden with numerous bulbs and wild flowers in spring and early summer. Wheelchair access dependent upon weather conditions.

6 18 BROWNSWOOD ROAD

Beaconsfield HP9 2NU. John & Bernadette Thompson, 01494 689959, tbernadette60@gmail.com. *Beaconsfield New Town. From New Town turn R into Ledborough Lane, L into Sandleswood Rd, 2nd R into Brownswood Rd*. Home-made teas. **Adm £3, chd free. Sun 15 June (2-5.30). Visitors also welcome by appt May to Sept.**

A plant-filled garden designed by Barbara Hunt. A harmonious arrangement of arcs and circles introduces a rhythm that leads through the garden. Sweeping box curves, gravel beds, brick edging and lush planting. A restrained use of purples and reds dazzle against a grey and green background. New auricula theatre.

7 BURROW FARM

Hambleden RG9 6LT. David Palmer, 01491 571256. *1m SE of Hambleden. On A4155 between Henley and Marlow, turn N at Mill End. After 300yds, R onto Rotten Row. After ½ m, Burrow Farm entrance on R*. Home-made teas. **Adm £5, chd free (share to Buckinghamshire Community Foundation). Sun 22 June, Sun 13 July (2-6). Visitors also welcome by appt May to July.**

Burrow Farm and the adjacent cottages (not open) are part Tudor and part Elizabethan, set in the Chilterns above Hambleden Valley where it meets the Thames. Views of pasture and woodlands across the ha-ha greatly enhance the setting. Special features are the parterre, arboretum and C15 barn, where home-made teas are served.

8 CEDAR HOUSE

Bacombe Lane, Wendover HP22 6EQ. Sarah Nicholson, 01296 622131, jeremynicholson@btinternet.com. *5m SE Aylesbury. From Gt Missenden take A413 into Wendover. Take 1st L before row of cottages, house at top of lane*. **Adm £3.50. Visitors welcome by appt May to Sept for groups of 10+.**

A chalk garden in the Chiltern Hills with a steep sloping lawn leading to a natural swimming pond with aquatic plants. Wild flowers with native orchids. Shaped borders hold a great variety of trees, shrubs and perennials. A lodge greenhouse and a good collection of half hardy plants in pots. Steep, sloping lawn.

Turn End

GROUP OPENING

9 CHEDDINGTON GARDENS

nr Leighton Buzzard LU7 0RQ. *11m E of Aylesbury, 7m S of Leighton Buzzard. Turn off B489 at Pitstone. Turn off B488 at Cheddington Station*. Home-made teas at Westend House and Bridge Cottage. **Combined adm £5, chd free (share to Methodist Church, St Giles Church and Village School). Sun 29 June (1.30-5.30).**

BRIDGE COTTAGE
Mr & Mrs B Hicks
Visitors also welcome by appt May to Sept.
01296 660313
georgeous1@gmail.com

CHEDDINGTON ALLOTMENTS
Cheddington Parish Council

CHEDDINGTON COMBINED SCHOOL SENSORY GARDEN
Cheddington Combined School

7 HIGH STREET
Irene & Tony Johnson

THE OLD POST OFFICE
Alan & Wendy Tipple

WESTEND HOUSE
His Honour Judge & Mrs Richard Foster
(See separate entry)

WOODSTOCK COTTAGE
Mr & Mrs D Bradford

A village grouping of varied and interesting gardens to view - incl the village school sensory garden which is maintained by the pupil's gardening club and the village allotments which has over 50 plots and benefits from wide views of the Chilterns. Partial wheelchair access.

10 CHESHAM BOIS HOUSE

85 Bois Lane, Chesham Bois HP6 6DF. Julia Plaistowe, 01494 726476, julia.plaistowe@yahoo.co.uk. *1m N of Amersham-on-the-Hill. Follow Sycamore Rd (main shopping centre road of Amersham) which becomes Bois Lane*. Home-made teas. **Adm £3.50, chd free. Sun 30 Mar (1.30-5); Sun 11 May, Sun 13 July (2-5.30). Visitors also welcome by appt Mar to Sept.**

3-acre plantswoman's garden with primroses, daffodils and hellebores in early spring. Interesting for most of the yr with lovely herbaceous borders, rill with small ornamental canal, walled garden, old orchard with wildlife pond, and handsome trees of which some are topiaried. It is a peaceful oasis. Has been featured in RHS journal The Garden and numerous local publications. Gravel in front of house.

11 126 CHURCH GREEN ROAD

Bletchley, Milton Keynes MK3 6DD. David & Janice Hale. *13m E of Buckingham, 11m N of Leighton Buzzard. Off B4034 into Church Green Rd, take L turn at mini-r'about.* Home-made teas. **Adm £3, chd free. Sun 22 June (2-6); Tue 24 June (2-5).**

A gentle sloping mature garden of 1/2 -acre is a plant lover's delight, which incl a small formal garden, shady areas and mixed borders of shrubs, perennials and roses. Features incl a thatched wendy house, pergola, pond, productive fruit and vegetable garden, greenhouse and patio.

12 ◆ CLIVEDEN

Taplow, Maidenhead SL6 0JA. National Trust, 01628 605069, www.nationaltrust.org.uk/cliveden. *2m N of Taplow. Leave M4 at J7, take A4 towards Maidenhead or M40 at J4, take A404 S & follow brown tourism signs.* Light refreshments. **Adm £9.90, chd £4.95. For NGS: Sat 26 Apr (10-5.30). For other opening times and information, please phone or see garden website.**

Set high above the R Thames, Cliveden's magnificent gardens and breath-taking views have been admired for centuries. Discover a garden that delights throughout the seasons with a colourful planting scheme for the famous Parterre, impressive floral displays, distinctive topiary and an outstanding sculpture collection. Garden highlights incl spring and summer floral displays on the parterre and in the long garden, autumn colour in the water garden and a new rose garden. Children's storybook-themed play area, yew tree maze, woodland play trail and a shop. Countryfile (May 2013), BBC London News (August 2013), The One Show (September 2013). Step-free route map available from information centre. Wheelchairs available to borrow.

13 ◆ COWPER & NEWTON MUSEUM GARDENS

Market Place, Olney MK46 4AJ. Mrs E Knight, 01234 711516, www.cowperandnewtonmuseum.org.uk. *5m N of Newport Pagnell. 12m S of Wellingborough. On A509. Please park in public car park in East St.* Home-made teas. **Adm £2.50, chd free. For NGS: Sat 7, Sun 8 June (10.30-4.30). For other opening times and information, please phone or see garden website.**

Restored walled flower garden with plants pre-1800, many mentioned by C18 poet, William Cowper, who said of himself 'Gardening was, of all employments, that in which I succeeded best'. Also summer house garden in Victorian kitchen style with organic, new and old vegetable varieties. Herb and medicinal plant borders in memory of the garden's original use by an apothecary. Lacemaking demonstrations and local artists painting live art.

14 CRAIGLEA HOUSE

Austenwood Lane, Chalfont St Peter, Gerrards Cross SL9 9DA. Jeff & Sue Medlock, 01753 884852, suemedlock@msn.com. *6m SE Amersham. From Gerrards Cross take B416 to Amersham. Take L fork after 1/2 m into Austenwood Lane, garden 1/3 m on R. Park at St Joseph's Church or Priory Rd.* Home-made teas. **Adm £4, chd free. Visitors welcome by appt Apr to Aug.**

Delightful 1-acre garden complements the Arts and Crafts House which it surrounds. The planting ranges from the formal rose garden, lawns, herbaceous borders and pergola, to the natural planting around wildlife ponds, apple trees and along a fairy inhabited fern walk. Garden contains a wide range of plants, including many hostas, a vegetable garden and many seats affording lovely views of garden.

GROUP OPENING

15 CUBLINGTON GARDENS

Cublington, Leighton Buzzard LU7 0LF. *5m SE Winslow, 5m NE Aylesbury. From Aylesbury take A413 Buckingham Rd. After 4m, at Whitchurch, turn R to Cublington.* Home-made teas at Victorian school, now the village hall. **Combined adm £4, chd free. Sun 8 June (2-5.30).**

LARKSPUR HOUSE
Mr & Mrs S Jenkins
Visitors also welcome by appt June to July.
01296 682615
gstmusketeers3@aol.com

OLD MANOR COTTAGE
Dr J Higgins

1 STEWKLEY ROAD
Tom & Helen Gadsby

3 diverse gardens in this attractive Buckinghamshire village listed as a conservation area. Each garden has its own character. Larkspur House is a beautifully maintained modern garden with hostas and alliums being firm favourites. It has a large orchard and newly planted meadow. Old Manor Cottage is a listed, timber-framed property with cottage garden giving all-yr colour, water features and courtyard for outside dining. 1 Stewkley Road has a strong focus on home-grown food with an idyllic organic kitchen garden, small orchard and courtyard plus family courtyard garden. Partial wheelchair access.

16 DANESFIELD HOUSE

Henley Road, Marlow SL7 2EY. Danesfield House Hotel, 01628 891010, www.danesfieldhouse.co.uk. *3m from Marlow. On the A4155 between Marlow and Henley-on-Thames. Signs on the LH-side - Danesfield House Hotel and Spa.* Reservations for luncheon or afternoon tea is essential. **Adm £4, chd free. Tue 5, Thur 7, Tue 12, Thur 14 Aug (10-4.30).**

The gardens at Danesfield were completed in 1901 by Robert Hudson, the Sunlight Soap magnate who built the house. Since the house opened as a hotel in 1991, the gardens have been admired by several thousand guests each year. However, in 2009, it was discovered that the gardens contained outstanding examples of pulhamite in both the formal gardens and the waterfall areas. The 100-yr-old topiary is also outstanding. Part of the grounds incl an Iron Age fort. Guided tours welcome on NGS open days. Pre-booking essential. Restricted wheelchair access to the gardens (gravel paths).

GROUP OPENING

17 DINTON VILLAGE GARDENS

Dinton HP17 8UN. *4m SW Aylesbury, 4m NE Thame. For Satnavs enter HP17 8UQ. 1/4 m off A418.* ***Please only use turning signed Ford and Dinton for free car park, clearly signed***. Home-made teas in village hall. **Combined adm £6, chd free. Sun 22 June (2-6).**

GRAPEVINE COTTAGE
Anne & Mark Seckington

GREENDALE
S A Eaton

HERMIT'S COTTAGE
Mr & Mrs M Usherwood

NEW HONEYSUCKLE COTTAGE
Mr & Mrs W Lee

INNISFREE
David & Rosemary Jackson

LAVENDER COTTAGE
Sara & Trevor Hopwood

ORCHARD COTTAGE
Harry & Barbara Bingham

WESTLINGTON FARM
Shaun & Catherine Brogan

WILLOW COTTAGE
Philip & Jennifer Rimell

Dinton is a very picturesque, secluded, historic village, set in countryside with views to the Chiltern Hills. A conservation area, it has many pretty, thatched, whitewashed, old cottages and has been featured in the Midsomer Murders TV series. The 9 colourful and very interesting gardens range from small, informal cottages through to medium and on to larger, country house styles, each one with a strikingly different character and purpose. All are within easy and peaceful walking distance of the car park and village hall. The lovely C11/12 Norman Church, a Grade I listed building, has an outstanding S-doorway and a 800-yr-old font (open to visitors). Wheelchair access and dogs allowed to 5 gardens. WC at village hall.

GROUP OPENING

18 ELLESBOROUGH VILLAGE GARDENS

Wendover HP17 0XD. *6m SE of Aylesbury, 4m NE of Princes Risborough. On B4010 1 1/2 m W of Wendover. Between village hall at Butlers Cross & church.* Tea at Homelands or church. **Combined adm £4.50, chd free. Sun 6 July (2-5).**

HOMELANDS
Jean & Tony Young
(See separate entry)

NEW ST PAULS HOUSE D
Mr David Porter

Homelands; a 3/4 -acre garden on chalk, wide range of features incl seating areas, wildlife pond and a mature wild flower meadow, deep borders and gravel beds. St Pauls House; a 1/2 -acre modern cottage garden. Stunning views over the Vale of Aylesbury, making the most of a tricky sloping site. Generous planting in a strong structure of beds and paths. Wheelchair access at Homelands only.

19 FRESSINGWOOD

Hare Lane, Little Kingshill, Great Missenden HP16 0EF. John & Maggie Bateson. *1m S of Gt Missenden, 4m W of Amersham. From the A413 at Chiltern Hospital, turn L signed Gt & Lt Kingshill. Take 1st L into Nags Head Lane. Turn R under railway bridge, then L into New Rd & continue to Hare Lane.* Home-made teas. **Adm £3.50, chd free. Sun 18 May (2-5.30).**
Thoughtfully designed garden with yr-round colour. Shrubbery with ferns, grasses and hellebores. Small formal garden, herb garden, pergolas with wisteria, roses and clematis. Topiary and landscaped terrace. Newly developed area incorporating water with grasses. Herbaceous borders and bonsai collection. Many interesting features.

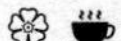

GROUP OPENING

20 GRANGE DRIVE WOOBURN

Wooburn Green HP10 0QD. *On A4094, 2m SW of A40, between Bourne End & Wooburn. From Wooburn Church, direction Maidenhead, Grange Drive is on L before r'about. From Bourne End, L at 2 mini-r'abouts, then 1st R.* Home-made teas. **Combined adm £3.50, chd free. Sun 22, Wed 25 June (2-5).**

MAGNOLIA HOUSE
Alan & Elaine Ford
(See separate entry)

THE SHADES
Pauline & Maurice Kirkpatrick

2 diverse gardens in a private tree-lined drive which formed the entrance to a country house now demolished. Magnolia House is a 1/2 -acre garden with many mature trees incl magnificent copper beech and magnolia reaching the rooftop, a small cactus bed, fernery, stream leading to pond and greenhouses with 2 small aviaries. Front garden now has natural pond and bees. The Shades drive is approached through mature trees and beds of herbaceous plants and 60 various roses. A natural well is surrounded by shrubs and acers. The garden was developed in 2010 to incl a natural stone lawn terrace and changes were made to the existing flower beds. A green slate water feature with alpine plants completes the garden. Partial wheelchair access.

A riot of intense but natural planting providing colour, perfume and contrasting foliage . . .

The Manor House

GROUP OPENING

21 GREAT BRICKHILL GARDENS

Milton Keynes MK17 9AS. *6m S of Milton Keynes. At Old Red Lion PH go up the Pound Hill. No. 2 is right opp the PH, No. 28 is further up on RH-side.* Refreshments available at Old Red Lion PH. **Combined adm £4, chd free. Sat 21 June, Sat 5 July (1-6).**

2 POUND HILL
Mr Ivan Mears

28 POUND HILL
Ms Beata Baker

2 village gardens in the picturesque hilltop village of Great Brickhill. 2 Pound Hill is a small terraced cottage garden full of unusual perennials and a huge collection of heucheras and hostas. 28 Pound Hill is a mature, ½ -acre garden. Extensive deep borders densely filled with shrubs and perennials in contrasting colours and textures. Many unusual plants, with over 50 different varieties of (mostly) English roses. Other features incl lily and aquatic plants' pond surrounded by naturalistic borders, fruit and vegetable plot and many exotic plants in pots.

22 HALL BARN

Windsor End, Beaconsfield HP9 2SG. The Hon Mrs Farncombe, jenefer@farncombe01.demon.co.uk. *½ m S of Beaconsfield. Lodge gate 300yds S off St Mary & All Saints' Church in Old Town centre. Please do not use satnavs.* **Adm £4, chd free. Visitors welcome by appt weekdays. Teas by arrangement for groups of 10+.**
Historical landscaped garden laid out between 1680-1730 for the poet Edmund Waller and his descendants. Features 300-yr-old cloud formation yew hedges, formal lake and vistas ending with classical buildings and statues. Wooded walks around the grove offer respite from the heat on sunny days. One of the original NGS garden openings of 1927. Open-air Shakespeare Festival for the mid 2 weeks in June. Gravel paths.

GROUP OPENING

23 HIGHER DENHAM GARDENS

Higher Denham UB9 5EA. *6m E of Beaconsfield. Turn off the A412 about ½ -mile N of junction with A40 into Old Rectory Lane. After 1m enter Higher Denham straight ahead. Tickets for all gardens available at the community hall.* Home-made teas at the community hall. **Combined adm £5, chd free (share to Higher Denham Community Association). Sun 25 May (1-5).**

NEW **LOWER ROAD**

NEW **30 LOWER ROAD**
Mr & Mrs Mike Macgowan

19 MIDDLE ROAD
Sonia Harris

5 SIDE ROAD
Jane Blythe

WIND IN THE WILLOWS
Ron James
(See separate entry)

5 gardens, incl 2 NEW, in the delightful chalk stream Misbourne Valley. Wind in the Willows has over 350 shrubs and trees, informal, woodland and wild gardens incl riverside and bog plantings and a collection of 80 hostas. 'Really different' and 'stunning' are typical visitor comments. 19 Middle Road has a terrace overlooking a garden crowded with as many plants as possible with some fruit bushes and vegetables. 5 Side Road is a medium-sized garden with lawns surrounded by beds of mixed flowering plants and shrubs and a feature for children. The 2 NEW gardens in Lower Road are medium-size, one a work in progress with raised beds perennials and shrubs incl roses, ceanothus and clematis and patio pots, the other a wildlife friendly garden with interesting shrubs, pond, vegetables and ferns. Wind in the Willows featured in Carol Klein's new book and Buckinghamshire Life. A few steps at 19 Middle Road and some lawn and gravel paths at Wind in the Willows.

24 HILL HOUSE, BUCKINGHAM
Castle Street, Buckingham MK18 1BS. Leonie & Peter Thorogood, 07860 714758, leonie@pjtassociates.com. *By parish church in Buckingham town centre. Signed off bypass at Tingewick Rd Industry turn off.* Cream teas in the parish church. **Adm £3, chd free. Sun 29 June (12.30-6). Visitors also welcome by appt May to Sept.**
1/3 -acre town garden on old castle walls by parish church in Buckingham conservation area. Aiming for ease of maintenance, yr-round interest and colour, incl good roses, hostas, and herbaceous. Slight slopes.

25 HILLESDEN HOUSE
Church End, Hillesden MK18 4DB. Mr & Mrs R M Faccenda, 01296 730451, suefaccenda@aol.com. *3m S of Buckingham. Next to church in Hillesden.* **Adm £4.50, chd free. Sun 15 June (2-5). Visitors also welcome by appt June to July for groups 15+.**
By superb church 'Cathedral in the Fields'. Carp lakes, fountains and waterfalls with mature trees. Rose, alpine and herbaceous borders, 5-acres of formal gardens with 80-acres of deer park and parkland. Wild flower areas and extensive lakes developed by the owner. Lovely walks and plenty of wildlife. Also a newly created woodland garden. No wheelchair access to lakes.

26 HOMELANDS
Springs Lane, Ellesborough, Aylesbury HP17 0XD. Jean & Tony Young, 01296 622306, young@ellesborough.fsnet.co.uk. *6m SE of Aylesbury. On the B4010 between Wendover & Princes Risborough. Springs Lane is between village hall at Butlers Cross and the church. Narrow lane with an uneven surface.* **Adm £3.50, chd free. Sun 10 Aug (2-5). Visitors also welcome by appt June to Aug.**
Secluded 3/4 -acre garden on difficult chalk, adjoining open countryside. Designed to be enjoyed from many seating positions. Progress from semi formal to wild flower meadow and wildlife pond. Deep borders with all season interest and gravel beds with exotic late summer and autumn planting.

27 KAYALAMI
The Pyghtle, off Village Road, Denham Village UB9 5BD. Hazel de Quervain, 07747 856468, hazel@connexions4africa.com. *3m NW of Uxbridge, 7m E of Beaconsfield. Village Rd is next to village green. The Pyghtle is opp Falcon PH and Kayalami is the 3rd house along.* Light refreshments. **Adm £4, chd free. Visitors welcome by appt June to July for groups of 30 max.**
A deep passion for gardening is evident everywhere in this stunning yet secluded 1-acre garden. For over 21-yrs Hazel and Tony, her gardener and friend, have created the garden of today. A riot of intense but natural planting providing colour, perfume and contrasting foliage. Herbaceous borders packed with hardy plants, shrubs and trees provide a magnificent backdrop to beautifully manicured lawns. Gravel drive, plenty of seats.

GROUP OPENING

28 LONG CRENDON GARDENS
Long Crendon HP18 9AN. *2m N of Thame. Long Crendon Village is situated on the B4011 Thame-Bicester Rd. Maps showing the location of the gardens will be available on the day.* Home-made teas at Church House located in the High St. **Combined adm £6, chd free (share to Long Crendon Day Centre and Community Library). Sun 27 Apr (2-6).**

BAKER'S CLOSE
Mr & Mrs Peter Vaines

BARRY'S CLOSE
Mr & Mrs Richard Salmon

48 CHILTON ROAD
Mr & Mrs M Charnock

25 ELM TREES
Carol & Mike Price

MANOR HOUSE
Mr & Mrs West

MULBERRY HOUSE
Ken Pandolfi & James Anderson

TOMPSONS FARM
Mr & Mrs T Moynihan

7 gardens to visit, 3 along the High St; Tompsons Farm: a large woodland garden with mature trees and lawns sweeping down to an ornamental lake; Mulberry House: a restored, old vicarage garden which incl a formal knot garden, a wooded walkway, pond, Zen style area and a notable Monkey Puzzle tree; Manor House: a large garden with 2 ornamental lakes and fine views towards the Chilterns and a large variety of spring flowering bulbs and shrubs. On the Bicester Road, 2 large gardens; Baker's Close: partly walled with terraced lawns, rockery, shrubs and a wild area, a spring planting of thousands of daffodils, narcissi and tulips; Barry's Close: has a collection of spring flowering trees forming a backdrop to borders, pools and a water garden. Then 2 cottage gardens; 25 Elm Trees: with a terrace, small orchard area, wildlife pond, rockery and deep borders; and 48 Chilton Road: with spring bulbs, shrubs, perennial borders and a summerhouse area. Restricted wheelchair access to some gardens.

A spring planting of thousands of daffodils, narcissi and tulips . . .

29 LORDS WOOD
Frieth Road, Marlow Common SL7 2QS. Mr & Mrs Messum. *1 1/2 m NW Marlow. From Marlow turn off the A4155 at Platts Garage into Oxford Rd, towards Frieth for 1 1/2 m. Garden is 100yds past the Marlow Common turn, on the L.* Home-made teas. **Adm £4, chd free. Thur 19 June, Thur 11 Sept (11-4.30).**
Lords Wood was built in 1899 and has been the Messums family home since 1974. The 5-acres of garden feature extensive borders in widely varying styles. From vegetable, flower and herb gardens, to large water gardens and rockery, orchard, woodland, and meadow with fantastic views over the Chilterns. We are always bringing new ideas to Lords Wood, you will find something different to enjoy with every visit. Partial wheelchair access; gravel paths and steep slopes.

30 MAGNOLIA HOUSE

Wooburn HP10 0QD. Alan & Elaine Ford, 01628 525818, www.lanford.co.uk/events. *On A9094, 2m SW of A40 between Bourne End & Wooburn.* Light refreshments. **Adm £3, chd free. Sun 2 Mar (11-2). Visitors also welcome by appt Feb to Sept.**

1/2 -acre, many mature trees incl magnificent copper beech and large magnolia. Wollemi pine, cactus, fernery, stream, 2 ponds, 2 greenhouses. 2 small aviaries, 2 beehives, 10,000 snowdrops and hellebores in spring. Collection of over 60 different hostas. Stay in our self-catering accommodation and enjoy the garden. It is constantly being updated and new features added. Partial wheelchair access.

Water garden with paths, bridges and walkways, fed by 14 chalk springs . . .

31 THE MANOR HOUSE

Church End, Bledlow, Nr Princes Risborough HP27 9PB. The Lord Carrington. *9m NW of High Wycombe, 3m SW of Princes Risborough. 1/2 m off B4009 in middle of Bledlow Village.* **Adm £5, chd free. Sun 4 May, Sun 15 June (2-5).**

Paved garden, parterres, shrub borders, old roses and walled kitchen garden. Water garden with paths, bridges and walkways, fed by 14 chalk springs. Also 2-acres with sculptures and landscaped planting. Limited access for wheelchairs to some parts of the gardens.

32 MARYFIELD

High Street, Taplow SL6 0EX. Jacqueline & Roger Andrews, 01628 667246, japrivate@btinternet.com. *1m S Cliveden, 1/2 m E Maidenhead. From M4 J7 or M40 J4 follow signs for Taplow. Drive past church & up High St. Maryfield is on bend of High St. Please enter through iron gates.* Home-made teas. **Adm £4.50, chd free. Sat 24, Sun 25 May (2-5). Visitors and groups also welcome by appt Apr to Sept.**

A 3-acre garden wrapped around our Victorian home in the heart of Taplow Village. Featuring grasses, a white garden, exotic garden and walled vegetable garden. Formal, structured planting with yew topiary and box hedging to prairie-style and ending in a woodland context. Adventurous planting combinations and contemporary designs. Lovely garden to explore or just to sit and have tea. Limited wheelchair access. Some narrow paths.

33 MOAT FARM

Water Lane, Ford, Aylesbury HP17 8XD. Mr & Mrs P Bergqvist, 01296 748560, patricia@quintadelarosa.com. *Turn up Water Lane by Dinton Hermit in the middle of Ford Village, after approx 200yds turn L over cattle grid between beech hedges into Moat Farm.* Home-made teas. **Visitors welcome by appt Apr to Sept for groups of 8-40.**

A country garden with herbaceous borders, roses, hostas, trees and water. A moat that flows through the garden and a 'blind' moat through the arboretum. Small walled garden and some vegetables.

34 MONTANA

Shire Lane, Cholesbury HP23 6NA. John & Diana Garner, 01494 758347, montana@cholesbury.net. *3m NW of Chesham. Leave A41 junction signed A4251 North Church. Follow Wigginton signs turning R before church. R after Champneys. 2nd R onto Shire Lane & Montana is 1/2 m on L.* Home-made teas. **Visitors welcome by appt Feb to June.**

A 1-acre country garden planted to attract birds and wildlife leading to 3-acres of mixed woodland. Snowdrops, daffodils, a multitude of spring bulbs and flowers, camellias, rhododendrons and sweet peas. Peaceful seating, meandering paths, chickens, a vegetable patch, greenhouses and 2 small ponds. Unusual flowering shrubs, herbaceous borders and a fernery.

35 ◆ NETHER WINCHENDON HOUSE

Nether Winchendon, Near Thame, Aylesbury HP18 0DY. Mr Robert Spencer Bernard, 01844 290101, www.netherwinchendonhouse.com. *6m SW of Aylesbury, 6m from Thame. Approx 4m from Thame on A418 turn 1st L to Cuddington, turn L at Xrds, down hill, turn R, and R again to parking by house.* Cream teas at the church (2.30-5). **Adm £4, chd free. For NGS: Mon 5, Mon 26 May, Mon 25 Aug (2-5.30). For other opening times and information, please phone or see garden website.**

Nether Winchendon House is set in 7-acres of garden with fine and rare trees and surrounded by parkland. A Founder Garden (1927). Medieval and Tudor house set in stunning landscape. The South Lawn runs down to the R Thame. Picturesque village with interesting church. Wheelchair access to the main features of the garden.

36 NORTH DOWN

Dodds Lane, Chalfont St Giles HP8 4EL. Merida Saunders, 01494 872928. *4m SE of Amersham, 4m NE of Beaconsfield. Opp the green in centre of village. At Crown Inn turn into UpCorner onto Silver Hill. At top of hill fork R into Dodds Lane. North Down is 7th on L.* Light refreshments. **Visitors and groups welcome by appt May to Sept for groups of 30 max. No coaches.**

A passion for gardening is evident in this plantswomans lovely 3/4 -acre garden which has evolved over the yrs with scenic effect in mind. Colourful and interesting through the yr. Large grassed areas with island beds of mixed perennials, shrubs and some unusual plants. Variety of rhododendrons, azaleas, acers, clematis and a huge Kiftsgate rose. Displays of sempervivum varieties, alpines, grasses and ferns. Small patio/water feature, greenhouse and an Italianate front patio to owner's design.

37 THE OLD SUN HOUSE

Pednor, Chesham HP5 2SZ. Mr & Mrs M Sharpley. *3m E of Gt Missenden, 2m W of Chesham. From Gt Missenden take B485 to Chesham, 1st L & follow signs approx 2m. From Chesham Church St (B485) follow signs approx 1 1/2 m.*

Home-made teas. **Adm £3.50, chd free. Mon 26 May (2-5.30).**
5-acre garden abundant with wildlife, on a Chiltern ridge giving superb views over farmland. The garden is surrounded by mature trees with inner plantings of unusual trees and shrubs. Features incl large ornamental pond, vegetable and herb garden, woodland walk, chainsaw tree sculpture, pheasantry and chickens. A natural not manicured garden. Gravel drive.

38 OVERSTROUD COTTAGE

The Dell, Frith Hill, Gt Missenden HP16 9QE. Mr & Mrs Jonathan Brooke, 01494 862701, susie@jandsbrooke.co.uk. *½ m E Gt Missenden. Turn E off A413 at Gt Missenden onto B485 Frith Hill to Chesham Rd. White Gothic cottage set back in lay-by 100yds uphill on L. Parking on R at church.* Cream teas at parish church. **Adm £3.50, chd £0.50. Sun 20 Apr, Sun 11 May, Sun 1, Sun 29 June (2-5). Visitors also welcome by appt Apr to July for groups of 15+.**
Artistic chalk garden on 2 levels. Collection of C17/C18 plants. Potager/herb garden, spring bulbs, hellebores, succulents, primulas, pulmonarias, geraniums, species/old fashioned roses and lily pond. Garden studio with painting exhibition. Cottage was once C17 fever house for Missenden Abbey. Share of flower painting proceeds to NGS.

39 11 THE PADDOCKS

Wendover HP22 6HE. Mr & Mrs E Rye, 01296 623870, pam.rye@talktalk.net. *5m from Aylesbury, on A413. From Aylesbury turn L at mini-r'about onto Wharf Rd. From Gt Missenden turn L at the Clock Tower, then R at mini-r'about onto Wharf Rd.* **Adm £2.50, chd free. Sat 21, Sun 22 June (2-5.30); Evening opening with wine on Fri 27 June (5-8.30); Sat 5, Sun 6 July (2-5.30). Visitors also welcome by appt June to July for groups of 10-30.**
Small peaceful garden with mixed borders of colourful herbaceous perennials and a special show of David Austin roses and a large variety of spectacular named 'Blackmore and Langdon' delphiniums. A tremendous variety of colour in a small area. The White Garden with a peaceful arbour, 'The Magic of Moonlight' created for the BBC. Most of the garden can be viewed from the lawn.

40 THE PLOUGH

Chalkshire Road, Terrick, Aylesbury HP17 0TJ. John & Sue Stewart. *2m W of Wendover. Entrance to garden and car park signed off B4009 Nash Lee Rd. 200yrds E of Terrick r'about. Access to garden from field car park.* Home-made teas. **Adm £3, chd free. Sun 11, Mon 26 May (1-5).**
Formal garden with open views to the Chiltern countryside and hills. Designed as a series of outdoor rooms around a listed former C18 inn, incl vegetable and fruit gardens, and a newly planted orchard featuring traditional varieties. Jams for sale made from fruits from the garden.

GROUP OPENING

41 QUAINTON GARDENS

Quainton HP22 4AY. *7m W of Aylesbury, 2m N of Waddesdon A41. Nr Waddesdon turn off A41. Maps given to all visitors.* Light refreshments at The Vine in Feb, and home-made teas at Banner Farmhouse in June, weather permitting, or at parish church. **Combined adm £4 (Feb), £5 (June) chd free. Sun 23 Feb (12-4); Sun 15 June (2-6); Sun 22 Feb 2015 (12-4).**

NEW **THE BOOT**
Paul & Gill.
Open June date only

CAPRICORNER
Mrs Davis

HOPE HOUSE
4 Station Road. Jane & Jeff.
Open June date only

MILL VIEW
Upper Street. Jane & Nigel Jackson
www.millviewquainton.com

135A STATION ROAD
Mr & Mrs Carter.
Open June date only

THORNGUMBALD
Jane Lydall
Visitors also welcome by appt Feb to Oct.
01296 655356
janelydall@gmail.com

THE VINE
Mr & Mrs D A Campbell
Visitors also welcome by appt Feb to July.
01296 655243
david@dacampbell.com

The village lies at foot of Quainton Hills with fine views over Vale of Aylesbury to Chiltern Hills. There is a C14 church with outstanding monuments, a C19 working windmill milling Quainton flour (open Sundays am), and a steam railway centre. Heavy clay but well-watered from the hills. The gardens are varied in their styles and content and also incl part of the allotments. No wheelchair access at The Vine or rear garden at Mill View.

42 RED KITES

46 Haw Lane, Bledlow Ridge HP14 4JJ. Mag & Les Terry, 01494 481474, les.terry@lineone.net. *4m S of Princes Risborough. Off A4010 halfway between Princes Risborough and West Wycombe. At Hearing Dogs sign in Saunderton turn into Haw Lane, then ¾ m on L.* Home-made teas. **Visitors welcome by appt Apr to Sept for groups of 15+.**
Chiltern hillside garden with terracing, slopes and superb views. The 1½ -acres are planted for yr-round interest and lovingly maintained, with mixed and herbaceous borders, wild flower orchard, established pond, vegetable garden, managed woodland area and hidden garden. Wide use of climbers and clematis throughout.

43 RIVENDELL

13 The Leys, Amersham HP6 5NP. Janice & Mike Cross. *Off A416. Take A416 N towards Chesham. The Leys is on L ½ m after Boot & Slipper PH. Park at Beacon School, 100yds N.* Home-made teas. **Adm £3, chd free. Mon 21 Apr, Sun 29 June (2-5).**

S-facing garden featuring a series of different areas, incl a raised woodland bed under mature trees, bog garden, gravel area with grasses and pond, auricula theatre, raised alpine bed, bug hotel, box-edged herbaceous beds surrounding a circular lawn with a rose and clematis arbour and containing a wide variety of shrubs, bulbs and perennials.

44 ROSE TREE COTTAGE

The Avenue, Worminghall, Aylesbury HP18 9LE. Roger & Penny Rowe, 01844 339250, roger@birdseye42.wanadoo.co.uk. *Worminghall, opp the church. On entering village look for turning to the Avenue and keep driving until the notice board at the end of road, parking available in this area.* Home-made teas. **Visitors welcome by appt Apr to June for groups of 12 max.**

A mature traditional cottage garden, with spring and summer interest with approx ½ -acre of roses, clematis, shrubs, fruit, and a vegetable and herb garden, set around a cottage. Wheelchair access possible but shallow steps may impede access to some areas of garden.

45 ◆ STOKE POGES MEMORIAL GARDENS

Church Lane, Stoke Poges, Slough SL2 4NZ. South Bucks District Council, 01753 523744, memorial.gardens@southbucks.gov.uk. *1m N of Slough, 4m S of Gerrards Cross. The car park for the Memorial Gardens is opp the gardens entrance. Disabled visitor parking in the gardens.* Home-made teas. **Adm £3.50, chd free. For NGS: Sun 27 Apr, Sun 18 May (2-5). For other opening times and information, please phone or see garden website.**

Unique 20-acre Grade I registered garden constructed 1934-9. Rock and water gardens, sunken colonnade, rose garden incl 500 individual gated gardens. Spring garden, bulbs, wisteria, rhododendrons. Beautiful autumn colours. Guided tours on the hour. Guide dogs only.

Rose walk with 350 roses . . .

46 TURN END

Townside, Haddenham, Aylesbury HP17 8BG. Peter Aldington, www.turnend.org.uk. *3m NE of Thame, 5m SW of Aylesbury. Turn off A418 to Haddenham. Turn at Rising Sun to Townside. Please park at a distance with consideration for neighbours.* Home-made teas. **Adm £3.50, chd £1. Mon 5 May (2-5.30).**

Intriguing series of garden rooms enveloping architect's own post war 2* listed house (not open). Sunken gardens, raised beds, formal box garden, richly planted borders, curving lawn and glades, framed by ancient walls and mature trees. Spring bulbs, irises, wisteria, roses and climbers. Courtyards with pools, secluded seating and Victorian Coach House. Open studios - displays and demonstrations by creative artists. Gravel and stone paths, narrow archways, some steps.

47 TYTHROP PARK

Kingsey HP17 8LT. Nick & Chrissie Wheeler. *2m E of Thame, 4m NW of Princes Risborough. Via A4129, at T-junction in Kingsey turn towards Haddenham, take L turn on bend. Parking in field on L.* Home-made teas. **Adm £6, chd free (share to St Nicholas Church, Kingsey). Sun 6 July (2-5).**

10-acres of gardens surrounding C17 grade I listed manor house. In the past 6-yrs the grounds at Tythrop have undergone some major changes, and now blend traditional styles with more contemporary planting. Features incl large intricate parterre, deep mixed borders, water features, large greenhouse, kitchen/cut flower garden, wild flower meadow, many old trees and shrubs.

48 THE WALLED GARDEN

Wormsley, Stokenchurch, High Wycombe HP14 3YE. Wormsley Estate. *Leave M40 at J5. Turn towards Ibstone. Entrance to estate is ¼ m on R. NB: 20mph speed limit on estate. Please DO NOT drive on grass verges.* Light refreshments. **Adm £6 incl teas, chd free. Sat 19 July (2-5). Advanced booking only, for timed tickets please phone 01483 211535 or visit www.ngs.org.uk.**

The Walled Garden at Wormsley Estate is a 2-acre garden providing flowers, vegetables and tranquil contemplative space for the occupiers of the main house. For many years the garden was neglected until Sir Paul Getty purchased the estate in the mid-1980s. In 1991 the garden was redesigned by the renowned garden designer Penelope Hobhouse. Wheelchair ramp available for garden access. Please ensure the requirement is mentioned upon booking.

49 WATERCROFT

Church Road, Penn HP10 8NX. Mr & Mrs Paul Hunnings, 01494 816535, info@maryberry.co.uk. *3m NW of Beaconsfield, 3m W of Amersham. On B474 from Beaconsfeld, 600yds on L past Holy Trinity Church, Penn. Some parking on site.* Home-made teas. **Visitors welcome by appt June to Aug, pm visits only.**

Mature 3-acre chalk and clay garden. Large weeping ash. Rose walk with 350 roses. Courtyard with new roses and summer pots and box topiary. Large natural old pond with diving ducks, newly extended pond edge planting and replanted perennial border. Italianate garden with 20-yr-old yew hedges and fine view. Wild flower meadow with wild roses. Formal herb garden with culinary herbs, small vegetable garden with hebe hedge. Glasshouse with unusual pelargoniums.

50 WESTEND HOUSE

Cheddington, Leighton Buzzard LU7 0RP. His Honour Judge & Mrs Richard Foster, 01296 661332, westend.house@hotmail.com. *5m N of Tring. From double mini-r'about in Cheddington take turn to Long Marston. Take 1st L and Westend House is on your R.* Home-made

teas. **Adm £3, chd free. Mon 21 Apr (2-5); Sun 3 Aug (2-6). Visitors also welcome by appt Apr to Sept for groups of 10+.**
2-acre garden restored and extended during the last 8-yrs featuring herbaceous and shrub borders, formal rose garden, wild flower area adjoining natural pond and new planting for 2014, vegetable potager and steel bird sculptures. Wood sculptures created from old tree stumps. Small orchard and adjoining paddock with rare breed hens, sheep and pigs. Some bespoke bird and butterfly sculptures for sale. Seasonal vegetables for sale. Wildlife pond with dragonflies, butterflies and much more. Access to wild flower garden and pond limited to one side.

51 THE WHITE HOUSE

Village Road, Denham Village UB9 5BE. Mr & Mrs P G Courtenay-Luck. *3m NW of Uxbridge, 7m E of Beaconsfield. Signed from A40 or A412. Parking in village road. The White House is in centre of village.* Home-made teas. **Adm £4, chd free. Sun 22 June (2-5).**
Well established 6-acre formal garden in picturesque setting. Mature trees and hedges, with R Misbourne meandering through lawns. Shrubberies, flower beds, rockery, rose garden and orchard. Large walled garden with Italian garden and developing laburnum walk. Herb garden, vegetable plot and Victorian greenhouses. Gravel entrance and path to gardens.

52 WHITEWALLS

Quarry Wood Road, Marlow SL7 1RE. Mr W H Williams, 01628 482573. *1/2 m S Marlow. From Marlow cross over bridge. 1st L, 3rd house on L with white garden wall.*
Adm £2.50, chd free. Sun 27 Apr, Sun 20 July, Sun 7 Sept (2-5). Visitors also welcome by appt Mar to Oct.
Thames-side garden approx 1/2 -acre with spectacular view of weir. Large wildlife pond, interesting planting of trees, shrubs, herbaceous perennials and bedding, and a large conservatory.

53 WIND IN THE WILLOWS

Moorhouse Farm Lane, Off Lower Road, Higher Denham UB9 5EN. Ron James, 07740 177038, r.james@company-doc.co.uk. *Moorhouse Farm Lane, off Lower Road, Higher Denham. Take lane next to the community centre & Wind in the Willows is the 1st house on L.*
Home-made teas. **Adm £4, chd free. Sun 16 Mar (2-5). Visitors also welcome by appt Feb to Oct (3-wks notice required).**
3-acre wildlife friendly yr-round garden comprising informal, woodland and wild gardens, separated by streams lined by iris and primulas. Over 350 shrubs and trees, many variegated or uncommon, marginal and bog plantings incl a collection of 80 hostas. 'Stunning' was the word most often used by visitors last year. 'Best private garden I have visited in 20-yrs of NGS visits' said one visitor. Selected to illustrate the water garden section of Carole Klein's forthcoming new book. Also featured in Buckingham Life. Lawn and gravel paths.

Acer Corner

Buckinghamshire County Volunteers

County Organiser
Maggie Bateson, 01494 866265, jmbateson@btopenworld.com

County Treasurer
Tim Hart, 01494 837328, tim.hart@virgin.net

Publicity
Sandra Wetherall, 01494 862264, sandra@robertjamespartnership.com

Assistant County Organisers
Rosemary Brown, 01296 429605, grahama.brown@virgin.net
Janice Cross, Rivendell, 01494 728291, gwendalice@aol.com
Judy Hart, 01494 837328, judy.hart@virgin.net
Margaret Higgins, 01844 347072, jhiggins816@btinternet.com
Mhairi Sharpley, 01494 782870, mhairisharpley@btinternet.com

CAMBRIDGESHIRE

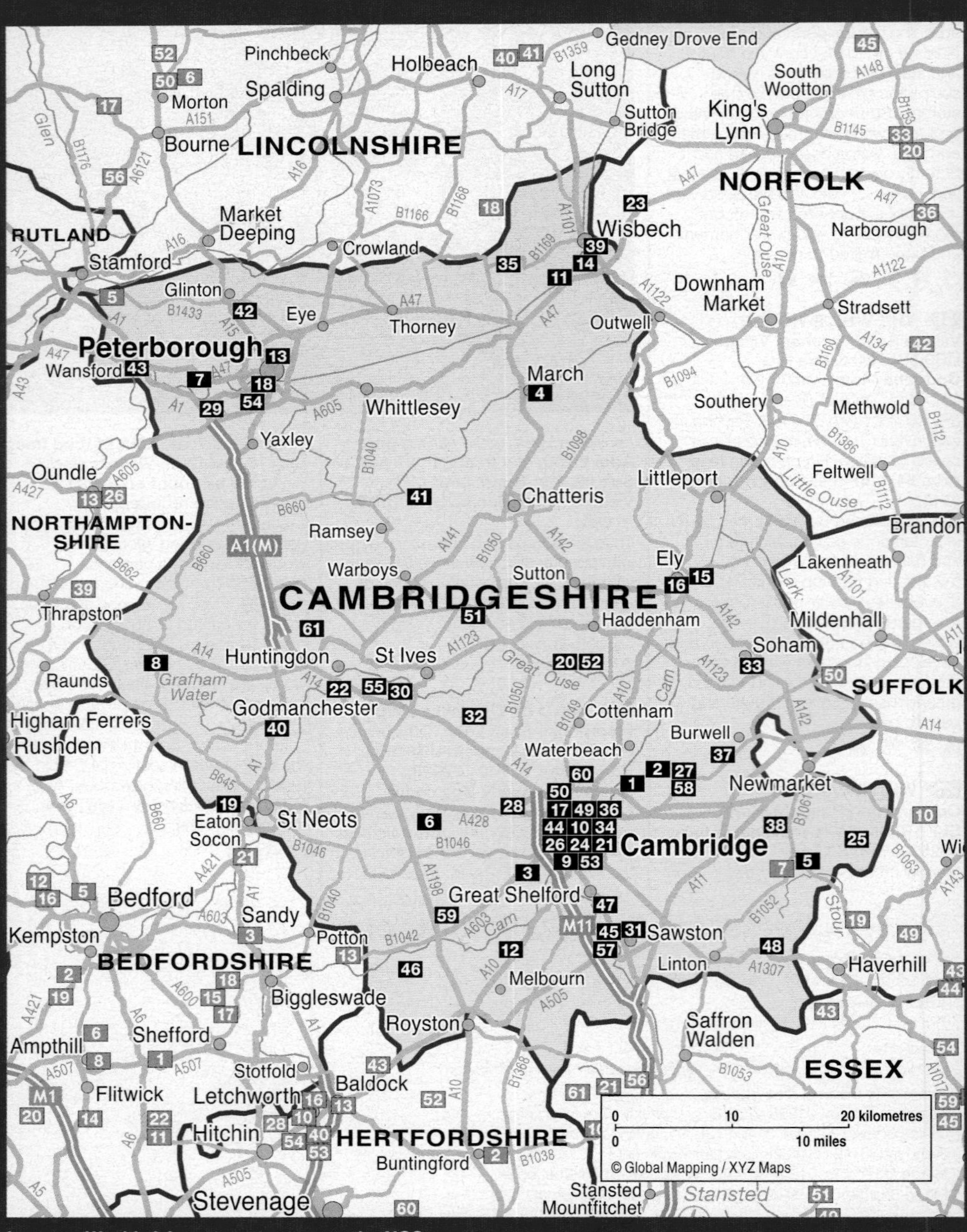

Opening Dates

All entries subject to change. For latest information check www.ngs.org.uk

January

Daily Wed 1 Jan to Sat 20 April
44 **Robinson College**

February

Sunday 23
43 6 Robins Wood

April

Sunday 6
3 Barton Gardens
25 Kirtling Tower
33 Netherhall Manor

Sunday 13
17 Fitzwilliam College
25 Kirtling Tower
49 Trinity College, Fellows' Garden
50 Trinity Hall - Wychfield

Sunday 27
12 Docwra's Manor

Cakes made with garden fruit where possible . . .

May

Sunday 4
9 Chaucer Road Gardens
33 Netherhall Manor

Monday 5
9 Chaucer Road Gardens

Sunday 11
27 Lode Gardens

Sunday 18
26 Leckhampton
52 Ty Gwyn
60 The Windmill

Sunday 25
21 Highsett Cambridge
37 The Paddock

June

Sunday 1
6 Cambourne Gardens
15 Ely Gardens 1
22 Island Hall
23 Kenilworth Smallholding

Festival Weekend

Saturday 7
11 Clear View
19 NEW Great Staughton, Staploe & Hail Weston Gardens
51 Twin Tarns
54 1A The Village

Sunday 8
3 Barton Gardens
8 Catworth, Molesworth, Spaldwick & Brington Gardens
11 Clear View
19 NEW Great Staughton, Staploe & Hail Weston Gardens
20 NEW Haddenham & Aldreth Gardens
27 Lode Gardens
28 Madingley Hall
35 The Old Rectory
51 Twin Tarns
54 1A The Village
56 NEW Wendens Ambo Gardens

Tuesday 10
2 Anglesey Abbey, Gardens & Lode Mill

Sunday 15
16 Ely Gardens 2
57 Whittlesford Gardens

Sunday 22
24 King's College Fellows' Garden
25 Kirtling Tower
41 Ramsey Forty Foot
48 Streetly End Gardens
60 The Windmill

Saturday 28
7 Castor House (Evening)
55 NEW Walden Cottage

Sunday 29
1 Abbots Way
13 289 Dogsthorpe Rd
45 Sawston Gardens
47 Stapleford Gardens
55 NEW Walden Cottage
61 Wytchwood

July

Daily 1 July to 31 December
44 **Robinson College**

Thursday 3
39 Peckover House

Sunday 6
10 Clare College Fellows' Garden
52 Ty Gwyn

Saturday 12
4 45 Beaver Lodge

Sunday 13
4 45 Beaver Lodge
27 Lode Gardens
31 Mary Challis Garden

Friday 18
5 NEW Burrough Green Gardens

Sunday 20
5 NEW Burrough Green Gardens

Sunday 27
59 Wimpole Estate

August

Saturday 2
36 NEW The Old Vicarage

Sunday 3
14 Elgood's Brewery Gardens
33 Netherhall Manor
34 Norfolk Terrace Garden
36 NEW The Old Vicarage

Sunday 10
33 Netherhall Manor

Sunday 31
7 Castor House

September

Sunday 14
13 289 Dogsthorpe Rd

Gardens open to the public

2 Anglesey Abbey, Gardens & Lode Mill
12 Docwra's Manor
14 Elgood's Brewery Gardens
30 The Manor, Hemingford Grey
39 Peckover House
44 Robinson College
59 Wimpole Estate

By appointment only

18 39 Foster Road
29 Manor House, Alwalton
32 5 Moat Way
38 Pavilion House
40 23a Perry Road
42 11 Redbridge
46 South Farm & Brook Cottage
53 Upwater Lodge
58 Wild Rose Cottage

Also open by appointment

8 32 High Street, Catworth, Molesworth, Spaldwick & Brington Gardens
8 7 Thrapston Road, Catworth, Molesworth, Spaldwick & Brington Gardens
9 16 Chaucer Road, Chaucer Road Gardens
11 Clear View
13 289 Dogsthorpe Rd
19 The Old Vicarage, Great Staughton, Staploe & Hail Weston Gardens

- **20** College Farm, Haddenham & Aldreth Garden
- **23** Kenilworth Smallholding
- **27** 21 Lode Road, Lode Gardens
- **33** Netherhall Manor
- **41** The Elms, Ramsey Forty Foot
- **43** 6 Robins Wood
- **48** Clover Cottage, Streetly End Gardens
- **48** Weaver's Cottage, Streetly End Gardens
- **51** Twin Tarns
- **52** Ty Gwyn
- **60** The Windmill

An Aladdin's Cave of plants, tucked away in a corner of a conservation village. . .

The Gardens

1 ABBOTS WAY

Horningsea CB25 9JN. Sally & Don Edwards, 01223 861234. *4m NE of Cambridge. ½ m from A14. No access from Abbots Way. Follow signs in Horningsea to car park & garden.* Home-made teas. **Adm £4, chd free (share to St Peters Church Horningsea). Sun 29 June (2-5.30).**
1¼ -acre sloping garden, with many herbaceous beds. Views to church and over the R Cam and its water meadows. Interesting plants and use of colour. 180ft double herbaceous borders; 116ft pergola with large collection of roses, clematis and other climbers. Natural pond with fish and bridge. Access for wheelchair users may be difficult from car park. Please phone ahead for alternative access from front of house.

2 ◆ ANGLESEY ABBEY, GARDENS & LODE MILL

Quy Road, Lode, Cambridge CB25 9EJ. National Trust, 01223 810080, www.nationaltrust.org.uk/angleseyabbey. *6m NE of Cambridge. From A14 J35, on B1102 through Stow-cum-Quy.* **Adm £6.60, chd £3.50. For NGS: Tue 10 June (10-5.30). For other opening times and information, please phone or see garden website.**

Anglesey is one of England's great gardens, with captivating views, vibrant colour and delicious fragrance for every season. Delight in the sweeping avenues, classical statuary and beautiful flower borders. June favourites incl the colourful herbaceous borders, rose garden and wildlife rich wild flower meadows. Take a tour with a garden guide and be inspired by the seasonal highlights. Large proportion of gardens fully accessible with hard surfaced paths.

GROUP OPENING

3 BARTON GARDENS

Wimpole Road, Barton, Cambridge CB23 7AE. *3½ m SW of Cambridge. Barton is on A603 Cambridge to Sandy rd, ½ m for J12 M11.* **Combined adm £5, chd free. Suns 6 Apr; 8 June (2-5).**

FARM COTTAGE
18 High Street. Dr R M Belbin

GLEBE HOUSE
1 High Street. David & Sue Rapley.
8 June only

114 HIGH STREET
Barton, Cambridge. Meta & Hugh Greenfield

KING'S TITHE
13a Comberton Road. Mrs Elizabeth Thorne.
6 April only

31 NEW ROAD
Barton, Cambridge. Dr & Mrs D Macdonald.
8 June only

THE SIX HOUSES
33-45 Comberton Road. Perennial (GRBS)

Varied group of large and small gardens reflecting different approaches to gardening.
Farm Cottage: landscaped cottage garden with herbaceous beds and themed woodland walk. Glebe House: 1-acre mature, partly wooded and walled garden with large duck pond formal fruit/herb garden, Italianate courtyard garden and a secret garden. 114 High Street: small cottage garden with an unusual layout comprising several areas incl vegetables, fruit and a secret garden. 31 New Road: large, wildlife friendly cottage garden with a good show of spring flowers, mature shrubs, trees and a kitchen garden. The Six Houses: recently renovated gardens, incl winter and dry gardens, lovely spring bulbs and a small wood. Kings Tithe is a spring garden with many bulbs, shrubs and fruit trees.

4 45 BEAVER LODGE

Henson Road, March, Cambs PE15 8BA. Mr & Mrs Maria & Paul Nielsen Bom. *A141 to Wisbech rd into March, turn L into Westwood Ave, follow rd leading to Henson Rd, turn R. Property opp school playground.* Light refreshments. **Adm £2.50, chd free. Sat 12, Sun 13 July (10.30-4).**
A delightful town garden divided into several rooms. A pergola leads to an ornamental pond with koi carp, surrounded by borders with a large variety of plants and ornamental trees. There is a fern area with ornamental waterfall. The whole garden has an Oriental theme with bonsais and statues.

GROUP OPENING

5 NEW BURROUGH GREEN GARDENS

Burrough Green, Newmarket CB8 9NF. *5m S of Newmarket. Take B1061 out of Newmarket, & Burrough Green is signed to L 1m after Dullingham. In middle of village, turn R to cross the Green.* Home-made teas and refreshments at Acorn House. **Combined adm £5, chd free. Fri 18 July (3-8); Sun 20 July (1-6).**

NEW ACORN HOUSE
Church Lane. Mr & Mrs David Swanney

NEW 7 ELIZABETH WAY
Mr & Mrs Robert King

Two very different gardens.
7 Elizabeth Way is an Aladdin's Cave of plants, tucked away in a corner of a conservation village. Being small, the garden has been interestingly designed to make maximum use of space, with over 50 varieties of clematis, and many varieties of heuchera. Also found in the terraced borders are a huge variety of herbaceous perennials, shrubs and other plants, which add colour and interest throughout the garden.
Acorn House is an elegant two-acre garden, only eight years old, offering

109 High Street, Great Staughton, Staploe & Hail Weston Gardens

many areas of interest. These include herbaceous borders, a mini arboretum with many different and unusual trees, a shady woodland walk, an orchard, and a vegetable plot. Seating throughout the garden. Gravel drive.

GROUP OPENING

6 CAMBOURNE GARDENS

Great Cambourne CB23 6AH. *8m W of Cambridge on A428. From A428 Cambourne junction into Great Cambourne. Follow NGS signs to start at any garden.* Teas at selected gardens and also available locally. **Combined adm £5, chd free. Sun 1 June (11-5).**

NEW **14 GRANARY WAY**
Great Cambourne, Cambridge. Mrs Jackie Hutchinson.
Exit A428 Cambourne, 2nd exit on next two roundabouts. At Morrisons turn left onto High Street then Monkfield Lane. right Greenhaze Lane

128 GREENHAZE LANE
Great Cambourne. Fran and John Panrucker.
At the end of Greenhaze Lane, up a short drive between nos. 126 & 130

22 JEAVONS LANE
Great Cambourne.
Mr Sheppard.
Entry via Chervil Way

5 MAYFIELD WAY
Great Cambourne.
Debbie & Mike Perry.
S on Cambourne Rd at r'about take 2nd exit onto Broad St L onto High St, R onto Monkfield Lane R onto Jeavons Lane

43 MONKFIELD LANE
Great Cambourne.
Tony & Penny Miles

6 ST JOHN'S WAY
Lower Cambourne.
Greg Barnes

A unique and inspiring modern group, all created from new build in just a few years. This selection of six demonstrates how imagination and gardening skill can be combined in a short time to create great effects from unpromising and awkward beginnings. The grouping includes a garden inspired by the French Riviera complete with a miniature meadow, a foliage garden, a stunning modern treatment featuring Astroturf at it's finest along with several more showing their owners' creativity and love of growing fine plants well. Cambourne is one of Cambridgeshire's newest communities, and this grouping showcases the happy, vibrant place it has become. No garden is more than 13 years old. and most are much younger. Featured on regional TV and regularly in the Cambridge News.

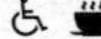

7 CASTOR HOUSE

Peterborough Road, Castor, Peterborough PE5 7AX. Ian & Claire Winfrey, www.castorhousegardens.co.uk. *4m W of Peterborough. House on main Peterborough rd in Castor. Parking in paddock off Water Lane.* Home-made teas. **Adm £4, chd free. Evening Opening wine, Sat 28 June (6-9.30); Sun 31 Aug (2-5).**
3 acre garden with 150yr old cedars, redesigned 2010. Italianate spring fed pond and stream gardens. Ornamental potager with greenhouse. Winter border, spring planted woodland garden. Peony and prunus walk. Rose and cottage gardens, 'Hot' double border. Planted for year round interest. 6 acre mature wood. Late C17 house (not open). 'Roaring 20s' jazz band 28 June. For more information please see garden website. Featured in Cambridgeshire Journal. Not suitable for wheelchairs.

GROUP OPENING

8 CATWORTH, MOLESWORTH, SPALDWICK & BRINGTON GARDENS

nr Huntingdon PE28 0PF. *10m W of Huntingdon. A14 W for Catworth, Molesworth & Brington exit at J16 onto B660. For Spaldwick exit A14 at J18.* Home-made teas at Molesworth House, Yew Tree Cottage and 7 Thrapston Rd. **Combined adm £4, chd free. Sun 8 June (2-6).**

32 HIGH STREET
Huntingdon. Colin Small
Visitors also welcome by appt June, evenings & weekends only.
01832 710269
sheila.small@btinternet.com

MOLESWORTH HOUSE
Molesworth. John Prentis.
Next to the church in Molesworth

7 THRAPSTON ROAD
Spaldwick.
Stewart & Mary Barnard.
Take J18 off A14 to centre of village, garden approx 50 metres from George PH
Visitors also welcome by appt May to July.
01480 890060
mnbarnard@btinternet.com

YEW TREE COTTAGE
Brington.
Christine & Don Eggleston.
Brington is approx 10m W of Huntingdon along the A14. Leave A14 at B660 to Brington past school, garden is 200yds up hill

4 varied gardens showing the best of planting, design and creativity representing classic tradition but with a modern twist. 32 High Street is a long narrow garden with many rare plants including ferns, herbaceous borders, woodland area and wildlife pond. Molesworth House is a Victorian Rectory garden with a bit of everything, old fashioned and proud of it but with a groovy tropical house. Yew Tree Cottage comprises flower beds, lawn, vegetable patch, boggy area, copse and orchard. Plants in pots and hanging baskets.
7 Thrapston Road comprises mature trees under planted with mixed borders of shrubs, bulbs, herbaceous plants and fish pond. A pleasant outlook to the rear over the village church. Wheelchair access limited.

GROUP OPENING

9 CHAUCER ROAD GARDENS

Chaucer Road, Cambridge CB2 7EB. *1m S of Cambridge. Off Trumpington Rd (A1309), nr Brooklands Ave junction. Parking available at MRC Psychology Dept on Chaucer Rd.* Tea at 16 Chaucer Road. **Combined adm £5, chd free. Sun 4, Mon 5 May (2-5).**

16 CHAUCER ROAD
Mrs V Albutt
Visitors also welcome by appt May.
07912 571680

NEW **18 CHAUCER ROAD**
Mr Simon Smith

16 Chaucer Road ½ -acre garden, divided by arches and hedges into separate areas, each with its own character. The garden is more open this year with some hedges removed. Spring flowering shrubs and trees, bulbs in borders and wildlife area. Waterproof footwear advised.
18 Chaucer Road recently designed ½ -acre town garden, divided in several distinct parts, with formal and informal planting and two garden houses. Raised planters with lavender and buxus, stone terracing and oak pergolas with wysteria and clematis connect differing sections. Cakes made with garden fruit where possible. Swings and climbing ropes. Stalls selling plants, cards, prints and fabric crafts. Some gravel areas and grassy paths with fairly gentle slopes.

10 CLARE COLLEGE FELLOWS' GARDEN

Trinity Lane, Cambridge CB2 1TL. The Master & Fellows, www.clare.cam.ac.uk. *Central to city. From Queens Rd or city centre via Senate House Passage, Old Court & Clare Bridge.* Light refreshments. **Adm £3.50, chd free. Sun 6 July (2-5.30).**
2 acres. One of the most famous gardens on the Cambridge Backs. Herbaceous borders; sunken pond garden, fine specimen trees and tropical garden. Gravel paths.

11 CLEAR VIEW

Cross Lane, Wisbech St Mary PE13 4TX. Margaret & Graham Rickard, 01945 410724, magsrick@hotmail.com. *3m SW of Wisbech. Approach village via Barton Rd from Wisbech, Leverington Common into Station Rd or Sandbank, & from Guyhirn. Yellow signs at most junctions.* Home-made teas. **Adm £3, chd free. Sat 7, Sun 8 June (10.30-5). Visitors also welcome by appt Apr to July.**
Approx 1½ -acre with lake incorporating large wildlife area, and wildlife meadow. Secluded cottage garden with many old fashioned plants, herbaceous border, gravel garden with raised bed and pond. Large rose beds, allotments and small orchard. Plenty of secluded seating. Gravel paths in cottage garden are too narrow but garden can be viewed from the picket fencing.

12 ◆ DOCWRA'S MANOR

2 Meldreth Road, Shepreth, Royston SG8 6PS. Mrs Faith Raven, 01763 260677, www.docwrasmanorgarden.co.uk. *8m S of Cambridge. ½ m W of A10. Garden is opp the War Memorial in Shepreth. King's Cross-Cambridge train stop 5 min walk.* Cream teas. **Adm £4, chd free. For NGS: Sun 27 Apr (2-5). For other opening times and information, please phone or see garden website.**
2½ acres of choice plants in a series of enclosed gardens. Tulips and Judas trees. Opened for the NGS for more than 40yrs. The garden is featured in great detail in a book published 2013 'The Gardens of England' edited by George Plumptre. Gravel paths. Wheelchair access to most parts of the garden.

13 289 DOGSTHORPE RD

Peterborough PE1 3PA. Mr & Mrs Michael & Julie Reid, 01733 553784, julie@juliereid.co.uk, www.facebook.com/AnArtistsGarden?ref=stream. *1m N of city centre. A47 Paston turn. Exit*

r'about South. Down Fulbridge rd to end & turn L into St Paul's Rd. Turn R at end down Dogsthorpe Rd. Garden 600 metres on R. Light refreshments. **Adm £3, chd free. Suns 29 June; 14 Sept (11-5). Visitors also welcome by appt June to Sept don't be shy!**
An artist's garden designed with the same sensitivity and expression as Julie puts into her work Divided into rooms using texture, form and colour. New planting and subtle structural and sculptural additions are thoughtfully added. Social and intimate seating all around the garden allows guests and gardeners to relax and enjoy. Sweet and savoury home-made refreshments all day. Open Artists Studio and Fine Art Exhibition. The garden feeds the art and the art feeds the garden.

14 ◆ ELGOOD'S BREWERY GARDENS
North Brink, Wisbech PE13 1LW. Elgood & Sons Ltd, 01945 583160, www.elgoods-brewery.co.uk. *1m W of town centre. Leave A47 towards Wisbech Centre. Cross river to North Brink. Follow river and brown signs to brewery and car park beyond.* Light refreshments. **Adm £3.50, chd free. For NGS: Sun 3 Aug (11.30-4.30). For other opening times and information, please phone or see garden website.**
Approx 4 acres of peaceful garden featuring 250yr old specimen trees providing a framework to lawns, lake, rockery, herb garden, dipping pool and maze. Wheelchair access to Visitor Centre and most areas of the garden.

GROUP OPENING

15 ELY GARDENS 1
ELY CB7 4TX. *14m N of Cambridge. Parking at Rosewell House off B1382 N of Ely, or Barton Rd car park. Map given at first garden visited.* Home-made tea and cake at Rosewell House. **Combined adm £5, chd free. Sun 1 June (2-6).**

THE BISHOPS HOUSE
The Bishop of Ely

BLACK HOSTELRY
Oyster Lane. Canon & Mrs David Pritchard.
Access via footpath around Ely Cathedral, through the Porta, or via Bishop's garden

12 & 26 CHAPEL STREET
Ken & Linda Ellis

50A PRICKWILLOW ROAD
Mr & Mrs J Hunter

ROSEWELL HOUSE
60 Prickwillow Road. Mr & Mrs A Bullivant.
On edge of Ely on B1382, turn R into Environment Agency office on Prickwillow Rd, 150 metres after mini r'about

A delightful and varied group of gardens in an historic Cathedral city. Take a leisurely circular walk of about 2m to access all gardens.
Rosewell House has splendid views of Cathedral and surrounding fenland. Herbaceous borders, roses, small pond and kitchen garden. Meadow with area of cornfield planting. Also 'Rhobile' moving sculptures by Andrew Jones and Fairtrade artes-mundi metal animal sculptures for sale. Close by, 50A Prickwillow Rd is an enthusiast's small walled garden with shade border, succulents and vegetable plot, the emphasis being on foliage. The Bishop's garden adjoining Ely Cathedral has mixed planting with roses, wisteria and more. Close by, The Black Hostelry, an ancient monastic building has a secluded garden with trees and shrubs. 12 & 26 Chapel Street: the former a small town garden reflecting the owners eclectic outlook, from alpine to herbaceous, all linked with a model railway! The latter a surprisingly long garden with shrubs and developing areas of herbaceous planting. An oasis of peace in the city. Wheelchair access to some areas of most gardens. Wheelchair access to some areas of most gardens.

GROUP OPENING

16 ELY GARDENS 2
Ely CB7 4HZ. *A10 from Cambridge (14m). All six gardens within the group are within easy walking distance of Barton Rd car park.* Home-made teas at 36 Barton Road. **Combined adm £5, chd free. Sun 15 June (2-5.30).**

NEW **41 ANNESDALE**
Dr Janet Fairweather.
Entry by the side entrance in Cutter Lane, exit by the front gate (signed)

40 BARTON ROAD
Mrs Diana Grove

42 BARTON ROAD
Mrs Grace Bent.
Close to Barton Road car park

NEW **42 CAMBRIDGE ROAD**
Mr & Mrs J & C Switsur.
On corner of Cambridge Rd & Tower Rd

HAZELDENE
36 Barton Road. Mike & Juliette Tuplin

NEW **ST. PETER`S CHURCH, BROAD ST**
Mrs Helen Yates.
Church is near the junction with Back Hill

These are a very disparate group of 6 large and small town gardens all within walking distance of Barton Rd car park. The gardens reflect a wide range of interests and expertise: Displays of summer flowers; an organic garden; expertise in growing fruit and vegetables. Two new small gardens are close to the river making a delightful walk which includes an artists garden and the herbaceous borders of St. Peter's Church. Hazeldene, 36 Barton Road has been featured in Amateur Gardening. St Peter's Church received an award from Ely in Bloom.

gardens reflect a wide range of interests and expertise . . .

17 FITZWILLIAM COLLEGE
Storeys Way, Cambridge CB3 0DG. Master and Fellows, www.fitz.cam.ac.uk. *1m NW of Cambridge city centre. Turn into Storeys Way from Madingley Rd (A1303) or from Huntingdon Rd (A1307). Free parking.* Light refreshments. **Adm £3, chd free. Sun 13 Apr (2-5).**
Traditional topiary, borders, woodland walk, lawns from the Edwardian period and specimen trees are complemented by modern planting and wild meadow. The avenue of limes, underplanted with spring bulbs, leads to The Grove, the 1813 house once belonging to the Darwin Family (not open). Some ramped pathways.

Fitzwilliam College

18 39 FOSTER ROAD
off Campaign Ave, Woodston, Peterborough PE2 9RS. Robert Marshall & Richard Handscombe, 01733 555978, robfmarshall@btinternet.com. *1m SW of Peterborough City Centre. A605 Oundle Rd, N into Sugar Way. Cross r'bout, L at 2nd r'bout to Campaign Ave. R at next r'bout on Campaign Ave. 2nd R to Foster Rd. L into cul-de-sac.* Light refreshments. **Adm £3.50, chd free. Visitors welcome by appt Feb to Oct, week days possible, groups up to 25 very welcome.**
Plantsman's garden in small, new estate plot. Mixed borders; woodland/shade; 'vestibule' garden; exotic and ferns; espaliered fruit; pergola; patio; pond; parterre; many pots; octagonal greenhouse; seating and sculpture. Uncommon snowdrops, over 200 hostas, plus daphnes, acers and other choice/unusual cultivars. Trees and hedges create enclosure and intimacy. 4 British Shorthair cats. Featured in local publications and Saturday Mail Magazine. Main garden and WC accessible by wheelchair. 3 very shallow steps to front and side garden. Admission also includes tea/coffee and biscuits.

GROUP OPENING

19 NEW GREAT STAUGHTON, STAPLOE & HAIL WESTON GARDENS
Staploe, St. Neots PE19 5JA. *109 High Street from A1 take B645 in direction of Kimbolton & High Ferrers, take 1st R signed Hail Weston and follow High St round is opp church & village hall. Old Farm Cottage leave St Neots on the Duloe Rd. Pass through Duloe. Continue to Staploe and house is last one on L. The Old Vicarage from A1 take B645 to Great Staughton. At end of village main st go straight ahead towards church. Garden before church on R.* Home-made teas. **Combined adm £3.50, chd free. Sat 7, Sun 8 June (1-5).**

109 HIGH STREET, HAIL WESTON D
Dawn Isaac.
www.dawn-isaac.com

OLD FARM COTTAGE
Staploe. Sir Graham & Lady Fry.

THE OLD VICARAGE
Great Staughton. Mr & Mrs Richard Edmunds.
Visitors also welcome by appt May to Oct.
01480 860397
elizabeth.edmunds4@btinternet.com

109 High Street set in 1/3 acre, this space has been designed to show that a practical family garden can still be beautiful. There is a large lawn with a sunken trampoline surrounded

by mixed borders, ornamental vegetable garden, children's play area and greenhouse. Old Farm Cottage flower garden surrounding thatched house (not open), with 3 acres of orchard, grassland, young woodland and pond maintained for wildlife. Present owners have planted a number of exotic trees as well as extending the area of native woodland. The Old Vicarage a good Old Vicarage garden, redesigned in 2008/9 to enhance original plan.

Sophisticated and urban feel creating a green and cool oasis in a small space . . .

GROUP OPENING

20 NEW HADDENHAM & ALDRETH GARDENS

Haddenham & Aldreth, Ely CB6 3PJ, www.artes-mundi.co.uk/garden. *5m SW of Ely; Aldreth is 2m S of Haddenham. From A142, take A1421.* Teas & home-made cakes at Ty Gwyn. **Combined adm £5, chd free. Sun 8 June (10-5).**

NEW COLLEGE FARM
Mr & Mrs J & S Waller
Visitors also welcome by appt May to Aug.
07779 302777
jeremyprimavera@aol.com
www.primaveragallery.co.uk

53 STATION ROAD
Jo Pooley.
Entering Haddenham village from N 200 metres on R

TY GWYN
Sian & Mark Hugo
(See separate entry)

Three very different gardens in 2 adjacent fen villages. Ty Gwyn, a 1 acre cottage garden with shrubs, perennials and climbers; cactus greenhouse, fish pond, animal sculptures and more. Fair Trade Gift Shop. Tea and home made cakes. College Farm offers open views, grass paths among wild flower meadow and ponds. Gallery. In contrast 53 Station Road is an intimate enclosed organic cottage garden, including roses and bearded irises. Limited wheelchair access to 53 Station Road.

GROUP OPENING

21 HIGHSETT CAMBRIDGE

Cambridge CB2 1NZ. *Centre of Cambridge. Via Station Rd, Tenison Rd, 1st L Tenison Ave, entrance ahead. Sat nav CB1 2DX.* Tea at 82 & 83 Highsett. **Combined adm £5, chd free. Sun 25 May (2-5).**

73 HIGHSETT
Mrs P Caldwell

79 HIGHSETT
Mrs J Evans

82 HIGHSETT
Mrs A Fleet

3 small delightful town gardens in central Cambridge. Fine specimen trees and interesting 1950/1960's houses designed by well-known architect Eric Lyons. No.73 the garden is dominated by a large fatsia japonica and overhanging birch trees creating shade and dappled sun. The main border was re-designed in 2012. Raised bed planting. Grasses and ferns intermingle with seasonal perennials in a palette of white and blue. The fence is covered with evergreen climbers and clematis. A sophisticated and urban feel creating a green and cool oasis in a small space. No.79 small town garden landscaped with a variety of herbs. Seating arranged in various places to take advantage of the sun. No.82 densely planted, colourful small garden to complement the lovely communal gardens of Highsett, one of Cambridge's secret gardens in the middle of the city.

22 ISLAND HALL

Godmanchester PE29 2BA. Mr Christopher & Lady Linda Vane Percy. *1m S of Huntingdon (A1). 15m NW of Cambridge (A14). In centre of Godmanchester next to free car park.* Home-made teas. **Adm £4, chd free. Sun 1 June (11-5).**

3-acre grounds. Mid C18 mansion (not open). Tranquil riverside setting with mature trees. Chinese bridge over Saxon mill race to an embowered island with wild flowers. Garden restored in 1983 to mid C18 formal design, with box hedging, clipped hornbeams, parterres, topiary and good vistas over borrowed landscape, punctuated with C18 wrought iron and stone urns. The ornamental island has been replanted with Princeton elms (ulmus americana).

23 KENILWORTH SMALLHOLDING

West Drove North, Walton Highway PE14 7DP. John & Marilyn Clarke, 07884 491105, bookings@kenilworthhouse.co.uk, www.kenilworthhouse.co.uk. *6m E of Wisbech. Off A47 through Walton Highway, at E end of village turn N towards Walpole St Peter, on 2nd sharp bend turn R into Farm Lane.* Home-made teas. **Adm £4, chd free. Sun 1 June (11-5). Visitors also welcome by appt Mar to Oct.**

Varied country garden set around 100yr-old Bramleys. Beds, large ponds, fern greenhouse, shade garden and herb bed. Working smallholding with goats and sheep. Tree lined path past paddocks to secluded mixed dessert apple orchard and copse. Japanese Garden. Teas served in outbuilding housing exhibition of the development of the smallholding and archaeology. Two awards Wisbech in Bloom - Wildlife friendly garden and Large out of town gardens (Highly Commended).

24 KING'S COLLEGE FELLOWS' GARDEN

Queen's Road, Cambridge CB2 1ST. Provost & Scholars of King's College. *In Cambridge, the Backs. Entry by gate at junction of Queen's Rd & West Rd. Parking at Lion Yard 10mins walk, or some pay & display places in West Rd & Queen's Rd.* Cream teas. **Adm £3.50, chd free. Sun 22 June (2-6).**

Fine example of a Victorian garden with rare specimen trees. With a small woodland walk and a kitchen/ allotment garden created in 2011 and new rose pergola and herbaceous border created in 2013. Gravel paths.

25 KIRTLING TOWER
Newmarket Road, Kirtling, nr Newmarket CB8 9PA. The Lord & Lady Fairhaven. *6m SE of Newmarket. From Newmarket head towards village of Saxon Street, through village to Kirtling, turn L at war memorial, signposted to Upend, entrance is signed on L.* Light refreshments. **Adm £5, chd free. Suns 6, 13 Apr; 22 June (11-4).**
Surrounded by a moat, formal gardens and parkland. In the spring swathes of daffodils, narcissi, crocus, muscari, chionodoxa and tulips. Closer to the house vast lawn areas, secret and cutting gardens. In the summer the walled garden has superb herbaceous borders with anthemis, hemerocalis, geraniums and delphiniums. The Victorian Garden is filled with peonies. Views of surrounding countryside. Display and demonstrations of stonemasonry from Lady Fairhaven's stone yard, and the chance to have a go yourself. A lot of the paths and routes around the garden are grass - they are accessible by wheelchairs, but can be hard work if wet.

26 LECKHAMPTON
37 Grange Road, Cambridge CB3 9BJ. Corpus Christi College. *Runs N to S between Madingley Rd (A1303) & A603. Entrance opp Selwyn College. No parking available on site.* Home-made teas. **Adm £4, chd free. Sun 18 May (2-6).**
10 acres comprising formal lawns and extensive wild gardens, featuring walkways and tree-lined avenues, fine specimen trees under-planted with spring bulbs, cowslips, anemones, fritillaries and a large area of lupins. Gravel and grass paths.

The garden is enclosed by a curving, swooping fence of woven willow . . .

GROUP OPENING

27 LODE GARDENS
Cambridgeshire CB25 9FW. *10m NE of Cambridge. Take B1102 from Stow-cum-Quy r'about, NE of Cambridge at junction with A14, Lode is 2m from r'about.* Home-made teas at Carpenter's End. **Combined adm £5, chd free. Suns 11 May; 8 June; 13 July (11-5).**

CARPENTERS END
Mr & Mrs Paul Webb

21 LODE ROAD
Mr Richard P Ayres
Visitors also welcome by appt May to Aug.
01223 811873

2 contrasting gardens set in a picturesque village to E of Anglesey Abbey Garden. 21 Lode Road is planted with bold groups of herbaceous plants creating an element of mystery and delight. Carpenters End displays shrubs, trees, herbaceous plants and a fine lawn.

28 MADINGLEY HALL
nr Cambridge CB23 8AQ. University of Cambridge, 01223 746222, reservations@madingleyhall.co.uk, www.madingleyhall.co.uk. *4m W of Cambridge. 1m from M11 J13.* Home-made teas at St Mary Magdalene Church adjacent to Madingley Hall Drive. **Adm £4, chd free. Sun 8 June (2.30-5.30).**
C16 Hall (not open) set in 8 acres of attractive grounds. Features incl landscaped walled garden with hazel walk, alpine bed, medicinal border and rose pergola. Meadow, topiary, mature trees and wide variety of hardy plants. Plant Heritage Cambs Group plant stall. St Mary Magdalene Church open throughout the event.

29 NEW MANOR HOUSE, ALWALTON
Church Street, Alwalton, Peterborough PE7 3UU. Malcolm & Jane Holmes, 01733 233435. *Alwalton Village. Turn into centre of old village, after church take R fork and continue for 100 metres.* Light refreshments. **Adm £5, chd free. Visitors welcome by appt Apr to July, groups up to 20.**
Walled garden divided into rooms. Wild garden overlooking Nene Valley. Topiary and mixed borders.

30 ◆ THE MANOR, HEMINGFORD GREY
nr Huntingdon PE28 9BN. Mrs D S Boston, 01480 463134, www.greenknowe.co.uk. *4m E of Huntingdon. Off A14. Entrance to garden by small gate off river towpath. No parking at house except for disabled by arrangement. Park in village.* **For opening times and information, please phone or see garden website.**
Garden designed and planted by author Lucy Boston, surrounds C12 manor house on which Green Knowe books based (house open by appt). 4 acres with topiary; over 200 old roses, extensive collection of irises incl Cedric Morris varieties and herbaceous borders with mainly scented plants. Meadow with mown paths. Enclosed by river, moat and wilderness. Late May splendid show of irises followed by the old roses. Care is taken with the planting to start the year with a variety of snowdrops and to extend the flowering season right through to the first frosts. Gravel paths but wheel chairs are encouraged to go on the lawns.

31 MARY CHALLIS GARDEN
High Street, Sawston CB22 3BG. A M Challis Trust Ltd. *7m SE of Cambridge. Entrance via lane between 60 High St & 66 High St (Billsons Opticians).* Home-made teas. **Adm £3, chd free. Sun 13 July (2-5.30).**
Given to Sawston in 2006 this 2 acre garden is being restored by volunteers: formal flower garden, vegetable beds with vine house, meadow and woodland, with concern for the flora and fauna - and the village children.

32 5 MOAT WAY
Swavesey CB24 4TR. Mr & Mrs N Kyberd, 01954 200568, n.kyberd@ntlworld.com. *Off A14, 2m beyond Bar Hill. Look for School Lane/Fen Drayton Rd, at mini r'about turn into Moat Way, no.5 is approx 100 metres on L.* **Adm £2.50, chd free. Visitors welcome by appt June to Sept.**
Colourful garden filled with collection

Elgood's Brewery Gardens

of trees, shrubs and perennials. Large patio area displaying many specimen foliage plants in planters, incl pines, hostas and acers.

33 NETHERHALL MANOR

Tanners Lane, Soham CB7 5AB. Timothy Clark, 01353 720269. *6m Ely, 6m Newmarket. Enter Soham from Newmarket, Tanners Lane 2nd R 100yds after cemetery. Enter Soham from Ely, Tanners Lane 2nd L after War Memorial*. Home-made teas. **Adm £3, chd free. Suns 6 Apr; 4 May; 3, 10 Aug (2-5). Visitors also welcome by appt Apr to Aug, refreshments by prior arrangement.**
An elegant garden 'touched with antiquity' Good Gardens Guide. An unusual garden appealing to those with an historical interest in the individual collections of genera and plant groups: March - old primroses, daffodils and Victorian double flowered hyacinths. May - old English tulips. Crown Imperials. Aug - Victorian pelargonium, heliotrope, calceolaria, dahlias. Author of Margery Fish's Country Gardening and Mary McMurtrie's Country Garden Flowers. Historic Plants 1500-1900. Double flowered Hyacinths.Tudor type primroses. Victorian Pelargoniums. The only bed of English tulips on display in the country. Featured in local newspapers. Flat lawn and paths.

34 NORFOLK TERRACE GARDEN

38 Norfolk Terrace, Cambridge CB1 2NG. John Tordoff & Maurice Reeve, 01223 312188, tordoffjohn@icloud.com. *Central Cambridge. A603 East Rd turn R into St Matthews St to Norfolk St, L into Blossom St & Norfolk Terrace is at the end*. Tea. **Adm £3, chd free. Sun 3 Aug (12-6).**
A small, paved courtyard garden in Moroccan style. Masses of colour in raised beds and pots, backed by Oriental arches. An ornamental pool done in patterned tiles offers the soothing splash of water. The owners' previous, London garden, was named by BBC Gardeners' World as 'Best Small Garden in Britain'.

35 THE OLD RECTORY

Main Road, Parson Drove, Wisbech PE13 4LF. Helen Roberts. *SW of Wisbech. From Peterborough on A47 follow signs to Parson Drove L after Thorney Toll. From Wisbech follow the B1166 through Levrington Common*. Home-made teas. **Adm £3.50, chd free. Sun 8 June (11-4).**
Walled Georgian cottage garden of 1 acre, opening into wild flower meadow and paddocks. Long herbaceous border, 2 ponds and unusual weeping ash tree. Terraced areas and outdoor kitchen! No hills but lovely open Fen views. New white border 2013.

36 NEW THE OLD VICARAGE
Thompsons Lane, Cambridge CB5 8AQ. Christa Pleasants. *St Clements Church Gardens, Cambridge. Enter Thompson's Lane from Bridge St. Old Vicarage is 1st house on R. Enter garden through iron gate, up two steps to path and lawn*. Home-made teas. **Adm £2.50, chd free. Sat 2, Sun 3 Aug (2-5).**
The garden to this distinctive historic house has been transformed since 2012 by designer Michael C Wood. Set within the churchyard of St Clement. The garden is enclosed by a curving, swooping fence of woven willow. New stone paving, structures and richly-textured planting have been worked around mature trees to create a delightful, calm oasis in this busy part of the city.

37 THE PADDOCK
43 Lower End, Swaffham Prior CB25 0HT. Judi & Mike Churcher. *10m E of Cambridge off B1102. On entering the village from Cambridge, The Paddock can be found at the far end on L, opp Rogers Rd*. Home-made teas. **Adm £3, chd free. Sun 25 May (2-6).**
Redesigned 8 years ago and still evolving. Gravel paths zig zag between shrub and perennial borders. On the way, relax on the deck; on a bench opposite a raised bed or on a swing seat in the gazebo. Children will love to explore the playhouse. Round a corner enjoy the colour on the 'flowery mead', where paths snake through herbaceous perennials and ornamental grasses. The village is famous for its 2 churches and a working windmill (certain dates only). The Devil's Dyke, NT Wicken Fen and NT Anglesey Abbey are nearby. Featured in Garden News Weekly.

38 PAVILION HOUSE
Station Road, Dullingham, nr Newmarket CB8 9UT. Mrs Gretta Bredin, 01638 508005, gretta@thereliablesauce.co.uk, www.pavilionhousebandb.co.uk. *4m S of Newmarket. Take turning off A1304, signed Dullingham, Pavilion House is 1m along this rd, 1st house on R. Parking will be signed*. **Adm £5, chd free. Visitors welcome by appt Apr to Sept, for individuals & groups, adm incls cream teas.**
Delightful S-facing 20yr old 1 acre country garden, with traditional colour themed borders. Expansive rural views, wild flower walk, free range bluebelle chickens and stunning raised bed organic vegetable potager. Superb cream teas. Gravel driveway.

New wildlife pond with small stumpery and woodland plus small seaside garden with beach hut . . .

39 ◆ PECKOVER HOUSE
North Brink, Wisbech PE13 1JR. National Trust, 01945 583463, www.nationaltrust.org.uk. *In the centre of Wisbech, on the north bank of R Nene. From Chapel Rd car park (free) walk towards river via Exchange Square on opp side of the rd. Turn R at river & walk 160yds*. Light refreshments. **Adm £5.30, chd £2.65. For NGS: Thur 3 July (11-5). For other opening times and information, please phone or see garden website.**
One of the best Victorian town house gardens, Peckover is a 2-acre site offering many areas of interest. These incl herbaceous borders, bedding, roses, trees, ponds, a propagation glasshouse, lawns, cut flower border, ferns, summerhouses and a newly restored orangery with 3 very old fruiting orange trees. Thur 3 July, coincides with Wisbech Rose Fair. Roses in the garden will be labelled and should be at their peak. The gardeners will be on hand to answer questions about the garden in general and roses in particular. Featured in English Gardens magazine and several other publications. Gravel paths.

40 23A PERRY ROAD
Buckden, St. Neots PE19 5XG. David & Valerie Bunnage, 01480 810553, d.bunnage@btinternet.com. *5m S of Huntingdon on A1. From A1 Buckden r'about take B661, Perry Rd approx 300yds on L*. **Adm £3.50, chd free. Visitors also welcome by appt May to Oct.**
Approx 1 acre garden consisting of many garden designs incl Japanese interlinked by gravel paths. Large selection of acers, pines, rare and unusual shrubs. Also interesting features. Plantsmans garden for all seasons, new wildlife pond with small stumpery and woodland plus small seaside garden with beach hut. Featured in Garden News.

GROUP OPENING

41 RAMSEY FORTY FOOT
nr Ramsey PE26 2YA. *3m N of Ramsey. From Ramsey (B1096) travel through Ramsey Forty Foot, just before bridge over drain, turn into Hollow Rd at The George PH, First Cottage 300yds on R, next door to The Elms*. Light refreshments at First Cottage. **Combined adm £3, chd free. Sun 22 June (2-6).**

THE ELMS
Mr R Shotbolt
Visitors also welcome by appt Apr to Sept. 01487 812601 richard@shotbolt.freeserve.co.uk

FIRST COTTAGE
Hollow Road. Mr & Mrs Fort

THE WILLOWS
Jane & Andrew Sills

3 interesting and contrasting gardens in the village of Ramsey Forty Foot. The Elms 1½ -acre water garden around C19 clay pit backed by massive elms. Large collection of shrubs, perennials, bog and aquatic plants. Woodland and arid plantings. First Cottage 150ft x 40ft garden with herbaceous borders, shrub beds, natural pond. Miniature steam railway. The Willows is a cottage garden with riverside location filled with old roses, herbaceous beds; shrubs, ferns, pond and vegetable garden. Some wheelchair access.

42 11 REDBRIDGE
Peterborough PE4 5DP. Mr & Mrs Mandy & Andy Knowles, 07976 224473, arknowles2@gmail.com. *Werrington, N Peterborough. 4m from city centre on A15. Turn E at Audi/BMW garage onto David's Lane. At T-lights turn L & Redbridge is 3rd turn on L*. Wine. **Adm £2, chd free. Visitors welcome by appt July to Sept.**
Unusual small walled garden with many tropical plants and ferns incl mature banana plants, ginger lilies, cannas, hostas, ligularia and a tall

paulownia pots containing red banana, yellow banana and strelitzia. Yellow Balue hardwood decking and wall covering and a glass wall separating a cobbled seating area from the garden. Climbers suspended on overhead steel cables.

43 6 ROBINS WOOD

Wansford, Peterborough PE8 6JQ. Carole & Forbes Smith, 01780 783094, caroleannsmith@tiscali.co.uk. *7m W of Peterborough on A1/A47 junction. From A47 turn towards Wansford. At Xrds by church turn W onto Old Leicester Rd. Approx 500yds turn R into Robins Field, follow on to Robins Wood.* Home-made teas. **Adm £2.50, chd free. Sun 23 Feb (11-4). Visitors also welcome by appt Jan to May.**

Small woodland garden with a collection of 300+ varieties of snowdrops. Various hellebore and corydalis followed by other spring woodland plants and bulbs. Small alpine plant house.

44 ◆ ROBINSON COLLEGE

Grange Road, Cambridge CB3 9AN. Warden and Fellows, 01223 339100, www.robinson.cam.ac.uk/about/gardens/ngs.php. *Grange Road, Cambridge. Garden at main Robinson College site, report to Porters' Lodge. There is only on-street parking.* **Adm £2.50, chd free. For NGS: Wed 1 Jan to Sun 20 Apr incl; Tue 1 July to Wed 31 Dec incl. Mon-Fri (10-4), Sat & Sun (2-4). For other opening times and information, please phone or see garden website.**

10 original Edwardian gardens are linked to central wild woodland water garden focusing on Bin Brook with small lake at heart of site. This gives a feeling of park and informal woodland, while at the same time keeping the sense of older more formal gardens beyond. Central area has a wide lawn running down to the lake framed by many mature stately trees with much of the original planting intact. More recent planting incl herbaceous borders and commemorative trees. No picnics. Children must be accompanied at all times. Ask at Porters' Lodge for wheelchair access.

GROUP OPENING

45 SAWSTON GARDENS

Sawston, nr Cambridge CB22 3HY. *5m SE of Cambridge. Halfway between Saffron Walden & Cambridge on A1301 close to A505 'McDonalds' r'about.* Cream teas at 'Sweet Tea' on High St. **Combined adm £5, chd free. Sun 29 June (1-6).**

NEW BROOK HOUSE
Mr & Mrs Ian & Mia Devereux.
Short walk S from the village centre; opp Hutchings & Harding chamois leather works

DRIFT HOUSE
19a Babraham Road.
Mr Alan & Mrs Jean Osborne

11 MILL LANE
Tim & Rosie Phillips.
Close to village centre. Approx 200yds W along Mill Lane from its junction with the High Street (Post Office corner)

35 MILL LANE
Doreen Butler.
Next to fire station. Approx halfway between the village centre and western by-pass

THE NEW VICARAGE
Revd Alan Partridge.
Behind the Church Hall. Enter through the Church Hall car park

22 ST MARY'S ROAD
Ann & Mike Redshaw.
Enter Church Lane at the War Memorial. 1st R onto St Mary's Rd

VINE COTTAGE
Dr & Mrs Tim Wreghitt

New entrant this year Brook House, has many lovely, recently designed and planted features set in 1½ acres. One of the many highlights is a stunning large walled garden not to be missed. Drift House has ⅓ acre of mature mixed planting in a 1960s garden, also featuring cloud pruned Junipers. 35 Mill Lane has colourful massed annual and perennial floral displays and fascinating water features. Find immaculate lush lawns, delightful mature mixed borders and large fruit cage at 11 Mill Lane.
The New Vicarage is a developing new garden with interestingly designed and planted borders.
22 St Mary's Road has views over SSSI meadows, wildlife friendly planting and charming colour-themed contemporary borders.
Vine Cottage's large mature garden has an intriguing secret Japanese courtyard. Many other features to be found, something for everyone. Great value seven gardens for £5. Enjoy a cream tea at 'Sweet Tea', or take up the exclusive discount offer for garden visitors at the Jade Fountain. With such a variety of gardens, clearly wheelchair access is variable.

46 SOUTH FARM & BROOK COTTAGE

Shingay-cum-Wendy, Royston SG8 0HR. Philip Paxman, 01223 207581, philip@south-farm.co.uk, www.southfarming.co.uk. *12m W of Cambridge. 500 metres S of A603/A1198. 5m N of Royston turn L to Wendy, then L again at sign to South Farm.* Light refreshments at South farm. **Adm £3.50, chd free. Visitors welcome by appt Apr to Sept, except August.**

Garden established over 30yrs on farmland site. 20 acres ring fenced by hardwood planting. Eco-garden with reed bed, wild flowers, ponds. Winter garden. New in 2011, 5 acre British Hardwood arboretum and heritage meadow established. Extensive vegetable garden. Restored listed barnyard (open). Also Private Nature Reserve with lake, otters, beautiful dragon flies and native crayfish, wild flowers. Neighbouring Brook Cottage (Mr & Mrs Charvile) Countryman's cottage garden. Abundant yr-long mixed colour, spilling over boundary stream, intermixed with traditional vegetables and poultry. Refreshments and light meals available using our own produce.

GROUP OPENING

47 STAPLEFORD GARDENS

Cambridge CB22 5DG. *4m S of Cambridge on A1301. L into Church St, then 1st L into Priam's Way.* Home-made teas. **Combined adm £4, chd free. Sun 29 June (2-6).**

NEW 6 FINCH'S CLOSE
Prof & Mrs S Sutton.
Cul-de-sac off Bar Lane

5 PRIAMS WAY
Tony Smith

Contrasting gardens showing a range of size, planting and atmosphere in this village just S of Cambridge. Priams Way forms an interlocking series of garden rooms including herbaceous beds, kitchen garden, alpine, pit and summer houses with sculptures set around.
6 Finch's Close small Spanish-styled patio leads to the fruit and vegetable garden and greenhouse. The borders around the lawn and wildlife pond are well-stocked with shrubs and mature trees whilst gentle musical chimes can be heard in the breeze.

GROUP OPENING

48 STREETLY END GARDENS

West Wickham CB21 4RP. *3m NW of Haverhill. On A1307 between Linton & Haverhill. Turn N at Horseheath towards West Wickham, from Horseheath turn L at triangle of grass & trees.* Home-made teas at Chequer Cottage. **Combined adm £4, chd free. Sun 22 June (12-5).**

CHEQUER COTTAGE
Mr & Mrs D Sills.
After triangle on RH bend, cottage on RH-side, look for B&B sign
01223 891522
stay@chequercottage.com
www.chequercottage.com

CLOVER COTTAGE
Mr Paul & Mrs Shirley Shadford.
At triangle on RH bend turn L, cottage on RH-side next to old windmill
Visitors also welcome by appt May to July, adm incl tea or coffee & biscuits.
01223 893122
shirleyshadford@live.co.uk

WEAVER'S COTTAGE NCH
Sylvia Norton.
After triangle on RH bend, cottage 100yds on RH-side
Visitors also welcome by appt Apr to Aug.
01223 892399

Find arches of roses and clematis at Clover Cottage and many varieties of hardy geraniums, and raised fruit/vegetable beds. Delightful pond and borders of English roses, climbers and herbaceous plants. Also ferns and shade plants and views over open countryside from summerhouse in sunken garden. At Chequer Cottage enjoy mixed cottage and contemporary planting of Monet style rose arch, perennial beds with many iris, delphiniums, roses. Unusual trees, pond, bog garden, art studio. Long vegetable garden, interesting walls, paths and rockery. In walled garden evergreen shrubs, damp shade and hot dry borders. Weaver's Cottage is a recently rejuvenated plantsman's paradise of many rare and unusual plants. National collection of lathyrus. Also wildlife pond, many new and old 'old' roses, mature shrubs, trees, perennials, bulbous plants. Raised scree bed, fruit and vegetable cage. Art studio open, art work for sale. Cakes, honey and preserves all home-made at Chequer Cottage. Plants and blank cards for sale of the cottage and flowers in the garden at Clover Cottage of the cottage.

NCH

49 TRINITY COLLEGE, FELLOWS' GARDEN

Queens Road, Cambridge CB3 9AQ. Master and Fellows' of Trinity College. *Short walk from city Centre. At the Northampton Street/Madingley Road end of Queens Road close to Garrett Hostel Lane.* Tea. **Adm £3.50, chd free. Sun 13 Apr (1-4).**
Garden of 8 acres, originally laid out in the 1870s by W B Thomas. Lawns with mixed borders, shrubs and specimen trees. Drifts of spring bulbs. Recent extension of landscaped area among new college buildings to W of main garden. Some gravel paths.

50 TRINITY HALL - WYCHFIELD

Storeys Way, Cambridge CB3 0DZ. The Master & Fellows, www.trinhall.cam.ac.uk/about/gardens. *1m NW of city centre. Turn into Storeys Way from Madingley Rd (A1303).* Home-made teas. **Adm £4.50, chd free (share to C.R.Y. (Cardiac Risk in the Young). Sun 13 Apr (11.30-3.30).**
A beautiful large garden that complements the interesting and varied architecture. The Edwardian Wychfield House and its associated garden areas contrast with the recent contemporary development located off Storeys Way. Majestic trees, a wide array of spring flowering bulbs, shady under storey woodland planting and established lawns, work together to provide a picturesque garden. Plant Sale. Some gravel paths.

Gentle musical chimes can be heard in the breeze . . .

51 TWIN TARNS

6 Pinfold Lane, Somersham PE28 3EQ. Michael & Frances Robinson, 01487 843376, mkrobinson12@aol.com. *Easy access from the A14. 4m NE of St Ives, Cambridgeshire. Turn onto Church St. Pinfold Lane is next to the church.* Home-made teas. **Adm £3.50, chd free. Sat 7, Sun 8 June (1-5). Visitors also welcome by appt May to Sept.**
One-acre wildlife garden with formal borders, kitchen garden and ponds, large rockery, mini woodland, wild flower meadow (June/July). Topiary, rose walk, willow sculptures. Character oak bridge. Hammock. Adjacent to C13 village church. Featured in Cambridgeshire Journal, Garden News, Landscape and on ITV's Love Your Garden.

Manor House, Alwalton

52 TY GWYN
6 The Borough, Aldreth CB6 3PJ. Sian & Mark Hugo, 01353 740586, sianandmark@artes-mundi.co.uk, www.artes-mundi.co.uk/garden. *7m SW of Ely. 2m S of Haddenham. The Borough is 2nd on L after entering Aldreth. Please park in High St, 2 mins from garden. Parking for elderly/disabled at garden.* Home-made teas. **Adm £3, chd free. Suns 18 May; 6 July (10-5). Also open with Haddenham & Aldreth Gardens, 8 June. Groups also welcome by appt May to July.**
1 acre cottage garden in small fenland hamlet. Grass path walks around mature trees, shrubs, perennials and climbers. Wild flower garden, cactus greenhouses, vegetable patch, orchard, fishpond, metal animal and bird sculptures. Free range chickens and ducks including rare breeds. Artes Mundi Fair Trade gift shop open.

53 UPWATER LODGE
23 Chaucer Road, Cambridge CB2 7EB. Mr & Mrs George Pearson 07890 080303 jmp@pearson.co.uk *Off Trumpington Rd, nr to Brooklands Ave junction.* Home-made teas. **Adm £5, chd free. Visitors welcome by appt April to Sept, parking for 8-10 cars available.**
6 acres with mature trees, fine lawns, old wisterias, and colourful borders. Small, pretty potager and newly planted vineyard. A network of paths through a bluebell wood leads down to water meadows and small flock of rare breed sheep by R Cam. Enjoy a walk by the river and watch the punts go by. Cakes made with home grown produce where possible. Some unusual recipes. Swings ropes and plenty of space. Gravel and mown grass paths, some gentle slopes.

54 1A THE VILLAGE
Orton Longueville, Peterborough PE2 7DN. Christine & George Stevenson. *2m W of Peterborough. Off A605 Oundle Rd. Car parking in the Orton Hall Hotel.* Home-made teas. **Adm £2.50, chd free. Sat 7 June (2-5); Sun 8 June (11-5).**
Cottage Garden featuring shrubs, herbaceous beds and arches supporting varieties of rose, honeysuckle and clematis. Gravel paths and drive.

55 NEW WALDEN COTTAGE
12 Common Lane, Hemingford Abbots, Huntingdon PE28 9AN. Mr & Mrs John & Anne Sink. *1m N of A14, 12m W of Cambridge & 3m E of Huntingdon. Take exit 25, follow signs to village. Cottage located 400yds from village centre on Common Lane on R.* **Adm £4, chd free. Sat 28, Sun 29 June (1-6).**
A 2½ acre garden behind a rose and wisteria covered cottage. Roses tumble over pergolas, herbaceous borders, fountains and ornaments. A large lawn area with a fish pond, parterre and trees. A woodland walk to the R Great Ouse with a jetty and seating area. Some grass paths.

GROUP OPENING

56 NEW WENDENS AMBO GARDENS
West End, Wendens Ambo, Saffron Walden CB11 4UJ. *2m W of Saffron Walden on B1383 Newport Rd, turn at the Fighting Cock PH into B1039 Royston Rd. Continue along Station Rd pass The Bell PH on L under M11, a further 300 metres are Courtlands Barn & Courtlands House. Parking available at Chinnel Barn (signed on the day).* Home-made teas. **Combined adm £3, chd free. Sun 8 June (2.30-5).**

NEW COURTLANDS BARN
Mr & Mrs Martin & Sarah Steer

NEW COURTLANDS HOUSE
Dr & Mrs C Glazebrook

Two contrasting gardens - Courtlands House a newly designed low maintenance minimalistic garden with interesting topiary, many varieties of hostas, colourful seasonal pots. Ferns and gunera thrive in shady areas.
Courtlands Barn is a country garden, vegetables in raised beds, bamboo hedging and colourful seasonal pots in a lovely country setting. Featured on BBC Radio Cambridge.

GROUP OPENING

57 WHITTLESFORD GARDENS
Whittlesford CB22 4NR. *7m S of Cambridge. 1m NE of J10 M11 & A505. Parking nr church, additional parking will be signed.* Home-made teas at the church. **Combined adm £4, chd free. Sun 15 June (2-6).**

MARKINGS FARM
32 West End. Mr & Mrs A Jennings.
Parking space

5 PARSONAGE COURT
Mrs L Button.
Please park on rd

RYECROFT
1 Middlemoor Road. Mr & Mrs Paul Goodman.
From village centre, past 'Tickell Arms' and 'Bees in the wall', L into Middlemoor Road, L turn and driveway 1st on L

11 SCOTTS GARDENS
Mr & Mrs M Walker

NEW SHEADS HOUSE
7 High Street. Mr & Mrs Matthew & Claire Roe

NEW WHITBY COTTAGE
20 West End. Mr & Mrs Simon & Laura Latham

There is a sense of going back to older gentler times with this collection of formal and country gardens. 2 new gardens this year, Whitby Cottage is a small claybat walled pretty cottage garden with interesting water features and large koi carp. Sheads House has 3 areas, formal planting around the house, a less formal wild flower area, and fruit and vegetable plots to rear behind a hedge. Ryecroft is a large elegant garden with trees, shrubs and restful patio area. Markings Farm is a lovely old fashioned country garden with a variety of shrubs and fabulous vegetable patch. Parsonage Court

has an arched walkway, shrubs, raised fish pond and delightful seating area around an old tree.
11 Scotts Gardens is a shady small walled cottage garden with chickens and a variety of shrubs and perennials.

58 WILD ROSE COTTAGE
Church Walk, Lode, Cambridge CB25 9EX. Mrs Joy Martin, 01223 811132, joymartin123@btinternet.com. *From A14 take the rd towards Burwell turn L in to Lode & park on L. Walk straight on between cottages to the archway of Wild Rose Cottage.* **Visitors welcome by appt.**
A real cottage garden overflowing with plants. Gardens within gardens of abundant vegetation, roses climbing through trees, laburnum tunnel, a daffodil spiral which becomes a daisy spiral in the summer. Circular vegetable garden and wildlife pond. Described by one visitor as a garden to write poetry in! Chickens, ducks and dog, circular veggie garden, wild life pond, and wild romantic garden!

59 ◆ WIMPOLE ESTATE
Arrington SG8 0BW. National Trust, 01223 206000, www.nationaltrust.org.uk/wimpole-estate. *7m N of Royston (A1198). 8m SW of Cambridge (A603). J12 off M11, 30 mins from A1(M).* Light refreshments in stable block. **Adm £4, chd £2. For NGS: Sun 27 July (10.30-5). For other opening times and information, please phone or see garden website.**
New border 2010; a prelude to the walled garden, our showpiece containing fruit, flowers, vegetables. Recreated Sir John Sloane glasshouse, financed with NGS help. Herbaceous borders over 100 metres long with mixed plantings of perennials, roses and choice shrubs. Dutch Garden and Victorian parterres. Expanding collection of fine trees and shrubs. Also National Collection of Juglans (walnuts). New border 2011 to produce cut flowers for the house and restaurant. Restored mushroom house and apple store in the bothy yard. Electric buggies available, please book before arrival.

60 THE WINDMILL
Cambridge Road, Impington CB24 9NU. Pippa & Steve Temple, 07775 446443, mill.impington@ntlworld.com, www.impingtonmill.org. *2½ m N of Cambridge. Off A14 at J32, B1049 to Histon, L into Cambridge Road at traffic lights, follow Cambridge Rd round to R, the Windmill is approx 400yds on L.* Home-made teas. **Adm £3, chd free. Suns 18 May; 22 June (2-5). Visitors also welcome by appt Apr to Oct.**
A previously romantic wilderness of 1½ acres surrounding windmill, now filled with bulbs, perennial beds, pergolas, bog gardens, grass bed and herb bank. Secret paths and wild areas maintain the romance. New - millstone seating area, water features and hot planting to contrast with the pastel colours of the remainder of the garden. Amazing compost area, plus the start of a vegetable garden. Smock windmill under restoration. Featured in Daily Mail, local press and on Radio Cambridgeshire.

61 WYTCHWOOD
7 Owl End, Great Stukeley, Huntingdon PE28 4AQ. Mr David Cox. *2m N of Huntingdon on B1043. Parking available at Great Stukeley Village Hall in Owl End.* Home-made teas. **Adm £3.50, chd free. Sun 29 June (1.30-5.30).**
A 2 acre garden. Brightly planted borders of perennials, annuals and shrubs, lawns and ponds. 1 acre of wild plants, grasses set among rowan, maple and birch trees leading to spinney planted with native trees, bulbs, ferns, hostas and foxgloves. Short gravel drive.

Secret paths and wild areas maintain the romance. New - millstone seating area . . .

Cambridgeshire County Volunteers

County Organiser
George Stevenson, 1a The Village, Orton Longueville, Peterborough, Cambridgeshire PE2 7DN, 01733 391506, chrisgeorge1a@aol.com

County Treasurer
Nicholas Kyberd, 5 Moat Way, Swavesey, Cambridge CB24 4TR, 01954 200568, n.kyberd@ntlworld.com

Publicity Officer
Angie Jones Willow Holt, Willow Hall Lane, Thorney, Peterborough PE6 0QN, 01733 222367 janda.salix@virgin.net

Booklet Coordinator
Robert Marshall, 39 Foster Road, Campaign Avenue, Woodston, Peterborough PE2 9RS, 01733 555978, robfmarshall@btinternet.com

Assistant County Organisers
Pam Bullivant, Rosewell House, 60 Prickwillow Road, Ely CB7 4TX, 01353 667355, pbu1@hotmail.co.uk
Nicole Langstaff, Phantom Cottage, Snailwell Road, Chippenham, Ely CB7 5QZ, 01638 720499, info@fineartmarketing.co.uk
Patsy Glazebrook, Courtlands, West End, Royston Road, Wendens Ambo, Saffron Walden CB11 4UJ, 01799 541180, glazebrc@doctors.org.uk
Michael Tuplin, 36 Barton Road, Ely CB7 4HZ 01353 612029 miketuplin@yahoo.co.uk
Annette White, Forestry Cottage, 9 West End, Woodditton, Newmarket CB8 9SW, 01638 730876, annette323@btinternet.com

CHESHIRE & WIRRAL

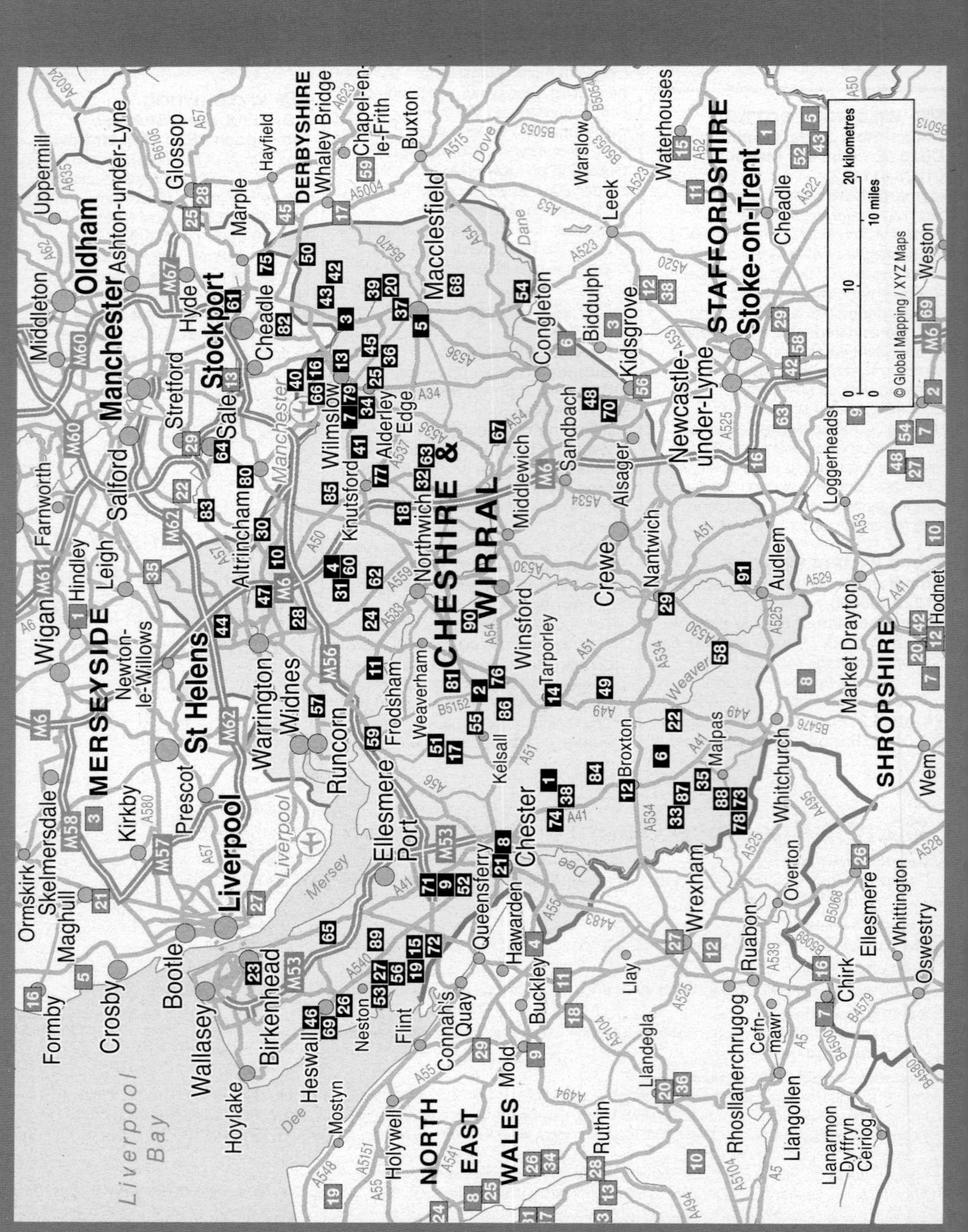

Opening Dates

All entries subject to change. For latest information check www.ngs.org.uk

February

Sunday 16
18 Bucklow Farm
30 Dunham Massey

March

Saturday 1
56 Ness Botanic Gardens

April

Sunday 6
62 Parm Place
74 Saighton Grange

Sunday 13
15 Briarfield

Saturday 19
65 Poulton Hall

Sunday 20
49 Long Acre
65 Poulton Hall

Monday 21
11 Bluebell Cottage Gardens

May

Sunday 4
41 Hillside
55 Mount Pleasant

Monday 5
41 Hillside
55 Mount Pleasant

Sunday 11
2 Abbeywood Gardens
30 Dunham Massey
86 Tirley Garth

Wednesday 14
85 Tatton Park

Thursday 15
22 Cholmondeley Castle Garden

Sunday 18
66 Quarry Bank House Garden
69 Riverside Lodge
86 Tirley Garth

Thursday 22
40 73 Hill Top Avenue (Evening)

Saturday 24
75 Sandsend

Sunday 25
51 Manley Knoll
75 Sandsend
84 Tattenhall Hall
89 Willaston Village Gardens

Monday 26
27 NEW Delfan
53 NEW Millheyes

Saturday 31
25 34 Congleton Road
60 The Old Parsonage
63 Peover Hall & Gardens
82 Sun House

June

Sunday 1
23 28 Christchurch Road
25 34 Congleton Road
32 Free Green Farm
60 The Old Parsonage
63 Peover Hall & Gardens
81 Stonyford Cottage
82 Sun House
86 Tirley Garth

Festival Weekend

Sunday 8
44 NEW Holly Mere
57 Norton Priory Museum & Gardens
65 Poulton Hall

Wednesday 11
85 Tatton Park

Saturday 14
5 Ashmead
17 Brooklands
21 Chester Cathedral
38 Hatton House Gardens
59 The Old Cottage

Sunday 15
5 Ashmead
17 Brooklands
18 Bucklow Farm
33 Grafton Lodge
59 The Old Cottage
84 Tattenhall Hall

Wednesday 18
58 NEW Oakfield Villa

Saturday 21
8 150 Barrel Well Hill
9 NEW Beechwood
52 NEW The Meadows
54 Millpool
58 NEW Oakfield Villa
71 NEW Rose Farm House
78 NEW Somerset House
83 Sycamore Cottage
88 NEW The White Cottage

Sunday 22
1 NEW Abbeydale House
8 150 Barrel Well Hill
9 NEW Beechwood
14 Bowmere Cottage
33 Grafton Lodge
36 Hare Hill Garden
45 Hunter's Croft
52 NEW The Meadows
54 Millpool
71 NEW Rose Farm House
78 NEW Somerset House
83 Sycamore Cottage
88 NEW The White Cottage

Saturday 28
35 NEW Hannets Cottage
80 199 Stockport Road

Sunday 29
10 Beechwood Cottage
19 Burton Village Gardens
29 Dorfold Hall
35 NEW Hannets Cottage
62 Parm Place
80 199 Stockport Road

An orchard and woodland borders with views to parkland . . .

July

Friday 4
77 Somerford

Saturday 5
39 18 Highfield Road
43 The Hollow

Sunday 6
30 Dunham Massey
31 The East Garden
39 18 Highfield Road
43 The Hollow
51 Manley Knoll
68 Ridge Hill

Saturday 12
16 Brooke Cottage
46 Inglewood
48 Little Moreton Hall
73 The Rowans
79 68 South Oak Lane
91 Yew Tree House Garden & Special Perennials Nursery

Sunday 13
16 Brooke Cottage
24 NEW Cogshall Grange
46 Inglewood
73 The Rowans
77 Somerford
79 68 South Oak Lane
91 Yew Tree House Garden & Special Perennials Nursery

Wednesday 16
91 Yew Tree House Garden & Special Perennials Nursery

Saturday 19
34 Greenways
64 17 Poplar Grove
91 Yew Tree House Garden & Special Perennials Nursery

Sunday 20
27 NEW Delfan
34 Greenways
53 NEW Millheyes
64 17 Poplar Grove
76 Sandymere
91 Yew Tree House Garden & Special Perennials Nursery

Wednesday 23
91 Yew Tree House Garden & Special Perennials Nursery

Saturday 26
7 NEW Barlow House Farm
28 NEW Dingle Farm

Sunday 27
3 Adlington Hall
7 NEW Barlow House Farm
28 NEW Dingle Farm

August

Saturday 2
28 NEW Dingle Farm
37 NEW Hathaway

Sunday 3
2 Abbeywood Gardens
4 Arley Hall & Gardens
28 NEW Dingle Farm
37 NEW Hathaway

Wednesday 6
91 Yew Tree House Garden & Special Perennials Nursery

Saturday 9
28 NEW Dingle Farm
91 Yew Tree House Garden & Special Perennials Nursery

Sunday 10
28 NEW Dingle Farm
40 73 Hill Top Avenue
44 NEW Holly Mere
77 Somerford
81 Stonyford Cottage
91 Yew Tree House Garden & Special Perennials Nursery

Saturday 16
35 NEW Hannets Cottage
47 Laskey Farm

Sunday 17
35 NEW Hannets Cottage
47 Laskey Farm

Wednesday 20
91 Yew Tree House Garden & Special Perennials Nursery

Monday 25
11 Bluebell Cottage Gardens

Sunday 31
91 Yew Tree House Garden & Special Perennials Nursery

September

Wednesday 3
91 Yew Tree House Garden & Special Perennials Nursery

Saturday 6
50 Lyme Park
55 Mount Pleasant
61 39 Osborne Street

Sunday 7
55 Mount Pleasant
61 39 Osborne Street

Saturday 13
91 Yew Tree House Garden & Special Perennials Nursery

Sunday 14
91 Yew Tree House Garden & Special Perennials Nursery

October

Sunday 5
67 The Quinta Arboretum

February 2015

Sunday 15
30 Dunham Massey

Created by a novice gardener using a very personal planting scheme ....

Gardens open to the public

2 Abbeywood Gardens
3 Adlington Hall
4 Arley Hall & Gardens
11 Bluebell Cottage Gardens
22 Cholmondeley Castle Garden
30 Dunham Massey
36 Hare Hill Garden
48 Little Moreton Hall
50 Lyme Park
55 Mount Pleasant
56 Ness Botanic Gardens
57 Norton Priory Museum & Gardens
63 Peover Hall & Gardens
66 Quarry Bank House Garden
67 The Quinta Arboretum
70 Rode Hall
81 Stonyford Cottage
85 Tatton Park

By appointment only

6 Bank House
12 Bolesworth Castle
13 Bollin House
20 4 Cheshire View
26 29 Dee Park Road
42 Hillside Cottage
72 Rosewood
87 The Well House
90 Wood End Cottage

Also open by appointment

14 Bowmere Cottage
15 Briarfield
16 Brooke Cottage
17 Brooklands
19 Lynwood, Burton Village Gardens
31 The East Garden
33 Grafton Lodge
34 Greenways
35 Hannets Cottage
46 Inglewood
47 Laskey Farm
49 Long Acre
51 Manley Knoll
54 Millpool
59 The Old Cottage
60 The Old Parsonage
61 39 Osborne Street
62 Parm Place
65 Poulton Hall
68 Ridge Hill
73 The Rowans
74 Saighton Grange
76 Sandymere
77 Somerford
79 68 South Oak Lane
80 199 Stockport Road
84 Tattenhall Hall

The Gardens

1 NEW ABBEYDALE HOUSE

Old Hall Lane, Hargrave, Chester CH3 7RT. Rob & Jane Windsor. *Midway between Tarporley/Chester. From A41 Chester to Whitchurch, after Waverton, past Black Dog PH, take L into Quarry Lane. T junction turn R through Old Waverton. Past church on L. Alongside canal on L, 1m over hump back bridge. L into Hargrave village. 1st L into Old Hall Lane, 1st L continuation of Old Hall Lane. Continue to end of lane.* Home-made teas. **Adm £3.50, chd free.** **Sun 22 June (11-4).**
1/2 acre country garden created from fields over 10yrs. Lovely unspoilt views over open countryside with a wavy hedge to protect from the westerlies but keep the views. Herbaceous, shrubs and annuals carefully colour co-ordinated. Raised bed kitchen garden and small orchard. Interesting trees and hard landscaping. Created by a novice gardener using a very personal

planting scheme. Views over open countryside. Attractive line of medlars and other mature trees. Hard landscaping incorporating dry stone wall of reclaimed Cheshire sandstone. Limited wheelchair access as some steps.

2 ◆ ABBEYWOOD GARDENS

Chester Road, Delamere, Northwich CW8 2HS. The Rowlinson Family, 01606 889477, www.abbeywoodgardenscheshire.co.uk. *11m E of Chester. On the A556 facing Delamere Church.* Light refreshments. **Adm £5, chd free. For NGS: Suns 11 May; 3 Aug (9-5). For other opening times and information, please phone or see garden website.**

Superb setting near Delamere Forest. Total area 45 acres incl mature woodland, new woodland and new arboretum all with connecting pathways. Approx 4½ acres of gardens surrounding large Edwardian House. Vegetable garden, exotic garden, chapel garden, pool garden, woodland garden, lawned area with beds.

3 ◆ ADLINGTON HALL

Macclesfield SK10 4LF. Mrs Camilla Legh, 01625 829206/827595, www.adlingtonhall.com. *4m N of Macclesfield. Well signed off A523 at Adlington.* Home-made teas. **Adm £6, chd free. For NGS: Sun 27 July (2-5). For other opening times and information, please phone or see garden website.**

6 acres of formal gardens with herbaceous borders, rose garden, rockeries, yew maze, water garden. Lawns with open views across ha-ha. 32-acre wilderness with mature plantings, various follies incl a 'Temple to Diana', woodland walk. Yew and ancient lime walks. Flower parterre. Recently restored Shell Cottage. Limited wheelchair access.

4 ◆ ARLEY HALL & GARDENS

Nr Northwich CW9 6NA. The Viscount Ashbrook, 01565 777353, www.arleyhallandgardens.com. *5m from Knutsford, Warrington & Northwich. Well signed from M6 J19 & 20, & M56 J9 & 10.* **Adm £10, chd £4. For NGS: Sun 3 Aug (11-5). For other opening times and information, please phone or see garden website.**

Ridge Hill

One of Britain's finest gardens, Arley has been lovingly created by the same family over 250yrs and is famous for its yew buttressed herbaceous border, avenue of ilex columns, walled garden, pleached lime avenue and Victorian Rootree. A garden of great atmosphere, interest and vitality throughout the seasons. Specialist nursery adjacent.

5 ASHMEAD

2 Bramhall Way, off Gritstone Drive, Macclesfield SK10 3SH. Peter & Penelope McDermott. *1m W of Macclesfield. Along Victoria Rd, 1st L after Macclesfield Hospital complex into Pavilion Way. L onto Gritstone Dr. Turn R into Bramhall Way, corner house. Travelling from Knutsford on A537 Chelford Rd turn L at Broken Cross r'about, straight across the next r'about at 'The Villas' down the hill passing the clock tower on your R, Pavilion Way is 1st R, then Gritstone Dr first L & Ashmead 1st R on the corner.* Home-made teas. **Adm £3, chd free. Sat 14, Sun 15 June (1-5).**

⅛ acre suburban cottage garden, featuring plant packed mixed borders, rock gardens, kitchen garden, island beds, water feature. The garden demonstrates how small spaces can be planted to maximum effect to create all round interest. Extensive range of plants favoured for colours, texture and scent. Pots used in a creative way to extend and enhance borders.

6 BANK HOUSE

Goldford Lane, Bickerton SY14 8LL. Dr & Mrs M A Voisey, 01829 782287, voisey598@btinternet.com. *4m NE of Malpas. 11m S of Chester on A41 turn L at Broxton r'about to Nantwich on A534. Take 5th R (1¾ m) to Bickerton. Take 2nd R into Goldford Lane. Bank House is nearly 1m on L. Field parking.* **Adm £4, chd free. Visitors welcome by appt Apr to July, children free if accompanied.**

1¾ -acre garden at the foot of Bickerton Hill, in area of outstanding beauty, with extensive views to Derbyshire and the Marches. Sheltered, terraced borders stocked with a wide range of shrubs, trees and herbaceous plants; established wild garden, Millennium garden with water features and productive vegetable garden. Unfenced swimming pool and ponds. Limited wheelchair access.

7 NEW **BARLOW HOUSE FARM**
Paddock Hill, Mobberley, Knutsford WA16 7DE. Jill Halman. *From Wilmslow follow the signs to Mobberley*. Cream teas. **Adm £3.50, chd free.** **Sat 26, Sun 27 July (12-5).**
My wife spends nearly all of her time in our off the beaten track garden. Your challenge will be to find a weed! Although not the largest (approx half an acre) the garden surrounds a C17 farmhouse (not open) with a half timbered barn incl a collection of vintage farm tools. The semi natural pond in the field gives added interest to the more traditional herbaceous beds and borders. Wheelcair access to most of the garden.

8 **150 BARREL WELL HILL**
Boughton, Chester CH3 5BR. Dr & Mrs John Browne. *On riverside ¾ m E of Chester off A5115. No parking adjacent to garden. Preferred access via Bithells Boats, on the hour from 11 - 4, from The Groves central Chester. Cost one way £3.50, child £2. Alternative access on foot from Boughton or bus to St Paul's church. Limited parking available locally, incl adj to Bill Smith Motors*. Home-made teas. **Adm £4, chd £2.** **Sat 21, Sun 22 June (11-5).**
Spectacular terraced garden with views over the R Dee to the Meadows and Clwyd Hills. Uniquely, preferred method of arrival is by leisurely river cruiser from Chester. Informal cottage style garden on historic site by the Martyrs Memorial. Lawns running down to the river, prolific shrub and flower beds, productive vegetable patch and soft and hard fruit areas, springs, stream and lily pond. Not suitable for wheelchairs or children under eight due to unprotected drop into river.

9 NEW **BEECHWOOD**
Meadow Court, off Townfield Lane, Mollington, Chester CH1 6NJ. Mr Dave & Mrs Sue Colegate. *3m N of Chester. Off A540 Parkgate Rd as signed. R from S, L from N. Parking will be signposted. For Satnav please use postcode CH1 6NR*. Tea at The Meadows. **Combined adm with The Meadows & Rose Farm House £5, chd free.** **Sat 21, Sun 22 June (1-5).** .
Set in ⅔ acre walled gardens (circa 1759), originally part of the Mollington Hall estate. Large natural pond with rose covered pergola pathway and bordered by huge hostas, ferns, grasses and gunnera manicata. Shady wild life area, rockery, number of quirky features incl Mollington Hall's original gasometer (rediscovered in 2006), now converted into sunken eating area, many mature trees. Winners of Cheshire Life Garden of The Year.

The grandest chicken shed outside Highgrove . . .

10 **BEECHWOOD COTTAGE**
64 Crouchley Lane, Lymm WA13 0AT. Ian & Amber Webb. *8m S of Altrincham. 4m from J7 or 2m J21 M6 onto A56 turn into Crouchley Ln past Lymm Rugby Club on R, 300yds on R (opp Crouchley Mews)*. Home-made teas. **Adm £4, chd free.** **Sun 29 June (11-5).** **Also open for 'Lymm Gardens' festival.**
2½ acre garden looking out to fields. Large lawn with herbaceous borders. Formal walkway with rose arches, topiary garden and orchard. Wild flower meadow - shaded area with tree ferns, hellebores and ferns. The grandest chicken shed outside Highgrove. Under cover tea room. Some gravel paths.

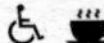

11 **◆ BLUEBELL COTTAGE GARDENS**
Lodge Lane, Dutton WA4 4HP. Sue & David Beesley, 01928 713718, www.bluebellcottage.co.uk. *5m NW of Northwich. From M56 (J10) take A49 to Whitchurch. After 3m turn R at T-lights towards Runcorn/Dutton. Then 1st turning L*. Home-made teas. **Adm £4, chd free.** **For NGS: Mons 21 Apr; 25 Aug (10-5).** **For other opening times and information, please phone or see garden website.**
1½ -acre south facing garden on a quiet rural lane in the heart of Cheshire. Packed with thousands of rare and familiar hardy herbaceous perennials, shrubs and trees. Unusual plants available at adjacent nursery. April opening usually co-incides with bluebells flowering in woods - access included in entry charge. Some gravel paths. Wheelchair access to 90% of garden.

12 **BOLESWORTH CASTLE**
Tattenhall CH3 9HQ. Mrs Anthony Barbour, 01829 782210, dcb@bolesworth.com. *8m S of Chester on A41. Enter by Lodge on A41*. **Adm £5, chd free.** **Visitors welcome by appt Apr to May, groups of 10+.**
One of the finest collections of rhododendrons, camellias and acers in any private garden in the NW. Set on a steep hillside accessed by a gently rising woodland walk and overlooking spectacular view of the Cheshire plain. Formal lawn beside castle with well stocked herbaceous borders. Terraces with lawn, rose gardens and many other plants.

13 **BOLLIN HOUSE**
Hollies Lane, Wilmslow SK9 2BW. Angela Ferguson & Gerry Lemon, 07828 207492, fergusonang@doctors.org.uk. *Hollies Lane is off Adlington Rd 2nd exit on L coming from Wilmslow. Proceed to turning circle at end of lane, take 2nd exit off to Bollin House*. Light refreshments. **Adm £4, chd free.** **Visitors welcome by appt May to July, if more than 10 cars let us know.**
There are two components to this garden, the formal garden and the wild flower meadow. The garden contains richly planted, deep, herbaceous borders with a wide plant variety. Also an orchard, wild flower area and vegetable garden. The meadow contains both cornfield annuals and perennial wild flower areas which are easily accessible with meandering mown paths. Ramps to gravel lined paths to most of the garden. Some narrow paths through borders. Mown pathways in the meadow.

14 **BOWMERE COTTAGE**
Bowmere Road, Tarporley CW6 0BS. Romy & Tom Holmes, 01829 732053, romy@holmes-email.co.uk. *10m E of Chester. From Tarporley High St (old A49) take Eaton Rd signed Eaton. After 100 metres take R fork into Bowmere Rd, Garden 100 metres on LH-side*. Home-made teas. **Adm £4, chd free.**

Sun 22 June (1.30-5.30). Visitors also welcome by appt June to Aug, teas incl in adm.
Mature 1-acre country style garden around a Grade II listed house (not open). Mixed shrub and herbaceous borders, pergolas, 2 plant filled courtyard gardens and small kitchen garden. Shrub and rambling roses, clematis, hardy geraniums and a wide and colourful range of plants make this a very traditional English garden. Cobbled drive and courtyard. Gravel paths. Featured in Concept For Living Magazine.

15 BRIARFIELD

The Rake, Burton, Neston CH64 5TL. Liz Carter, 0151 336 2304, carter.burton@virgin.net. *9m NW of Chester. Turn off A540 at Willaston-Burton Xrds T-lights & follow rd for 1m to Burton village centre*. Home-made teas in St Nicholas' Church, close to the garden. **Adm £4, chd free. Sun 13 Apr (1-5). Visitors also welcome by appt Apr to Sept.**
Tucked under the S-facing side of Burton Wood the garden is home to many specialist and unusual plants, some available in plant sale. This 2-acre garden is on two sites, a couple of minutes along an unmade lane. Shrubs, bulbs, alpines and several water features compete for attention as you wander through four distinctly different gardens. Always changing, Liz can't resist a new plant! Plants sold (50% to NGS) in Neston Market each Friday morning and from the house.

16 BROOKE COTTAGE

Church Road, Handforth SK9 3LT. Barry & Melanie Davy, 01625 536511, barry.davy@ntlworld.com. *1m N of Wilmslow. Ctr of Handforth, behind Health Centre. Turn off Wilmslow Rd at St Chads, follow Church Rd round to R. Garden last on L. Parking in Health Centre car park*. Home-made teas. **Adm £3.50, chd free. Sat 12, Sun 13 July (12-5). Visitors also welcome by appt May to Aug.**
Garden designer's plant-filled garden surrounded by trees and shrubs. 3 distinct areas & planting styles. Woodland garden: unusual water feature, 20+ fern varieties incl tree ferns, astrantias, hydrangeas, foxgloves, shade-loving plants. Container garden: huge variety of hostas, banana, ligularias, dahlias, bamboo, daylilies, pond. Colourful naturalistic style herbaceous borders, island beds, grasses, late flowering plants.

My wife spends nearly all of her time in our off the beaten track garden. Your challenge will be to find a weed . . . !

17 BROOKLANDS

Smithy Lane, Mouldsworth CH3 8AR. Barbara & Brian Russell-Moore, ngsmouldsworth@aol.co.uk. *1½ m N of Tarvin. 5½ m S of Frodsham. Smithy Lane is off B5393 via A54 Tarvin/Kelsall rd or the A56 Frodsham/Helsby rd*. Home-made teas. **Adm £4, chd free. Sat 14, Sun 15 June (2-5). Visitors also welcome by appt May to Sept, for groups of 10+.**
Lovely country style, ¾ -acre garden with backdrop of mature trees and shrubs. The planting is based around azaleas, rhododendrons, mixed shrub and herbaceous borders. Small vegetable garden, supported by a greenhouse.

18 BUCKLOW FARM

Pinfold Lane, Plumley, Knutsford WA16 9RP. Dawn & Peter Freeman. *2m S of Knutsford. M6 J19, A556 Chester. L at 2nd set of T-lights. In 1¼ m, L at concealed Xrds. 1st R. From Knutsford A5033, L at Sudlow Lane, becomes Pinfold Lane*. Home-made teas. **Adm £3.50, chd free (share to Knutsford Methodist Church). Sun 16 Feb (1-3.30); Sun 15 June (2-5).**
Country garden with shrubs, perennial borders, rambling roses, herb garden, vegetable patch, wildlife pond/water feature and alpines. Landscaped and planted over the last 26yrs with recorded changes. Free range hens. Carpet of snowdrops and spring bulbs. Leaf, stem and berries to show colour in autumn and winter. Cobbled yard from car park, but wheelchairs can be dropped off near gate.

GROUP OPENING

19 BURTON VILLAGE GARDENS

Neston, Cheshire CH64 5SJ. *9m NW of Chester. Turn off A540 at Willaston-Burton Xrds T-lights & follow rd for 1m to Burton. Maps given to visitors. Buy your ticket at first garden*. Home-made teas in village hall. **Combined adm £5, chd free. Sun 29 June (11-5).**

BANK COTTAGE
Bunny Beecroft

BRIARFIELD
Liz Carter
(See separate entry)

◆ BURTON MANOR WALLED GARDEN
Burton Manor Gardens Ltd
www.burtonmanorgardens.wordpress.com
For other opening times and information, please see garden website

LYNWOOD
Burton. Pauline Wright.
Through Burton village centre towards Ness Gardens
Visitors also welcome by appt May to July.
0151 336 2311

MAPLE HOUSE
Ingrid & Neil Sturmey

Burton is a medieval villlage about a mile from Ness Gardens. Five gardens are open, each with its own unique character. Lynwood, a plantswoman's garden, has a superb view across the river Dee to the Clwyd hills and an extensive natural sandstone outcrop, while Maple House merges into the Cheshire countryside with an informal wildlife area surrounding the pond. Briarfield's sheltered site, nestling under the south side of Burton Wood (National Trust), is home to many specialist and unusual plants, some available in the plant sale. Period planting surrounds the restored Edwardian glasshouse in Burton Manor's walled garden. At Bank Cottage, a small cottage garden backing onto the cricket field, the borders are packed with old fashioned flowers growing together to create a painter's garden with topiary and roses. Four plant sales; convenient car parks. Celebration of Flowers in Church.

Sandymere

20 4 CHESHIRE VIEW

Kerridge, Macclesfield SK10 5AU. Peter & Georgie Everson, 01625 572445, pandg@uwclub.net. *3m from Macclesfield. A523 from Macclesfield. A5090 turn 1st R to Kerridge. After 1½ m pass Bull's Head on R and park on rd. Garden is 5min walk over stone stile and 2 fields. Owner will meet you in village by appointment. Ignore sat nav.* Light refreshments. **Adm £3, chd free. Visitors welcome by appt July to Aug, only suitable for active and able visitors.**

A magical ⅔ acre hillside garden at 650ft with W facing views over the Cheshire plain to Alderley Edge and Mersey estuary. Magnificent sunsets. Landscaped on several levels using old railway sleepers with shrubs, late herbaceous perennials and a background of wooded slopes. Visitors must be able bodied and wear stout footwear. Featured in Amateur Gardening.

21 CHESTER CATHEDRAL

Chester CH1 2HU. Dean of Chester Cathedral. *Centre of Chester. Admission at SW entrance on St Werburgh St.* Refreshments and lunches in Norman and C12 monk's refectory. **Adm £3, chd free. Sat 14 June (11-4).**

Cloister Garth 2004 (Cheshire Garden of Distinction), haven of peace and tranquillity surrounded by ancient architecture, sculpture fountain and exotic plants. 2012 Jubilee Garden with abundance of herbaceous and rare trees, fern border and new developments in Abbey Street and Cathedral Green. Gardens designed by botanist and maintained by volunteers. Open day followed by (horticultural) Choral Evensong at 4.15pm in iconic C14 quire, sung by Cathedral Nave Choir. Custos hortorum philipbhunt@hotmail.co.uk.

22 ◆ CHOLMONDELEY CASTLE GARDEN

Cholmondeley, Nr Malpas SY14 8AH. Lavinia, Dowager Marchioness of Cholmondeley, 01829 720383, www.cholmondeleycastle.com. *4m NE of Malpas. Signed from A41 Chester-Whitchurch rd & A49 Whitchurch-Tarporley rd.* Light refreshments. **Adm £6, chd £3. For NGS: Thur 15 May (11-5). For other opening times and information, please phone or see garden website.**

Over 20 acres of romantically landscaped gardens with fine views and eye-catching water features, but still manages to retain its intimacy. Beautiful mature trees form a background to spring bulbs, exotic plants in season incl magnolias, rhododendrons, azaleas, camellias and many others, particularly *Davidia Involucrata* which will be in flower in late May. Magnificent magnolias. Partial wheelchair access.

23 28 CHRISTCHURCH ROAD

Oxton CH43 5SF. Tom & Ruth Foster. *1m SW of Birkenhead. At M53 J3 take A552 to Birkenhead. Cross junction at T-lights after Sainsbury's. At next T-lights bear L. Take 2nd L. Christchurch R is after church.* **Adm £3.50, chd free. Sun 1 June (1-5).**

Grade II listed Victorian Folly with crenellated towers forms a unique feature in this ¼ -acre plot. The garden is on different levels with many seating areas, terraced banks, planted sandstone walls, water features, herbaceous borders, lawns, trees (many acers) and a Japanese style garden. All areas are connected by a series of tunnels, pathways and steps.

24 NEW COGSHALL GRANGE

Hall Lane, Antrobus, Northwich CW9 6BJ. *3m NW of Northwich. Take A599 Northwich to Warrington. Turn into Wheatsheaf Lane or Well Lane. Head S on Sandiway Lane to grass triangle & then R into Hall Lane.* Light refreshments. **Adm £5, chd free. Sun 13 July (1-5).**

Set in the historic landscape of a late Georgian country house this is a contemporary garden, designed by the internationally renowned garden designer, Tom Stuart-Smith. The gardens contain a mixture of both informal and formal elements, modern herbaceous plantings, a walled garden, wild flower meadows, an orchard and woodland borders with views to parkland and the surrounding countryside. Featured in House and Garden and Gardens Illustrated.

25 34 CONGLETON ROAD
Alderley Edge SK9 7AB. Mr Nicholas Clayton. *400 yards S of Alderley Edge on the A34. Park on rd.* Teas. **Adm £4, chd free. Sat 31 May; Sun 1 June (12-6).**
W-facing, 1-acre garden with views on a fine day to the Clwydian Range. Mature rhododendron, magnolias and wisteria with early clematis, hellebores and a range of unusual herbaceous plants and young specimen trees.

26 29 DEE PARK ROAD
Gayton CH60 3RG. E Lewis, 0151 342 5893, eileen.lewis29@tiscali.co.uk. *7m S of Birkenhead. From Devon Doorway/Glegg Arms rbout at Heswall travel towards Chester on A540 for approx. 1/4 m. R into Gayton Lane, then 5th L.* **Adm £3, chd free. Visitors welcome by appt June to Sept.**
Plant packed garden with newly designed bed of predominantly silver leaved plants. Mature trees, topiary, cottage garden perennials, climbing roses, clematis, gravel areas, alpines, and thymes. A gated entrance by an arbour leads to a garden room featuring more roses and clematis.

27 NEW DELFAN
Burton Road, Little Neston, Neston CH64 4AF. Chris Sullivan. *10m NW of Chester. Off A540. M53 J4, follow signs M56 & A5117 (signed N Wales). Turn onto A540 follow signs for Hoylake. Garden is 1m past Ness Gardens. Garden is situated between Neston & Ness Gardens nr to Marshlands Rd. Parking at St Michael's Church.* Tea at St Michael's Church. **Combined adm with Mill Heyes £4, chd free. Mon 26 May; Sun 20 July (2-5).**
The garden is surrounded by mature trees. Spring borders with Camellias and Rhododendrons, followed by herbaceous borders offering colour and variety of planting. The borders provide fragrance with roses climbing up obelisks. A tender plant area and fern bed sit amongst the cottage garden plants. Late summer colour is provided by echinaceas, heleniums and dahlias.

28 NEW DINGLE FARM
Dingle Lane, Appleton, Warrington WA4 3HR. Robert Bilton, www.dinglefarmonline.co.uk. *2m N from M56 J10. A49 towards Warrington, R at T-lights onto Stretton Rd, 1m turn L at The Thorn PH, after 1m turn L into Dingle Lane. Plenty of parking.* Home-made teas at Dingle Farm Tea Rooms, all day. **Adm £3, chd free. Sats, Suns 26, 27 July; 2, 3, 9, 10 Aug (10-5).**
The garden is only 3yrs old but gives the impression of being more established. Features include a large pond, wild flower garden, vegetable patch with chicken run and a wooded area. The garden is overlooked by the world famous Dingle Farm Tea Rooms, Art Studio & Gift Shop set in the beautiful Cheshire countryside. Woodland walks adjacent to the site.

29 DORFOLD HALL
Nantwich CW5 8LD. Mr & Mrs Richard Roundell. *1m W of Nantwich. On A534 between Nantwich & Acton.* Teas. **Adm £6, chd £2.50. Sun 29 June (2-5.30).**
18-acre garden surrounding C17 house (not open) with formal approach; lawns and herbaceous borders; spectacular spring woodland garden with rhododendrons, azaleas, magnolias and bulbs.

30 ◆ DUNHAM MASSEY
Altrincham WA14 4SJ. National Trust, 0161 941 1025, www.nationaltrust.org.uk/dunham massey. *3m SW of Altrincham. Off A56; M6 exit J19; M56 exit J7. Foot: close to Trans-Pennine Trail & Bridgewater Canal. Bus: Nos 38 & 5.* **Adm £8, chd £4. For NGS: Sun 16 Feb (11-4); Suns 11 May; 6 July (11-5.30); 15 Feb 2015. For other opening times and information, please phone or see garden website.**
Enjoy the elegance of this vibrant Edwardian garden. Richly planted borders packed with colour and texture, sweeping lawns, majestic trees and shady woodland all await your discovery. Explore the largest Winter Garden in Britain and marvel at the colourful, scent-filled Rose Garden. Water features. C18 Orangery, rare Victorian Bark House. Visitors to the garden, incl NT members, should collect ticket from Ticket Office at Visitor Reception.

A tender plant area and fern bed sit amongst the cottage garden plants . . .

31 THE EAST GARDEN
Arley Hall, Northwich CW9 6LZ. Mrs Jane Foster & Mrs Tessa Holmes, 01565 777231, jmefoster@btinternet.com. *6m W of Knutsford. Follow brown signs for Arley Hall from M6 Junc 19 & 20 and M56 Junc 9 & 10.* Home-made teas. **Adm £4.50, chd free. Sun 6 July (11-5.30). Combined adm £9 with Arley Hall Gardens. Visitors also welcome by appt June to Aug.**
Two modern, very attractive gardens made since 1992 on the site of the C19 East Garden by the owners of Arley Hall Nursery and the East House, Arley Hall. Old shrub roses, early summer perennials and circular herbaceous borders enclosed by yew hedges. Many varieties of hardy herbaceous perennials - the speciality of the nursery. Wheelchair access throughout.

32 FREE GREEN FARM
Free Green Lane, Lower Peover WA16 9QX. Sir Philip & Lady Haworth. *3m S of Knutsford. Near A50 between Knutsford and Holmes Chapel. Off Free Green Lane.* Home-made teas. **Adm £5, chd free. Sun 1 June (2-6).**
2-acre garden with pleached limes, herbaceous borders, ponds, parterre; garden of the senses and British woodland. Topiary. Assortment of trees, and ten different forms of hedging. Wheelchair access not easy in the wood.

33 GRAFTON LODGE

Stretton, Tilston, Malpas SY14 7JE. Simon Carter & Derren Gilhooley, 01829 250670, simoncar@aol.com. *For Sat Nav please use SY14 7JA NOT 7JE. 12m S of Chester. A41 S from Chester toward Wrexham on the A534 at Broxton r'about. Pass Carden Park hotel - turn L at Cocko Barton PH to Stretton & Tilston.* Light refreshments. **Adm £4, chd free. Suns 15, 22 June (12-5.30). Visitors also welcome by appt June to July.**

Vibrantly colourful garden of 2 acres crammed with herbaceous plants, shrubs and roses. There are lawns, natural and formal ponds, specimen trees, mixed hedges and garden rooms including herb garden, standard rose circle, large pergola with sprawling roses and climbers, herbaceous beds, perfumed gazebo, roof terrace with far reaching views.

34 GREENWAYS

82 Knutsford Road, Alderley Edge SK9 7SF. Jenny & Roger Lloyd, 01625 583488, jenny.plants@btinternet.com. *1m west of Alderley Edge. 1m from Alderley Edge & Wilmslow on B5085 to Knutsford. Close to Chorley Village Hall. Parking at Village Hall. Disabled parking at house.* Home-made teas. **Adm £4, chd free. Sat 19, Sun 20 July (2-6). Visitors also welcome by appt May to Aug, max 50.**

Even more plants now in this obsessive collector's garden. Over 400 named varieties and much more. Plant maps available. A personal collection of unusual and familiar perennials and shrubs set in 1½ acres, displaying a diversity of planting styles in a range of growing conditions. Sculpture exhibition and new children's quiz. Unfenced pools. Wheelchair access possible throughout garden.

35 NEW HANNETS COTTAGE

Tilston Road, Kidnal, Malpas SY14 7DH. Doris Bamforth, 01948 860979, deabamforth@aol.com. *Approx 1m NW of Malpas town centre. From Malpas town centre up High St towards Tilston. You are now on Tilston Rd. Continue for 800 metres. Do not use sat-nav.* Home-made teas. **Adm £4, chd free. Sats, Suns 28, 29 June; 16, 17 Aug (1-5.30). Visitors also welcome by appt May to Aug, groups of 10 - 20.**

This ½ acre cottage garden surrounds a typical Cheshire, grade 2 listed, cottage (not open). Different rooms for sun and shade lovers will show you how to create interest and movement. Unusual plants (plus good plant stall), various water features, cosy seats and lovely views will make your visit to this quirky and much loved garden one to remember. Limited wheelchair access.

36 ◆ HARE HILL GARDEN

Prestbury Road, Over Alderley SK10 4PY. National Trust, www.nationaltrust.org.uk. *2m E of Alderley Edge. Between Alderley Edge & Prestbury. Turn off N at B5087 at Greyhound Rd.* **Adm £5, chd £2.50. For NGS: Sun 22 June (10-5). For other opening times and information, please see garden website.**

Attractive spring garden featuring a fine display of rhododendrons and azaleas and many other specimen trees and shrubs. 10-acre garden incl a walled garden which hosts many wall shrubs incl clematis and vines and wisteria; recently introduced White Borders for Summer interest. Most paths wheel chair accessable, some steps but alternate routes available.

37 NEW HATHAWAY

1 Pool End Road, Tytherington, Macclesfield SK10 2LB. Mr & Mrs Cordingley. *2m N of Macclesfield, ½ m from The Tytherington Club. Stockport: follow A523 to Butley Ash, R on A538 Tytherington. Knutsford: follow A537 at A538, L for Tytherington. Leek: follow A523 at A537 L & 1st R A53.* Home-made teas. **Adm £3.50, chd free. Sat 2, Sun 3 Aug (10.30-4).**

Garden of approx ⅓ acre. SW facing. Garden laid out in two parts. Large lawn area surrounded by mature, colourful perennial borders. Rose arbour, small pond with koi, patio, raised fruit and cut flower bed. Small mature wooded area with winding paths on a lower level. Front, laid to lawn with two main borders separated by a small grass area. Good wheelchair access to most of garden except wood area.

38 HATTON HOUSE GARDENS

Hatton Heath, Chester CH3 9AP. Judy Halewood. *4m SE of Chester. From Chester on A41 2km past The Black Dog PH. From Whitchurch on A41 7km past the Broxton r'about.* Light refreshments. **Adm £5, chd free. Sat 14 June (11-5.30).**

Approx 8 acres of beautifully landscaped gardens both formal and natural. Pathways leading through extensive herbaceous borders give way to lawns, azalea rock gardens, waterfalls and wild flowers. The 2 acre lake is rich in wildlife and flanked by woodland, wildflowers, bulbs, bridges and follies. Some areas are still under development. All of the gardens are wheelchair friendly apart from the Sunken Garden.

> Cosy seats and lovely views will make your visit to this quirky and much loved garden one to remember . . .

39 18 HIGHFIELD ROAD

Bollington, Macclesfield SK10 5LR. Mrs Melita Turner. *3m N of Macclesfield. A523 to Stockport. Turn R at B5090 r'about signed Bollington. Pass under viaduct. Take next R (by Library) up Hurst Lane. Turn R into Highfield Rd.* Home-made teas. **Adm £3, chd free. Sat 5, Sun 6 July (11-4).**

This small terraced garden packed with plants was designed by Melita and has evolved over the past 7yrs. This plantswoman is a plantaholic and RHS Certificate holder. An attempt has been made to combine formality through structural planting with a more casual look influenced by the style of Christopher LLoyd.

40 73 HILL TOP AVENUE

Cheadle Hulme SK8 7HZ. Mr & Mrs Martin Land. *4m S of Stockport. Turn off A34 (new bypass) at r'about signed Cheadle Hulme (B5094). Take 2nd turn L into Gillbent Rd, signed*

Cheadle Hulme Sports Centre. Go to end, small r'about, turn R into Church Rd. 2nd rd on L is Hill Top Ave. From Stockport or Bramhall turn R or L into Church Rd by The Church Inn. Hill Top Ave is 1st rd on R. Light refreshments. **Adm £3.50, chd free (share to Arthritis Research UK). Evening Opening wine, Thur 22 May (5.30-8); Sun 10 Aug (2-6).**
1/6 -acre plantswoman's garden. Well stocked with a wide range of sun-loving herbaceous plants, shrub and climbing roses, many clematis varieties, pond and damp area, shade-loving woodland plants and small unusual trees, in an originally designed, long narrow garden.

41 HILLSIDE

Mill Lane, Mobberley WA16 7HY. Paul Hales & Mark Rubery. *2m E of Knutsford. Entrance off Mill Lane, next to Roebuck Inn. Roebuck is signed off Mobberley Rd.* Cream teas. **Adm £5, chd £2 (share to Blackbrook Zoological Park). Sun 4, Mon 5 May (11-5).**
A magnificent 6-acre garden, home to a huge collection of rare birds incl 90 flamingos. The various ponds are adorned with delightful palm trees, bonsais, agaves and citrus trees. On the opposite side is a woodland setting that features a large, delightful waterfall surrounded by many mature plants and trees.

42 HILLSIDE COTTAGE

Shrigley Road, Pott Shrigley SK10 5SG. Anne & Phil Geoghegan, 01625 572214, annegeoghegan@btinternet.com. *6m N of Macclesfield. On A523 at Legh Arms T-lights turn to Pott Shrigley. Take 3rd. L after approx 1½ m. After 1m at Green Close Methodist Church turn R to garden.* Home-made teas. **Visitors welcome by appt June to Aug, groups of 10+. Adm £6 incl teas or wine.**
A 1/4 -acre garden with panoramic views over the treetops. Packed with colourful perennials, roses, clematis, shrubs and small trees. Landscaped on several discreet levels with various places to sit and enjoy the garden and views beyond. There is a small walled garden with water feature and a summerhouse, conservatory and rose covered arbour. Limited wheelchair access.

43 THE HOLLOW

Moggie Lane, Adlington, Macclesfield SK10 4NY. Rob & Jan Wiper. *7m N of Macclesfield. On A523 from Macclesfield to Stockport in Poynton turn R at mini r'about (Johnsons Dry Cleaners) into Dickens Lane follow rd into Moggie Lane.* Home-made teas. **Adm £4, chd free. Sat 5, Sun 6 July (1.30-5).**
Modern 2½ acre garden. Long lavender borders greet you into a diverse garden with summer perennial beds, climbing plant covered gazebo and pergola, large cascade, koi and lily pond. Small fruit orchard, vegetable kitchen beds. Small woodland belt with bridge covered stream and wild flower meadow. Many garden sculptures.

Partly walled garden at the rear combines the relaxed and varied planting . . .

44 NEW HOLLY MERE

4 Radley Lane, Houghton Green, Warrington WA2 0SY. Angela & Graham Harrop. *2m N of Warrington. Leave M6 J22 to Newton. 250yds L into Highfield Lane. At T-junction L into Middleton Lane. 1st R into Delph Lane. Over M62, R into Mill Lane. L into Radley Lane.* Tea. **Adm £3.50, chd free. Suns 8 June; 10 Aug (11-5).**
½ acre garden. Some specimen trees and shrubs. Extensive borders of interesting herbaceous perennials (some colour themed), roses and grasses. Many AGM plants. Small kitchen garden.

45 HUNTER'S CROFT

Wilmslow Road, Mottram St. Andrew SK10 4QH. Len & Mary Beth Morris. *Located on A538, Wilmslow Road. ½ m from The Bull's Head PH toward Prestbury.* Home-made teas. **Adm £4, chd free. Sun 22 June (12-5).**
Set in approximately 1½ acres, Hunter's Croft has a real mix of borders from architectural, hot to herbaceous. Japanese inspired rockery from which water flows into a pond below with a bog garden. Woodland, greenhouse with herb garden, raised vegetable beds and meadow. All with the backdrop of the Cheshire countryside!

46 INGLEWOOD

4 Birchmere, Heswall CH60 6TN. Colin & Sandra Fairclough, 0151 3424645, sandra.fairclough@tiscali.co.uk, www.inglewood-birchmere.blogspot.co.uk. *6m S of Birkenhead. From A540 Devon Doorway/Clegg Arms r'about go through Heswall. ¼ m after Tesco, R into Quarry Rd East, 2nd L into Tower Rd North & L into Birchmere.* Home-made teas. **Adm £4, chd free. Sat 12, Sun 13 July (1.30-5). Visitors also welcome by appt May to July.**
Beautiful ½ acre garden with stream, large koi pond, 'beach' with grasses, wildlife pond and bog area. Brimming with shrubs, bulbs, acers, conifers, rhododendrons, herbaceous plants and hostas. Interesting features include hand cart, antique mangle, wood carvings, bug hotel and Indian dog gates leading to a secret garden. Lots of seating to admire the views and enjoy refreshments.

47 LASKEY FARM

Laskey Lane, Thelwall, Warrington WA4 2TF. Howard & Wendy Platt, 07740 804825, wendy_platt1@excite.com, www.laskeyfarm.com. *3m From M6/M56. From M56/M6 follow directions to Lymm. At T-junction turn L onto Booths Lane in Warrington direction. Turn R onto Lymm Rd. Turn R onto Laskey Lane.* Home-made teas. **Adm £4, chd free. Sat 16, Sun 17 Aug (11-5). Visitors also welcome by appt May to Aug groups of 10+.**
1-acre garden packed with late summer colour which incl herbaceous borders, rose garden, vegetable area and parterre while the greenhouse contains a collection of pelargoniums and tropical plants. There are a number of interconnected pools for wildlife, fish and terrapin pond and a number of new features are planned for 2014. Large greenhouse. Featured in Garden News and Warrington Guardian. Most areas of the garden may be accessed by wheelchair.

48 ◆ LITTLE MORETON HALL

Congleton CW12 4SD. National Trust, 01270 272018, www.nationaltrust.org.uk/littlemoretonhall. *4m S of Congleton. On A34.* **Adm £9, chd £4.50. For NGS: Sat 12 July (11-5). For other opening times and information, please phone or see garden website.**

1½ -acre garden surrounded by a moat, next to finest example of timber-framed architecture in England. Herb and historic vegetable garden, orchard and borders. Knot garden. Adm incl entry to the Hall with optional free guided tours. Picnic lawn at front of hall. Wheelchairs available, ground floor of hall and garden accessible. Please be aware that the courtyard is cobbled.

49 LONG ACRE

Wyche Lane, Bunbury CW6 9PS. Margaret & Michael Bourne, 01829 260944, mjbourne249@tiscali.co.uk. *3½ m SE of Tarporley. In Bunbury village, turn into Wyche Lane by Nags Head PH car park, garden 400yds on L. Disabled parking in lane adjacent to garden.* Home-made teas. **Adm £4, chd free (share to Guide Dogs for the Blind & St Boniface Church Flower Fund). Sun 20 Apr (2-5). Visitors also welcome by appt Apr to June, groups of 10+.**

Plantswoman's garden of approx 1 acre with unusual plants and trees, pool gardens, exotic conservatory, herbaceous, specialise in proteas, S African bulbs and clivia. Spring garden with camellias, magnolias, bulbs. Wheelchair access to most areas.

50 ◆ LYME PARK

Lyme Park, Disley SK12 2NR. National Trust, 01663 762023, www.nationaltrust.org.uk/lyme-park/. *6m SE of Stockport. Just W of Disley on A6. Once you see the brown signs, follow them, not Satnav.* **Adm £7, chd £3.50. For NGS: Sat 6 Sept (11-5). For other opening times and information, please phone or see garden website.**

Neglected in the 1940's, and now gloriously restored this 17-acre garden is a relaxed space to enjoy picnics and stroll amongst high Victorian style bedding, the Dutch garden, luxurious Gertrude Jekyll style herbaceous borders, and Edwardian rose garden, An orangery, rare trees, reflection lake, dramatic ravine garden, and mixed borders contrast with sweeping moorland beyond. House and park are also open. Please ask at admissions for wheelchair access. The garden is on many levels, with steps, but an accessible route is available.

51 MANLEY KNOLL

Manley Road, Manley WA6 9DX. Mr & Mrs James Timpson, 01928 740458, james@timpson.com, www.manleyknoll.com. *3m N of Tarvin. On B5393, via Ashton & Mouldsworth. 3m S of Frodsham, via Alvanley.* Home-made teas. **Adm £3.50, chd free. Suns 25 May; 6 July (12-5). Visitors also welcome by appt Apr to Oct.**

Arts and Crafts garden created early 1900s. Covering 6 acres, divided into different rooms encompassing parterres, clipped yew hedging and ornamental ponds. Banks of rhododendron and azaleas frame a far-reaching view of the Cheshire Plain. Also a magical quarry/folly garden with waterfall.

52 NEW THE MEADOWS

Townfield Lane, Mollington, Chester CH1 6NJ. Peter & Ruth Bowler. *3m N of Chester off A540 Parkgate Rd as signed. R from S, L from N. Parking will be signed.* Home-made teas. **Combined adm with Beechwood and Rose Farm House £5, chd free. Sat 21, Sun 22 June (1-5).**

A cobbled drive with borders of mixed planting between old brick walls leads to a lawned area with mature trees. Partly walled garden at the rear combines the relaxed and varied planting of a cottage garden with some formality incl yew hedging in the centre. Approx 1 acre garden surrounding the former gardener's cottage to Mollington Hall (now demolished). Cobbled drive and some gravel paths.

53 NEW MILLHEYES

Little Neston, Neston CH64 4AF. Mr & Mrs Clive & Jane Harding. *10m NW of Chester. M53 J4, follow signs M56 and A5117. Turn onto A540 & follow signs for Hoylake. Garden is 1m further along from Ness Gardens (signed locally). Parking at St Michael's Church.* Home-made teas at St Michael's Church. **Adm £4, chd free. Mon 26 May, Sun 20 July (2-5). Combined with Delfan.**

Informally planted garden set in ¾ acre. Hedge enclosed front garden with circular lawn and deep herbaceous/perennial border. Vegetable plot. Sandstone terraced back garden with wildlife pond, wisteria pergola, perennial borders and seating areas. Views over to the Welsh hills. Front garden wheelchair accessible. Restricted access in back garden.

54 MILLPOOL

Smithy Lane, Bosley SK11 0NZ. Joe & Barbara Fray, 01260 226581. *5m S of Macclesfield. Just off A523 at Bosley. Turn L 1m S of A54 T-lights. From Leek, turn R, 2½ m N of The Royal Oak PH at Rushton. Please follow direction to parking areas. No parking at garden.* Light refreshments. **Adm £3.50, chd free. Sat 21, Sun 22 June (1-5). Visitors also welcome by appt May to Sept, 10-40 people max.**

Garden designed to extend the seasons with colour, texture and scent. Lush herbaceous borders and areas of deep shade. Small stream, pond and bog garden. Gravel plantings, containers and a fine collection of bonsai trees. An ever increasing collection of modern ceramics and a most productive vegetable garden in tubs and baskets. Children's interest trail and craft activities and large plant sale.

55 ◆ MOUNT PLEASANT

Yeld Lane, Kelsall CW6 0TB. Dave Darlington & Louise Worthington, 01829 751592, www.mountpleasantgardens.co.uk. *8m E of Chester. Off A54 at T-lights into Kelsall. Turn into Yeld Lane opp Farmers Arms PH, 200yds on L. Do*

not follow Sat Nav directions. Tea. **Adm £5, chd £1. For NGS: Sun 4, Mon 5 May; Sat 6, Sun 7 Sept (12-5). For other opening times and information, please phone or see garden website.**
10 acres of landscaped garden and woodland started in 1994 with impressive views over the Cheshire countryside. Steeply terraced in places. Specimen trees, rhododendrons, azaleas, conifers, mixed and herbaceous borders; 4 ponds, formal and wildlife. Vegetable garden, stumpery with tree ferns, sculptures, wild flower meadow and Japanese garden. Bog garden, tropical garden. September Sculpture Exhibition. Please ring prior to visit for wheelchair access.

56 ◆ NESS BOTANIC GARDENS

Ness, Neston CH64 4AY. The University of Liverpool, 0845 0304063, www.nessgardens.org.uk. *10 NW of Chester. Off A540. M53 J4, follow signs M56 & A5117 (signed N Wales). Turn onto A540 follow signs for Hoylake. Ness Gardens is signed locally*. **Adm £6.50, chd £3. For NGS: Sat 1 Mar (10-4.30). For other opening times and information, please phone or see garden website.**
Gardens cover some 64 acres, having a distinctly maritime feel and housing The National Collection of Mountain Ash (Sorbus). Among some of the significant specimens that still flourish in the gardens are Pieris Forrestii which was collected for Bulley by George Forrest in Yunnan. Winter garden features, including many varieties of snowdrops. Mobility scooters and wheelchairs available free - advance booking recommended.

57 ◆ NORTON PRIORY MUSEUM & GARDENS

Tudor Road, Manor Park, Runcorn WA7 1SX. Norton Priory Museum Trust, 01928 569895, www.nortonpriory.org. *2m SE of Runcorn. If using Sat-Nav try WA7 1BD and follow the brown Norton Priory signs*. **Adm £3.50, chd £3.50. For NGS: Sun 8 June (12-4). For other opening times and information, please phone or see garden website.**
Over 40 acres of gardens and grounds, with summerhouses, stream glade and medieval herb garden. 2½ -acre Georgian Walled Garden, with rosewalk, colour borders, soft fruit and cottage garden. Home to the National Collection of Tree Quince (Cydonia Oblonga). Historic Pear orchard and wild flower meadow.

NCH

Somerford

58 NEW OAKFIELD VILLA

Nantwich Road, Wrenbury, Nantwich CW5 8EL. Carolyn & Jack Kennedy. *6m S of Nantwich & 6m N of Whitchurch. Garden on main rd through village next to Dairy Farm. Parking in field between Oak Villas & School 1min walk to garden*. Home-made teas. **Adm £3, chd free. Wed 18, Sat 21 June (10.30-5).**
Romantic S-facing garden of densely planted borders and creative planting in containers, incl climbing roses, clematis and hydrangeas. Divided by screens into rooms, the garden incl a small fishpond and water feature. Pergola clothed in beautiful climbers provides relaxed sheltered seating area. Small front garden. Some gravelled areas.

59 THE OLD COTTAGE

44 High Street, Frodsham WA6 7HE. John & Lesley Corfield, 07591 609311, corfield@rock44.plus.com. *DO NOT FOLLOW SATNAV - no parking at garden. On A56 close to Frodsham town centre. Follow signs from town centre to railway car park, garden signed from there (short walk). Or park in town centre and follow signs uphill N to cottage*. Home-made teas. **Adm £4, chd free. Sat 14, Sun 15 June (1-6). Visitors also welcome by appt June to Aug.**
At the rear of the Grade II listed C16 cottage (not open) are ⅔ acre, organic and wildlife friendly garden featuring many aspects that support various forms of wildlife. Steps lead up to a large vegetable and herb garden, with further mixed planting in herbaceous borders. Wildlife pond and bog garden. Further areas of fruit trees and shady woodland borders. Extensive views over Mersey estuary. Partial wheelchair access - please ring for details.

60 THE OLD PARSONAGE

Arley Green, via Arley Hall & Gardens CW9 6LZ. The Viscount & Viscountess Ashbrook, 01565 777277, www.arleyhallandgardens.com. *5m NNE of Northwich. 3m NNE of Great Budworth. M6 J19 & 20 & M56 J10. Follow signs to Arley Hall & Gardens. From Arley Hall notices to Old Parsonage which lies across park at Arley Green.* Home-made teas. **Adm £4.50, chd free (share to Save The Children Fund). Sat 31 May, Sun 1 June (2-5.30). Visitors also welcome by appt May to June, groups of 10+.**

2-acre garden in attractive and secretive rural setting in secluded part of Arley Estate, with ancient yew hedges, herbaceous and mixed borders, shrub roses, climbers, leading to woodland garden and unfenced pond with gunnera and water plants. Rhododendrons, azaleas, meconopsis, cardiocrinum, some interesting and unusual trees. Wheelchair access over mown grass.

Pergola clothed in beautiful climbers provides relaxed sheltered seating area . . .

61 39 OSBORNE STREET

Bredbury, Stockport SK6 2DA. Geoff & Heather Hoyle, geoff.hoyle@btinternet.com, www.youtube.com/user/Dahliaholic. *1½ m E of Stockport, just off B6104. Follow signs for Lower Bredbury/Bredbury Hall. Leave M60 at J27 (from S and W) or J25 (from N and E). Osborne St is adjacent to pelican crossing on B6104.* Light refreshments. **Adm £3.50, chd free. Sat 6, Sun 7 Sept (1-5). Visitors also welcome by appt Sept.**

This dahliaholic's garden contains over 300 dahlias in 150+ varieties, mostly of exhibition standard. Shapely lawns are surrounded by deep flower beds that are crammed with dahlias of all shapes, sizes and colours, and complemented by climbers, soft perennials and bedding plants. An absolute riot of early autumn colour. The garden comprises two separate areas, both crammed with very colourful flowers. The dahlias range in height from 18 inches to 8 feet tall, and are in a wide variety of shapes and colours. They are interspersed with salvias, fuchsias, argyranthemums, and bedding plants. The garden is on YouTube: search for Dahliaholic. Featured on BBC Gardeners World, and in Amateur Gardener, Daily Mail, and Landscape.

62 PARM PLACE

High Street, Great Budworth CW9 6HF. Peter & Jane Fairclough, 01606 891131, janefair@btinternet.com. *3m N of Northwich. Great Budworth on E side of A559 between Northwich & Warrington, 4m from J10 M56, also 4m from J19 M6. Parm Place is W of village on S side of High Street.* Home-made teas. **Adm £4, chd free (share to Great Ormond Street Hospital). Suns 6 Apr; 29 June (1-5). Visitors also welcome by appt Apr to July.**

Well-stocked ½ -acre plantswoman's garden with stunning views towards S Cheshire. Curving lawns, shrubs, colour co-ordinated herbaceous borders, roses, water features, rockery, gravel bed with grasses. Fruit and vegetable plots. In spring large collection of bulbs and flowers, camellias, hellebores and blossom. Parterre new last year.

63 ◆ PEOVER HALL & GARDENS

Over Peover, Knutsford WA16 9HW. Randle Brooks, 01565 724220, www.peoverhall.com. *4m S of Knutsford. A50/Holmes Chapel Rd/Whipping Stocks PH turn onto Stocks Lane. Approx 0.9m turn onto Grotto Lane. ¼ m turn onto Goostrey Lane. Main entrance on bend.* Light refreshments The Park House Tea Room and Paddock offers lovely cream teas, homemade cakes and refreshments on open days. **Adm £4, chd free. For NGS: Sat 31 May, Sun 1 June (2-5). For other opening times and information, please phone or see garden website.**

Set in 15 acres, 'garden rooms' filled with clipped box, topiary, lily ponds, herb, walled gardens, Romanesque loggia, C19 dell, rhododendrons, pleached limes. Grade I Carolean Stables - more architecturally important than the house itself. Featured in Cheshire Life '10 Glorious Gardens'. Partial wheelchair access to garden.

64 17 POPLAR GROVE

Sale M33 3AX. Mr Gordon Cooke. *3m N of Altrincham. From the A6144 at Brooklands Stn turn into Hope Rd. Poplar Grove 3rd on R.* Home-made teas. **Adm £4, chd free. Sat 19, Sun 20 July (2-5).**

This S-facing suburban garden is on many levels. Its strongly diagonal design features a pebble mosaic 'cave', topiary, sculpture garden, living roof and exotic planting. A mix of formality and dense planting in the contemporary 'English' style. Exhibition of Garden Ceramics.

65 POULTON HALL

Poulton Lancelyn, Bebington CH63 9LN. The Lancelyn Green Family, 0151 3342057, jlgpoulton@talktalk.net, www.poultonhall.co.uk. *2m S of Bebington. From M53, J4 towards Bebington; at T-lights R along Poulton Rd; house 1m on R.* Cream teas. **Adm £4, chd free. Sat 19, Suns 20 Apr; 8 June (2-5). Visitors also welcome by appt Apr to July, teas by arrangement.**

3 acres; lawns fronting house, wild flower meadow. A surprising approach to the walled garden, with reminders of Roger Lancelyn Green's retellings, Excalibur, Robin Hood and Jabberwocky. Scented sundial garden for the visually impaired. Memorial sculpture for Richard Lancelyn Green by Sue Sharples. Rose, nursery rhyme, witch, herb and oriental gardens. Organ Music at 4pm in the music room of the Hall. There are often choirs or orchestral music in the garden. Level gravel paths. Separate access (not across parking field) for wheelchairs.

66 ◆ QUARRY BANK HOUSE GARDEN
Quarry Bank Road, Styal SK9 4LA. National Trust, 01625 527 468, www.nationaltrust.org.uk. *2m N of Wilmslow. Follow NT signs.* Light refreshments. **Adm £6, chd £3. For NGS: Sun 18 May (10.30-5). For other opening times and information, please phone or see garden website.**
A 'picturesque' valley garden created in the 1790s by cotton mill owner Samuel Greg. The garden is mainly a spring garden, with many fine azaleas and rhododendrons. Some rhododendrons are unique to the garden having been commissioned and introduced by the Greg family during C19. Parts of lower garden are accessible and a map is provided to show the route. Mobility scooter available.

67 ◆ THE QUINTA ARBORETUM
Swettenham CW12 2LD. Tatton Garden Society, 01477 537698, www.tattongardensociety.co.uk. *4m NW of Congleton. Turn off A54 N 2m W of Congleton or turn E off A535 at Twemlow Green, NE of Holmes Chapel. Follow signs to Swettenham. Park at Swettenham Arms PH.* **Adm £5, chd free. For NGS: Sun 5 Oct (12-4). For other opening times and information, please phone or see garden website.**
The 28-acre arboretum has been established since 1960s and contains around 10,000 trees and shrubs of over 2,000 species, some very rare. Incl National Collections of Pinus and Fraxinus, large collection of oak, a collection of hebes and autumn flowering shrubs. A lake and way-marked walks. A guided tour at 2pm is incl. Care required but wheelchairs can access much of the arboretum on the mown paths.
NCH

68 RIDGE HILL
Ridgehill, Sutton, Macclesfield SK11 0LU. Mr & Mrs Martin McMillan, 01260 252353, pat@normanshall.co.uk. *2m SE of Macclesfield. From Macclesfield take A523 to Leek. After Silk Rd look for T-lights signed Langley, Wincle & Sutton. Turn L into Byron's Lane, under canal bridge, 1st L to Langley at junction Church House PH. Ridge Hill Rd is opp turn up Ridge Hill Rd, garden on R.* Light refreshments. **Adm £5, chd free. Sun 6 July (10-4.30). Visitors also welcome by appt Apr to May on 27, 29, 30 April; 1, 2, 3, 4, 6, 8, 9, 10, 11 May.**
4 acre garden set in the hills above Macclesfield overlooking the Cheshire plain. Herbaceous borders, old Rose garden, shrubbery with rhododendron, azaleas, water features, topiary, plus a new Victorian greenhouse and potager. Raffle. Garden accessories, teas/coffee, home made cakes, plants, wine and soft drinks.

69 RIVERSIDE LODGE
19 Oldfield Road, Heswall CH60 6SN. Tim & Margaret Ransome. *7m S Birkenhead. From Devon Doorway/Glegg Arms r'about go N on Telegraph Rd for 1½ m. Turn L at Quarry Rd West. Garden in Oldfield Rd facing junction with Quarry Rd West.* Home-made teas by Marie Curie. **Adm £4, chd free. Sun 18 May (1-4.30).**
¾ -acre garden set in mature trees and shrubs. Spectacular stonework terracing with views to Welsh Hills, reflecting pool, gazebo, herbaceous and mixed planting, gravel area and rose arches. The front garden has been redesigned by the garden owners and features a Westmorland Green Slate water feature. Garden can be viewed from wheelchair accesible areas.

70 ◆ RODE HALL
Church Lane, Scholar Green ST7 3QP. Sir Richard & Lady Baker Wilbraham, 01270 873237, www.rodehall.co.uk. *5m SW of Congleton. Between Scholar Green (A34) & Rode Heath (A50).* **For opening times and information, please phone or see garden website.**
Nesfield's terrace and rose garden with view over Humphry Repton's landscape is a feature of Rode gardens, as is the woodland garden with terraced rock garden and grotto. Other attractions incl the walk to the lake, restored ice house, working walled kitchen garden and Italian garden. Fine display of snowdrops in February. Daily for Snowdrop Walks 8 Feb - 16 March (except Mons) 12-4pm. Partial wheelchair access, gravel and woodchip paths, but WC and tearooms accessed easily.

71 NEW ROSE FARM HOUSE
Townfield Lane, Mollington, Chester CH1 6NJ. Mr & Mrs Carl Stagg. *3 m N of Chester off A540 Parkgate Rd as signed. R from S, L from N. Parking will be signed.* **Combined adm with Beechwood and The Meadows £5, chd free. Sat 21, Sun 22 June (1-5).**
Set in ½ acre, enclosed in part by a brick wall in the style of the Georgian Estate wall opposite. Much history and originally laid out in the 1920's and 30's and changed over time. An informal cottage style incl herbaceous border, roses, shrubbery, vegetable patch, fruit trees and bushes and water feature. Home movies of the garden in 1935 should be on show.

72 ROSEWOOD
Old Hall Lane, Puddington, Neston CH64 5SP. Mr & Mrs C E J Brabin, 0151 353 1193, angela.brabin@btinternet.com. *6m N of Chester. From A540 turn down Puddington Lane, 1½ m. Park by village green. Walk 30yds to Old Hall Lane, turn L through archway into garden.* Home-made teas. **Adm £3, chd free. Visitors welcome by appt, individuals, medium or large groups.**
All yr garden; thousands of snowdrops in Feb, Camellias in autumn, winter and spring. Rhododendrons in April/May and unusual flowering trees from March to June. Autumn Cyclamen in quantity from Aug to Nov. Perhaps the greatest delight to owners is a large Cornus capitata, flowering in June. Bees kept in the garden. Honey sometimes available.

The East Garden

73 THE ROWANS

Oldcastle Lane, Threapwood, nr Malpas SY14 7AY. Paul Philpotts & Alan Bourne, 01948 770522, alanandpaul@btinternet.com. *3m SW of Malpas. Leave Malpas on B5069 for Wrexham, after 3m, take 1st L after Threapwood Shop/PO into Chapel Lane, L into Oldcastle Lane, garden 1st Bungalow on R.* Home-made teas. **Adm £4, chd free. Sat 12, Sun 13 July (2-5.30). Visitors also welcome by appt June to July, refreshments by arrangement.**
This 1-acre award winning garden, has an Italianate theme. Divided into numerous formal and natural areas, in which to sit and enjoy the views and feature statuary. Many mature and unusual trees, several ponds, herbaceous borders, vegetable plots, greenhouse, extensive Hosta collection, tranquil secret garden. Something of interest for every visitor with new features added for 2014. Featured in Amateur Gardening Magazine and Garden News. Winners of Cheshire West and Chester Councils Best Front Garden - Something Blooming Special competition.

74 SAIGHTON GRANGE

Saighton CH3 6EN. The Governors of Abbey Gate College, 01244 564184, alan.kift@abbeygatecollege.co.uk, www.abbeygatecollege.co.uk. *4m SE of Chester. Take A41 towards Whitchurch. At far end of Waverton turn R to Saighton Grange at the end of village.* Home-made teas. **Adm £4, chd free. Sun 6 Apr (1-4). Visitors also welcome by appt Apr to Sept.**
6½ acres of garden designed by Inigo Triggs for the 2nd Duke of Westminster in 1901. Redesigned for the 4th Duchess during the 1960's by Russell, of Castle Howard fame. Now undergoing third development. Present emphasis on a spring garden with magnolias, daffodils and bluebell woodland walk, but development continues to introduce later flowering plants to extend the season.

75 SANDSEND

126 Hibbert Lane, Marple SK6 7NU. David & Audrey Bomford. *5m SE of Stockport. Leave M60 at J27. A626 to Marple R at Texaco garage, R at mini r'about into Hibbert Lane ½ m on R. Or A6 from Stockport via Hazel Grove to High Lane, L at Horseshoe PH into Windlehurst Rd 1¾ m towards Marple. Hibbert Lane starts at canal bridge on L 200yds past bridge.* Home-made teas. **Adm £3.50, chd free. Sat 24, Sun 25 May (1-5).**
Mature garden set back from the road, trees and shrubs give all-yr-round colour to the front garden. Long back garden with raised beds, lawns and winding paths is a journey through varied planting with seats to view all aspects. Small pond, acers, hostas, azaleas, rockeries and herbaceous. Sun and shade and abundant birdsong in surrounding mature trees. Home made teas, cake sale.

76 SANDYMERE

Middlewich Road, Cotebrook CW6 9EH. John & Alex Timpson, 07886 368014, tscheers@btinternet.com. *5m N of Tarporley. On A54 about 300yds W of T-lights at Xrds of A49/A54.* Home-made teas. **Adm £5, chd free. Sun 20 July (2.30-5.30). Visitors also welcome by appt May to Sept, min 20.**
16 landscaped acres of beautiful Cheshire countryside with terraces,

walled garden and amazing hosta garden. Long views, native wildlife and tranquillity of 3 lakes. Elegant planting schemes, shady seats and sun-splashed borders, mature pine woods and rolling lawns accented by graceful wooden structures. Different every year. Kitchen garden with organically grown vegetables, fruit cage and small orchard, also extensive range of penstemon plants. Limited access for wheelchairs.

77 SOMERFORD
19 Leycester Road, Knutsford WA16 8QR. Emma Dearman & Joe Morris, 01565 621095, emmadearman1@gmail.com. *1m from centre of Knutsford. From Knutsford town centre, take Toft Rd (A50) direction Holmes Chapel (S). After approx 1m, turn sharp L into Leycester Rd, immed after Esso garage. Cross Legh Rd. Somerford is found on your L opp Leycester Close. Park on Leycester Rd or Legh Rd with consideration to residents.* Home-made teas. **Adm £4, chd free. Evening opening adm £5 incl glass of wine Fri 4 July (6-8.30); Suns 13 July; 10 Aug (12-5). Visitors also welcome by appt June to Aug, groups of 10+.**
Majestic trees surround this 1½ acre garden which has been completely re-designed and planted. Hard landscaping and sculptures complement lush herbaceous and perennial borders. Croquet and pond lawns are separated by a vast oak pergola. Cube-headed hornbeams lead into the snail-trail walk and informal lawn and fernery. Stable courtyard with box parterres. Most of the garden is accessible by wheelchair. Ring for further information.

78 NEW SOMERSET HOUSE
Sarn Road, Threapwood, Malpas SY14 7AW. Sir John & Lady Susan Clark. *Just off B5069 3¼ m W of Malpas. From East leave A41 at Hampton for Malpas 1½ m turn 1st L past church 3m B5069. W from A525 go Bangor on Dee take B5069 4m to Threapwood on Sarn Rd.* Home-made teas. **Combined adm with The White Cottage £4, chd free. Sat 21, Sun 22 June (1-5).**
A cottage garden that has evolved over 30yrs. An old orchard is set behind a trellis dividing it from the front lawn surrounded by beds containing herbaceous plants, shrubs and roses. Surrounded by more beds pond and rockery with a large rose bed and bank with mature trees beyond. Separated by the drive is an extensive vegetable garden, large pond with shade plants and new orchard.

You will not believe how many plants there are in such a small garden . . .

79 68 SOUTH OAK LANE
Wilmslow SK9 6AT. Caroline & David Melliar-Smith, 01625 528147, caroline.ms@btinternet.com. *¾ m SW of Wilmslow. From M56 (J6) take A538 (Wilmslow) R into Buckingham Rd. From centre of Wilmslow turn R onto B5086, 1st R.into Gravel Ln, 4th R. into South Oak Ln.* **Adm £3.50, chd free. Sat 12, Sun 13 July (11-4.30). Visitors also welcome by appt May to Aug, max 20.**
With year-round colour, scent and interest, this attractive, narrow, hedged cottage garden has evolved over the years into 5 natural 'rooms'. These Hardy Plant Society members passion for plants, reflected in shrubs, trees, flower borders and pond, creates havens for wildlife. Share this garden with its varied history from the 1890's. Some rare and unusual hardy and shade loving plants. Featured in Amateur Gardening, Garden News and Cheshire life.

80 199 STOCKPORT ROAD
Timperley WA15 7SF. Eric & Shirley Robinson, 0161 980 1368, shirley233@sky.com. *1½ m NE of Altrincham. Take A560 out of Altrincham, in 1m take B5165 towards Timperley. B5165 is Stockport Rd.* Home-made teas. **Adm £3, chd free. Sat 28, Sun 29 June (1-5). Visitors also welcome by appt May to Aug.**
Cottage-style garden full of colourful herbaceous perennials, shrubs and hostas, with a brick-built pond complete with small koi and goldfish. You will not believe how many plants there are in such a small garden. Small front garden with water feature and small shaded plant area.

81 ◆ STONYFORD COTTAGE
Stonyford Lane, Oakmere CW8 2TF. Janet & Tony Overland, 01606 888128, www.stonyfordcottagegardens.co.uk. *5m SW of Northwich. From Northwich take A556 towards Chester. ¾ m past A49 junction turn R into Stonyford Lane. Entrance ½ m on L.* Cream teas. **Adm £4, chd free. For NGS: Suns 1 June; 10 Aug (1.30-5). For other opening times and information, please phone or see garden website.**
Set around a tranquil pool this Monet style landscape has a wealth of moisture loving plants, incl iris and candelabra primulas. Drier areas feature unusual perennials and rarer trees and shrubs. Woodland paths meander through shade and bog plantings, along boarded walks, across wild natural areas with views over the pool to the cottage gardens. Unusual plants available at the adjacent nursery. Open Tues - Sun & BH Mons Apr - Sept 10-5. Some gravel paths.

82 SUN HOUSE
66 Bridge Lane, Bramhall, Stockport SK7 3AW. Peter & Susan Hale. *3½ m S of Stockport. Sun House is on Bridge Lane (A5143) between junction with A5102 at the Bramall Hall r'about and Bramhall Moor Lane.* Home-made teas. **Adm £3.50, chd free. Sat 31 May; Sun 1 June (1.30-5.30).**
⅓ acre garden enclosed by mature trees, it has a dry acid sandy soil which has been addressed by building numerous ponds and bog areas. A wide range of herbaceous plants, mosaic and ceramic decorations, gravel garden, vegetable plot and chickens plus two life-sized terracotta warriors. Display and sale of ceramics and crafts. New exploration trail for children each year. Some paths need care, unfenced ponds.

83 SYCAMORE COTTAGE
Manchester Road, Carrington, Manchester M31 4AY. Mrs C Newton. *From M60 J8 take Carrington turn (A6144) through 2 sets of lights past Windmill PH. Garden about 1m past the PH opp Air Products on R. From M6 J20 follow signs for Lymm. In Lymm town centre follow signs for Partington/Carrington (A6144) follow for 5 or 6m. Garden on L opp Air Products*. Light refreshments. **Adm £3.50, chd free. Sat 21, Sun 22 June (1-5).**
Approx 1/5 acre cottage garden split into distinct areas, with woodland banking, natural spring, well and ponds. Also features decking with two seating areas and summer house. Garden featured on Cupranols TV advert.

84 TATTENHALL HALL
High Street, Tattenhall CH3 9PX. Jen & Nick Benefield, Chris Evered & Jannie Hollins, 01829 770654, janniehollins@gmail.com. *8m S of Chester on A41. Turn L to Tattenhall, through village, turn R at Letters PH, past war memorial on L through Sandstone pillared gates. Park on rd or in village car park*. Tea. **Adm £4.50, chd free. Suns 25 May; 15 June (2-5). Visitors also welcome by appt Apr to Sept, limited parking facilities.**
Plant enthusiasts garden around Jacobean house (not open). 4 1/2 acres, wild flower meadows, interesting trees, large pond, stream, walled garden, colour themed borders, succession planting, spinney walk with shade plants, yew terrace overlooking meadow, views to hills. Glasshouse and vegetable garden. Wildlife friendly sometimes untidy garden, interest throughout the year, continuing to develop. Gravel paths, cobbles and some steps.

85 ◆ TATTON PARK
Knutsford WA16 6QN. National Trust, leased to Cheshire East Council, 01625 374400, www.tattonpark.org.uk. *2 1/2 m N of Knutsford. Well signed on M56 J7 & from M6 J19*. **Adm £6, chd £4. For NGS: Weds 14 May; 11 June (10-6). For other opening times and information, please phone or see garden website.**
Features include orangery by Wyatt, fernery by Paxton, restored Japanese garden, Italian and rose gardens. Greek monument and African hut. Hybrid azaleas and rhododendrons; swamp cypresses, tree ferns, tall redwoods, bamboos and pines. Fully restored productive walled gardens.

Flower beds meander along the drive with roses, astrantias, geraniums, violas and other summer flowering plants . . .

86 TIRLEY GARTH
Mallows Way, Willington, nr Tarporley CW6 0RQ. *2m N of Tarporley. 2m S of Kelsall. Entrance 500yds from village of Utkinton. At N of Tarporley take Utkinton rd*. Home-made teas. **Adm £5, chd free. Suns 11, 18 May; 1 June (1-5).**
40-acre garden, terraced and landscaped, designed by Thomas Mawson (considered the leading exponent of garden design in early C20), it is the only Grade II* Arts and Crafts garden in Cheshire that remains complete and in excellent condition. The gardens are an important example of an early C20 garden laid out in both formal and informal styles. By early May the garden is bursting into flower with almost 3000 Rhododendron and Azalea many 100 years old. Exhibition by local Artists.

87 THE WELL HOUSE
Wet Lane, Tilston, Malpas SY14 7DP. Mrs S H French-Greenslade, 01829 250332. *3m NW of Malpas. On A41, 1st turn R after Broxton r'about, L on Malpas Rd through Tilston. House & antique shop on L*. **Adm £5, chd free. Visitors welcome by appt Feb to Oct not open in August. Refreshments by appt.**
1-acre cottage garden, bridge over natural stream, spring bulbs, perennials, herbs and shrubs. Triple ponds. Adjoining 3/4 -acre field made into wild flower meadow; first seeding late 2003. Large bog area of kingcups and ragged robin. Febuary for snowdrop walk. Coach parties welcome.

88 NEW THE WHITE COTTAGE
Threapwood, Malpas SY14 7AL. Chris & Carol Bennion. *3m SW of Malpas. From Malpas take Wrexham Rd B5069 W for 3m. From Bangor on Dee take B5069 E to Threapwood. Car Park in field opp shop & garage.* **Combined adm with Somerset House £4, chd free. Sat 21, Sun 22 June (1-5).**
Pretty, 1/2 acre cottage garden with countryside views containing a mixture of mature trees, shrubs, herbaceous plants, bulbs and small orchard. Open spaces and secluded areas merge to provide new interest at every corner. Greenhouse featured in several gardening magazines. Flower beds meander along the drive with roses, astrantias, geraniums, violas and other summer flowering plants. A brick built greenhouse, various arches, pergola and dovecote. Several mature trees and a variety of hedging. Superb views over Cheshire countryside. NB this garden sits alongside a Nature Conservation Zone.

GROUP OPENING

89 WILLASTON VILLAGE GARDENS
Willaston CH64 1TE. *From Chester, take A540 direction West Kirby; turn R on B5151 to Willaston; at village centre turn R onto Hooton Rd; Change Lane is 3/4m on R opp garage. From Hooton Stn, 15 mins walk along B5133 (Hooton Rd) in direction of Willaston; Change Lane on LH-side opp garage. From M53, leave at J5; join A41 direction Queensferry, N Wales; after 1/4m turn R at T-lights onto B5133; Hooton Stn is on L after 3/4 m. All 3 gardens entered from Change Hey garden. Parking available in field at bottom of Change Lane on RH-side.* Home-made teas at Change Hey. **Combined adm £4.50, chd free. Sun 25 May (2-5).**

CHANGE HEY
Change Lane. Keith & Joan Butcher

THE DUTCH HOUSE
Park Road. Michael Ring

SILVERBURN
Prof M P & Dr A M Escudier

3 very different gardens in design and planting. Change Hey: 2 acre garden with mature trees, developing woodland area underplanted with rhododendrons and azaleas.
The Dutch House: 1/3 acre cottage-style garden with some formality. The rear garden vista, terminating with a 1920 Boulton and Paul revolving summerhouse, is surrounded on 2 sides by mature beech, oak and pine trees. Some gravel paths.
Silverburn: ½ -acre garden designed by present owners. A plantsperson's garden with varied plantings in the herbaceous beds and mixed borders, species and old-fashioned roses, rhododendrons, azaleas, attractive trees, vegetable garden and small orchard. Bridge linking Silverburn and Change Hey not suitable for wheelchairs. Alternative (separate) wheelchair access possible.

Cogshall Grange

90 WOOD END COTTAGE
Grange Lane, Whitegate, Northwich CW8 2BQ. Mr & Mrs M R Everett, 01606 888236, woodendct@supanet.com. *4m SW of Northwich. Turn S off A556 (Northwich bypass) at Sandiway PO T-lights; after 1¾ m, turn L to Whitegate village; opp school follow Grange Lane for 300yds.* Home-made teas. **Adm £4, chd free.** **Visitors welcome by appt May to July.**
Plantsman's ½ acre garden in attractive setting, sloping to a natural stream bordered by shade and moisture-loving plants. Background of mature trees. Well stocked herbaceous borders, trellis with roses and clematis, magnificent delphiniums, many phlox and choice perennials. Interesting shrubs and flowering trees. Vegetable garden.

91 YEW TREE HOUSE GARDEN & SPECIAL PERENNIALS NURSERY
Hall Lane, Hankelow, nr Audlem CW3 0JB. Janet & Martin Blow, www.specialperennials.com. *Just off A529, 5m S of Nantwich, 1m N of Audlem. From Nantwich follow signs to Audlem. From Market Drayton follow signs to Audlem then Nantwich. Map on our website.* **Adm £2.50, chd free. Sats, Suns, Weds 12, 13, 16, 19, 20, 23 July; 6, 9, 10, 20, 31 Aug; 3, 13, 14 Sept (2-5).**
Small garden planted in an exuberant cottage style with an abundance of interesting and unusual plants: no lawns just lots of lovely flowers! Specialities include heleniums, day lilies, phlox, centaurea, monarda, grasses plus lots more. The garden is a haven for bees and butterflies. Attached small nursery selling plants grown in the garden. No WC at garden: nearest public facilities Audlem 1m. National Collection of Heleniums (best Aug - Sep). National Collection of Centaurea. For special National Collection weekends see our website. Partial wheelchair access.

Cheshire & Wirral County Volunteers

County Organiser
John Hinde, 3 Earle Drive, Parkgate, Neston CH64 6RY, 0151 353 0032, john.hinde@maylands.com

County Treasurer
Andrew Collin, 8 Collingham Green, Little Sutton, Ellesmere Port CH66 4NX, 0151 339 3614, andrewcollin@btinternet.com

Publicity
Graham Beech, 01625 402946, gb.ngs@talktalk.net

Booklet Co-ordinator
John Hinde, 3 Earle Drive, Parkgate, Neston CH64 6RY, 0151 353 0032, john.hinde@maylands.com

Assistant County Organisers
Janet Bashforth, janetbashforth@talktalk.net
Sue Bryant, 0161 928 3819, suewestlakebryant@btinternet.com
Jean Davies, 01606 892383, misjeandavies@gmail.com
Sandra Fairclough, Inglewood, 4 Birchmere, Heswall, Wirral CH60 6TN, 0151 3424645, sandra.fairclough@tiscali.co.uk
Juliet Hill, 01829 732804, hill573@btinternet.com
Romy Holmes, Bowmere Cottage, Bowmere Road, Tarporley CW6 0BS, 01829 732053, romy@holmes-email.co.uk

CORNWALL

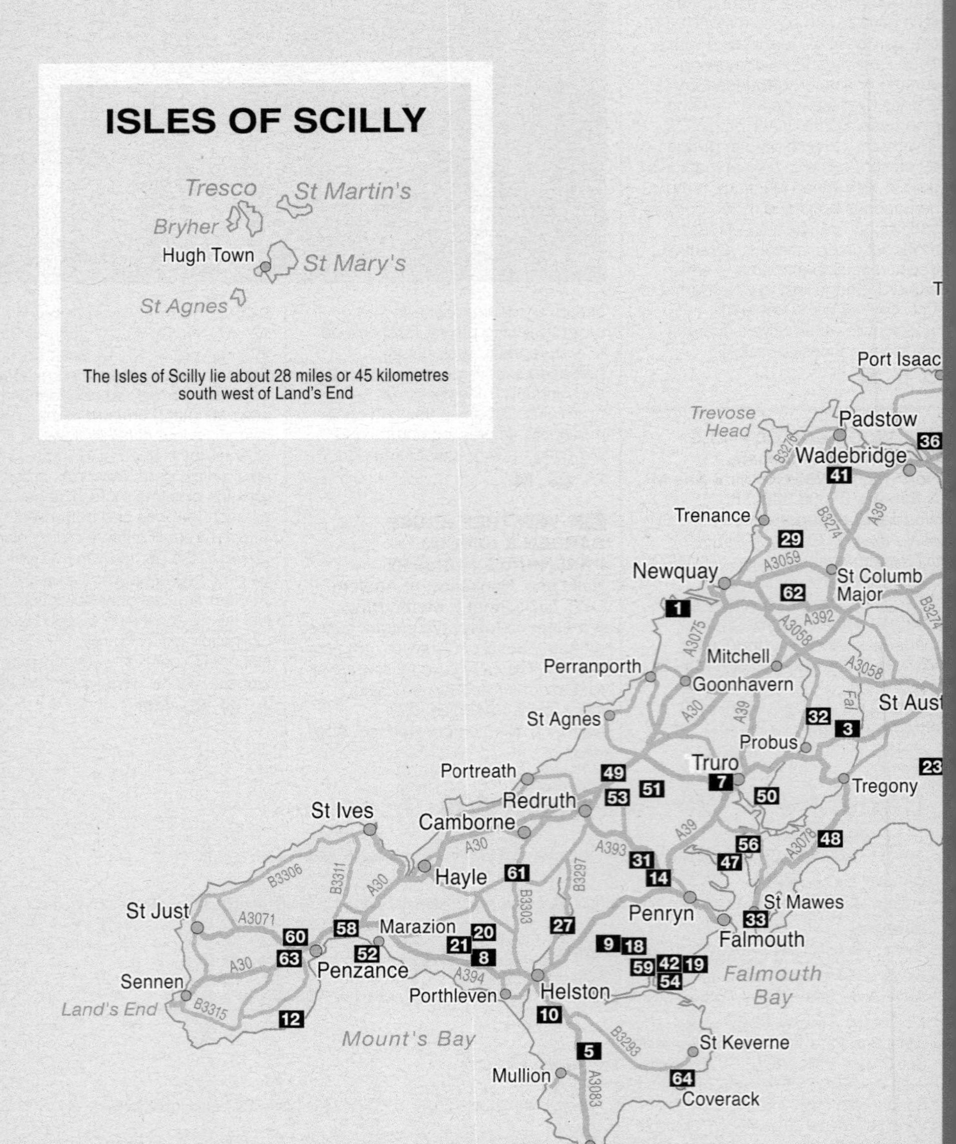
ISLES OF SCILLY
Tresco
St Martin's
Bryher
Hugh Town
St Mary's
St Agnes
The Isles of Scilly lie about 28 miles or 45 kilometres south west of Land's End
Port Isaac
Trevose Head
Padstow
36
Wadebridge
41
B3276
B3274
A39
Trenance
29
Newquay
A3059
St Columb Major
62
1
A3075
A3058
A392
B3274
Mitchell
Perranporth
Goonhavern
A3058
St Agnes
A30
A39
Fal
32
3
St Aust
Probus
Truro
49
7
23
Portreath
53
51
50
Tregony
Redruth
St Ives
Camborne
A30
A393
A39
56
48
47
A3078
Hayle
61
31
B3306
B3311
A30
B3297
14
St Just
A3071
St Mawes
Penryn
58
Marazion
20
B3303
27
33
60
Falmouth
21
9
18
63
52
8
59
42
19
A30
Penzance
Falmouth Bay
Sennen
A394
54
Porthleven
Helston
Land's End
B3315
10
12
Mount's Bay
B3293
5
St Keverne
Mullion
64
A3083
Coverack
Lizard Point
Lizard

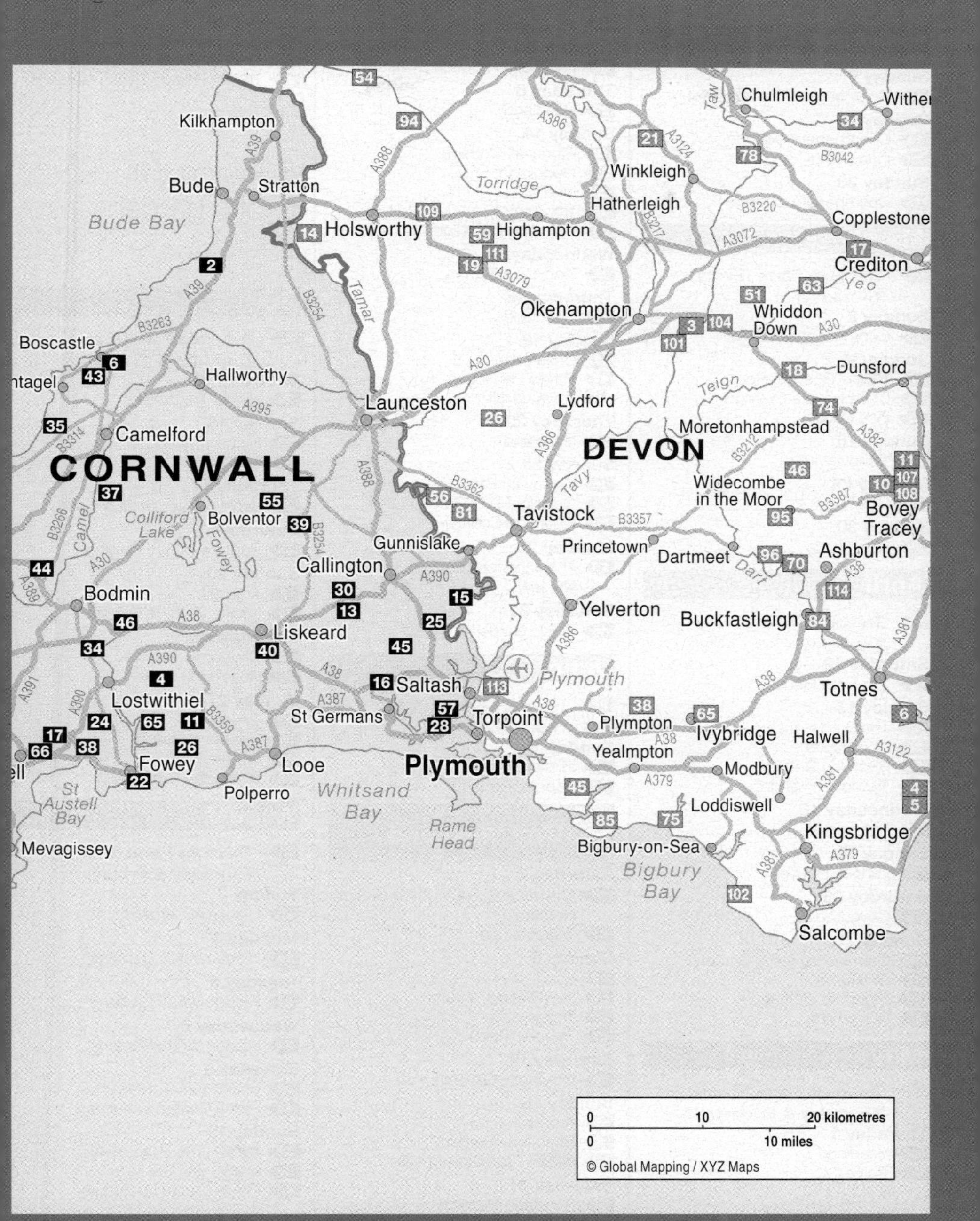

CORNWALL
DEVON
Kilkhampton
Bude
Stratton
Bude Bay
Holsworthy
Highampton
Hatherleigh
Winkleigh
Chulmleigh
Copplestone
Crediton
Okehampton
Whiddon Down
Dunsford
Boscastle
Hallworthy
Launceston
Lydford
Moretonhampstead
Camelford
Widecombe in the Moor
Bovey Tracey
Colliford Lake
Bolventor
Tavistock
Gunnislake
Callington
Princetown
Dartmeet
Ashburton
Bodmin
Yelverton
Buckfastleigh
Liskeard
Saltash
Plymouth
Totnes
Lostwithiel
St Germans
Torpoint
Plympton
Ivybridge
Halwell
Fowey
Looe
Yealmpton
Modbury
St Austell Bay
Polperro
Whitsand Bay
Loddiswell
Rame Head
Kingsbridge
Mevagissey
Bigbury-on-Sea
Bigbury Bay
Salcombe
Torridge
Tamar
Teign
Tavy
Camel
Fowey
Dart
Yeo
Taw
0 10 20 kilometres
0 10 miles
© Global Mapping / XYZ Maps

Opening Dates

All entries subject to change. For latest information check www.ngs.org.uk

February

Sunday 9
13 Coombegate Cottage

Sunday 16
13 Coombegate Cottage
28 Ince Castle

Sunday 23
13 Coombegate Cottage

March

61 **Trevoole Farm (Every Thursday)**

Sunday 2
13 Coombegate Cottage

Sunday 9
7 NEW Bosvigo House
13 Coombegate Cottage
28 Ince Castle

Sunday 16
60 Trengwainton

Monday 24
15 Cotehele

Sunday 30
28 Ince Castle

April

61 **Trevoole Farm (Every Thursday)**

Saturday 12
2 The Barn House

Sunday 13
2 The Barn House
28 Ince Castle
50 Riverside Cottage
63 Trewidden Garden

Wednesday 16
44 Pencarrow

Sunday 20
32 Ladock House

Saturday 26
12 Chygurno

Sunday 27
10 Carminowe Valley Garden
12 Chygurno
18 Ethnevas Cottage
47 Polgwynne

May

61 **Trevoole Farm (Every Thursday & Friday)**

Thursday 1
22 Headland
56 Trelissick

Sunday 4
4 Boconnoc
19 Glendurgan
33 Lamorran House

Monday 5
40 Moyclare

Tuesday 6
34 Lanhydrock House & Gardens

Thursday 8
22 Headland

Sunday 11
18 Ethnevas Cottage
20 Godolphin
28 Ince Castle
55 Trebartha
66 Woodland Cottage

Wednesday 14
5 Bonython Manor

Thursday 15
22 Headland

Sunday 18
11 Casa Laguna
42 Navas Hill House
62 Trewan Hall

Thursday 22
22 Headland

Sunday 25
16 Cutlinwith Farm
21 Godolphin Hill Garden Lady
50 Riverside Cottage

Monday 26
29 The Japanese Garden & Bonsai Nursery

Saturday 31
46 Pinsla Garden & Nursery

June

61 **Trevoole Farm (Every Thursday & Friday)**

Sunday 1
46 Pinsla Garden & Nursery
53 Scorrier House

Festival Weekend

Saturday 7
29 The Japanese Garden & Bonsai Nursery
61 Trevoole Farm

Sunday 8
35 Long Hay
52 St Michael's Mount
60 Trengwainton
61 Trevoole Farm

Saturday 14
6 Boscastle Gardens

Sunday 15
1 Arundell
6 Boscastle Gardens
57 NEW Trematon Castle

Saturday 21
51 Roseland House

Sunday 22
8 Brea Mor
10 Carminowe Valley Garden
36 Lower Amble Gardens
51 Roseland House

Sunday 29
3 Benallack Barn
21 Godolphin Hill Garden Lady
45 NEW Pillaton Parish Gardens

Spectacular exotic garden . . .

July

61 **Trevoole Farm (Every Thursday & Friday)**

Saturday 12
26 Higher Trenedden

Sunday 13
26 Higher Trenedden
59 Trenarth

Thursday 17
34 Lanhydrock House & Gardens

Saturday 19
48 Poppy Cottage Garden

Sunday 20
1 Arundell
48 Poppy Cottage Garden

Saturday 26
12 Chygurno
51 Roseland House

Sunday 27
12 Chygurno
51 Roseland House
64 Waters Edge
66 Woodland Cottage

August

61 **Trevoole Farm (Every Thursday & Friday)**

Sunday 3
25 Highcroft Gardens

Monday 4
24 Hidden Valley Gardens

Tuesday 5
24 Hidden Valley Gardens

Wednesday 6
24 Hidden Valley Gardens

Saturday 9
38 Marsh Villa Gardens
46 Pinsla Garden & Nursery

Sunday 10
27 NEW The Homestead
38 Marsh Villa Gardens
46 Pinsla Garden & Nursery

Sunday 17

25 Highcroft Gardens

Sunday 31

9 Bucks Head House Garden
10 Carminowe Valley Garden

September

61 **Trevoole Farm (Every Thursday & Friday)**

Saturday 13

14 Cosawes Barton

October

61 **Trevoole Farm (Every Thursday & Friday)**

Sunday 12

55 Trebartha
58 Tremenheere Sculpture Garden

November

61 **Trevoole Farm (Every Thursday)**

Monday 17

15 Cotehele

December

61 **Trevoole Farm (Every Thursday until 18 December)**

Gardens open to the public

4 Boconnoc
5 Bonython Manor
7 Bosvigo House
12 Chygurno
15 Cotehele
17 Eden Project
19 Glendurgan
20 Godolphin
21 Godolphin Hill Garden Lady
22 Headland
23 The Lost Gardens of Heligan
24 Hidden Valley Gardens
29 The Japanese Garden & Bonsai Nursery
30 Ken Caro
33 Lamorran House
34 Lanhydrock House & Gardens
38 Marsh Villa Gardens
40 Moyclare
44 Pencarrow
46 Pinsla Garden & Nursery
48 Poppy Cottage Garden
51 Roseland House
52 St Michael's Mount
54 Trebah
56 Trelissick
57 Trematon Castle
58 Tremenheere Sculpture Garden
60 Trengwainton
63 Trewidden Garden

Waters Edge

By appointment only

31 Kennall House
37 Lower Hamatethy
39 Middlewood House
41 Nanfenten
43 The Old Rectory, Trevalga
49 Primrose Farm
65 Waye Cottage

Also open by appointment

1 Arundell
6 Half Acre, Boscastle Gardens
8 Brea Mor
9 Bucks Head House Garden
13 Coombegate Cottage
16 Cutlinwith Farm
18 Ethnevas Cottage
25 Highcroft Gardens
45 Pillaton Parish Gardens
50 Riverside Cottage
59 Trenarth
61 Trevoole Farm
64 Waters Edge

The Gardens

1 ARUNDELL

West Pentire, Crantock TR8 5SE. Brenda & David Eyles, 01637 831916, david@davideyles.com. *1m W of Crantock. From A3075 take signs to Crantock. At junction in village keep straight on to West Pentire (1m). Park in field (signed) or public car parks at W Pentire.* Cream teas. **Adm £4, chd free. Suns 15 June; 20 July (1-5). Visitors also welcome by appt May to Aug.**

A garden where no garden should be! - on windswept N coast NT headland between 2 fantastic beaches. 1 acre set around original farm cottage. Front: cottage garden. Side: small Mediterranean courtyard. Rear: rockery and shrubbery leading up to a 'Stumpery' and Fernery and on to a stream and pond, herbaceous borders, Beth Chatto Dry garden, a small pinetum and spectacular exotic garden. Featured in Gardeners World with Joe Swift and Coast and Cornwall Today magazines. Wheelchair access from public car park with entrance via rear gate. 14 shallow steps in centre of garden useable with care in wheelchair.

2 THE BARN HOUSE

Higher Penhalt, Poundstock, Bude EX23 0DG. Tim & Sandy Dingle, 01288 361356, timdingle237@btinternet.com. *5m S of Bude. 1m off A39 to Widemouth Bay. Take Millook rd by Widemouth Manor Hotel. Follow rd for 1m, signed L at top of hill.* Home-made teas. **Adm £3.50, chd free. Sat 12, Sun 13 Apr (11-4).**

Garden that shows you can battle with the elements above dramatic cliffs of N Cornish coast and win. 1/2 -acre garden designed for yr-round interest with many colourful and unusual plants. Divided and enclosed by sheltering hedges. Herbaceous borders, prairie bed, pond, kitchen garden and patio. A walk through fields and wooded valley often gives glimpses of abundant wildlife and wild flowers. April opening - demonstration of willow-weaving by Hilary Workman. Partial wheelchair access.

3 BENALLACK BARN

Grampound Road, Truro TR2 4BY. Linda Pelham, 01726 883618, info@benallack.net, www.benallack.net. *Between Grampound & Grampound Rd. From Truro, L to Grampound Road, 1st R. From A30, exit Fraddon to Grampound Rd, 1st L after village. From St Austell, R at pet shop in Grampound.* Cream teas. **Adm £3.50, chd free. Sun 29 June (1-5).**
3-acre garden surrounding 400 yr-old converted barn, sloping towards Fal River valley. Gravelled, S-facing courtyard with climbers and planted granite troughs; sculptured cotoneaster hedges and colour-themed herbaceous borders; bog garden; small orchard; vegetable garden, greenhouse; wild meadow leading to small lake with island and summerhouse surrounded by giant gunneras, grasses and perennials.

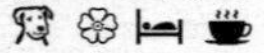

4 ◆ BOCONNOC

Lostwithiel PL22 0RG. Anthony Fortescue, 01208 872507. *Off A390 between Liskeard & Lostwithiel. From East Taphouse follow signs to Boconnoc. (Sat Nav does not work well in this area).* Home-made teas in Stable Yard. **Adm £4.50, chd free. For NGS: Sun 4 May (2-5). For other opening times and information, please phone.**
20-acre gardens surrounded by parkland and woods with magnificent trees, flowering shrubs and stunning views. The gardens are set amongst mature trees which provide the backcloth for exotic spring flowering shrubs, woodland plants, with newly-planted magnolias and a fine collection of hydrangeas.

5 ◆ BONYTHON MANOR

Cury Cross Lanes, Helston TR12 7BA. Mr & Mrs Richard Nathan, 01326 240550, www.bonythonmanor.co.uk. *5m S of Helston. On main A3083 Helston to Lizard Rd. Turn L at Cury Cross Lanes (Wheel Inn). Entrance 300yds on R.* Home-made teas. **Adm £6, chd £2. For NGS: Wed 14 May (2-4.30). For other opening times and information, please phone or see garden website.**
Magnificent 20-acre colour garden incl sweeping hydrangea drive to Georgian manor (not open). Herbaceous walled garden, potager with vegetables and picking flowers; 3 lakes in valley planted with ornamental grasses, perennials and South African flowers. A 'must see' for all seasons colour.

GROUP OPENING

6 BOSCASTLE GARDENS

Boscastle PL35 0BJ. *5m N of Camelford. Park in doctor's surgery car park at top of village (clearly signed). Limited parking for disabled at both gardens. Maps provided.* Home-made teas at Half Acre. **Combined adm £3.50, chd free. Sat 14, Sun 15 June (1.30-5.30).**

HALF ACRE
Boscastle. Carole Vincent Visitors also welcome by appt. 01840 250263 concretecarole@btinternet.com

WILDWOOD
Doctors Hill. Alex Stewart

Boscastle Harbour is well-known to visitors. Both gardens are in older part of village, overlooking cliff, land and sea. Half Acre: sculpture in an acre of 3 gardens: Cottage, small wood, the Blue Circle garden, constructed in colour concrete with coastal planting. Studio open. Paintings exhibition. Wildwood: garden of magic deception. Front traditional, rear - lawns leading to wood with pond, tree ferns and shade-loving shrubs.

7 NEW ◆ BOSVIGO HOUSE

Bosvigo Lane, Truro TR1 3NH. Wendy Perry, 01872 275774, www.bosvigo.com/. *Truro City Centre. At Highertown, nr Sainsbury r'about, turn down Dobbs Lane. After 500yds, entrance to house is on L, after sharp LH-bend.* Home-made teas in the Servants Hall. **Adm £5, chd free. For NGS: Sun 9 Mar (2-5.30)**
The 3-acre garden surrounding the Georgian house (not open) and Victorian conservatory includes a woodland garden. A sinuous path winds between heavily planted areas in the woodland. In spring, before the leaves open on the beech and sycamore, the area is carpeted with drifts of snowdrops, hellebores, wood anemones, epimediums, erythroniums and scented narcissus.

8 BREA MOR

Tresowes Hill, Ashton, Helston TR13 9TB. Eileen Clarke, 01736 762721, eileenjclarke@gmail.com. *Tresowes Hill, Ashton. 5m from Helston on A394 towards Penzance. Turn R at Ashton Garage towards Godolphin, Breamor exactly ½ m on R from main rd.* Home-made teas. **Adm £3.50, chd free (share to St Julia's Hospice Appeal). Sun 22 June (2-5). Visitors also welcome by appt May to Sept, for groups of 10, between 12-5.**
Situated on side of Tregonning Hill overlooking Mounts Bay. Wide variety of trees, shrubs and perennial plants. Fern garden, 2 ponds, roses. Developed over 25 years. Designed for bees, birds and butterflies.

9 BUCKS HEAD HOUSE GARDEN

Trengove Cross, Constantine TR11 5QR. Deborah Baker, 01326 340844, deborah.baker@falmouth.ac.uk. *5m SW of Falmouth. A394 towards Helston, L at Edgcumbe towards Gweek/Constantine. Proceed for 0.8 m then L towards Constantine. Further 0.8m, garden on L at Trengove.* Home-made teas. **Adm £3.50, chd free. Sun 31 Aug (12-4.30). Visitors also welcome by appt July to Sept.**
Enchanting cottage gardens and young woodland of native and rare trees, shrubs and perennials. The site of 1½ acres is an exposed S-facing Cornish hillside with panoramic views. Nurtured by essential windbreaks, the inspiring collection of plants are chosen to create a calm and tranquil retreat. Limited wheelchair access to lower garden and to woodland.

10 CARMINOWE VALLEY GARDEN

Tangies, Gunwalloe TR12 7PU. Mr & Mrs Peter Stanley, 01326 565868, stanley.m2@sky.com. *3m SW of Helston. A3083 Helston-Lizard rd. R opp main gate to Culdrose. 1m downhill, garden on R.* Home-made teas. **Adm £4, chd free. Sun 27 Apr, Sun 22 June, Sun 31 Aug (12-5).**

Overlooking the beautiful Carminowe Valley towards Loepool this abundant garden combines native oak woodland, babbling brook and large natural pond with more formal areas. Wild flower meadow, mown pathways, shrubberies, orchard, nectar beds, cutting garden, kitchen garden, summerhouse. Enclosed cottage garden, tulips in spring and roses early summer provide huge contrast. Gravel paths, slopes.

11 CASA LAGUNA

School Rd, Lanreath, Looe PL13 2NX. Ivor & Margaret Dungey. *5m SW of East Taphouse. From A390 take B3359 signed Looe Lanreath. Lanreath village 5m. Garden 150yds from village hall car park where parking available.* Tea. **Adm £3.50, chd free. Sun 18 May (11-4).**

Drive with shrubs leading to colourful spring garden, approx ½ acre. Azaleas, camellias and rhododendrons in arrangement of beds. Assortment of conifers, all intermingled with seasonal bulbs and small plants. Disabled parking at house. Reasonably level garden, no steps.

12 ◆ CHYGURNO

Lamorna TR19 6XH. Dr & Mrs Robert Moule, 01736 732153. *4m S of Penzance. Off B3315. Follow signs for The Cove Restaurant. Garden is at top of hill, past Hotel on L.* **Adm £5, chd free. For NGS: Sat 26, Sun 27 Apr, Sat 26, Sun 27 July (2-5). For other opening times and information, please phone.**

Beautiful, unique, 3-acre cliffside garden overlooking Lamorna Cove. Planting started in 1998, mainly S-hemisphere shrubs and exotics with hydrangeas, camellias and rhododendrons. Woodland area with tree ferns set against large granite outcrops. Garden terraced with steep steps and paths. Plenty of benches so you can take a rest and enjoy the wonderful views. Well worth the effort. Also open Weds, Thurs (2-5), Apr - Sept. Featured in Gardens Illustrated.

13 COOMBEGATE COTTAGE

St Ive, Liskeard PL14 3LZ. Michael Stephens, 01579 383520, mike@coombegate.wanadoo.co.uk. *4m E of Liskeard. From A390 at St Ive take turning signed Blunts. After 100 metres turn L & continue to the bottom of the hill.* Home-made teas in Village Hall. **Adm £3.50, chd free. Every Sun 9 Feb to 9 Mar (1-4). Visitors also welcome by appt Feb to Mar.**

Prepare to be entranced by how colourful, fragrant and interesting a garden can be in winter and early spring. See what use has been made of a beautiful one acre steep valley site. All the winter favourites including drifts of snowdrops. Also more unusual seasonal plants, many available in the excellent plant sale. Open unless ice/snow - phone to check if in doubt.

Prepare to be entranced by how colourful, fragrant and interesting a garden can be in winter and early spring . . .

14 COSAWES BARTON

Ponsanooth, nr Truro TR3 7EJ. Louise Bishop, 01872 864026, info@cosawesbarton.co.uk, www.cosawesbarton.co.uk. *8½m W of Truro. A39 Truro - Falmouth rd. At Treluswell r'about take A393 Redruth/Ponsanooth rd. After Burnt House 1st L. ¾m nr 30mph sign, house on R.* Light refreshments. **Adm £4, chd free. Sat 13 Sept (10-4).**

An idyllic spot. Gardens surround C18 farmhouse, cottage and courtyard. Inner courtyard garden, a formal, very well-established area and extensive wooded walks covering 14 acres. There are gorgeous views over the Kennal Valley and to the North beyond. Featured in Cornwall Today and Cornwall Life.

15 ◆ COTEHELE

Saltash PL12 6TA. National Trust, 01579 351346, www.nationaltrust.org.uk. *2m E of St Dominick. 4m from Gunnislake. (Turn at St Annís Chapel); 8m SW of Tavistock; 14m from Plymouth via Tamar Bridge.* Cream teas in the Barn Restaurant and The Edgcumbe. **Adm £6.50, chd £3.25 (Mar); £5, chd free (Nov). For NGS: Mons 24 Mar; 17 Nov (11-4). For other opening times and information, please phone or see garden website.**

Formal garden, orchards and meadow. Terrace garden falling to sheltered valley with ponds, stream and unusual shrubs. Historic collection of daffodils. Fine Tudor house (one of the least altered in the country); armour, tapestries, furniture. Gravel paths, some steep slopes in Valley Garden.

16 CUTLINWITH FARM

Tideford, Saltash PL12 5HX. Peter & Mary Hamilton, 01752 851599, maryphamilton@btinternet.com. *1½m N of Tideford, 5m W of Saltash. Tideford is on the A38 between Liskeard & Landrake. Yellow signs from Tideford & Landrake.* Home-made teas. **Adm £3.50, chd free. Sun 25 May (2-5.30). Visitors also welcome by appt.**

3-acre garden in small valley. Begun 12yrs ago and now beginning to mature. The design aim is to have all yr round interest. Features trees, borders, water garden incl stream and ponds. Developing acer, magnolia and bluebell walk leading to woodland paths. Music in the garden incl local brass band. Other countrytype attractions arranged as available like falconry, beekeeping. Cream teas. Featured on Radio Cornwall and in Cornish Times. Wheel Chair access is limited as the garden is in a Valley and some paths are inevitable steep or steps are used to get from one level to another.

Waye Cottage

17 ◆ EDEN PROJECT
Bodelva PL24 2SG. The Eden Trust, 01726 811911, www.edenproject.com. *4m E of St Austell. Brown signs from A30 & A390.* **For opening times and information, please phone or see garden website.**
Described as the eighth wonder of the world, the Eden Project is a global garden for the C21. Discover the story of plants that have changed the world and which could change your future. The Eden Project is an exciting attraction where you can explore your relationship with nature, learn new things and get inspiration about the world around you. Year-round programme of talks, events and workshops. Please call our Access Team in advance to book a power chair or manual wheelchair.

18 ETHNEVAS COTTAGE
Constantine, Falmouth TR11 5PY. Lyn Watson, 01326 340076. *6m SW of Falmouth. Nearest main rds A39, A394. Follow signs to Constantine. At Lower Village sign, at bottom of winding hill, turn off on private lane. Garden 3/4 m up hill.* Home-made teas. **Adm £3.50, chd free. Suns 27 Apr; 11 May (12-4). Visitors also welcome by appt Mar to Sept, max 10.**
Isolated granite cottage in 2 acres. Intimate flower and vegetable garden. Bridge over stream to large pond and primrose path through semi-wild bog area. Hillside with grass paths among native and exotic trees (40 different conifers). Many camellias and rhododendrons. Mixed shrub and herbaceous beds, wild flower glade, spring bulbs. Plantaholics' garden.

19 ◆ GLENDURGAN
Mawnan Smith, Falmouth TR11 5JZ. National Trust, 01326 252020, www.nationaltrust.org.uk/glendurgan. *5m SW of Falmouth. Follow rd out of Mawnan Smith to Helford Passage. Brown signs to Glendurgan.* Light refreshments. **Adm £8, chd £4. For NGS: Sun 4 May (10.30-5.30). For other opening times and information, please phone or see garden website.**
Three valleys of natural beauty and amazing plants. Discover lush tender plantings in the jungle-like lower valley and spiky arid plants basking on sunny upper slopes. Wander down to hamlet of Durgan on R Helford. Banks of wild flowers teeming with wildlife - and a 180 yr-old maze!

20 ◆ GODOLPHIN
Godolphin Cross, Helston TR13 9RE. National Trust, 01736 763194, www.nationaltrust.org.uk/godolphin. *5m NW of Helston. From Helston take A394 to Sithney Common, turn R B3302 to Leedstown, turn L, follow signs. From Hayle B3302 Leedstown, turn R, follow signs.* Light refreshments. **Adm £5.60, chd £2.80. For NGS: Sun 11 May (10-5). For other opening times and information, please phone or see garden website.**
A near-miraculous survival from C14 and C16, unchanged by fashions through the centuries. The garden is not about flowers and plants but about the surviving remains of a medieval pattern. Acquired by the National Trust in 2007. Limited wheelchair access, gravel paths, steep slopes, uneven surfaces and steps.

21 ◆ GODOLPHIN HILL GARDEN LADY
Trewithen Terrace, Godolphin, Helston TR13 9TQ. Mr J & Mrs V L Marshall, 07899 803899, www.thegardenlady.co.uk. *1m S of Godolphin Cross. From Godolphin Cross follow sign for Ashton. R at top of hill, signed Millpool & Trescowe. 300yds down Trewithen Terrace on R.* Light refreshments. **Adm £3.50, chd free. For NGS: Suns 25 May; 29 June (11-5). For other opening times and information, please phone or see garden website.**
Set high on the southern slope of Godolphin Hill, this natural, informal and bio-diverse 3 acre garden has evolved over 20 years, working with nature rather than against it. Long borders containing large variety of species, shrubs and rambling roses along with herbs and herbaceous perennials. Wildlife pond, butterfly meadow, bee friendly lawn, cut flower garden all surrounded by hedgerows full of rambling roses. Displays of many moths found here in the gardens. These never fail to delight and fascinate visitors who think that only butterflies are colourful. Featured in Cornwall Today.

22 ◆ HEADLAND
Battery Lane, Polruan-by-Fowey PL23 1PW. Jean Hill, 01726 870243, www.headlandgarden.co.uk. *1/2 m SE of Fowey across estuary. Passenger ferry from Fowey then 10 min walk along West St & Battery Lane. From E use second car park in Polruan on L then turn L on foot down hill.* Light refreshments. **Adm £3.50, chd free. For NGS: Thurs 1, 8, 15, 22 May (2-6). For other opening times and information, please phone or see garden website.**

1¼-acre cliff garden with magnificent sea, coastal and estuary views on 3 sides. Planted to withstand salty gales yet incl subtropical plants with intimate places to sit and savour the views. Paths wind through the garden past rocky outcrops down to a secluded swimming cove. Open Thurs May - Aug (2-6). Partial wheelchair access, wheelchair users please phone beforehand.

Romantic garden at the end of winding lanes, surrounding C17 pink brick castle . . .

23 ◆ THE LOST GARDENS OF HELIGAN

Pentewan, St Austell PL26 6EN. Heligan Gardens Ltd, 01726 845100, www.heligan.com. *5m S of St Austell. From St Austell take B3273 signed Mevagissey, follow signs.* **For opening times and information, please phone or see garden website.**

Lose yourself in The Nation's Favourite Garden (BBC poll) and discover the mysterious world of The Lost Gardens. With the finest productive gardens in Britain, a pioneering wildlife project and exotic subtropical jungle just some of the attractions waiting to be explored, you are sure to have a magical day out. Wheelchair access to Northern gardens. Armchair tour shows video of unreachable areas. Wheelchairs available at reception.

24 ◆ HIDDEN VALLEY GARDENS

Treesmill, Par PL24 2TU. Tricia Howard, 01208 873225, www.hiddenvalleygardens.co.uk. *2m SW of Lostwithiel. Yellow sign directions on A390 between Lostwithiel (2m) & St Austell (5m), directing onto B3269 towards Fowey, followed by a R turn.* Cream teas. **Adm £4, chd free. For NGS: Mon 4, Tue 5, Wed 6 Aug (10-6). For other opening times and information, please phone or see garden website.**

Award-winning 3-acre colourful garden in 'hidden' valley with nursery. Cottage-style planting with herbaceous beds and borders, grasses, ferns and fruit. Gazebo with country views. Iris fairy well. Fishpond, Japanese garden and vegetable potager. August opening for special displays of agapanthus, dahlias, asters and crocosmia collections. Cream Teas. Children's and Wildlife quiz. Special drop off parking for wheelchair access directly into garden area. Some gentle sloping ground.

25 HIGHCROFT GARDENS

Cargreen, Saltash PL12 6PA. Mr & Mrs B J Richards, 01752 848048, gardens@bjrichardsflowers.co.uk, www.bjrichardsflowers.co.uk. *5m NW of Saltash. 5m from Callington on A388 take Landulph Cargreen turning. 2m on, turn L at Landulph Xrds. Parking by Methodist Church.* Cream teas in Methodist Church. **Adm £4, chd free. Suns 3, 17 Aug (1.30-5.30). Visitors also welcome by appt July to Sept.**

3-acre garden in beautiful Tamar Valley. Japanese-style garden, hot border, pastel border, grasses, arboretum with hemerocallis and new blue borders. Prairie planting containing 2,500 plants of herbaceous and grasses. Buddleia and shrub rose bank. Pond. All at their best in July, Aug and Sept. Collection of hydrangeas and agapanthus.

26 HIGHER TRENEDDEN

Peakswater, nr Pelynt PL13 2QE. Judy & Kevin Channer. *Between Pelynt & Fowey. Off Bodinnick Ferry rd, B3359, from East Taphouse or Pelynt. Turn off at 90 degree turn, follow sign for Valleybrook Cottages & NGS signs.* Home-made teas. **Adm £3.50, chd free. Sat 12, Sun 13 July (1-4.30).**

4-acre garden set in quiet valley with countryside views, ranges from established cottage garden to arboretum (planted 2006), with specimen trees, meadow with large pond, and board walk through marshland with an abundance of wild flowers. Gravel paths and several seating areas.

27 NEW THE HOMESTEAD

Crelly, Trenear, Wendron TR13 0EU. Shirley Williams & Chris Tredinnick, 01326 562808, homesteadholidays@btconnect.com. *3m N of Helston. From Helston B3297 towards Redruth, 3m. Entrance 3rd on R 200 metres past signpost Crelly/Bodilly & bus shelter.* Light refreshments. **Adm £4, chd free. Sun 10 Aug (1-4.30).**

3 acres of divided gardens giving all-yr round interest and 3 acres of wildlife habitat and deciduous woodland with primroses in spring. Cornish variety apple orchard where chickens, ducks and geese roam free. Vegetable and cutting garden, mature garden with pond and mixed borders. Archways, pergolas, seating, water features, hot and shady areas, walled garden, Japanese area. Sculptures sited throughout. Unfenced pond. Uneven paths which can be slippery.

28 INCE CASTLE

Saltash PL12 4RA. Lord & Lady Boyd. *3m SW of Saltash. From A38 at Stoketon Cross take turn signed Trematon, then Elmgate. No large coaches.* Home-made teas. **Adm £3.50, chd free. Sun 16 Feb (11-3); Suns 9, 30 Mar; 13 Apr; 11 May (2-5).**

Romantic garden at the end of winding lanes, surrounding C17 pink brick castle on a peninsula in the R Lynher. Old apple trees with bulbs, woodland garden with fritillaries, camellias and rhododendrons. Extraordinary 1960s shell house on edge of formal garden.

29 ◆ THE JAPANESE GARDEN & BONSAI NURSERY

St Mawgan TR8 4ET. Mr & Mrs Hore, 01637 860116, www.japanesegarden.co.uk. *6m E of Newquay. Japanese Garden Brown & White Rd Signs on A3059 & B3276. St. Mawgan village is directly below Newquay Airport.* **Adm £4.50, chd £2. For NGS: Mon 26 May, Sat 7 June (10-6). For other opening times and information, please phone or see garden website.**

East meets West in unique Garden for All Seasons. Spectacular Japanese maples and azaleas, symbolic teahouse, koi pond, bamboo grove, stroll, woodland, zen and moss gardens. An oasis of tranquillity. Entrance free to adjacent specialist Bonsai and Japanese Garden Nurseries. Some gravel paths.

30 ◆ KEN CARO

Bicton, nr Liskeard PL14 5RF. Mr & Mrs K R Willcock, 01579 362446. *5m NE of Liskeard. From A390 to Callington turn off N at St Ive. Take Pensilva Rd, follow brown tourist signs, approx 1m off main rd. Plenty of parking.* **For opening times and information, please phone.**

Connoisseurs garden full of interest all yr round. Lily ponds, panoramic views, plenty of seating, picnic area, in all 10 acres. Garden started in 1970, recently rejuvenated. Woodland walk, which has one of the largest beech trees. Good collection of yellow magnolias and herbaceous plants. Daily 16 Mar to 30 Sept (10-5.30), adm £5. Partial wheelchair access.

31 KENNALL HOUSE

Ponsanooth TR3 7HJ. Mr & Mrs N Wilson-Holt, 01872 870557, kennallvale@hotmail.com. *4m NW of Falmouth. A393 Falmouth to Redruth, L at Ponsanooth PO for 0.3m. Garden at end of drive marked Kennall House.* **Adm £4.50, chd free. Visitors welcome by appt Feb to Nov.**

12-acre garden/arboretum, beautifully situated in Kennall Valley. Incl typical British species and exotics. Wide variety of trees incl new plantings of rare specimens. Fast-flowing stream with ponds and walled garden. All yr interest.

32 LADOCK HOUSE

Ladock TR2 4PL. Kate & Simon Holborow. *7m E of Truro. Just off B3275. Adjacent to church.* Cream teas in church. **Adm £4, chd free. Sun 20 Apr (2-5).**

Georgian Old Rectory with 4 acres of lawns, rhododendrons, camellias and azaleas with many woodland glades, all planted in last 35 yrs. Many fine trees have survived the gales of the 80's and 90's. Slowly being developed maintaining the essential integrity of developments in 60's, 70's and 80's.

33 ◆ LAMORRAN HOUSE

Upper Castle Road, St Mawes, Truro TR2 5BZ. Robert Dudley-Cooke, 01326 270800, www.lamorrangarden.co.uk. *A3078, R past garage at entrance to St Mawes. ¾ m on L. ¼ m from castle if using passenger ferry service.* **Adm £6, chd free. For NGS: Sun 4 May (11-4). For other opening times and information, please phone or see garden website.**

4-acre subtropical garden overlooking Falmouth bay. Designed by owner in an Italianate/Cote d'Azur style. Extensive collection of Mediterranean and subtropical plants incl large collection of palms Butia capitata/Butia yatay and tree ferns. Reflects both design and remarkable micro-climate. Beautiful collection of Japanese azaleas and tender rhododendrons. Large collection of S-hemisphere plants. Italianate garden with many water features. Champion trees.

34 ◆ LANHYDROCK HOUSE & GARDENS

Property Office, Bodmin PL30 5AD. National Trust, 01208 265950, www.lanhydrock@nationaltrust.org.uk. *2½ m SE of Bodmin. 2½ m on B3268. Stn: Bodmin Parkway 1¾ m walk.* Cream teas. **Adm £7, chd £3.50. For NGS: Tue 6 May, Thur 17 July (10-5.30). For other opening times and information, please phone or see garden website.**

Large formal garden laid out in 1857. Ornamental parterres. Many fine specimens of rhododendrons and magnolias. Good summer colour with herbaceous borders and roses. Woodland walks. Lovely views. Mainly Victorian country house, though some parts date back to the C17, with over 50 rooms open to the public. Formal and woodland gardens. Garden tours most days of the week. Wheelchair access route around formal garden. Gravel paths and slopes to higher woodland garden.

35 LONG HAY

Treligga, Delabole PL33 9EE. Bett & Mick Hartley. *10m N of Wadebridge. B3314 Pendoggett to Delabole Rd. L at Westdowns from Pendoggett, R from Delabole. Signed Treligga (N). After entering hamlet, follow parking signs.* Cream teas. **Adm £4, chd free. Sun 8 June (11-5.30).**

⅔ -acre abundant cottage garden with beautiful vistas of the N coast and sea. Herbaceous beds, shrubs, pond, greenhouse and lawns. Natural meadow of 1 acre overlooking sea with paths leading to copse, vegetable plots, orchard and greenhouse. Cornish coastal garden in beautiful but harsh environment.

A surprise around every corner with beautiful views . . .

GROUP OPENING

36 LOWER AMBLE GARDENS

Chapel Amble, Wadebridge PL27 6EW. *3m N of Wadebridge. Take lane signed Middle & Lower Amble opp PO 1m to L turn by pond Parking in field beyond farmhouse.* Cream teas. **Combined adm £4, chd free. Sun 22 June (2-6).**

LOWER AMBLE FARMHOUSE
Mr & Mrs Laurence Grand

MILLPOND COTTAGE
Sheilagh Lees

Hamlet developed from farm buildings of early 1800s, originally a mill farm powered by water from the stream, ponds and underground leats running down S-facing hillside to R Amble and Walmsley Bird Sanctuary. Peaceful end-of-the-rd location with views across valley and up to Bodmin Moor. Large 20yr-old garden (Millpond Cottage) with emphasis on herbaceous plants, roses and hardy geraniums; vegetable garden and orchard. Lower Amble Farmhouse: an acre of garden leading into a four acre deciduous woodland with pond and wild flower orchard. Disabled parking in Millpond Cottage drive or access through side gate.

37 NEW LOWER HAMATETHY
St. Breward, Bodmin PL30 4PG. Mrs Yolande Hall, 01208 851212. *6m N of Bodmin. From St Breward pass church on R. Top of hill then down to LH bend, take small lane 2nd R. Garden 1st L.* Light refreshments. **Adm £3, chd free.** **Visitors welcome by appt May to July.**
Mature moorland garden bisected by stream on edge of Bodmin Moor. Woodland trees. Best in spring.

38 ◆ MARSH VILLA GARDENS
St Andrew's Road, Par PL24 2LU. Judith Stephens, 01726 815920, www.marshvillagardens.com. *5m E of St Austell. Leave A390 at St Blazey T-lights, by church, into Station Rd, then 1st L, garden 600yds on L.* Home-made teas. **Adm £4.50, chd free. For NGS: Sat 9, Sun 10 Aug (10-6). For other opening times and information, please phone or see garden website.**
Traditional English garden with mature trees, shrubs, lawns and overflowing flower beds. 100yds hornbeam avenue divides garden, separating many different planting schemes. Enjoy marshland walks and natural water features. 3 acres full of ideas for budding gardeners. Good wheelchair access, some hard gravel paths.

39 MIDDLEWOOD HOUSE
Middlewood, North Hill, Launceston PL15 7NN. Brian & Cathy Toole, 01566 782118, cathy.toole@btinternet.com. *On B3254, 7m S of Launceston, 7m N of Liskeard. At north end of village on B3254, lay-by directly outside house. Parking for up to 6 cars only & coaches up to 16-seater.* Cream teas. **Adm £3.50, chd free. Visitors welcome by appt Apr to July, 6 parking spaces - so car-sharing helps.**
Beautiful, tranquil 1¼ -acre garden nestling in Lynher valley. In a series of semi-formal destinations, spring shrubs and flowers are complemented by extensive herbaceous beds. Fernery, raised beds, water features, wooden and other architectural structures. Garden is sloped but good paths allow wheelchair access to most of it.

40 ◆ MOYCLARE
Lodge Hill, Liskeard PL14 4EH. Elizabeth & Philip Henslowe, 01579 343114, www.moyclare.co.uk. *1m S of Liskeard centre. Approx 300yds S of Liskeard railway stn on St Keyne-Duloe rd (B3254).* Home-made teas. **Adm £3.50, chd free. For NGS: Mon 5 May (2-5). For other opening times and information, please phone or see garden website.**
Gardened by one family for over 80yrs; mature trees, shrubs and plants (many unusual, many variegated). Once most televised Cornish garden. Now revived and rejuvenated and still a plantsman's delight, still full of character. Camellia, brachyglottis and astrantia (all 'Moira Reid') and cytisus 'Moyclare Pink' originated here. Meandering paths through fascinating shrubberies, herbacious borders and sunny corners. Wellstocked pond. Wildlife habitat area. Featured on Austrian TV and in Die Geheimen Garten von Cornwall. Most of the garden can be enjoyed by wheel-chair users.

41 NANFENTEN
Little Petherick, Wadebridge PL27 7QT. Trevor & Jackie Bould, 01841 540480, nanfentensgarden@hotmail.co.uk, www.nanfentensgarden.com. *3m W of Wadebridge, A389 to Little Petherick. Turn into lane next to white cottage almost opp church, Nanfenten 150 metres on L. Limited parking, larger groups please use village hall car park.* Home-made teas. **Adm £3.50, chd free. Visitors welcome by appt May to Aug, individuals or groups all welcome.**
⅔ -acre plantsman's garden on side of valley. Views of Petherick Creek to Padstow. Cottage-style planting on difficult terrain. Many beautiful roses. Steep sloping aspect to rear garden with wide variety of shrubs and plants. Unusual sloping water feature. Pergola and summerhouse. A surprise around every corner with beautiful views. Many seating areas.

42 NAVAS HILL HOUSE
Bosanath Valley, Mawnan Smith, Falmouth TR11 5LL. Aline & Richard Turner. *1½ m from Trebah & Glendurgan Gardens. Head for Mawnan Smith.* Cream teas. **Adm £3.50, chd free. Sun 18 May (2-5.30).**
8½ -acre garden divided into various zones; kitchen garden with greenhouses, potting shed, fruit cages, orchard; 2 plantsman areas with specialist trees and shrubs; walled rose garden; ornamental garden with water features and rockery; wooded areas with bluebells and young large leafed rhododendrons. Seating areas with views across wooded valley, not a car in sight! Limited wheelchair access, some gravel and grass paths.

43 THE OLD RECTORY, TREVALGA
Trevalga, Boscastle PL35 0EA. Jacqueline M A Jarvis, 01840 250512. *Coastal rd between Tintagel & Boscastle. At Trevalga Xrds turn inland away from hamlet. Garden ½ m up narrow, steep hill.* Light refreshments. **Adm £3.50, chd free. Visitors welcome by appt Mar to Nov, limited parking.**
North Cornish coast - challenging, exposed, NW-facing garden with panoramic sea views. 'From Field to Garden' a 25 yr project by artist owner. ½ m inland, elevation 500ft, informal incl woodland, perennial borders, sunken and walled areas. Has lookout at front of garden (4 stair - spiral stair access) with stunning views across circa 50 miles of the coastline - Hartland Point to Pendeen. Featured in Cornish Guardian by Michael Williams. Gravel driveways - wheelchairs would be difficult but not impossible Not all parts of garden accessible.

44 ◆ PENCARROW
Washaway, Bodmin PL30 3AG. Molesworth-St Aubyn family, 01208 841369, www.pencarrow.co.uk. *4m NW of Bodmin. Signed off A389 & B3266.* **Adm £5.50, chd £2.50. For NGS: Wed 16 Apr (10-5.30). For other opening times and information, please phone or see garden website.**
50 acres of tranquil, family-owned Grade II* listed gardens. Superb specimen conifers, azaleas, magnolias and camellias galore. 700 varieties of rhododendron give a blaze of spring colour; blue hydrangeas line the mile long carriage drive throughout the summer. Discover the Iron Age hill fort, lake, Italian gardens and granite rockery. Free parking, dogs welcome, cafe and children's play area. Gravel paths, some steep slopes.

GROUP OPENING

45 NEW PILLATON PARISH GARDENS
Pillaton, Saltash PL12 6QS, 01579 350629, tony@laurillard.eclipse.co.uk. *4m S of Callington. Signs from r'abouts on A388 at St Mellion & Hatt or on A38 at Landrake. 1st garden in centre of village opp Weary Friar PH. Roadside parking. No parking in PH car park.* Home-made teas available at all 3 gardens. **Combined adm £5, chd free. Sun 29 June (12-5). Visitors also welcome by appt for coach parties only.**

NEW SOUTH LEA
Viv & Tony Laurillard

NEW STONECROFT
John & Anne Soul

NEW NORTH SILLATON FARMHOUSE
Linda Mavin

In quiet village in SE Cornwall with C12 church and thriving village PH, set in rolling farmland above River Lynher valley. The first 2 gardens, each about 0.3 acres, are right in village, whilst 3rd, at about 1 acre, is 1½ m away. South Lea: presents a tropical theme around front and, at rear, sun terrace, sloping and level lawns, herbaceous borders, fair-sized pond and newly created shady woodland area. Stonecroft: small, enclosed garden. Split level lawns and 2 large fenced ponds full of assorted fish with waterfall, surrounded by greenhouse, patio and flowerbeds of shrubs, colourful bedding and vegetables. North Sillaton Farmhouse: property was bought at Duchy auction 29yrs ago. Apart from privet hedge, everything has since been added. Mixed garden on S-facing slope with pond, vegetable beds, small orchard, houses for plants and hens and poly-tunnel. To the north is a Cornish hedge. Several sheltered areas to sit. Sloping lawns, soft paths. Limited wheelchair access at South Lea and Stonecroft (both have paved areas overlooking most of garden).

Home-made teas at all three gardens . . .

46 ◆ PINSLA GARDEN & NURSERY
Cardinham PL30 4AY. Mark & Claire Woodbine, 01208 821339, www.pinslagarden.net. *3½ m E of Bodmin. From A30 or Bodmin take A38 towards Plymouth, 1st L to Cardinham & Fletchers Bridge, 2m on R.* Home-made teas. **Adm £3, chd free. For NGS: Sats, Suns 31 May; 1 June; 9, 10 Aug (9-5.30). For other opening times and information, please phone or see garden website.**
Romantic 1½ acre artist's garden set in tranquil woodland. Naturalistic cottage garden planting surrounds our C18 fairytale cottage. Imaginative design, intense colour and scent, bees and butterflies. Unusual shade plants, acers and ferns. Fantastic range of plants and statues on display and for sale. Friendly advice in nursery. Gravel paths.

47 POLGWYNNE
Feock TR3 6SG. Amanda & Graham Piercy. *5m SW of Truro. Take A39 out of Truro signed Falmouth. At Playing Place turn L onto B3289. After 2m look for NGS signs.* Home-made teas. **Adm £4, chd free. Sun 27 Apr (2-5.30).**
Wonderful 4-acre garden by the sea. New cottage garden planting. Walled gardens, terraced lawns, and formal pond. Vegetable and picking gardens, with greenhouses whose mechanisms were described in The Journal of the RHS in 1852. Many unusual plants and what is believed to be the largest female Ginkgo biloba in Britain. Partial wheelchair access, gravel paths, some slopes.

48 ◆ POPPY COTTAGE GARDEN
Ruan High Lanes, Truro TR2 5JR. Tina & David Primmer, 01872 501411, www.poppycottagegarden.co.uk. *On the Roseland Peninsula. Turn off the A390 Truro - St Austell rd onto the A3078 to St Mawes. Garden 4m out of Tregony.* Home-made teas. **Adm £3.50, chd free. For NGS: Sat 19, Sun 20 July (2-5.30). For other opening times and information, please phone or see garden website.**
Situated on the beautiful Roseland peninsula, this 1-acre garden is a plantsman's paradise. Planted for yr-round interest and divided into rooms, its intense planting of shrubs and herbaceous under-planted with bulbs provides colourful and intriguing surprises around every corner. Small orchard with ornamental ducks and chickens. Featured on BBC Gardeners World.

49 PRIMROSE FARM
Skinners Bottom, Redruth TR16 5EA. Barbara & Peter Simmons, 01209 890350, babs.simmons@btinternet.com, www.primrosefarmgarden.blogspot.com. *6m N of Truro. At Chiverton Cross r'about on A30 take Blackwater turn. Down hill, R by Red Lion PH up North Hill, 1st L (mini Xrd), garden approx ½ m on L.* Home-made teas. **Adm £3.50, chd free. Visitors welcome by appt May to Sept, groups welcome.**
Rambling informal cottage-style garden with woodland glade. Mature trees and shrubs, herbaceous and mixed borders. Patio area with exotic plants. Gravel path to pergola with scented climbers and summerhouse. Vegetable patch and wildlife pond. New secret garden. A plantsman's garden.

50 RIVERSIDE COTTAGE
St. Clement, Truro TR1 1SZ. Billa & Nick Jeans, 01872 263830, billajeans@gmail.com. *1½ m SE of Truro. From Trafalgar r'about on A39 in Truro, follow signs for St Clement, up St Clement Hill. R at top of hill, continue to car park by river.* Home-made teas. **Adm £3.50, chd free. Sun 13 Apr, Sun 25 May (2-5). Visitors also welcome by appt Apr to May.**
Small garden on beautiful St Clement Estuary. Cottage garden. Small Victorian orchard and nut walk with wild flower areas, borders and vegetable patch. Steep paths and steps but plenty of seats. Walk through to C13 St Clement Church and 'living churchyard'.

51 ◆ ROSELAND HOUSE
Chacewater TR4 8QB. Mr & Mrs Pridham, 01872 560451, www.roselandhouse.co.uk. *4m W of Truro. At Truro end of main st. Parking in village car park (100yds) or on surrounding rds.* Home-made teas. **Adm £4, chd free. For NGS: Sats, Suns 21, 22 June; 26, 27 July (1-5). For other opening times and information, please phone or see garden website.**
The 1-acre garden is a mass of rambling roses and clematis. Ponds and borders alike are filled with plants, many rarely seen in gardens. National Collection of clematis viticella cvs can be seen in garden and display tunnel, along with a huge range of other climbing plants. Some slopes.

52 ◆ ST MICHAEL'S MOUNT
St Michaels Mount, Marazion TR17 0HS. James & Mary St Levan, 01736 710507, www.stmichaelsmount.co.uk. *2½ m E of Penzance. ½ m from shore at Marazion by Causeway; otherwise by motor boat.* **Adm £5, chd £2. For NGS: Sun 8 June (10.30-5). For other opening times and information, please phone or see garden website.**
Infuse your senses with colour and scent in the unique sub-topical gardens basking in the mild climate and salty breeze. Clinging to granite slopes the terraced beds tier steeply to the ocean's edge, boasting tender exotics from places such as Mexico, the Canary Islands and South Africa. The Laundry Lawn, Mackerel Bank,

Woodland Cottage

Pill Box, Gun Emplacement, Tiered Terraces, The Well, Tortoise Lawn. Walled Gardens, Seagull Seat. ITV's This Morning team sent Diarmuid Gavin to undertake some abseil planting. The garden lawn can be accessed with wheelchairs although further exploration is limited due to steps and steepness.

53 SCORRIER HOUSE
Scorrier, Redruth TR16 5AU. Richard & Caroline Williams. *2½ m E of Redruth. Signed from the B3207. And the Redruth Truro rd B3287.* Home-made teas. **Adm £4, chd free. Sun 1 June (2-5.30).**
Scorrier House and gardens have been in the Williams family for 7 generations. The gardens are set in parkland with a new conservatory, formal garden with herbaceous borders and walled garden with camellias, magnolias and rare trees, some collected by the famous plant collector William Lobb. Unfenced swimming pool.

54 ◆ TREBAH
Mawnan Smith TR11 5JZ. Trebah Garden Trust, 01326 252200, www.trebah-garden.co.uk. *4m SW of Falmouth. Follow tourist signs from Hillhead r'about on A39 approach to Falmouth or Treliever Cross r'about on junction of A39-A394. Parking for coaches.* **For opening times and information, please phone or see garden website.**
26-acre S-facing ravine garden, planted in 1830s. Extensive collection rare/mature trees/shrubs incl glades; huge tree ferns 100yrs old, subtropical exotics. Hydrangea collection covers 2½ acres. Water garden, waterfalls, rock pool stocked with mature koi carp. Enchanted garden for plantsman/artist/family. Play area/trails for children. Use of private beach. Amazing spring colour, two and a half acres of hyrangeas in summer and autumn, private beach, childrens trails and play areas. Steep paths in places. 2 motorised vehicles available, please book in advance.

55 TREBARTHA
nr Launceston PL15 7PE. The Latham Family. *6m SW of Launceston. North Hill, SW of Launceston nr junction of B3254 & B3257. No coaches.* Home-made teas. **Adm £5, chd free. Suns 11 May; 12 Oct (2-5).**
Wooded area with lake surrounded by walks of flowering shrubs; woodland trail through fine woods with cascades and waterfalls; American glade with fine trees. Major but exciting clearance and replanting is underway in these fine landscape/woodland gardens which will not interfere with your walk but we do request that visitors keep to the signed paths and other directions.

56 ◆ TRELISSICK

Feock TR3 6QL. National Trust, 01872 862090, www.nationaltrust.org.uk/trelissick. *4m S of Truro. From A39 Truro to Falmouth, turn onto B3289 at Playing Place. Follow signs to Trelissick & King Harry Ferry*. Light refreshments in Crofters. **Adm £8, chd £4. For NGS: Thur 1 May (10.30-5.30). For other opening times and information, please phone or see garden website.**

Woodland garden with fantastic views out to water on 3 sides. Contrasts between light and shade and inspiration from gardening in a variety of woodland environments. Mixed borders designed for long term interest with a mixture of popular hardy favourites and tender exotics with foliage interest. Four summer-houses with lovely views. Guided tour of garden to learn about woodland gardening and mixed borders for lasting impact 2.30pm. Partially accessible by wheelchair, map provided. Two manual wheelchairs available and also power mobility vehicles, ring to book these in advance.

enchanting ¾ acre cottage garden and 6½ acre woodland . . .

57 NEW ◆ TREMATON CASTLE

Castle Hill, Trematon, Saltash PL12 4QW. Bannerman, 01752 847986, www.bannermandesign.com. *2m SW of Saltash. Arrive from Trematon village not through Saltash via Forder as lane very narrow & steep. A38, turning signed Trematon, 1m from Saltash Services r'about. R at T-junction in Trematon (Longlands and Trehan), or straight on if coming from W. At fork L to Trehan. Parking ½ m past castle sign*. **Adm £5, chd free. For NGS: Sun 15 June (2-5). For other opening times and information, please phone or see garden website.**

Property of Duchy of Cornwall since the Conquest, Trematon is a perfect miniature motte and bailey castle. On R Lynher estuary, '... one of the superb views of Cornwall ... all the more romantic for being still a private residence' (John Betjeman). Julian and Isabel Bannerman have begun to create a garden playing on its pre-Raphaelite glories, wild flowers, orchard, woodland, scented borders, seaside and exotic planting.

58 ◆ TREMENHEERE SCULPTURE GARDEN

Penzance TR20 8YL. Drs Neil Armstrong & Jane Martin, 01736 448089, www.tremenheere.co.uk. *1m E of Penzance. From Gulval church proceed ¾ m due E. L at sign Entrance, gates straight ahead*. **Adm £6.50, chd £3. For NGS: Sun 12 Oct (10-5). For other opening times and information, please phone or see garden website.**

Spectacular valley setting overlooking St Michael's Mount provides microclimate for large scale subtropical planting. Habitats from ponds to hot slopes provide wide variety of landscaping styles. High quality contemporary sculpture by internationally-renowned artists.

59 TRENARTH

High Cross, Constantine TR11 5JN. Lucie Nottingham, 01326 340444, lmnottingham@tiscali.co.uk, www.trenarthgardens.com. *6m SW of Falmouth. Main rd A39/A394 Truro to Helston, follow Constantine signs. High X garage turn L for Mawnan, 30yds on R down dead end lane, Trenarth is ½ m at end*. Light refreshments. **Adm £4, chd free. Sun 13 July (4-8). Visitors also welcome by appt Mar to Oct please contact before visiting. Guided tours.**

4-acres round C17 farmhouse in peaceful pastoral setting. Yr-round interest. Emphasis on tender, unusual plants, structure and form. C16 courtyard, listed garden walls, yew rooms, vegetable garden, traditional potting shed, orchard, new woodland area and palm and gravel gardens. Circular walk down ancient green lane via little lake to Trenarth Bridge, returning through bluebell woods. Abundant wildlife. Bees in tree bole, lesser horseshoe bat colony, swallows and house martins nesting, wild flowers and butterflies. New 'benchmarked' walk, and 'wolery'.

60 ◆ TRENGWAINTON

Madron, Penzance TR20 8RZ. National Trust, 01736 363148, www.nationaltrust.org.uk/trengwainton. *2m NW of Penzance. ½ m W of Heamoor. On Penzance-Morvah rd (B3312), ½ m off St Just rd (A3071). Signed from A30*. **Adm £7.50, chd £3.75. For NGS: Suns 16 Mar; 8 June (10.30-5). For other opening times and information, please phone or see garden website.**

Glorious spring displays of magnolias, rhododendrons, azaleas and camellias; walled kitchen garden built to dimensions of Noahs Ark and breathtaking views across Mounts Bay. Lose yourself amongst winding, wooded paths, picnic by the stream or simply find a quiet corner to sit within Trengwainton's peaceful 25 acres. WW2 'Dig for Victory' allotment, complete with reproduction Anderson shelter. Free guided tour 11.30am. Featured on 'Hungry Sailors' TV programme. Main drive tarmac, other paths gravel. Slope, wheelchair assistance may be needed. 2 manual wheelchairs available, booking essential.

61 TREVOOLE FARM

Trevoole, Praze-an-Beeble, Camborne TR14 0RN. Mr & Mrs Stevens, 01209 831243, beth@trevoolefarm.co.uk, www.trevoolefarm.co.uk. *3m SSW of Camborne. From Camborne on B3303 towards Helston. Past Pendarves Nature Reserve, L into lane just after 2 mine chimneys*. Light refreshments. **Adm £3, chd free. Every Thur 6 Mar to 18 Dec (10-4); Every Friday 2 May to 31 Oct (10-4); Sat 7, Sun 8 June (10-4). Visitors also welcome by appt Mar to Oct.**

The gardens are nestled around C18 smallholding. Old farmhouse and shade garden, charming courtyard of restored granite buildings. Old orchard and herb garden. Patchwork potager. Bog garden, shepherd's hut cottage garden and rose walk. Featured in Country Living and Cornwall Life. Gravel paths.

62 TREWAN HALL

St Columb TR9 6DB. Mrs Jo Davies, www.trewan-hall.co.uk. *6m E of Newquay. N of St Columb Major, off A39 to Wadebridge. 1st turning on L signed to St Eval & Talskiddy. Entrance ¾ m on L in woodland. Map*

on website. Home-made teas. **Adm £3.50, chd free. Sun 18 May (2-5).**
Set within 36 acres of parkland, fields and broadleaved woodland, with features incl flower borders, rose beds, kitchen garden enclosed by recently-restored cob wall and traditional orchard with beehive. Driveway bordered by mature rhododendron and hydrangea leading to Grade II star listed C17 manor house (not open). Children's play area. Long standing David Bellamy Gold Conservation Award. Disabled WC.

63 ◆ TREWIDDEN GARDEN

Buryas Bridge, Penzance TR20 8TT. Richard Morton, Head Gardener, 01736 363021/351979, www.trewiddengarden.co.uk. *2m W of Penzance. Entry on A30 just before Buryas Bridge. Sat nav TR19 6AU.* Cream teas. **Adm £6, chd free. For NGS: Sun 13 Apr (10.30-4.30). For other opening times and information, please phone or see garden website.**
Historic Victorian garden with magnolias, camellias and magnificent tree ferns planted within ancient tin workings. Tender, rare and unusual exotic plantings create a riot of colour thoughout the season. Water features, specimen trees and artefacts from Cornwall's tin industry provide a wide range of interest for all.

64 WATERS EDGE

North Corner, Coverack TR12 6TG. Lizzie Cartwright, lizzie@lizziebrownart.co.uk, www.lizziebrownart.co.uk. *10m from Helston. From Helston take B3293. Park in Coverack car parks, follow yellow signs, garden next to Porthgwarra Nursing Home.* Home-made teas. **Adm £3, chd free. Sun 27 July (11-4). Visitors also welcome by appt July to Aug.**
Coverack, on the unique Lizard Peninsula, is a Conservation Area and SSSI. Small, narrow, sheltered garden, lush and blue in July with swathes of agapanthus. Hidden seating, stream, pond, sculptures and artist's studio to enjoy. Homemade cakes on terrace with stunning views of harbour, beach and sea. Artist's painting studio and sculptures in the garden. Children's Creature Trail and craft table. Featured in the book Die Geheimen Garten von Cornwall.

65 WAYE COTTAGE

Lerryn, nr Lostwithiel PL22 0QQ. Malcolm & Jennifer Bell, 01208 872119. *4m S of Lostwithiel. Village parking, garden 10min, level stroll along riverbank/stepping stones.* Home-made teas. **Adm £3.50, chd free. Visitors welcome by appt May to Sept, garden clubs welcomed at reduced rate.**
Never immaculate but abundantly-planted, this 1-acre cottage garden has a large and interesting collection of plants, some rare and unusual, together with delightful bonsai theatre. Wander along the meandering paths, sit on the many benches and enjoy stunning river views. Steep and sadly only for those sound in wind and limb. Attractive riverside village with pub and shop which supplies picnics to eat on trestle tables on the village green.

66 WOODLAND COTTAGE

Tregrehan Mills, St Austell PL25 3TL. Terry & Cassie Corby, www.woodlandcottage.weebly.com. *2m E of St Austell. From St Austell take A390, 1st L after St Austell Garden Centre, continue through village for 1m.* Light refreshments. **Adm £4, chd free. Suns 11 May; 27 July (12-5).**
An enchanting 3/4 acre cottage garden and 6 1/2 acre woodland, which hides an old ruined tin mine. Sloping lawns with island beds. Spring and summer colour from rhododendrons, azaleas, large range of perennials and over 250 varieties of hemerocallis. Grotto with mature tree ferns. Many seating areas incl a pretty summerhouse. Cornish industrial heritage: tin mine/engine house; china clay works; quarry. Parts of the woodland are very steep and not for the faint hearted.

Cornwall County Volunteers

County Organiser
Bryan Coode, Carwinnick, Grampound, Truro TR2 4RJ, 01726 882488, bhcoode@btconnect.com

County Treasurer
Andrew Flint, Wheal Eliza, Boscundle, St.Austell PL25 3RJ, 01726 879336, flints@elizaholidays.co.uk

Booklet Coordinator
Peter Stanley, Mazey Cottage, Tangies, Gunwalloe, Helston TR12 7PU, 01326 565868, stanley.m2@sky.com

Publicity
Nutty Lim, Kilmarth, Par PL24 2TL, 01726 815247, christianne.gf.lim@gmail.com

Assistant County Organisers
Ginnie Clotworthy, Trethew, Lanlivery, Bodmin PL30 5BZ, 01208 872612, giles.clotworthy@btopenworld.com
William Croggon, Creed Lodge, Creed, Grampound, Truro TR2 4SL, 01872 530499, wrcroggon@btinternet.com
Sar Gordon, Hillburn Cottage, Henwood, Liskeard PL14 5BP, 01579 362076, sar.gordon@virgin.net
Caroline Latham, Stonaford Manor, North Hill, Launceston PL15 7PE, 01566 782970
Katie Nichols, Tresithick House, St Erme, Truro TR4 9AU, 01872 275786, katherinemlambert@gmail.com
Alison O'Connor, Tregoose, Grampound, Truro TR2 4DB, 01726 882460, tregoose@tregoose.co.uk
Marion Stanley, Mazey Cottage, Tangies, Gunwalloe, Helston TR12 7PU, 01326 565868, stanley.m2@sky.com
Virginia Vyvyan-Robinson, Mellingey Mill House, St Issey, Wadebridge PL27 7QU, 01841 540511, mellingey@btinternet.com
Ian Wright, Garden Adviser, The National Trust, Cornwall Office, Lanhydrock, Bodmin PL30 4DE, 07884 425899, ian.wright@nationaltrust.org.uk

CUMBRIA

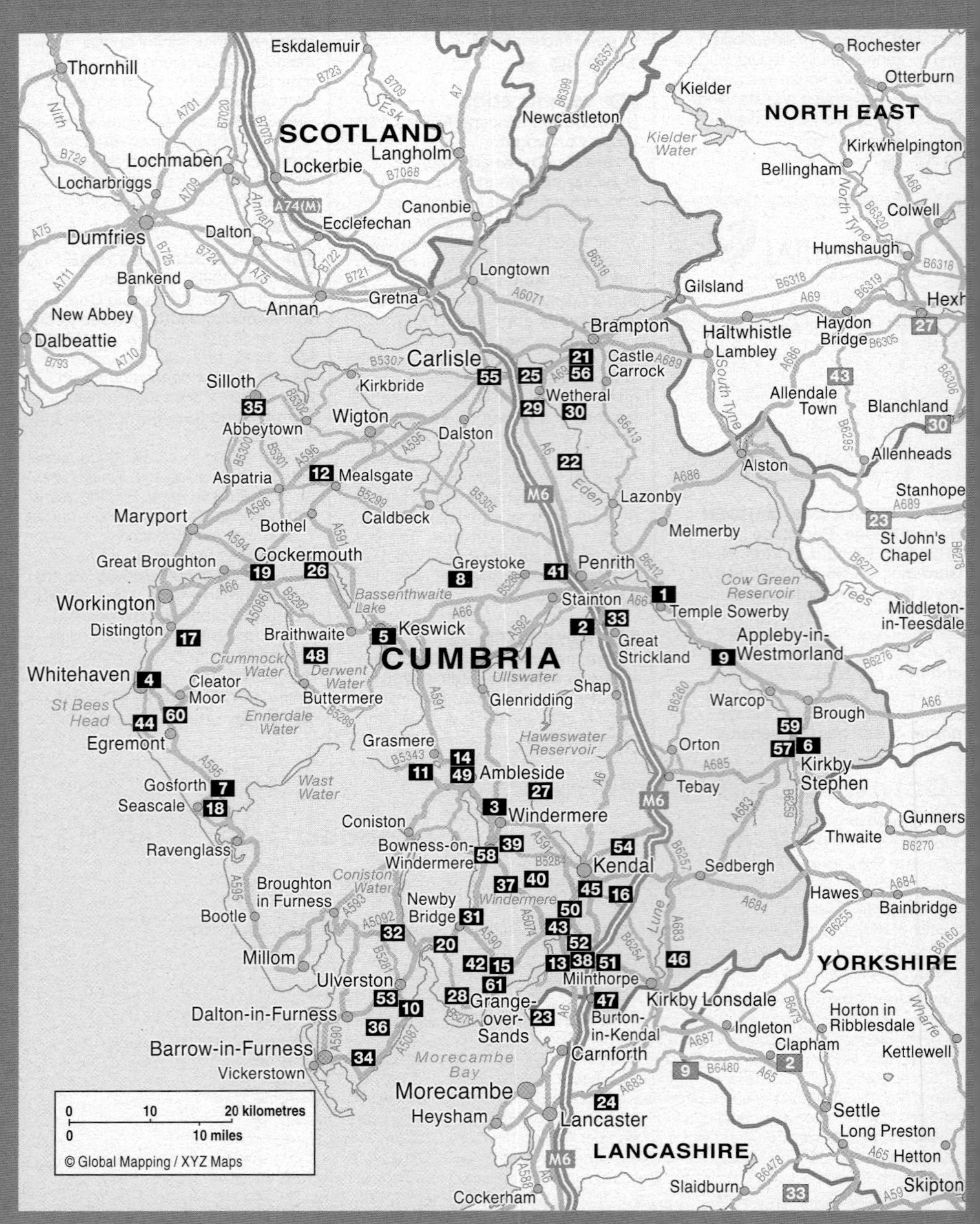
SCOTLAND
NORTH EAST
CUMBRIA
YORKSHIRE
LANCASHIRE
Eskdalemuir
Thornhill
Lochmaben
Lockerbie
Langholm
Locharbriggs
Canonbie
Ecclefechan
Dumfries
Dalton
Bankend
New Abbey
Dalbeattie
Annan
Gretna
Longtown
Newcastleton
Kielder
Kielder Water
Rochester
Otterburn
Kirkwhelpington
Bellingham
Colwell
Humshaugh
Gilsland
Brampton
Haltwhistle
Haydon Bridge
Lambley
Castle Carrock
Carlisle
Kirkbride
Silloth
Abbeytown
Wigton
Dalston
Wetheral
Allendale Town
Blanchland
Alston
Allenheads
Aspatria
Mealsgate
Caldbeck
Lazonby
Stanhope
Maryport
Bothel
Melmerby
St John's Chapel
Great Broughton
Cockermouth
Greystoke
Penrith
Workington
Bassenthwaite Lake
Stainton
Temple Sowerby
Cow Green Reservoir
Middleton-in-Teesdale
Distington
Braithwaite
Keswick
Great Strickland
Appleby-in-Westmorland
Whitehaven
Crummock Water
Derwent Water
Ullswater
Cleator Moor
Buttermere
Glenridding
Shap
Warcop
Brough
St Bees Head
Ennerdale Water
Egremont
Grasmere
Haweswater Reservoir
Orton
Kirkby Stephen
Gosforth
Wast Water
Ambleside
Tebay
Seascale
Windermere
Coniston
Thwaite
Gunners
Ravenglass
Bowness-on-Windermere
Kendal
Sedbergh
Broughton in Furness
Coniston Water
Newby Bridge
Hawes
Bainbridge
Bootle
Millom
Ulverston
Milnthorpe
Kirkby Lonsdale
Dalton-in-Furness
Grange-over-Sands
Burton-in-Kendal
Horton in Ribblesdale
Ingleton
Clapham
Barrow-in-Furness
Carnforth
Kettlewell
Vickerstown
Morecambe Bay
Morecambe
Heysham
Lancaster
Settle
Long Preston
Hetton
Slaidburn
Skipton
Cockerham
0 10 20 kilometres
0 10 miles
© Global Mapping / XYZ Maps

Opening Dates

All entries subject to change. For latest information check www.ngs.org.uk

February

Sunday 16
38 Lower Rowell Farm & Cottage
51 Summerdale House

Monday 24
53 Swarthmoor Hall

Tuesday 25
53 Swarthmoor Hall

Wednesday 26
53 Swarthmoor Hall

Thursday 27
53 Swarthmoor Hall

Friday 28
53 Swarthmoor Hall

Wild meadow and large pond area home to moisture-loving plants, tame hens and wild moorhens . . .

March

51 Summerdale House (Every Friday from 7 March)

Saturday 1
53 Swarthmoor Hall

Sunday 2
51 Summerdale House
53 Swarthmoor Hall

Monday 3
53 Swarthmoor Hall

Tuesday 4
53 Swarthmoor Hall

Wednesday 5
53 Swarthmoor Hall

Thursday 6
53 Swarthmoor Hall

Friday 7
53 Swarthmoor Hall

Saturday 8
53 Swarthmoor Hall

Sunday 9
53 Swarthmoor Hall

Monday 10
53 Swarthmoor Hall

Tuesday 11
53 Swarthmoor Hall

Wednesday 12
53 Swarthmoor Hall

Thursday 13
53 Swarthmoor Hall

Friday 14
53 Swarthmoor Hall

Saturday 15
53 Swarthmoor Hall

Sunday 16
53 Swarthmoor Hall

Sunday 23
1 Acorn Bank
14 Dora's Field
27 Holehird Gardens
49 Rydal Hall

April

51 Summerdale House (Every Friday)

Friday 18
11 Copt Howe

Monday 21
11 Copt Howe

Wednesday 23
11 Copt Howe

Friday 25
11 Copt Howe

Saturday 26
10 Conishead Priory & Buddhist Temple

Sunday 27
10 Conishead Priory & Buddhist Temple
22 Hazel Cottage

Wednesday 30
11 Copt Howe

May

51 Summerdale House (Every Friday)

Friday 2
8 Chapelside
33 NEW Larch Cottage Nurseries

Saturday 3
8 Chapelside

Sunday 4
8 Chapelside
51 Summerdale House
58 Windy Hall

Friday 9
11 Copt Howe

Saturday 10
5 Bishop's House

Sunday 11
13 Dallam Tower
56 West Garth Cottage

Monday 12
11 Copt Howe

Wednesday 14
11 Copt Howe

Friday 16
8 Chapelside
11 Copt Howe

Saturday 17
8 Chapelside
11 Copt Howe

Sunday 18
1 Acorn Bank
3 Beck Lodge
8 Chapelside
22 Hazel Cottage
39 Matson Ground

Wednesday 21
11 Copt Howe

Friday 23
11 Copt Howe

Saturday 24
11 Copt Howe

Wednesday 28
11 Copt Howe

Friday 30
8 Chapelside
11 Copt Howe

Saturday 31
8 Chapelside

June

51 Summerdale House (Every Friday)

Sunday 1
8 Chapelside
17 Gilgarran Gardens
26 Higham Hall
58 Windy Hall
61 Yewbarrow House

Wednesday 4
11 Copt Howe

Friday 6
11 Copt Howe

Festival Weekend

Saturday 7
38 Lower Rowell Farm & Cottage

Sunday 8
1 Acorn Bank
23 Hazelwood Farm
35 Lilac Cottage Garden
38 Lower Rowell Farm & Cottage

Wednesday 11
11 Copt Howe

Thursday 12
49 Rydal Hall

Friday 13
8 Chapelside
11 Copt Howe

Saturday 14
8 Chapelside

Sunday 15
8 Chapelside
12 Crookdake Farm
20 Haverthwaite Lodge

Langholme Mill

© Linda Greening

Tuesday 17
- 11 Copt Howe

Wednesday 18
- 9 Church View
- 41 Newton Rigg College Gardens (Afternoon & evening)

Friday 20
- 11 Copt Howe

Sunday 22
- 21 Hayton Village Gardens
- 24 Heywood House
- 34 Leece & Dendron Village Gardens
- 43 Orchard Cottage

Wednesday 25
- 11 Copt Howe
- 20 Haverthwaite Lodge
- 31 Lakeside Hotel & Rocky Bank

Thursday 26
- 49 Rydal Hall

Friday 27
- 8 Chapelside
- 11 Copt Howe

Saturday 28
- 5 Bishop's House
- 8 Chapelside
- 46 Park House
- 48 Rannerdale Cottage

Sunday 29
- 2 Askham Hall
- 8 Chapelside
- 16 Ewebank Farm
- 24 Heywood House
- 30 Ivy House
- 46 Park House
- 47 Pear Tree Cottage
- 48 Rannerdale Cottage
- 51 Summerdale House

July

- 51 **Summerdale House (Every Friday)**

Sunday 6
- 36 Little Urswick Village Gardens
- 44 Orchard House
- 61 Yewbarrow House

Friday 11
- 8 Chapelside

Saturday 12
- 8 Chapelside

Sunday 13
- 8 Chapelside
- 57 Westview
- 59 Winton Park

Wednesday 16
- 9 Church View

Thursday 17
- 27 Holehird Gardens

Saturday 19
- 50 Sizergh Castle

Sunday 20
- 19 NEW Hames Hall Residential Home
- 45 8 Oxenholme Road
- 54 NEW Tenter End Barn
- 60 Woodend House

Friday 25
- 33 NEW Larch Cottage Nurseries

Sunday 27
- 29 Holme Meadow

August

- 51 **Summerdale House (Every Friday)**

Sunday 3
- 6 NEW Boxwood House
- 18 Hall Senna
- 23 Hazelwood Farm
- 42 NEW The Old Vicarage and Fell Cottage
- 61 Yewbarrow House

Sunday 10
- 36 Little Urswick Village Gardens

Sunday 17
- 40 NEW Middle Blakebank

Wednesday 20
- 9 Church View

Sunday 24
- 4 Berriedale
- 51 Summerdale House

Wednesday 27
- 20 Haverthwaite Lodge
- 31 Lakeside Hotel & Rocky Bank

Thursday 28
- 28 Holker Hall Gardens

Saturday 30
- 52 Sunnyside

Sunday 31
- 52 Sunnyside

September

Sunday 7
- 61 Yewbarrow House

Wednesday 17
- 9 Church View

Sunday 21
- 20 Haverthwaite Lodge

October

Wednesday 1
- 41 Newton Rigg College Gardens

Wednesday 15
- 9 Church View

Sunday 19
- 37 Low Fell West

February 2015

Sunday 15
- 51 Summerdale House

Gardens open to the public

- 1 Acorn Bank
- 10 Conishead Priory & Buddhist Temple
- 14 Dora's Field
- 27 Holehird Gardens
- 28 Holker Hall Gardens
- 49 Rydal Hall

Look out for exciting Designer Gardens D

By appointment only

Also open by appointment

Take a walk through this peaceful natural garden . . .

The Gardens

1 ◆ ACORN BANK

Temple Sowerby CA10 1SP. National Trust, 017683 61893, www.nationaltrust.org.uk. *6m E of Penrith. Off A66; ½ m N of Temple Sowerby. Bus: Penrith-Appleby or Carlisle-Darlington; alight Culgaith Rd end.* Tea. **Adm £6, chd £3. For NGS: Suns 23 Mar; 18 May; 8 June (10-5). For other opening times and information, please phone or see garden website.**

Sheltered and tranquil, walled gardens contain a herb garden with more than 250 medicinal and culinary plants. Traditional apple orchards and mixed borders. Beyond the walls lie woodland walks with a wonderful display of snowdrops, daffodils and wild flowers in spring. Dogs welcome on leads on woodland walks. 23 March, NGS Cumbria 'Wordsworth's Daffodil Legacy'. Walled gardens accessible with grass and firm gravel paths, woodland paths have steep gradients and some steps. Access map and information available.

2 ASKHAM HALL

Askham, Penrith CA10 2PF. Countess of Lonsdale, www.askhamhall.co.uk. *5m S of Penrith. Turn off A6 for Lowther and Askham.* Cream teas. **Adm £5.50, chd free (share to Askham and Lowther Churches). Sun 29 June (2-5).**

Askham Hall is a pele tower, incorporating C14, C16 and early C18 elements in courtyard plan (opening this year as luxury accommodation). Splendid formal outlines of garden with terraces of herbaceous borders and topiary, dating back to C17. Meadow area with trees and pond. Wheelchair access limited to certain routes and parts of the gardens.

3 BECK LODGE

Bridge Lane, Troutbeck, Windermere LA23 1LA. Mrs Rachel Crowfoot. *2½ m N of Windermere. From Windermere after Lakes School, turn R into Bridge Lane, off A591. Garden on R in ½ m.* Home-made teas. **Adm £3.50, chd free. Sun 18 May (10.30-4).**

Set in the beautiful Troutbeck Valley this enchanting 1¼ -acre garden is overflowing with colourful rhododendrons, azaleas, magnolias and spring bulbs. A charming pergola is clothed in a mantle of blue wisteria complementing well kept lawns and mixed borders. There is a small but very productive fruit and vegetable garden and stunning views of Lake Windermere.

4 BERRIEDALE

15 Loop Road South, Whitehaven CA28 7TN. Enid & John Stanborough, 01946 695467. *From S, A595 through T-lights onto Loop Rd approx 150yds on R. From N, A595 onto Loop Rd at Pelican Garage, garden approx 1½ m on L.* Home-made teas. **Adm £3, chd free. Sun 24 Aug (2-5). Visitors also welcome by appt, refreshments must be ordered in advance.**

Large cottage style garden divided into several areas including Japanese style, wildlife, patio, large vegetable garden with fruit trees, show class vegetables and flowers. Large front garden, 2 lawns surrounded by flower borders and small pond. Large pond with seating area leading to greenhouse of fuchsias and plants for sale. Oil paintings by local artist. Limited wheelchair access. Able to access most of flower garden. Vegetable garden can be accessed by separate entrance.

5 BISHOP'S HOUSE

Ambleside Road, Keswick CA12 4DD. Mrs Alison Newcome. *Turn off the A591, signed to Castlerigg Manor. House is on L just before St Johns church.* Home-made teas. **Adm £3, chd free. Sats 10 May; 28 June (2-6).**

The garden is approx 1 acre and comprises a mixture of woodland garden, small rockery, herbaceous bed, pond, orchard area, trees and shrubs. A Garden 'in the making' only having been recreated in the last three years, so a lot of the structures and plantings are new amidst the mature beech and yew trees which provided the starting point of this development. Gravel paths.

6 NEW BOXWOOD HOUSE

Hartley, Kirkby Stephen CA17 4JH. Colin & Joyce Dirom, 01768 371306, boxwoodhouse@hotmail.co.uk. *In the centre of Hartley approx, 1m from Kirkby Stephen. Exit M6 at J38.Follow A685, R in Kirkby Stephen for Hartley. From A66 exit at Brough onto A685, 1st L in Kirkby St for Hartley.* Light refreshments. **Adm £3.50, chd free. Sun 3 Aug (11-5). Visitors also welcome by appt June to Aug, for groups of 10-30.**

Take a walk through this peaceful natural garden. Packed herbaceous borders, herb, hosta and heuchera beds plus the tranquil pond are designed to be wildlife friendly. The summer house provides one of the many seating areas around the garden overlooking productive vegetable plot and fruit trees, whilst a meadow walk leads to a stunning view of the whole garden.

7 BUCKBARROW HOUSE
Denton Park Court, Gosforth CA20 1BN. John Maddison, 019467 25431, jhnmaddison@gmail.com. *13m S of Whitehaven. L off A595 into Gosforth, after village centre, L at fork. Next L into Denton Park, keep bearing R into Denton Park Court to number 8.* **Adm £5, chd free. Visitors welcome by appt May to June.**
Small densely-planted garden with a number of compartments incl wildlife pond, shrub area, cottage garden borders, and natural stream. Also Japanese style garden area, including small gravel garden. Decking area. Decorative stone front garden. Favourite plant acers. A visitor said 'A small garden which appears to be much larger than it is!'. Increasing Japanese Garden influence.

8 CHAPELSIDE
Mungrisdale, Penrith CA11 0XR. Tricia & Robin Acland, 017687 79672. *12m W of Penrith. On A66 take minor rd N signed Mungrisdale. After 2m, sharp bends, garden on L immed after tiny church on R. Park at foot of our short drive.* **Adm £3, chd free (share to Mungrisdale Parish Church). Fris, Sats, Suns 2, 3, 4, 16, 17, 18, 30, 31 May; 1, 13, 14, 15, 27, 28, 29 June; 11, 12, 13 July (1-5). Visitors also welcome by appt Apr to Sept, refreshments for groups by arrangement.**
1-acre mature organic garden below fell, around C18 farmhouse and outbuildings, latter mainly open. Tiny stream, large pond. Alpine, herbaceous, raised, gravel, damp and shade beds, bulbs in grass. Extensive range of plants, many unusual. art constructions in and out, local stone used creatively. Fine views, so unkind winds.

9 CHURCH VIEW
Bongate, Appleby-in-Westmorland CA16 6UN. Mrs H Holmes, 017683 51397, engcougars@btinternet.com, www.engcougars.co.uk/church-view. *0.4 miles S Appleby town centre. A66 N take B6542 for 2m St Michael's Church on L garden opp. A66 S take B6542 & continue to Royal Oak Inn, garden next door, opp church.* Tea and biscuits. **Adm £3.50, chd free. Weds 18 June; 16 July; 20 Aug; 17 Sept; 15 Oct (12-4). Visitors also welcome by appt.**
A modern cottage garden with coherent layers of colour, texture and interest. From spring bulbs, through the lushness of summer roses and herbaceous plants galore, to the inherent richness of late perennials and graceful grasses well into late autumn. Plants occupy every inch of this garden for all seasons! Also vegetables in a raised bed system. Approx 2/5 acre. Featured in Garden News, Lancashire Life, Cumberland and Westmorland Herald & Cumbria Life. Part of the garden is readily accessible in a wheelchair, but the main garden is on a sloping site with gravel paths.

10 ◆ CONISHEAD PRIORY & BUDDHIST TEMPLE
A5087 Coast Road, Ulverston LA12 9QQ. Manjushri Kadampa Meditation Centre, 01229 584029, www.manjushri.org. *2m S of Ulverston on A5087 Coast Rd. 30 mins from M6 J36, follow A590 to Ulverston then L onto A5087 Coast Rd signed Bardsea & 'Coastal route to Barrow'.* Light refreshments. **Adm £3.60, chd free. For NGS: Sat 26, Sun 27 Apr (11-5). For other opening times and information, please phone or see garden website.**
40 acres of gardens and woodland surrounding Romantic Gothic mansion. Temple garden an oasis of peace, wildlife garden, arboretum, cottage gardens. Free map with 3 woodland walks. 6 minute woodland walk to Morecambe Bay. 'It is an amazing house, one of the most spectacular in Cumbria', Hunter Davies in 'Best of Lakeland'. Free guided tours of Temple and part of house. Cafe and gift shop. Disabled WC near Temple.

11 COPT HOWE
Chapel Stile, Great Langdale, Ambleside, Cumbria LA22 9JR. Professor R N Haszeldine. Please tel 01539 437685 for weekly recorded message. *5m W of Ambleside. On B5343, 1/4 m past Chapel Stile. Park by side of rd. Please tel for info re special needs transport provided up the drive.* **Adm £4.50, chd free. For NGS: Fri 18, Mon 21, Wed 23, Fri 25, Wed 30 Apr; Fri 9, Mon 12, Wed 14, Fri 16, Sat 17, Wed 21, Fri 23, Sat 24, Wed 28, Fri 30 May; Wed 4, Fri 6, Wed 11, Fri 13, Tue 17, Fri 20, Wed 25, Fri 27 June (12.30-4.30).**
2-acre plantsman's mountain paradise garden. Superb views Langdale Pikes. Extensive collections of acers, camellias, azaleas, rhododendrons, oaks, beeches, rare shrubs, trees, unusual perennials; herbaceous and bulbous species; alpines, trough gardens; rare conifers; expedition plants from worldwide mountainous regions. Outstanding spring and autumn colour. Wildlife sanctuary, red squirrels, badgers, slow-worms, lizards, hotel for wild birds. Major new viewing routes and features. 25yr of opening for NGS. Surrounded by central hills of the Lake District, views in all directions, pools with fish, mountain streams, waterfalls. Neolithic rock carvings. Original stone carvings. Complete tranquility restores the spirit. Featured in GGG and many papers, magazine articles, radio and TV programmes. Not suitable for wheelchair access. Owner is now 89 and finds a walking stick helpful and good walking shoes essential.

Outstanding spring and autumn colour. Wildlife sanctuary, red squirrels, badgers, slow-worms, lizards, hotel for wild birds . . .

12 CROOKDAKE FARM
Aspatria, Wigton CA7 3SH. Kirk & Alannah Rylands, 016973 20413, alannah.rylands@me.com. *3m NE of Aspatria. Between A595 & A596. From A595 take B5299 at Mealsgate signed Aspatria. After 2m turn sharp R in Watch Hill signed Crookdake. House 1m on L.* Home-made teas. **Adm £3.50, chd free. Sun 15 June (1-5). Visitors also welcome by appt June to July.**
Windswept informal farmhouse (not open) garden with a careful colour combination of planting sympathetic

to the landscape incl various different areas with densely planted herbaceous borders, vegetable patch, wild meadow and large pond area home to moisture-loving plants, tame hens and wild moorhens. Opening supported by old vehicle enthusiasts. All types of old vehicles encouraged to attend.

13 DALLAM TOWER

Milnthorpe LA7 7AG. Mr & Mrs R T Villiers-Smith. *7m S of Kendal. 7m N of Carnforth. Nr junction 36 off the M6. A6 & B5282. Stn: Arnside, 4m; Lancaster, 15m.* Cream teas. **Adm £3.50, chd free.** **Sun 11 May (2-5).**
Large garden; natural rock garden, water garden; wood walks, lawns, shrubs. C19 cast iron orangery. Limited wheelchair access. Deep gravel paths.

14 ◆ DORA'S FIELD

Rydal, Ambleside LA22 9LX. National Trust, www.nationaltrust.org.uk. *1½ m N of Ambleside. Follow A591 from Ambleside to Rydal. Dora's Field is next to St Mary's Church.* **Adm by donation.** **For NGS: Sun 23 Mar (11-4). For other opening times and information, please see garden website.**
Named for Dora, the daughter of the poet William Wordsworth. Wordsworth planned to build a house on the land but, after her early death, he planted the area with daffodils in her memory. Now known as Dora's field the area is renowned for its spring display of daffodils. 23rd March 2014; Wordsworth's Daffodil Legacy.

15 ELLER HOW HOUSE

Lindale, Grange-Over-Sands LA11 6NA. John & Helen Churchill, 015395 32479, ellerhowhouse@hotmail.co.uk. *Off A590 above Lindale. On L if travelling towards Levens. Gateposts with large pieces limestone & avenue of trees. Can send detailed directions by email.* **Adm £3.50, chd free.** **Visitors welcome by appt Feb to Oct, groups of 2-12.**
A romantic Regency house and grounds with 12 acres of steep fellside garden, designed by the architect George Webster as his family home. Wild daffodils abound in the woods and on the hillside. Eleven acres of Repton style landscaped woodland with meandering pathways, a lake with bridge and cascade, ruined folly, reposoir, sea view and rocky outcrops. Snowdrops from mid February. Daffodils from mid March. Bluebells from mid April. Autumn colours during October.

16 EWEBANK FARM

Old Hutton, Kendal LA8 0NS. Sue & Barry Sharkey. *3m NE of Kendal. Oxenholme Stn - B6254 - Old Hutton. 3rd turning on L. R turns at next 2 junctions. M6 take J37 A684 Sedbergh. 1st R & R again. After 3m turn L. Ewebank.* Home-made teas. **Adm £3.50, chd free.** **Sun 29 June (1-5).**
Relaxing, rural, flower arrangers garden, friendly hens and suggestions of music. Large lawn sloping down to a steam where curved decking follows the gentle contours of the land. Planting mostly formal with areas of shade for ferns, hostas and other moisture-loving plants. Mixed borders, statues, topiary, orchard and espaliered apples.

GROUP OPENING

17 GILGARRAN GARDENS

Gilgarran, Nr Distington, Workington CA14 4RD. *5m N of Whitehaven, 5m E of Workington. Follow A595 to Distington. Turn from the bypass & take the rd to Distington Crematorium. Follow rd for approx 2m.* Home-made teas at 1 The Avenue. **Combined adm £4, chd free.** **Sun 1 June (12-5).**

NEW MEADOWSIDE
Gilgarran Park. Mr & Mrs Don & Mandy Wright

NEW STACKYARD
Mr & Mrs Pam & Leslie Easdon

STILEFIELD
13 Pinewoods. Brian & Alice Middleton

6 THE AVENUE
Brian & Avril Dixon

WOODSIDE HOUSE
17 Gilgarran Park. David & Brenda Forster

Five contrasting gardens in this peaceful rural hamlet overlooking the Cumbrian coast and fells, each with their own distinctive character, using colour, texture and foliage to best advantage. Well-stocked gardens vary from formal landscaping to woodland and wildlife gardens, and a variety of tranquil water features. Plant Sale at Stilefield.

18 HALL SENNA

Hallsenna, Gosforth, Holmrook CA19 1YB. Chris & Helen Steele, 01946 725436, helen.steele5@btinternet.com. *2m SW of Gosforth. Follow main A595 either N or S. 1m S of Gosforth turn down lane opp Seven Acres Caravan Park, proceed for approx 1m.* Home-made teas. **Adm £3, chd free.** **Sun 3 Aug (10.30-5). Visitors also welcome by appt May to Sept, access is via a public bridleway, no coaches.**
Tucked away within the hamlet of Hallsenna close to the West Cumbrian coast this garden provides the visitor with many different aspects of gardening. The 1 acre site includes borders fully planted for year round colour and many delightful structures built to provide interest, and punctuate your journey through the garden. New water feature completed during 2011. Garden tombola, plant sales, home made teas. Wheelchair access is limited due to steep slopes on entry into the garden.

19 NEW HAMES HALL RESIDENTIAL HOME

Hames Hall - Care Home, Gote Road, Cockermouth CA13 0NN. Amanda Root. *1/2 m NW of town centre. From A595 take A5086 off r'about to Cockermouth. Hames Hall 1/2 m on L. From town centre take A5086.* Home-made teas. **Adm £3, chd free.** **Sun 20 July (2-5).**

Hames Hall Community Garden is a thriving project between Riversmeet Co-Operative and Lakeland Care. Nine volunteers have worked to restore this lovely walled garden whose origins go back to 1836 when it was the kitchen garden for the Hall. Our aim is to involve the residents of Hames Hall by encouraging them to use the raised bed. We grow vegetables, herbs, flowers, soft fruit and apples. Featured in News and Star and on Radio Cumbria. Level, wheelchair friendly access to all main parts of the garden.

20 HAVERTHWAITE LODGE

Haverthwaite LA12 8AJ. David Snowdon, 015395 39841, sheena.taylforth@lakesidehotel.co.uk. *100yds off A590 at Haverthwaite. Turn E off A590 opp Haverthwaite railway stn.* Light refreshments at Lakeside Hotel. **Adm £3, chd free.** **Suns, Weds 15, 25 June; 27 Aug; 21 Sept (11-4).** **Combined with Lakeside & Rocky Bank 25 June; 27 Aug, adm £6. Visitors also welcome by appt Mar to Oct.**

Traditional Lake District garden that has been redesigned and replanted. Gardens on a series of terraces leading down to the R Leven and incl: rose garden, cutting garden, dell area, rock terrace, herbaceous borders and many interesting mature shrubs. In a stunning setting the garden is surrounded by oak woodland and was once a place of C18 and C19 industry.

GROUP OPENING

21 HAYTON VILLAGE GARDENS

Hayton, Brampton CA8 9HR. *7m E of Carlisle. 5m E of M6 J43. 1/2 m S of A69, 3m E of Brampton signed to Hayton. Maps of gardens with tickets, Park on one side of road only please.* Home-made teas at Hayton Village Primary School. **Combined adm £3.50, chd free (share to Hayton Village Primary School).** **Sun 22 June (12-5.30).**

BRACKENHOW
Susan & Jonny Tranter

THE CEDARS
Mrs Lynda Hayward

HAYTON C OF E PRIMARY SCHOOL
Hayton C of E Primary School

KINRARA
Tim & Alison Brown

LITTLE GARTH
Dugald Campbell

MEADOW VIEW
Mr Andrew Welsh

MILLBROOK
Emily & Angus Dawson

STONECHATS
Anna & Mic Mayhew

Easily accessible village of many characterful old sandstone properties, green with ancient walnut tree, church and Inn (weekend meals and WCs). Not far from Hadrian's Wall, Talkin Tarn, N. Pennine fells, Eden Valley and small market town of Brampton with particular attractions such as a Philip Webb church (Burne Jones stained glass). Gardens of varied size and styles all within 1/2 m, mostly of old stone cottages. Smaller and larger cottage gardens, courtyards and containers, steep wooded slopes, sweeping lawns, exuberant borders, frogs, pools and poultry, colour and texture throughout. Homemade teas at the school. Pimms or similar depending on weather! Informal treasure hunt for children young and old. Gardens additional to those listed also generally open and views into numerous others. Varying degrees of access from full to minimal.

22 HAZEL COTTAGE

Armathwaite CA4 9PG. Mr D Ryland & Mr J Thexton. *8m SE of Carlisle. Turn off A6 just S of High Hesket signed Armathwaite, after 2m house facing you at T-junction.* Home-made teas. **Adm £3.50, chd free.** **Suns 27 Apr; 18 May (12-5).**

Developing flower arrangers and plantsmans garden. Extending to approx 5 acres. Incls herbaceous borders, pergola, ponds and planting of disused railway siding providing home to wildlife. Many variegated and unusual plants. Varied areas, planted for all seasons, S-facing, some gentle slopes.

23 HAZELWOOD FARM

Hollins Lane, Silverdale, Carnforth LA5 0UB. Glenn & Dan Shapiro, www.hazelwoodfarm.co.uk. *4m NW of M6 J35. From Carnforth follow signs to Silverdale, after 1m turn L signed Silverdale, after level xing turn L then 1st L into Hollins Lane. Farm on R.* Home-made teas. **Adm £3.50, chd free.** **Sun 8 June, Sun 3 Aug (11-5).**

A theatre of light curtained by backdrops of woodland. Steep paths winding up and through natural limestone cliff, intersected by a tumbling rill joining ponds, provide staging for alpine gems and drifts of herbaceous, prairie and woodland planting. Old and English roses, bulbs and the National Collection of Hepatica. Wildlife friendly garden surrounded by NT access land. New bird, bee and butterfly garden. Featured on ITV 'Love Your Garden' with Alan Titchmarsh.

NCH

> Pond for ducks and bantams roam free . . . enjoy views of garden and greenhouse to take shelter in . . .

24 HEYWOOD HOUSE

Littledale Road, Brookhouse LA2 9PW. Mike & Lorraine Cave, 01524 770977. *4m E of Lancaster. From J34 M6, follow A683 to Caton/Kirkby Lonsdale. At mini island turn R to Brookhouse. At Black Bull PH turn R, garden 3/4 m on LH-side.* Home-made teas. **Adm £3.50, chd free.** **Suns 22, 29 June (1-5).**

Secluded 2-acre garden with many unusual trees and shrubs, sweeping lawns with beautiful herbaceous borders leading to large natural wildlife pond, gravel garden, pergolas with an abundance of roses and climbers, rockery, folly, woodland garden with natural stream, under development. Garden railway train rides for adults and children.

25 NEW HIGH HOLLINS

Aglionby, Carlisle CA4 8AG. Janice & Nick Stewardson, 01228 513799, jlstewardson@btconnect.com. *2m E of Carlisle. ½ m from M6 J43 on A69. 1st white house on R in lay-by after R turn to Scotby. Parking along Scotby Rd.* Home-made teas. **Adm £3.50, chd free. Visitors welcome by appt June to July, enquire for special requests.**

1 acre S facing plantsman's garden hidden behind trees containing mature shrubs, herbaceous borders, rose covered pergola, gravel garden, alpine beds, orchard with wild flowers, soft fruit and vegetable garden. Pond for ducks and bantams roam free. Seating positioned to enjoy views of garden and greenhouse to take shelter in.

26 HIGHAM HALL

Bassenthwaite Lake, Cockermouth CA13 9SH. Higham Hall College, www.highamhall.com. *Northern edge of Lake District, between Cockermouth & Keswick. From Penrith (M6,J40) or Keswick, follow the A66, after Bassenthwaite Lake turn R. From Cockermouth, follow A66 for 3m, turn L at B5291.* Home-made teas. **Adm £3.50, chd free. Sun 1 June (10-4).**

C19 Gothic mansion (not open) set in approximately 6 acres of mature garden with wonderful open views of Skiddaw and surrounding fells. Many interesting trees and perennials, stream with wildlife pond, large lawn, raised bed cut flower and vegetable area. Woodland walks with many wild birds and a chance to see red squirrels. Plant sales. Garden Tour available on NGS day at 11:30am.

27 ◆ HOLEHIRD GARDENS

Patterdale Road, Windermere LA23 1NP. Lakeland Horticultural Society, 015394 46008, www.holehirdgardens.org.uk. *1m N of Windermere. On A592, Windermere to Patterdale rd.* **Adm £4, chd free. For NGS: Sun 23 Mar; Thur 17 July (10-5). For other opening times and information, please phone or see garden website.**

The garden is run by volunteers with the aim of promoting knowledge of the cultivation of plants particularly suited to Lakeland conditions. One of the best labelled gardens in the UK. National Collections of *Astilbe*,

Low Fell West

Polystichum (ferns) and meconopsis. Set on the fellside with stunning views over Windermere the walled garden gives protection to mixed borders whilst alpine houses protect an always colourful array of tiny gems. Consistently voted among the top gardens in Britain and Europe. Wheelchair access limited to walled garden and beds accessible from drive.

NCH

28 ◆ HOLKER HALL GARDENS

Cark-in-Cartmel, Grange-over-Sands LA11 7PL. Lord & Lady Cavendish, 015395 58328, www.holker.co.uk. *4m W of Grange-over-Sands. 12m W of M6 (J36) Follow brown tourist signs.* Cream teas in Courtyard Cafe. **Adm £8, chd free. For NGS: Thur 28 Aug (10.30-5.30). For other opening times and information, please phone or see garden website.**

25 acres of romantic gardens, with peaceful arboretum, inspirational formal gardens, flowering meadow and labyrinth. Spring sees thousands of bulbs and flowers. Summer brings voluptuous mixed borders and bedding. Discover unusually large rhododendrons, magnolias and azaleas, and the National Collection of Stryracaceae. Discover our latest garden feature - The Pagan Grove, designed by Kim Wilkie. Guided tour of the gardens, take the opportunity to tour the gardens with our experienced guide. Donation required.

NCH

29 HOLME MEADOW

1 Holme Meadow, Cumwhinton, Carlisle CA4 8DR. John & Anne Mallinson, 01228 560330, jwai.mallinson@btinternet.com. *2m S of Carlisle. From M6 J42 take B6263 to Cumwhinton, in village take 1st L then bear R at Lowther Arms, Holme Meadow is immed on R.* Tea. **Adm £3, chd free. Sun 27 July (11-5). Visitors also welcome by appt June to Aug.**

Village garden developed and landscaped from scratch by owners. Incl shrubbery, perennial beds supplemented by annuals, pergola and trellis with climbers, slate beds and water feature, ornamental copse, wild flower meadow and kitchen garden. Designed, planted and maintained to be wildlife friendly.

30 IVY HOUSE

Cumwhitton, Brampton CA8 9EX. Martin Johns & Ian Forrest. *6m E of Carlisle. At the bridge at Warwick Bridge on A69 take turning to Great Corby & Cumwhitton. Through Great Corby & woodland until you reach a T-junction Turn R.* Home-made teas. **Adm £3.50, chd free.** **Sun 29 June (1-5).**

Approx 2 acres of sloping fell-side garden with meandering paths leading to a series of 'rooms': pond, fern garden, gravel garden with assorted grasses, vegetable and herb garden. Copse with meadow leading down to beck. Trees, shrubs, bamboos and herbaceous perennials planted with emphasis on variety of texture and colour. Featured in Cumbria Life. Steep slopes.

A natural stream runs into a small lake – a haven for wildlife and birds . . .

31 LAKESIDE HOTEL & ROCKY BANK

Lake Windermere, Newby Bridge, Ulverston LA12 8AT. Mr N Talbot, 015395 30001, sheena.taylforth@lakesidehotel.co.uk, www.lakesidehotel.co.uk. *1m N of Newby Bridge. Turn N off A590 across R Leven at Newby Bridge along W side of Windermere.* Light refreshments Lakeside Hotel. **Combined adm £6, chd free, with Haverthwaite Lodge. Weds 25 June; 27 Aug (11-4). Visitors also welcome by appt Mar to Oct.**

Two diverse gardens on the shores of Lake Windermere. Lakeside has been created for year round interest, packed with choice plants, incl some unusual varieties. Main garden area with herbaceous borders and foliage shrubs, scented and winter interest plants and seasonal bedding. Roof garden with lawn, espaliered local heritage apple varieties and culinary herbs. Lawn art on front lawn. Rocky Bank is a traditional garden with rock outcrops. Planted with unusual specimen alpines. Herbaceous borders, shrubs and ornamental trees. Woodland area with species rhododendrons. Working greenhouse and polytunnels. Wild flower garden and cut flower garden. Wheelchair access not available at Rocky Bank.

32 LANGHOLME MILL

Woodgate, Lowick Green LA12 8ES. Judith & Graham Sanderson, 01229 885215, judith@themill.biz. *7m NW of Ulverston. Take A590 towards Ulverston. At Greenodd turn R on to A5902 towards Broughton. Langholme Mill is approx. 3m along this rd on the LH-side.* **Adm £3, chd free. Visitors welcome by appt Apr to Oct, please phone Judith to arrange.**

Approx 1 acre of mature woodland garden with meandering lakeland stone paths surrounding the mill race stream which can be crossed by a variety of bridges. The garden hosts well established bamboo, rhododendrons, hostas, acers and astilbes and a large variety of country flowers. Featured in Cumbria Life & Westmorland Gazette.

33 NEW LARCH COTTAGE NURSERIES

Melkinthorpe, Penrith CA10 2DR. Joy Batey. *From N leave M6 J40 take A6 S. From S leave M6 J39 take A6 N signposted off A6.* Light refreshments in Green House Restaurant. **Adm £3.50, chd free.** **Fri 2 May, Fri 25 July (1-4).**

For 2 days only Larch Cottage Nurseries are opening the new lower gardens and chapel for NGS visitors. The gardens incl lawns, flowing perennial borders, rare and unusual shrubs, trees, small orchard and kitchen garden. A natural stream runs into a small lake - a haven for wildlife and birds. At the head of the lake stands a chapel, designed and built by Peter for family use only. Larch Cottage has a Japanese Dry garden, ponds and Italianesque columned garden specifically for shade plants. Newly designed and constructed lower gardens and chapel. 'A Plant Kingdom' - English Garden. 'A haven, imbued with the spirit of the Mediterranean world' - Cumbria Life 'One of the best 50 garden centres in the UK' - 'A place of pilgrimage for plantaholics who love the rare and unusual' The Independent. The gardens are accessible to wheelchair users although the paths are rocky in places.

GROUP OPENING

34 LEECE & DENDRON VILLAGE GARDENS

Cumbria LA12 0QP. *2m E of Barrow-in-Furness. J36 on M6 onto A590 to Ulverston. Take A5087 Coast Rd to Barrow. Approx 8m (opp sea wall), turn R for Leece, & a further ½ m for Dendron.* Light refreshments at Leece Village Hall. **Combined adm £3.50, chd free. Sun 22 June (11-5).**

BRIAR HOUSE
Jeff & Gill Lowden

NEW **BROW EDGE**
Mrs Lynn Furzeland-Ridgway

THE DIN DRUM, DENDRON
Mr & Mrs Adrian & Julie Newnham.
Dendron is a small village, just off the main road between Gleaston and Leece

3 PEAR TREE COTTAGE
Jane & Rob Phizacklea

ST MARGARETS, LEECE
Mr & Mrs Lyn & Sabine Dixon

WINANDER
Mrs Enid Cockshott

Two small close villages on the Furness Peninsula 1½ m from Morecambe Bay, rural but not remote, with working farms centred around a small tarn. Gardens of varying size and individual styles, all of which enjoy wonderful views. Features incl a willow yurt, green roof, a white garden, hay meadow with maze, mature trees, herbaceous borders, wildlife ponds and streams, bees, cottage garden, alpines, perennials, shrubs, water features, climbers... and much, much more!

35 LILAC COTTAGE GARDEN

Lilac Cottage, Blitterlees, Silloth CA7 4JJ. Jeff & Lynn Downham, 0169 7332171, lilaccottage@tiscali.co.uk. *1m S of Silloth. On B5300 Maryport to Silloth rd.* Home-made teas. **Adm £3, chd free. Sun 8 June (11-4). Visitors also welcome by appt Apr to Aug.**

Approx 1-acre garden set in compartments in a coastal setting. Featuring raised and woodland gardens, herbaceous borders, large lawned areas and a recently converted sandstone gazebo into a superb garden room. Each garden has an individual theme, well stocked with plants and shrubs and seasonal vegetables.with colour and interest in early spring which continues throughout summer and into autumn. The raised garden is the only area not accessible by wheelchair users.

GROUP OPENING

36 LITTLE URSWICK VILLAGE GARDENS

nr Ulverston LA12 0PL. *4m W of Ulverston. A590 from Ulverston approx 2m to Little Urswick.* Home-made teas at Redmayne Hall. **Combined adm £3.50, chd free. Suns 6 July; 10 Aug (11-5).**

BECKSIDE FARM
Anna Thomason

BURNSMEAD FARM
Richard & Anne Kenyon.
In centre of Little Urswick, above the village green

CORNAA
Mike & Bev Williams.
Behind the green, up short drive

EAST VIEW
Simon & Sally Barton

21 GREENBANK GARDENS
Inez Rixom

NEW **HAZEL COTTAGE**
Mrs Norma Steer

HILL COTTAGE
Mrs Christine Winder

REDMAYNE HALL
Jennie Werry

A small quiet village on the Furness Peninsula with houses set around small village green. Eight very diverse gardens varying in size with individual attractions and interests.

37 LOW FELL WEST

Crosthwaite, Kendal LA8 8JG. Barbie & John Handley, 01539 568297, barbie@handleyfamily.co.uk. *4.6m S of Bowness. Off A5074, turn W just S of Damson Dene Hotel. Follow lane for ½ m.* Home-made teas. **Adm £3.50, chd free. Sun 19 Oct (10.30-5). Visitors also welcome by appt Apr to Oct, for groups of 10+.**
This 2 acre woodland garden in the tranquil Winster Valley has extensive views to the Pennines. The garden, restored since 2003, incl expanses of rock planted sympathetically with grasses, unusual trees and shrubs, climaxing for autumn colour. There are areas of plant rich meadows and native hedges. A woodland area houses a gypsy caravan and there is direct access to Cumbria Wildlife Trust's Barkbooth Reserve of Oak woodland and open fellside. Limited wheelchair access, rough paths, steep slopes.

38 LOWER ROWELL FARM & COTTAGE

Milnthorpe LA7 7LU. John & Mavis Robinson & Julie & Andy Welton, 015395 62270 or 015395 64135. *2m NE of Milnthorpe. Signed to Rowell off B6385. Garden ½ m up lane on L.* Home-made teas. **Adm £3.50, chd free. Sun 16 Feb; Sat 7, Sun 8 June (1-5). Visitors also welcome by appt May to Aug, groups of 15+.**
Approx ¾ -acre garden. Borders and beds with shrubs and interesting herbaceous perennials. Retro greenhouse and vegetable plots. Very peaceful with open views to Farleton Knott, Pennines and Lakeland hills. Adjacent cottage garden also open. Featured in Lake Disrict Life and Lancashire Life magazine.

39 MATSON GROUND

Windermere LA23 2NH. Matson Ground Estate Co Ltd, 015394 47892, info@matsonground.co.uk. *⅔ m E of Bowness. ⅔ m E of Bowness. Turn N off B5284 signed Heathwaite. From East 100yds after Windermere Golf Club, from West 100yds after Windy Hall Rd.* Home-made teas. **Adm £3.50, chd free. Sun 18 May (1-5). Visitors also welcome by appt.**
2 acre formal garden with a mix of established borders, wildflower areas and a stream leading to a large pond and developing aboretum. Rose garden, rockery and topairy terrace borders; white garden. Walled kitchen garden with raised beds, fruit trees and greenhouse. The garden is constantly developing and regular visitors will see changes each year.

40 NEW MIDDLE BLAKEBANK

Underbarrow, Kendal LA8 8HP. Mrs Hilary Crowe. *Lyth Valley between Underbarrow & Crosthwaite. The Garden is on Broom Lane, a turning off the main rd between Underbarrow & Crosthwaite signed Red Scar & Broom Farm.* Home-made teas. **Adm £3.50, chd free. Sun 17 Aug (10.30-4.30).**
The garden overlooks the Lyth Valley with extensive views south to Morcombe Bay and east to the Howgills. It comprises 4 acres of orchard, wild flower meadow and plantings that take the garden through to early autumn.

41 NEWTON RIGG COLLEGE GARDENS

Newton Rigg, Penrith CA11 0AH. 01768 893640, shelagh.todd@newtonrigg.ac.uk, www.askham-bryan.ac.uk. *1m W of Penrith. 3m W from J40 & J41 off M6. ½ m off the B5288 W of Penrith.* Tea. **Adm £4, chd free. Afternoon & evening opening Wed 18 June (3-8.30); Wed 1 Oct (3-6).**
The Educational Gardens and Grounds have much of horticultural interest incl herbaceous borders, eight ponds, expanded organic garden with fruit cage and display of composting techniques, woodland walk, scented garden, 2 arboretums, annual Pictorial Meadows, Pleached Hornbeam Walkway and extensive range of ornamental trees and shrubs. Guided tour of the gardens by the horticultural team at Newton Rigg, incl the organic garden, ornamental garden, the aboretum and herbaceous borders. Expert staff available for information on courses in horticulture, garden design and floristry as well as an extensive range of land based subjects.

The Old Vicarage & Fell Cottage

42 NEW THE OLD VICARAGE AND FELL COTTAGE

Field Broughton, Grange-Over-Sands LA11 6HW. Louise Shrapnel & Malcolm Slater. *1½ m N of Cartmel. In the centre of Field Broughton village, next to the Parish Rooms. Parking on the village 'green' near to the church, 5min walk to the gardens.* Home-made teas. **Adm £4, chd free. Sun 3 Aug (11-5).**

Small walled cottage garden in the centre of the village. On multiple levels, planted for summer colour. Fish pond, vegetable area and greenhouse. Sunny and sheltered seating areas. Combined with part of the garden of a gentleman's residence, planted with a variety of interesting trees and shrubs.

43 ORCHARD COTTAGE

Hutton Lane, Levens, Kendal LA8 8PB. Shirley & Chris Band, 015395 61005, chrisband67@gmail.com. *6m S of Kendal. Turn N off A590 or A6 signed Levens. From Xrds by Methodist Church, 300 metres down Hutton Lane. Park near this Xrds. Garden access via 'The Orchard'.* Light refreshments at Levens Village Institute. **Adm £3.50, chd free. Sun 22 June (1-5). Visitors also welcome by appt Mar to Oct groups up to 50.**

¾ acre sloping garden in old orchard. Plantsperson's paradise with winding paths, diverse habitats, secret vistas, hidden places. All yr round interest and colour. Collections of ferns (100+), hellebores (70+), grasses, cottage plants, geraniums. Auricula theatres, 'imaginary' stream, bog garden. Trees support clematis, roses and honeysuckle. Wildlife friendly. Featured in Amateur Gardening and Lancashire Magazine.

44 ORCHARD HOUSE

Main Street, St. Bees CA27 0AA. Dr Juliet Rhodes. *From railway stn approx 500yds uphill (towards Egremont). Park at station, limited on street parking. From Main St, wooden gates to gravel drive.* Home-made teas. **Adm £3, chd free. Sun 6 July (10.30-5).**

Surprisingly generous secluded cottage style garden behind Georgian house on village main street sheltered from coastal winds by tall trees. Designed and developed by owner since 2005 its varied planting is enhanced by local red sandstone in walls and paving. Features incl a well, woodland area, greenhouse, vegetable plot, espaliered fruit trees, gravel garden, wild flower area, bees and hens.

45 8 OXENHOLME ROAD

Kendal LA9 7NJ. Mr & Mrs John & Frances Davenport, 01539 720934, frandav8@btinternet.com. *SE Kendal. From A65 (Burton Rd, Kendal/Kirkby Lonsdale) take B6254 (Oxenholme Rd). No.8 is 1st house on L beyond red post box.* Teas. **Adm £3.50, chd free. Sun 20 July (10-5). Visitors also welcome by appt May to Oct.**

Artist and potters garden of approx ½ acre of mixed planting designed for year-round interest, incl two small ponds. The garden runs all round the house with a gravel garden at the front, as well as a number of woodland plant areas.

46 PARK HOUSE

Barbon, Kirkby Lonsdale LA6 2LG. Mr & Mrs P Pattison, 015242 76346, philip@ppattison.co.uk. *2½ m N of Kirkby Lonsdale. Off the A683 Kirkby Lonsdale to Sedburgh rd. Follow signs into Barbon village.* Cream teas. **Adm £5, chd free. Sat 28 June (10.30-4.30); Sun 29 June (11-4). Visitors also welcome by appt May to Sept groups of 10+.**

Romantic Manor house. Extensive vistas. Formal tranquil pond encased in yew hedging. Meadow with meandering pathways, water garden filled with bulbs and ferns. Formal lawn gravel pathways, cottage borders with hues of soft pinks and purples. Shady border, kitchen garden. An evolving garden to follow.

47 PEAR TREE COTTAGE

Dalton, Burton-in-Kendal LA6 1NN. Linda & Alec Greening, 01524 781624, linda.greening@virgin.net, www.peartreecottagecumbria.co.uk. *5m from J35 & J36 of M6. From northern end of Burton-in-Kendal (A6070) turn E into Vicarage Lane & continue approx 1m.* **Adm £3.50, chd free. Sun 29 June (11-4.30). Also open Summerdale House. Visitors also welcome by appt June to July groups of 15+.**

⅓ -acre cottage garden in a delightful rural setting. A peaceful and relaxing garden, harmonising with its environment and incorporating many different planting areas, from packed herbaceous borders and rambling roses, to wildlife pond, bog garden and gravel garden. A plantsperson's delight, including over 200 different ferns, and many other rare and unusual plants. Featured on Alan Titchmarsh's 'Love Your Garden' (ITV).

48 RANNERDALE COTTAGE

Buttermere CA13 9UY. The McElney Family. *8m S of Cockermouth. 10m W of Keswick. B5289 on Crummock Water, in the Buttermere Valley.* Home-made teas. **Adm £3.50, chd free. Sat 28, Sun 29 June (12-5).**

½ -acre garden with beck and woodland walk overlooking Crummock Water with splendid mountain views. Herbaceous, shrubs, roses, perennial geraniums, tree peonies, pond with fish. The house and garden were badly damaged during flash flooding in 2012.

49 ◆ RYDAL HALL

Ambleside LA22 9LX. Diocese of Carlisle, 01539 432050, www.rydalhall.org. *2m N of Ambleside. E from A591 at Rydal signed Rydal Hall.* Light refreshments. **Adm by donation. For NGS: Sun 23 Mar, Thurs 12, 26 June (10-5). For other opening times and information, please phone or see garden website.**

Formal Italianate gardens designed by Thomas Mawson in 1911 set in 34 acres. The gardens have recently been restored over a 2yr period returning to their former glory. Informal woodland garden, leading to C17 viewing station/summerhouse, fine herbaceous planting, community vegetable garden, orchard and apiary. Opening for Wordsworth's Daffodil Legacy - 23rd March.

50 ◆ SIZERGH CASTLE

nr Kendal LA8 8AE. National Trust, 015395 69811, www.nationaltrust.org.uk. *3m S of Kendal. Approach rd leaves A590 close to & S of A590/A591 interchange.* Light refreshments. **Adm £5.20, chd £2.60. For NGS: Sat 19 July (11-5). For other opening times and information, please phone or see garden website.**

⅔ -acre limestone rock garden, largest owned by National Trust; collection of Japanese maples, dwarf conifers, hardy ferns; hot wall border with fruiting trees. Wild flower areas, herbaceous borders, 'Dutch' garden. Terraced garden and lake; kitchen garden; fruit orchard with spring bulbs. National Collection of *Asplenium scolopendrium, Cystopteris, Dryopteris, Osmunda*.

NCH

51 SUMMERDALE HOUSE

Nook, nr Lupton LA6 1PE. David & Gail Sheals, 015395 67210, sheals@btinternet.com, www.summerdalegardenplants.co.uk. *7m S of Kendal, 5m W of Kirkby Lonsdale. From J36 M6 take A65 towards Kirkby Lonsdale, at Nook take R turn Farleton.* Home-made bread and soup (Feb, March Sun only), Home-made teas (Sun only). **Adm £4, chd free. Suns 16 Feb; 2 Mar; Every Fri 7 Mar to 29 Aug; Suns 4 May; 29 June; 24 Aug (11-4.30), Sun 15 Feb 2015. Also open on 29 June Pear Tree Cottage. Visitors also welcome by appt Feb to Aug, groups of 12+.**

1½ -acre part-walled country garden set around C18 former vicarage. Several defined areas have been created by hedges, each with its own theme and linked by intricate cobbled pathways. Beautiful setting with fine views across to Farleton Fell. Traditional herbaceous borders, ponds, woodland and meadow planting provide year round interest. Large collections of auricula, primulas and snowdrops. Adjoining specialist nursery growing a wide range of interesting and unusual herbaceous perennials. Home made jams and chutneys for sale.

52 SUNNYSIDE

Woodhouse Lane, Heversham, Milnthorpe LA7 7EW. Bill & Anita Gott, 015395 63249, willgottatsunnyside@hotmail.co.uk. *1½ m N of Milnthorpe. From A6 turn into Heversham, then R at church signed Crooklands in ½ m turn L down lane.* Home-made teas. **Adm £3.50, chd free. Sat 30, Sun 31 Aug (1-5). Visitors also welcome by appt June to July, groups of 10-25. Refreshments by arrangement.**

½ -acre country cottage garden with a well at the bottom, 3 greenhouses, pond, mixed borders and a stunning display of prize winning dahlias. Large immaculate vegetable garden. Orchard with free range hens and usually we have chicks. Area to attract bees and butterflies. Featured in Lake District Life & Lancashire Life Magazine.

53 ◆ SWARTHMOOR HALL

Ulverston LA12 0JQ. Jane Pearson, 01229 583204, www.swarthmoorhall.co.uk. *1½ m SW of Ulverston. A590 to Ulverston. Turn off to Ulverston railway station. Brown tourist signs to hall, R into Urswick Rd, then R into Swarthmoor Hall Lane.* **Adm by donation. For NGS: Open Mon 24 Feb to Sun 16 March (10.30-3.30). For other opening times and information, please phone or see garden website.**

Wild purple crocus meadow in late February early March depending on weather, earlier if mild winter later if cold and frosty. Also, good displays of snowdrops, daffodils and tulips.

> Walks on the wild side around a mere and woodlands. Many birds can be seen at various feeding stations . . .

54 NEW TENTER END BARN

Docker, Kendal LA8 0DB. Mrs Hazel Terry, 01539 824447, hnterry@btinternet.com. *3m N Kendal. From Kendal take the A685 Appleby rd. Then 2nd on R to Docker. At the junction bear L.* Home-made teas. **Adm £3.50, chd free. Sun 20 July (11-5). Visitors also welcome by appt June to Sept, for groups of 4+.**

3 acres of cultivated and natural areas, in a secretive rural setting. A patio garden, large lawns, herbaceous borders and a small vegetable patch. Walks on the wild side around a mere and woodlands. Many birds can be seen at various feeding stations, also waterfowl on the mere. All managed by one OAP. Rather uneven around the woodland paths. Could be difficult around mere in wet weather.

Lemon drizzle cake, Victoria sponge ... yummy!

55 ◆ TULLIE HOUSE

Castle Street, Carlisle CA3 8TP. Tullie House Museum and Art Gallery Trust, www.tulliehouse.co.uk. *City Centre. Signed as Museum on brown signs, see website for map.* **For opening times and information, please see garden website.**

Open all year this tranquil garden in city centre setting incl an area developed during 2012 to reflect a Roman peristyle garden with Roman influenced planting incl figs, vines, myrtle, acanthus, herbs. Delightful garden to front of Jacobean house with mature Arbutus unedo and Cornus kousa growing alongside Fatsia japonica variegata and Eucryphia glutinosa. The garden surrounds the Jacobean building of the museum which displays a fine collection of Pre-raphelite artworks and porcelain, well worth a visit as is the rest of the museum displaying Roman, Natural and Social History objects. Interactive and fun the museum has something for everyone.

56 WEST GARTH COTTAGE

Hayton, Brampton CA8 9HL. Debbie Jenkins, www.westgarth-cottage-gardens.co.uk. *5m E of Carlisle. M6 J 43 E A69 5m E of Carlisle, 3m W of Brampton. turn for Hayton. Park in central village, cottage 2 mins walk.* Home-made teas. **Adm £3.50, chd free.** **Sun 11 May (1-5).**

An Artist's garden. A canvas of colours and textures. An acre of hidden walled gardens to capture and delight the senses. Parterres, stream, sculptures, sundial garden, leading to a relaxing wild garden with beautiful plantings for every season, many tulips, fragrant old roses and white perennials. Garden studio/gift shop, cottage perennials. Featured in Cumbria Life. Access to most areas, level ground.

57 WESTVIEW

Fletcher Hill, Kirkby Stephen CA17 4QQ. Reg & Irene Metcalfe. *Kirkby Stephen town centre, T-lights opp Antiques & Collectables.* Refreshments at Winton Park. **Combined adm £5, chd free with Winton Park.** **Sun 13 July (11-5).**

Tucked away behind the town centre, this secret walled cottage garden is a little haven. The main garden is filled with perennials, shrubs and large collection of hostas, with small wildlife pond. The adjacent prairie-style nursery beds are at their best in July. Choose your own plants from the nursery beds and we will dig them up for you.

An Artist's garden. A canvas of colours and textures. An acre of hidden walled gardens to capture and delight the senses . . .

58 WINDY HALL

Crook Road, Windermere LA23 3JA. Diane & David Kinsman, 015394 46238, dhewitt.kinsman@gmail.com. *½ m S of Bowness-on-Windermere. On western end of B5284 (Crook Rd) up Linthwaite House Hotel driveway.* Home-made teas. **Adm £4.50, chd free.** **Suns 4 May; 1 June (10-5).** **Visitors also welcome by appt Apr to Oct, guided tours for group of 8+.**

2 people, 4-acres, 6ft rain and 30+ years. Fellside woodland with rhododendrons, camellias, magnolias, hydrangeas, bluebells and foxgloves. Pond, kitchen, 'privy' and 'best' gardens, Japanese influenced quarry garden. Waterfowl garden with stewartias and large gunneras, alpine area with very small gunneras. Moss path and wild flower meadow. Abundant wildlife with many native birds nesting in the garden. National Collections of *Aruncus* & *Filipendula*. Exotic waterfowl and pheasants. Black, multi-horned Hebridean sheep.

NCH

59 WINTON PARK

Appleby Road, Kirkby Stephen CA17 4PG. Mr Anthony Kilvington. *2m N of Kirkby Stephen. On A685 turn L signed Gt Musgrave/Warcop (B6259). After approx 1m turn L as signed.* Light refreshments. **Combined adm £5, chd free with Westview.** **Sun 13 July (11-5).**

3-acre country garden bordered by the banks of the R Eden with stunning views. Many fine conifers, acers and rhododendrons, herbaceous borders, hostas, ferns, grasses and several hundred roses. Four formal ponds plus rock pool. Featured in Lake District Life and Lancashire Life magazine. Partial wheelchair access.

60 WOODEND HOUSE

Woodend, Egremont CA22 2TA. Grainne & Richard Jakobson, 01946 813017, gmjakobson22@gmail.com. *2m S of Whitehaven. Take the A595 from Whitehaven towards Egremont. On leaving Bigrigg take 1st turn L. Go down hill, garden at bottom on R opp Woodend Farm.* Home-made teas. **Adm £3, chd free.** **Sun 20 July (11-5.30).** **Visitors also welcome by appt Apr to Sept, max no 25.**

Secluded garden in quiet location set against background of mature trees. Relaxed style of planting, colour themed with unusual plants. The garden, mainly on a slope, surrounds an attractive Georgian house with meandering gravel paths. A wildlife friendly garden incl small wildlife pond, summer wild flower meadow and mini native woodland and shady walk.

61 YEWBARROW HOUSE

Hampsfell Road, Grange-over-Sands LA11 6BE. Jonathan & Margaret Denby, 015395 32469, jonathan@bestlakesbreaks.co.uk, www.yewbarrowhouse.co.uk. *¼ m from town centre. Turn left from Hampsfell Rd onto a lane signposted 'Charney Wood/Yewbarrow Wood'.* Cream teas. **Adm £4, chd free.** **Suns 1 June; 6 July; 3 Aug; 7 Sept (11-4).** **Visitors also welcome by appt May to Oct.**

Mediterranean style garden on 4½ -acre elevated site with magnificent views over Morecambe Bay. The garden features a restored walled Victorian kitchen garden; Italianate terrace garden; exotic gravel garden; fern garden, Japanese Hot Spring pool. Dahlia trial beds, Orangery, Sculpture and Sensory gardens.

Boxwood House

Cumbria County Volunteers

County Organiser

Diane Hewitt, Windy Hall, Crook Road, Windermere LA23 3JA, 015394 46238, dhewitt.kinsman@gmail.com

County Treasurer

Derek Farman, Mill House, Winster, Windermere, Cumbria LA23 3NW, 015394 44893, derek@derejam.myzen.co.uk

Booklet Coordinator

Diane Hewitt, dhewitt.kinsman@gmail.com

Assistant County Organisers

Central (Publicity, Gardens & Special Interest) Carole Berryman, 1 Cragwood Cottages, Ecclerigg, Windermere LA23 1LQ, 01539 443649, carole.berryman@student.sac.ac.uk

North Alannah Rylands, Crookdake Farm, Aspatria, Wigton CA7 3SH, 016973 20413, alannah.rylands@me.com

East Alec & Linda Greening, Pear Tree Cottage, Dalton, Burton-in-Kendal, Carnforth LA6 1NN, 01524 781624, linda.greening@virgin.net

West Chris & Helen Steele, Hall Senna, Gosforth, Holmbrook CA19 1YB, 019467 25436, helen.steele5@btinternet.com

Publicity (Web) Tony Connor, 01524 781119, tonconnor@aol.com

Borders Liaison Sue Clapperton, 01387 381004, charlieclapperton@hotmail.com

DERBYSHIRE

YORKSHIRE
DERBYSHIRE
NOTTINGHAM-SHIRE
STAFFORDSHIRE
LEICESTERSHIRE
Oldham
Manchester
Stockport
Macclesfield
Stoke-on-Trent
Sheffield
Rotherham
Doncaster
Chesterfield
Derby
Nottingham
Mansfield
Burton upon Trent
Derwent Reservoir
East Midlands
0 10 20 kilometres
0 10 miles
© Global Mapping / XYZ Maps

Opening Dates

All entries subject to change. For latest information check www.ngs.org.uk

February

Saturday 22
7 Bluebell Arboretum and Nursery

March

Sunday 16
7 Bluebell Arboretum and Nursery

Saturday 22
16 Coxbench Hall

Sunday 30
7 Bluebell Arboretum and Nursery

April

Sunday 13
4 334 Belper Road
7 Bluebell Arboretum and Nursery
29 37 High Street, Repton

Friday 18
1 12 Ansell Road

Monday 21
9 The Burrows Gardens

Saturday 26
47 Old English Walled Garden, Elvaston Castle Country Park

Sunday 27
7 Bluebell Arboretum and Nursery
66 35 Wyver Lane

May

Friday 2
53 Renishaw Hall & Gardens

Sunday 4
16 Coxbench Hall

Monday 5
1 12 Ansell Road
9 The Burrows Gardens
56 Tilford House

Sunday 11
7 Bluebell Arboretum and Nursery

Wednesday 14
64 Windward

Sunday 18
2 Askew Cottage
13 10 Chestnut Way
24 Fir Croft
49 The Paddock
64 Windward

Wednesday 21
4 334 Belper Road

Saturday 24
21 Dove Cottage

Sunday 25
7 Bluebell Arboretum and Nursery
21 Dove Cottage
25 Gamesley Fold Cottage
30 Highfield House
43 Meynell Langley Trials Garden

Monday 26
1 12 Ansell Road
9 The Burrows Gardens
36 The Leylands
57 Tissington Hall

Saturday 31
4 334 Belper Road
42 Melbourne Hall Gardens

June

Sunday 1
24 Fir Croft
42 Melbourne Hall Gardens
59 Westgate

Enjoy a lovely cream tea at 12 Ansell Road . . .

Festival Weekend

Saturday 7
33 The Holly Tree

Sunday 8
1 12 Ansell Road
7 Bluebell Arboretum and Nursery
13 10 Chestnut Way
25 Gamesley Fold Cottage
60 Wharfedale

Saturday 14
46 9 Newfield Crescent
54 Rosebank

Sunday 15
6 NEW 53 Birchover Way
12 Cherry Hill
24 Fir Croft
44 Moorfields
46 9 Newfield Crescent
66 35 Wyver Lane

Monday 16
9 The Burrows Gardens

Saturday 21
17 Craigside
34 Holme Grange
48 Owl End

Sunday 22
7 Bluebell Arboretum and Nursery
14 Clovermead
17 Craigside
28 High Roost
43 Meynell Langley Trials Garden
48 Owl End
63 26 Windmill Rise

Monday 23
17 Craigside

Friday 27
32 The Hollies (Evening)

Saturday 28
8 Brick Kiln Farm
23 NEW Elmton Gardens
59 Westgate

Sunday 29
21 Dove Cottage
23 NEW Elmton Gardens
30 Highfield House
37 The Lilies
50 Park Hall
60 Wharfedale

July

Saturday 5
52 Rectory House

Sunday 6
13 10 Chestnut Way
29 37 High Street, Repton
39 Locko Park
58 13 Westfield Road

Wednesday 9
64 Windward

Friday 11
53 Renishaw Hall & Gardens

Saturday 12
34 Holme Grange
41 2 Manvers Street
45 New Mills School Business & Enterprise College

Sunday 13
7 Bluebell Arboretum and Nursery
27 Hardwick Estate
41 2 Manvers Street
45 New Mills School Business & Enterprise College
64 Windward

Monday 14
9 The Burrows Gardens

Wednesday 16
56 Tilford House

Saturday 19
11 Calke Abbey

Sunday 20
15 The Cottage
19 8 Curzon Lane
43 Meynell Langley Trials Garden
60 Wharfedale

Saturday 26
3 Barlborough Gardens
63 26 Windmill Rise

Sunday 27
3 Barlborough Gardens
7 Bluebell Arboretum and Nursery
14 Clovermead
19 8 Curzon Lane
63 26 Windmill Rise

You are always welcome at an NGS garden!

August

Sunday 3
10 Byways
15 The Cottage
40 9 Main Street

Wednesday 6
1 12 Ansell Road

Sunday 10
7 Bluebell Arboretum and Nursery
13 10 Chestnut Way
16 Coxbench Hall
49 The Paddock
51 22 Pinfold Close
60 Wharfedale
65 Woodend Cottage

Monday 11
11 Calke Abbey

Wednesday 13
1 12 Ansell Road

Saturday 16
47 Old English Walled Garden, Elvaston Castle Country Park

Sunday 17
15 The Cottage
55 Thornbridge Hall

Sunday 24
7 Bluebell Arboretum and Nursery
43 Meynell Langley Trials Garden
58 13 Westfield Road
60 Wharfedale

Monday 25
9 The Burrows Gardens
57 Tissington Hall

Sunday 31
37 The Lilies

September

Sunday 7
38 Littleover Lane Allotments

Sunday 14
7 Bluebell Arboretum and Nursery

Monday 15
9 The Burrows Gardens

Sunday 21
43 Meynell Langley Trials Garden

Sunday 28
7 Bluebell Arboretum and Nursery

October

Sunday 12
2 Askew Cottage
7 Bluebell Arboretum and Nursery
43 Meynell Langley Trials Garden

Wednesday 22
7 Bluebell Arboretum and Nursery

November

Saturday 15
7 Bluebell Arboretum and Nursery

Visit a garden on National Gardens Weekend 7 & 8 June

Gardens open to the public

7 Bluebell Arboretum and Nursery
9 The Burrows Gardens
11 Calke Abbey
27 Hardwick Estate
35 Lea Gardens
42 Melbourne Hall Gardens
43 Meynell Langley Trials Garden
47 Old English Walled Garden, Elvaston Castle Country Park
53 Renishaw Hall & Gardens
57 Tissington Hall

In April see our hellebores, cowslips and try our home-made soups . . . .

By appointment only

5 Birchfield
18 Cuckoostone Cottage
20 Dam Stead
22 The Dower House
26 Green Meadows
31 Hillside
61 24 Wheeldon Avenue
62 26 Wheeldon Avenue

Also open by appointment

1 12 Ansell Road
2 Askew Cottage
4 334 Belper Road
8 Brick Kiln Farm
10 Byways
12 Cherry Hill
13 10 Chestnut Way
14 Clovermead
15 The Cottage
17 Craigside
19 8 Curzon Lane
21 Dove Cottage
25 Gamesley Fold Cottage
28 High Roost
30 Highfield House
34 Holme Grange
36 The Leylands
38 Littleover Lane Allotments
40 9 Main Street
41 2 Manvers Street
44 Moorfields
46 9 Newfield Crescent
49 The Paddock
50 Park Hall
54 Rosebank
56 Tilford House
58 13 Westfield Road
59 Westgate
60 Wharfedale
64 Windward
65 Woodend Cottage
66 35 Wyver Lane

The Gardens

1 12 ANSELL ROAD

Ecclesall, Sheffield S11 7PE. Dave Darwent, 01142 665881, dave@poptasticdave.co.uk, www.poptasticdave.co.uk/_/Horticulture.html. *Approx 3m SW of City Centre. Travel to Ringinglow Rd (88 bus), then Edale Rd (opp Ecclesall C of E Primary School). 3rd R - Ansell Rd. No 12 on L ³/₄ way down, solar panel on roof.* Cream teas, gluten-free options and savoury items available. **Adm £2.50, chd free. Fri 18 Apr, Mon 5, Mon 26 May (11-5); Sun 8 June (11-8); Wed 6, Wed 13 Aug (3-8.30). Visitors also welcome by appt Apr to Aug, max group 25.**
Established 1930s, the garden contains many original plants maintained in the original style. Traditional rustic pergola and dwarf-wall greenhouse. Owner (grandson of first owner) aims to keep the garden as a living example of how inter-war gardens were cultivated to provide decoration and produce. More detail online. Featured on BBC 1 The One Show and BBC Radio Sheffiled. Also featured in Sheffield Telegraph, Sheffield Star, Dronfield Eye, Amateur Gardening and The Telegraph (Gardening supplement).

2 ASKEW COTTAGE

23 Milton Road, Repton, Derby DE65 6FZ. Louise Hardwick, 01283 701608, louise.hardwick@hotmail.co.uk. *6m S of Derby. From A38/A50 junction S of Derby. Follow signs to Willington then Repton on B5008. In Repton turn 1st L then bear sharp R into Milton Rd.* Light refreshments. **Adm £3, chd free. Sun 18 May, Sun 12 Oct (2-6). Visitors also welcome by appt May to Oct, adm £6 incl refreshments.**
The rear garden comprises several different areas, all connected with flowing curved paths. Formal hedges give structure and features in the

garden incl a box-edged herb garden, a small wildlife pool and bog garden, a kitchen garden with raised beds, a circle of meadow grass set within a 'cloud' box hedge, trained apple trees and plenty of interesting shrubs and perennials. Featured in The Derbyshire Magazine.

GROUP OPENING

3 BARLBOROUGH GARDENS

Barlborough, Chesterfield S43 4ER, 07956 203184, christine.r.sanderson@uwclub.net. *7m NE of Chesterfield. Off A619 midway between Chesterfield & Worksop. ½ m E M1 J30. Follow signs for Barlborough then NGS signs. Parking available in village centre. Map detailing all gardens issued with admission ticket. Coach parking available at the Royal Oak PH in village centre.* Light refreshments at Church Institute. **Combined adm £5, chd free. Sat 26, Sun 27 July (1-6).**

CLARENDON
Neil & Lorraine Jones

GOOSE COTTAGE
Mick & Barbara Housley

THE HOLLIES
Vernon Sanderson
(See separate entry)

LINDWAY
Thomas & Margaret Pettinger

ROSE COTTAGE
Kathy & Steve Thomson

NEW **WOODSIDE HOUSE**
Tricia & Adrian Murray-Leslie

Barlborough is an attractive historic village and a range of interesting buildings can be seen all around the village centre. The village is situated close to Renishaw Hall for possible combined visit. Opening coincides with the village well dressing and St James's Church Flower Festival. Partial wheelchair access at Rose Cottage and The Hollies. Access to rear of Clarendon via stone slabs.

4 334 BELPER ROAD

Stanley Common DE7 6FY. Gill & Colin Hancock, 01159 301061, www.hamescovert.com. *7m N of Derby. 3m W of Ilkeston. On A609, ¾ m from Rose & Crown Xrds (A608). Please park in field up farm drive or Working Men's Club rear car park if wet.* Home-made teas. **Adm £3, chd free. Sun 13 Apr (12-5); Wed 21 May (2-8); Sat 31 May (12-5). Visitors also welcome by appt Apr to July, adm £6 incl tea/coffee/cake and our personal attention.**

334 Belper Road

Relax in our constantly evolving country garden with informal planting and features with plenty of seating to enjoy our highly recommended home-made cakes. Take a stroll across the field into the young 10-acre wood with wild flower glades to a ½ -acre lake. In April see our hellebores, cowslips and try our home-made soups. Paths round wood and lake not suitable for wheelchairs.

5 BIRCHFIELD

Dukes Drive, Ashford in the Water, Bakewell DE45 1QQ. Brian Parker, 01629 813800. *2m NW of Bakewell. On A6 to Buxton between New Bridge & Sheepwash Bridge.* **Adm £3, chd free (share to Thornhill Memorial Trust). Visitors welcome by appt all yr, adm £3 April - Sept, £2 Oct - March.**

Beautifully situated ¾ -acre part terraced garden with pond and a 1¼ -acre arboretum and wild flower meadow. An extremely varied selection of trees, shrubs, climbers, perennials, bulbs, grasses and bamboos, all designed to give yr-round colour. Featured in Garden News and Peak Advertiser.

6 NEW 53 BIRCHOVER WAY

Allestree, Derby DE22 2QG. Mrs Jannice Grundy. *3m N of Derby city centre from A38 N bound take slip rd to Uni, turn L at T-lights, 1st R past Uni. Parking permitted on yellow lines on a Sunday.* Light refreshments. **Adm £3, chd free. Sun 15 June (1-4).**

A stunning garden, with many types of plants, flowers, fruit trees and more. The variety of fruit is incredible, incl cooking and eating apples, plums, tomato, cucumber, pears and cherries, a delight to see all yr round. There is a beautiful pond with water plants and lilies and a green house where a loving gardener raises her plants from seedlings.

7 ◆ BLUEBELL ARBORETUM AND NURSERY

Annwell Lane, Smisby, Ashby de la Zouch LE65 2TA. Robert & Suzette Vernon, 01530 413700, www.bluebellnursery.com. *1m NW of Ashby-de-la-Zouch. Arboretum is clearly signed in Annwell Lane, 1/4 m S, through village of Smisby off B5006, between Ticknall & Ashby-de-la-Zouch. Free parking.* **Adm £3, chd free. For NGS: Sat 22 Feb, Suns 16, 30 Mar; Suns 13, 27 Apr; Suns 11, 25 May; Suns 8, 22 June; Suns 13, 27 July; Suns 10, 24 Aug; Suns 14, 28 Sept; Sun 12, Wed 22 Oct, Sat 15 Nov (10.30-4). For other opening times and information, please phone or see garden website.**

Beautiful 9-acre woodland garden with a large collection of rare trees and shrubs. Interest throughout the yr with spring flowers, cool leafy areas in summer and sensational autumn colour. Many information posters describing the more obscure plants. Bring wellingtons in wet weather. Adjacent specialist tree and shrub nursery. Please be aware this is not a wood full of bluebells, despite the name. The woodland garden is fully labelled and the staff can answer questions or talk at length about any of the trees or shrubs on display. Please wear sturdy, waterproof footwear during wet weather! Full wheelchair access in dry, warm weather however grass paths in garden can become wet and inaccessible in snow or after rain.

Special delight for children is a secret tree den . . .

8 BRICK KILN FARM

Hulland Ward, Ashbourne DE6 3EJ. Mrs Jan Hutchinson, 01335 370440, robert.hutchinson123@btinternet.com. *4m E of Ashbourne (A517). 1m S of Carsington Water. From Hulland Ward take Dog Lane past church 2nd L. 100yds on R. From Ashbourne A517 Bradley Corner turn L follow sign for Carsington Water 1m on L.* **Adm £3.50, chd free (share to Great Dane Adoption Society). Sat 28 June (2-5). Visitors also welcome by appt May to Aug.**

A small country garden which wraps around an old red brick farmhouse accessed through a courtyard with original well. Irregularly shaped lawn bounded by wide herbaceous borders leading to duck pond and pet's memorial garden. 'A description that did not disappoint' - Ashbourne Telegraph. Can be viewed online on Peak District TV. Level garden, some uneven flagstones, gravel drive.

9 ◆ THE BURROWS GARDENS

Burrows Lane, Brailsford DE6 3BU. Mr B C Dalton, 01335 360745, www.burrowsgardens.com. *5m SE of Ashbourne; 5m NW of Derby. Look for yellow AA signs. A52 from Derby: turn L opp sign for Wild Park Leisure 1m before village of Brailsford. 1/4 m.* Home-made teas. **Adm £4, chd free. For NGS: Mon 21 Apr; Mons 5, 26 May; Mons 16 June, 14 July; Mon 25 Aug; Mon 15 Sept (10.30-4.30). For other opening times and information, please phone or see garden website.**

5 acres of stunning garden set in beautiful countryside where immaculate lawns show off exotic rare plants and trees, mixing with old favourites in this outstanding garden. A huge variety of styles from temple to Cornish, Italian and English, gloriously designed and displayed. This is a must-see garden. Open every Tues, Fri, and Sun from April - September incl. Look out for Special events such as Shakespeare productions and Wine tasting. Most of garden can be accessed by wheelchair users.

10 BYWAYS

7A Brookfield Avenue, Brookside, Chesterfield S40 3NX. Terry & Eileen Kelly, 01246 566376, telkel1@aol.com. *1 1/2 m W of Chesterfield. Follow A619 from Chesterfield towards Baslow. Brookfield Av is 2nd R after Brookfield Sch. Please park on Chatsworth Rd (A619).* Home-made teas. **Adm £2.50, chd free (share to Ashgate Hospice). Sun 3 Aug (12.30-5.30). Visitors also welcome by appt 21 July to 24 August.**

Winners of the best back garden over 80sq m, Chesterfield in Bloom 2012. Well established perennial borders incl helenium, monardas, phlox, penstenom, grasses, acers (30+). Rock and alpine gardens and planters containing hostas, ferns, roses and fuchsias. Enjoy the view from any of the 5 seating areas around the garden. Featured in Derbyshire Reflections and Chesterfield Twist.

11 ◆ CALKE ABBEY

Ticknall DE73 7LE. National Trust, 01332 865587, www.nationaltrust.org.uk. *10m S of Derby. On A514 at Ticknall between Swadlincote & Melbourne.* **Adm £5, chd £2.50. For NGS: Sat 19 July, Mon 11 Aug (10-5). For other opening times and information, please phone or see garden website.**

Late C18 walled gardens gradually repaired over the last 25yrs. Flower garden with summer bedding, herbaceous borders and the unique auricula theatre. Georgian orangery, impressive collection of glasshouses and garden buildings. Icehouse and recently repaired grotto. Vegetable garden growing heirloom varieties of fruit and vegetables, often on sale to visitors. Electric buggy available for those with mobility problems.

12 CHERRY HILL

The Nook, Eyam, Derbyshire S32 5QP. June Elizabeth Skinner, 01433 631036, juneliza.s@btinternet.com, www.peakdistrictart.com. *6m NW of Chatsworth in Peak National Park. Off A623. In Eyam past church on R take 1st R up Hawkhill Rd. Car Park opp museum. 200yds up hill walk on to The Nook, entrance drive on R.* Home-made teas. **Adm £3.50, chd free. Sun 15 June (1-5). Visitors also welcome by appt Apr to July.**

One-acre naturally planted artists' garden. The S-facing aspect is a delightful blend of herbaceous borders, secret areas, and a geranium carpeted orchard. Sculptures hidden amongst the foliage reflect the quirky and different style, which the present owner has brought to this garden. Artist's Studio open with a display of ceramics for sale. Garden sculptures made by the owner to be found around the garden. Special delight for children is a secret tree den. Wonderful cakes baked by my husband!

13 10 CHESTNUT WAY

Repton DE65 6FQ. Robert & Pauline Little, 01283 702267, rlittleq@gmail.com, www.littlegarden.org.uk. *6m S of Derby. From A38, S of Derby, follow signs to Willington, then Repton. In Repton turn R at r'about. Chestnut Way is ¼ m up hill, on L.* Home-made teas. **Adm £3, chd free. Sun 18 May, Sun 8 June, Sun 6 July, Sun 10 Aug (1-5.30). Combined with Woodend Cottage & 22 Pinfold Close. Combined adm £6, (Sun 10 Aug only). Visitors also welcome by appt Apr to Sept. Adm £6 incl home-made teas and guided tour. Groups 10+.**

Lose yourself in an acre of sweeping mixed borders, spring bulbs, mature trees to a stunning butterfly bed, young arboretum, established prairie and annual meadow. Meet a pair of passionate, practical, compost loving gardeners who gently manage this plantsman's garden. Designed and maintained by the owners. Expect a colourful display throughout the year. Plenty of seats, conservatory if wet. Excellent plant stall. Special interest in viticella clematis and organic vegetables. All in all a happy garden. Featured in Garden News, Country Images and Burton Mail. Level garden, good solid paths to main areas. Some grass/bark paths.

14 CLOVERMEAD

Commonpiece Lane, Findern DE65 6AF. David & Rosemary Noblet, 01283 702237, daverose1221@btinternet.com. *4m S of Derby. From Findern village green, turn R at church into Lower Green, R turn into Commonpiece Lane, approx 500yds on R.* Home-made teas. **Adm £3, chd free. Sun 22 June, Sun 27 July (1-5.30). Visitors also welcome by appt May to Aug.**

Cottage garden set in approx 1-acre. Garden rooms packed full of perennial flowers. Honeysuckle, roses, jasmine and sweet peas scent the air. Clematis ramble everywhere over 100 varieties. Pergolas and archways give height to the garden. Fishponds and bandstand with seating. Greenhouses, large vegetable plot, wildlife orchard. New long rose walk. Pathway to village nature park and canal. Featured in Derbyshire Life and on Radio Derby.

15 THE COTTAGE

25 Plant Lane, Old Sawley, Long Eaton NG10 3BJ. Ernie & Averil Carver, 01158 491960. *2m SW of Long Eaton. From town centre take B6540 to Old Sawley, R at Nags Head PH into Wilne Rd 400yds take R turn Plant Lane at The Railway Inn. Gdn 200yds on R.* Light refreshments. **Adm £3, chd free (share to Canaan Trust and Diabetic UK). Sun 20 July, Sun 3, Sun 17 Aug (12-5). Visitors also welcome by appt July to Aug, adm £5 incl light refreshments.**

Cottage garden full of colour steeped in herbaceous borders. Annual plants raised from the greenhouse. Number of surprising features. Summerhouse in a walled sheltered garden, providing a charming environment. After a short break for tea and home-made cakes why not step back in time to a bygone era and visit our Victorian nursery and the maid's room (extra cost). Victorian attic rooms open, additional adm £1.50. Featured in The Derbyshire magazine and The Derby Evening Telegraph. Some gravelled areas.

16 COXBENCH HALL

Alfreton Road, Coxbench, Derby DE21 5BB. Mr Brian Ballin. *4m N of Derby close to A38. After passing through Little Eaton, turn L onto Alfreton Rd. After 1m Coxbench Hall is on L next to Fox & Hounds PH between Little Eaton & Holbrook.* Home-made teas. **Adm £3, chd free. Sat 22 Mar, Sun 4 May, Sun 10 Aug (2.30-4.30).**

Formerly the ancestral home of the Meynell family, the gardens reflect the Georgian house standing in 4½ -acres of grounds most of which is accessible and wheelchair friendly. The garden has 2 fishponds connected by a stream, a sensory garden for the sight impaired, a short woodland walk through shrubbery, a vegetable plot and seasonal displays in the mainly lawned areas. As a Residential Home for the Elderly, our Gardens are developed to inspire our residents from a number of sensory perspectives - different colours, textures and fragrances of plants, growing vegetables next to the C18 potting shed. A recently discovered C18 well is to be uncovered. Wheelchair access not available to woodland area.

17 CRAIGSIDE

Reservoir Road, Whaley Bridge SK23 7BW. Jane & Gerard Lennox, 01663 732381, jane@lennoxonline.net. *11m SE of Stockport. 11m NNW of Buxton. Turn off A6 onto A5004 to Whaley Bridge. Turn at train station 1st L under railway bridge onto Reservoir Rd. Park on roadside or in village.* Home-made teas. **Adm £3.50, chd free. Sat 21, Sun 22, Mon 23 June (1-5). Visitors also welcome by appt May to Sept.**

1 acre garden rising steeply from the Reservoir giving magnificent views across Todbrook reservoir into Peak District. Gravel paths, stone steps with stopping places. Many mature trees incl 450yr old oak. Spring bulbs, summer fuchsias, herbaceous borders, alpine bed, steep mature rockery many heucheras and hydrangeas. Herbs, vegetables and fruit trees.

18 CUCKOOSTONE COTTAGE

Chesterfield Road, Matlock Moor, Matlock DE4 5LZ. Barrie & Pauline Wild, 07960 708415, paulinewild@sky.com. *2½ m N of Matlock on A632. Past Matlock Golf Course look for Cuckoostone Lane on L. Turn here & follow for ¼ m. 1st cottage on bend.* Light refreshments. **Adm £4, chd free. Visitors and groups welcome by appt May to Sept.**

Situated on a sloping, SW-facing rural hillside at 850ft, this ½ -acre is a plantsman's garden. Colour themed borders, several ponds, bog garden and conservatory. Large collection of unusual trees, shrubs and perennials make this a yr-round garden but best from late May to late summer. In total over 1200 different species of plants, shrubs, trees.

Lindway, Barlborough Gardens

19 8 CURZON LANE

Alvaston, Derby DE24 8QS. Mrs Marian Gray, 01332 601596, maz@curzongarden.com, www.curzongarden.com. *2m SE of Derby city centre. From city centre take A6 (London Rd) towards Alvaston. Curzon Lane on L, approx ½ m before Alvaston shops.* **Adm £2.50, chd free. Sun 20, Sun 27 July (1-6). Visitors also welcome by appt July.**
Mature garden with lawns, borders packed full with perennials, shrubs and small trees, tropical planting. Ornamental and wildlife ponds, greenhouse, gravel area, large patio with container planting. Also recently added extra mixed borders and potager garden. Featured as Garden of the Week in Garden News magazine.

20 DAM STEAD

3 Crowhole, Barlow, Dronfield S18 7TJ. Derek & Barbara Saveall, 01142 890802, barbarasaveall@hotmail.co.uk. *Chesterfield B6051 to Barlow. Tickled Trout PH on L. Springfield Rd on L then R on unnamed rd. Last cottage on R.* Light refreshments. **Adm £2.50, chd free. Visitors welcome by appt Apr to Sept.**
Approx 1 acre with stream, weir, fragrant garden, rose tunnel, orchard garden and dam with an island. Long woodland path, alpine troughs, rockeries and mixed planting. A natural wildlife garden-large summerhouse with seating inside and out. 3 village well-dressings and carnival over one week mid-August.

21 DOVE COTTAGE

off Watery Lane, Clifton, Ashbourne DE6 2JQ. Stephen & Anne Liverman, 01335 343545, astrantiamajor@hotmail.co.uk. *1½ m SW of Ashbourne. Enter Clifton village. Turn R at Xrds by church. After 100yds turn L, Dove Cottage 1st house on L. Always well signed on open days.* Light refreshments. **Adm £4, chd free (share to British Heart Foundation). Sat 24, Sun 25 May, Sun 29 June (11-4). Visitors also welcome by appt Apr to July.**
Much admired, long standing NGS ¾ -acre cottage garden by the R Dove, with collections of new and traditional hardy plants and shrubs, notably Astrantias, alchemillas, alliums, geraniums, hostas, variegated and silver foliage plants. This plantsman's garden is noted for the number of separate areas, incl a ribbon border of purple flowering plants and foliage, woodland glade planted with daffodils and shade loving plants. Anne delivers a number of day courses for the Royal Horticultural Society in the garden, during the yr.

22 THE DOWER HOUSE

Church Square, Melbourne DE73 8JH. William & Griselda Kerr, 01332 864756, griseldakerr@btinternet.com. *6m S of Derby. 5m W of exit 23A M1. 4m N of exit 13 M42. In Church Square, turn R at blue sign giving church service times - just before you go past the church - gates are 50 yards ahead.* **Adm £3.50, chd free. Visitors welcome by appt, advance booking only, max 6 weeks in advance. Refreshments available for groups (min 10, max 25) on request at time of booking.**
Beautiful view of Melbourne Pool from balustraded terrace running length of 1831 house. Garden drops steeply by way of paths and steps to lawn with long herbaceous border best in June and late summer beds good in August and September. Rose tunnel, glade, orchard, area of woodland, hellebore bed lovely in early spring, peony bed, rockery, herb garden, other small lawns and vegetable garden. Featured on Radio Derby and Derbyshire Life. Wheelchair access to most of garden.

GROUP OPENING

23 NEW ELMTON GARDENS

Elmton, Worksop S80 4LS. *2m from Creswell, 3m from Clowne, 5m from J30, M1. From M1 take A616 to Newark. Follow approx 4m. Turn R at Elmton signpost. At junction turn R.* Cream teas in School Room next to the church. **Combined adm £4, chd free. Sat 28, Sun 29 June (12-5).**

NEW PEAR TREE COTTAGE
Geoff & Janet Cutts

NEW PINFOLD
Nikki Kirsop

NEW WILMOTS
Barbara Kirsop

Elmton is a lovely little village situated on a stretch of rare magnesian limestone in the middle of attractive farm land. There are about 40 houses, a PH, a church, art gallery and a village green. This weekend is our 'Well Dressing' weekend. There are 3 boards to see in different locations around the village. At Spring Cottage there is a small art gallery that you would be welcome to visit and in the church there will be an exhibition of local history devised by the History Group. Food and drink also available throughout the day at the Elm Tree PH. Received silver award, Villages in Bloom. Pinfold awarded the Frank Constable award and Gold Judges Award.

24 FIR CROFT

Froggatt Road, Calver S32 3ZD. Dr S B Furness, www.alpineplantcentre.co.uk. *4m N of Bakewell. At junction of B6001 with A625 (formerly B6054), adjacent to Power Garage.* **Adm by donation. Sun 18 May, Sun 1, Sun 15 June (2-5).**

Massive scree with many varieties. Plantsman's garden; rockeries; water garden and nursery; extensive collection (over 3000 varieties) of alpines; conifers; over 800 sempervivums, 500 saxifrages and 350 primulas. Tufa and scree beds.

25 GAMESLEY FOLD COTTAGE

Gamesley Fold, Glossop SK13 6JJ. Mrs G Carr, 01457 867856, www.gamesleyfold.co.uk. *2m W of Glossop. Off A626 Glossop - Marple Rd nr Charlesworth. Turn down lane directly opp St. Margaret's School, white cottage at bottom. Parking in adjacent field.* Home-made teas. **Adm £2.50, chd free. Sun 25 May, Sun 8 June (1-4). Visitors also welcome by appt May to July.**

Old-fashioned cottage garden. Spring garden with herbaceous borders, shrubs and rhododendrons, wild flowers and herbs in profusion to attract butterflies and wildlife. Good selection of herbs and cottage garden plants for sale. Featured in local press.

26 GREEN MEADOWS

Cross Lane, Monyash, Bakewell DE45 1JN. Mr & Mrs Mike Cullen, 01629 810234, culherbs@btinternet.com. *5m W of Bakewell. From centre Bakewell take B5055 to Monyash. At Xrds by village green go straight onto Tagg Lane. At 2nd bend turn R into Cross Lane.* Home-made teas. **Adm £3, chd free. Visitors welcome by appt June to Sept, max 12 visitors.**

Compact cottage garden surrounded by enclosures, in superb countryside with far reaching views of the Dales. Herbaceous borders, shrubs, wild flowers, lavender hedges and kit parterre in daily use filled with a profusion of herbs to attract butterflies and wildlife. Water features and limestone garden. Large greenhouse and raised beds. Featured in The Derbyshire magazine, Garden News, Amateur Gardening Weekly and Reflections Magazine.

27 ◆ HARDWICK ESTATE

Doe Lea, Chesterfield S44 5QJ. National Trust, 01246 858400, www.nationaltrust.org.uk. *8m SE of Chesterfield. S of A617. Signed from J29 M1.* **Adm £7, chd £3.50. For NGS: Sun 13 July (9-6). For other opening times and information, please phone or see garden website.**

The gardens are beautifully presented in a series of courtyards, where you can move from one garden 'room' to the next to explore the herb garden, orchards and colourful borders which are planted up each yr with many unusual tender perennials. Gardens are wheelchair accessible. An electric shuttle bus is provided from the Visitor Centre to the Hall for those who have difficulties walking.

28 HIGH ROOST

27 Storthmeadow Road, Simmondley, Glossop SK13 6UZ. Peter & Christina Harris, 01457 863888, peter-harris9@sky.com. *¾ m SW of Glossop. M67 take A57, R at Mottram (1st T-lights) through Broadbottom & Charlesworth. In Charlesworth turn R up Town Lane by side of Grey Mare PH, cont up High Lane, past Hare & Hounds, take 2nd L Storthmeadow Rd. From Glossop, A57 towards Manchester, L at 2nd mini r'about, up Simmondley Lane, R into Storthmeadow Rd. On rd parking nearby, please do not block drives.* Light refreshments. **Adm £2.50, chd free (share to Manchester Dogs Home). Sun 22 June (12-4). Visitors also welcome by appt June to July.**

Garden on terraced slopes, views over fields and hills. Winding paths, archways and steps explore different garden rooms packed with plants, designed to attract wildlife. Alpine bed, vegetable garden, water features, statuary, troughs and planters. A garden which needs exploring to discover its secrets tucked away in hidden corners. Craft Stall, childrens garden quiz and Lucky dip. Featured in Daily Mail Plus App.

29 37 HIGH STREET, REPTON

Repton DE65 6GD. David & Jan Roberts. *6m S of Derby. From A38, A50 junction S of Derby follow signs to Willington, then Repton. In Repton continue past island & shops. Garden on L.* Home-made teas. **Adm £3, chd free. Sun 13 Apr, Sun 6 July (2-5.30).**

Over 1 acre of gardens with bridge over Repton Brook which meanders through. Formal and wildlife ponds, mixed borders of herbaceous, shrubs and trees. Rhododendrons and woodland, grasses, ferns and bamboos. Vegetable garden and greenhouses, container planting for spring and summer colour and alpine troughs. A surprising garden for all seasons with interest for everyone. Brook flows through the garden. Partial access for wheelchairs.

A garden which needs exploring to discover its secrets . . .

30 HIGHFIELD HOUSE

Wingfield Road, Oakerthorpe, Alfreton DE55 7AP. Paul & Ruth Peat and Janet & Brian Costall, 01773 521342, highfieldhouseopengardens@hotmail.co.uk, www.highfieldhouse.weebly.com. *Rear of Alfreton Golf Club. A615 Alfreton-Matlock Rd.* Home-made teas. **Adm £3, chd free. Sun 25 May, Sun 29 June (11-5.30). Visitors also welcome by appt May to July.**

Lovely country garden of approx one acre, incorporating a shady garden, woodland, tree house, laburnum tunnel, orchard, parterre, herbaceous borders and productive vegetable garden. Walk to Derbyshire Wildlife Trust Nature Reserve to see the beautiful spotted Orchids. A lovely day out and you must try our AGA baked cakes and light lunches. Featured in Reflections, Derbyshire magazine and Gardeners Weekly. Some steps, slopes and gravel areas.

31 HILLSIDE

286 Handley Road, New Whittington, Chesterfield S43 2ET. Mr E J Lee, 01246 454960, eric.lee5@btinternet.com. *3m N of Chesterfield. Between B6056 & B0652 N of village. SatNav friendly.* **Adm £2.50, chd free. Visitors and groups welcome by appt.**

1/3 -acre sloping site. Herbaceous borders, rock garden, alpines, streams, pools, bog gardens, asiatic primula bed, and alpine house. Acers, bamboos, collection of approx 150 varieties of ferns, eucalypts, euphorbias, grasses, conifers, Himalayan bed. 1000+ plants permanently labelled. Yr-round interest.

32 THE HOLLIES

S43 4EH. Vernon Sanderson, 87 Clowne Road, Barlborough, Chesterfield, 07956 203184, christine.r.sanderson@uwclub.net. *7m NE of Chesterfield. Off A619 midway between Chesterfield & Worksop. 1/2 m E M1, J30. Follow signs for Barlborough then yellow NGS signs.* Wine and canapés will be served. **Evening Opening £3, chd free, Light refreshments, Fri 27 June (6-9).**

The Hollies maximises the unusual garden layout and includes a shade area, patio garden, cottage border and a fruit and vegetable plot. Tombola stall with home made goodies as prizes. Local singing quartet will be providing entertainment during opening. Partial wheelchair access.

33 THE HOLLY TREE

21 Hackney Road, Hackney, Matlock DE4 2PX. Carl Hodgkinson. *1/2 m NW of Matlock, off A6. Take A6 NW past bus stn & 1st R up Dimple Rd. At T-junction, turn R & immed L, for Farley & Hackney. Take 1st L onto Hackney Rd. Continue 3/4 m.* Home-made teas. **Adm £3, chd free. Sat 7 June (11-4.30).**

The garden is in excess of 1 1/2 acres and set on a steeply sloping S-facing site, sheltering behind a high retaining wall and incl a small arboretum, bog garden, herbaceous borders, pond, vegetables, fruits, apiary and chickens. Extensively terraced with many paths and steps and with spectacular views across the Derwent valley to Snitterton and Oker.

34 HOLME GRANGE

Holme Lane, Bakewell DE45 1GF. Mrs Shirley Stubbs, 01629 814728, shirleystubbs@hotmail.co.uk. *Close to centre of Bakewell. From Bakewell centre, take A619 towards Baslow, over river bridge, 1st L into Holme Lane. Follow lane which runs between meadows. Holme Grange is on R, bounded by stone wall. Parking, go past entrance & take track to R.* Home-made teas. **Adm £3.50, chd free. Sat 21 June, Sat 12 July (11-4). Visitors also welcome by appt May to July for groups 10+.**

Holme Grange has a garden of about an acre, and offers a range of mixed borders, large lawned area and woodland offering some unusual trees, shrubs and plants. Featured in Sheffield Weekend Telegraph.

35 ◆ LEA GARDENS

Lea, nr Matlock DE4 5GH. Mr & Mrs J Tye, 01629 534380, www.leagarden.co.uk. *5m SE of Matlock. Off A6 & A615.* **For opening times and information, please phone or see garden website.**

Rare collection of rhododendrons, azaleas, kalmias, alpines and conifers in delightful woodland setting. Gardens are sited on remains of medieval quarry and cover about 4 acres. Specialised plant nursery of rhododendrons and azaleas on site. Open daily 20 March to 31 July (9-5) Plant sales by appointment out of season. Visitors welcome throughout the yr. Tea shop on site. Gravel paths, steep slopes. Free access for wheelchair users.

36 THE LEYLANDS

Moorwood Lane, Owler Bar (Holmesfield), Nr Sheffield S17 3BS. Richard & Chris Hibberd, 01142 890833, hibberd3@btinternet.com. *2m W of Dronfield. Take B6054, (Sheffield ring rd/Owler Bar). Moorwood Lane is 1m from Owler Bar junction with A621 (Sheffield -Bakewell).* Home-made teas. **Adm £3, chd free (share to Water Aid). Mon 26 May (11.30-3). Visitors also welcome by appt May to July for groups 6+.**

Situated on the edge of the Peak District National Park. A 2-acre country garden on a sloping site, with family ties from 1947. The garden has been developed by the current owners over recent decades, as a means of accommodating the wide variety of plants, habitats and water systems. Paths winding through the plantings provide further interest. A wildlife and family friendly, Plantsman's garden. Children's trails and play equipment. Hard drive with loose gravel surface. Most of garden viewed from grass; mostly wheelchair accessible inclines.

Paths winding through the plantings provide further interest. A wildlife and family friendly garden . . .

37 THE LILIES

Griffe Grange Valley, Grangemill, Matlock DE4 4BW. Chris & Bridget Sheppard, www.thelilies.com. *4m N Cromford. On A5012 via Gellia Rd 4m N Cromford. 1st house on R after junction with B5023 to Middleton. From Grangemill 1st house on L after Stancliffe Quarry.* Home-made teas and light lunches. **Adm £3, chd free. Sun 29 June, Sun 31 Aug (11.30-5).**

1-acre garden gradually restored over the past 7yrs situated at the top of a wooded valley, surrounded by wildflower meadow and ash woodland. Area adjacent to house with seasonal planting and containers, mixed shrubs and perennial borders many raised from seed. 3 ponds, vegetable plot, barn conversion with separate cottage style garden. Natural garden with stream developed from old mill pond. Walks in large wild flower meadow and ash woodland both SSSI's. Handspinning and natural dyeing display using materials from the garden and wool from sheep in the meadow. Spinning demonstration in August. Light lunches served as well as home made teas. Featured in The Derbyshire magazine and on BBC East Midlands Today. Also Garden of the Week in Amateur Gardening Magazine. Steep slope from car park, limestone chippings at entrance, some boggy areas if wet.

ALLOTMENTS

38 LITTLEOVER LANE ALLOTMENTS

19 Littleover Lane, Derby DE23 6JH. Littleover Lane Allotments Assoc, 07745 227230, davidkenyon@tinyworld.co.uk, www.littleoverlaneallotments.org.uk. *3m SW of Derby. Off Derby ring rd A5111 into Stenson Rd. R into Littleover Lane. Garden on L. On street parking opp Foremark Ave.* Light refreshments. **Adm £3, chd free. Sun 7 Sept (11-5). Visitors also welcome by appt Apr to Oct for groups 4 to 25.**

Allotment site with over 180 plots cultivated in a variety of styles. Range of heritage and unusual vegetable varieties grown. Annual produce show. Disabled WC. Site slopes so some plots may not be accessible to wheelchairs as avenues are stoned.

39 LOCKO PARK

Spondon, Derby DE21 7BW. Mrs Lucy Palmer, www.lockopark.co.uk. *6m NE of Derby. From A52 Borrowash bypass, 2m N via B6001, turn to Spondon. More directions on www.lockopark.co.uk. NB. Satnav input via Locko Rd.* Home-made teas. **Adm £3, chd free. Sun 6 July (2-5).**

An original 1927 open garden for the NGS. Large garden; pleasure gardens; rose gardens designed by William Eames. House (not open) by Smith of Warwick with Victorian additions. Chapel (open) Charles II, with original ceiling. Limited wheelchair access, steps to main garden.

40 9 MAIN STREET

Horsley Woodhouse DE7 6AU. Ms Alison Napier, 01332 881629, ibhillib@btinternet.com. *3m SW of Heanor. 6m N of Derby. Turn off A608 Derby to Heanor rd at Smalley, towards Belper, (A609). Garden on A609, 1m from Smalley turning.* Cream teas. **Adm £2.50, chd free. Sun 3 Aug (1.30-4.30). Visitors also welcome by appt Apr to Sept, refreshments by arrangement.**

1/3 -acre hilltop garden overlooking lovely farmland view. Terracing, borders, lawns and pergola create space for an informal layout with planting for colour effect. Features incl large wildlife pond with water lilies, bog garden and small formal pool. Emphasis on carefully selected herbaceous perennials mixed with shrubs and old-fashioned roses. Additions incl gravel garden for sun-loving plants and scree garden, both developed from former drive. Wheelchair-adapted WC.

41 2 MANVERS STREET

Ripley DE5 3EQ. Mrs D Wood & Mr D Hawkins, 01773 743962, davidshawkins@tiscali.co.uk. *Ripley Town centre to Derby rd turn L opp Leisure Centre onto Heath Rd. 1st turn R onto Meadow Rd, 1st L onto Manvers St.* Home-made teas. **Adm £2.50, chd free. Sat 12, Sun 13 July (2-5). Visitors also welcome by appt July to Aug.**

Summer garden with backdrop of neighbouring trees, 10 borders bursting with colour surrounded by immaculate shaped lawn. Perennials incl 26 clematis, annuals, baskets, tubs and pots. Ornamental fish pond. Water features, arbour and summerhouse. Plenty of seating areas to take in this awe-inspiring oasis. Winners of the Daily Mirror Diarmuid Gavin Cup for Most Inspiring Garden and Ripley Town Council, Best Back Garden.

42 ◆ MELBOURNE HALL GARDENS

Church Square, Melbourne, Derby DE73 8EN. The Melbourne Trust, 01332 862502, www.melbournehall.com. *6m S of Derby. At Melbourne Market Place turn in to Church St, go down to Church Sq. Garden entrance across visitor centre next to tea room.* **Adm £4.50, chd £3.50. For NGS: Sat 31 May, Sun 1 June (1.30-5.30). For other opening times and information, please phone or see garden website.**

A 17 acre historic garden with an abundance of rare trees and shrubs, woodland and waterside planting with extensive herbaceous borders. Meconopsis, candelabra primulas, styrax japonica, cornus kousa 'Eddies white wonder'. The other garden features incl Bakewells wrought iron arbour, a yew tunnel and fine C18 statuary and water features. Light refreshments in tea room next to garden entrance in visitor centre. Gravel paths, uneven surface in places, some steep slopes.

43 ◆ MEYNELL LANGLEY TRIALS GARDEN

Lodge Lane (off Flagshaw Lane), Nr Kirk Langley, Derby DE6 4NT. Robert & Karen Walker, 01332 824358, www.meynell-langley-gardens.co.uk. *4m W of Derby, nr Kedleston Hall. Head W out of Derby on A52. At Kirk Langley turn R onto Flagshaw Lane (signed to Kedleston Hall) then R onto Lodge Lane. Follow Meynell Langley Gdns.* **Adm £3, chd free. For NGS: Sun 25 May, Sun 22 June, Sun 20 July, Sun 24 Aug, Sun 21 Sept, Sun 12 Oct (11-4.30). For other opening times and information, please phone or see garden website.**

Formal 3/4 -acre Victorian-style garden established 20 yrs, displaying and trialling new and existing varieties of bedding plants, herbaceous perennials and vegetable plants grown at the adjacent nursery. Over 180 hanging baskets and floral displays. 85 varieties of apple, pear and other fruit. Summer fruit pruning demonstrations late summer and apple tasting in October. Summer fruit tree pruning demonstrations on July NGS day and Apple tasting on October NGS day. Adjacent tea rooms serving light lunches and refreshments daily. Level ground and firm grass. Full disabled access to tea rooms.

44 MOORFIELDS

257/261 Chesterfield Road, Temple Normanton, Chesterfield S42 5DE. Peter, Janet & Stephen Wright, 01246 852306, peterwright100@hotmail.com. *4m SE of Chesterfield. From Chesterfield take A617 for 2m, turn on to B6039 through Temple Normanton, taking R fork signed Tibshelf. Garden ¼ m on R. Limited parking on site.* Light refreshments. **Adm £3, chd free. Sun 15 June (1-5). Visitors also welcome by appt Apr to July for groups 10+.**
Two adjacent gardens, the larger developed from field over last few yrs and has newly extended gravel garden, herbaceous island beds, small wild flower area, large wildlife pond, orchard and soft fruit, vegetable patch. Show of late flowering tulips. Smaller back and front gardens of No. 257 feature herbaceous borders. Views across to mid-Derbyshire. Free-range eggs for sale.

45 NEW MILLS SCHOOL BUSINESS & ENTERPRISE COLLEGE

Church Lane, New Mills, High Peak SK22 4NR. Mr C Pickering, www.newmillsschool.co.uk/ngs.html. *12m NNW of Buxton. From A6 take A6105 signed New Mills, Hayfield. At C of E Church turn L onto Church Lane. School on L. Parking on site.* Light refreshments in School Library. **Adm £3, chd free. Sat 12 July (10-5); Sun 13 July (1-5).**
Mixed herbaceous perennials/shrub borders, with mature trees and lawns and gravel border situated in the semi rural setting of the High Peak incl a Grade II listed building with 4 themed quads. Ramps allow wheelchair access to most of outside, flower beds and into Grade II listed building and library.

46 9 NEWFIELD CRESCENT

Dore, Sheffield S17 3DE. Mike & Norma Jackson, 01142 366198, mandnjackson@googlemail.com. *Dore - SW Sheffield. Turn off Causeway Head Rd on Heather Lea Av. 2nd L into Newfield Crescent. Parking on roadside.* Home-made teas. **Adm £3, chd free. Sat 14, Sun 15 June (2-6). Visitors also welcome by appt Apr to Oct.**
Mature, wildlife friendly garden planted to provide all-yr interest. Upper terrace with alpines in troughs and bowls. Lower terrace featuring pond with cascade and connecting stream to second pond. Bog garden, rock gardens, lawn alpine bed, wilder areas, mixed borders with trees, shrubs and perennials. Featuring azaleas, rhododendrons, primulas. Wheelchair access without steps to top terrace offering full view of garden.

Take in the peaceful atmosphere and enjoy the scents and colours . . .

47 ◆ OLD ENGLISH WALLED GARDEN, ELVASTON CASTLE COUNTRY PARK

Borrowash Road, Elvaston, Derby DE72 3EP. Derbyshire County Council, 01332 571342, www.derbyshire.gov.uk/elvaston. *4m E of Derby. Signed from A52 & A50. Car parking charge applies.* Light refreshments. **Adm £2.50, chd free. For NGS: Sat 26 Apr, Sat 16 Aug (12-4). For other opening times and information, please phone or see garden website.**
Visit Elvaston Castle and discover the beauty of the Old English walled garden. Take in the peaceful atmosphere and enjoy the scents and colours of all the varieties of trees, shrubs and plants. Spring bulbs, summer bedding, large herbaceous borders and new for 2014 the Sensory Garden created by the Parish Plan Volunteer group. Estate gardeners on hand during the day.

48 OWL END

Newfield Lane, Dore, Sheffield S17 3DB. Sue & Roger Thompson, 01142 350830, owlend@gmail.com. *5m SW Sheffield City Centre. Turn off A625 at Dore Moor Inn & follow yellow NGS signs. Please park giving consideration to neighbours.* Home-made teas. **Adm £3.50, chd free. Sat 21, Sun 22 June (1.30-5).**
Large garden of 1½ -acres with additional woodlands and meadow. Herbaceous and mixed borders. Vegetables, soft fruit, greenhouse and polytunnel. Views towards Blackamoor. Two-storey Wendy House. Woodland and wilder areas as well as varied borders. Wheelchair access to main part of garden, but care needed beyond this due to some sloping areas.

49 THE PADDOCK

12 Mankell Road, Whittington Moor, Chesterfield S41 8LZ. Mel & Wendy Taylor, 01246 451001. *2m N of Chesterfield. Whittington Moor just off A61 between Sheffield & Chesterfield. Parking available at Lidl supermarket, garden signed from here.* Home-made teas. **Adm £3, chd free. Sun 18 May, Sun 10 Aug (11-5). Visitors also welcome by appt May to Sept.**
½ -acre garden incorporating small formal garden, stream and koi filled pond. Stone path over bridge, up some steps, past small copse, across the stream at the top and back down again. Past herbaceous border towards a pergola where cream teas can be enjoyed.

50 PARK HALL

Walton Back Lane, Walton, Chesterfield S42 7LT. Kim & Margaret Staniforth, 01246 567412, kim.staniforth@btinternet.com. *2m SW of Chesterfield centre. From town on A 619 L into Somersall Lane. On A632 R into Acorn Ridge. Park on field side of Walton Back Lane only.* Home-made teas. **Adm £4, chd free (share to Bluebell Wood Childrens Hospice). Sun 29 June (2-5.30). Visitors also welcome by appt Apr to July for groups +20.**
Romantic 2-acre plantsmans garden, in a stunningly beautiful setting surrounding C17 house (not open) 4 main rooms-terraced garden, parkland area with forest trees, croquet lawn, sunken garden with arbours, pergolas, pleached hedge, topiary, statuary, roses, rhododendrons, camellias, several water features. Newly planted driveside. Two steps down to gain access to garden.

Treat yourself to a plant from the plant stall

51 22 PINFOLD CLOSE

Repton DE65 6FR. Mr O Jowett, 01283 701964, owenjowett@btinternet.com. *6m S of Derby. From A38, A50 J, S of Derby follow signs to Willington then Repton. Off Repton High St find Pinfold Lane, Pinfold Close 1st L.* **Sun 10 Aug (1-5.30). Combined with 10 Chestnut Way & Woodend Cottage. Combined adm £6, single garden adm £3, chd free.**

Small garden with an interest in tropical plants. Palms, gingers, tree ferns, cannas, bananas. Mainly foliage plants.

52 RECTORY HOUSE

Kedleston, Derby DE22 5JJ. Helene Viscountess Scarsdale. *5m NW Derby. A52 from Derby turn R Kedleston sign. Drive to village turn R. Brick house standing back from rd on sharp corner.* Home-made teas. **Adm £3.50, chd free. Sat 5 July (2-5).**

The 3 acre garden planted with wildlife in mind has rare trees a shrub border with rare varieties, grasses, rhododendrons, azaleas and shrub roses. Large pond with candelabra primulas, gunneras, and darmeras with winding paths. Small potager and orchard. Summerhouse to sit in and plenty of seats. Limited wheelchair access. Uneven grass paths.

53 ◆ RENISHAW HALL & GARDENS

Renishaw, nr Sheffield S21 3WB. Alexandra Haywood, 01246 432310, www.renishaw-hall.co.uk. *10m from Sheffield city centre. By car: Renishaw Hall only 3m from J30 on M1, well signed from junction r'about.* **Adm £6.50, chd free. For NGS: Fri 2 May, Fri 11 July (10.30-4.30). For other opening times and information, please phone or see garden website.**

Renishaw Hall and Gardens boasts 7 acres of stunning gardens created by Sir George Sitwell in 1885. The Italianate gardens feature various 'rooms' with extravagant herbaceous borders. Rose gardens, rare trees and shrubs, National Collection of Yuccas, sculptures, woodland walks and lakes create a magical and engaging garden experience. Open Wed to Sun, BH Mons, 29 March to 28 Sept. Wheelchair route around garden.

Byways

54 ROSEBANK

303 Duffield Road, Allestree, Derby DE22 2DF. Patrick & Carol Smith, 01332 559161, padsmith@ntlworld.com. *2m N of Derby. Follow A6 from Derby towards Matlock. On crossing A38 island continue for 150 metres turning L into Gisborne Crescent then R into service rd.* Cream teas. **Adm £2.50, chd free. Sat 14 June (2-6). Visitors also welcome by appt Apr to Sept for groups 20 max.**

Interesting garden of variety on a gentle, upward sloping site. Access by steps and path incl colourful borders with imaginative planting and a water feature in a natural setting. Small orchard and soft fruit garden, lawns, including a camomile lawn, rockery, shrubs, trees and greenhouse. Wildlife friendly. Children welcomed. The garden has an Auricula Theatre which houses a vivid display of Streptocarpus during the Summer. A running computer display in the summerhouse features the garden in different seasons together with photographs and wildlife information such as a checklist of birds observed in the garden. Wheelchair access to front and terrace in rear garden. Remainder of garden difficult.

55 THORNBRIDGE HALL

Ashford in the Water DE45 1NZ. Jim & Emma Harrison. *2m NW of Bakewell. From Bakewell take A6, signed Buxton. After 2m, R onto A6020. ½ m turn L, signed Thornbridge Hall.* Light refreshments. **Adm £4.50, chd free. Sun 17 Aug (10-4).**

A stunning 10-acre garden overlooking rolling Derbyshire countryside. This C19, rarely opened garden has many distinct areas incl Italian garden with statuary, knot garden, water garden, 100ft herbaceous border, working potager, scented terrace, koi lake, thatched summer house and glasshouses. Gravel paths, steep slopes, steps.

56 TILFORD HOUSE
Hognaston, Ashbourne DE6 1PW. Mr & Mrs P R Gardner, 01335 372001, peter.rgardner@mypostoffice.co.uk. *5m NE of Ashbourne. A517 Belper to Ashbourne. At Hulland Ward follow signs to Hognaston. Down hill (2m) to bridge. Roadside parking 100 metres.* Home-made teas. **Adm £3, chd free. Mon 5 May, Wed 16 July (2-5). Visitors also welcome by appt May to July.**
A 1½ acre streamside country garden. Woodland, wildlife areas and ponds lie alongside colourful borders. Collections of primulas, hostas, iris and clematis as well as many unusual plants and trees. Raised vegetable beds and fruit trees. Relax in a magical setting to listen to the sounds of the countryside.

This leads to a small area at rear of garden given to more natural planting. . .

57 ◆ TISSINGTON HALL
nr Ashbourne DE6 1RA. Sir Richard & Lady FitzHerbert, 01335 352200, www.tissingtonhall.co.uk. *4m N of Ashbourne. E of A515 on Ashbourne to Buxton rd.* **Adm £5, chd £2. For NGS: Mon 26 May, Mon 25 Aug (12-3). For other opening times and information, please phone or see garden website.**
Large garden celebrating over 75yrs in the NGS, with stunning Rose garden on West Terrace, herbaceous borders and 5 acres of grounds. Award-winning Tearooms in the Village. The Old Coach House Tearooms Tel 01335 350501. Wheelchair access advice from ticket seller.

58 13 WESTFIELD ROAD
Swadlincote DE11 0BG. Val & Dave Booth, 01283 221167, valerie.booth@sky.com. *5m E of Burton-on-Trent, off A511. Take A511 from Burton on Trent. Follow signs for Swadlincote. Turn R into Springfield Rd, take 3rd R into Westfield Rd.* Home-made teas. **Adm £3, chd free. Sun 6 July, Sun 24 Aug (1-5.30). Visitors also welcome by appt June to Aug for groups 10+. Adm £5.00 inc tea and cake.**
A garden on 2 levels of approx ½ an acre. Packed herbaceous borders designed for colour. Roses and clematis scrambling over pergolas. Shrubs, baskets and tubs. Greenhouses, raised bed vegetable area, fruit trees and bushes. Free range chicken area. Plenty of seating.

59 WESTGATE
Combs Road, Combs, Chapel-en-le-Frith, High Peak SK23 9UP. Maurice & Christine Lomas, ca-lomas@sky.com. *N of Chapel-en-le-Frith off B5470. Turn L immed before Hanging Gate PH, signed Combs Village. ¾ m on L by railway bridge.* **Adm £3, chd free. Sun 1, Sat 28 June (1-5). Visitors also welcome by appt May to Aug 10+.**
Large sloping garden in quiet village with beautiful views. Features incl mixed borders and beds containing many perenials, hosta and heuchera. Large rockery. Vegetable and fruit beds Natural pond and stream with bog area and two formal ponds. New wild flower area.

60 WHARFEDALE
34 Broadway, Duffield, Belper DE56 4BU. Roger & Sue Roberts, 01332 841905, roberts34@btinternet.com, www.garden34.co.uk. *4m N of Derby. Turn onto B5023 Wirksworth rd (Broadway) off A6 midway between Belper & Derby.* Home-made teas. **Adm £3, chd free. Sun 8, Sun 29 June, Sun 20 July, Sun 10, Sun 24 Aug (11-5). Visitors also welcome by appt June to Aug for groups 20+.**
Back by popular demand after 4yrs! Plant enthusiasts' garden with over 800 varieties of unusual shrubs, trees, perennials and bulbs. Themed borders incl new Piet Oudolf inspired, late summer tropical and single colour schemes. Italianate walled scented garden and woodland with pond and raised walkway. Japanese tea garden with stream and pavilion. Cottage garden to front. Eclectic and unusual garden providing lots of ideas. 18yrs mature.

61 24 WHEELDON AVENUE
Derby DE22 1HN. Laura Burnett, 01332 384893 or 01332 342204. *1m N Derby city centre. Off Kedleston Rd with limited on street parking.* Teas at 28 Wheeldon Avenue. **Combined with 26 Wheeldon Avenue. Combined adm £4, single garden adm £3, chd free. Visitors welcome by appt (24 & 26 Wheeldon Av) May - July for groups 4+.**
Small Victorian garden, with original walling supporting many shrubs and climbers with contrasting colour and texture. Circular lawn surrounded by herbaceous border with main colour scheme of blue, purple, black, yellow and orange tones. This leads to a small area at rear of garden given to more natural planting to suit shade and natural habitat. This is a garden produced on a low income budget, with varied tones and textures throughout the planting. Photo of garden used on front cover of a book on designing small gardens by Ian Cook. Selection of fruit trees planted for this year.

62 26 WHEELDON AVENUE
Derby DE22 1HN. Ian Griffiths, 01332 342204, ig@moodyandwoolley.co.uk. *1m N of Derby. 1m from city centre & approached directly off the Kedleston Rd or from A6 Duffield Rd via West Bank Ave. Limited on-street parking.* Teas at 28 Wheeldon Avenue. **Combined with 24 Wheeldon Avenue. Combined adm £4, single garden adm £3, chd free. Visitors welcome by appt (24 & 26 Wheeldon Av) May - July for groups 4+.**
Tiny Victorian walled garden near to city centre. Lawn and herbaceous borders with newly expanded old rose collection, lupins, delphiniums and foxgloves. Small terrace with topiary, herb garden and lion fountain. Rose collection. Featured in Daily Telegraph and on BBC TV.

63 26 WINDMILL RISE

Belper DE56 1GQ. Kathy Fairweather. *From Belper Market Place take Chesterfield Rd towards Heage. Top of hill, 1st R Marsh Lane, 1st R Windmill Lane, 1st R Windmill Rise - limited parking only.* Home-made teas. **Adm £3, chd free (share to local charities). Sun 22 June, Sat 26, Sun 27 July (11-4).**
A very original and unusual plant lovers' organic garden full of surprises which are impossible to glimpse from the road. Large variety of plants, some unusual and rare. Garden divided into sections: woodland, Japanese, secret garden, cottage, edible. Fish and wildlife ponds, small stream. Specimen fir tree of most unusual shape. Lush, restful atmosphere with paths meandering to many seating areas. Featured in Derby Telegraph, Belper News and Belper Annual Calendar.

64 WINDWARD

62 Summer Lane, Wirksworth, Matlock DE4 4EB. Audrey & Andrew Winkler, 01629 822681, audrey.winkler@w3z.co.uk, www.grandmafrogsgarden.co.uk. *5m S of Matlock. From Wirksworth Market Place take the B5023 towards Duffield. After 300yds turn R onto Summer Lane at mini r'about. Windward is approx 500yds on R.* Home-made teas. **Adm £3, chd free (share to Ruddington Framework Knitters Museum). Wed 14, Sun 18 May, Wed 9, Sun 13 July (2-5). Visitors also welcome by appt Apr to Sept for groups of 10+.**
An informal green garden of 1 acre, with pockets of colour throughout the yr. Wildlife friendly, with flowers, shrubs and trees, catering for allcomers - from the smallest insect to the bigger birds - incl the occasional peregrine falcon. Paths wind around the garden, making sure you don't miss anything, with interesting details tucked away to surprise you. A garden for all seasons. Although on the edge of a small town, the garden is remarkably peaceful.

65 WOODEND COTTAGE

134 Main Street, Repton DE65 6FB. Wendy & Stephen Longden, 01283 703259, wendylongden@btinternet.com. *6m S of Derby. From A38, S of Derby, follow signs to Willington, then Repton. In Repton straight on at r'about through village.Garden is 1m on R.* Home-made teas. **Sun 10 Aug (1-5.30). Combined with 22 Pinfold Close and 10 Chestnut Way. Combined adm £6, single garden adm £3, chd free. Visitors also welcome by appt during Aug.**
Plant lover's garden with glorious views on a sloping 2½ -acre site developed organically for yr-round interest. On lower levels herbaceous borders are arranged informally and connected via lawns, thyme bed, pond and pergolas. Mixed woodland and grassed labyrinth lead naturally into fruit, vegetable and herb potager with meadows beyond. Especially colourful in July and Aug. Easy and unusual perennials and grasses for sale. Why not visit St Wystans Church, Repton during you by appiontment visit. Featured in Garden News. Wheelchair access on lower levels only.

66 35 WYVER LANE

Belper DE56 2UB. Jim & Brenda Stannering, 01773 824280, Wyver35@gmail.com. *8m N of Derby. Cross R Derwent heading out of Belper signed Ashbourne.* **Adm £2.50, chd free. Sun 27 Apr, Sun 15 June (1-5). Visitors also welcome by appt Apr to Oct.**
Cottage garden of approx 500sq yds on side of R Derwent opp Belper River Gardens. Full of hardy perennial plants with pergola, troughs, greenhouse, small pond. Demonstration of patchwork, embroidery, doll making etc by garden owner on request.

  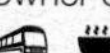

Derbyshire County Volunteers

County Organiser
Irene Dougan, 2 Home Farm, Main Street, Kirk Ireton, Ashbourne DE6 3JP, 01335 370958, emily.dougan@btinternet.com

County Treasurer
Robert Little, 10 Chestnut Way, Repton DE65 6FQ, 01283 702267, rlittleq@gmail.com

Publicity
Christine Morris, 9 Langdale Avenue, Ravenshead NG15 9EA, 01623 793827, christine@ravenshead.demon.co.uk

Booklet Distribution
Kathy Fairweather, 26 Windmill Rise, Belper DE56 1GQ, 01773 825255, kathyf100@hotmail.com

ACO/Booklet Coordiantor
Dave Darwent, 12 Ansell Road, Ecclesall, Sheffield S11 7PE, 01142 665881, dave@poptasticdave.co.uk

Assistant County Organisers
Jane Lennox, Craigside, Reservoir Road, Whaley Bridge SK23 7BW, 01663 732381, jane@lennoxonline.net
Gill & Colin Hancock, 334 Belper Road, Stanley Common, nr Ilkeston DE7 6FY, 01159 301061
Pauline Little, 10 Chestnut Way, Repton DE65 6FQ, 01283 702267, rlittleq@gmail.com
Christine Sanderson, The Hollies, 87 Clowne Road, Barlborough, Chesterfield S43 4EH, 01246 570830, christine.r.sanderson@uwclub.net
Kate & Peter Spencer, Merle Close, 41 Summer Lane, Wirksworth, Matlock DE4 4EB, 01629 822499

DEVON

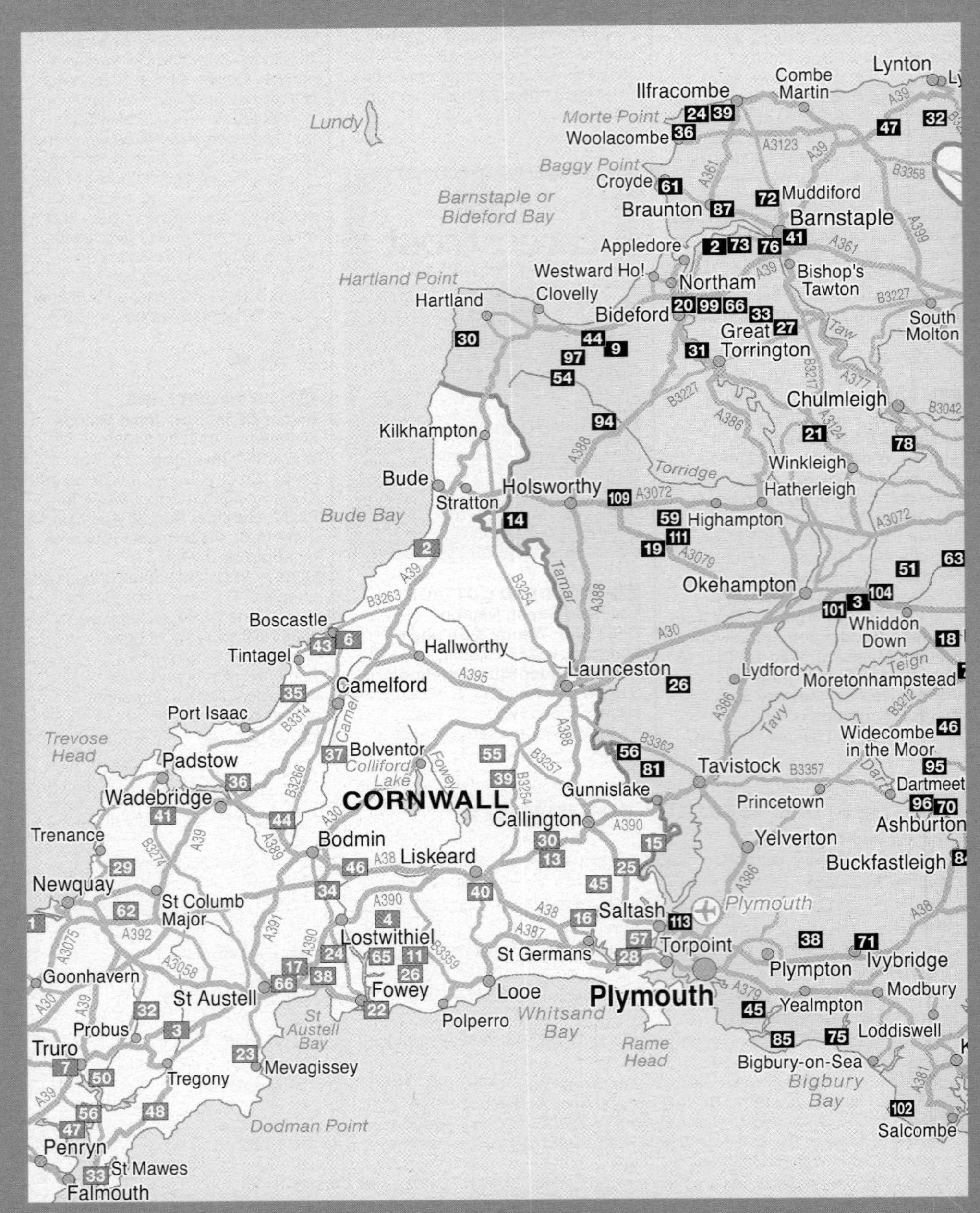
Lundy
Ilfracombe
Combe Martin
Lynton
Morte Point
Woolacombe
Baggy Point
Croyde
Braunton
Muddiford
Barnstaple
Barnstaple or Bideford Bay
Appledore
Bishop's Tawton
Westward Ho!
Northam
Hartland Point
Hartland
Clovelly
Bideford
Great Torrington
South Molton
Chulmleigh
Kilkhampton
Winkleigh
Torridge
Bude
Stratton
Holsworthy
Hatherleigh
Highampton
Bude Bay
Tamar
Okehampton
Whiddon Down
Boscastle
Tintagel
Hallworthy
Camelford
Launceston
Lydford
Moretonhampstead
Teign
Port Isaac
Trevose Head
Padstow
Bolventor
Colliford Lake
Fowey
Tavy
Widecombe in the Moor
Tavistock
Dart
Dartmeet
Wadebridge
CORNWALL
Gunnislake
Princetown
Ashburton
Trenance
Callington
Bodmin
Liskeard
Yelverton
Buckfastleigh
Newquay
St Columb Major
Saltash
Plymouth
Lostwithiel
St Germans
Torpoint
Plympton
Ivybridge
Goonhavern
St Austell
Fowey
Looe
Plymouth
Modbury
Yealmpton
Probus
St Austell Bay
Polperro
Whitsand Bay
Loddiswell
Truro
Rame Head
Bigbury-on-Sea
Mevagissey
Tregony
Bigbury Bay
Dodman Point
Salcombe
Penryn
St Mawes
Falmouth

Foreland Point
Bridgwater Bay
Porlock
Minehead
Burnham-on-Sea
Highbridge
Cheddar
Wedmore
Wells
Shepton Mallet
Dunster
Watchet
Wheddon Cross
Williton
Exford
Street
Glastonbury
Bridgwater
Westonzoyland
SOMERSET, BRISTOL AREA & S. GLOS
Bruton
Castle Cary
Bishop's Lydeard
Dulverton
Wiveliscombe
Milverton
Somerton
Taunton
Langport
Wellington
Bampton
Ilchester
Yeovil
Sherborne
Ilminster
South Petherton
Witheridge
Hemyock
Chard
DEVON
Tiverton
Yarcombe
Crewkerne
Middlemarsh
Bickleigh
Cullompton
Copplestone
Beaminster
DORSET
Crediton
Honiton
Axminster
Maiden Newton
Ottery St Mary
Exeter
Lyme Regis
Bridport
Dorchester
Dunsford
Topsham
Sidford
Seaton
Abbotsbury
Sidmouth
Broadwey
Bovey Tracey
Budleigh Salterton
Exmouth
Dawlish
Lyme Bay
Weymouth
Teignmouth
Fortuneswell
Newton Abbot
Torquay
Bill of Portland
Totnes
Paignton
Brixham
Halwell
Dartmouth
Kingsbridge
Start Bay
Start Point
0 10 20 kilometres
0 10 miles
© Global Mapping / XYZ Maps

Opening Dates

All entries subject to change.
For latest information check
www.ngs.org.uk

February

Sunday 2
21 Cherubeer Gardens

Saturday 8
65 Little Cumbre

Sunday 9
65 Little Cumbre
68 Littleham House Cottage

Friday 14
21 Cherubeer Gardens

Saturday 15
35 1 Feebers Cottage
65 Little Cumbre

Sunday 16
35 1 Feebers Cottage
65 Little Cumbre
68 Littleham House Cottage

March

Sunday 2
34 East Worlington House

Sunday 9
34 East Worlington House

Sunday 23
41 Gorwell House
100 Summers Place

Friday 28
45 The Haven

Saturday 29
45 The Haven

Sunday 30
46 Heathercombe
112 Wood Barton
113 Woodvale Cottage
115 Yonder Hill

Monday 31
115 Yonder Hill

April

39 **The Gate House (Daily)**
115 **Yonder Hill (every Sunday & Monday)**

Saturday 5
19 Chapel Farm House
31 The Downes

Sunday 6
31 The Downes
85 Rowden House

Monday 7
31 The Downes

Tuesday 8
31 The Downes

Wednesday 9
31 The Downes

Thursday 10
31 The Downes

Friday 11
31 The Downes

Saturday 12
31 The Downes

Sunday 13
22 Chevithorne Barton
41 Gorwell House

Wednesday 16
89 Shapcott Barton Estate

Saturday 19
42 Haldon Grange
53 Holbrook Garden

Sunday 20
3 Andrew's Corner
7 Bickham Gardens
42 Haldon Grange
53 Holbrook Garden
57 Kia-Ora Farm & Gardens
68 Littleham House Cottage
87 St Merryn
89 Shapcott Barton Estate
112 Wood Barton

Monday 21
42 Haldon Grange
53 Holbrook Garden
57 Kia-Ora Farm & Gardens
112 Wood Barton

Tuesday 22
7 Bickham Gardens

Wednesday 23
7 Bickham Gardens

Saturday 26
19 Chapel Farm House
42 Haldon Grange
91 Sidbury Manor

Sunday 27
42 Haldon Grange
68 Littleham House Cottage
91 Sidbury Manor

Subtropical planting in a small garden . . .

May

39 **The Gate House (Daily)**
115 **Yonder Hill (every Sunday & Monday)**

Saturday 3
28 Dicot
42 Haldon Grange
52 Hillrise
75 Mothecombe House

Sunday 4
3 Andrew's Corner
28 Dicot
42 Haldon Grange
49 NEW Higher Ash Farm
52 Hillrise
57 Kia-Ora Farm & Gardens
75 Mothecombe House
101 Taikoo
104 2 Town Barton
107 Whitstone Bluebells

Monday 5
3 Andrew's Corner
28 Dicot
37 Fursdon
42 Haldon Grange
57 Kia-Ora Farm & Gardens

Wednesday 7
42 Haldon Grange

Saturday 10
10 Bovey Country Gardens
13 Brendon Gardens
17 Carpenter's Cottage
26 Coombe Trenchard
42 Haldon Grange
78 The Old Glebe
88 Sedgewell Coach House Gardens
96 NEW Spitchwick Manor

Sunday 11
7 Bickham Gardens
10 Bovey Country Gardens
13 Brendon Gardens
17 Carpenter's Cottage
18 Castle Drogo
26 Coombe Trenchard
36 Foamlea
42 Haldon Grange
78 The Old Glebe
84 Ridgehill
88 Sedgewell Coach House Gardens
96 NEW Spitchwick Manor
109 Wick Farm Gardens

Monday 12
60 Knightshayes Court Garden

Tuesday 13
7 Bickham Gardens

Wednesday 14
7 Bickham Gardens
42 Haldon Grange

Friday 16
19 Chapel Farm House

Saturday 17
19 Chapel Farm House
42 Haldon Grange
61 Langtrees
63 Lewis Cottage
74 Moretonhampstead Gardens
78 The Old Glebe
79 The Old Vicarage

Sunday 18
22 Chevithorne Barton
41 Gorwell House
42 Haldon Grange
46 Heathercombe

49 NEW Higher Ash Farm
61 Langtrees
63 Lewis Cottage
74 Moretonhampstead Gardens
78 The Old Glebe
79 The Old Vicarage
87 St Merryn
95 Southcombe Gardens

Monday 19
74 Moretonhampstead Gardens

Wednesday 21
42 Haldon Grange

Saturday 24
53 Holbrook Garden
54 NEW Hole Farm
97 NEW Springfield

Sunday 25
3 Andrew's Corner
5 Ash Tree Farm
16 Cadhay
32 Durcombe Water
46 Heathercombe
53 Holbrook Garden
54 NEW Hole Farm
57 Kia-Ora Farm & Gardens
95 Southcombe Gardens
97 NEW Springfield
109 Wick Farm Gardens

Monday 26
3 Andrew's Corner
5 Ash Tree Farm
16 Cadhay
32 Durcombe Water
53 Holbrook Garden
57 Kia-Ora Farm & Gardens
95 Southcombe Gardens
109 Wick Farm Gardens

Saturday 31
19 Chapel Farm House
42 Haldon Grange
46 Heathercombe
48 High Garden

June

39 The Gate House (Daily)
40 Goren Farm (Every evening)
115 Yonder Hill (Every Sunday & Monday)

Sunday 1
3 Andrew's Corner
21 Cherubeer Gardens
36 Foamlea
38 NEW Galen Way
42 Haldon Grange
46 Heathercombe
48 High Garden
50 Higher Burnhaies
57 Kia-Ora Farm & Gardens
64 Little Ash Bungalow
95 Southcombe Gardens

Friday 6
69 The Lookout

Sidbury Manor

Festival Weekend

Saturday 7
11 Bovey Tracey Gardens
20 Cherry Trees Wildlife Garden
40 Goren Farm
63 Lewis Cottage
70 Lower Spitchwick Garden
86 Runnymede

Sunday 8
11 Bovey Tracey Gardens
20 Cherry Trees Wildlife Garden
37 Fursdon
40 Goren Farm
46 Heathercombe
47 Heddon Hall
56 NEW Hotel Endsleigh
63 Lewis Cottage
69 The Lookout
70 Lower Spitchwick Garden
86 Runnymede
95 Southcombe Gardens

Friday 13
90 Shutelake

Saturday 14
1 Abbotskerswell Gardens
9 Bocombe Mill Cottage
12 Bramble Torre
19 Chapel Farm House
28 Dicot
40 Goren Farm
53 Holbrook Garden
58 Kilmington (Shute Road) Gardens
59 NEW Kingswood House
83 Regency House
87 St Merryn
90 Shutelake
92 Sidmouth Gardens
96 NEW Spitchwick Manor
105 Venn Cross Railway Gardens
110 Willand Old Village Gardens
111 Winsford Walled Garden

Sunday 15
1 Abbotskerswell Gardens
7 Bickham Gardens
9 Bocombe Mill Cottage
12 Bramble Torre
14 NEW The Bridge Mill
27 The Croft
28 Dicot
30 Docton Mill
36 Foamlea
40 Goren Farm
41 Gorwell House
53 Holbrook Garden
57 Kia-Ora Farm & Gardens
58 Kilmington (Shute Road) Gardens
59 NEW Kingswood House
72 Marwood Hill
81 Portington
83 Regency House
87 St Merryn
90 Shutelake
92 Sidmouth Gardens
95 Southcombe Gardens
96 NEW Spitchwick Manor
101 Taikoo
105 Venn Cross Railway Gardens
110 Willand Old Village Gardens

June contd

39 The Gate House (Daily)
40 Goren Farm (Every evening)
115 Yonder Hill (Every Sunday & Monday)

Tuesday 17
7 Bickham Gardens

Wednesday 18
7 Bickham Gardens

Friday 20
16 Cadhay

Saturday 21
25 Collepardo
52 Hillrise
73 NEW The Mill House
99 Stone Farm

Sunday 22
25 Collepardo
50 Higher Burnhaies
52 Hillrise
73 NEW The Mill House
81 Portington
95 Southcombe Gardens
99 Stone Farm
104 2 Town Barton
114 Yolland Gardens

Monday 23
25 Collepardo

Tuesday 24
25 Collepardo

Wednesday 25
25 Collepardo

Thursday 26
25 Collepardo

Friday 27
25 Collepardo

Saturday 28
4 Ash Gardens
9 Bocombe Mill Cottage
23 Cleave Hill
25 Collepardo
44 Harbour Lights
61 Langtrees
97 NEW Springfield

Sunday 29
4 Ash Gardens
9 Bocombe Mill Cottage
23 Cleave Hill
25 Collepardo
44 Harbour Lights
46 Heathercombe
51 NEW Higher Cullaford
57 Kia-Ora Farm & Gardens
61 Langtrees
97 NEW Springfield
109 Wick Farm Gardens

Monday 30
24 Cliffe

July

24 Cliffe (Daily)
39 The Gate House (Daily)
40 Goren Farm (Every evening)
115 Yonder Hill (Every Sunday & Monday)

Wednesday 2
37 Fursdon

Saturday 5
19 Chapel Farm House
40 Goren Farm
48 High Garden
59 NEW Kingswood House
73 NEW The Mill House

Sunday 6
36 Foamlea
40 Goren Farm
46 Heathercombe
51 NEW Higher Cullaford
59 NEW Kingswood House
73 NEW The Mill House

Saturday 12
40 Goren Farm
82 Prospect House
103 Teignmouth Gardens
105 Venn Cross Railway Gardens
106 Weirfield Meadows Allotment Gardens

Sunday 13
7 Bickham Gardens
40 Goren Farm
47 Heddon Hall
57 Kia-Ora Farm & Gardens
72 Marwood Hill
82 Prospect House
94 NEW South Worden
103 Teignmouth Gardens
105 Venn Cross Railway Gardens
106 Weirfield Meadows Allotment Gardens

Tuesday 15
7 Bickham Gardens

Wednesday 16
7 Bickham Gardens

Friday 18
16 Cadhay

Saturday 19
29 Dittisham Gardens
77 The Old Dairy
89 Shapcott Barton Estate

Sunday 20
27 The Croft
29 Dittisham Gardens
41 Gorwell House
54 NEW Hole Farm
56 NEW Hotel Endsleigh
77 The Old Dairy
87 St Merryn
89 Shapcott Barton Estate
97 NEW Springfield
113 Woodvale Cottage

Tuesday 22
89 Shapcott Barton Estate

Wednesday 23
89 Shapcott Barton Estate

Saturday 26
28 Dicot
33 East Woodlands Farmhouse
63 Lewis Cottage
89 Shapcott Barton Estate

Sunday 27
28 Dicot
33 East Woodlands Farmhouse
57 Kia-Ora Farm & Gardens
63 Lewis Cottage
67 Littlecourt Cottages
76 20 Old Bideford Road
89 Shapcott Barton Estate
94 NEW South Worden
98 Squirrels
104 2 Town Barton
109 Wick Farm Gardens

Monday 28
67 Littlecourt Cottages

August

24 Cliffe (Daily)
39 The Gate House (Daily)
115 Yonder Hill (Every Sunday & Monday)

Saturday 2
59 NEW Kingswood House
98 Squirrels
111 Winsford Walled Garden

Sunday 3
59 NEW Kingswood House
85 Rowden House
98 Squirrels

Saturday 9
13 Brendon Gardens

Sunday 10
7 Bickham Gardens
13 Brendon Gardens
57 Kia-Ora Farm & Gardens
94 NEW South Worden
108 Whitstone Farm

Tuesday 12
7 Bickham Gardens

Wednesday 13
7 Bickham Gardens

Saturday 16
19 Chapel Farm House
73 NEW The Mill House
89 Shapcott Barton Estate

Sunday 17
27 The Croft
49 NEW Higher Ash Farm
64 Little Ash Bungalow
73 NEW The Mill House
89 Shapcott Barton Estate

Saturday 23
53 Holbrook Garden
70 Lower Spitchwick Garden
79 The Old Vicarage
92 Sidmouth Gardens

Sunday 24
2 32 Allenstyle Drive
32 Durcombe Water
53 Holbrook Garden
57 Kia-Ora Farm & Gardens
70 Lower Spitchwick Garden
79 The Old Vicarage
92 Sidmouth Gardens

Monday 25
2 32 Allenstyle Drive
32 Durcombe Water
53 Holbrook Garden
57 Kia-Ora Farm & Gardens
92 Sidmouth Gardens

Saturday 30
63 Lewis Cottage
88 Sedgewell Coach House Gardens
99 Stone Farm

Sunday 31
2 32 Allenstyle Drive
63 Lewis Cottage
88 Sedgewell Coach House Gardens
99 Stone Farm

September

24 **Cliffe (Daily to 12 September)**
39 **The Gate House (Daily)**
115 **Yonder Hill (Every Sunday & Monday)**

Saturday 6
19 Chapel Farm House
59 NEW Kingswood House
74 Moretonhampstead Gardens
82 Prospect House

Sunday 7
2 32 Allenstyle Drive
7 Bickham Gardens
57 Kia-Ora Farm & Gardens
59 NEW Kingswood House
74 Moretonhampstead Gardens
82 Prospect House

Tuesday 9
7 Bickham Gardens

Wednesday 10
7 Bickham Gardens

Saturday 13
105 Venn Cross Railway Gardens

Sunday 14
18 Castle Drogo
37 Fursdon
41 Gorwell House
54 NEW Hole Farm
97 NEW Springfield
105 Venn Cross Railway Gardens

Saturday 20
93 NEW South Wood Farm

Sunday 21
93 NEW South Wood Farm
100 Summers Place

October

39 **The Gate House (Daily)**

Sunday 5
21 Cherubeer Gardens
49 NEW Higher Ash Farm
113 Woodvale Cottage

Sunday 12
3 Andrew's Corner
83 Regency House

Sunday 19
7 Bickham Gardens

Saturday 25
19 Chapel Farm House

February 2015

Sunday 1
21 Cherubeer Gardens

Sunday 8
68 Littleham House Cottage

Sunday 15
68 Littleham House Cottage

Friday 20
21 Cherubeer Gardens

Gardens open to the public

8 Blackpool Gardens
15 Burrow Farm Gardens
16 Cadhay
18 Castle Drogo
30 Docton Mill
37 Fursdon
47 Heddon Hall
53 Holbrook Garden
56 Hotel Endsleigh
60 Knightshayes Court Garden
71 Lukesland
72 Marwood Hill
80 Plant World
89 Shapcott Barton Estate
111 Winsford Walled Garden

By appointment only

6 Avenue Cottage
43 Hamblyn's Coombe
55 Hollycombe House
62 Lee Ford
66 Little Webbery
102 Tamarisks

. . . a hidden oasis of plants and views . . .

Also open by appointment

1 Abbotskerswell Gardens
1 Fairfield, Abbotskerswell Gardens
2 32 Allenstyle Drive
3 Andrew's Corner
5 Ash Tree Farm
7 Bickham Gardens
9 Bocombe Mill Cottage
12 Bramble Torre
13 Brendon Gardens
14 The Bridge Mill
21 Cherubeer Gardens
23 Cleave Hill
24 Cliffe
25 Collepardo
27 The Croft
33 East Woodlands Farmhouse
36 Foamlea
38 Galen Way
40 Goren Farm
41 Gorwell House
42 Haldon Grange
44 Harbour Lights
45 The Haven
46 Heathercombe
48 High Garden
49 Higher Ash Farm
52 Hillrise
57 Kia-Ora Farm & Gardens
61 Langtrees
63 Lewis Cottage
64 Little Ash Bungalow
65 Little Cumbre
68 Littleham House Cottage
73 The Mill House
74 Sutton Mead, Moretonhampstead Gardens
75 Mothecombe House
79 The Old Vicarage
81 Portington
82 Prospect House
83 Regency House

Yonder Hill

The Gardens

GROUP OPENING

1 ABBOTSKERSWELL GARDENS

Abbotskerswell TQ12 5PN, 01626 356004, christinemack@clara.co.uk. *2m SW of Newton Abbot town centre. A 381 Newton Abbot/Totnes Road. Sharp L turn from NA, R from Totnes. Field parking at Fairfield. Maps available at all gardens*. Home-made teas at Church House. **Combined adm £5, chd free (share to Friends of St Marys).** **Sat 14, Sun 15 June (1-5).** **Visitors also welcome by appt Apr to Aug, number of gardens available agreed on request.**

ABBOTSFORD
Mrs W Grierson.
Maps at all locations

ABBOTSKERSWELL ALLOTMENTS
Margaret Crompton

1 ABBOTSWELL COTTAGES
Ford Road. Jane Taylor

BRIAR COTTAGE
1 Monk's Orchard. Peggy & David Munden

NEW 3 CORN PARK ROAD
Mrs Margie Tomlinson

8 COURT FARM BARNS
Wilton Way. Pat Mackness

FAIRFIELD
Christine & Brian Mackness
Visitors also welcome by appt Apr to Aug.
01626 356004
christinemack@clara.co.uk

KARIBU
35 Wilton Way. Jenny & Dave Brook

In 2014 Abbotskerswell Gardens adds another new garden - Corn Park Road, a prize winning small garden, majors on pots and hanging baskets. The allotments have 22 plots showing a wide range of skills and production methods. 1 Abbotswell Cottages is a delightful garden which hides its charms - until you enter the back garden! A further 5 gardens in this lovely village display beautiful cottage planting, wild flower areas, specialist plants, dramatic terracing, and yet more redevelopment areas incorporating imaginative hard landscaping. We welcome people to picnic in the field or arboretum at Fairfield if the weather is good. Children will enjoy the miniature Shetland ponies, plus finding their way through winding paths among high grasses. See You Tube Abbotskerswell Gardens 2011 for a taster. Featured in Newton Abbot and Mid Devon Advertiser. Disabled access to 4 gardens.

2 32 ALLENSTYLE DRIVE

Yelland, Barnstaple EX31 3DZ. Steve & Dawn Morgan, 01271 861433, fourhungrycats@aol.com, www.devonsubtropicalgarden.co.uk. *5m W of Barnstaple. Take B3233 towards Instow. Through Bickington & Fremington. L at Yelland sign into Allenstyle Rd. 1st R into Allenstyle Dr. Light blue bungalow*. Light refreshments. **Adm £3.50, chd free.** **Sun 24, Mon 25, Sun 31 Aug, Sun 7 Sept (11-5.30).** **Visitors by appt will be warmly welcomed during Aug.**
Subtropical planting in small (50x100ft) garden in mild estuary location. Bananas, hedychiums (gingers), palms, colocasia, aroids, brugmansias, exotic collection of passionflowers, prairie planting and much more. Lots of seating so you can take your time and enjoy our late summer burst of scent, colour and high impact planting. Featured in Garden News and on Radio Devon.

3 ANDREW'S CORNER

Belstone EX20 1RD. Robin & Edwina Hill, 01837 840332, edwinarobinhill@btinternet.com, www.belstonevillage.net. *3m E of Okehampton. Signed to Belstone. In village signed Skaigh. Parking restricted but cars may be left on nearby common*. Home-made teas.

Treat yourself to a plant from the plant stall

Adm £3.50, chd free. Sun 20 Apr, Sun 4, Mon 5, Sun 25, Mon 26 May, Sun 1 June, Sun 12 Oct (2.30-5.30). Visitors also welcome by appt Feb to Nov.
Well-established, wildlife-friendly, well-labelled plantsman's garden in stunning high moorland setting. Variety of garden habitats incl woodland areas, bog garden, pond; wide range of unusual trees, shrubs, herbaceous plants for yr-round effect including blue poppies, rhododendrons, bulbs and maples; spectacular autumn colour. Organic kitchen garden, greenhouses and chickens. Family quiz sheet. Featured on BBC Radio Devon and in Devon Country Gardener. Wheelchair access difficult when wet.

GROUP OPENING

4 ASH GARDENS

Ash, Dartmouth TQ6 0LR. *2m SW of Dartmouth. Leave A3122 at Halwell for Dartmouth. R at Sportsman's Arms follow signs to Ash. 1½ m at 2nd X-rds, park at Ash Tree Farm.* Home-made teas. **Combined adm £4.50, chd free.** Sat 28, Sun 29 June (2-6).

ASH TREE FARM
Ms Stevie Rogers
(See separate entry)

BAY TREE COTTAGE
Jenny Goffe

NEW **HIGHER ASH FARM**
Mr Michael Gribbin
(See separate entry)

3 delightful gardens of contrasting styles in the tiny hamlet of Ash. For Ash Tree Farm and Higher Ash Farm: see separate entries. The beautiful intimate little garden at Bay Tree Cottage sits in a quiet secluded valley with wonderful sunlit views across open farmland. The perfect curved lawn leads the eye to small 'rooms' filled with surprise and clever planting. Ornamental trees punctuate the boundary and a tiny vegetable garden of raised beds overflows with produce. Bring photos or drawings of your garden and discuss your ideas or problems with a member of the Society of Garden Designers and a previous judge at Chelsea Flower Show.

5 ASH TREE FARM

Ash Cross, Dartmouth TQ6 0LR. Ms Stevie Rogers, 01803 712437, stevie@ashtreefarm.com, www.ashtreefarm.com. *2m SW of Dartmouth. See Ash Gardens for directions.* Home-made teas. **Adm: £4, chd free.** Sun 25, Mon 26 May (2-5.30). **Also open 28 & 29 June with Ash Gardens. Visitors also welcome by appt Mar to Apr.**
Our rainbow garden is an interesting, informative and unconventional new garden, full of original ideas. Colour-themed, cottage garden style plantings. Whole garden planted for the benefit of wildlife. Wildflower banks and orchard, kitchen garden and wildlife pond. Level pathways, accessible to wheelchairs and buggies, plenty of seating. Unusual and contemporary sculptures by Bob Dawson on display throughout the garden. The farm is also home to the Ash Rescue Centre (ARC) making it a sanctuary for rescued and retired horses. Access to farm walks available. All pathways are level and accessible to wheelchairs unless very wet. Plenty of seating around the garden for the less mobile.

Unconventional new garden, full of original ideas . . .

6 NEW AVENUE COTTAGE

Ashprington, Totnes TQ9 7UT. Mr Richard Pitts and Mr David Sykes, 01803 732769, richard.pitts@btinternet.com, avenuecottage.com. *3m SW of Totnes. A 381 Totnes to Kingsbridge for 1m; L for Ashprington; into village then L by PH. Garden ¼ m on R after Sharpham Estate sign.* Home-made teas. **Adm £4, chd free.** Visitors welcome by appt **Apr to Oct.**
11 acres of mature and young trees and shrubs. Once part of an C18 landscape, the neglected garden has been cleared and replanted over the last 25 yrs. Good views of Sharpham House and R Dart. Azaleas and hydrangeas are a feature.

GROUP OPENING

7 BICKHAM GARDENS

Kenn EX6 7XL, 01392 832671, jandjtremlett@hotmail.com. *6m S of Exeter. 1m off A38. Leave A38 at Kennford Services, follow signs to Kenn. 1st R in village, follow lane for ¾ m to end of no through rd.* Cream teas. **Combined adm £4.50, chd free.**
Suns, Tues. Weds (2-5pm)
20, 22, 23 Apr,
11, 13, 14 May,
15, 17, 18 June,
13, 15, 16 July,
10, 12, 13 Aug,
7, 9, 10 Sept,
19 Oct.
Visitors also welcome by appt Apr to Oct, coaches by arrangement.

BICKHAM COTTAGE NCH
Steve Eyre

BICKHAM HOUSE
John & Julia Tremlett.
Leave A38 at Kennford Services, follow signs to Kenn, 1st R in village, follow lane for ¾ m to end of no through rd

Adj gardens in private valley under Haldon Hills. Bickham House: 7-acre garden with much recent replanting. Colour co-ordinated borders, mature trees incl massive tulip tree. Fernery and water garden. Formal parterre with lily pond. 1-acre walled garden with profusion of vegetables and flowers. Palm tree avenue leading to summerhouse. Spring garden incl cowslips, bluebells. Alpine house with over 100 immaculately displayed plants. Wide selection of well-grown plants for sale. Bickham Cottage: small cottage garden divided into separate areas by old stone walls and hedge banks. Front garden with mainly South African bulbs and plants. Lawn surrounded by borders incl agapanthus, eucomis, crocosmia, dierama. Stream garden with primulas. Pond with large koi carp. National collection of Nerine sarniensis and cultivars, 450 varieties in glasshouses. October opening for National Collection of Nerines, 3500 pots with in excess of 450 varieties. Featured in Daily Telegraph, Western Morning News, Devon Country Gardener, Amateur Gardener, RHS Plantsman.

8 ◆ BLACKPOOL GARDENS
Dartmouth TQ6 0RG. Sir Geoffrey Newman, 01803 771801, www.blackpoolsands.co.uk. *3m SW of Dartmouth. From Dartmouth follow brown signs to Blackpool Sands on A379. Entrance to gardens via Blackpool Sands car park.* **For opening times and information, please phone or see garden website.**
Tenderly restored C19 subtropical plantsman's garden with collection of mature and newly-planted tender and unusual trees, shrubs and carpet of spring flowers. Paths and steps lead gradually uphill and above the Captain's seat offering spectacular coastal views. Recent plantings follow the S hemisphere theme with callistemons, pittosporums, acacias and buddlejas. Open 1 Apr - Sept (10-4) weather permitting.

9 BOCOMBE MILL COTTAGE
Bocombe, Parkham, Bideford EX39 5PH. Mr Chris Butler & Mr David Burrows, 01237 451293, www.bocombe.co.uk. *6m E of Clovelly, 9m SW of Bideford. From A39 just outside Horns Cross village, turn to Foxdown. At Xrds follow signs for parking.* Home-made teas. **Adm £4, chd £1. Sat 14, Sun 15, Sat 28, Sun 29 June (12-5). Groups of 10+ also welcome by appt Mar to Sept.**
An undulating organic landscape of 5 acres punctuated with gardens and features. Flower gardens walk around house plus relaxing circular walk around a mile, boots suggested. Streams, bog gardens, pools, a dozen water features. White pergola. grotto and hermitage. Hillside orchard. Soft fruit and kitchen gardens. Garden kaleidoscope. Wild meadow, a wildlife haven. Garden Plan includes 60 specimen trees. Goats on hillside. Featured in The Garden magazine (RHS) and Western Morning News.

GROUP OPENING

10 BOVEY COUNTRY GARDENS
Bovey Tracey TQ13 9LQ. *6m N of Newton Abbot. Gateway to Dartmoor. Gardens between Shewte Cross and cattle grid to moor (2m) on Manaton Rd from fire station r'about. Limited parking at Down Park, parking at Three Corners; extra parking for Holne Brake over cattle grid.* Home-made teas at Three Corners. **Combined adm £4, chd free. Sat 10, Sun 11 May (2-5).**

DOWN PARK
Shewte Cross. Susan Macready.
1m from Fire Station r'about on Manaton Rd. Parking available

HOLNE BRAKE
Michael & Jennifer Pery.
R after cattle grid on rd to Manaton Rd, 2m from fire stn r'about

THREE CORNERS
Manaton Rd. Jonathan & Sue Clarke.
Up Manaton Rd from Bovey Fire Stn, 1st R after turning to Haytor before Shewte Cross

3 very different gardens on Western edge of Bovey Tracey towards Dartmoor. On moorland rd towards Manaton is Three Corners, a classic style country garden laid out in 1930s style with croquet lawn, grass tennis court, vegetable garden and vine-clad pergola. Close by is Down Park, a colourful mature garden with a great variety of rhododendrons, azaleas, camellias and unusual shrubs. A mile beyond at cattle grid is Holne Brake, an artist's moorland garden with woodland walks and spectacular views of Lustleigh Cleave. A blaze of colour in spring. Recent clearing of rhododendron ponticum has opened ground for planting of specimen trees and creation of new pond. New Raven Bench made from 110ft douglas fir, the tree house and folly. Dogs allowed to Holne Brake. Wheelchair access to 2 gardens.

Much redevelopment and revels in interesting garden and planting styles . . .

GROUP OPENING

11 BOVEY TRACEY GARDENS
Bovey Tracey TQ13 9NA. *6m N of Newton Abbot. Gateway to Dartmoor. Take A382 to Bovey Tracey. Car parking at Mary St, Station Rd, library, car parks and Little Bradley Pottery Rd and Parke.* Home-made teas at Gleam Tor. **Combined adm £4.50, chd free. Sat 7, Sun 8 June (2-6).**

BOVEY COMMUNITY GARDEN
Parke. NT and Bovey Tracey Climate Action.
Follow signs to Parke, parking in visitors' car park
www.boveycommunitygarden.org.uk

5 BRIDGE COTTAGES
Pottery Rd. Cath Valentine.
Down lane at base of Pottery Rd, near r'about, opp Mike Harding Landrover dealership

GLEAM TOR
Brimley Rd. Gillian & Colin Liddy.
Last house on L at end of Brimley Rd before rd narrows

NEW LITTLE BRADLEY HOUSE
Off Bradley Rd B3344

PARKE VIEW
Fore St. Peter & Judy Hall.
Next to The Old Cottage tea shop

11 ST PETER'S CLOSE
Pauline and Keith Gregory.
Parking available in surrounding rds

23 STORRS CLOSE
Mr Roger Clark & Ms Chie Nakatani

Pretty cob and Dartmoor granite-built town by R Bovey. 7 enormously varied gardens in or close to the town. Storrs Close, plantsman's paradise with plants grown from seed from around the world. St Peter's Close: small town garden packed with interesting plants and an art exhibition. Gleam Tor: abundance of herbaceous colour and new curved wall garden with prairie planting. New for 2014, beautiful re designed wildlife pond area. 5 Bridge Cottages: productive, colourful and quirky cottage garden. Little Bradley has seen much redevelopment and revels in interesting garden and planting styles with ponds small walled herb/flower garden and ornamental areas. Parke view an acre of garden with meandering stone walls and unusual plants. In the walled garden at the NT's Parke is a successful community garden, with productive fruit trees, and many vegetables (inc. heritage varieties). Limited wheelchair access at some gardens.

12 BRAMBLE TORRE
Dittisham, nr Dartmouth TQ6 0HZ. Paul & Sally Vincent, 01803 722227, salv@hotmail.co.uk, www.rainingsideways.com. *¾ m from Dittisham. Leave A3122 at Sportsman's Arms. Drop down into Village, at Red Lion turn L to Cornworthy. Continue ¾ m Bramble Torre straight ahead*. Cream teas. **Adm £4, chd free. Sat 14, Sun 15 June (2-6). Visitors also welcome by appt Apr to July.**
Set in 20 acres of farmland, the 3-acre garden follows a rambling stream through a steep valley: lily pond, herbaceous borders, camellias, shrubs and roses dominated by huge embothrium glowing scarlet in late spring against a sometimes blue sky! A formal herb and vegetable garden runs alongside the stream while chickens scratch in an orchard of Dit'sum plums and cider apples. Well behaved dogs on leads welcome. Limited wheelchair access, parts of garden very steep and uneven. Tea area with wheelchair access and excellent garden view.

GROUP OPENING

13 BRENDON GARDENS
Brendon, Lynton EX35 6PU, 01598 741343, lalindevon@yahoo.co.uk. *1m S of A39 North Devon coast rd, between Porlock and Lynton*. Cream teas. **Combined adm £4.50, chd free. Sat 10, Sun 11 May; Sat 9, Sun 10 Aug (12-5). Visitors also welcome by appt May to Sept.**

1 DEERCOMBE COTTAGES
Valerie and Stephen Exley.
From village green in Brendon drive into village and park in Village hall car park. Garden 250 yds on L. Set down possible close to garden

NEW HALL FARM
Brendon, Lynton. Mrs Janie Scott.
From village green in Brendon, over bridge turn R.100 yds on R. Some parking in stable yard

HIGHER TIPPACOTT FARM
Tippacott Lane. Angela & Malcolm Percival.
From Xrds at Brendon village green follow signs to Tippacott, 1m to T-junction fronting moor. Turn R, proceed 200 yds. Parking on R

A stunningly beautiful part of Exmoor Nat Park nestling in the E Lyn river valley surrounded by heather moorland, dramatic coastline close by. Excellent walking; along river to Rockford, across moorland & coastpath. 1 Deercombe Cottage: delightful small garden situated in steeply wooded valley overlooking lane and river, created using ditched stone to provide a variety of levels to display planting rich in contrasting foliage and variety of perennials. Hall Farm: a beautiful and mature garden. The inner cottage garden opens out into a tranquil area with lake, borders, shrubs, lawns and woodland all flowing together harmoniously in 2-acre valley setting with lovely views. Walks beyond the garden. Higher Tippacott: on open moor high above Brendon alt 950ft overlooking its own pretty valley pasture and stream. Sunny levels of interesting herbaceous planting, stone walls and old barns, blending into its surroundings. Vegetable patch high up with distant sea view. Chickens. All organic.

14 NEW THE BRIDGE MILL
Mill Lane, Bridgerule, Holsworthy EX22 7EL. Rosie Beat, 01288 381341, rosie@thebridgemill.org.uk, www.thebridgemill.org.uk. *In Bridgerule village on R Tamar between Bude and Holsworthy. Between chapel by river bridge and church at top of hill towards Holsworthy. See above website for detailed directions*. Home-made teas. **Adm £3.50, chd free. Sun 15 June (11-5). Groups of 10+ also welcome by appt June to July.**
1-acre organic gardens set around mill house and restored water mill. Small cottage garden; herb garden with medicinal and dye plants; very productive vegetable garden and new woodland and water garden behind the mill. The 16-acre smallholding will be open for lake, pond and riverside walks. Friendly sheep, pigs and poultry! The Bridge Mill is open for educational visits throughout the yr to school and adult groups. Details on website. Regular features in Country Smallholding magazine. Wheelchair access to at least half the garden. Toilet with access for wheelchairs.

15 ◆ BURROW FARM GARDENS
Dalwood, Axminster EX13 7ET. Mary & John Benger, 01404 831285, enquiries@burrowfarmgardens.co.uk, www.burrowfarmgardens.co.uk. *3½ m W of Axminster. From A35 turn N at Taunton Xrds then follow brown signs*
Beautiful 10-acre garden with unusual trees, shrubs and herbaceous plants. Traditional summerhouse looks towards lake and ancient oak woodland with rhododendrons and azaleas. Early spring interest and superb autumn colour. The more formal Millennium garden features a rill. Anniversary Garden featuring late summer perennials and grasses. A photographers dream. Open 1 April - 31 Oct (10 - 7). Café and gift shop. Various events incl plant fair and open air Shakespeare held at garden each year. Visit events page on Burrow Farm Gardens website for more details. Featured in Country Homes and Interiors magazine.

16 ◆ CADHAY

Ottery St Mary EX11 1QT. Rupert Thistlethwayte, 01404 813511, jayne@cadhay.org.uk, www.cadhay.org.uk. *1m NW of Ottery St Mary. On B3176 between Ottery St Mary and Fairmile. From E exit A30 at Iron Bridge. From W exit A30 at Patteson's Cross.* Home-made teas. **Adm £3, chd £1. For NGS: Sun 25, Mon 26 May, Fri 20 June, Fri 18 July (2-5). For other opening times and information, please phone or see garden website.**

Tranquil 2-acre setting for Elizabethan manor house. 2 medieval fish ponds surrounded by rhododendrons, gunnera, hostas and flag iris. Roses, clematis, lilies and hellebores surround walled water garden. 120ft herbaceous border walk informally planted with cottage garden perennials and annuals. Walled kitchen gardens have been turned into allotments and old garden store is now tearoom. Featured in Devon Life. Gravel paths.

17 CARPENTER'S COTTAGE

Knowle, Crediton EX17 5BX. Mrs Joan Tolley. *4m W of Crediton. From Crediton A377 W, after 4m L to Knowle. From Copplestone A377 E, after 1m turn R to Knowle. Park in Church car park.* Home-made teas. **Adm £3, chd free. Sat 10, Sun 11 May (2-5).**

1-acre plantaholic's cottage garden. Winding paths throughout densely planted areas take you through exotic planting, acer glade, white garden, wildlife ponds and many shady areas with unusual woodland planting and late spring bulbs.

18 ◆ CASTLE DROGO

Drewsteignton EX6 6PB. National Trust, 01822 820320, www.nationaltrust.org.uk. *12m W of Exeter. 5m S of A30. Follow brown signs.* Light refreshments. **Adm £6.50, chd £3.50. For NGS: Sun 11 May, Sun 14 Sept (9.30-5.30). For other opening times and information, please phone or see garden website.**

Medium-sized Grade II* listed garden with formal structures designed by Edwin Lutyens and George Dillistone during the late 1920s. These consist of formal rose beds, herbaceous borders, shrubbery and circular croquet lawn surrounded by mature yew hedges. Rhododendron garden overlooks spectacular views of Teign valley gorge and Dartmoor. Garden tours. Partial wheelchair access, purpose-built access path to main terrace.

Friendly sheep, pigs and poultry . . . !

19 CHAPEL FARM HOUSE

Halwill Junction, Beaworthy EX21 5UF. Robin & Toshie Hull, 01409 221594. *12m NW of Okehampton. On A3079. At W end of village.* Home-made teas. **Adm £2.50, chd free. Sats 5, 26 Apr; Fri 16, Sats 17, 31 May; Sats 14 June; 5 July; 16 Aug; 6 Sept; 25 Oct (11-5).**

Approx 1/2 -acre garden started in 1992 by present owners, landscaped with shrub borders, heathers, rhododendrons and azaleas. Alpine bed. Kitchen garden. 2 small greenhouses for mixed use. Small bonsai collection. 3 acres of mixed young woodland with wildlife and flowers. Japanese garden and stone lantern. Gravel car park and paths.

20 CHERRY TREES WILDLIFE GARDEN

5 Sentry Corner, East the Water, Bideford EX39 4BW. Henry and Evelyn Butterfield, cherrytrees.weebly.com. *From Bideford Old Bridge, follow up hill past The Royal Hotel. Follow signs to Sentry Corner (approx 3/4 m), parking at Pollyfield Centre.* Light refreshments. **Adm £3, chd free. Sat 7, Sun 8 June (2-5).**

Small demonstration garden showing what can be done to bring wildlife into the town. Incl courtyard garden, summer cornfield meadow, cottage garden border, mini copse and 2 small ponds. Newly-constructed folly and stumpery. Enjoy a friendly chat about wildlife gardening over tea and biscuits with the owners. Photo collection of garden's wildlife visitors. Small natural history collection.

GROUP OPENING

21 CHERUBEER GARDENS

Dolton EX19 8PP, 01805 804265, hynesjo@gmail.com, www.sites.google.com/site/cherubeergardens/the-gardens. *8m SE of Great Torrington. 2m E of Dolton. From A3124 turn S towards Stafford Moor Fisheries, take 1st R, gardens 500m on L.* Home-made teas Higher Cherubeer. **Combined adm £4, chd free. Sun 2, Fri 14 Feb (2-5); Sun 1 June, Sun 5 Oct (2.30-5.30); Sun 1, Fri 20 Feb 2015 (2-5). Groups of 10+ also welcome by appt Feb all gardens and Mar to Oct Cherubeer and Higher Cherubeer.**

CHERUBEER
Janet Brown

HIGHER CHERUBEER NCH
Jo & Tom Hynes

MIDDLE CHERUBEER
Heather Hynes.
not open in the summer

The 3 Cherubeers, a family affair, form a small hamlet in rolling farmland at 500 ft at the top of a SW facing valley. Despite the exposed location and stony acid clay soil, the gardens provide a wealth of colour right through the season. Cherubeer: cottage garden set around a C15 thatched house (not open). Ponds, paths, and steps filled with colourful perennials and herbs set off by mature shrubs and trees. Higher Cherubeer: 1-acre country garden with gravelled courtyard, raised beds and alpine house, large herbaceous border, shady woodland beds with over 200 varieties of snowdrops, colourful collection of basketry willows, vegetable garden and National Collection of hardy cyclamen. Middle Cherubeer: colourful small garden. 3 separate areas with bog garden, pond and massed herbaceous perennials interlinked with paths. Many cyclamen and snowdrop bank. Partial wheelchair access due to slopes and gravel. Very little wheelchair access at Cherubeer.

22 CHEVITHORNE BARTON
Tiverton EX16 7QB. Michael & Arabella Heathcoat Amory, pottinger985@btinternet.com. *3m NE of Tiverton. Through Sampford Pev and Halberton to Tiverton, past Golf Club, turn R. R at next junction. Over bridge, L through Craze Lowman, carry on to T-junc, R then 1st L.* Home-made teas. **Adm £4, chd free.** Sun 13 Apr, Sun 18 May (2-5).
Terraced walled garden, summer borders and romantic woodland of rare trees and shrubs. In spring, garden features large collection of magnolias, camellias, rhododendrons and azaleas. Also incl one of only two NCCPG oak collections situated in 12 hectares of parkland and comprising over 200 different species.

23 CLEAVE HILL
Membury, Axminster EX13 7AJ. Andy & Penny Pritchard, 01404 881437, penny@tonybengerlandscaping.co.uk. *4m NW of Axminster. From Membury Village, follow rd down valley. 1st R after Lea Hill B&B, last house on drive, approx 1m.* Light refreshments. **Adm £3.50, chd free.** Sat 28, Sun 29 June (11-5.30). **Visitors also welcome by appt coaches can only park 1 mile away.**
Artistic garden in pretty village situated on edge of Blackdown Hills. Cottage-style garden, planted to provide all-season structure, texture and colour. Designed around pretty thatched house and old stone barns. Wonderful views, attractive vegetable garden and orchard, wild flower meadow. Featured on BBC Radio Devon's The Potting Shed.

24 CLIFFE
Lee, Ilfracombe EX34 8LR. Dr & Mrs Humphreys, 07854 131935, gill.heavens@virgin.net, www.ontheedgegardening.wordpress.com. *3m W of Ilfracombe. Past sea front at Lee, towards top of steep hill on coast rd. Entrance through black wrought iron gates on L. Car park at bottom of hill.* **Adm £3, chd free.** Mon 30 June to Fri 12 Sept incl (10-4). **Visitors also welcome by appt Apr to Sept.**
Cliff-side terraced garden with spectacular coastal views. Diverse range of habitats from Mediterranean to woodland. Colourful herbaceous borders throughout summer and exotic hedychiums, canna and salvias flowering into autumn.

Mardon, Moretonhampstead Gardens

25 COLLEPARDO
3 Keyberry Park, Newton Abbot TQ12 1BZ. Betty & Don Frampton, 01626 354580, collepardo@btinternet.com. *Take A380 Newton Abbot. From Newton Abbot (Penn Inn) r'about follow sign for town centre. 1st L slip rd before T-lights, then 1st R, 2nd L.* Home-made teas. **Adm £3, chd free.** Sat 21 June to Sun 29 June incl (11-5). **Visitors also welcome by appt May to June for groups of 10+.**
1/3 -acre garden laid out in series of interlinked colour-themed garden rooms, explored via 400 metres of meandering paths. Circular rockery of 30 metres enclosing new lawn. Herbaceous and shrub borders, pond, raised walkway, and gazebo allow the visitor every opportunity to view 1,500 varieties of hardy plants, shrubs and trees. 1st prize in Large Garden competition, Newton Abbot in Bloom.

26 COOMBE TRENCHARD
Lewtrenchard EX20 4PW. Philip & Sarah Marsh, 01566 783179, Sarah@coombetrenchard.co.uk, www.coombetrenchard.co.uk. *14m N of Tavistock and W of Okehampton. In Lewdown take turning for Lewtrenchard, at bottom of hill turn R opp Lewtrenchard Manor Hotel. Garden 100yds on R up unmarked lane.* Cream teas. **Adm £5, chd free.** Sat 10, Sun 11 May (11-5).
Coombe Trenchard's 8-acre Arts & Crafts garden was designed in 1906 by architect Walter Sarel, with terraces, garden buildings, paths and bridges. Still a work in progress, forgotten paths, woodland garden, water gardens and the pattern of long forgotten Edwardian planting schemes are being discovered and restored. Featured in Devon Life magazine, The Valley (SW publication on AONB), The Dartmoor Magazine, Western Morning News and The Telegraph. Mostly wheelchair access. Gravel paths in woodland.

27 THE CROFT
Yarnscombe, Barnstaple EX31 3LW. Sam & Margaret Jewell, 01769 560535. *8m S of Barnstaple, 10m SE of Bideford, 12m W of South Molton, 4m NE of Torrington. From A377, turn W opp Chapelton railway stn. Follow Yarnscombe signs, after 3m. From B3232, ¼ m N of Huntshaw Cross TV mast, turn E and follow Yarnscombe signs for 2m. Parking in Village Hall Car Park.* **Adm £3.50, chd free (share to N Devon Animal Ambulance). Suns 15 June; 20 July; 17 Aug (2-6). Visitors also welcome by appt Mar to Nov minimum of 3 days notice required.**
1-acre plantswoman's garden featuring exotic Japanese garden with tea house, koi carp pond and cascading stream, tropical garden with exotic shrubs and perennials, herbaceous borders with unusual plants and shrubs,bog garden with collection of irises, astilbes and moisture-loving plants, duck pond. Exotic borders, new beds around duck pond and bog area, large collection of rare and unusual plants.

28 DICOT
Chardstock EX13 7DF. Mr & Mrs F Clarkson, www.dicot.co.uk. *5m N of Axminster. Axminster to Chard A358 at Tytherleigh to Chardstock. R at George Inn, L fork to Hook, R to Burridge, 2nd house on L.* Home-made teas. **Adm £3.50, chd free. Sat 3, Sun 4, Mon 5 May, Sat 14, Sun 15 June, Sat 26, Sun 27 July (2-5.30).**
Secret garden hidden in East Devon valley. 3 acres of unusual and exotic plants - some rare. Rhododendrons, azaleas and camellias in profusion. Meandering stream, fish pool, Japanese-style garden and interesting vegetable garden with fruit cage, tunnel and greenhouses. Surprises round every corner. Partial wheelchair access.

GROUP OPENING

29 DITTISHAM GARDENS
Dittisham, nr Dartmouth TQ6 0ES, 01803 722227, salv@hotmail.co.uk, www.dittisham.org.uk. *On R Dart at Dittisham between Totnes and Dartmouth. Leave A3122 Dartmouth rd at Hemborough Post by Sportsmans Arms PH. Continue 2½ m then down steep hill with river views into village.* Cream teas at Dittisham Village Hall. **Combined adm £5, chd free. Sat 19, Sun 20 July (2-6).**

CAMELOT
Lower St. Stella Stothart

DEEDAS COTTAGE
Manor St. Mrs Gail Mosley

DOVE COTTAGE
The Level. Mrs M Pusey

NEW DUKES HOUSE
Lower St. Mr & Mrs Nigel Long.
Rectory Lane

FERRY VIEW
The Lane. Mr & Mrs J Young

NEW LYNDHURST
Lower St. Mr & Mrs David Hunt

SHEARWATER
Riverside Rd. Mr & Mrs Smith.
Enter village leaving church on L. Follow wide rd (Riverside Rd) passing field on R. Shearwater 1st house after small lane to The Ham on R

Dittisham overlooks the widest stretch of the beautiful R Dart just 3m up river from Dartmouth. The village, protected from the worst weather by rolling hills and the temperance of the Gulf Stream, is a gardener's paradise! Thatched cottages with gardens filled with all the old fashioned favourites, look out across the water towards Dartmoor in the distance. There are modern gardens too with contemporary planting, terraced gardens clinging to the hillside and the famous Dit'sum Plum orchards flourish still. Delicious home made cream teas can be had in the Village Hall overlooking the river. Read more about the village on www.dittisham.org.uk. Beautiful village on steep slopes overlooking R Dart opp National Trust property Greenway (Agatha Christie). Very limited wheelchair access; the village is very steep.

30 ◆ DOCTON MILL
Lymebridge, Hartland EX39 6EA. Lana & John Borrett, 01237 441369, doctonmill@tiscali.co.uk, www.doctonmill.co.uk. *8m W of Clovelly. Follow brown tourist signs on A39 nr Clovelly.* Cream teas. **Adm £4.50, chd free. For NGS: Sun 15 June (10-5). For other opening times and information, please phone or see garden website.**
Situated in stunning valley location. Garden surrounds original mill pond and the microclimate created within the wooded valley enables tender species to flourish. Recent planting of herbaceous, stream and summer garden give variety through the season. Light lunches and cream teas all day.

31 THE DOWNES
Monkleigh, Bideford EX39 5LB. Richard Stanley-Baker, 07729 511671/07413 593557, downes.gardens@gmail.com, downes-gardens.com. *3m NW of Great Torrington. On A386 between Bideford & Torrington. Drive leads off A386 4½ m from Bideford, 2½ m from Torrington. Do not go to Monkleigh.* Cream teas. **Adm £5, chd free. Sat 5, Sun 6, Mon 7, Tue 8, Wed 9, Thur 10, Fri 11, Sat 12 Apr (12-4.30).**
15 acres of landscaped lawns with spectacular views over Torridge Valley. Arboretum with woodland walk, narcissi, bluebells. Unusual trees and shrubs sourced by two generations of Stanley-Bakers, from all over the world. Energetic programme of new plantings and border restoration initiated by new Head Gardener, Nigel Alford. Lovely garden environment, open to the public for some 30yrs, and features many specimen shrubs and trees. It borders on the Tarka Trail, and itself offers a lovely woodland walks - especially good at bluebell time, and is delightfully secluded, rich in wild life. The garden has some steep slopes however, with due care, wheelchair access should be manageable, preferably when accompanied by friend.

32 DURCOMBE WATER
Furzehill, Barbrook, Lynton EX35 6LN. Pam & David Sydenham, 01598 753658, pam.sydenham@virgin.net. *3m S of Lynton. From Lynmouth head for*

Barnstaple. AT the T-junction in Barbrook (petrol station opposite) turn L, follow yellow signs. A39 from Blackmore Gate. Home-made teas. **Adm £4, chd free. Sun 25, Mon 26 May, Sun 24, Mon 25 Aug (11-5).**
Stunning views across Exmoor. A silent relaxing 2½ acres, enlivened with streams, ponds and waterfalls falling 40ft through 8 tiered ponds. Different types of garden - cottage, landscaped terraces, oriental and art gallery, each with colour, scents and beauty. A feast of colour with rhododendrons, azaleas, perennials and shrubs. Lots of seats to enjoy the peace, views and beauty. The garden has been created single-handedly by the owner over the last 12 years since his retirement, and is maintained solely by him. Superb views, water features, peace and quiet.

33 EAST WOODLANDS FARMHOUSE

Newton Tracey, Barnstaple EX31 3PP. Ann & Richard Harding, 01271 858776, hardingfarmhouse@aol.com, www.the-farmhouse.co.uk. *5m NE of Great Torrington, 5m S of Barnstaple, off B3232. From Great Torrington turn R into single track rd before Alverdiscott; and from Barnstaple turn L after Alverdiscott. 1m down rd R fork at Y-junction*. Home-made teas. **Adm £3.50, chd free. Sat 26, Sun 27 July (2-5). Visitors also welcome by appt Apr to Sept, phone or email at least 1 month prior to visit.**
From 1-acre blank landscape, East Woodlands has been transformed into a hidden oasis of swaying grasses, spectacular bamboos and cool to hot terraces. Little havens have been created where you can sit and enjoy the garden with its rolling, tireless views. Pond (unfenced) and bog garden. A potager's delight. Featured in North Devon Journal, Torrington Crier. Partial wheelchair access.

34 EAST WORLINGTON HOUSE

East Worlington, Witheridge, Crediton EX17 4TS. Mr & Mrs Barnabas Hurst-Bannister. *In centre of East Worlington, 2m W of Witheridge. In Witheridge (B3137 Tiverton/South Molton) into square and R at sign to East Worlington. Along West St to Drayford Lane, 1.4m R at T-junction in Drayford, over bridge then L to Worlington. 0.3m enter East Worlington, L at T-junction. East Worlington House after parish hall on L*. Cream teas in thatched parish hall next to house. **Adm £3, chd free. Sun 2, Sun 9 Mar (1.30-5).**
Thousands of Crocuses. In 2-acre garden, set in lovely position with views down the valley to Little Dart river, these spectacular crocuses have spread over many years through the garden and into the neighbouring churchyard. Cream teas in the parish hall (in aid of its thatch fund) next door. Disabled parking at the house. Parking nearby. Dogs on leads please.

35 1 FEEBERS COTTAGE

Broadclyst EX5 3DQ. Mr & Mrs M J Squires. *8m NE of Exeter. From B3181 Exeter to Taunton bear E at Dog Village towards Whimple. After 1½ m fork L for Westwood*. Light refreshments. **Adm £3, chd free. Sat 15, Sun 16 Feb (12-3).**
Mature but evolving cottage garden of 1 acre, with a maze of pathways, alpine area, herbaceous plants, trees, shrubs and vegetable garden. Many varieties of snowdrops in spring. Wheelchair access if dry.

36 FOAMLEA

Chapel Hill, Mortehoe EX34 7DZ. Beth Smith, 01271 871182, bethmortepoint@fmail.co.uk. *¼ m S of Mortehoe village. A361 N from Barnstaple. L onto B3343 to Mortehoe car park. No parking at or near garden. On foot L past church, down hill, then 200yds*. Home-made teas. **Adm £3, chd free. Suns 11 May; 1, 15 June; 6 July (2-5). Visitors also welcome by appt May to Sept, max 20.**
11 yr old collection of plants thriving in open cliff top site with uninterrupted view to Morte Point (NT). The mild climate and a gradient providing natural drainage favour many temperate and semi-tropical species. Wide range of shrubs and perennials. Drystone walling, slate steps and shillet paths feature throughout. Colour-schemed areas, rockery and mixed plantings. National Collection of phlomis. Featured in Coast magazine and RHS The Garden magazine.

NCH

Quirky garden full of surprises . . .

37 ◆ FURSDON

Cadbury, Thorverton, Exeter EX5 5JS. David & Catriona Fursdon, 01392 860860, admin@fursdon.co.uk, www.fursdon.co.uk. *2m N of Thorverton. From Tiverton S on A396. Take A3072 at Bickleigh towards Crediton. L after 2½ m. From Exeter N on A396. L to Thorverton and R in centre*. Light refreshments in the Coach Hall. **Adm £4, chd free. For NGS: Mon 5 May, Sun 8 June, Wed 2 July, Sun 14 Sept (12-5). For other opening times and information, please phone or see garden website.**
The garden surrounds Fursdon, home of same family for 7 centuries. Hillside setting with extensive views S over parkland and beyond. Sheltered by house, hedges and cob walls, there are terraces of roses, herbs and perennials in mixed traditional and contemporary planting. Woodland walk and pond in meadow garden. Fursdon House open for guided tours on NGS days. Some steep slopes and gravel paths.

38 NEW GALEN WAY

Sparkwell, Plymouth PL7 5DF. Mr & Mrs Peter & Ann Tremain, 01752 837532. *Car parking Sparkwell Hall PL7 5DD. Follow signs approx 300yds. Limited disabled park at Galen Way*. Home-made teas. **Adm £4, chd free. Sun 1 June (12-5). Visitors also welcome by appt Apr to Aug.**
Quirky garden full of surprises, developed over last 40yrs. Incl fish ponds, floating Island, water wheel, cave and sunken greenhouse. Fully organic and compost system. Vegetable garden (no dig system). Flower borders with shrubs. Various seating areas and a 'follow the sun house'! Complete walled Garden. Mostly wheelchair access.

The Lookout

39 THE GATE HOUSE

Lee EX34 8LR. Mrs D Booker, 01271 862409. *3m W of Ilfracombe. Park in Lee village car park. Take lane alongside The Grampus PH. Garden approx 30 metres past inn buildings.* **Adm by donation. Tue 1 Apr to Fri 31 Oct incl (10-4) by appt (open most days but wise to check by tel/email).**

Described by many visitors as a peaceful paradise, this streamside garden incl collection of over 100 rodgersia (at their best end of June), interesting herbaceous areas, patio gardens with semi-hardy exotics, many unusual mature trees and shrubs and large organic vegetable garden. Level gravel paths.

40 GOREN FARM

Broadhayes, Stockland, Honiton EX14 9EN. Julian Pady, 01404 881335, gorenfarm@hotmail.com, www.goren.co.uk. *6m E of Honiton, 6m W of Axminster. Old Taunton Rd from Shute on A35 or Otter Vale motors on A30. 100 metres north of the Stockland television mast, signed at Ridge Cross.* Light refreshments. **Adm £3, chd free. Evening Openings £3, chd free, Sun 1 June to Thur 31 July incl (5-9); Sat 7, Sun 8, Sat 14, Sun 15 June; Sat 5, Sun 6, Sat 12, Sun 13 July (10-5). Visitors also welcome by appt June to Aug.**

Wander through 50 acres of natural species rich wild flower meadows. Dozens of varieties of wild flowers and grasses. Orchids early June, butterflies July. Stunning views of Blackdown Hills. Georgian house and gardens, guided walks 10.30 and 2.30 on open weekends, evenings, or by appointment. Partial wheelchair access to meadows.

41 GORWELL HOUSE

Goodleigh Rd, Barnstaple EX32 7JP. Dr J A Marston, 01271 323202, artavianjohn@gmail.com, www.gorwellhousegarden.co.uk. *¾ m E of Barnstaple centre on Bratton Fleming rd. Drive entrance between two lodges on L.* Cream teas. **Adm £4, chd free. Sun 23 Mar, Sun 13 Apr, Sun 18 May, Sun 15 June, Sun 20 July, Sun 14 Sept (2-6). Visitors also welcome by appt Mar to Oct, groups preferred.**

Created mostly since 1979, this 4-acre garden overlooking the Taw estuary has a benign microclimate which allows many rare and tender plants to grow and thrive, both in the open and in the walled garden. Several strategically-placed follies complement the enclosures and vistas within the garden. Opening in March especially for the magnolias. Featured in N Devon Journal, The English Garden and Devon Life magazines and on BBC Radio Devon. Mostly wheelchair access but some steep slopes.

42 HALDON GRANGE

Dunchideock, Exeter EX6 7YE. Ted Phythian, 01392 832349. *5m SW of Exeter. From A30 at Exeter go through Ide Village to Dunchideock 5m. Turn L to Lord Haldon, Haldon Grange is next L. From A38 (S) turn L on top of Haldon Hill follow Dunchideock signs, R at village centre (at thatched house) to Lord Haldon.* Home-made teas. **Adm £3.50, chd free. Sat 19, Sun 20, Mon 21, Sat 26, Sun 27 Apr, Sat 3, Sun 4, Mon 5, Wed 7, Sat 10, Sun 11, Wed 14, Sat 17, Sun 18, Wed 21, Sat 31 May, Sun 1 June (1-5). Visitors also welcome by appt Apr to June.**

12-acre well-established garden with camellias, magnolias, azaleas, various shrubs and rhododendrons; rare and mature trees; small lake and ponds with river and water cascades. 5-acre arboretum planted 2011 with wide range of trees and shrubs. Wheelchair access to main features.

43 HAMBLYN'S COOMBE

Dittisham, Dartmouth TQ6 0HE. Bridget McCrum, 01803 722228. *3m N of Dartmouth. From A3122 L to Dittisham. In village R at Red Lion, The Level, then Rectory Lane, past River Farm to Hamblyn's Coombe.* **Adm by donation. Visitors welcome by appt.**

7-acre garden with stunning views across the river to Greenway House and sloping steeply to R Dart at bottom of garden. Extensive planting of trees and shrubs with unusual design features accompanying Bridget McCrum's stone carvings and bronzes. Wild flower meadow and woods. Good rhododendrons and camellias, ferns and bamboos, acers and hydrangeas. Exceptional autumn colour.

44 HARBOUR LIGHTS
Horns Cross, Bideford EX39 5DW. Brian & Faith Butler, 01237 451627, brian.nfu@gmail.com. *7m W of Bideford, 3m E of Clovelly. On the main A39 between Bideford and Clovelly, half way between Hoops Inn and Bucks Cross.* Cream teas. **Adm £3.50, chd free. Sat 28, Sun 29 June (11-6). Also open Springfield, Woolsery. Groups of 10+ also welcome by appt June to Aug.**
½ -acre colourful garden with Lundy Views. A garden of wit, humour, unusual ideas and surprises. Water features, shrubs, harbaceous, foliage area, grasses in an unusual setting, fernery, bonsai and polytunnel. Interesting time saving ideas.You will never have seen a garden like this! Superb conservatory for cream teas. Free leaflet. We like our visitors to leave with a smile! Child friendly. A 'must visit' garden. Intriguing artwork of various kinds. Featured in Amateur Gardening.

HARCOMBE HOUSE
See Dorset

30ft pergola covered with seagull rose and clematis . . .

45 THE HAVEN
Wembury Road, Hollacombe, Wembury, South Hams PL9 0DQ. Mrs S Norton & Mr J Norton, 01752 862149, suenorton1@hotmail.co.uk. *20 minutes from Plymouth city centre. Use A379 Plymouth to Kingsbridge rd. At Elburton r'about follow signs to Wembury. Parking on roadside. Bus stop outside, route 48 from Plymouth.* Cream teas. **Adm £3.50, chd free. Fri 28, Sat 29 Mar (10.30-4.30). Visitors also welcome by appt Mar to Aug.**
½ -acre sloping plantsman's garden in the South Hams AONB. Views of South Hams countryside. Tea room and seating areas. 2 ponds. Substantial collection of large flowering Asiatic and hybrid tree magnolias. Large collection of camellias including camellia reticulata. Rare dwarf, weeping and slow growing conifers. Daphnes, early azaleas and rhododendrons, spring bulbs, fritillaria and hellebores. Large flowering tree magnolias, michelias, manglietias, camellia, camellia reticulata, weeping conifers, rare conifers, early azaleas, bulbs, fritillaria, daphnes, hellebores. Wheelchair access to top part of garden only.

46 HEATHERCOMBE
Manaton, nr Bovey Tracey TQ13 9XE. Claude & Margaret Pike Woodlands Trust, 01626 354404, gardens@pike.me.uk, www.heathercombe.com. *7m NW of Bovey Tracey. From Bovey Tracey take rd to Becky Falls and Manaton. Continue on same rd for 2m beyond village to Heatree Cross then follow signs to Heathercombe.* Cream teas. **Adm £4.50, chd free (share to Rowcroft Hospice). Sun 30 Mar (1.30-5.30); Every Sun 18 May to 8 June (1.30-5.30); Sat 31 May, Sun 29 June, Sun 6 July (1.30-5.30). Visitors also welcome by appt Apr to Oct.**
Tranquil valley with tumbling streams and quiet ponds, setting for 30 acres of spring and summer interest - daffodils, extensive bluebells complementing large displays of rhododendrons, lovely cottage gardens, interesting herbaceous planting, woodland walks, many specimen trees, bog and fern gardens, orchard and wild flower meadow. Fine sculptures, seats and mainly level sandy paths. Featured on Radio Devon 'The Potting Shed'.

47 ◆ HEDDON HALL
Parracombe EX31 4QL. Mr & Mrs de Falbe, 01598 763541, Jdefalbe@gmail.com, www.heddonhall.co.uk. *10m NE of Barnstaple. Follow A39 towards Lynton around Parracombe (avoiding village centre), then L towards village; entrance 200 yds on L.* Home-made teas. **Adm £5, chd free. For NGS: Sun 8 June, Sun 13 July (11-4). For other opening times and information, please phone or see garden website.**
Stunning walled garden laid out by Penelope Hobhouse with clipped box and cordoned apple trees, herbaceous secret garden and natural rockery leading to a bog garden and three stew ponds. Very much a gardeners' garden, beautifully maintained, with many rare species, ferns, mature shrubs and trees all thriving in 4 acres of this sheltered Exmoor valley. Wheelchair access to walled garden only.

48 HIGH GARDEN
Chiverstone Lane, Kenton EX6 8NJ. Chris & Sharon Britton, 01626 899106, highgarden@highgarden.co.uk. *5m S of Exeter on A379 Dawlish Rd. Leaving Kenton towards Exeter, L into Chiverstone Lane, 50yds along lane. Entrance clearly marked.* Home-made teas. **Adm £3, chd free. Sat 31 May, Sun 1 June, Sat 5 July (2-5.30). Visitors also welcome by appt May to July, all size groups catered for.**
Stunning recently-developed garden of over 4 acres with huge range of interesting, rare and exciting plants. 70m double herbaceous border for high summer colour. Tropical border, large vegetable and fruit garden. Adjoining plantsman's nursery open on NGS days and all yr Tuesday to Friday. Slightly sloping site but the few steps can be avoided.

49 NEW HIGHER ASH FARM
Ash, Dartmouth TQ6 0LR. Mr Michael Gribbin, 07595 507516, matthew.perkins18@yahoo.co.uk. *Leave A3122 at Halwell for Dartmouth. R at Sportsman's Arms to Ash After 1½ m at 2nd Xrds turn R to Higher Ash Farm.* Home-made teas. **Adm £4.50, chd free. Sun 4, Sun 18 May, Sun 17 Aug, Sun 5 Oct (2-5). Also open 28 & 29 June with Ash Gardens. Visitors also welcome by appt Apr to Oct.**
Evolving garden, high up in South Devon countryside. Sitting in 2.5 acres there is a large kitchen garden terraced into the hillside with adjoining orchard under planted with a variety of daffodils. A vibrant array of azaleas and rhododendrons surround the barns and courtyard. The farmhouse is surrounded by a mix of herbaceous borders, shrubs and lawns. Pond, stream, autumn interest.

50 HIGHER BURNHAIES
Butterleigh, Cullompton, Devon EX15 1PG. Richard & Virginia Holmes, 01884 855748. *Butterleigh. From Butterleigh take rd to Silverton at T-junction. After ¼ m, take unmarked L fork, continue to hamlet. Very narrow lanes*. Home-made teas. **Adm £4, chd free. Sun 1, Sun 22 June (2-6).**
2½ -acre site started in 1997. Situated in the beautiful Burn Valley, a plantsman's garden of herbaceous plantings with trees, shrubs, ponds and wildlife. Informal, country feel with Devon lane and wilderness walk. Vegetable garden. Uneven ground and steps. Wheelchair access is limited with steps and uneven ground.

51 NEW HIGHER CULLAFORD
Spreyton, Crediton EX17 5AX. Dr. and Mrs. Kennerley. *Approx ¾ m from centre of Spreyton, 20m W of Exeter, 10 E of Okehampton. From A30 at Whiddon Down follow signs to Spreyton. Yellow signs from A3124 and Spreyton parish church*. Cream teas. **Adm £3.50, chd free. Sun 29 June, Sun 6 July (1.30-5).**
Traditional cottage-style garden developed over past 10yrs from steep field and farmyard on northern edge of Dartmoor National Park. Mixed borders of herbaceous plants, roses and shrubs. 30ft pergola covered with seagull rose and a variety of clematis, raised vegetable beds and wildlife pond. New polytunnel and fruit trees.

52 HILLRISE
24 Windsor Mead, Sidford EX10 9SJ. Mr & Mrs D Robertshaw, 01395 514991. *1m N of Sidmouth. Off A3052 approx ¼ m W of Sidford T-lights (towards Exeter) signed R to Windsor Mead. R at top of hill, last on R*. Tea. **Adm £3.50, chd £1.50. Sat 3, Sun 4 May, Sat 21, Sun 22 June (1.30-5.30). Visitors also welcome by appt May to Sept max 15.**
Plant enthusiasts' garden on S-facing slope. Fine countryside and sea views. Yr-round colour and interest from wide variety of plants. Borders for New Zealand plants, cannas, dahlias, grasses with kniphofias and hemerocalis, kaleidoscope border. Shaded area for woodland plants. Greenhouse with pelargoniums, cacti and succulents. Troughs, hostas, colourful shrubs and trees and ferns. Some slopes.

53 ◆ HOLBROOK GARDEN
Sampford Shrubs, Sampford Peverell EX16 7EN. Martin Hughes-Jones & Susan Proud, 01884 821164, www.holbrookgarden.com. *1m NW from M5 J27. From M5 J27 follow signs to Tiverton Parkway. At top of slip rd off A361 follow brown signs to Holbrook Garden*. **Adm £4, chd free. For NGS: Sat 19, Sun 20, Mon 21 Apr, Sat 24, Sun 25, Mon 26 May, Sat 14, Sun 15 June, Sat 23, Sun 24, Mon 25 Aug (10-5). For other opening times and information, please phone or see garden website.**
2-acre S-facing garden with plantings inspired by natural plant populations; the garden continually evolves - many experimental plantings - wet garden, stone garden. Perfumes, songbirds and nests everywhere in spring and early summer. Fritillaries, pulmonarias April; crocosmia, heleniums, Salvias, late perennials Aug/Sept. Productive vegetable garden and poly-tunnel.

54 NEW HOLE FARM
Woolsery, Bideford EX39 5RF. Heather Alford. *11m SW of Bideford. Follow directions for Woolfardisworthy, signed from A39 at Bucks Cross. From village follow NGS signs from school for approx 2m*. Home-made teas in converted barn. **Adm £3.50, chd free. Sat 24, Sun 25 May, Sun 20 July, Sun 14 Sept (2-6).**
3 acres of exciting gardens with established pergola walk, waterfall, ponds, vegetable and bog garden.Terraces and features including the round house have all been created using natural stone from the original farm quarry. Peaceful walks through Culm grassland and water meadows border the river Torridge and host a range of wildlife and is home to a herd of pedigree native Devon cattle. Riverside walk not accessible with wheelchair.

55 HOLLYCOMBE HOUSE
Manor Rd, Bishopsteignton TQ14 9SU. Jenny Charlton & Graham Jelley, 01626 870838, hollycombealpacas@live.co.uk, www.hollycombealpacas.co.uk. *Situated between Newton Abbot and Teignmouth. From Newton Abbot A381, L after Jack's Patch GC, or from Teignmouth R at sign Old Walls Vineyard - Church Rd - R at PH, Radway Hill, L Manor Rd, R at Rock*. Cream teas. **Adm £3.50, chd free. Visitors welcome by appt Apr to Sept.**
Nearly 5 acres of stunning garden with views over Teign Estuary. Some say the best view Devon. Stylish borders, shrubs for every day of the year. Organic vegetables in raised beds - compost from alpacas! Attractive large pond, water lilies, koi carp, call ducks, alpacas with their babies and free range chickens all create an area of individuality: also we have Harley the Harris Hawk! Limited wheelchair access to view pond, white silkie chickens, ducks, fish & alpacas.

56 NEW ◆ HOTEL ENDSLEIGH
Milton Abbot, Tavistock PL19 0PQ. Helen Costello, 01822 870000, mail@hotelendsleigh.com, www.hotelendsleigh.com/garden. *7m NW of Tavistock, midway between Tavistock and Launceston. From Tavistock, take B3362 to Launceston. 7m to Milton Abbot then 1st L. From Launceston & A30, B3362 to Tavistock. At Milton Abbot L opp school*. Home-made teas available in lovely old stable yard opp Hotel's main entrance. **Adm £5, chd free. For NGS: Sun 8 June, Sun 20 July (12-5). For other opening times and information, please phone or see garden website.**
200 year old Repton-designed garden in three parts; formal gardens around the house, picturesque Dell with pleasure dairy and rockery, arboretum.The gardens were laid out in 1814 and have been renovated over last 10yrs. Bordering R Tamar, it is a hidden oasis of plants and views.

57 KIA-ORA FARM & GARDENS

Knowle Lane, Cullompton EX15 1PZ. Mrs M B Disney, 01884 32347, rosie@kia-orafarm.co.uk, www.kia-orafarm.co.uk. *On W side of Cullompton and 6m SE of Tiverton. M5 J28 off Swallow Way nr Cullompton Rugby Club.* Homemade traditional Devon cream teas and wide selection of home-made cakes, to be enjoyed inside or out. Proceeds not for NGS. **Adm £3, chd free. Suns, Mons 20, 21 Apr; 4, 5, 25, 26 May; Suns 1, 15, 29 June; 13, 27 July; 10, 24 Aug, Mon 25 Aug; Sun 7 Sept (2-5.30). Visitors also welcome by appt Mar to Sept.**

Charming, peaceful 10-acre garden with lawns, lakes, & ponds. Water features with swans, ducks & other wildlife. Mature trees, shrubs, rhododendrons, azaleas, heathers, roses, herbaceous borders and rockeries. Nursery avenue, novelty crazy golf. Lots to see and enjoy.

GROUP OPENING

58 KILMINGTON (SHUTE ROAD) GARDENS

Kilmington, Axminster EX13 7ST, www.Kilmingtonvillage.com. *1½ m W of Axminster. Signed off A35.* Home-made teas at Bywood. **Combined adm £5, chd free. Sat 14, Sun 15 June (1.30-5).**

BREACH
J A Chapman & B J Lewis.
Off Shute Rd

BYWOOD
David and Sandra Ingles

SPINNEY TWO
Paul & Celia Dunsford

WAYSFIELD
Mrs Sydie Bones

Set in rural E Devon in AONB yet easily accessed from A35. 4 gardens within ¼ m circle. Spinney Two: ½ -acre on southerly slope with yr-round colour, foliage and texture. Spring flowering bulbs, shrubs and trees including acers and cornus, climbers including clematis and roses. Mixed borders and vegetable plot. Breach: set in over 3 acres with majestic woodland partially underplanted with rhododendrons, also extensive areas of grass, colourful beds, ponds, orchard and vegetable garden. Waysfield: ½ -acre country garden, mixed borders with interesting planting, small pond, sunken terrace and expansive views across Axe valley. Bywood: adjoining Waysfield. 1½ acres of well kept grounds with excellent views. An ideal setting for teas.

59 NEW KINGSWOOD HOUSE

West Chilla, Nr. Highampton, Beaworthy EX21 5JS. Mr & Mrs G King. *From Hatherleigh: 2½ m after Highampton turn L at sign Chilla 2. From Holsworthy: 2m after Brandis Corner turn R at sign Chilla 2.* Cream teas. **Adm £3.50, chd free. Sat 14, Sun 15 June, Sat 5, Sun 6 July, Sat 2, Sun 3 Aug, Sat 6, Sun 7 Sept (10.30-4).**

Garden in secluded woodland setting. 3-acre lake with 4 islands, 2 with bridges. 10 acres of wild garden, an abundance of wild flowers and grasses. Lake is surrounded by mature trees, shrubberies and flower gardens, bog garden with waterfall. Over 1m of woodland walks. Cream teas can be served on the island where there is summerhouse and seating, or on terrace. Wheelchair lift and car ramp to lake and patio level.

60 ◆ KNIGHTSHAYES COURT GARDEN

Tiverton EX16 7RQ. National Trust, 01884 254665, www.nationaltrust.org.uk. *2m N of Tiverton. Via A396 Tiverton to Bampton rd; turn E in Bolham, signed Knightshayes; entrance ½ m on L.* **Adm £8.10, chd £4.05. For NGS: Mon 12 May (11-4). For other opening times and information, please phone or see garden website.**

Large, beautiful 'Garden in the Wood', 50 acres of landscaped gardens with pleasant walks and views over Exe valley. Choice collections of unusual plants, incl acers, birches, rhododendrons, azaleas, camellias, magnolias, roses, spring bulbs, alpines and herbaceous borders; formal gardens; walled kitchen garden.

61 LANGTREES

10 Cott Lane, Croyde, Braunton EX33 1ND. Paul & Helena Petrides, 01271 890202, angelrest@lineone.net, www.langtrees.info. *10m W of Barnstaple. From Braunton direction Cott Lane on R as road narrows towards village centre. No parking in lane, parking in village car park 200yds L.* Home-made teas. **Adm £4, chd free. Sat 17, Sun 18 May, Sat 28, Sun 29 June (1-6). Visitors also welcome by appt visitors always welcome.**

1-acre plantsman's garden with eclectic selection of plants. Many S hemisphere shrubs and other tender species. Yr-round interest with landscaping and design features. Flowers all seasons from rhododendrons, viburnums and magnolias in spring to salvias, cannas and ginger lilies in autumn. Interesting selection of trees.

Bog garden with waterfall . . .

62 LEE FORD

Knowle, Budleigh Salterton EX9 7AJ. Mr & Mrs N Lindsay-Fynn, 01395 445894, crescent@leeford.co.uk. *3½ m East of Exmouth in village of Knowle. For Sat Nav use postcode EX9 6AL.* Home-made teas. **Adm £6, chd free (share to Lindsay-Fynn Trust). Visitors welcome by appt groups of 20+ discount, entrance £5 per head.**

Extensive, formal and woodland garden, largely developed in 1950s, but recently much extended with mass displays of camellias, rhododendrons and azaleas, incl many rare varieties. Traditional walled garden filled with fruit and vegetables, herb garden, bog garden, rose garden, hydrangea collection, greenhouses. Ornamental conservatory with collection of pot plants. Lee Ford has direct access to the Pedestrian route and National Cycle Network route 2 which follows the old railway line that linked Exmouth to Budleigh Salterton. Garden is ideal destination for cycle clubs or rambling groups. Formal gardens are lawn with gravel paths. Moderately steep slope to woodland garden on tarmac with gravel paths in woodland.

63 LEWIS COTTAGE

Spreyton, nr Crediton EX17 5AA. Mr & Mrs M Pell and Mr R Orton, 07773 785939, richard@yaxleyhall.com, https://www.greenplantswap.co.uk /growers/Lewis-Cottage-Plants. *5m NE or Spreyton, 8m W of Crediton. From Hillerton Cross, keep Stone Cross to your R. Drive approx 1.5m, Lewis Cottage on L, proceed across cattle grid.* Home-made teas. **Adm £4, chd free. Sat 17, Sun 18 May, Sat 7, Sun 8 June, Sat 26, Sun 27 July, Sat 30, Sun 31 Aug (11-6). Visitors also welcome by appt May to Oct garden clubs and private groups of up to 20.**

Located on SW-facing slope in rural Mid Devon, the 4-acre garden at Lewis Cottage has evolved primarily over last two decades, harnessing and working with the natural landscape. Using informal planting and natural formal structures to create a garden that reflects the souls of those who garden in it, it is an incredibly personal space that is a joy to share.

64 LITTLE ASH BUNGALOW

Fenny Bridges, Honiton EX14 3BL. Helen & Brian Brown, 01404 850941, helenlittleash@hotmail.com. *3m W of Honiton. Leave A30 at Iron Bridge from Honiton 1m, Patteson's Cross from Exeter 1/2 m and follow NGS signs.* Home-made teas. **Adm £3.50, chd free. Sun 1 June, Sun 17 Aug (1.30-5.30). Visitors also welcome by appt June to Sept groups of 10 or more only, coaches welcome.**

Plantswoman's 1 1/2 acre garden packed with different and unusual herbaceous perennials, shrubs and bamboos. Designed for yr-round interest, wildlife and owners' pleasure. Inspirational colour coordinated mixed borders provide interest through late spring, summer and autumn. Natural stream, pond and damp woodland area, mini wildlife meadows and gravel/alpine garden. BBC Radio Devon, Western Morning News, Express & Echo. Grass paths.

65 LITTLE CUMBRE

145 Pennsylvania Road, Exeter EX4 6DZ. Dr Margaret Lloyd, 01392 258315. *1m due N of city centre. From town centre take Longbrook St, continue N up hill approx 1m. Near top of hill. P bus within 75 yds of gate, every 20 mins, hourly on Sundays.* **Adm £3.50, chd free. Sat 8, Sun 9, Sat 15, Sun 16 Feb (12-3.30). Visitors also welcome by appt Feb to Apr for groups of 10 plus.**

1-acre garden and woodland on S-facing slope with extensive views. Interesting areas of garden on different levels linked by grassy paths. Wonderful display of snowdrops, many varieties, and colourful hellebores. Scented winter shrubs and camellias, spring bulbs. Top garden managed to encourage wildlife. Limited wheelchair access.

66 LITTLE WEBBERY

Webbery, Bideford EX39 4PS. Mr & Mrs J A Yewdall, 01271 858206, jyewdall1@gmail.com. *2m E of Bideford. From Bideford (East the Water) along Alverdiscott Rd, or from Barnstaple to Torrington on B3232. Take rd to Bideford at Alverdiscott, pass through Stoney Cross.* Teas by arrangement. **Adm £4, chd free. Visitors welcome by appt Apr to Oct.**

Approx 3 acres in valley setting with pond, lake, mature trees, 2 ha-has and large mature raised border. Large walled kitchen garden with yew and box hedging incl rose garden, lawns with shrubs and rose and clematis trellises. Vegetables and greenhouse and adjacent traditional cottage garden.

67 LITTLECOURT COTTAGES

Seafield Road, Sidmouth EX10 8HF. Geoffrey Ward & Selwyn Kussman. *500yds N of Sidmouth seafront.* Home-made teas. **Adm £3.50, chd free. Sun 27, Mon 28 July (2-5).**

Oasis of calm in middle of Sidmouth. A series of rooms for the plantaholic. Courtyard gardens behind house; in front, main lawn and water feature. Rare and tender plants everywhere. Exceptional basket colour. New features in front garden.

68 LITTLEHAM HOUSE COTTAGE

11 Douglas Avenue, Exmouth EX8 2EY. Pat & Phil Attard, 01395 266750, patricia.attard@sky.com. *1/4 m from Exmouth seafront Orcombe end. E along seafront L into Maer Rd by Fortes Kiosk. Public car park on R. Short 250yd walk to Douglas Ave. Follow NGS signs.* Light refreshments. **Adm £3.50, chd free. Sun 9, Sun 16 Feb (12-3.30); Sun 20, Sun 27 Apr (2-5); Sun 8, Sun 15 Feb 2015 (12-3.30). Visitors also welcome by appt Feb to Sept.**

This secret spring garden is full of colour, foliage and flair. Winding paths lead you to horticultural surprises round every corner; spring bulbs, flowering shrubs and other treasures abound in this cottage garden. Organically-grown vegetables, herbs and a variety of fruit trees - something for everyone. Featured on BBC TV and in Devon Life and Gardener's World. Limited wheelchair access - gravel paths.

Designed for year-round interest, wildlife and owners' pleasure . . .

69 THE LOOKOUT

Sowden Lane, Lympstone EX8 5HE. Will & Jackie Michelmore, jm@lookoutlandscapes.co.uk, www.lympstone.org/businesses/ lookout-landscapes/. *9m SE of Exeter, 2m N of Exmouth off A376. A376 to Exmouth. 1st R after Marine Camp signed Lower Lympstone, 1st R in village into The Strand, past Londis shop into Sowden Lane. No on-site or road parking. If dry, nearby field parking will be signed. Otherwise please use village car park at Underhill between Londis & Globe In - 8min walk. New Exe estuary trail adj - plenty of bike parking!* Cream teas. **Adm £4, chd free. Fri 6 June (2-5); Sun 8 June (2-6).**

2 wildlife-friendly acres on edge of Exe Estuary. Lovingly created from derelict site to harmonise with coastal location and maximise on far reaching views. Flotsam and jetsam sit

Heathercombe

amongst naturalistic seaside planting to give that washed up from the beach look. Circular walk through wild flower meadow to pond, through copse and along riverbank. Walled mediterranean courtyard, small jungly area. Giant sandpit with buckets and spades for children. Photographic display showing how the site has evolved from 1920's to present day. Love-Local stall featuring nautically inspired Westcountry craft. Featured in Western Morning News and on BBC Radio Devon. Limited wheelchair access, some gravel paths, steps and slopes. Drop off area at gate. Level access to stalls and refreshments.

70 LOWER SPITCHWICK GARDEN

Poundsgate TQ13 7NU. Pauline Lee, 01364 631593, Paulineleeceramics@hotmail.com. *4 m NW of Ashburton. By Spitchwick Common, nr New Bridge, Dartmoor.* Home-made teas. **Adm £3.50, chd free.** Sat 7, Sun 8 June, Sat 23, Sun 24 Aug (1.30-5.30).

Beautiful valley alongside the R Dart. East Lower Lodge: atmospheric woodland garden with imaginative planting in natural setting. Contains jungle area with bamboo tea-house, meandering grass pathways, lawns, borders with stream, potager and vegetable garden. Ceramic sculpture inspired by plant forms, and artist's studio.

71 ◆ LUKESLAND

Harford, Ivybridge PL21 0JF. Mrs R Howell & Mr & Mrs J Howell, 01752 691749, lorna.lukesland@gmail.com, www.lukesland.co.uk. *10m E of Plymouth. Turn off A38 at Ivybridge. 1½ m N on Harford rd, E side of Erme valley*

24 acres of flowering shrubs, wild flowers and rare trees with pinetum in Dartmoor National Park. Beautiful setting of small valley around Addicombe Brook with lakes, numerous waterfalls and pools. Extensive and unusual collection of rhododendrons, a champion Magnolia campbellii and a huge Davidia involucrata. Superb spring and autumn colour. Impressive recovery from a severe flood in July 2012. Children's trail. Open Suns, Weds and BH (11-5) 30 Mar-15 June and 5 Oct-16 Nov. Adm £5, chd free. Partial wheelchair access.

72 ◆ MARWOOD HILL

Marwood EX31 4EB. Dr J A Snowdon, 01271 342528, info@marwoodhillgarden.co.uk, www.marwoodhillgarden.co.uk. *4m N of Barnstaple. Signed from A361 & B3230. Look out for Brown Signs. See website for map. New Coach and Car Park.* **Adm £6, chd free.** For NGS: Sun 15 June, Sun 13 July (10-5). **For other opening times and information, please phone or see garden website.**

Marwood Hill is a very special private garden covering an area of 20 acres with lakes and set in a valley tucked away in North Devon. From the early spring snowdrops through to late autumn there is always a colourful surprise around every turn. National Collections of Astilbe, Iris Ensata and Tulbaghia large collections of Camellia, Rhododendron and Magnolia. Winner of MacLaren Cup at Rhododendron and Camellia Show RHS Rosemoor. Featured on Gardeners World. Various articles in national publications. Partial wheelchair access.

NCH

73 NEW THE MILL HOUSE

Fremington, Barnstaple EX31 3DQ. Martin & Judy Ash, martin_s_ash@yahoo.co.uk. *3m W of Barnstaple. Off A39, take A3125 N. At 3rd r'about (Cedars) L on B3233. In Fremington L at top of Church Hill onto Higher Rd. All parking signed 100m away.* Home-made teas. **Adm £3.50, chd free.** Sat 21, Sun 22 June, Sat 5, Sun 6 July, Sat 16, Sun 17 Aug (10-5). **Groups of 10+ also welcome by appt June to Aug.**

A 3/4 acre witty garden, designed around the thatched Mill House and bordered by Fremington water; the topography is the first wow factor here. Stepped ups and downs, ins and outs, surprises around every corner. There is so much on a small scale; bridges, borders, ponds, walkways, rockery, terracing, lawns, bog garden, quarry garden, wild garden, a small art gallery, oh and a henge.

There is so much on a small scale . . .

GROUP OPENING

74 MORETONHAMPSTEAD GARDENS

Moretonhampstead TQ13 8PW, 01647 440296, Miranda@allhusen.co.uk. *12m W of Exeter & N of Newton Abbot. On E slopes of Dartmoor National Park. Parking at both gardens.* Scrummy teas at both gardens. **Combined adm £4.50, chd free.** Sat 17, Sun 18, Mon 19 May, Sat 6, Sun 7 Sept (2-6).

MARDON
Graham & Mary Wilson.
From centre of village, head towards church, turn L into Lime St. Bottom of hill on R

SUTTON MEAD
Edward & Miranda Allhusen.
1/2 m N of village on A382. R at de-restriction sign
Visitors also welcome by appt, mini bus possible.
01647 440296
miranda@allhusen.co.uk

2 large gardens close to moorland town. One in a wooded valley, the other higher up with magnificent views of Dartmoor. Dogs on leads welcome. Plant sale, teas are a must. Both have mature orchards and year round vegetable gardens. Substantial rhododendron, azalea and tree planting, croquet lawns, summer colour and woodland walks through hydrangeas and acers. Something for all the family. Mardon: 4 acres based on its original Edwardian design. Long herbaceous border, rose garden and formal granite terraces supporting 2 borders of agapanthus. Fernery beside stream-fed pond with its thatched boathouse. New arboretum with 60 specimen trees. Sutton Mead: Paths wander through tranquil woodland, unusual planting. Lawns surrounding granite-lined pond with seat at water's edge. Elsewhere dahlias, grasses, bog garden, rill-fed round pond, secluded seating and an unusual concrete greenhouse. A garden of variety. Featured in Western Morning News, Express and Echo.

75 MOTHECOMBE HOUSE

Holbeton, nr Plymouth PL8 1LB. Mr & Mrs A Mildmay-White, 01752 830444, annemildmay@gmail.com, www.flete.co.uk. *12m E of Plymouth. From A379 between Yealmpton and Modbury turn S for Holbeton. Continue 2m to Mothecombe.* Home-made teas. **Adm £4, chd free.** Sat 3, Sun 4 May (2-5). **Visitors also welcome by appt Feb to Oct.**
Queen Anne house (not open) with Lutyens additions and terraces set in private estate hamlet. Walled pleasure gardens, borders and Lutyens courtyard. Orchard with spring bulbs, unusual shrubs and trees, camellia walk. Autumn garden, streams, bog garden and pond. Bluebell woods leading to private beach. Yr-round interest. Sandy beach at bottom of garden, unusual shaped large liriodendron tulipifera. New planting of bee-friendly walled garden. Gravel paths, one slight slope.

76 20 OLD BIDEFORD ROAD

Sticklepath, Barnstaple EX31 2DE. Ian and Jenny Allen. *1m W of Barnstaple town centre. From Stones r'about by new bridge take B3233 (sp Petroc) to top of Sticklepath Hill. L at r'about into Old Torrington Rd then R into Old Bideford Rd.* Home-made teas. **Adm £3.50, chd free.** Sun 27 July (2-5).
Approx 1/4 -acre plantsman's garden. Colourful hot and cool borders with stunning colour associations surround 3 lawns and are packed with hundreds of perennials, annuals, grasses and shrubs plus ornamental trees; a tapestry of colour and texture - secluded and restful. Copies of garden plan and plant list available. Plant stall contains divisions and cuttings from many of the garden's plants. Wheelchair access for small/average size chair.

77 THE OLD DAIRY

Sidbury, Sidmouth EX10 0QR. Alison Carnwath & Peter Thomson. *1/2 m from Sidbury. Enter village of Sidbury from either Honiton or Sidford and turn into Church St which is next to church. Yellow signs visible at church.* Home-made teas. **Adm £5, chd free.** Sat 19, Sun 20 July (1-5).
Extensive woodland and semi-formal areas providing short or longer walks. Roses, herbaceous borders, late rhododendrons, bog garden and greenhouse. Care needed in boggy areas. Panoramic views over Sid and Roncombe valleys. Continue from house along East Devon way to extend your experience of glorious East Devon.

78 THE OLD GLEBE

Eggesford EX18 7QU. Mr & Mrs Nigel Wright. *20m NW of Exeter. Turn S off A377 at Eggesford Stn (halfway between Exeter & Barnstaple), cross railway drive uphill (signed Brushford) for 3/4m, turn R into drive.* Home-made teas. **Adm £3.50, chd £1 (share to Friends of Eggesford All Saints Trust).** Sat 10, Sun 11, Sat 17, Sun 18 May (2-5).
7-acre garden of former Georgian rectory (not open) with mature trees and several lawns, courtyard, walled herbaceous borders, bog garden and small lake; emphasis on species and hybrid rhododendrons and azaleas, 750 varieties. Adjacent rhododendron nursery open by appt.
Rhododendrons magnificent in May.

79 THE OLD VICARAGE

West Anstey, South Molton EX36 3PE. Tuck & Juliet Moss, 01398 341604, julietmoss@btinternet.com. *9m E of South Molton. From S Molton go E on B3227 to Jubilee Inn. Follow NGS signs to house. From Tiverton r'about take A396 7m to B3227 (L) to Jubilee Inn.* Cream teas. **Adm £3.50, chd free.** Sat 17, Sun 18 May, Sat 23, Sun 24 Aug (12-5). **Visitors also welcome by appt May to Aug.**
Croquet lawn leads to multi-level garden overlooking three large ponds with winding paths, climbing roses and overviews. Brook with waterfall flows through garden past fascinating summerhouse built by owner. Benched deck overhangs first pond. Features rhododendrons, azaleas and primulas in spring and large collection of Japanese iris in summer.

80 ◆ PLANT WORLD

St Marychurch Road, Newton Abbot TQ12 4SE. Ray Brown, 01803 872939, raybrown@plant-world-seeds.com, www.plant-world-gardens.co.uk. *2m SE of Newton Abbot. 1 1/2 m from Penn Inn r'about. Follow brown tourist signs at end of A380 dual carriageway from Exeter.* **For opening times and**

information, please phone or see garden website.
The 4 acres of landscape gardens with fabulous views have been called Devon's 'Little Outdoor Eden'. Representing each of the five continents, they offer an extensive collection of rare and exotic plants from around the world. Superb mature cottage garden and Mediterranean garden will delight the visitor. Attractive new viewpoint café and shop. Open 29 Mar - mid Oct (9.30-5.00). Featured in Your Perfect Garden Magazine, Country Gardener Magazine, The Times (on blue poppies) and Herald Express on Cardiocrinum giganteum. Wheelchair access to the cafe and nursery only.

81 PORTINGTON

nr Lamerton PL19 8QY. Mr & Mrs I A Dingle, 01822 870364. *3m NW of Tavistock. From Tavistock B3362 to Launceston. 1/4 m beyond Blacksmiths Arms, Lamerton, fork L (signed Chipshop). Over Xrds (signed Horsebridge) 1st L, L again (signed Portington). From Launceston turn R at Carrs Garage and R again (signed Horsebridge), then as above.* Home-made teas. **Adm £3, chd free (share to Mary Budding Trust). Sun 15, Sun 22 June (2-5.30). Visitors also welcome by appt.**
Garden in peaceful rural setting with fine views over surrounding countryside. Mixed planting with shrubs and borders. Walk to small lake through woodland and fields, which have been designated a county wildlife site.

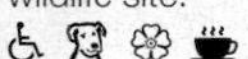

82 PROSPECT HOUSE

Lyme Road, Axminster EX13 5BH. Peter Wadeley, 01297 631210, wadeley@btinternet.com. *1/2 m uphill from centre of Axminster. Just before service station.* Home-made teas. **Adm £3.50, chd free. Sat 12, Sun 13 July, Sat 6, Sun 7 Sept (1.30-5). Groups of 6+ also welcome by appt June to Oct.**
1-acre plantsman's garden hidden behind high stone walls with Axe Valley views. Well-stocked borders with rare shrubs, many reckoned to be borderline tender. 200 varieties of salvia, and other late summer perennials including rudbeckia, helenium, echinacea, helianthus, crocosmia and grasses creating a riot of colour. A gem, not to be missed. Featured in Western Morning News, Garden News Magazine and BBC Gardeners' World feature on salvias.

83 REGENCY HOUSE

Hemyock EX15 3RQ. Mrs Jenny Parsons, 01823 680238, jenny.parsons@btinternet.com, www.regencyhousehemyock.co.uk. *8m N of Honiton. M5 J26. From Hemyock take Dunkeswell-Honiton Rd. Entrance 1/2 m on R from Catherine Wheel PH and church. Disabled parking (only) at house.* Home-made teas. **Adm £4.50, chd free. Sat 14, Sun 15 June, Sun 12 Oct (2-5.30). Visitors also welcome by appt Mar to Oct no coaches.**
5-acre plantsman's garden approached across private ford. Many interesting and unusual trees and shrubs. Visitors can try their hand at identifying plants with the plant list. Plenty of space to eat your own picnic. Walled vegetable and fruit garden, lake, ponds, bog plantings and sweeping lawns. Horses, Dexter cattle and Jacob sheep.

84 RIDGEHILL

5 Dart Bridge Road, Buckfastleigh TQ11 0DY. Paul & Pip Wadsworth, www.facebook.com/ridgehillgarden.devon. *On Eastern edge of Buckfastleigh. A38, either direction. Dart Bridge exit Buckfastleigh/ Buckfast/Totnes. Turn to B'leigh/ B'fast. Over Dart L into Dart Bridge Rd. Ridgehill 400yds on R.* Home-made teas. **Adm £3.50, chd free. Sun 11 May (1-5).**
Compact, half acre, mature garden in Dart valley. Several distinct, heavily-planted beds, many uncommon plants, alpine/rockery, wildlife pond, herbaceous and ferns, copse, grasses & bamboo, small orchard, fruit and veg, work area, shrubbery, roses. Several DIY projects using fencing poles, footer boards and old tools! Child's Find The Animal Quiz and other surprises.

85 ROWDEN HOUSE

Stoke Road, Noss Mayo, Plymouth PL8 1JG. Mr & Mrs Andrew Kingsnorth. *1/2 m from village of Noss Mayo. From Plymouth or Modbury take A379 to Yealmpton. Opp The Volunteer turn off on B3186 to Noss Mayo. After 3m take L turn signed Bridgend and Noss Mayo. At bottom cross creek through village to church. Bear L after 1/2 m last house on R.* Home-made teas. **Adm £3, chd free (share to Operation Hernia). Sun 6 Apr, Sun 3 Aug (1-5).**
Beautiful 1-acre sloping S-facing garden in rural setting with views across adjacent fields. Landscaped with drystone walls, steps and grassy paths, mature trees and shrubs provide a framework for underplanted bulbs and perennial beds, giving yr-round interest. A pond and stream complete the bucolic picture.

86 RUNNYMEDE

2 Orchard Close, Manor Road, Sidmouth EX10 8RS. Veronica Wood. *12m SE of Exeter. 12m SE of Exeter, A3052 to Sidmouth. 1st R, B3176. 1 1/2 m, R at Manor Pavillion Theatre, 1/2 m to Manor Rd car park (advised). Alternatively if using Google Maps arrive lower end Witheby (rd at rear of Runneymede) and follow NGS pedestrian directions on rear fence. Disabled parking only at Orchard Close.* Home-made teas. **Adm £3, chd free. Sat 7, Sun 8 June (2-5.30).**
On western edge of Sidmouth. Beautiful tranquil garden about 1/4 acre artistically landscaped with circles, pool and rill designed by Naila Green RHS Chelsea medallist. Abundance of colourful and unusual plants. Woodland and gravel areas. Microclimate, tender plants, plentiful seating, level paths. Raised vegetable beds and greeenhouse with vines. Featured in Sidmouth Herald.

Little Ash Bungalow

87 ST MERRYN
Higher Park Road, Braunton EX33 2LG. Dr W & Mrs Ros Bradford, 01271 813805, ros@st-merryn.co.uk. *5m W of Barnstaple. On A361, R at 30 mph sign then L into Seven Acre Lane, at top of lane R into Higher Park Rd. Pink house 200 yds on R.* Cream teas. **Adm £3.50, chd free. Sun 20 Apr, Sun 18 May, Sat 14, Sun 15 June, Sun 20 July (2-6). Groups of 10+ also welcome by appt Mar to Aug.**
Very sheltered, peaceful, gently sloping, south-facing, artist's garden, emphasis on shape, colour, scent and all-year round interest. A garden for pleasure with thatched summerhouse leading down to herbaceous borders. Winding crazy paving paths, many seating areas. Shrubs, mature trees, fish ponds, grassy knoll, gravel areas, hens. Many environmental features. Open gallery (arts & crafts).

88 SEDGEWELL COACH HOUSE GARDENS
Olchard TQ12 3GU. Heather Jansch, www.heatherjansch.com. *4m N of Newton Abbot. 12m S of Exeter on A380, L for Olchard, straight ahead on private drive.* **Adm £4, chd free. Sats, Suns 10, 11 May; 30, 31 Aug (11-5).**
Heather Jansch, world-famous sculptor, brings innovative use of recycled materials to gardening. 14 acres incl stunning driftwood sculpture, fabulous views from thrilling woodland bluebell trail down to timeless stream-bordered water meadow walk, pools, herbaceous border, medicinal herb garden. Plentiful seating, come and picnic.

89 ◆ SHAPCOTT BARTON ESTATE
(East Knowstone Manor), East Knowstone, South Molton EX36 4EE. Anita Allen, 01398 341664. *13m NW of Tiverton. J25 M5 take Tiverton exit. 6½ m to r'about take exit South Molton 10m on A361. Turn R signed Knowstone. Leave A361 travel ¼ m to Roachhill through hamlet turn L at Wiston Cross, entrance on L ¼ m.* Light refreshments. **Adm £4, chd free (share to Cats Protection). For NGS: Wed 16, Sun 20 Apr, Sat 19, Sun 20, Tue 22, Wed 23, Sat 26, Sun 27 July, Sat 16, Sun 17 Aug (10.30-4.30). For other opening times and information, please phone or see garden website.**
Large, ever developing garden of 200-acre estate around ancient historic manor house. Wildlife garden. Restored old fish ponds, stream and woodland rich in birdlife. Exotic breeds of poultry. Unusual fruit orchard. Scented bulbs in Apr. Flowering burst July/Aug of National Plant Collections *Leucanthemum superbum* (shasta daisies) and Buddleja davidii. Many butterfly plants incl over 40 varieties of phlox. Kitchen garden and standard orchard.
NCH

90 SHUTELAKE
Butterleigh EX15 1PR. Jill & Nigel Hall, 01884 38812, jill22hall@gmail.com. *3m W of Cullompton; 3m S of Tiverton. Follow signs for Silverton from Butterleigh village. Take L fork 100yds after entrance to Pound Farm. Car park sign on L after 150yds.* Light refreshments in large studio barn conversion overlooking garden provides venue for lunch/tea refreshments even if weather inclement. **Adm £4, chd free. Fri 13, Sat 14 June (11-5.30); Sun 15 June (2-5.30). Also open on Sunday 15th June neighbouring Higher Burnhaies. Visitors also welcome by appt Mar to Oct cars/minibus only.**
Cross a stream by bridge to a secluded S-facing tiered garden with a Mediterranean feel. Borders, ponds, lake, arbours, sculptures, woodland walk. Special young gardeners' activities.

91 SIDBURY MANOR
Sidbury, Sidmouth EX10 0QE. Sir John & Lady Cave, www.sidburymanor.co.uk. *1m NW of Sidbury. Signed in Sidbury Village off A375 between Honiton and Sidmouth.* Home-made teas. **Adm £4.50, chd free. Sat 26, Sun 27 Apr (2-5).**
Built in the 1870s this Victorian manor house built by owner's family and set within East Devon AONB comes complete with 20 acres of garden incl substantial walled gardens, an extensive arboretum containing many fine trees and shrubs, a number of champion trees, and areas devoted to magnolias, rhododendrons and camellias. Partial wheelchair access.

Plantaholic's garden crammed with shrubs, perennials . . . little old fashioned 'sweetie shop' nursery . . .

GROUP OPENING

92 SIDMOUTH GARDENS

Sidmouth, EX10 9JP & EX10 8XQ. *Road plan provided at each Garden.* Home-made teas. **Combined adm £4, chd free.** Sat 14, Sun 15 June, Sat 23, Sun 24, Mon 25 Aug (2-5.30).

BYES REACH
Lynette Talbot & Peter Endersby.
Easterly on A3052. R at Sidford X-lights. In 3/4 m turn L into Coulsdon Rd. On foot, enter back gate via Livonia Field bike path
Visitors also welcome by appt June to Aug for groups of 8+.
01395 578081
lfisher@talktalk.net

ROWAN BANK
44 Woolbrook Park. Barbara & Alan Mence.
A3052.10 m from Exeter turn R at bottom of hill beyond Bowd Inn into Woolbrook Rd. After 1/2 m turn R beside St Francis Church. Garden on L

Situated on Jurassic Coast World Heritage Site, Sidmouth has fine beaches, beautiful gardens and magnificent coastal views.
2 contrasting gardens about 1 mile apart. Byes Reach: edible garden of 1/5 acre. Potager style, raised beds, espalier fruit trees on arched walkway, designed for those with mobility problems. Herbaceous borders, colour-themed flower beds combining perennials, herbs, ferns and hostas. Pond, rockery, greenhouse and studio. Backing onto The Byes nature reserve and R Sid, offering an opportunity for a short walk from the garden gate. Rowan Bank is approx 1/4 acre on steep NW- facing slope, generously planted with trees, shrubs, perennials and bulbs for yr-round interest. Steps lead to a wide zigzag path rising gently to woodland edge of birch and rowan, with a shady seat under Mexican pine. Benches at every corner and summerhouse looking towards wooded hills. Wheelchair access at Byes Reach, regret none at Rowan Bank.

93 NEW SOUTH WOOD FARM

Cotleigh, Honiton EX14 9HU. Dr Clive Potter, C.potter@imperial.ac.uk. *3m NE of Honiton. From Honiton head N on A30, take 1st R past Otter Dairy layby. Follow for 1m. Go straight over Xrds and take first L. Entrance on R.* Home-made teas. **Adm £4, chd free.** Sat 20, Sun 21 Sept (2-5).
Large country garden surrounding a listed C17 Devon farmhouse set deep in the Blackdown Hills. Includes walled courtyard planted with late summer herbaceous and yew topiary, kitchen garden of raised beds with step over pears, fruit cages and trained fruit trees, sunken dry stream bed walk and reflecting pond, formal plum orchard, nuttery and traditional Devon cobbled yard with lean to glasshouse. Gravel pathways, cobbles and steps.

94 NEW SOUTH WORDEN

West Putford, Holsworthy EX22 7LG. Colonel Michael French, 01409 261448, mike@southworden.co.uk, www.southworden.co.uk. *2m from main A388 at Venn Green Xrds Milton Damerel. On A388 Holsworthy to Bideford rd pick up NGS signs at Venn Green Xrds Milton Damerel.* Home-made teas. **Adm £3.50, chd free.** Sun 13, Sun 27 July, Sun 10 Aug (2-5.30). **Visitors also welcome by appt Apr to Sept.**
3/4 -acre peaceful garden in the beautiful Devon countryside. Cottage garden divided by rose and clematis clad pergola. Several large herbaceous beds incl white and hot beds, conifer bed, 70 roses, peonies and sweet peas. Separate 1/2 -acre woodland garden with large circular wildflower beds. Japanese-inspired garden containing dry rivers, bonsai, water features and seating. Stunning views. Quintessential Cottage garden, large 9 ton granite stone with a circular hole, two water features, various statues and interesting garden ornaments. Mainly flat but some gravel and grass pathways.

GROUP OPENING

95 SOUTHCOMBE GARDENS

Dartmoor, Widecombe-in-the-Moor TQ13 7TU, 01364 621332, amandasabin1@hotmail.com. *6m W of Bovey Tracey. B3387 from Bovey Tracey after village church take rd SW for 400yds then sharp R signed Southcombe, after 200yds pass C17 farmhouse and park on L.* Home-made teas at Southcombe Barn. **Combined adm £4.50, chd free.** Sun 18, Sun 25, Mon 26 May, Sun 1, Sun 8, Sun 15, Sun 22 June (2-5). **Visitors also welcome by appt May to July.**

SOUTHCOMBE BARN
Amanda Sabin & Stephen Hobson
Visitors also welcome by appt May to June.
01364 621332
amandasabin1@hotmail.com

SOUTHCOMBE HOUSE
Dr & Mrs J R Seale
Visitors also welcome by appt June to July.
01364 621365

Village famous for its Fair, Uncle Tom Cobley and its C14 church - the Cathedral of the Moor. Featured in RHS The Garden. Southcombe Barn is the woodland end of Southcombe Gardens. In May and June it is dazzlingly colourful. Grass paths wind through 3 acres of flowering and exotic trees with shade patches and sunny clearings full of wild and garden flowers. Sit on a bench, feast on colour and listen to bees. Southcombe House: 5 acres, SE-facing garden, arboretum and orchid-rich restored wild flower meadow with bulbs in spring and four orchid species (early purple, southern marsh, common spotted and greater butterfly). On steep slope at 900ft above sea level with fine views to nearby tors. Spectacular teas too!

96 NEW SPITCHWICK MANOR
Poundsgate, Newton Abbot TQ13 7PB. Mr & Mrs P Simpson. *4m NW of Ashburton. Princetown rd from Ashburton through Poundsgate 1st R at Lodge. From Princetown L at Poundsgate sign. Past Lodge. Park after 300yds at Xrds.* Home-made teas. **Adm £5, chd free. Sat 10, Sun 11 May, Sat 14, Sun 15 June (11-4.30).**
6½ -acre garden with extensive beautiful views. Mature garden undergoing refreshment. A variety of different areas; lower walled garden with glass houses, formal rose garden with fountain, camellia walk with small leat and secret garden with Lady Ashburton's plunge pool built 1763. 2.6 acre vegetable garden sheltered by high granite walls housing 9 allotments and lily pond. Mostly wheelchair access.

This unique mix of nature and nurture has created a quiet haven for gardeners and wildlife alike . . .

97 NEW SPRINGFIELD
Woolsery, Bideford EX39 5PZ. Ms Asta Munro, 01237 431162. *Ignore SatNav. 8m W of Bideford. 3m S of Clovelly. Turn off A39 at Buck's Cross. T-junction at school turn L past village hall. L signed Putford. 1m L.* Home-made teas. **Adm £3.50, chd free. Sat 24, Sun 25 May (1-6); Sat 28, Sun 29 June (12-6); Sun 20 July, Sun 14 Sept (1-6). Also open 28/29 June Harbour Lights. Visitors also welcome by appt Apr to Oct.**
2 acre S sloping rural plot with views. Plantaholic's garden crammed with shrubs, perennials inc 100+ hardy geraniums. Paved suntrap with containers. Gravel area surrounded with herbs, aromatic, silver and pastel plants. Shade area. Small wildlife pond. Meadow with meandering paths. Kitchen garden fruit, veg, edible flowers. Wildlife haven inc bats. Little old fashioned 'sweetie shop' nursery.

98 SQUIRRELS
98 Barton Road, Torquay TQ2 7NS. Graham & Carol Starkie, 01803 329241, calgra@talktalk.net. *5m S of Newton Abbot. From Newton Abbot take A380 to Torquay. After ASDA store on L, turn L at T-lights up Old Woods Hill. 1st L into Barton Rd. Bungalow 200yds on L.* Home-made teas. **Adm £3.50, chd free. Sun 27 July, Sat 2, Sun 3 Aug (2-5). Visitors also welcome by appt July to Aug.**
Plantsman's small town environmental garden, landscaped with small ponds and 7ft waterfall. Interlinked areas incl Japanese, Italianate, Tropical. Specialising in fruit incl peaches, figs, kiwi. Tender plants incl bananas, tree fern, brugmansia, lantanas, oleanders. Collections of fuchsia, abutilons, bougainvilleas. Colourful pergolas, many clematis. Perennial borders. Many nesting boxes, ducks on slug patrol. Environmentally friendly water features and waterfall. 22 cleverly hidden water storage containers. Advice on free electric from solar (p.v.) panels and solar hot water heating. Fruit pruning advice. Featured on BBC Radio 4 Gardeners Question Time, BBC Radio Devon and in local newspaper and Devon Life magazine. Environmentally Friendly Garden Winner and Superclass Gold Medal Winner. No wheelchair access. Mainly level paths. Parking nearby. Conservatory for shelter and seating.

99 STONE FARM
Alverdiscott Rd, Bideford EX39 4PN. Mr & Mrs Ray Auvray. *1½ m from Bideford towards Alverdiscott. From Bideford cross river using Old Bridge and turn L onto Barnstaple Rd. 2nd R onto Manteo Way and 1st L at mini r'about.* Home-made teas. **Adm £3.50, chd free. Sat 21, Sun 22 June, Sat 30, Sun 31 Aug (2-5).**
1-acre country garden with striking herbaceous borders, dry stone wall terracing, white garden, dahlia bed wild meadow area and woodland area. We also have an extensive fully organic vegetable garden with raised beds, soft fruit cage and polytunnels, together with an orchard with traditional varieties of apples, pears and nuts. Some gravel paths but access to whole garden with some help.

100 SUMMERS PLACE
Little Bowlish, Whitestone EX4 2HS. Mr & Mrs Stafford Charles, 01647 61786. *6m NW of Exeter. From M5, A30 Okehampton. After 7m, R to Tedburn St Mary, immed R at r'about past golf course. 1st L after ½ m signed Whitestone, straight ahead at Xrds, follow signs. From Exeter on Whitestone rd 1m beyond Whitestone, follow signs from Heath Cross. From Crediton, follow Whitestone rd through Fordton.* Home-made teas. **Adm £4, chd free. Sun 23 Mar, Sun 21 Sept (12-5). Visitors also welcome by appt Mar to Oct, 48 hrs notice required. Refreshments by arrangement.**
Extensive woodland garden, interesting trees, shrubs, herbaceous and wildflowers, bulbs in spring, autumn fruit and colour, Paths, steps and walkways lead to follies, sculptures, ponds, streamside strolls, grass steps to dewpond with Dartmoor views, Conservation and planting equally emphasized. Intimate house garden, rare breed poultry. Children (prize trail) & dog friendly.

101 TAIKOO
Belstone EX20 1QZ. Richard & Rosamund Bernays. *3m SE of Okehampton. Fork L at stocks in middle of village. Keep left. Entrance to Car Park 300yds on R.* Cream teas. **Adm £3.50, chd free. Sun 4 May, Sun 15 June (2-5).**
3-acre hillside moorland garden, recently extended to include heathers, grasses and moorland plants. Interesting collections of rhododendrons, acers, fuchsias, hydrangeas, magnolias, camellias, Chinese and Himalayan roses and other shrubs and trees. Herb garden. Sculptures and water features. Magnificent views over Dartmoor from terraces of Taipan's house (not open).

102 TAMARISKS
Inner Hope Cove, Kingsbridge TQ7 3HH. Barbara Anderson, 01548 561745, bba@talktalk.net. *6m SW of Kingsbridge. Follow signs through Hope Cove to Inner Hope Cove and the sea.* **Adm £3.50, chd free (share to Butterfly Conservation). Visitors welcome by appt.**
Sloping ⅓ acre directly above the sea with magnificent views, rustic steps, extensive stonework, ponds,

rockeries, and a wild terrace overlooking sea. Very colourful demonstration of seaside planting: hydrangeas, mallows, crocosmia, achillea, sea holly, convolvulus, lavender, sedum, roses, grasses, ferns, conifers, fruit trees. A bird and butterfly haven. Butterfly Conservation and BTO Birdwatch. Craft exhibition and sale of enamel work, bowls, jewellery and photos of local area.

GROUP OPENING

103 TEIGNMOUTH GARDENS

Teignmouth TQ14 8TW. *1m from Teignmouth town centre. From Teignmouth take A379 towards Dawlish, at top of hill L into New Rd, park in New Rd, walk back to A379 and follow signs to gardens.* Home-made teas at High Tor. **Combined adm £4, chd free.** **Sat 12, Sun 13 July (2-5).**

BERRY COTTAGE
Cliff Road. Maureen Fayle

HIGH TOR
Cliff Road. Gill Treweek

NEW LITTLE CLANAGE
Oak Hill Cross Rd.
Mrs Gill Derbyshire.
No parking available in road

PINEWOOD
52 Woodland Ave.
Pam & Ron Martin.
1m up hill on rd from Teignmouth to Dawlish. 3rd rd from brow of hill

Joining Teignmouth Gardens in 2014 is the imaginatively planted garden at Little Clanage. Designed for low maintenance with a huge selection of interesting shrubs and trees, superb views of the sea and lots of hidden nooks and crannies, Little Clanage is an exciting addition to the three existing gardens. The artist owner of Berry Cottage has developed a lovely secluded wildlife haven and will have a display of her stunning artwork. At Pinewood a variety of colourful plants are divided into several rooms with panoramic views over Lyme Bay. High Tor is a large sunny garden with sea views and abundant cottage garden style planting. Featured in Teignmouth Post.

104 2 TOWN BARTON

South Tawton, Okehampton EX20 2LP. Susan & Mark Freeman. *4km W of Okehampton. Off A30 W at Whiddon Down towards Sticklepath. After 4m, R at Ford Cross towards S Tawton. Straight at Xrds, village ½ m. Park in village square.* Home-made teas. **Adm £3, chd free.** **Sun 4 May, Sun 22 June, Sun 27 July (11-5).**
Small, diverse garden, hidden in heart of S Tawton, every inch edible, useful and beautiful. Developed as sustainable forest garden with numerous fruit and nut trees underplanted with unusual soft fruit and spice bushes. Ground cover of perennial vegetables, herbs, wild flowers and plants for dyeing and basket-making. Guided tours at The Church House.

GROUP OPENING

105 VENN CROSS RAILWAY GARDENS

Venn Cross, Waterrow, Taunton TA4 2BE, 01398 361392, venncross@btinternet.com. *Devon/Somerset border. 4m W of Wiveliscombe, 6m E of Bampton on B3227. Easy access. Ample tarmac parking.* Home-made teas.
Combined adm £4, chd free. **Sat 14, Sun 15 June, Sat 12, Sun 13 July, Sat 13, Sun 14 Sept (2-5.30).**
Visitors also welcome by appt.

THE ENGINE HOUSE
Waterrow, Taunton. Kevin & Samantha Anning
Visitors also welcome by appt.
01398 361392
venncross@btinternet.com

STATION HOUSE
Pat & Bill Wilson

Set in beautiful countryside straddling Devon/Somerset border between Bampton and Wiveliscombe. 2 large adjoining gardens covering site of former station and goods yard on GWR line between Taunton and Barnstaple. The Engine House: approx 4 acres with colour from trees, shrubs and bulbs in spring to the wildflower meadow, bog gardens and sweeping herbaceous borders as summer progresses. Streams, ponds (incl koi), vegetable plot, hornbeam walkway and woodland paths. Railway and sculptural features add interest throughout. New pond and borders for 2014. Station House: 2-acre sheltered garden in deep cutting. Site of old station. Steep banks featuring hostas and other plants. Deep herbaceous beds packed with flowers. Vegetable beds. Tunnel (no entry permitted) at end forming part of dell garden. Access to top of tunnel with view of garden. Woodland walk. Historic railway interest (many photographs) and garden sculptures. Featured in Exmoor magazine and on BBC Radio Devon. Wheelchair access to main areas. Some gravel paths, gentle grass slopes.

ALLOTMENTS

106 WEIRFIELD MEADOWS ALLOTMENT GARDENS

Near Trews Weir, Exeter EX2 4DJ. Mrs Beverley Langley, www.weirfieldmeadows.co.uk. *Riverside Valley Park, Trews Weir Reach, Exeter. Cross suspension bridge and entrance to allotment gardens is on L. See website for alternative directions and parking.* Home-made teas. **Adm £3, chd free.** **Sat 12, Sun 13 July (11-4).**
In an enviable setting with almost ¼ m of river frontage on the Exe, these working allotments provide a tranquil oasis in the City of Exeter. Each allotment has its own unique style, with an abundance of fruits, vegetables and flowers. Together with hedgerows, mature trees and riverbank, this unique mix of nature and nurture has created a quiet haven for gardeners and wildlife alike. Limited wheelchair access.

107 WHITSTONE BLUEBELLS
Bovey Tracey, Newton Abbot TQ13 9NA, 01626 832258, katie@whitstonefarm.co.uk. *Whitstone Lane. From A382 turn towards hospital (sign opp golf range), after 1/3 m L at swinging sign 'Private road leading to Whitstone'. Follow NGS signs.* Teas at Whitstone Farm. **Combined adm £4, chd free.** Sun 4 May (2-5). **Visitors also welcome by appt Apr to May to Whitstone Farm only.**
Stunning spring gardens each with its own character and far reaching views over Dartmoor. Whitstone House has clouds of bluebells throughout woodland walk area and at Whitstone Farm: bluebells intermingle among camellias, azaleas, rhododendrons and magnolias. Plus a magnificent display of architectural metal, wood and stone sculptures, ornaments, gates and benches. An exhibition of work by Matt Dingle, a talented Devon Blacksmith, artist and forgemaster, will also be on display at Whitstone Farm.

108 WHITSTONE FARM
Whitstone Lane, Bovey Tracey TQ13 9NA. Katie & Alan Bunn, 01626 832258, katie@whitstonefarm.co.uk. *1/2 m N of Bovey Tracey. From A382 turn towards hospital (sign opp golf range), after 1/3 m L at swinging sign 'Private road leading to Whitstone'. Follow NGS signs.* Home-made teas. **Adm £4, chd free.** Sun 10 Aug (2-5). **Visitors also welcome by appt July to Aug group and society tours by appointment.**
Nearly 4 acres of steep hillside garden with stunning views of Haytor and Dartmoor. Arboretum planted 40 yrs ago of over 200 trees from all over the world, incl magnolias, camellias, acers, alders, betula, davidias and sorbus. Major plantings of rhododendron and cornus. Late summer opening for flowering eucryphias. National Collection of Eucryphias. Beautiful all-yr round garden.

NCH

109 WICK FARM GARDENS
Cookbury, Holsworthy EX22 6NU. Martin & Jenny Sexton, 01409 253760, www.wickfarmgardens.co.uk. *3m E of Holsworthy. From Holsworthy take Hatherleigh Rd for 2m, L at Anvil Corner, 1/4 m then R to Cookbury, garden 1 1/2 m on L.* Cream teas. **Adm £4, chd free.** Suns 11, 25 May, Mon 26 May; Suns 29 June; 27 July (11-6). **Visitors also welcome by appt May to Sept.**
8-acre pleasure garden with many attractive features, arranged around house into rooms. Fernery, small ornamental pond, borders, sculptures, long border around lake with large variety of plants to attract butterflies and bees. Arboretum with over 300 varieties of trees. Ample seating, tropical oasis, croquet lawn. Stonehenge with sacrificial stone! Picnic area. Bluebell walk of approx 1m. Some gravel paths, motor wheelchair friendly.

GROUP OPENING

110 WILLAND OLD VILLAGE GARDENS
Willand Old Village, Cullompton EX15 2RH. *From J27 or J28 of M5 follow signs B3181 to Willand. Turn at PO sign, gardens approx 200 yds, follow yellow signs. Parking in village.* Home-made teas. **Combined adm £3.50, chd free.** Sat 14, Sun 15 June (2-5.30).

CHURCH LEA
Mrs D Anderson

NEW **THE FIRS**
Silver Street, Willand, Mrs Sylvia Statham

NONSUCH, DYE HOUSE LANE
E Whiteley

NEW **THE VILLAGE ALLOTMENTS**
Silver Street, Willand, c/o Mrs S. Statham

Close to attractive old village centre and church (also open). Few slopes make this a particularly welcoming environment for wheelchair users. Church Lea: ideas for limited space in an evolving garden, pond, rockery with alpines, many pots create a garden within a garden, vegetables, fruit and vistas. Nonsuch: imaginative use of space in tranquil garden. Year round interest, established shrubs, herbaceous and summer bedding, plus friendly bantams. The Firs: bounded by the old drovers road, a wildlife garden, pond, flowers, shrubs and woodpile for encouraging wildlife. New this year visit the 56 Allotments and award winning compost scheme boasting 10,000 bags of compost from residents' green waste. Gardens, village and church have good accessibility for wheelchair users with modest slopes and few changes of level. Allotments have partial access.

111 ◆ WINSFORD WALLED GARDEN
Halwill Junction EX21 5XT. Dugald and Adel Stark, 01409 221477, dugald@dugaldstark.co.uk, www.winsfordwalledgarden.info. *10m NW of Okehampton. On A3079 follow brown tourism signs from centre of Halwill Junction (1m). Straight on through Anglers Paradise.* Home-made teas. **Adm £4, chd free.** For NGS: Sats 14 June; 2 Aug (10-5).
Under new ownership of the landscape painter, Dugald Stark. Historic walled gardens, redesigned and brimming with colourful and interesting planting. Large restored Victorian glasshouses and extensive mature bamboo grove. Studio open. Garden open May - Sept, Wed - Sun (10-5).

112 WOOD BARTON
Kentisbeare EX15 2AT. Mrs Richard Horton, 01884 266285. *8m SE of Tiverton, 3m E of Cullompton. 3m from M5 J28. A373 Cullompton to Honiton. 2m L to Bradfield/Willand, Horn Rd. After 1m at Xrds turn R. Farm drive 1/2 m on L. Bull on sign.* Home-made teas. **Adm £4, chd free.** Sun 30 Mar, Sun 20, Mon 21 Apr (2.30-5.30). **Visitors also welcome by appt Mar to Oct, cup of tea incl in adm fee.**
Established 2-acre arboretum with species trees on S-facing slope. Magnolias, 2 davidia, azaleas, camellias, rhododendrons, acers; several ponds and water feature. Autumn colour. New planting of woodland trees and bluebells opp house (this part not suitable for wheelchairs but dogs are welcome here). Sculptures and profiles in bronze resin. Featured in Countryside Magazine.

113 WOODVALE COTTAGE
Truro Drive, Plymouth PL5 4LA. Mr & Mrs Graham Lindsay. *NW of Plymouth. From A38 Plymouth Parkway take St Budeaux exit follow*

signs for Crownhill. At T-lights, L Budshead Rd, L Milford Ln, L Truro Dr. 300m V sharp L. Light refreshments. **Adm £4, chd free.** **Suns 30 Mar; 20 July; 5 Oct (12-4.30).**
Surprising and beautiful waterside garden in wooded valley. The garden is still being developed but already contains large variety of trees, shrubs, bulbs and flowers for yr-round colour and interest. Water features, small orchard, vegetable and fruit gardens along with network of winding pathways, some steep. Opening times and dates chosen around tide times. Craft stalls on some opening dates check NGS website for up to date details. Wheelchair access to main garden only, some pathways are rustic and steep.

GROUP OPENING

114 YOLLAND GARDENS

Yolland Hill, Ashburton TQ13 7JP. *Just S of Ashburton. A38 S ignore 1st slip rd to Ashburton next L in front of sign Motel Services Not 24hrs. A38 N ignore 1st slip rd to Ashburton take 2nd, at T-junction turn R, follow rd round to join A38 towards Plymouth, take next L.* Cream teas. **Combined adm £5, chd free.** **Sun 22 June (11-5.30).**

SOUTH BARTON
Angie & Tim Guy

YOLLAND BARTON
Richard and Pamela Nock

YOLLAND HOUSE
Whistley Hill. Peter & Sue Munday

3 gardens in secluded wooded valley that was a dairy farm 30 yrs ago. Extensive tree planting at that time now gives shelter with wide variety of fine evergreen and deciduous specimens. Yolland Barton: large garden designed around many exciting granite features for which 300 tons of stone was brought in mostly from redundant Georgian and Victorian buildings. The garden has been extensively planted with shrubs, herbaceous and alpine plants to complement these features. South Barton has an old-fashioned country garden air and is planted to provide a haven for butterflies and bees. Granite walls and meandering paths. Yolland House: 4-acre landscaped, terraced garden with park-like grounds and specimen trees. Small lake, home to ducks, geese and moorhens. Substantial granite rockery with paths and steps lead back to car park.

115 YONDER HILL

Shepherds Lane, Colaton Raleigh, Sidmouth EX10 0LP. Judy McKay, Eddie Stevenson, Sharon Attrell, Bob Chambers, 07864 055532, judy@yonderhill.me.uk, www.yonderhill.org.uk. *4m N of Budleigh Salterton B3178 between Newton Poppleford and Colaton Raleigh. Take turning signed to Dotton and immed R into small lane, 1/4 m 1st R at top of hill opp public footpath.* Cream teas. **Adm £3, chd £1.** **Every Mon & Sun 30 Mar to 29 Sept (1-4.30).** **Visitors also welcome by appt Apr to Sept.**
An experience to awaken the senses and soothe the soul. Leave your cares at the gate and enjoy a warm welcome to 3 1/2 acres planted with love. Blazing mixed borders buzzing with insects, cool woods alive with birdsong, rustling bamboos, delicious scents. Eucalyptus, grass, conifer and fern collections, rare plants, unusual planting, wildlife ponds, new meadow, woodland tunnel, seats everywhere. Garden attracts great variety of wildlife. Butterfly safaris and moth trapping available July - August. phone to book. Featured in Express & Echo. Limited wheelchair access, some slopes. Wheelchair and large mobility scooter available, phone to book. Disabled toilet.

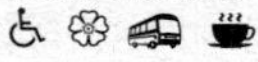

Enjoy a warm welcome to 3 1/2 acres planted with love . . .

Devon County Volunteers

County Organisers and Central Devon area
Edward & Miranda Allhusen, Sutton Mead, Moretonhampstead TQ13 8PW, 01647 440296, miranda@allhusen.co.uk

County Treasurer
Julia Tremlett, Bickham House, Kenn, Nr Exeter EX6 7XL, 01392 832671, jandjtremlett@hotmail.com

Publicity
Brian Mackness, Fairfield, Vicarage Road, Abbotskerswell TQ12 5PN, 01626 356004, brianmackness@btinternet.com
Cath Pettyfer, Mill Cottage, Bondleigh, North Tawton EX20 2AH, 01837 89024, cathpettyfer@tiscali.co.uk

Show Gardens
Dorothy Anderson, Church Lea, Willand Old Village, Cullompton EX15 2RH, 01884 33415, dorothyanderson321@btinternet.com

Assistant County Organisers
North East Devon Jill Hall, Shutelake Farm, Butterleigh, Cullompton EX15 1PR, 01884 38812, jill22hall@gmail.com
Plymouth Maria Ashurst, 57 Fegen Road, Plymouth PL5 1HY, 01752 351396, maria.ashurst@sky.com
West Devon Sara-Jane Cumming, Broad Park, Coryton, Tavistock EX20 4AA, 01822 860281, sj@broadparkdesigns.co.uk
North Devon Jo Hynes, Higher Cherubeer, Dolton, Winkleigh EX19 8PP, 01805 804265, hynesjo@gmail.com
Exeter Jenny Phillips, 25 Rosebarn Avenue, Exeter EX4 6DY, 01392 254076, jennypips25@hotmail.co.uk
Exmoor Juliet Moss, The Old Vicarage, West Anstey EX36 3PE, 01398 341604, julietm@onetel.com
South Devon Sally Vincent, Bramble Torre, Dittisham, Dartmouth TQ6 0HZ, 01803 722227, salv@hotmail.co.uk
East Devon Peter Wadeley, Prospect House, Lyme Road, Axminster EX13 5BH, 01297 631210, wadeley@btinternet.com
Torbay Christine Mackness, Fairfield, Vicarage Road, Abbotskerswell TQ12 5PN, 01626 356004, christinemack@clara.co.uk

DORSET

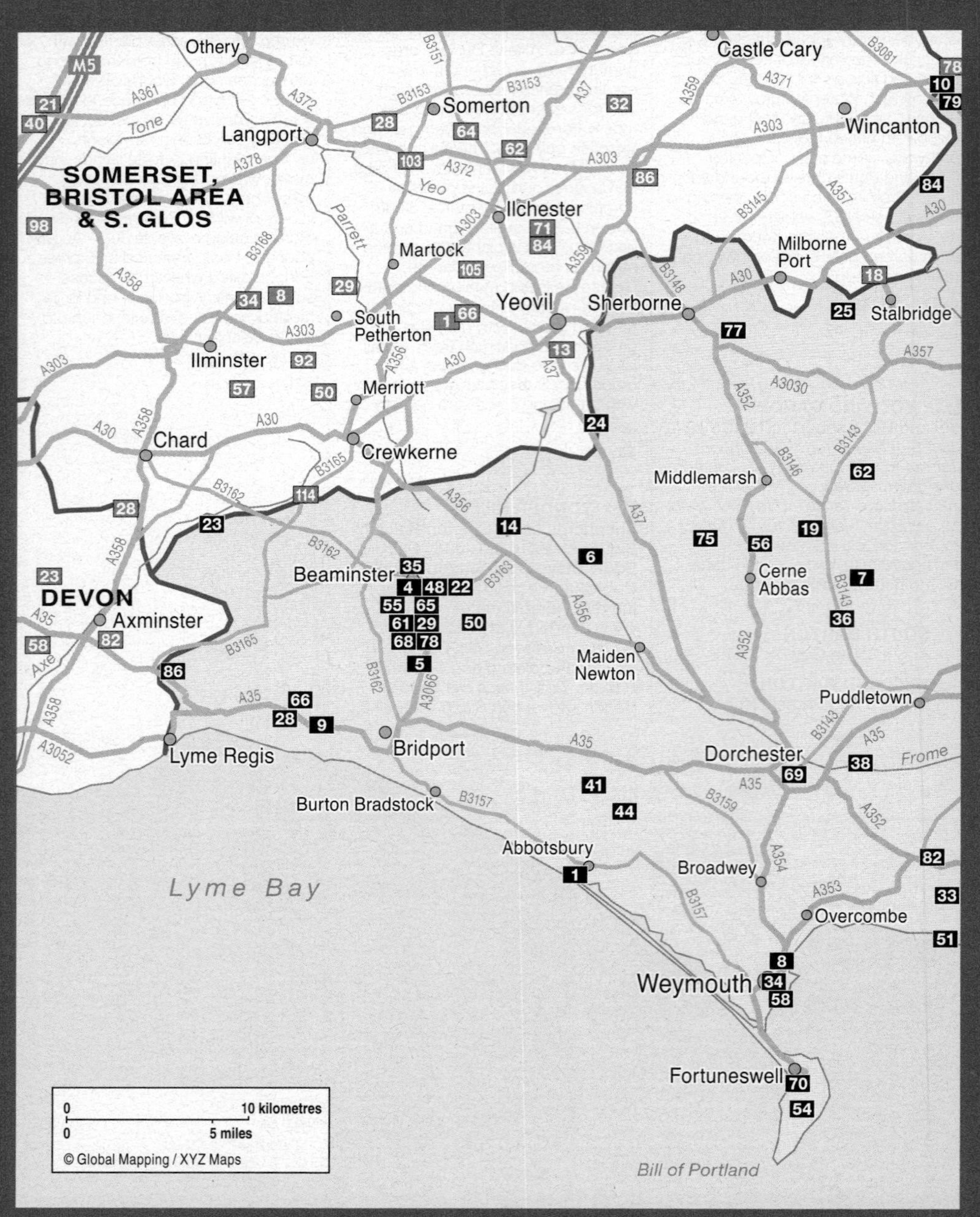

SOMERSET, BRISTOL AREA & S. GLOS
DEVON
Othery
Langport
Somerton
Castle Cary
Wincanton
Ilchester
Martock
Yeovil
Sherborne
Milborne Port
Stalbridge
South Petherton
Ilminster
Merriott
Crewkerne
Chard
Middlemarsh
Cerne Abbas
Beaminster
Axminster
Maiden Newton
Puddletown
Lyme Regis
Bridport
Dorchester
Burton Bradstock
Abbotsbury
Broadwey
Overcombe
Weymouth
Fortuneswell
Bill of Portland
Lyme Bay
Tone
Yeo
Parrett
Axe
Frome
M5
A361
A372
B3151
B3153
A37
A359
A371
B3081
A303
A378
A357
A30
B3145
B3148
B3168
A358
A356
A3030
A352
B3143
B3146
B3165
B3162
B3163
A35
A3066
A3052
B3157
B3159
A354
A353
0
10 kilometres
0
5 miles
© Global Mapping / XYZ Maps

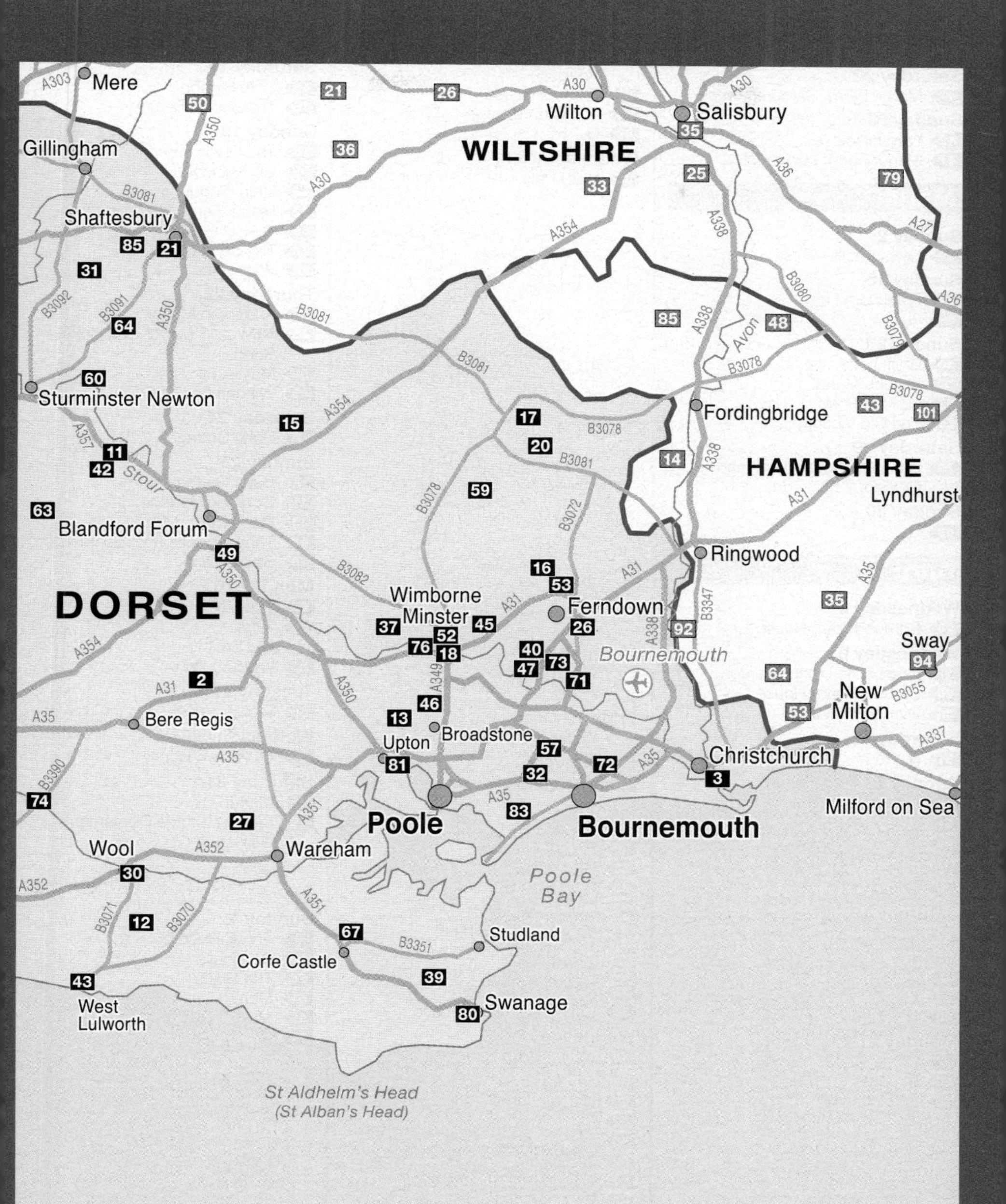
Mere
Gillingham
Shaftesbury
Sturminster Newton
Blandford Forum
DORSET
WILTSHIRE
HAMPSHIRE
Wilton
Salisbury
Fordingbridge
Lyndhurst
Ringwood
Wimborne Minster
Ferndown
Bournemouth
Sway
New Milton
Christchurch
Milford on Sea
Bere Regis
Broadstone
Upton
Poole
Bournemouth
Wool
Wareham
Poole Bay
Studland
Corfe Castle
Swanage
West Lulworth
St Aldhelm's Head
(St Alban's Head)
Stour
Avon

Opening Dates

All entries subject to change. For latest information check www.ngs.org.uk

February

Saturday 22
47 Manor Farm, Hampreston

Sunday 23
42 Lawsbrook
47 Manor Farm, Hampreston

March

Sunday 2
42 Lawsbrook

Sunday 16
24 Frankham Farm
69 Q

Sunday 23
10 Chiffchaffs
30 Herons Mead
32 22 Holt Road
64 The Old Vicarage

Saturday 29
79 Snape Cottage Plantsman's Garden

Sunday 30
69 Q

April

Wednesday 2
20 Edmondsham House

Wednesday 9
17 Cranborne Manor Garden
20 Edmondsham House
36 Ivy House Garden

Saturday 12
51 Marren

Sunday 13
19 Domineys
51 Marren
69 Q

Wednesday 16
20 Edmondsham House

Saturday 19
63 Old Smithy

Sunday 20
9 Chideock Manor
26 The Glade
30 Herons Mead

Monday 21
9 Chideock Manor
20 Edmondsham House
36 Ivy House Garden

Wednesday 23
20 Edmondsham House

Saturday 26
8 24 Carlton Road North
79 Snape Cottage Plantsman's Garden

Sunday 27
6 Broomhill
7 Butts Cottage
8 24 Carlton Road North
13 Corfe Barn
24 Frankham Farm
32 22 Holt Road
46 NEW 17 Lower Golf Links Road
55 The Mill House
64 The Old Vicarage
69 Q

Wednesday 30
35 Horn Park

Delicious home-made cakes and clotted cream teas . . .

May

Friday 2
39 Knitson Old Farmhouse

Saturday 3
39 Knitson Old Farmhouse

Sunday 4
26 The Glade
30 Herons Mead
33 Holworth Farmhouse
36 Ivy House Garden
39 Knitson Old Farmhouse
83 24a Western Avenue

Monday 5
33 Holworth Farmhouse
36 Ivy House Garden
39 Knitson Old Farmhouse

Wednesday 7
18 Deans Court

Sunday 11
29 Hatchlands
52 Mayfield
55 The Mill House
62 The Old Rectory, Pulham
67 NEW Puddledock Cottage
68 2 Pyes Plot
86 Wolverhollow

Monday 12
58 'OLA'

Tuesday 13
5 Braddocks
86 Wolverhollow

Wednesday 14
74 NEW Sculpture by the Lakes

Saturday 17
43 Little Bindon
75 The Secret Garden

Sunday 18
26 The Glade
32 22 Holt Road
43 Little Bindon
47 Manor Farm, Hampreston
69 Q
75 The Secret Garden
85 Wincombe Park

Thursday 22
2 Anderson Manor
46 NEW 17 Lower Golf Links Road
52 Mayfield
85 Wincombe Park

Saturday 24
7 Butts Cottage

Sunday 25
7 Butts Cottage
11 Coombe Cottage
13 Corfe Barn
48 The Manor House, Beaminster
78 Slape Manor

Monday 26
48 The Manor House, Beaminster
58 'OLA'
63 Old Smithy
86 Wolverhollow

Tuesday 27
86 Wolverhollow

Wednesday 28
59 Old Down House

Saturday 31
51 Marren
79 Snape Cottage Plantsman's Garden

June

Sunday 1
3 Annalal's Gallery
19 Domineys
26 The Glade
51 Marren
52 Mayfield
71 Resting Laurels

Wednesday 4
28 NEW Harcombe House
59 Old Down House

Thursday 5
2 Anderson Manor
28 NEW Harcombe House

You are always welcome at an NGS garden!

Festival Weekend

Saturday 7
7 Butts Cottage
15 Cottage Row (Evening)
21 NEW Edwardstowe
28 NEW Harcombe House
54 Mews Cottage

Sunday 8
7 Butts Cottage
15 Cottage Row
21 NEW Edwardstowe
24 Frankham Farm
25 Frith House
28 NEW Harcombe House
47 Manor Farm, Hampreston
54 Mews Cottage
59 Old Down House

Monday 9
58 'OLA'

Tuesday 10
5 Braddocks
66 Pilsdon View

Wednesday 11
6 Broomhill
52 Mayfield

Thursday 12
46 NEW 17 Lower Golf Links Road

Friday 13
39 Knitson Old Farmhouse
82 Warmwell House

Saturday 14
9 Chideock Manor
39 Knitson Old Farmhouse

Sunday 15
9 Chideock Manor
22 Farrs
32 22 Holt Road
33 Holworth Farmhouse
39 Knitson Old Farmhouse
46 NEW 17 Lower Golf Links Road
52 Mayfield
69 Q
82 Warmwell House

Tuesday 17
65 Parnham House

Wednesday 18
35 Horn Park
74 NEW Sculpture by the Lakes

Thursday 19
84 Weston House

Friday 20
30 Herons Mead (Evening)

Saturday 21
8 24 Carlton Road North
12 Coombe Keynes Gardens
65 Parnham House

Sunday 22
4 NEW Beaminster Gardens
8 24 Carlton Road North

The Old Rectory, Pulham
© Val Corbett

10 Chiffchaffs
12 Coombe Keynes Gardens
27 Greenacres
30 Herons Mead
60 The Old Rectory, Manston
72 25 Richmond Park Avenue

Tuesday 24
44 Littlebredy Walled Gardens

Wednesday 25
4 NEW Beaminster Gardens
60 The Old Rectory, Manston

Saturday 28
37 Kingston Lacy
79 Snape Cottage Plantsman's Garden

Sunday 29
3 Annalal's Gallery
13 Corfe Barn
37 Kingston Lacy
66 Pilsdon View

July

80 NEW **Stone Rise (Every Wednesday)**

Tuesday 1
44 Littlebredy Walled Gardens

Thursday 3
72 25 Richmond Park Avenue

Saturday 5
45 55 Lonnen Road

Sunday 6
6 Broomhill
45 55 Lonnen Road
57 4 Noel Road

Tuesday 8
5 Braddocks
66 Pilsdon View

Wednesday 9
18 Deans Court
55 The Mill House (Evening)
68 2 Pyes Plot (Evening)

Thursday 10
84 Weston House

Saturday 12
17 Cranborne Manor Garden

Sunday 13
14 Corscombe House
31 Hilltop
72 25 Richmond Park Avenue
73 357 Ringwood Road

Saturday 19
34 Holy Trinity Environmental Garden

Sunday 20
3 Annalal's Gallery
22 Farrs
27 Greenacres
31 Hilltop
33 Holworth Farmhouse
34 Holy Trinity Environmental Garden
53 Meadow Views
54 Mews Cottage
57 4 Noel Road

Thursday 24
76 The Secret Garden and Serles House

Saturday 26
66 Pilsdon View

Sunday 27
- 16 Cottesmore Farm
- 31 Hilltop
- 32 22 Holt Road
- 67 NEW Puddledock Cottage
- 72 25 Richmond Park Avenue
- 76 The Secret Garden and Serles House

Wednesday 30
- 73 357 Ringwood Road
- 80 NEW Stone Rise

August

- 80 NEW **Stone Rise (Every Wednesday)**

Saturday 2
- 45 55 Lonnen Road
- 54 Mews Cottage

Sunday 3
- 31 Hilltop
- 45 55 Lonnen Road
- 47 Manor Farm, Hampreston
- 54 Mews Cottage
- 62 The Old Rectory, Pulham
- 70 NEW Queen Ann House
- 76 The Secret Garden and Serles House
- 83 24a Western Avenue

Wednesday 6
- 47 Manor Farm, Hampreston
- 62 The Old Rectory, Pulham

Thursday 7
- 76 The Secret Garden and Serles House

Sunday 10
- 16 Cottesmore Farm
- 19 Domineys
- 31 Hilltop
- 76 The Secret Garden and Serles House

Wednesday 13
- 28 NEW Harcombe House

Thursday 14
- 28 NEW Harcombe House

Saturday 16
- 21 NEW Edwardstowe
- 28 NEW Harcombe House

Sunday 17
- 3 Annalal's Gallery
- 6 Broomhill
- 16 Cottesmore Farm
- 21 NEW Edwardstowe
- 22 Farrs
- 28 NEW Harcombe House
- 31 Hilltop
- 53 Meadow Views

Sunday 24
- 11 Coombe Cottage
- 32 22 Holt Road
- 33 Holworth Farmhouse
- 54 Mews Cottage
- 73 357 Ringwood Road
- 76 The Secret Garden and Serles House

Monday 25
- 76 The Secret Garden and Serles House

Sunday 31
- 76 The Secret Garden and Serles House

September

Thursday 4
- 76 The Secret Garden and Serles House

Saturday 6
- 76 The Secret Garden and Serles House

Sunday 7
- 49 Manor House, Lower Blandford St Mary
- 54 Mews Cottage
- 70 NEW Queen Ann House
- 76 The Secret Garden and Serles House

Wednesday 10
- 49 Manor House, Lower Blandford St Mary

Sunday 14
- 10 Chiffchaffs
- 22 Farrs
- 76 The Secret Garden and Serles House

Sunday 21
- 30 Herons Mead

October

Wednesday 1
- 20 Edmondsham House

Wednesday 8
- 20 Edmondsham House

Sunday 12
- 24 Frankham Farm

Wednesday 15
- 20 Edmondsham House

Wednesday 22
- 20 Edmondsham House

November

Sunday 2
- 42 Lawsbrook

Gardens open to the public

- 1 Abbotsbury Gardens
- 10 Chiffchaffs
- 17 Cranborne Manor Garden
- 20 Edmondsham House
- 23 Forde Abbey Gardens
- 31 Hilltop
- 33 Holworth Farmhouse
- 37 Kingston Lacy
- 38 Kingston Maurward Gardens and Animal Park
- 40 Knoll Gardens
- 44 Littlebredy Walled Gardens
- 50 Mapperton Gardens
- 56 Minterne House
- 77 Sherborne Castle
- 79 Snape Cottage Plantsman's Garden
- 81 Upton Country Park

By appointment only

- 41 Langebride House

Also open by appointment

- 3 Annalal's Gallery
- 5 Braddocks
- 6 Broomhill
- 7 Butts Cottage
- 9 Chideock Manor
- 11 Coombe Cottage
- 13 Corfe Barn
- 15 Cottage Row
- 18 Deans Court
- 19 Domineys
- 24 Frankham Farm
- 25 Frith House
- 26 The Glade
- 30 Herons Mead
- 32 22 Holt Road
- 35 Horn Park
- 36 Ivy House Garden
- 39 Knitson Old Farmhouse
- 42 Lawsbrook
- 45 55 Lonnen Road
- 51 Marren
- 52 Mayfield
- 54 Mews Cottage
- 55 The Mill House
- 60 The Old Rectory, Manston
- 62 The Old Rectory, Pulham
- 63 Old Smithy
- 64 The Old Vicarage
- 66 Pilsdon View
- 69 Q
- 71 Resting Laurels
- 72 25 Richmond Park Avenue
- 73 357 Ringwood Road
- 74 Sculpture by the Lakes
- 75 The Secret Garden
- 83 24a Western Avenue
- 86 Wolverhollow

Visit a garden in your own time – look for by appointment gardens

The Gardens

1 ◆ ABBOTSBURY GARDENS

nr Weymouth DT3 4LA. Ilchester Estates, 01305 871412, info@abbotsburygardens.co.uk, www.abbotsburygardens.co.uk. *8m W of Weymouth. From B3157 Weymouth-Bridport, 200yds W of Abbotsbury village.* **For opening times and information, please phone or see garden website.**
30 acres, started in 1760 and considerably extended in C19. Much recent replanting. The maritime micro-climate enables Mediterranean and southern hemisphere garden to grow rare and tender plants. National collection of Hoherias (flowering Aug in NZ garden). Woodland valley with ponds, stream and hillside walk to view the Jurassic Coast. Open all yr except Christmas week. Featured on Countrywise and Gardeners' World. Limited wheelchair access, some very steep paths and rolled gravel.

NCH

2 ANDERSON MANOR

Anderson, Blandford Forum DT11 9HD. Jeremy & Rosemary Isaac, www.andersonmanor.co.uk. *3m E Bere Regis, 12m W Wimborne, 8m SW Blandford. Turn off A31 at Red Post Xrds to Anderson, follow rd around corner, entrance on R.* Home-made teas. **Adm £4.50, chd free. Thurs 22 May, 5 June (2-5).**
Approx 3 acres of mature topiary, old roses and herbaceous borders surrounding Elizabethan/Jacobean manor house (Grade 1 listed, not open). Formal garden, gazebos, bowling green, walled garden, parterre and orchard. Yew and box hedges, pleached lime walk, old rose walk by R Winterborne and avenue of walnut trees. C12 church open next to house. Separate car parking via Church Lane. All gardens accessible. No gravel, mainly grass.

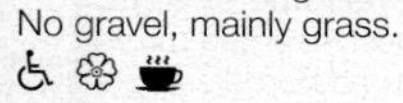

3 ANNALAL'S GALLERY

25 Millhams Street, Christchurch BH23 1DN. Anna & Lal Sims, 01202 567585, anna.sims@ntlworld.com, www.annasims.co.uk. *Town centre. Park in Saxon Square PCP - exit to Millham St via alley at side of church.* **Adm £3, chd free. Suns 1, 29 June; 20 July; 17 Aug (2-4). Visitors also welcome by appt.**
Enchanting 100 yr-old cottage, home of two Royal Academy artists. 32ft x 12½ ft garden on 3 patio levels. Pencil gate leads to colourful scented Victorian walled garden. Sculptures and paintings hide among the flowers and shrubs. Featured on BBC Radio Solent, live broadcast.

GROUP OPENING

4 NEW BEAMINSTER GARDENS

Shadrack Street, Beaminster DT8 3BE. *6m N of Bridport, 6m S of Crewkerne on B3162. All gardens within short walk of Town Sq or Main car park. In pairs, all well signed from Town Square. Lots of yellow arrows and balloons.* Home-made teas on Sunday 22 June at Barton End and on Wed 25 June in the Strode Room by church, well signed. **Combined adm £5, chd free. Sun 22, Wed 25 June (2-5).**

NEW BARTON END
50 Fleet Street. Mr & Mrs Philip Crawford

NEW 29 FLEET STREET
Mrs Jane Pinkster

NEW SHADRACK HOUSE
Shadrack Street. Mr & Mrs Hugh Lindsay

NEW SHORTS ORCHARD
Shorts Lane. Mrs Sally Mallinson

Three charming small town gardens, one by the river, and one a much larger town garden. All a total delight, masses of roses, unusual climbers, shrubs and swathes of perennials. A first opening for all four gardens. All except Shadrack House wheelchair friendly.

5 BRADDOCKS

Oxbridge, Bridport DT6 3TZ. Dr & Mrs Roger Newton, 01308 488441, rogernewton329@btinternet.com. *3m N of Bridport. From Bridport, A3066 to Beaminster 3m, just before Melplash, L into Camesworth Lane signed Oxbridge. Single track rd, down steep hill. Garden signed.* Home-made teas. **Adm £4, chd free. Tues 13 May; 10 June; 8 July (2-5). Visitors also welcome by appt Apr to Sept.**
3 acres of plant-packed sloping gardens, conceived, planted and looked after by owner. 'A feast of a garden at all times of the year'. Wild flower meadows and water. Herbaceous, underplanted shrubs and roses of all types and hues. Shady woodland garden and fine mature specimen trees. The steep slopes and gravel paths make the garden unsuitable for wheelchairs.

> All a total delight . . . swathes of perennials . . .

6 BROOMHILL

Rampisham DT2 0PU. Mr & Mrs D Parry, 01935 83266, carol.parry2@btopenworld.com. *11m NW of Dorchester. From Yeovil, A37 towards Dorchester, 7m turn R signed Evershot. From Dorchester, A37 to Yeovil, 4m L A356 signed Crewkerne, 6m R to Rampisham. From Crewkerne A356, 1½ m after Rampisham Garage L to Rampisham - follow signs.* Home-made teas. **Adm £4, chd free. Sun 27 Apr, Wed 11 June, Sun 6 July, Sun 17 Aug (2-5). Visitors also welcome by appt May to Aug.**
Once a farmyard now a delightful, tranquil garden set in 1½ acres. Island beds and borders are planted with shrubs, roses, masses of perennials and choice annuals to give vibrancy and colour from spring to autumn. Lawns and paths lead to a less formal area with, a large wildlife pond, shaded areas, a bog garden and a late summer border. Featured in Roger Lane's Gardens of Dorset.

7 BUTTS COTTAGE

Plush DT2 7RJ. John & Jane Preston, 01300 348545. *9m N Dorchester. At Piddletrenthide (on B3143) take turning E to Plush; after 1½ m follow 'no through rd' sign then 1st R.* **Adm £3.50, chd free. Sun 27 Apr; Sats, Suns 24, 25 May; 7, 8 June (2-5). Groups of 10+ also welcome by appt May/June.**
Tranquil village garden of ¾ acre sheltered by mature beech trees around C18 cottage in fold of N Dorset Downs. Stream, pond, wild flowers and marsh orchids. Pleasant place to sit or wander amongst wide variety of flowers, vegetables, shrubs and trees. Partial wheel chair access.

Knoll Gardens

8 24 CARLTON ROAD NORTH

Weymouth DT4 7PY. Anne Mellars and Rob Tracey, 01305 786121, mellie_52@hotmail.com. *8m S of Dorchester. A354 from Dorchester, R into Carlton Rd N. On R after Alexandra Rd. From Town Centre follow esplanade towards A354 Dorchester and L into Carlton Rd N.* Home-made teas. **Adm £3, chd free. Sats, Suns 26, 27 Apr; 21, 22 June (2-5).**

Long garden on several levels. Steps and narrow sloping paths lead to beds and borders overflowing with trees, shrubs and herbaceous plants. Unusual plants including exotics in interesting combinations merit a second look. A garden of discovery reflecting an interest in texture, shape, colour, wildlife and above all plants.

9 CHIDEOCK MANOR

Chideock, nr Bridport DT6 6LF. Mr & Mrs Howard Coates, 0788 555 1795, deidrecoates@btinternet.com. *2m W of Bridport on A35. In centre of village turn N at church. The Manor is 1/4 m along this rd on R.* Home-made teas. **Adm £5, chd free. Sun 20, Mon 21 Apr, Sat 14, Sun 15 June (2-5). Visitors also welcome by appt Mar to Oct.**

6/7 acres of formal and informal gardens. Bog garden beside stream and series of ponds. Yew hedges and mature trees. Lime and crab apple walks, herbaceous borders, colourful rose and clematis arches, fernery and nuttery. Walled vegetable garden and orchard. Woodland and lakeside walks. Fine views. Partial wheelchair access.

10 ◆ CHIFFCHAFFS

Chaffeymoor, Bourton, Gillingham SP8 5BY. Mr K R Potts, 01747 840841. *3m E of Wincanton. W end of Bourton. N of A303 On border of Somerset and Wiltshire.* **Adm £3.50, chd free. For NGS: Suns 23 Mar; 22 June; 14 Sept (2-5). For other opening times and information, please phone or see garden website.**

A well known mature garden for all seasons planted round stone cottage with many interesting plants, bulbs, shrubs, herbaceous border and shrub roses. Attractive walk to woodland garden with far-reaching views across Blackmore Vale. New stream and waterfall feature.

11 COOMBE COTTAGE

Shillingstone DT11 0SF. Mike & Jennie Adams, 01258 860220, mikeadams611@gmail.com. *5m NW of Blandford. On main rd (A357) in middle of village between Gunn Lane and Old Ox PH. Parking advised in Gunn Lane.* **Adm £3, chd free. Sun 25 May, Sun 24 Aug (2-6). Visitors also welcome by appt.**

0.4-acre profusely-planted mixed garden with broad borders edged by walls, hedges, fences and arbours. Cottage favourites jostle with more unusual herbaceous and bulbous perennials, shrubs, trees and climbers, and self-seeders rub shoulders with late-flowering and bold-leaved subtropicals. Large glasshouse and some non-botanical surprises. Licensed tea-room, The Willows, 3 mins walk away, is open when Coombe Cottage is open.

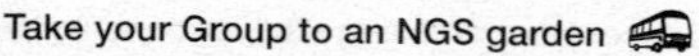
Take your Group to an NGS garden

12 COOMBE KEYNES GARDENS

Coombe Keynes, Wareham BH20 5PS. *All within Combe Keynes village. Map provided on arrival. Turn left off the B3071 Wool/West Lulworth, signed Coombe Keynes 300 yards to village. Park as indicated.* Cream teas in Coombe Keynes Village Church. **Combined adm £5, chd free. Sat 21, Sun 22 June (12.30-5).**

Situated in delightful and secluded hamlet of stone and thatched cottages, former farmyard houses and buildings, C13/C19 church, all renovated and adapted over last 30yrs around small green, conservation area. AONB, adjacent to Jurassic Coast World Heritage Site. Series of village gardens, some classic, some courtyard, some long established, others recently created incl an outstanding vegetable garden (featured in Amateur Gardener), orchards and ponds, vicarage garden adjoining and incl churchyard. Cream teas and some individual stalls in gardens (profits to the Coombe Keynes Church Preservation Trust). Partial wheelchair access.

13 CORFE BARN

Corfe Lodge Road, Broadstone BH18 9NQ. Mr & Mrs John McDavid, 01202 694179. *1m W of Broadstone centre. From main r'about in Broadstone, W along Clarendon Rd ¾ m, N into Roman Rd, after 50yds W into Corfe Lodge Rd.* Home-made teas. **Adm £2.50, chd free. Suns 27 Apr; 25 May; 29 June (2-5). Visitors also welcome by appt May to July.**

Very varied garden in pleasant semi-rural environment extending to about ⅔ acre. Mixture of usual and unusual trees, shrubs and flowers on three levels in and out of the barnyard. Eucalyptus, trees, clematis, roses.

14 CORSCOMBE HOUSE

Corscombe DT2 0NU. Jim Bartos. *3½ m N of Beaminster. On A356 take southern of two signed turnings E to Corscombe, then R signed Church; or on A37 turn W signed Corscombe, L signed Church.* Cream teas in vicarage garden. **Adm £4.50, chd free. Sun 13 July (2-5.30).**

Strong architectural hedges define multiple rooms on different levels with yew columns, parterre and cool beds in lower garden, reflecting pool and hot beds in upper garden, wild flower meadow and orchard, part-walled vegetable garden and secret garden with Mediterranean planting and lemons in pots.

> This sophisticated cottage garden reflects the owners' love of unusual plants . . .

15 COTTAGE ROW

School Lane, Tarrant Gunville, nr Blandford Forum DT11 8JJ. Carolyn & Michael Pawson, 01258 830212, michaelpawson637@btinternet.com. *6m NE of Blandford Forum. From Blandford take A354 towards Salisbury, L at Tarrant Hinton. After 1½ m R in Tarrant Gunville into School Lane.* Cream teas. **Adm £4, chd free. Evening Opening £4, chd free, wine, Sat 7 June (5-8); Sun 8 June (2-5.30). Visitors also welcome by appt May to Aug, roses and clematis at best June/July.**

Maturing ½ -acre partly walled garden. Formal and informal areas separated by yew hedges. Pergola, arbours, brick paths, tree house, kitchen garden and the sound of water. This sophisticated cottage garden reflects the owners' love of unusual plants, structure and an artist's eye for sympathetic colour also evident in new box plantings.

16 COTTESMORE FARM

Newmans Lane, West Moors, Ferndown BH22 0LW. Paul & Valerie Guppy. *Newmans Lane, 1m N of West Moors. Off B3072 Bournemouth to Verwood rd. Car parking in owner's field.* Home-made teas. **Adm £4, chd free. Suns 27 July; 10, 17 Aug (2-5).**

His and hers gardens of over an acre. Wander through a plantsman`s tropical paradise of giant gunneras, bananas, bamboos and over 100 Chusan palms into her cottage garden. Large borders and sweeping island beds with 28 different phlox, heliopsis, heleniums, roses and much more combine to drown you in scent and colour. Butterflies and other insects abound here and in the wild flower area.

17 ◆ CRANBORNE MANOR GARDEN

Cranborne BH21 5PP. Viscount Cranborne, 01725 517248, www.cranborne.co.uk. *10m N of Wimborne on B3078. Enter garden via Cranborne Manor Garden Centre, on L as you enter top of village of Cranborne.* Light refreshments. **Adm £6, chd £1. For NGS: Wed 9 Apr; Sat 12 July (9-4). For other opening times and information, please phone or see garden website.**

Beautiful and historic garden laid out in C17 by John Tradescant and enlarged in C20, featuring several gardens surrounded by walls and yew hedges: blue and white garden, cottage-style and mount gardens, water and wild garden. Many interesting plants, with fine trees and avenues. Mostly wheelchair access.

18 DEANS COURT

Deans Court Lane, Wimborne Minster BH21 1EE. Sir William Hanham, 01202 849314, www.deanscourt.org. *¼ m SE of Minster. Pedestrians: From Deans Court Lane, continuation of High St, over Xrds at Holmans shop (BH21 1EE). Cars: Entrance on Poole Rd, Wimborne (A349); heading S, 300 m on R after Rodways r'about (BH21 1QF).* **Adm £4, chd free (share to Friends of Victoria Hospital). Weds 7 May; 9 July (11-6). Groups of 15+ also welcome by appt.**

13 acres of peaceful, partly wild gardens in ancient setting with mature specimen trees, Saxon fish pond, herb garden and apiary beside R Allen close to town centre. Apple orchard with wild flowers. 1st Soil Association accredited kitchen garden within C18 serpentine walls. Lunches and teas served in garden and tea room, using estate produce (also for sale). Tours of house by owner, pre-booking essential. Follow signs for parking closer to the gardens. Some paths have deep gravel.

19 DOMINEYS

Lockets Lane, Buckland Newton, Dorchester DT2 7BS. Mr & Mrs W Gueterbock, 01300 345295, www.domineys.com. *11m N of Dorchester, 11m S of Sherborne. 2m E A352 or take B3143. No thro' road between church & Gaggle of Geese. Enter 100 yd on L.* Home-made teas. **Adm £4, chd free. Suns 13 Apr; 1 June; 10 Aug (2-6). Visitors also welcome by appt, refreshments by request.**

Welcome to 50 years of change, in attractive thatched cottage setting, superb soil with a good micro climate and plant diversity to enjoy at every season. Naturalised arboretum. Trees, shrubs, herbaceous, bulbs, annuals and pots, fruit and vegetables. Rarities mixed with favourites. Varied layout with something to see around every corner. Growing experience has made a place to relate to and share. Wheelchair access excludes arboretum.

20 ◆ EDMONDSHAM HOUSE

Edmondsham, nr Cranborne, Wimborne BH21 5RE. Mrs Julia Smith, 01725 517207, Julia.edmondsham@yahoo.co.uk. *9m NE of Wimborne. 9m W of Ringwood. Between Cranborne & Verwood. Edmondsham off B3081.* Tea, coffee, cake Weds (3.30-4) in April & Oct only. **Adm £2.50, chd 50p, under 5's free. For NGS: Weds 2, 9, 16, Mon 21, Wed 23 Apr; Weds 1, 8, 15, 22 Oct (2-5).**
For other opening times and information, please phone or email.

6 acres of mature gardens, grounds, views, trees and shaped hedges surrounding C16/C18 house, giving much to explore incl church. Large Victorian walled garden is productive and managed organically (since 1984) using 'no dig' vegetable beds. Wide herbaceous borders planted for seasonal colour. Traditional potting shed and working areas. House also open on NGS days.

21 NEW EDWARDSTOWE

50-52 Bimport, Shaftesbury SP7 8BA. Mike & Louise Madgwick. *Park in town's main car park, garden 500m. Walk along Bimport (B3091) to end, Edwardstowe last house on L.* **Adm £3.50, chd free. Sat 7, Sun 8 June (2-5); Sat 16, Sun 17 Aug (11-5).**

An evolving cottage garden with all yr-round interest, set behind oldest house in Shaftesbury. An enormous magnolia tree greets visitors exiting the courtyard drive to long lawns, divided by two colourful borders and a self-sufficiency vegetable garden. Chickens and bees complete the scene. Seasonal plant and produce sales.

22 FARRS

Whitcombe Rd, Beaminster DT8 3NB.
Mr & Mrs John Makepeace, www.johnmakepeacefurniture.com. *Southern edge of Beaminster. On B3163. Car parking on site only for those in wheelchairs. Enter through garden door in wall adjacent to Museum. Park in the Square or side streets.* Light refreshments. **Adm £5, chd free. Suns 15 June; 20 July; 17 Aug; 14 Sept (11-5).**

Enjoy several distinctive walled gardens, rolling lawns, sculpture and giant topiary around the house. John's inspirational grasses garden, Jennie's riotous potager with cleft-oak fruit cage. Glasshouse, straw bale studio, geese in orchard. Remarkable trees, planked and drying in open-sided barn. House also open on NGS days with selection of furniture by John Makepeace, and paintings, sculpture and applied arts by living artists. Midday talks by John and Jennie Makepeace and Neil Lucas. Plants for sale. Featured in English Garden and Hortus. Some gravel paths, alternative wheelchair route through orchard.

23 ◆ FORDE ABBEY GARDENS

Chard TA20 4LU. Mr & Mrs Julian Kennard, 01460 221290, info@fordeabbey.co.uk, www.fordeabbey.co.uk. *4m SE of Chard. Signed off A30 Chard-Crewkerne & A358 Chard-Axminster. Also from Broadwindsor B3164.* **For information, please phone or see garden website.**

30 acres of fine shrubs, magnificent specimen trees, ponds, herbaceous borders, rockery, bog garden containing superb collection of Asiatic primulas, Ionic temple, working walled kitchen garden supplying the tearoom. Centenary fountain, England's highest powered fountain. Gardens open daily (10-6, last adm 4.30pm). Please ask at reception for best wheelchair route. Wheelchairs available to borrow/hire, advance booking advised.

24 FRANKHAM FARM

Ryme Intrinseca, Sherborne DT9 6JT. Susan Ross, Andy & Sue 01935 872819, neilandsusan@blueyonder.co.uk. *3m S of Yeovil. A37 Yeovil-Dorchester; turn E; drive 1/4 m on L.* Home-made teas. **Adm £3, chd free. Suns 16 Mar; 27 Apr; 8 June; 12 Oct (2-5). Visitors welcome by appointment**

3½-acre garden, created since 1960 by the late Jo Earle for yr-round interest. This large and lovely garden is filled with a wide variety of well grown plants, roses, unusual, labelled shrubs and trees from around the world. Productive vegetable garden. Climbers cover the walls. Spring bulbs through to autumn colour, particularly oaks. Sorry, no dogs.

Chickens and bees complete the scene. Seasonal plant and produce sales . . .

25 FRITH HOUSE

Stalbridge DT10 2SD. Mr & Mrs Patrick Sclater, 01963 250809, rosalynsclater@btinternet.com. *5m E of Sherborne. Between Milborne Port and Stalbridge. From A30 1m, follow sign to Stalbridge. From Stalbridge 2m and turn W by PO.* Home-made teas. **Adm £4, chd free. Sun 8 June (2-5). Groups welcome by appt May-July incl, Mon-Fri only.**

Approached down long drive with fine views. 4 acres of garden around

Edwardian house and self-contained hamlet. Range of mature trees, lakes and flower borders. House terrace edged by rose border and featuring Lutyensesque wall fountain and game larder. Well-stocked kitchen gardens.

26 THE GLADE

Woodland Walk, Ferndown BH22 9LP. Mary & Roger Angus, 01202 872789, mary@gladestock.co.uk. *3/4 m NE of Ferndown, nr Tricketts Cross r'about. N off Wimborne Rd East, Woodland Walk is a single track lane with no parking. Please leave cars on main road and access on foot (5 mins/330 yds).* Home-made & cream teas. **Adm £3.50, chd free. Suns 20 Apr; 4, 18 May; 1 June (1-5). Groups of 20+ also welcome by appt Apr to June, refreshments by arrangement.**

The name captures the setting. Award-winning 1 3/4 -acre spring garden. Terraced lawns for lingering over tea. Woodland walks through blossom trees, wild anemones, primroses and bluebells. Extensive shrubbery with camellias, azaleas and rhododendrons. Stream and large wildlife pond with primulas, marginals and waterlilies. Bog garden, wet meadow, spring bulbs and herbaceous and mixed borders. Featured in Gardens of Dorset. Gravel, grass and slopes make wheelchair access difficult, notably if wet. Drop-off/pick-up for those with restricted mobility by arrangement only. Please phone.

27 GREENACRES

Bere Road, Coldharbour, Wareham BH20 7PA. John & Pat Jacobs. *2 1/2 m NW of Wareham. From r'about adjacent to stn take Wareham-Bere Regis rd. House 1/2 m past Silent Woman Inn on R.* Home-made teas. **Adm £3.50, chd free. Sun 22 June, Sun 20 July (2-5.30).**

Approx 1-acre plantswoman's garden situated in Wareham Forest. Lawns punctuated by colourful island beds designed mainly for summer interest. Unusual perennials, shrubs and specimen trees, spectacular flowering Tulip Tree. Themed areas and stone water feature with 2 ponds. Stumpery with collection of ferns and grasses. Live music. Static display of radio controlled aircraft. Plenty of off-road parking.

28 NEW HARCOMBE HOUSE

Pitmans Lane, Morcombelake, Bridport DT6 6EB. Jan & Martin Dixon. *A35 4m W of Bridport - ignore satnav. From Bridport: R to Whitchurch just past The Artwave Gallery. Immed R, bear L into Pitmans Lane. Approx 800m, park in paddock on L.* Home-made teas. **Adm £4, chd free. Wed 4, Thur 5, Sat 7, Sun 8 June; Wed 13, Thur 14, Sat 16, Sun 17 Aug (10-5).**

Landscaped into the hillside with wonderful views across Lyme Bay, the garden is laid out as a series of gravel paths and terraces connected by steps. Featuring mature shrubs and perennials, many of which are unusual and visually stunning, the garden offers something for every season. The garden will present a challenge to the less mobile visitor and is unsuitable for wheelchairs and buggies. Wonderful views. Mature trees and shrubs for all seasons. Pond with water lilies and fish. Not suitable for wheelchairs.

29 HATCHLANDS

Netherbury DT6 5NA. Dr & Mrs John Freeman. *2m SW of Beaminster. Turn R off A3066 Beaminster to Bridport Rd, signed Netherbury. Car park at Xrds at bottom of hill. 200yds up bridle path.* Home-made teas. **Adm £5, chd free. Sun 11 May (1-5). Also open The Mill House and 2 Pyes Plot.**

Country hillside garden within 3 acres. Tall yew and box hedges, rose gardens, herbaceous and fuchsia beds and many hardy geraniums beneath a long Georgian brick wall. Open sloping lawns and croquet court, spring-fed pond and mature broadleaf trees in woodland area.

30 HERONS MEAD

East Burton Road, East Burton, Wool BH20 6HF. Ron & Angela Millington, 01929 463872, ronamillington@btinternet.com. *6m W of Wareham on A352. Approaching Wool from Wareham, turn R just before level crossing into East Burton Rd. Herons Mead 3/4 m on L.* Home-made teas. **Adm £3, chd free. Suns 23 Mar; 20 Apr; 4 May (2-5). Evening Opening £4, chd free, wine, Fri 20 June (6-8); Suns 22 June; 21 Sept (2-5). Also open 4 May Holworth Farmhouse. Groups of 10+ also welcome by appt Mar to Sept.**

1/2 -acre plantlover's garden full of interest from spring (bulbs, 200 hellebores, pulmonaria, fritillaries) through abundant summer perennials, old roses scrambling through trees and late-seasonal exuberant plants amongst swathes of tall grasses. Wildlife attractive, especially bees and butterflies. Tiny woodland. Cacti. 'Out of the ordinary' (WI Life). 'Interesting and Unique' (Dorset Life). Local community choir singing 20 June.

31 ◆ HILLTOP

Woodville, Stour Provost SP8 5LY. Josse & Brian Emerson, 01747 838512, www.hilltopgarden.co.uk. *7m N of Sturminster Newton, 5m W of Shaftesbury. On B3092 turn E at Stour Provost Xrds, signed Woodville. After 1 1/4 m thatched cottage on R. On A30, 4m W of Shaftesbury, turn S opposite Kings Arms.* Home-made teas. **Adm £2.50, chd free. For NGS: Every Sun 13 July to 17 Aug (2-6). For other opening times and information, please phone or see garden website.**

Summer at Hilltop is a gorgeous riot of colour and scent, the old thatched cottage barely visible amongst the flowers. Unusual annuals and perennials grow alongside the traditional and familiar, boldly combining to make a spectacular display, which attracts an abundance of wildlife. Always something new, the unique, gothic garden loo a great success. Nursery.

32 22 HOLT ROAD

Branksome, Poole BH12 1JQ. Alan & Sylvia Lloyd, 01202 387509, alan.lloyd22@ntlworld.com. *2½ m W of Bournemouth Square, 3m E of Poole Civic Centre. From Alder Rd turn into Winston Ave, 3rd R into Guest Ave 2nd R into Holt Rd at end of cul-de-sac. Park in Holt Rd or alternatively in Guest Ave.* Home-made teas. **Adm £3.50, chd free. Suns 23 Mar; 27 Apr; 18 May; 15 June; 27 July; 24 Aug (2-5.30). Also open 27 April 17 Lower Golf Links Rd. Groups of 10+ also welcome by appt Mar to Oct.**

¾ -acre walled garden for all seasons. Garden seating throughout the diverse planting areas, comprising Mediterranean courtyard garden, wisteria pergola. Walk up slope beside rill and bog garden to raised bed vegetable garden. Return through shrubbery and rockery back to waterfall cascading into a pebble beach. Partial wheelchair access.

Landscaped into the hillside with wonderful views across Lyme Bay . . .

33 ◆ HOLWORTH FARMHOUSE

Holworth, nr Dorchester DT2 8NH. Anthony & Philippa Bush, 01305 852242, www.inarcadia-gardendesign.co.uk. *7m E of Dorchester. 1m S of A352. Follow signs to Holworth. Through farmyard with duckpond on R. 1st L after 200yds of rough track. Ignore 'no access' signs.* Home-made teas on NGS days in the garden. **Adm £3.50, chd free. For NGS: Sun 4, Mon 5 May; Suns 15 June; 20 July; 24 Aug (2-5). Also open 4 May Herons Mead, and 15 June Warmwell House. For other opening times and information, please phone or see garden website.**

This unusual garden is tucked away without being isolated and has an atmosphere of extraordinary peace and tranquility. At no point do visitors perceive any idea of the whole, but have to discover, by degrees and at every turn, its element of surprise, its variety of features and its appreciation of space. At all times you are invited to look back, to look round and to look up. Birds and Butterflies. Limited wheelchair access.

34 HOLY TRINITY ENVIRONMENTAL GARDEN

Cross Rd, Weymouth DT4 9QX. Holy Trinity C E Primary School & Nursery, holytrinityenvironmentalgarden.blogspot.co.uk. *1m W of Weymouth centre. Follow A354 from Weymouth harbour junction by Asda. R at top of hill into Wyke Rd. 3rd L into Cross Rd. 200yds on R school car park.* Home-made teas. **Adm £3.50, chd free. Sat 19, Sun 20 July (1-5).**

This award-winning wildlife garden was started in 2008 with the donation of a winning RHS Show garden. There are also children's raised beds; large wildlife pond; WWII garden with genuine Anderson shelter; small orchard and bird garden. Dorset's largest living willow classroom which seats 30 is now well established and a recently installed composting toilet complements the garden. Butterfly hunt for children. Wheelchair access to most of garden and WC.

35 HORN PARK

Tunnel Rd, Beaminster DT8 3HB. Mr & Mrs David Ashcroft, 01308 862212, angieashcroft@btinternet.com. *1½ m N of Beaminster. On A3066 from Beaminster, L before tunnel (see signs).* Home-made teas. **Adm £4.50, chd free. Weds 30 Apr; 18 June (2.30-4.30). Visitors also welcome by appt Apr to Oct, Tues to Thurs only.**

Large, plantsman's garden with magnificent view to sea. Many rare and mature plants and shrubs in terraced, herbaceous, rock and water gardens. Woodland garden and walks in bluebell woods. Good autumn colouring. Wild flower meadow with 164 varieties incl orchids. Some parts may be inaccessible to wheelchairs due to steep inclines.

36 IVY HOUSE GARDEN

Piddletrenthide DT2 7QF. Bridget Bowen, 01300 348255, bridgetpbowen@hotmail.com. *9m N of Dorchester. On B3143. In middle of Piddletrenthide village, opp PO/village stores near Piddle Inn.* Home-made teas. **Adm £4, chd free. Wed 9, Mon 21 Apr; Sun 4, Mon 5 May (2-5). Groups of 10+ also welcome by appt Apr to May.**

Unusual and challenging ½ -acre garden set on steep hillside with fine views. A wildlife-friendly garden with mixed borders, ponds, propagating area, vegetable garden, fruit cage, greenhouses and polytunnel, chickens and bees, nearby allotment. Daffodils, tulips and hellebores in quantity for spring openings. Come prepared for steep terrain and a warm welcome! Wildlife-friendly, run on organic lines with plants to attract bees and other insects. Insect-friendly plants usually for sale. Honey and hive products available and weather permitting, an observation hive of honey bees is set up.

37 ◆ KINGSTON LACY

Wimborne Minster BH21 4EA. National Trust, 01202 883402, kingstonlacy@nationaltrust.org.uk, www.nationaltrust.org.uk. *1½ m W of Wimborne Minster. On the Wimborne-Blandford rd B3082.* **Adm £8, chd £4. For NGS: Sat 28, Sun 29 June (10.30-6). For other opening times and information, please phone or see garden website.**

35 acres of formal garden, incorporating a parterre and sunk garden planted with Edwardian schemes during the spring and summer. 5 acre kitchen garden and allotments, Victorian fernery containing over 35 varieties. Rose garden, mixed herbaceous borders, vast formal lawns and a Japanese garden restored to Henrietta Bankes' creation of 1910. 2 National Collections: Convallaria and Anemone nemorosa. Deep gravel on some paths but lawns suitable for wheelchairs. Slope to visitor reception and S lawn.

Farrs

38 ◆ KINGSTON MAURWARD GARDENS AND ANIMAL PARK

Kingston Maurward, Dorchester DT2 8PX. Kingston Maurward College, 01305 215003, www.kmc.ac.uk/gardens. *1m E of Dorchester. Off A35. Follow brown Tourist Information signs.* **For information, please phone or see garden website.**

35 acres of gardens laid out in C18 and C20 with 5-acre lake. Generous terraces and gardens divided by hedges and stone balustrades. Stone features and interesting plants. Elizabethan walled garden laid out as demonstration. National Collections of penstemons and salvias. Open 2 Jan to 20 Dec (10-5.30). Partial wheelchair access, gravel paths, steep slope to lake.

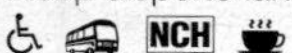

39 KNITSON OLD FARMHOUSE

Corfe Castle, Wareham BH20 5JB. Rachel Helfer, 01929 421681, rachel@knitson.co.uk. *1m NW of Swanage. 3m E of Corfe Castle. Signed L off A351 to Knitson. Very narrow rds for 1m. Ample parking in yard or in adjacent field.* Cream teas. **Adm £3, chd free. Fri 2, Sat 3, Sun 4, Mon 5 May; Fri 13, Sat 14, Sun 15 June (1-5). Visitors also welcome by appt Apr to Oct max 25.**

Mature cottage garden with exceptional views nestled at base of chalk downland in dry coastal conditions. Herbaceous borders, rockeries, climbers and shrubs. Evolved and designed over 50yrs for yr-round colour and interest. Large wildlife friendly kitchen garden for self-sufficiency. Rachel is delighted to welcome visitors and discuss gardening. Uneven, sloping paths.

40 ◆ KNOLL GARDENS

Hampreston BH21 7ND. Mr Neil Lucas, 01202 873931, www.knollgardens.co.uk. *2½ m W of Ferndown. ETB brown signs from A31. Large car park.* **For opening times and information, please phone or see garden website.**

Exciting collection of grasses and perennials thrive within an informal setting of shrubs, mature and unusual trees. Mediterranean-style gravel garden, Dragon Garden and Decennium border planted in the naturalistic style. National Collection of pennisetum. Some slopes. Various surfaces including gravel, paving, grass and bark.

41 LANGEBRIDE HOUSE

Long Bredy DT2 9HU. Mrs J Greener, 01308 482257. *8m W of Dorchester. S off A35, midway between Dorchester and Bridport. Well signed. 1st gateway on L in village.* **Adm £5, chd free. Visitors welcome by appt Feb to July.**

This old rectory garden has carpets of anemones spreading out under the huge copper beech tree on the lawn. Sheets of crocus are interspersed with snowdrops and other early spring bulbs. A lovely place to visit, especially in early spring. Large variety of daffodils, flowering shrubs, trees, with herbaceous borders and a kitchen garden. Some steep slopes.

42 LAWSBROOK

Brodham Way, Shillingstone, Dorset DT11 0TE. Clive, Faith & Gina Nelson, 01258 860148, cne70bl@aol.com, www.facebook.com/Lawsbrook. *5m NW of Blandford. Follow signs to Shillingstone on A357. Turn off A357 at old PO, continue up Gunn Lane, 2nd junction on R, 1st house on R (200yds).* Home-made teas. **Adm £3, chd free. Sun 23 Feb, Sun 2 Mar, Sun 2 Nov (10-4). Individuals/ groups also welcome by appt Feb to Nov.**

6 acres. Over 200 trees incl the mature and unusual. Formal borders, wild flower and wildlife areas, vegetable garden. Relaxed and friendly, lovely opportunity for family walks in all areas including wildlife, stream, meadow. Children and dogs welcome. Yr-round interest incl extensive snowdrops, hellebores and bulbs in early spring through full summer colour to intense autumn hues. Large and unusual labelled tree collection. Garden activities for all the family. More than an acre coverage of snowdrops in the early spring. Gravel path at entrance, grass paths over whole garden.

43 LITTLE BINDON

Main Road, West Lulworth BH20 5RJ. The Weld Estate/Mr Richard Wilkin. *5m West of Wareham. Far side of Lulworth Cove.* Light refreshments. **Adm £3, chd free. Sat 17, Sun 18 May (12-4.30).**
Remote and romantic C11 monastic chapel. Wild, secret garden. Bluebells and spring bulbs. Exuberant rose growth, sculptured vegetation, winding paths and vistas to adjacent cliffs and hills. Complete tranquillity. Challenging access as on far side of Lulworth Cove, repaid by this special and unusual place, dramatic coastal scenery en route and beyond. Featured in Dorset Life.

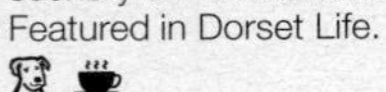

44 ◆ LITTLEBREDY WALLED GARDENS

Littlebredy DT2 9HL. The Walled Garden Workshop, 01305 898055, secretary@wgw.org.uk, www.littlebredy.com. *8m W of Dorchester. 10m E of Bridport. 1½ m S of A35. NGS days: park on village green then walk 300yds. For the less mobile (and on normal open days) use Gardens Car Park.* Home-made teas. **Adm £4, chd free. For NGS: Tues 24 June; 1 July (2-7). For information, please phone or see garden website.**
1-acre walled garden on S-facing slopes of Bride River Valley. Herbaceous borders, riverside rose walk, lavender parterre and potager vegetable and cut flower gardens. Original Victorian glasshouses, one under renovation. Gardens also open 2-5pm on Wed, Sun and some BHs (see website) from Easter to end Sept, weather permitting. Partial wheelchair access, some steep grass slopes. For disabled parking please follow signs to main entrance.

45 55 LONNEN ROAD

Colehill, Wimborne BH21 7AT. Malcolm Case & Jenny Parr, 01202 883549. *1½ m N of Wimborne. From Canford Bottom r'about where A31 meets B3073, exit N marked Colehill for 1¼ m, R into Lonnen Rd.* Home-made teas. **Adm £3, chd free. Sats, Suns 5, 6 July; 2, 3 Aug (2-5). Visitors also welcome by appt July/Aug.**
Perfectionist's garden on 3 levels, with colour co-ordinated planting using wide range of plants, with borrowed view over adjacent fields. Circular box parterre infilled with vegetables. Watering cans hang in a row behind tool shed, by bridge over little stream. Lots for the eye and senses to enjoy.

46 NEW 17 LOWER GOLF LINKS ROAD

Broadstone, Poole BH18 8BQ. Dr & Mrs Nicholas Dunn. *½ m N of Broadstone centre. Approaching from Gravel Hill, along Dunyeats Rd, Lower Golf Links Road is 2nd turn on R, past the Middle School.* Home-made teas. **Adm £3.50, chd free. Sun 27 Apr, Thur 22 May; Thur 12, Sun 15 June (2-5). Also open 22 Holt Rd 27 April.**
Town garden of 2/3 acre, created in a heathland suburb. Originally mainly acid-loving plants, now, after much clearance and soil enrichment, plants for all seasons. There is a prominent vegetable garden with raised beds, chickens, fruit trees and a pond as well as borders. Something of interest all year round, but particularly impressive in spring and early summer. Vegetable garden with raised beds. All the work and design done solely by the owners. Gravel drive and stone steps. Garden on a slight slope. Not suitable for wheelchairs.

47 MANOR FARM, HAMPRESTON

Wimborne BH21 7LX. Guy & Anne Trehane. *2½ m E of Wimborne, 2½ m W of Ferndown. From Canford Bottom r'about on A31, take exit B3073 Ham Lane. ½ m turn R at Hampreston Xrds. House at bottom of village.* Home-made teas. **Adm £3.50, chd free. Sat 22, Sun 23 Feb (12-3); Suns 18 May; 8 June; 3 Aug (1-5); Wed 6 Aug (2-5).**
Traditional farmhouse garden designed and cared for by 3 generations of the Trehane family. Last year marked the celebration of 100 years of farming and gardening at Hampreston. Garden is noted for its herbaceous borders and rose beds within box and yew hedges. Mature shrubbery, water and bog garden. Opening for hellebores in Feb. Dorset Hardy Plant Society sales at later openings.

48 THE MANOR HOUSE, BEAMINSTER

North St, Beaminster DT8 3DZ. Christine Wood. *200yds N of town square. North St, starts at Red Lion off Beaminster Square. Park in Sq or public car park, 5 mins walk from the Square. Limited disabled parking on site.* Home-made teas. **Adm £5, chd free. Sun 25, Mon 26 May (11-5). Also open 25 May Slape Manor.**
Set in heart of Beaminster, 16½ acres of stunning parkland with mature specimen trees, lake and waterfall. Recently restored walled garden - serendipity. Designed and planted over last 6 yrs as a formal garden. Entire garden is an ongoing project with woodland walk and wild flower meadow recently introduced.

49 MANOR HOUSE, LOWER BLANDFORD ST MARY

Church Lane, Lower Blandford St Mary, Blandford DT11 9ND. Mr & Mrs Jeremy Mains. *¼ m E of Blandford. Signed off A350 to Poole from Blandford Forum Ring Road (Tesco r'about).* Home-made teas. **Adm £4, chd free. Sun 7, Wed 10 Sept (2-5).**
Traditional 3-acre walled garden surrounding Jacobean House (not open). Formal rose beds with mixed herbaceous borders. Working fruit and vegetable garden. Large and varied shrub borders with extensive collection of roses.

50 ◆ MAPPERTON GARDENS

nr Beaminster DT8 3NR. The Earl & Countess of Sandwich, 01308 862645, www.mapperton.com. *6m N of Bridport. Off A356/A3066. 2m SE of Beaminster off B3163.* **For information, please phone or see garden website.**
Terraced valley gardens surrounding Tudor/Jacobean manor house. On

upper levels, walled croquet lawn, orangery and Italianate formal garden with fountains, topiary and grottos. Below, C17 summerhouse and fishponds. Lower garden with shrubs and rare trees, leading to woodland and spring gardens. Garden open 1 Mar to 31 Oct (except Sats) (11-5); café open 1 Apr to 30 Sept. Partial wheelchair access (lawn and upper levels).

51 MARREN

Holworth, Dorchester DT2 8NJ. Mr & Mrs Peter Cartwright, 01305 851503, wcartwright@tiscali.co.uk, www.wendycartwright.net. *SE of Dorchester. Don't use sat nav. Off A353 at Poxwell, L towards Ringstead, straight on to NT Car Park. Drive straight through CP over top to gate marked No Cars. Walk.* Home-made teas. **Adm £3.50, chd free. Sats, Suns 12, 13 Apr; 31 May; 1 June (2-5). Visitors also welcome by appt Apr to June, refreshments by arrangement.**

4 acres. Gardening on slopes with terraces. Nature has been subtly tamed giving satisfactory shapes and allowing glimpses over to Portland and Weymouth. Formality by house with Italianate courtyard and hornbeam arbour gives Mediterranean feel. Strong structure and effective planting creates lovely spaces where bees and butterflies feed and dance. A 'fedge' in willow. Hornbeam house. Italianate courtyard with fountain. Hornbeam arbour on terrace. Willow arbour at the bottom. Tree sculptures. Not suitable for wheelchairs. Disabled access to house for tea by prior arrangement.

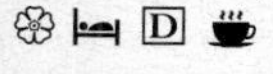

52 MAYFIELD

4 Walford Close, Wimborne Minster BH21 1PH. Mr & Mrs Terry Wheeler, 01202 849838, terry.wheeler@tesco.net. *1/2 m N of Wimborne. B3078 out of Wimborne, R into Burts Hill, 1st L into Walford Close.* Home-made teas. **Adm £3, chd free (share to The Friends of Victoria Hospital, Wimborne). Sun 11, Thur 22 May; Sun 1, Wed 11, Sun 15 June (1.30-5). Groups of 6+ also welcome by appt May to June.**

Town garden of approx 1/4 acre. Front: formal hard landscaping planted with drought-resistant shrubs and perennials. Shaded area has wide variety of hostas. Back garden contrasts with a seductive series of garden rooms containing herbaceous perennial beds separated by winding grass paths and rustic arches. Pond, vegetable beds and greenhouses containing succulents and vines. Display of artwork by local sculptor and craftsman Chris Davies. www.recyclart.co.uk.

New waterfall with stepped alpine bed behind pond . . .

53 MEADOW VIEWS

32 Riverside Road, West Moors, Ferndown BH22 0LQ. Sue & Norman Lynch. *2m from Ferndown towards Verwood, off B3072. From Station Rd through West Moors going N, turn L. Last house on R. Parking in rd, avoiding driveways.* Home-made teas. **Adm £2.50, chd free. Suns 20 July; 17 Aug (2-5).**

Discover peace and tranquillity at this small, informal garden overlooking Mannington Brook and open farmland. Island beds with colourful herbaceous mixed planting and two themed areas. Damselflies dance in the sunshine and the lobster pot sits near the water's edge with the latest catch!

54 MEWS COTTAGE

34 Easton Street, Portland DT5 1BT. Peter & Jill Pitman, 01305 820377, penstemon@waitrose.com. *3m S of Weymouth. Situated on top of the island, 50yds past Punchbowl Inn, small lane on L. Park in main street & follow signs.* Home-made teas. **Adm £2, chd free. Sat 7, Sun 8 June; Sun 20 July (2-5); Sat 2 Aug (11-4), Suns 3, 24 Aug; 7 Sept (2-5). Also open 3 Aug & 7 Sept Queen Ann House. Visitors also welcome by appt June to Sept.**

New waterfall with stepped alpine bed behind pond now completed for 2014, also reorganisation of National Collection of cultivar Penstemon, and crevice bed for species penstemon grown from APS seed. Well established agapanthus. Raised beds of wild orchids, roscoea and bletilla with several new stunning dierama provide colour late in the season. Ceramics by Tiffany. 2 small steps to WC Wheelchair access to WC and on three paths - fourth path walking only.

NCH

55 THE MILL HOUSE

Crook Hill, Netherbury DT6 5LX. Michael & Giustina Ryan, 01308 488267, themillhouse@dsl.pipex.com. *1m S of Beaminster. Turn R off A3066 Beaminster to Bridport rd at signpost to Netherbury. Car park at Xrds at bottom of hill.* Cream teas. **Adm £5, chd free. Suns 27 Apr; 11 May (1-5). Evening Opening £5, chd free, wine, Wed 9 July (5.30-8). Combined with Pye's Plot, Netherbury 11 May, 9 July, 2 gardens £7. Visitors also welcome by appt Apr to Aug min 6, max 30.**

6½ acres of garden around R Brit, mill stream and mill pond. Formal walled, terraced and vegetable gardens. Bog garden. Emphasis on spring bulbs, scented flowers, hardy geraniums, lilies, clematis and water irises. Wander through the wild garden planted with many rare and interesting trees including conifers, magnolias, fruit trees and oaks underplanted with bulbs. Featured in Country Life. Partial wheelchair access.

56 ◆ MINTERNE HOUSE

Minterne Magna, Dorchester DT2 7AU. The Hon Henry & Mrs Digby, 01300 341370, www.minterne.co.uk. *2m N of Cerne Abbas. On A352 Dorchester-Sherborne rd.* **For information please phone or see garden website.**

20 acres wild woodland gardens landscaped in C18, laid out in a horseshoe over 1m round. Home to the Churchill and Digby families for 350yrs. From spring to autumn the magnificent mature and newly-planted specimen shrubs and trees create surprises and superb vistas around the lake, ending with sensational autumn colouring. Open mid Feb to 9 Nov (10-6). Plant sale Sun 18 May. Regret unsuitable for wheelchairs.

bank. Circular sunken stone walled area with box bushes and statuary. Lovingly restored from neglected overgrown jungle.

Cottesmore Farm

57 4 NOEL ROAD

Wallisdown, Bournemouth BH10 4DP. Lesley & Ivor Pond. *4m NE of Poole. From Wallisdown Xrds enter Kinson Rd. Take 5th rd on R, Kingsbere Ave. Noel Rd is first on R.* Home-made teas. **Adm £3.50, chd free. Suns 6, 20 July (2-5).**
Exciting small garden, 100ft x 30ft, with big ideas. On sloping ground many Roman features incl water and impressive temple. Most planting is in containers. Several new features. Camera is a must. Come and give us your opinion 'Is this garden over the top?'. Steps to upper part of the garden.

58 'OLA'

47 Old Castle Road, Rodwell, Weymouth DT4 8QE. Jane Uff & Elaine Smith. *1m from Weymouth centre. Follow signs to Portland. Off Buxton Rd, lower end of Old Castle Rd. Bungalow just past Sandsfoot Castle ruins/gardens. Easy access by foot off Rodwell Trail at Sandsfoot Castle.* Home-made teas. **Adm £3.50, chd free. Mons 12, 26 May; 9 June (2-5).**
Seaside garden with stunning views overlooking Portland Harbour. 1930s-designed garden, once part of Sandsfoot Castle estate. Mixed herbaceous borders, shrubs and roses. Rockeries, fish pond, vegetables, orchard and 7 dwarfs

59 OLD DOWN HOUSE

Horton, Wimborne BH21 7HL. Dr & Mrs Colin Davidson, 07765 404248, olddown@btinternet.com. *7½ m N of Wimborne. Horton Inn at junction of B3078 with Horton Road, pick up yellow signs which take you up through North Farm. No garden access from Matterley Drove.* Home-made teas. **Adm £3, chd free. Wed 28 May; Wed 4, Sun 8 June (2-5).**
Nestled down a farm track, this ¾-acre garden on chalk surrounds C18 farmhouse. Stunning views over Horton Tower and farmland. Cottage garden planting with formal elements, climbing roses clothe pergola and house walls along with stunning wisteria sinensis and banksia rose. Part-walled potager. Featured in Dorset Life. Not suitable for wheelchairs.

60 THE OLD RECTORY, MANSTON

Manston, Sturminster Newton DT10 1EX. Andrew & Judith Hussey, 01258 474673, judithhussey@hotmail.com. *6m S of Shaftesbury, 2½ m N of Sturminster Newton. From Shaftesbury, take B3091. On reaching Manston, past Plough Inn, L for Child Okeford on R-hand bend. Old Rectory last house on L.* Home-made teas. **Adm £4, chd free. Sun 22, Wed 25 June (2-5). Groups of 4+ also welcome by appt May to Sept.**
Beautifully restored 5-acre garden. S-facing wall with 120ft herbaceous border edged by old brick path. Enclosed yew hedge flower garden. Wild flower meadow marked with mown paths and young plantation of mixed hardwoods. Well-maintained walled Victorian kitchen garden. Knot garden introduced in 2011 now well established. New garden room with box and rose and yew introduced in 2013. Featured in Dorset Life and Dorset Magazine.

62 THE OLD RECTORY, PULHAM

Dorchester DT2 7EA. Mr & Mrs N Elliott, 01258 817595. *13m N of Dorchester. 8m SE of Sherborne. On B3143 turn E at Xrds in Pulham.*

Signed Cannings Court. **Adm £5, chd free. Sun 11 May; Sun 3, Wed 6 Aug (2-5). Groups of 15+ also welcome by appt May to Aug.**
4 acres formal and informal gardens surround C18 rectory with splendid views. Yew hedges enclose circular herbaceous borders with late summer colour. Exuberantly planted terrace with purple and white beds. Box parterres, mature trees, pond, fernery, ha-ha, pleached hornbeam circle. 10 acres woodland walks. Flourishing and newly extended bog garden with islands; awash with primulas and irises in May. Home-made teas and cakes 11 May & 3 Aug, interesting plants for sale. Featured in Country Life, Home and Gardens, Country Homes and Interiors. Mostly wheelchair access.

63 OLD SMITHY

Ibberton DT11 0EN. Carol & Clive Carsley, 01258 817361. *9m NW of Blandford Forum. From Blandford A357 to Sturminster Newton. After 6.5m L to Okeford Fitzpaine. Follow signs to Ibberton, 3m, park by village hall, 5 min walk to garden*. Home-made teas in village hall. **Adm £3.50, chd free. Sat 19 Apr; Mon 26 May (2-5). Visitors also welcome by appt Mar to Aug.**
Worth driving twisty narrow lanes to reach rural 2½ -acre streamside garden framing thatched cottage. Back of beyond setting which inspired international best seller Mr Rosenblum's List. Succession of ponds. Mown paths. Spring bulbs, aquilegia and hellebores. Sit beneath rustling trees. Views of Bulbarrow and church. Featured in Period Living.

64 THE OLD VICARAGE

East Orchard, Shaftesbury SP7 0BA. Miss Tina Wright, 01747 811744. *4½ m S of Shaftesbury, 3½ m N of Sturminster Newton. On B 3091, Shaftesbury side of 90° bend. Drop passengers at lay-by with telephone box and park in narrow rd to East Orchard nr church*. Home-made teas. **Adm £4, chd free. Suns 23 Mar (1-4.30); 27 Apr (2-5). Individuals and groups also welcome by appt.**
Featured in the Mail on Sunday after winning the best large Dorset Wildlife Friendly garden in 2012, this inspirational garden has yr-round interest, with many ideas to take away. Early bulbs in spring, herbaceous borders, roses, berrying shrubs and mature trees as well as unusual water features and a fantastic tree viewing platform. Dogs welcome and children can pond dip. Swing and tree platform overlooking Duncliffe woods. Teas indoors and various shelters around the garden if wet. Not suitable for wheelchairs if very wet.

> Big lovingly created garden . . . myriad of butterflies and bees . . .

65 PARNHAM HOUSE

Beaminster DT8 3LZ. Mr & Mrs M B Treichl. *1m S of Beaminster. Turn R off A3066 1m S Beaminster. Follow signs*. **Adm £5, chd free. Tue 17, Sat 21 June (2-5).**
Beautifully presented spacious gardens surrounding Elizabethan Manor House. Terraced formal gardens on South side of house with topiary features leading to lake within deer park setting. Walled gardens with themed borders and vegetable area. House not open. Partial wheelchair access, gravel paths and steep grass slopes.

66 PILSDON VIEW

Junction Butts Lane & Pitman's Lane, Ryall, Bridport DT6 6EH. D Lloyd, 01297 489377, davidlloyd001@hotmail.com. *5m W of Bridport, through Chideock. From E through Morecombelake A35. Take the Ryall turning opp Felicity's farm shop on A35. Garden ¾ m on L at junction Butts Lane/Pitmans Lane. High hedge with PO box in wall*. **Adm £4, chd free. Tue 10, Sun 29 June; Tue 8, Sat 26 July (12-4). Visitors also welcome by appt June to July, no coaches.**
Started over 25 yrs ago, the hard landscaping provides different levels with breathtaking views over the Marshwood Vale towards Pilson Pen. A mature copper beech and evolving garden gives all yr round interest. Water features with wildlife add to the essence of the garden. Bring your own picnic. Mostly wheelchair access.

67 NEW PUDDLEDOCK COTTAGE

Scotland Heath, Norden, nr Corfe Castle, Wareham BH20 5DY. Mr Malcolm Orgee. *From Wareham to Corfe Castle turn L at Norden Park and Ride then L signed Slepe and Arne. Garden 500m on R*. Light refreshments. **Adm £3, chd free. Suns 11 May; 27 July (12-4).**
Puddledock Cottage was originally a quarryman's cottage. Newly renovated, it now stands at the centre of a big lovingly created garden with streams and ponds edged with nectar rich plants that attract a myriad of butterflies and bees. Shady walks snake though birch and willow, under-planted with rhododendrons and ferns. Views to Corfe Castle and Scotland Heath. Good wheelchair access.

68 2 PYES PLOT

St. James Road, Netherbury, Bridport DT6 5LP. Ms Sarah Porter. *2m SW of Beaminster. Turn off A3066. Go over R Brit into centre of village. L into St James Rd, signed to Waytown, R corner Hingsdon Lane*. **Adm £3, chd free. Sun 11 May (2-5.30). Evening Opening £3, chd free, light refreshments, Wed 9 July (5-7.30). Combined with The Mill House both days, 2 gardens £7, home-made teas at The Mill House 11 May.**
Small but perfectly formed front and back courtyard garden, created from new in 2007. Cream walls and black paintwork make a striking framework for softer planting. Climbing plants, foliage and running water feature enhance the tranquil feel to this space, which uses every inch creatively. Featured in Dorset Life and Good Housekeeping.

69 Q
113 Bridport Road, Dorchester DT1 2NH. Heather & Chris Robinson, 01305 263088, hev.robinson@talktalk.net. *Approx 300m W of Dorset County Hospital. From Top o' Town r'about head W towards Dorset County Hospital, Q 300 metres further on.* Home-made teas. **Adm £3, chd free. Suns 16, 30 Mar, 13 Apr (2-4.30); 27 Apr, 18 May, 15 June (2-5). Visitors also welcome by appt Feb to Sept, parties up to 40 would like 1wks notice.**
A town garden for all seasons where every inch counts. Themed rooms transport you from the hustle and bustle of town life. Garden reflects the owners many interests, featuring unusual spring bulbs, 100+ clematis plus other climbers, trees, herbaceous plants, shrubs and bedding plants, water features, gravel, veg and fruit trees. Mothering Sunday and Fathers Day celebrated for participants. On other dates there will be talks on plant regeneration and craft demonstrations with opportunity to purchase examples. Small number of paths available for wheelchair users.

70 NEW QUEEN ANN HOUSE
Fortuneswell, Portland DT15 1LP. Mrs Margaret Dunlop, 01305 820028, margaretdunlop@tiscali.co.uk. *4m S of Weymouth. Follow A354 to Portland. Up hill into one way traffic. When two way traffic 50 metres on L.* Cream teas. **Adm £3.50, chd free. Sun 3 Aug; Sun 7 Sept (2-5). Also open 3 Aug & 7 Sept Mews Cottage.**
A hidden gem with sectioned areas/gardens with different planting. Fern garden, tropical garden, English garden with rockery and two ponds. Also a single cast ornate cast-iron horses drinking trough.

71 RESTING LAURELS
14 Chine Walk, Ferndown BH22 8PU. Paul Jefferies, 01202 578728, wendyjefferies@live.co.uk. *2m SE of Bournemouth International Airport. From Parley Cross T-lights, off Christchurch Rd B3073 towards Longham/Wimborne, 1st R turn.* Home-made teas. **Adm £3, chd free. Sun 1 June (11-4). Visitors also welcome by appt May/June, refreshments by arrangement.**
The immaculate lawns set off the planting in this ¾ -acre green oasis. The difficult sandy soil supports many mature trees and shrubs with good focal points and an exciting pond area. Organic kitchen garden. Spring and autumn colour. Featured in Amateur Gardener.

A hidden gem . . .

72 25 RICHMOND PARK AVENUE
Bournemouth BH8 9DL. Barbara Hutchinson and Mike Roberts, 01202 531072, barbarahutchinson@tiscali.co.uk. *2.5 miles NE Bournemouth town centre. From T-lights at junction with Alma Rd and Richmond Park Rd, head N on B3063 Charminster Rd, 2nd turning on R into Richmond Park Ave.* Home-made teas. **Adm £3, chd free. Sun 22 June (11-5); Thur 3 July (2-5); Suns 13, 27 July (11-5). Visitors also welcome by appt July for groups of 10+.**
Beautifully designed town garden with pergola leading to ivy canopy over raised decking. Cascading waterfall connects 2 wildlife ponds enhanced with domed acers. Circular lawn with colourful herbaceous border planted to attract bees and butterflies. Fragrant S-facing courtyard garden at front, sparkling with vibrant colour and Mediterranean planting incl Asian lilies, brugmansias and lemon tree. Partial wheelchair access.

73 357 RINGWOOD ROAD
Ferndown BH22 9AE. Lyn & Malcolm Ovens, 01202 896071, malcolm@mgovens.freeserve.co.uk, www.lynandmalc.co.uk. *¾ m S of Ferndown. On A348 towards Longham. Parking in Glenmoor Rd or other side rds. Avoid parking on main rd.* Home-made teas. **Adm £3, chd free. Sun 13 July (11-5), Wed 30 July (2-5); Sun 24 Aug (11-5). Visitors also welcome by appt July/Aug.**
The original Dorset His and Hers garden. Hers in cottage style with clematis, phlox, lilies, roses, monarda, encouraging butterflies and bees, providing a riot of colour and perfume into late summer. Walk through a Moorish keyhole doorway into His exotic garden with brugmansias, canna, oleander, banana, dahlia and bougainvillea. A good example of what can be achieved in a small plantaholics' garden. Ferndown Common nearby. Featured in The Mail On Sunday and on Radio Solent.

74 NEW SCULPTURE BY THE LAKES
Pallington Lakes, Pallington, Dorchester DT2 8QU. Mrs Monique Gudgeon, 07720 637808, sbtl@me.com, www.sculpturebythelakes.co.uk. *6m E of Dorchester. ½ m E of Tincleton, see beech hedge and security gates. From other direction 0.8m from Xrds.* **Adm £5. Regret no children under 12 admitted. Weds 14 May; 18 June (11-5). Visitors also welcome by appt.**
A recently created modern garden with inspiration taken from all over the world. Described as a modern arcadia it follows in the traditions of the landscape movement, but for the 21st century. Where sculpture has been placed, the planting palette has been kept simple, but dramatic, so that the work remains the star. Home to renowned British sculptor Simon Gudgeon, the sculpture park features over 30 of his most iconic pieces including Isis, which is also in London's Hyde Park and a dedicated gallery where some of his smaller pieces can be seen and purchased. Featured on BBC South Today. Disabled access is limited although it is possible to go round the paths on a mobility scooter or electric wheelchair if care is taken.

75 THE SECRET GARDEN
The Friary, Hilfield DT2 7BE. The Society of St Francis, 01300 341345, hilfieldssf@franciscans.org.uk, www.hilfieldfriary.org.uk. *10m N of Dorchester, on A352 between Sherborne & Dorchester. 1st L after Minterne Magna, 1st turning on R signed The Friary. From Yeovil turn off A37 signed Batcombe, 3rd turning on L.* Home-made teas. **Adm £3.50, chd free. Sat 17, Sun 18 May (2-5). Visitors also welcome by appt.**
Ongoing reclamation of neglected woodland garden. Vegetables and courtyard garden. New plantings from modern day plant hunters. Mature trees, bamboo, rhododendrons,

azaleas, magnolias, camellias, other choice shrubs with a stream on all sides crossed by bridges, and in spring a growing collection of loderi hybrids with other choice shrubs. Stout shoes recommended for woodland garden. Friary grounds open where meadows, woods and livestock can be viewed. There is also a Friary Shop selling a variety of gifts.

76 THE SECRET GARDEN AND SERLES HOUSE

47 Victoria Road, Wimborne BH21 1EN. Ian Willis, 01202 880430. *Centre of Wimborne. On B3082 W of town, very near hospital, Westfield car park 300yds. Off-road parking close by*. **Adm £3, chd free (share to Wimborne Civic Society and NADFAS). Thur 24, Sun 27 July; Sun 3, Thur 7, Sun 10, Sun 24, Mon 25, Sun 31 Aug; Thur 4, Sat 6, Sun 7, Sun 14 Sept (2.30-5).**

Alan Titchmarsh described this amusingly creative garden as 'one of the best 10 private gardens in Britain'. The ingenious use of unusual plants complements the imaginative treasure trove of garden objects d'art. The enchanting house is also open. Gentle live music accompanies your tour as you step into a world of whimsical fantasy that is theatrical and unique. Live piano music at each opening. Wheelchair access to garden only. Narrow steps may prohibit wide wheelchairs.

77 ◆ SHERBORNE CASTLE

New Rd, Sherborne DT9 5NR. Mr J K Wingfield Digby, 01935 812072, www.sherbornecastle.com. *½ m E of Sherborne. On New Road B3145. Follow brown signs from A30 & A352.* **For opening times and information, please phone or see garden website.**

40+ acres. A Capability Brown garden with magnificent vistas across the surrounding landscape, incl lake and views to ruined castle. Herbaceous planting, notable trees, mixed ornamental planting and managed wilderness are linked together with lawn and pathways. Dry grounds walk. Partial wheelchair access, gravel paths, steep slopes, steps.

78 SLAPE MANOR

Netherbury DT6 5LH. Mr & Mrs Antony Hichens. *1m S of Beaminster. Turn W off A3066 to Netherbury. House ⅓ m S of Netherbury on back rd to Bridport signed Waytown.* Home-made teas. **Adm £4, chd free. Sun 25 May (2-6). Also open The Manor House, Beaminster.**

River valley garden with spacious lawns and primula fringed streams down to lake. Magnificent hostas and gunneras, horizontal cryptomeria Japonica 'Elegans'. Wellingtonias, ancient wisterias and rhododendrons.

79 ◆ SNAPE COTTAGE PLANTSMAN'S GARDEN

Chaffeymoor, Bourton, nr Gillingham SP8 5BZ. Ian & Angela Whinfield, 01747 840330 (evenings), www.snapecottagegarden.co.uk. *5m NW of Gillingham. On border of Somerset & Wiltshire, at W end of Bourton, N of A303. Opp Chiffchaffs, 5 mins from Stourhead (NT).* Delicious home made cakes and clotted cream Teas. **Adm £3.50, chd free. For NGS: Sats 29 Mar; 26 Apr; 31 May; 28 June (2-5). For other opening times and information, please phone or see garden website.**

Mature country garden containing exceptional collection of hardy plants and bulbs, artistically arranged in informal cottage garden style, organically managed and clearly labelled. Specialities incl snowdrops, hellebores, 'old' daffodils, pulmonarias, auriculas, herbs, irises and geraniums. Wildlife pond, beautiful views, tranquil atmosphere. The home of Snape Stakes plant supports. Widely televised and featured in many magazines, incl Country Living, Great British Gardens Revival.

80 NEW STONE RISE

25 Newton Road, Swanage BH19 2EA. Mrs Suzanne Nutbeem. *½ m S of Swanage town centre. From town follow signs to Durlston Country Park. At top of hill turn R at red postbox into Bon Accord Rd. 4th turn R into Newton Rd.* **Adm £3, chd free. Every Wed 2 July to 27 Aug (2-5.30).**

Access down stone steps. Pause at top of metal stairs then descend into transformed stone quarry. Explore densely planted beds in a relatively confined space. Pieces of London Bridge lurk in the stonework. 'An intriguing garden with exceptional richness and arrangements of colour, textures and form'.

81 ◆ UPTON COUNTRY PARK

Upton, Poole BH17 7BJ. Borough of Poole, 01202 262753, uptoncountrypark@poole.gov.uk, www.uptoncountrypark.com. *3m W of Poole town centre. On S side of A35/A3049. Follow brown signs.* **For information, please phone or see garden website.**

Over 100 acres of award-winning parkland incl formal gardens, walled garden, woodland and shoreline. Maritime micro-climate offers a wonderful collection of unusual trees, vintage camellias and stunning roses. Home to Upton House, Grade II* listed Georgian mansion. Regular special events. Plant centre, art gallery and tea rooms. Open 8am - 9 pm May - September and 8am - 6pm October - April.

82 WARMWELL HOUSE

Warmwell DT2 8HQ. Mr & Mrs H J C Ross Skinner. *7m SE of Dorchester. Warmwell is signed off A352 between Dorchester & Wool. House is in centre of village. Entrance to car park through double gates ¼ m N on B3390.* Home-made teas. **Adm £4, chd free. Fri 13, Sun 15 June (2-5). Also open 15 June Holworth Farmhouse.**

An old garden set round Jacobean house (not open). Formal square garden has mixed borders, adjacent to pleached lime lawn. Various borders below maze on hill overlooking house and countryside. Slopes and gravel make wheelchair access difficult.

WATERDALE HOUSE

See Wiltshire

© Louise Jolley

Herons Mead

83 24A WESTERN AVENUE
Branksome Park, Poole BH13 7AN. Mr Peter Jackson, 01202 708388, peter@branpark.wanadoo.co.uk. *3m W of Bournemouth. From S end Wessex Way (A338) take The Avenue. At T-lights turn R into Western Rd. At church turn R into Western Ave.* Home-made teas. **Adm £3.50, chd free. Suns 4 May; 3 Aug (2-5.30). Visitors also welcome by appt Apr to Sept refreshments by arrangement, min 12.**
'This secluded and magical 1-acre garden captures the spirit of warmer climes and begs for repeated visits' (Gardening Which?). Rose, wall, courtyard, woodland and herbaceous gardens. June sees rose garden at its best; herbaceous borders and lush subtropical planting flourish with 2nd flush of roses in August. Topiary and natural wood sculptures. Wheelchair access to ³/₄ garden.

84 WESTON HOUSE
Buckhorn Weston, Gillingham SP8 5HG. Mr & Mrs E A W Bullock. *4m W of Gillingham, 3m SE of Wincanton. From A30 turn N to Kington Magna, continue towards Buckhorn Weston & after railway bridge take L turn towards Wincanton. 2nd on L is Weston House.* Tea, coffee, biscuits and cakes. **Adm £4, chd free. Thur 19 June, Thur 10 July (10-6).**
Delightful colourful, scented garden of spring flowers, summer borders, old-fashioned roses and interesting trees. 1¹/₂ acres of beauty and peace with views of Blackmore Vale. Beyond the lawn, grass paths lead to wild flower meadows attracting butterflies and other insects. Natural pond shelters newts and dragonflies. Gravel yard and gentle slope to patio.

85 WINCOMBE PARK
Shaftesbury SP7 9AB. John & Phoebe Fortescue. *2m N of Shaftesbury. A350 Shaftesbury to Warminster, past Wincombe Business Park, 1st R signed Wincombe & Donhead St Mary. ³/₄ m on R.* Cream teas. **Adm £3.50, chd free. Sun 18, Thur 22 May (2-5).**
Extensive mature garden with sweeping panoramic views over lake and woods. Regeneration in progress. Azaleas, rhododendrons and camellias in flower amongst shrubs and unusual trees. Beautiful walled kitchen garden. Partial wheelchair access, slopes and gravel paths.

86 WOLVERHOLLOW
Elsdons Lane, Monkton Wyld DT6 6DA. Mr & Mrs D Wiscombe, 01297 560610. *4m N of Lyme Regis. 4m NW of Charmouth. Monkton Wyld is signed from A35 approx 4m NW of Charmouth off dual carriageway. Wolverhollow is next to the church.* Home-made teas. **Adm £3.50, chd free. Sun 11, Tue 13, Mon 26, Tue 27 May (11-5). Visitors also welcome by appt May to Oct.**
Over 1 acre of informal garden on different levels. Lawns lead past borders and rockeries down to a shady lower garden. Numerous paths take you past a variety of uncommon shrubs and plants. The managed meadow has an abundance of primulas growing close to the stream. A garden not to be missed!

Pause at top of metal stairs then descend into transformed stone quarry . . .

Dorset County Volunteers

County Organiser
Harriet Boileau, Witcham Farm, Rampisham, Dorchester DT2 0PX, 01935 83612, h.boileau@btinternet.com

County Treasurer
Richard Smedley, 60 Huntly Road, Bournemouth BH3 7HJ, 01202 528286, richard@carter-coley.co.uk

Publicity Officer
Gillian Ford, Rosemary Cottage, Rampisham DT2 0PX, 01935 83645, gillianford33@btinternet.com

Booklet Editor
Judith Hussey, The Old Rectory, Manston, Sturminster Newton DT10 1EX, 01258 474673, judithhussey@hotmail.com

Assistant County Organisers
North Central Caroline Renner, Croft Farm, Fontmell Magna, Shaftesbury SP7 0NR, 01747 811140, croftfarm@talktalk.net
North East/Ferndown/Christchurch Mary Angus, The Glade, Woodland Walk, Ferndown BH22 9LP, 01202 872789, mary@gladestock.co.uk
North West & Central Victoria Baxter, Longburton House, Longburton, Sherborne DT9 5NU, 01935 815992, victoria@lborchard.co.uk
Central East/Bournemouth Trish Neale, Badbury View, 3 Witchampton Mill, Witchampton, Wimborne BH21 5DE, 01258 840345, trishneale1@yahoo.co.uk
South Central Helen Hardy, The Manor, Winterborne Tomson, Blandford Forum DT11 9HA, 01929 471379, helliehardy@hotmail.co.uk
West Central Paul Stopford Adams, Steppes Farm, Frampton, Dorchester DT2 9NJ, 01300 320283, psa@stopford-adams.com
South/Portland Caroline Edwards, Westbrook House, Upwey, Weymouth DT3 5QB, 01305 812929, caroline@westbrookhousedorset.co.uk
South West Christine Corson, Stoke Knapp Cottage, Norway Lane, Stoke Abbott, Beaminster DT8 3JZ, 01308 868203, christinekcorson@gmail.com

ESSEX

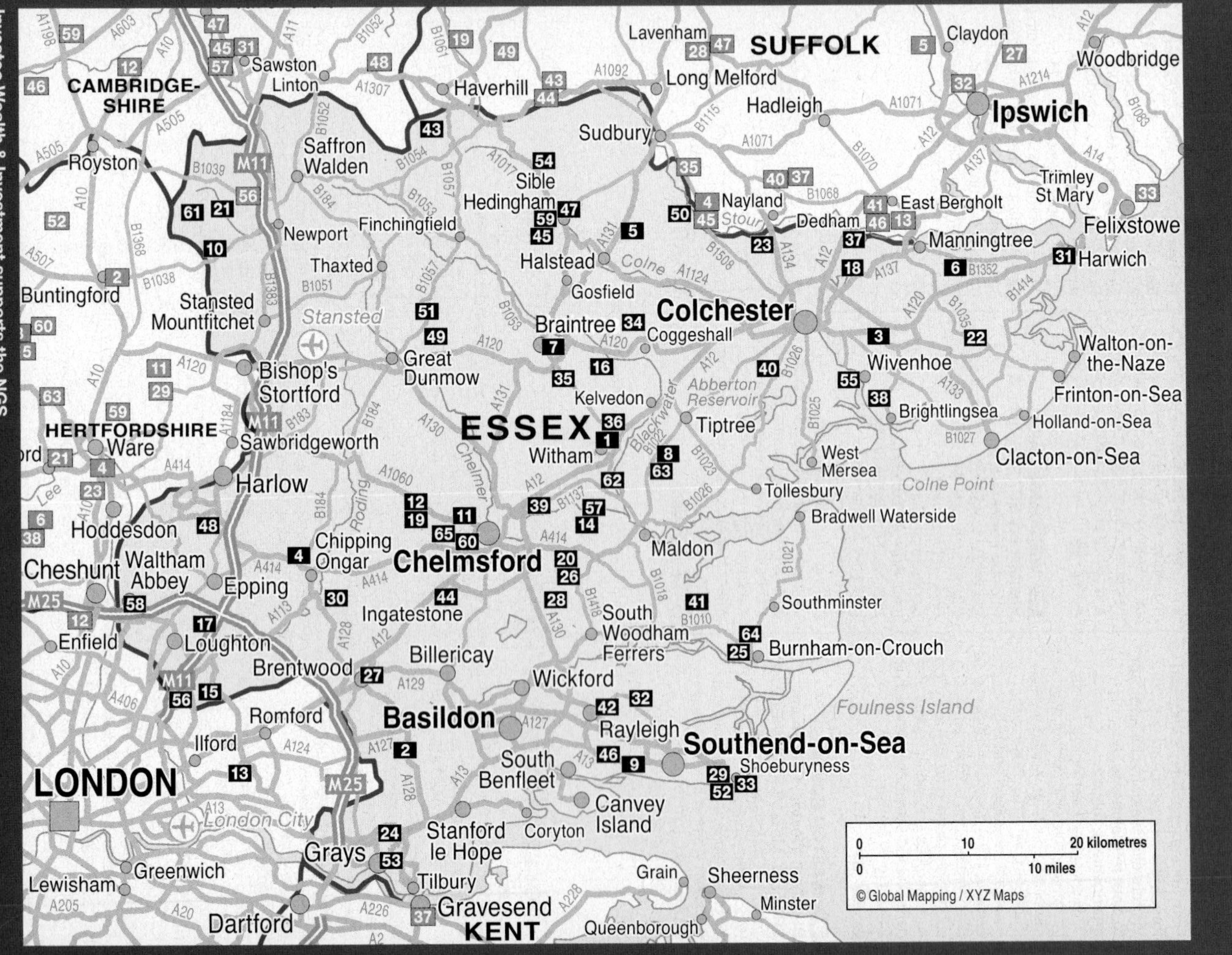

SUFFOLK
ESSEX
CAMBRIDGE-SHIRE
HERTFORDSHIRE
KENT
LONDON
Lavenham
Claydon
Woodbridge
Long Melford
Hadleigh
Ipswich
Sawston
Linton
Haverhill
Sudbury
Royston
Saffron Walden
Sible Hedingham
Trimley St Mary
Felixstowe
Nayland
East Bergholt
Dedham
Stour
Manningtree
Harwich
Newport
Finchingfield
Halstead
Colne
Thaxted
Gosfield
Buntingford
Stansted Mountfitchet
Stansted
Braintree
Coggeshall
Colchester
Walton-on-the-Naze
Wivenhoe
Great Dunmow
Bishop's Stortford
Kelvedon
Abberton Reservoir
Frinton-on-Sea
Brightlingsea
Holland-on-Sea
Tiptree
Blackwater
Witham
West Mersea
Clacton-on-Sea
Sawbridgeworth
Ware
Harlow
Chelmer
Tollesbury
Colne Point
Bradwell Waterside
Hoddesdon
Roding
Chipping Ongar
Chelmsford
Maldon
Cheshunt
Waltham Abbey
Epping
Ingatestone
Southminster
South Woodham Ferrers
Enfield
Loughton
Billericay
Burnham-on-Crouch
Brentwood
Wickford
Foulness Island
Romford
Basildon
Rayleigh
Southend-on-Sea
Ilford
South Benfleet
Shoeburyness
LONDON
Canvey Island
London City
Stanford le Hope
Coryton
Grays
Tilbury
Grain
Sheerness
Greenwich
Lewisham
Gravesend
Minster
Dartford
Queenborough
0 10 20 kilometres
0 10 miles
© Global Mapping / XYZ Maps

Opening Dates

All entries subject to change. For latest information check www.ngs.org.uk

February

Saturday 22
39 The Old Rectory

Sunday 23
39 The Old Rectory
65 Writtle College

April

16 **Feeringbury Manor (Every Thursday & Friday)**

Sunday 13
44 Peacocks
52 South Shoebury Hall

Tuesday 15
12 Dragons

Thursday 17
2 Barnards Farm

Sunday 20
55 Tudor Roost
63 Wood View

Monday 21
55 Tudor Roost

Thursday 24
2 Barnards Farm

Friday 25
62 Wickham Place Farm

Sunday 27
57 Ulting Wick

Wednesday 30
20 Furzelea

May

2 **Barnards Farm (Every Thursday)**
16 **Feeringbury Manor (Every Thursday & Friday)**

Friday 2
64 Woodpeckers

Saturday 3
64 Woodpeckers

Sunday 4
43 Parsonage House
55 Tudor Roost
63 Wood View

Monday 5
55 Tudor Roost
63 Wood View

Friday 9
57 Ulting Wick
62 Wickham Place Farm

Tuesday 20
12 Dragons

Friday 23
62 Wickham Place Farm

Sunday 25
21 NEW Great Becketts
27 The Lembic
36 Miraflores
45 Peppers Farm
61 Wickets

Monday 26
47 Rookwoods

Friday 30
28 The Limes (Evening)

Saturday 31
6 Chippins
28 The Limes

June

2 **Barnards Farm (Every Thursday)**
16 **Feeringbury Manor (Every Thursday & Friday)**

Sunday 1
20 Furzelea
27 The Lembic
38 Moverons
39 The Old Rectory
47 Rookwoods
51 Snares Hill Cottage

Friday 6
11 8 Dene Court
62 Wickham Place Farm

Festival Weekend

Saturday 7
1 Barnardiston House
61 Wickets (Evening)

Sunday 8
24 Julie's Garden
33 NEW The Major's House
46 Reprise
54 Spencers
61 Wickets
65 Writtle College

Thursday 12
14 Elwy Lodge

Sunday 15
1 Barnardiston House
10 Deers
15 Fairwinds
17 56 Forest Drive
25 NEW Keeway
44 Peacocks
56 37 Turpins Lane

Tuesday 17
11 8 Dene Court
12 Dragons

Saturday 21
36 Miraflores

Sunday 22
9 Court View
21 NEW Great Becketts
36 Miraflores
61 Wickets

Thursday 26
14 Elwy Lodge

Saturday 28
7 352 Coggeshall Road
32 NEW 262 Main Road
33 NEW The Major's House (Evening)

Sunday 29
2 Barnards Farm
4 Blake Hall
6 Chippins
7 352 Coggeshall Road
17 56 Forest Drive
56 37 Turpins Lane
59 Washlands

Garden and woodland bring surprise and delight . . .

July

2 **Barnards Farm (Every Thursday)**
16 **Feeringbury Manor (Every Thursday & Friday)**

Friday 4
11 8 Dene Court

Saturday 5
19 Fudlers Hall

Sunday 6
30 Little Myles
53 Southview
59 Washlands

Friday 11
14 Elwy Lodge
37 Monks Cottage

Sunday 13
17 56 Forest Drive
46 Reprise
52 South Shoebury Hall
56 37 Turpins Lane

Tuesday 15
11 8 Dene Court
12 Dragons

Wednesday 16
35 60 Mill Lane

Saturday 19
48 69 Rundells

Sunday 20
9 Court View
14 Elwy Lodge
26 Kingsteps

Friday 25
11 8 Dene Court

Saturday 26
32 NEW 262 Main Road
55 Tudor Roost

Sunday 27
19 Fudlers Hall
53 Southview
55 Tudor Roost

Artist's garden and plantaholics paradise packed with interest . . .

August

2 Barnards Farm (Every Thursday)

Saturday 2
31 447 Main Road

Sunday 3
31 447 Main Road
46 Reprise

Tuesday 5
12 Dragons

Friday 8
11 8 Dene Court

Sunday 10
9 Court View
13 6 Elms Gardens
35 60 Mill Lane

Saturday 16
29 Little Foxes
32 NEW 262 Main Road

Sunday 17
29 Little Foxes

Tuesday 19
11 8 Dene Court
12 Dragons

Sunday 24
10 Deers
55 Tudor Roost
60 45 Waterhouse Lane (Evening)

Monday 25
55 Tudor Roost

Sunday 31
26 Kingsteps
60 45 Waterhouse Lane (Evening)

September

16 Feeringbury Manor (Every Thursday & Friday)

Thursday 4
2 Barnards Farm

Saturday 6
38 Moverons

Sunday 7
2 Barnards Farm
9 Court View
38 Moverons
43 Parsonage House
58 Waltham Abbey

Wednesday 10
20 Furzelea

Friday 12
62 Wickham Place Farm

Sunday 14
14 Elwy Lodge
51 Snares Hill Cottage
54 Spencers
57 Ulting Wick

Tuesday 16
12 Dragons

Friday 19
57 Ulting Wick

Saturday 20
8 60 Colchester Road

Sunday 21
8 60 Colchester Road

Friday 26
64 Woodpeckers

Saturday 27
64 Woodpeckers

October

Sunday 26
65 Writtle College

Gardens open to the public

3 Beth Chatto Gardens
34 Marks Hall Gardens & Arboretum
54 Spencers

By appointment only

5 Byndes Cottage
18 Fountain Farm
22 Hannams Hall
23 Horkesley Hall
41 One Brook Hall Cottages
42 Orchard Cottage
49 St Helens
50 Shrubs Farm

Also open by appointment

1 Barnardiston House
2 Barnards Farm
6 Chippins
7 352 Coggeshall Road
8 60 Colchester Road
9 Court View
11 8 Dene Court
12 Dragons
14 Elwy Lodge
15 Fairwinds
16 Feeringbury Manor
17 56 Forest Drive
20 Furzelea
24 Julie's Garden
36 Miraflores
37 Monks Cottage
38 Moverons
39 The Old Rectory
44 Peacocks
45 Peppers Farm
46 Reprise
47 Rookwoods
48 69 Rundells
51 Snares Hill Cottage
52 South Shoebury Hall
53 Southview
55 Tudor Roost
56 37 Turpins Lane
57 Ulting Wick
60 45 Waterhouse Lane
61 Wickets
62 Wickham Place Farm
63 Wood View
64 Woodpeckers

The Gardens

1 BARNARDISTON HOUSE

35 Chipping Hill, Witham CM8 2DE. Ruth & Eric Teverson, 01376 502266, ruthteverson@yahoo.co.uk. *10m NE of Chelmsford. A12 S-bound J22 & A12 N-bound J21to town centre. Into Collingwood Rd at George PH. L at 2 mini r'abouts. Garden opp. White Horse PH. Use postcode CM8 2JU.* Light refreshments. **Adm £3, chd free. Sat 7, Sun 15 June (2-5.30). Visitors also welcome by appt June to Sept.**

A medium-sized town garden, designed and created over last 16yrs by the owners. A wide range of unusual and insect friendly plants, as well as fruit, heritage vegetables and succulents are grown, all of which must enjoy hot and dry conditions. Partial wheelchair access.

2 BARNARDS FARM

Brentwood Road, West Horndon, Brentwood CM13 3LX. Bernard & Sylvia Holmes & The Christabella Charitable Trust, 01277 811262, sylvia@barnardsfarm.eu, www.barnardsfarm.eu. *5m S of Brentwood. On A128 1½ S of A127 Halfway House flyover.From Junction continue on A128 under the railway bridge. Garden on R just past bridge.* Light refreshments (Thurs), home-made teas (Suns). **Adm £6, chd free (Thurs), adm £7.50, chd free (Suns) (share to St Francis Church). Every Thur 17 Apr to 4 Sept (11-4.30); Suns 29 June; 7 Sept (2-5.30). Visitors also welcome by appt May to Sept, group visits on non open days: minimum 12 visitors.**

A garden for all seasons, tastes and ages: 60 sculptures from the grand to the quirky carefully placed in the 17 hectares of garden and woodland bring surprise and delight. Daffodils along the stream, crab apple blossom; rose covered belvedere; summer flowers and climbers around the house; veg. plot; Japanese garden; fountains, ponds, lake: frogs, dragonflies, butterflies and bees; autumn colours. Barnards Miniature Railway rides (BMR). Sunday extras: Bernard's Sculpture tour 3pm;. Veteran and vintage vehicle collection; 1920s Cycle shop Collect loyalty points on Thur visits and earn a free Sun or Thur visit. Aviators welcome (PPO), see website for details. Wheelchair accessible WC Golf buggy tour available.

NCH

3 ◆ BETH CHATTO GARDENS

Elmstead Market, Colchester CO7 7DB. Mrs Beth Chatto, 01206 822007, www.bethchatto.co.uk. *¼ m E of Elmstead Market. On A133 Colchester to Clacton Rd in village of Elmstead Market.* **Adm £6.95, chd free (under 14). For opening times and information, please phone or see garden website.**

Internationally famous gardens, including dry, damp and woodland areas. The result of over fifty years of hard work and application of the huge body of plant knowledge possessed by Beth Chatto and her late husband Andrew. Visitors cannot fail to be affected by the peace and beauty of the garden. Large plant nursery and modern Tea Room. Disabled WC and parking.

4 BLAKE HALL

Bobbingworth CM5 0DG. Mr & Mrs H Capel Cure, www.blakehall.co.uk. *10m W of Chelmsford. Just off A414 between Four Wantz r'about in Ongar & Talbot r'about in North Weald. Signed on A414.* Home-made teas served in C17 barn. **Adm £4, chd free. Sun 29 June (11-5).**

25 acres of mature gardens within the historic setting of Blake Hall (not open). Arboretum with broad variety of specimen trees. Spectacular rambling roses clamber up ancient trees. Traditional formal rose garden and herbaceous border. Sweeping lawns. Some gravel paths.

Barnards Farm

© Mike Howes

5 BYNDES COTTAGE

Pebmarsh, nr Halstead CO9 2LZ. David & Margaret MacLennan, 01787 269500, byndes2@btinternet.com. *2m N of Halstead. On A131 from Halstead to Sudbury, take R turning signed Pebmarsh & Bures. 3rd house on L before Pebmarsh village round sharp bend.* Light refreshments. **Adm £5, chd free. Visitors welcome by appt, groups of 10+ only. Refreshments incl in adm.**

7-acre garden planted and maintained by enthusiastic owners who enjoy giving a conducted tour to groups. Extensive mix of borders, trees and shrubs with diverse and interesting plantings. Practical ideas for maintenance and conservation. National collection of Galanthus. Open all year round including snowdrop time (late Jan to early March). Mostly grass with some paving and gravel.

NCH

6 CHIPPINS

Heath Road, Bradfield CO11 2UZ. Kit & Ceri Leese, 01255 870730, ceriandkit1@btinternet.com. *3m E of Manningtree. On B1352, take main rd through village. Bungalow is directly opp primary school.* Home-made teas. **Adm £3.50, chd free. Sat 31 May; Sun 29 June (11-4.30). Visitors also welcome by appt May to July, groups very welcome.**

Artist's garden and plantaholics paradise packed with interest. Springtime heralds irises, hostas and alliums. Stream and wildlife pond brimming with bog plants. Summer hosts an explosion of colour-abundance of tubs and hanging baskets. Wide borders feature hemerocallis with swathes of lilies, later dahlias and exotics (South African streptocarpus, aeonium and unusual agaves). Kit is a landscape artist, pictures always on display.

7 352 COGGESHALL ROAD

Braintree CM7 9EH. Sau Lin Goss, 01376 329753, Richandsally.goss@yahoo.com. *15m W of Colchester, 10m N of Chelmsford. From M11 J8 take A120 Colchester. Follow A120 to Braintree r'about (McDonalds). 1st exit into Cressing rd follow to T-lights. R into Coggeshall rd.* Light refreshments. **Adm £3, chd free. Sat 28, Sun 29 June (1.30-5.30). Visitors also welcome by appt June to Aug, min 10, max 30.**

Sau Lin arrived from Hong Kong to become enthralled with English gardening. 'My little heaven', she says of her garden which has themed areas, perennials, roses and many other plants. Japanese mixed border, fruit trees and shrubs. Seating and relaxing areas, fish pond with plants and wildlife. Mediterranean patio with water feature and wide array of pots. Featured in Evening Echo. Partial wheelchair access, ramp from patio to main garden.

8 60 COLCHESTER ROAD

Great Totham, nr Maldon CM9 8DG. Mrs Sue Jackman, 01621 891155, susanjackman750@hotmail.com. *5m NE of Maldon. On B1022 Maldon to Colchester Rd at Totham North.* Home-made teas. **Adm £3.50, chd free. Sat 20, Sun 21 Sept (11-4). Visitors also welcome by appt, for groups of 20+.**

A 3/4 acre keen plantwoman's garden with large colour-themed borders, situated in both sun and shade. Borders are planted for a long season of interest with many unusual species, particularly perennials. Rock garden full of spring and autumn bulbs and alpines. A rill leading to watersteps, and circular pool overlooked by a summerhouse. Small vegetable garden.

9 COURT VIEW

276 Manchester Drive, Leigh-on-Sea SS9 3ES. Ray Spencer & Richard Steers, 01702 713221, arjeyeski@courtview.demon.co.uk, www.facebook.com/courtview.ngs essex. *4m W of Southend. From A127. signed at Progress Rd junction towards Leigh on Sea along the Fairway. Follow signs. From A13. follow signs from Kingswood Chase junction.* Home-made teas. **Adm £3.50, chd free. Suns 22 June; 20 July; 10 Aug; 7 Sept (1-5). Visitors also welcome by appt June to Sept, weekdays only, with homemade lunch or cream tea.**

Front garden densely planted with shrubs and perennials. Exuberant rear garden reached beyond a clematis, hosta and fern walk. Bold planting, fiery colours and scented plants surround many seating areas. Water and sculpture add to the sensory experience. White garden, mini-orchard and greenhouse beyond bamboo grove. Featured in Southend Evening Echo, Pride Life magazine, and on BBC Radio Essex.

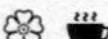

10 DEERS

Clavering CB11 4PX. Mr S H Cooke. *7m N of Bishop's Stortford. On B1038. Turn W off B1383 (old A11) at Newport and follow signs to Clavering then Langley and 1st L to Ford End.* Home-made teas. **Adm £5, chd free (share to Clavering Jubilee Field in August only). Suns 15 June; 24 Aug (2-5).**

9 acres. Judged by visitors to be a romantic set of gardens. The river Stort runs through the gardens. Shrub and herbaceous borders, 3 ponds with water lilies, old roses in formal garden, pool garden, walled vegetable garden, moon gate, field and woodland walks. Plenty of seats to enjoy the tranquility of the gardens. Dogs on leads.

11 8 DENE COURT

Chignall Road, Chelmsford CM1 2JQ. Mrs Sheila Chapman, 01245 266156. *W of Chelmsford (Parkway). Take A1060 Roxwell Rd for 1m. Turn R at T-lights into Chignall Rd. Dene Court 3rd exit on R. Parking in Chignall Rd.* **Adm £3, chd free. Fri 6, Tue 17 June; Fri 4, Tue 15, Fri 25 July; Fri 8, Tue 19 Aug (2-5). Also open Dragons 17 June, 15 July, 19 Aug. Visitors also welcome by appt June to Sept, refreshments by arrangement.**

Beautifully maintained and designed compact garden (250sq yds). Owner is well-known RHS gold medal-winning exhibitor (now retired). Circular lawn, long pergola and walls festooned with roses and climbers. Large selection of unusual clematis. Densely-planted colour coordinated perennials add interest from May to Sept in this immaculate garden. Featured in Essex Chronicle.

12 DRAGONS

Boyton Cross, Chelmsford CM1 4LS. Mrs Margot Grice, 01245 248651, mandmdragons@tiscali.co.uk. *5m W of Chelmsford. On A1060. 1/2 m W of The Hare PH or 1/2 m E of Temple.* Teas. **Adm £3.50, chd free. Tues 15 Apr; 20 May; 17 June; 15 July; 5, 19 Aug; 16 Sept (11-5). Also open 8 Dene Court, 17 June, 15 July, 19 Aug. Visitors also welcome by appt, refreshments on request.**

A plantswoman's 3/4 -acre garden, planted to encourage wildlife. Sumptuous colour-themed borders with striking plant combinations, featuring specimen plants, fernery, clematis, mature dwarf conifers and grasses. Meandering paths lead to ponds, patio, scree garden and small vegetable garden. Two summerhouses, one overlooking stream and farmland.

13 6 ELMS GARDENS

Dagenham RM9 5TX. Peter & Kathy Railton. *1m from Becontree Heath. A124 Wood Ln towards Barking. Elms Gdns located off Five Elms Rd/Halbutt St.* Home-made teas. **Adm £3, chd free. Sun 10 Aug (1-5).**

Plant lovers garden (approx 80ft x 60ft) featuring wide range of herbaceous plants and shrubs with year round interest. Colourful begonias in baskets and containers. Large collection of Heucheras create foliage interest. Magnificent Magnolia grandifloras. Winding paths lead to quiet seating, Koi fishpond and small woodland shade area.

14 ELWY LODGE

West Bowers Rd, Woodham Walter CM9 6RZ. David & Laura Cox, 01245 222165, elwylodge@gmail.com. *Just outside Woodham Walter village. From Chelmsford, A414 to Danbury. L at 2nd mini r'about into Little Baddow Rd. From Colchester, A12 to Hatfield Peverel, L onto B1019. Follow NGS signs.* Light refreshments. **Adm £3.50, chd free. Thurs 12, 26 June; Fri 11, Suns 20 July; 14 Sept (10.30-5.30). Also open Kingsteps, 20 July, Ulting Wick, 14 Sept. Visitors also welcome by appt May to Oct, (not August), adm £6 incl refreshments.**

Rural location offering peace, tranquility and lovely countryside views. Scented roses in front garden leading to flowing lawns, herbaceous/shrub borders, trees, wildlife pond and meadow area. The garden then slopes down to a secluded chamomile-scented lower garden with raised vegetable beds, soft fruits and fruit trees. This is an ever-changing garden being developed to blend with the rural setting. Sloping uneven lawn in parts. Please check wheelchair access with garden owner before visiting.

15 FAIRWINDS

Chapel Lane, Chigwell Row, Chigwell IG7 6JJ. Sue & David Coates, 07731 796467, scoates@forest.org.uk. *2m SE of Chigwell. Grange Hill Tube, turn R at exit, 10 mins walk uphill. Near M25 J26 & N Circular, turn off Lambourne Rd signed Chigwell. Park in Lodge Close Car Park.* Home-made teas. **Adm £4, chd free. Sun 15 June (1-5). Also open 37 Turpins Lane & 56 Forest Drive, Theydon Bois. Visitors also welcome by appt June to Sept, refreshments only by arrangement. Groups preferred.**
Country garden with a rich variety of planting styles. Gravelled front garden. Side entrance leads to an area with themed large mixed borders and an ornamental greenhouse. Central area includes a patio, fire pit, woodland, bug house and 'Eglu'. Beware dragons and chickens! Rustic fence separates wildlife pond and vegetable plot. Featured in parish council magazine. Space for 2 disabled cars to park by the house. Wood chip paths in woodland area may require assistance.

16 FEERINGBURY MANOR

Coggeshall Road, Feering, Colchester CO5 9RB. Mr & Mrs Giles Coode-Adams, 01376 561946, seca@btinternet.com. *12m SW of Colchester. Between Feering & Coggeshall on Coggeshall Rd, 1m from Feering village.* **Adm £5, chd free (share to Firstsite). Every Thur & Fri 3 Apr to 25 July (9-4); Every Thur & Fri 4 Sept to 26 Sept (9-4). Visitors also welcome by appt.**
There is always plenty to see in this 10 acre garden leading down to the R Blackwater. Spectacular tulips in April and May lead on to a huge number of different and colourful plants, many unusual, culminating in a purple explosion of michaelmas daisies in Sept. A small arboretum is planted with rare trees collected on Japanese expedition with Kew Gardens. Sculpture by Ben Coode-Adams. Featured in The English Garden. No wheelchair access to arboretum, steep slope.

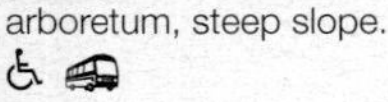

17 56 FOREST DRIVE

Theydon Bois CM16 7EZ. John & Barbara, 01992 814459, john.vale@live.co.uk. *2m S of Epping. J26 on M25 onto A121 to Wake Arms r'about 2nd exit B 172 into Theydon Bois. Turn L at The Bull PH 1st L into rd. Central line station 2nd on R.* Cream teas, self service tea,coffee and soft drinks available in the summer house. **Adm £3, chd free. Suns 15, 29 June; 13 July (12-6). Also open Fairwinds 15 June & 37 Turpins Lane 15, 29 June. Visitors also welcome by appt June to Aug, viewing after midday on weekdays due to parking.**
Elegant, tranquil garden set on a sloping site, developed by us since 1996, featuring specimen trees and plants. Shaded seating areas in this surprisingly secluded natural garden allow visitors to sit and watch the birds and admire Gladys in her reflective pool. Along with a collection of historic motorcycles.

18 FOUNTAIN FARM

Wick Lane, Ardleigh, Colchester CO7 7RG. Mr & Mrs C P Tootal, 01206 230558, christootal@aol.com. *4m NE of Colchester. A12/120 take Harwich/Clacton Turn L to 'Gnome Magic' Past Crown PH. Wick Lane next turning R. From Colchester A137 to Manningtree L after PH L at Xrds.* Home-made teas. **Adm £3.50, chd free. Visitors welcome by appt May to Sept.**
5 acres on the bank of Ardleigh Reservoir, surrounding listed farmhouse and 2 Essex barns (one listed). The garden has evolved over 40 yrs and is divided into small 'rooms' arising from the old farmyards. Two 10-yr-old areas of wild flowers, vegetable garden and more formal area of grass from the front of the house down to the reservoir. Trees and shrubs, many planted soon after our arrival in 1971. Gravel drive but access possible. Some paths may be bumpy.

19 FUDLERS HALL

Fox Road, Mashbury, Chelmsford CM1 4TJ. Mr & Mrs A J Meacock. *7m NW of Chelmsford. Chelmsford take A1060, R into Chignal Rd. 1/2 m L to Chignal St James approx 5m 2nd R into Fox Rd signed Gt. Waltham. From Gt Waltham take Barrack Lane.* Tea. **Adm £4, chd free. Sat 5, Sun 27 July (2-6).**
An award winning, romantic 2 acre garden surrounding C17 farmhouse with lovely pastoral views. Old walls divide garden into many rooms, each having a different character, featuring long herbaceous borders, ropes and pergolas festooned with rambling old fashioned roses. Enjoy the vibrant hot border in late summer. Yew hedged kitchen garden. Ample seating.

A garden to explore. Perennials and climbers are the focus . . .

20 FURZELEA

Bicknacre Road, Danbury CM3 4JR. Avril & Roger Cole-Jones, 01245 225726, randacj@gmail.com. *4m E of Chelmsford, 4m W of Maldon A414 to Danbury. At village centre turn S into Mayes Lane Take first R past Cricketers PH, L on to Bicknacre Rd see NT carpark on L garden further on R.* Home-made teas. **Adm £4, chd free. Wed 30 Apr; Sun 1 June; Wed 10 Sept (11-5). Visitors also welcome by appt May to Sept, groups 10+.**
A Victorian country house surrounded by a garden designed, created and maintained by the owners to provide maximum all year round interest. Spring planting includes tulips and alliums, Summer brings roses, peonies, and poppies and in autumn annuals, perennials, dahlias and grasses mix with topiary and shrubs to give colour, scent and form. Opp Danbury Common (NT), short walk to Danbury Country Park and Lakes and short drive to RHS Hyde Hall. Featured in The English Garden and Garden Answers. Limited wheelchair access, some steps and gravel paths.

Byndes Cottage

21 NEW GREAT BECKETTS
Duddenhoe End Road, Arkesden, Saffron Walden CB11 4HG. Mr & Mrs John Burnham. *5m W of Saffron Walden 10m N of Bishops Stortford. Approx 2/3 m NW of Arkesden in the direction of Duddenhoe End, near Newland End. Access from S on B1038 via Arkesden village or from N on B1039.* Home-made teas at Wickets, Langley Upper Green village hall. **Adm £4, chd free. Suns 25 May; 22 June (1-5). Combined with Wickets, Langley Upper Green, adm £7.**
In the middle of arable farm land, surrounding tudor house and outbuildings: a garden to explore. Perennials and climbers are the focus. Several perennial borders; courtyard; pergola; arbour; herb garden; two ponds; cutting garden; mini-orchard; paths through two established meadows. Newly planted trees and meadows on 5 additional acres across the road.

22 HANNAMS HALL
Thorpe Road, Tendring CO16 9AR. Mr & Mrs W Gibbon, 01255 830292, w.gibbon331@btinternet.com. *10m E of Colchester. From A120 take B1035 at Horsley Cross, through Tendring Village (approx 3m) pass Cherry Tree PH on R, after 1/3 m over small bridge 1st house L.* Tea. **Adm £5.50, chd free. Visitors welcome by appt** Feb to Nov **spring bulbs and autumn colour.**
C17 house (not open) set in 6 acres of formal and informal gardens and grounds with extensive views over open countryside. Herbaceous borders and shrubberies, many interesting trees incl flowering paulownias. Lawns and mown walks through wild grass and flower meadows, woodland walks, ponds and stream. Walled vegetable potager and orchard. Lovely autumn colour.

23 HORKESLEY HALL
Little Horkesley, Colchester CO6 4DB. Mr & Mrs Johnny Eddis, 01206 271371, pollyeddis@hotmail.com. *3m N of Colchester. W of A134. Next to Little Horkesley Church and access is via church car park.* Tea. **Adm £4, chd free. Visitors welcome by appt, very flexible and a warm welcome assured!**
8 acres of romantic garden surrounding classical house (not open) in mature parkland setting. Stream feeds 2 lakes. Wonderful trees some very rare. Largest ginkgo tree outside Kew. Walled garden, pear avenue, acer walk. Blossom and spring bulbs. Formal terrace overlooking sweeping lawns to wild woodland. A timeless garden. Wonderful bird life, vast plane trees and stunning tree barks. Limited wheelchair access to some areas, gravel paths and slopes but quite easy access to tea area which has lovely views over lake and garden.

24 JULIE'S GARDEN
163 Whitmore Avenue, Stifford Clays, Grays RM16 2HT. Julie Sadgrove & Harry Edwards, 01375 377780, juliesadgrove@hotmail.co.uk. *2m E of Lakeside shopping centre. Exit A13 at Grays, take Orsett turn off at r'about. 2nd R into Kingsman Drive, L into Whitmore Av.* Home-made teas. **Adm £3, chd free. Sun 8 June (12-4). Visitors also welcome by appt July.**
Now for something different. Quirky, unusual small garden (100ft x 30ft) where art and plants combine to bring colour, life and interest. A personal constantly-evolving space which reflects the owners' numerous, varied interests and talents, made using recycled resources. A surprise around every corner, incl African, Australian, Indian and beach artefacts and themes. Variety of arts and crafts made from recycled resources.

25 NEW KEEWAY
Ferry Road, Creeksea, nr Burnham-On-Crouch CM0 8PL. John & Sue Ketteley. *2m W of Burnham-on-Crouch. B1010 to Burnham on Crouch. At town sign take 1st R into Ferry Rd signed Creeksea & Burnham Golf Club & follow NGS signs.* Home-made teas. **Adm £3.50, chd free. Sun 15 June (2-5).**
Large, mature country garden with stunning views over the R Crouch. Formal terraces surround the house with steps leading to sweeping lawns, mixed borders packed full of bulbs and early perennials, a formal rose and herb garden with interesting water feature. Further afield there are wilder areas, fields and paddocks. A productive greenhouse, vegetable and cutting gardens complete the picture.

26 KINGSTEPS
Moor Hall Lane, Danbury CM3 4ER. Mr David Greenwood. *Bicknacre/Danbury. A414 from Chelmsford Turn R at The Bell in Danbury. L at T junction approx 1½ m. R turn by post box into Moor Hall Lane*. Cream teas. **Adm £3, chd free. Suns 20 July; 31 Aug (12-5). Also open Elwy Lodge 20 July.**
Country garden in ½ acre plot. Gardens front and rear with good selection of herbaceous plants and shrubs, roses, fuchsias, dahlias, begonias, bedding plants, tubs and hanging baskets. Fish pond with Koi carp and others. Well kept lawns and plenty of colour, especially late summer. Large horse chestnut tree in rear. Many seating areas.

27 THE LEMBIC
Hallwood Crescent, Shenfield, Brentwood CM15 9AA. Charmaine & Fred Cox. *½ m NE of Brentwood. Yellow signs on N side of A1023 between Brentwood & Shenfield*. Home-made teas. **Adm £3, chd free. Suns 25 May; 1 June (2-5).**
½ acre garden in quiet cul-de-sac. Fully grown forest trees and mature shrubs featuring rhododendron, azalea and acer. Perennial border and interesting walkways between shrubs. Large sculpture incorporating an analemma and garden seats designed for contemplation while enjoying your tea and home-made cake. Interview with Charmaine for the October issue of Essex Life. Wheelchair access, main garden accessible.

28 THE LIMES
The Tye, East Hanningfield CM3 8AA. Stan & Gil Gordon. *6m SE of Chelmsford. In centre of East Hanningfield across village green opp The Windmill PH*. Home-made teas. **Adm £3.50, chd free. Evening Opening £3.50, chd free, wine, Fri 30 May (6-9); Sat 31 May (2-6).**
Plant lovers' 1-acre well-established 'garden of many rooms' surrounding Victorian house (not open). Owner-designed to lure you round this tranquil garden with mature trees, interesting planting of shrubs, perennials, grasses, roses and clematis. Also orchard, soft fruit and vegetable area, formal garden and courtyard pots. Lots to enjoy, several seats and easy parking nearby. Approx 1m from RHS garden Hyde Hall. Gravel drive and grass paths.

29 LITTLE FOXES
Marcus Gardens, Thorpe Bay, Southend-on-Sea SS1 3LF. Mrs Dorothy Goode. *2½ m E of Southend. From Thorpe Bay Stn (S-side) proceed E, take 4th on R into Marcus Ave then 2nd L into Marcus Gardens*. Home-made teas. **Adm £3, chd free. Sat 16, Sun 17 Aug (2-5).**
A ⅓ acre garden offers a relaxing afternoon in beautiful surroundings. Island beds packed with flowers and foliage. 400ft herbaceous and shrub borders. Trees and conifers provide seclusion. August features Salvias, Agapanthus, Dahlia, Alstromeria and burgundy Eucomis. Water feature and pots incl 25 hostas. A seaside stroll is close by. Featured on BBC Radio Essex, and in Southend Evening Echo.

Greenhouse, vegetable and cutting gardens complete the picture . . .

30 LITTLE MYLES
Ongar Road, Stondon Massey, nr Brentwood CM15 0LD. Judy & Adrian Cowan. *1½ m SE of Chipping Ongar. Off A128 at Stag PH, Marden Ash, towards Stondon Massey. Over bridge, 1st house on R after S bend. 400yds Ongar side of Stondon Church*. Home-made teas. **Adm £3.50, chd £1. Sun 6 July (11-4).**
Romantic garden surrounded by wild flowers and grasses, set in 3 acres. Full borders, hidden features, meandering paths, pond, hornbeam pergola and fountains. Herb garden, full of nectar-rich and scented herbs, used for handmade herbal cosmetics. Asian garden with pots, statues and bamboo, ornamental vegetable patch, woven willow Gothic window feature and wire elephant. Crafts and handmade herbal cosmetics for sale. Gravel paths.

31 447 MAIN ROAD
Harwich CO12 4HB. J Shrive & S McGarry. *1m out of Dovercourt town centre. A120 to Harwich. St over Churchhill r'about onto bypass. Turn R at next r'about and up Parkeston Hill, turn R at mini r'about. 300 yds on L*. Home-made teas. **Adm £3, chd free. Sat 2 Aug (11-4); Sun 3 Aug (11-3).**
Come and view something different. No bedding plants or shrubs, unless you want to argue about the huge Banana plants being a shrub. Large town garden totally redesigned in 2007 as a tropical oasis, with its own Treasure island and treasure chest. A decking area for teas and Sharon's Mums delicious cakes! Featured in Colchester Gazette.

32 NEW 262 MAIN ROAD
Hawkwell, Hockley SS5 4NW. Karen Mann. *3m NE of Rayleigh. From the A127 at Rayleigh Weir take the B1013 towards Hockley. Garden on the L after the White Hart PH and village green*. Home-made teas. **Adm £3.50, chd free. Sat 28 June; Sat 26 July; Sat 16 Aug (1-5.30).**
The garden comprises of 185 metres of island beds and borders sited on ⅓ acre. Some of the borders are elevated from the house resulting in steep banks which provide a different and interesting aspect. Salvia, dahlia, hedychium, brugmansia peak in the summer months. There is disabled parking at the front of the house.

33 NEW THE MAJOR'S HOUSE
9 Warrior Square Road, Shoebury Garrison, Shoeburyness, Southend-On-Sea SS3 9PZ. Sharon & Richard Spence. *4m E of Southend. Head E on Thorpe Bay Esplanade, then Shoebury Common Rd adjacent to the seafront. After the Harvester PH, turn R into the Garrison*. Home-made teas. **Adm £3.50, chd free. Sun 8 June (11-5). Musical Evening Opening £15, wine, Sat 28 June (5.30-9.30).**
12yr old garden in a Grade 2 listed Victorian property (not opening) set in the historical Shoebury Garrison. The garden features traditional planting, mixed borders, herb garden, topiary and formal lawns. Many spring bulbs. Lots of seating areas to enjoy the garden. Gravel paths. Within a five minute stroll of the stunning beach. Musical evening on June 28. Admission by pre-purchased ticket. Contact arjeyeski@courtview.demon.co.uk tel 01702 713221.

34 ◆ MARKS HALL GARDENS & ARBORETUM

Coggeshall CO6 1TG. Marks Hall Estate, 01376 563796, www.markshall.org.uk. *1½ m N of Coggeshall. Follow brown & white tourism signs from A120 Coggeshall bypass.* **Adm £5, chd £2, family ticket £12. For opening times and information, please phone or see garden website.**

The walled garden is a unique blend of traditional long borders within C17 walls and 5 contemporary gardens. Inventive landscaping, grass sculpture and stunningly colourful mass plantings. On opp lake bank is millennium walk designed for winter interest, scent and colour, surrounded by over 100 acres of arboretum, incl species from all continents. New bridge across the brook making central area usable whatever the weather, from snowdrops to autumn colour. Hard paths now lead to all key areas of interest.

35 60 MILL LANE

Tye Green, Cressing CM77 8HW. Pauline & Arthur Childs. *2m S of Braintree. 15m W of Colchester, 5m N of Witham. From M11 J8 follow A120 to Braintree r'about McDonalds, take B1018 to Witham approx ¾ m turn R into Mill Lane.* Home-made teas. **Adm £2.50, chd free. Wed 16 July; Sun 10 Aug (2-5).**

A hidden little gem. Plantaholic's paradise packed with interesting flowers and ferns. Very colourful garden with hostas, penstemons, fuchsias and clematis in profusion, some rather unusual. 3 water features add a sense of calm. Relax on patio with delicious home-made cakes while admiring our beautiful containers, topiary and hanging baskets. Cressing Temple Barns nearby.

36 MIRAFLORES

5 Rowan Way, Witham CM8 2LJ. Yvonne & Danny Owen, 01376 515187, danny@dannyowen.co.uk. *ACCESS via CM8 2PS. The house postcode is not to be used, as access is from the REAR of the garden using postcode CM8 2PS, and please follow yellow signs.* Home-made teas. **Adm £3, chd free. Sun 25 May; Sat 21, Sun 22 June (1-5). Visitors also welcome by appt May to June minimum 10 for groups.**

An award-winning, medium-sized garden described by one visitor as a 'little bit of heaven'. A blaze of colour with roses and clematis, pergola rose arch, triple fountain with box hedging, the water attracts many birds. Clematis and poppies galore. Come and see our 'Folly'. Exuberant, cascading hanging baskets, as featured in Garden Answers and Essex Life. Tranquil seating areas and cakes to die for. Gentle instrumental background music. Camera enthusiasts welcome. Owner is a professional who can advise on flower photography and macro.

Beautiful and very peaceful 4 acre garden in touch with its surroundings and enjoying stunning estuary views . . .

37 MONKS COTTAGE

Monks Lane, Dedham nr Colchester CO7 6DP. Nicola Baker, 01206 322210, nicola_baker@tiscali.co.uk. *6m NE of Colchester. Leave Dedham village with the church on L. Take 2nd main rd on R (Coles Oak Lane) Monks Lane is first rd on L. Car park signs in Coles Oak Lane.* Home-made teas. **Adm £3.50, chd free. Fri 11 July (11-5). Visitors also welcome by appt May to July, small groups.**

½ acre cottage garden on a sloping site in the heart of Constable country. Colour-themed borders filled with bulbs, shrubs and perennials. Mature trees and pond. Highlights include roses, clematis and box-edged parterre beds filled with tulips and then later, dahlias. Features incl boggy area with strong foliage shapes and a small woodland garden. Gin-and-tonic balcony with views of the garden.

38 MOVERONS

Brightlingsea CO7 0SB. Lesley Orrock & Payne Gunfield, 01206 305498, lesleyorrock@me.com, www.moverons.co.uk. *7m SE of Colchester. At old church turn R signed Moverons Farm. Follow lane & garden signs for approx 1m. Beware some sat navs take you the wrong side of the river.* Home-made teas. **Adm £4, chd free. Sun 1 June; Sat 6, Sun 7 Sept (11-5). Visitors also welcome by appt June to Sept, for groups of 10+.**

Beautiful and very peaceful 4 acre garden in touch with its surroundings and enjoying stunning estuary views. A wide variety of planting in mixed borders to suit different growing conditions. A small courtyard, reflection pool garden, 2 large natural ponds all enhanced with a growing collection of metal sculptures. Magnificent mature trees some over 300yrs old give this garden real presence. Featured in Essex Life Magazine.

39 THE OLD RECTORY

Church Road, Boreham CM3 3EP. Sir Jeffery & Lady Bowman, 01245 467233, bowmansuzy@btinternet.com. *4m NE of Chelmsford. Take B1137 Boreham Village, turn into Church Rd at the Lion PH. ½ m along on R opp church.* Hot soup and filled rolls (Feb) Home-made teas (June). **Adm £5, chd free. Sat 22, Sun 23 Feb (12-3); Sun 1 June (2-5). Visitors also welcome by appt Feb to June, evening visits with wine possible.**

2½ -acre garden surrounding C15 house (not open). Ponds, stream, with bridges and primulas, small wild flower meadow and wood with interesting trees and shrubs, herbaceous borders with emphasis on complementary colours. Vegetable garden. February opening for crocus, snowdrops and cyclamen. Possibly largest gunnera in Essex. Lovely views over Chelmer/Blackwater canal. Featured in Country Homes and Interiors. Gravel drive but large part of garden accessible.

41 ONE BROOK HALL COTTAGES

Steeple Road, Latchingdon CM3 6LB. John & Corinne Layton, 01621 741680, corinne@arrow250.fsnet.co.uk. *1m from Latchingdon Church. From*

Maldon drive through Latchingdon to mini r'about at church taking exit towards Steeple & Bradwell. Approx 1m turn R at bungalow onto gravel drive. Home-made teas. **Adm £3.50, chd free. Visitors welcome by appt May to Sept, weekdays only.**
Uniquely designed contemporary cottage garden planted in a naturalistic style containing many nectar rich plants. Deck with a boardwalk leading to a wildlife pond. Pretty lawn edged with box and pleached limes with several small terraces from which to enjoy the view. Narrow paths and steep steps not suitable for people with walking difficulties. Footpath walk to R Blackwater. Winner of Daily Mail Garden Award and described by judges as a 'subtle organic masterpiece' Featured in House Beautiful and Garden Style magazines.

42 ORCHARD COTTAGE

219 Hockley Road, Rayleigh SS6 8BH. Heather & Harry Brickwood, 01268 743838, henry.brickwood@homecall.co.uk. *1m NE from Rayleigh town centre. Leave A127 at Rayleigh Weir and take B1013 towards Rayleigh. Pass through Rayleigh and proceed towards Hockley. Please park opp on grass verge*. Home-made teas. **Adm £4, chd free. Visitors welcome by appt June to July, groups 8+.**
Award winning 3/4 -acre garden. Central bed in the front is a mass of colour; June features 500+ aquilegias, backed up by roses, lilies and numerous other perennials; July will see exuberant lilies, hemerocallis, agapanthus and rudbeckia. There is a pond and stream and many flowering shrubs. Owner is a Chelsea Gold medal winner. Garden has over 2500 lilies. Featured on Gardeners World & The ABC of Gardening and in Garden News, The Essex Chronicle.

43 PARSONAGE HOUSE

Wiggens Green, Helions Bumpstead, Haverhill CB9 7AD. The Hon & Mrs Nigel Turner. *3m S of Haverhill. From the Xrds in the village centre go up past the Church for approx 1m. Parking on R through a five bar gate into the orchard*. Home-made teas. **Adm £3.50, chd free. Suns 4 May; 7 Sept (2-5).**
C15 house (not open) surrounded by 3 acres of formal gardens with mixed borders, topiary, pond, potager and greenhouse. Further 3-acre wild flower meadow with orchids and rare trees and further 3 acre orchard of old East Anglian apple varieties. Featured in Country Life, Hortus, The English Garden and Gardens Illustrated. Gravel drive and small step into WC.

44 PEACOCKS

Roman Road, Margaretting CM4 9HY. Phil Torr, 07802 472382, phil.torr@btinternet.com. *Margaretting Village Centre. From village Xrds go 75yds in the direction of Ingatestone, entrance gates will be found on L set back 50 feet from the road frontage*. Light refreshments. **Adm £4, chd free (share to St Francis Hospice). Sun 13 Apr (2-5); Sun 15 June (2-6). Visitors also welcome by appt Apr to June, adm incl refreshments.**
5-acre garden surrounding Regency house (not opewn) with mature native and specimen trees. Restored horticultural buildings. Formal walled garden (2nd under construction), long herbaceous/mixed border. Vegetable garden. Restored temple and lake. Large areas for wildlife incl woodland walk and orchard/flower meadow.

45 PEPPERS FARM

Forry Green, Sible Hedingham CO9 3RP. Mrs Pam Turtle, 01787 460221, pam@peppersfarm.entadsl.com. *1m SW of Sible Hedingham. From South after Gosfield L for Southey Green. L for Forry Green. From N for Sible Hedingham R at Sugar Loaves, Rectory Rd. L at White Horse until Forry Green*. Home-made teas. **Adm £3.50, chd free. Sun 25 May (2-5). Visitors also welcome by appt Mar to Oct.**
1/2 acre country garden set high on quiet rural green with farmland views. Hedges divide informal borders featuring flowering shrubs, fruit and specimen trees, many grown from seed. Beautiful alpine scree and sinks overlook spring fed pond. Garden owner has been a 'seedaholic' since small enough to seek fairies in tulips. Partial wheelchair access, large pond with steep sides. Some gravel.

46 REPRISE

5 Mornington Crescent, Hadleigh, Benfleet SS7 2HW. David & Rosemary King, 01702 557632, david.rosie@talktalk.net. *5m W of Southend-on-Sea. A13 E through Hadleigh town, Woodfield Rd L. A13 W pass Hadleigh Boundary sign, Woodfield Rd R. Follow signs*. Home-made teas. **Adm £3, chd free. Suns 8 June; 13 July; 3 Aug (2-5). Visitors also welcome by appt June to Aug, adm incl cream tea.**
A 250 sq-metre garden, created over 5yrs. Patio, with flower-filled containers, gives garden views. The gravel path winds through colourful perennials to a secluded seating area beneath an apple tree and climbers. Beyond the lawn is a pond, backed by shrubs and trees. Vegetable plot and greenhouse tucked away completes the scene. Featured in Evening Echo.

47 ROOKWOODS

Yeldham Road, Sible Hedingham CO9 3QG. Peter & Sandra Robinson, 01787 460224, sandy1989@btinternet.com. *8m NW of Halstead. Entering Sible Hedingham from the direction of Haverhill on A1017 take 1st R just after 30mph sign*. Home-made teas. **Adm £4, chd free. Mon 26 May; Sun 1 June (11.30-4.30). Visitors also welcome by appt May to Sept.**
Tranquil garden with mature and young trees and shrubs. Herbaceous borders with columns of tumbling roses. Pleached hornbeam leading to wild flower bed all being warmed by Victorian red brick wall enhanced with clematis and vitis coignetiae. Wander through meadow of buttercups to ancient oak wood. Enjoy tea relaxing under dreamy wisteria. Gravel drive.

48 69 RUNDELLS

Harlow CM18 7HD. Mr & Mrs K Naunton, 01279 303471, k_naunton@hotmail.com. *Harlow. M11 J7 A414 exit, lights take L exit Southern Way, mini r'about 1st exit Trotters Rd leading into Commonside Rd, take 2nd L into Rundells.* Home-made teas. **Adm £2.50, chd free. Sat 19 July (2-5). Visitors also welcome by appt June to Sept, please give plenty of notice.**

As featured on Alan Tichmarsh's first 'Love Your Garden' series ('The Secret Garden') 69 Rundells is a very colourful, small town garden packed with a wide variety of shrubs, perennials, herbaceous and bedding plants in over 200 assorted containers. Hard landscaping on different levels incls summer house, various seating areas and water features. Steep steps. Access to adjacent allotment, open to view. Honey and other produce for sale (conditions permitting). Full size hot tub/jacuzzi.

49 ST HELENS

High Street, Stebbing CM6 3SE. Stephen & Joan Bazlinton, 01371 856495, revbaz@care4free.net. *3m E of Great Dunmow. Leave Gt Dunmow on B1256. Take 1st L to Stebbing, at T-junction turn L into High St, garden 2nd on R.* Tea. **Adm £4, chd free (share to Dentaid). Visitors welcome by appt Apr to Aug.**

A garden of contrasts due to moist and dry conditions, laid out on a gentle Essex slope from a former willow plantation. These contours give rise to changing vistas and unanticipated areas of seclusion framed with hedging and generous planting. Walkways and paths alongside natural springs and still waters. Featured in Amateur Gardening. Limited wheelchair access.

50 SHRUBS FARM

Lamarsh, Bures CO8 5EA. Mr & Mrs Robert Erith, 01787 227520, bob@shrubsfarm.co.uk, www.shrubsfarm.co.uk. *1 1/4 m from Bures. On rd to Lamarsh, the drive is signed to Shrubs Farm.* Home-made teas. **Adm £5, chd free. Visitors welcome by appt Apr to Oct, groups of any size.**

2 acres with shrub borders, lawns, roses and trees. 50 acres parkland and meadow with wild flower paths and woodland trails. Over 70 species of oak. Superb 10m views over Stour valley. Ancient coppice and pollards incl largest goat (pussy) willow (*Salix caprea*) in England. Wollemi and Norfolk pines, and banana trees. Full size black rhinoceros. Display of Bronze age burial urns. Guided Tour to incl park and ancient woodland. Restored C18 Essex barn is available for refreshments. Some ground maybe boggy in wet weather.

> Ancient coppice and pollards including largest goat (pussy) willow (Salix caprea) . . .

51 SNARES HILL COTTAGE

Duck End, Stebbing CM6 3RY. Pete & Liz Stabler, 01371 856565, lizstabler@hotmail.com. *Between Dunmow & Bardfield. On B1057 from Great Dunmow to Great Bardfield, 1/2 m after Bran End on L.* Home-made teas. **Adm £4, chd free. Suns 1 June; 14 Sept (10.30-4). Visitors also welcome by appt Apr to Oct.**

A 'quintessential English Garden' - Gardeners World. Our quirky 1 1/2 acre garden has surprises round every corner and many interesting sculptures. A natural swimming pool is bordered by romantic flower beds, herb garden and Victorian folly. A bog garden borders woods and leads to silver birch copse, beach garden and 'Roman' temple. Natural Swimming Pond.

52 SOUTH SHOEBURY HALL

Church Road, Shoeburyness SS3 9DN. Mr & Mrs M Dedman, 01702 299022, michael@shoeburyhall.co.uk. *4m E of Southend-on-Sea. Enter Southend on A127 to Eastern Ave A1159 signed Shoebury. R at r'about to join A13. Proceed S to Ness Rd. R into Church Rd. Garden on L 50 metres.* Home-made teas. **Adm £3.50, chd free. Suns 13 Apr; 13 July (2-5). Visitors also welcome by appt Apr to Sept.**

Delightful, 1-acre established walled garden surrounding Grade II listed house (not open) and bee house. New agapanthus and hydrangea beds. April is ablaze with 3000 tulips and fritillaria. July shows 170+ varieties of agapanthus. Unusual trees, shrubs, rose borders, with 40yr old plus geraniums, Mediterranean and Southern Hemisphere planting in dry garden. St Andrews Church open to visitors. Garden close to sea.

53 SOUTHVIEW

11 Palmers Avenue, Grays RM17 5TX. Mrs Juliana Baker, 01375 375881, juliebaker28@gmail.com. *1/2 m E of Grays Town Centre. Follow Orsett Rd which runs into Palmers Ave (A1013), from Lodge Lane (A1013) follow Southend Rd into Palmers Ave.* Cream teas. **Adm £3, chd free. Suns 6, 27 July (12-4.30). Visitors also welcome by appt July to Sept.**

A delightful traditionally designed town garden, with a cottage style front garden. Side access with pots at different levels, our take on vertical gardening! Patio and plenty of seating. Lawn surrounded with densely planted borders. Beyond the pond is a secret garden and the summerhouse with a 'living roof'. Mirrors create illusion of depth and allow a view of summerhouse roof. 'Secret garden' is a tranquil area for contemplation. Wheelchair access through the rear gate from adjacent rd (500yds approx).

54 ◆ SPENCERS

Tilbury Road, Great Yeldham CO9 4JG. Mr & Mrs Colin Bogie, 01787 238175, www.spencersgarden.net. *Just N of Gt Yeldham on Tilbury Rd. In village centre, turn at 'Blasted Oak' (huge oak stump) onto Tilbury Rd. Spencers is clearly signed on L after approx 1/4 m.* Home-made teas. **Adm £5, chd free. For NGS: Suns 8 June; 14 Sept (2-5). For other opening times and information, please phone or see garden website.**

Romantic C18 walled garden laid out by Lady Anne Spencer, overflowing with blooms following Tom Stuart-Smith's renovation. Huge wisteria, armies of Lord Butler delphiniums ('Rab' lived at Spencers). Many varieties of roses, spectacular herbaceous borders, vibrant clover lawn, oldest greenhouse in Essex. Mature parkland with many ancient trees. Victorian woodland garden. Open Thurs May to Sep 2-5, and otherwise by appointment.

55 TUDOR ROOST

18 Frere Way, Fingringhoe, Colchester CO5 7BP. Chris & Linda Pegden, 01206 729831, pegdenc@gmail.com. *5m S of Colchester. In centre of village by Whalebone PH, follow sign to Ballast Quay, after 1/2 m turn R into Brook Hall Rd, then 1st L into Frere Way.* Home-made teas. **Adm £3.50, chd free. PLEASE CONFIRM OPENING DATES ON NGS WEBSITE OR TEL Suns, Mons 20, 21 Apr; 4, 5 May; 26, 27 July; 24, 25 Aug (2-5). Visitors also welcome by appt Apr to Aug, min 10, adm £6 incl Tea & Cake.**

An unexpected hidden colourful 1/4 - acre garden. Well manicured grassy paths wind round island beds and ponds. Densely planted subtropical area with architectural and exotic plants - cannas, bananas, palms, agapanthus, agaves and tree ferns surround a colourful gazebo. Garden planted to provide yr-round colour and encourage wildlife. Many peaceful seating areas. Within 1m of Fingringhoe Wick Nature Reserve. Local pub that serves meals. Featured in Garden News, Colchester Gazette and on Radio Essex - Down to Earth.

56 37 TURPINS LANE

Chigwell, Woodford Green IG8 8AZ. Fabrice Aru & Martin Thurston, 0208 5050 739, martin.thurston@talktalk.net. *Between Woodford & Epping. Tube: Chigwell, 2m from North Circular Rd at Woodford, follow the signs for Chigwell (A113) through Woodford Bridge into Manor Rd and turn L, Bus 275.* **Adm £3, chd free. Suns 15, 29 June; 13 July (11-5). Also open Fairwinds 15 June, 56 Forest Drive. Visitors also welcome by appt May to Sept, maxi 10.**

An unexpected hidden, magical, small part-walled garden showing how much can be achieved in a small space. An oasis of calm with densely planted rich, lush foliage, tree ferns, hostas, topiary and an abundance of well maintained shrubs complemented by a small pond and 3 water features designed for yr round interest. Awarded 2nd place by Gardening News for Best Small Garden.

37 Turpins Lane

57 ULTING WICK

Crouchmans Farm Road, Maldon CM9 6QX. Mr & Mrs B Burrough, 01245 380216, philippa.burrough@btinternet.com, www.ultingwickgarden.co.uk. *3m NW of Maldon. Take turning to Ulting off B1019 as you exit Hatfield Peverel. Garden on R after 2m.* Light refreshments incl home-made soup and rolls (Sun). Self service teas (Fri). **Adm £5, chd free (share to All Saints Ulting Church). Suns, Fris 27 Apr; 9 May; 14 Sept; 19 Sept (Sun 11-5), (Fri 2-5). Visitors also welcome by appt Mar to Oct, coaches welcome, groups 15+.**

Listed black barns provide backdrop for colourful, exuberant and dramatic planting in 8 acres. Thousand of tulips, flowing freestyle spring planting, herbaceous borders, pond, mature weeping willows, productive kitchen garden, late hot summer displays of dahlias, grasses and annuals. Drought tolerant wild flower meadow and front border. Woodland. Many plants propagated in-house. All Saints Ulting will be open in conjunction with the garden for talks on its history (not in May). Featured in Garden's Illustrated, Country Life and BBC Garden's World. Some gravel around the house but main areas of interest are accessible for wheelchairs.

GROUP OPENING

58 WALTHAM ABBEY

Waltham Abbey EN9 1LG. *8m W of Epping Town. M25, J26 to Waltham Abbey. At T-lights by McD turn R to r'about. Take 2nd exit to next r'about. Take 3rd exit (A112) to T-lights. L to Monkswood Av.* Home-made teas at Silver Birches, Quendon Drive. **Combined adm £5, chd free. Sun 7 Sept (12-6).**

NEW 62 EASTBROOK ROAD
Caroline Cassell.
Off Honey Lane, walking distance from Halfhides & The Glade Way approx 7 mins

39 HALFHIDES
Chris Hamer

76 MONKSWOOD AVENUE
Cathy & Dan Gallagher

SILVER BIRCHES
Quendon Drive. Linda & Frank Jewson

Historic Waltham Abbey is near Epping Forest. The Abbey is purported to be last resting place of King Harold. Lee Valley Regional Park is nearby. Silver Birches boasts 3 lawns on 2 levels. This surprisingly secluded garden has many mixed borders packed with early autumnal colour. Mature shrubs and trees create a short woodland walk. Crystal clear water flows through a shady area of the garden. At 39 Halfhides the garden has evolved over 45yrs. It features mixed shrubs and perennial borders on 2 levels. Waterfall linking two ponds leads to shade garden. Alpines thrive on scree and in troughs. Beautiful autumn colour. 76 Monkswood Ave is a plantswoman's garden. Mixed borders filled with specimen trees, shrubs and perennials incl asters, dahlias and late-flowering anemones. Wildlife pond. 62 Eastbrook Rd is a small cottage garden, traditional perennial planting, topiary and circular themed hard landscaping.
62 Eastbrook Rd not suitable for wheelchairs.

59 WASHLANDS

Prayors Hill, Sible Hedingham CO9 3LE. Tony & Sarah Frost. *1/4 m NW of Sible Hedingham Church. At Sugar Loaves PH on A1017 turn SW into Rectory Rd, R at White Horse PH, pass St Peters Church on RH-side, 1/4 m NW on Prayors Hill.* Home-made teas. **Adm £3.50, chd free. Suns 29 June; 6 July (2-6).**
Informal, tranquil garden approx 1 acre with good views over rolling countryside. Features incl a recently restored horse pond. Wide herbaceous, shrub and woodland borders incl roses and peonies. Many young and mature trees enhance the garden. A developing retirement project. Pond has steep banks. Woodland walk unsuitable for wheelchairs.

Peaceful country garden 'Far from the Madding Crowd' . . .

60 45 WATERHOUSE LANE

Chelmsford CM1 2TE. Peter & Julie Richmond, 01245 269277, richmond876@btinternet.com. *W side of Chelmsford between Widford & Chelmsford. Waterhouse Lane is on A1016 between Rainsford Lane & Westway. Parking in Bilton Rd opp & between 2 car showrooms. No restriction in Bilton Rd on Sundays.* **Evening Openings £15, wine, Sun 24, Sun 31 Aug (7-9.30). Visitors also welcome by appt June to Sept for groups of 10+.**
A plantsman's garden full of artistic and creative ideas with a wide variety of planting to suit different growing conditions. A stream and crystal clear pond lead you up the garden on a timbered boardwalk, past tropical planting to a seating area for informal dining and relaxed living. Behind the scenes, 2 greenhouses and a charming potting area are also home to 2 beehives and more flower beds. The evening opening will be an illuminated garden visit with entrance, wine and canapés. Numbers will be strictly limited to 30. Tickets £15.00 per head must be booked in advance (tel and email above). Featured in Amateur Gardening, Mail on Sunday and Bo Bygg Og Bolig (Homes and Garden in Norway). Also inspirational garden for Alan Titchmarsh's 'Love Your Garden'.

61 WICKETS

Langley Upper Green CB11 4RY. Susan & Doug Copeland, 01799 550553, susan.copeland2@btinternet.com. *7m W of Saffron Walden, 10m N of Bishops Stortford. At Newport take B1083. After 3m turn R at Clavering, signed Langley. Upper Green is 3m further on. At cricket green turn R. House 200m on R.* Home-made teas in village hall [opp] or in garden. **Adm £4, chd free. Sun 25 May (1-5). Evening Opening wine, Sat 7 June (4-8); Suns 8, 22 June (1-5). Combined adm £7 with Great Becketts 25 May, 22 June. Visitors also welcome by appt Apr to June, min 10+.**
Peaceful country garden 'Far from the Madding Crowd'. Wide, informal mixed borders include camassia, shrub roses and alliums. Two landscaped meadows and shepherd's hut with fine pastoral views. Large lily pond sheltered by silver birch. Curvilinear design links themed planting areas. Espalier apples enclose parterre with sweet peas, delphiniums, lavender. Secluded gravel garden. Featured in Essex Life, Country Homes and Interiors and on BBC Radio Essex. Gravel drive.

62 WICKHAM PLACE FARM

Station Road, Wickham Bishops, Witham CM8 3JB. Mrs J Wilson, 01621 891282, info@wickhamplacefarm.co.uk, www.wickhamplacefarm.co.uk. *2 1/2 m SE of Witham. On B1018 from Witham to Maldon. After going under A12 take 3rd L (Station Rd). 1st house on L. Different parking areas may be in use, follow signs.* Teas. **Adm £4, chd free (share to Farleigh Hospice). Fris 25 Apr; 9, 23 May; 6 June; 12 Sept (11-4). Visitors also welcome by appt, coaches/groups (min 15) any day/time. All year.**
14 acres for all seasons. 2 acre walled garden is home to climbers, shrubs, perennials and bulbs. Renowned for enormous wisterias in May (one over 250ft long) with further flowering in July. Ponds, intricate box knot garden and lovely woodland

walks with rabbit resistant plants. In September cyclamen carpet the woodland, replacing earlier bluebells. Adjacent to unique wooden trestle railway viaduct. Note. Wisterias face all aspects, extending flowering time during May. Featured in Gardeners World, Daily Mail, Express, Telegraph & Times. Local TV News, radio and press.

63 WOOD VIEW

24 Chapel Road, Great Totham, nr Maldon CM9 8DA. Edwin Parsons & Ian Roxburgh, 07540 798135, edwin@edwin.freeserve.co.uk, www.woodviewgardenessex.co.uk. *5m NE of Maldon. Situated in Great Totham North. Chapel Rd is off B1022 Maldon/Colchester Rd.* Home-made teas at URC Hall (opp). **Adm £3.50, chd free. Suns 20 Apr; 4, Mon 5 May (1-5). Visitors also welcome by appt Mar to May, pre booked groups - adm incl refreshments.**

Plantsman's contemporary garden containing unusual species, designed and maintained by the garden owners. Pergolas and terraces create seating areas in this haven for wildlife. Some rarer plants and species collected from our travels around the UK from Tresco to Shetland incl flowering Embothrium Coccineum, the Chilean Flame Tree, not usually found outside Cornwall. Crocus, swathes of primroses and narcissus. As spring moves on, tulips come into display. 3 allotments nearby. Refreshments, car parking and WC are available.

64 WOODPECKERS

Mangapp Chase, Burnham-on-Crouch CM0 8QQ. Neil & Linda Holdaway, & Lilian Burton, 01621 782137, lindaholdaway@btinternet.com, www.essexgardens.co.uk. *1m N of Burnham-on-Crouch. B1010 to Burnham-on-Crouch. Just beyond town sign turn L into Green Lane. Turn L after 1/2 m. Garden 200yds on R.* Light refreshments. **Adm £3.50, chd free. Fri 2, Sat 3 May, Fri 26, Sat 27 Sept (12-5). Visitors also welcome by appt Apr to Sept, for groups with home-made lunch or tea.**

Hedges divide and add structure to the exuberant planting in this 1 1/2 -acre country garden Spring brings blossom, wild flowers, drifts of bulbs and in the wide densely planted borders, a stunning display of tulips in late April/early May. Roses take centre stage in high summer and later in the year, nectar rich varieties of perennials encourage bees and clouds of butterflies. Featured in Period Homes magazine.

65 WRITTLE COLLEGE

Writtle CM1 3RR. Writtle College, 01245 424200 Ex 26020, tom.cole@writtle.ac.uk, www.writtle.ac.uk. *4m W of Chelmsford. On A414, nr Writtle village, clearly signed.* Light refreshments The Garden Room (main campus) and The Lordship tea room (Lordship campus). **Adm £4, chd free. Suns 23 Feb; 8 June; 26 Oct (10-3).**

15 acres; informal lawns with naturalised bulbs and wild flowers. Large tree collection, mixed shrubs, herbaceous borders. Landscaped gardens designed and built by students. Development of 13-acre parkland. Orchard meadow started. Landscaped glasshouses and wide range of seasonal bedding. NEW tropical 'HOT' bedding area added to quadrant garden. Herbaceous perennial borders renovated during 2012/13. Extended naturalised bulb areas on front campus lawns. Some gravel, however majority of areas accessible to all.

Essex County Volunteers

County Organiser
Susan Copeland, Wickets, Langley Upper Green, Saffron Walden CB11 4RY, 01799 550553, susan.copeland2@btinternet.com

County Treasurer
Neil Holdaway, Woodpeckers, Mangapp Chase, Burnham-on-Crouch CM0 8QQ, 01621 782137, mail@neilholdaway.com

Publicity & Assistant County Organisers
Doug Copeland, Wickets, Langley Upper Green, Saffron Walden CB11 4RY, 01799 550553, dougcopeland@btinternet.com
Linda Holdaway, Woodpeckers, Mangapp Chase, Burnham-on-Crouch CM0 8QQ, 01621 782137, lindaholdaway@btinternet.com
Ray Spencer, Court View, 276 Manchester Drive, Leigh-on-Sea SS9 3ES, 01702 713221, arjeyeski@courtview.demon.co.uk

Booklet Coordinator
Doug Copeland, Wickets, Langley Upper Green, Saffron Walden CB11 4RY, 01799 550553, dougcopeland@btinternet.com

Groups and Talks Coordinator
Linda Holdaway, Woodpeckers, Mangapp Chase, Burnham-on-Crouch CM0 8QQ, 01621 782137, lindaholdaway@btinternet.com

Assistant County Organiser
Richard Steers, Court View, 276 Manchester Drive, Leigh-on-Sea SS9 3ES, 01702 713221, arjeyeski@courtview.demon.co.uk

GLOUCESTERSHIRE

(for South Gloucestershire see Somerset, Bristol Area & S Glos)

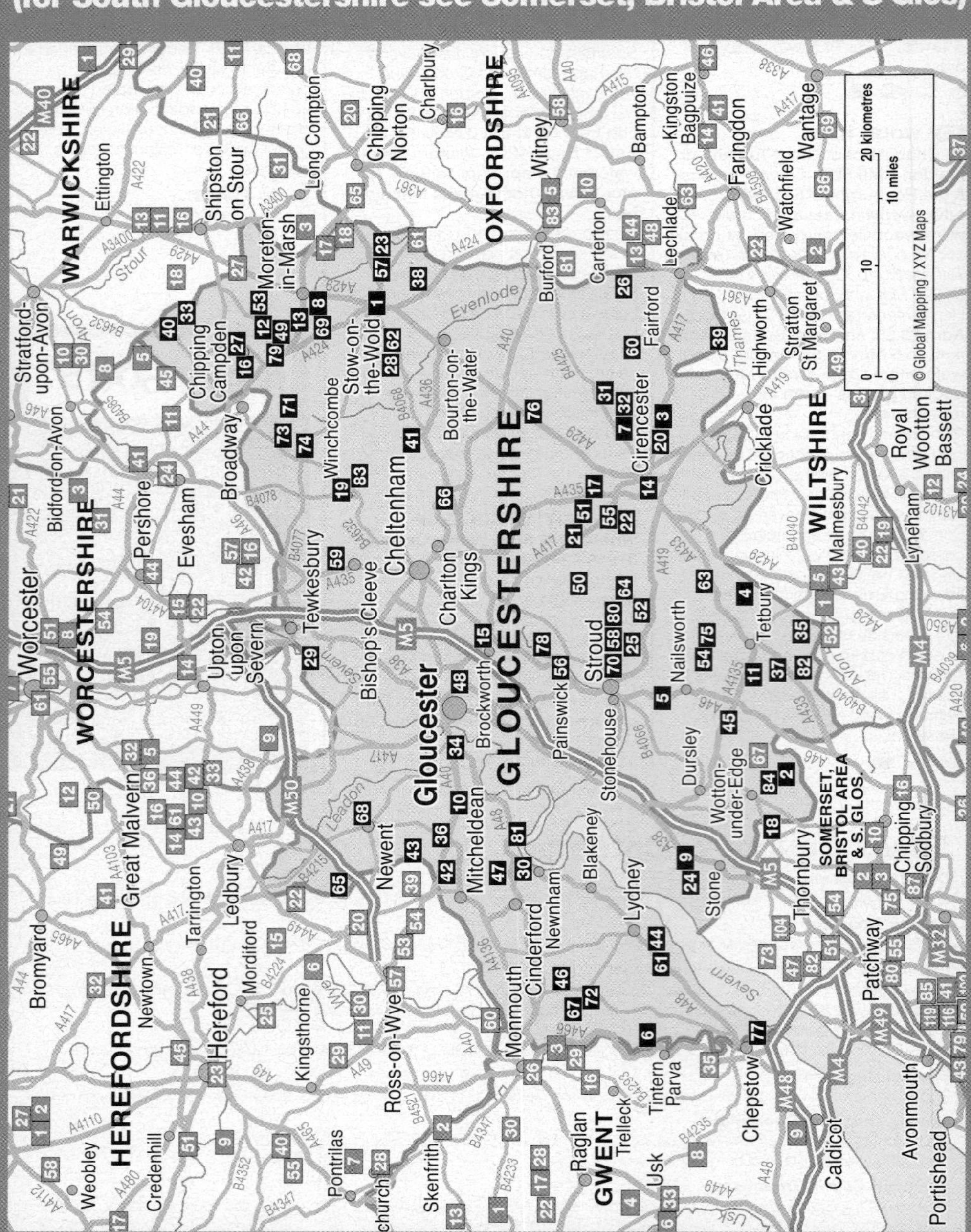

Opening Dates

All entries subject to change. For latest information check www.ngs.org.uk

February

Sunday 2
36 Home Farm

Sunday 9
39 Kempsford Manor

Sunday 16
36 Home Farm
39 Kempsford Manor
78 Trench Hill

Monday 17
55 The Old Rectory, Duntisbourne Rous

Sunday 23
24 Dr Jenner's House & Garden
78 Trench Hill

March

Sunday 2
8 Batsford Arboretum and Garden Centre

Sunday 16
36 Home Farm

April

Thursday 3
7 Barnsley House

Sunday 6
1 Abbotswood
34 Highnam Court
72 South Lodge

Sunday 13
36 Home Farm
39 Kempsford Manor
53 The Old Chequer

Monday 14
40 Kiftsgate Court
55 The Old Rectory, Duntisbourne Rous

Sunday 20
11 Beverston Castle
39 Kempsford Manor
50 Misarden Park
78 Trench Hill
79 Upton Wold

Monday 21
11 Beverston Castle
78 Trench Hill

Tuesday 22
46 Meadow Cottage

Saturday 26
29 NEW Forthampton Court

Sunday 27
12 Blockley Gardens
36 Home Farm

5 year project to create a haven for wildlife . . .

May

Saturday 3
72 South Lodge

Sunday 4
25 Eastcombe, Bussage and Brownshill Gardens
34 Highnam Court
61 Ramblers

Monday 5
25 Eastcombe, Bussage and Brownshill Gardens

Sunday 11
39 Kempsford Manor
74 Stanway Fountain & Water Garden

Wednesday 14
23 Daylesford House
44 Lydney Park Spring Garden

Saturday 17
19 Charingworth Court
72 South Lodge

Sunday 18
19 Charingworth Court
20 The Coach House Garden
39 Kempsford Manor
49 Mill Dene Garden
63 Rodmarton Manor
76 Stowell Park

Wednesday 21
43 Lower Farm House

Saturday 24
37 Hookshouse Pottery

Sunday 25
18 Charfield Village Gardens
37 Hookshouse Pottery
46 Meadow Cottage
48 9 Merevale Road
57 NEW Pasture Farm
66 Sandywell. Barn House

Monday 26
18 Charfield Village Gardens
37 Hookshouse Pottery
43 Lower Farm House
57 NEW Pasture Farm
66 Sandywell. Barn House

Tuesday 27
37 Hookshouse Pottery

Wednesday 28
37 Hookshouse Pottery

Thursday 29
37 Hookshouse Pottery

Friday 30
37 Hookshouse Pottery

Saturday 31
37 Hookshouse Pottery
42 Longhope Gardens

June

Sunday 1
17 Cerney House Gardens
31 NEW Greenacres
34 Highnam Court
37 Hookshouse Pottery
42 Longhope Gardens

Wednesday 4
78 Trench Hill

Festival Weekend

Saturday 7
5 Atcombe Court
84 Wortley Farm House

Sunday 8
4 Ashley Grange
12 Blockley Gardens
35 Hodges Barn
61 Ramblers
77 NEW Three Salmons House
84 Wortley Farm House

Monday 9
35 Hodges Barn
66 Sandywell. Barn House

Wednesday 11
16 Campden House
27 Ernest Wilson Memorial Garden
62 Rockcliffe House
78 Trench Hill

Friday 13
83 Woodlands Farm

Saturday 14
21 Cotswold Farm
42 Longhope Gardens
65 Rose Cottage
70 NEW Slad Valley House
83 Woodlands Farm

Sunday 15
9 Berkeley Castle
21 Cotswold Farm
42 Longhope Gardens
45 Matara Gardens of Wellbeing
52 Oakridge Lynch Open Gardens
54 The Old Rectory, Avening
65 Rose Cottage
73 Stanton Village Gardens
75 NEW 18 Star Lane

Wednesday 18
16 Campden House
27 Ernest Wilson Memorial Garden
78 Trench Hill

Saturday 21
10 Berrys Place Farm

Sunday 22
10 Berrys Place Farm
49 Misarden Park
58 Paulmead
60 Quenington Gardens
72 South Lodge
76 Stowell Park
80 Wells Cottage

Tuesday 24
46 Meadow Cottage

Wednesday 25
10 Berrys Place Farm
28 Eyford House
62 Rockcliffe House
78 Trench Hill

Thursday 26
10 Berrys Place Farm

Friday 27
71 Snowshill Manor & Garden

Saturday 28
64 Rookwoods

Sunday 29
30 The Gables
38 Icomb Gardens
51 Moor Wood
69 Sezincote

Beautiful rose arbour leading to lake and summerhouse . . .

July

Saturday 5
29 NEW Forthampton Court
33 Hidcote Manor Garden

Sunday 6
3 NEW Ampney Brook House
14 25 Bowling Green Road
32 Herbs for Healing
34 Highnam Court

Monday 7
14 25 Bowling Green Road

Sunday 13
11 Beverston Castle
14 25 Bowling Green Road
41 Littlefield Garden
57 NEW Pasture Farm

Monday 14
14 25 Bowling Green Road

Sunday 20
6 Barn House
14 25 Bowling Green Road
41 Littlefield Garden
66 Sandywell. Barn House
78 Trench Hill
82 Westonbirt School Gardens

Monday 21
14 25 Bowling Green Road

Wednesday 23
28 Eyford House

Tuesday 29
46 Meadow Cottage

August

Sunday 3
34 Highnam Court

Sunday 10
67 NEW Scatterford

Monday 11
40 Kiftsgate Court

Sunday 17
13 Bourton House Garden
32 Herbs for Healing

Sunday 24
78 Trench Hill

Tuesday 26
46 Meadow Cottage

Sunday 31
30 The Gables

September

Thursday 4
16 Campden House
27 Ernest Wilson Memorial Garden

Sunday 7
3 NEW Ampney Brook House
34 Highnam Court

Sunday 14
6 Barn House
74 Stanway Fountain & Water Garden
78 Trench Hill
81 Westbury Court Garden

Monday 15
55 The Old Rectory, Duntisbourne Rous

Sunday 21
15 Brockworth Court

October

Sunday 26
1 Abbotswood

February 2015

Sunday 1
36 Home Farm

Sunday 15
36 Home Farm
78 Trench Hill

Sunday 22
24 Dr Jenner's House & Garden
78 Trench Hill

Gardens open to the public

8 Batsford Arboretum and Garden Centre
13 Bourton House Garden
17 Cerney House Gardens
20 The Coach House Garden
24 Dr Jenner's House & Garden
32 Herbs for Healing
33 Hidcote Manor Garden
39 Kempsford Manor
40 Kiftsgate Court
44 Lydney Park Spring Garden
45 Matara Gardens of Wellbeing
49 Mill Dene Garden
50 Misarden Park
56 Painswick Rococo Garden
63 Rodmarton Manor
69 Sezincote
71 Snowshill Manor & Garden
74 Stanway Fountain & Water Garden
81 Westbury Court Garden
82 Westonbirt School Gardens

By appointment only

2 Alderley Grange
22 Daglingworth House
26 Eastleach House
47 The Meeting House
59 Pear Tree Cottage
68 Schofields

Also open by appointment

3 Ampney Brook House
6 Barn House
7 Barnsley House
11 Beverston Castle
14 25 Bowling Green Road
15 Brockworth Court
18 Pemberley Lodge, Charfield Village Gardens
19 Charingworth Court
21 Cotswold Farm
30 The Gables
36 Home Farm
42 Longhope Gardens
42 Springfield House, Longhope Gardens
46 Meadow Cottage
51 Moor Wood
53 The Old Chequer
55 The Old Rectory, Duntisbourne Rous
66 Sandywell. Barn House
67 Scatterford
72 South Lodge
75 18 Star Lane
78 Trench Hill
80 Wells Cottage

The Gardens

1 ABBOTSWOOD

Stow-on-the-Wold GL54 1EN. Dikler Farming Co. *1m W of Stow-on-the-Wold. On B4068 nr Lower Swell or B4077 nr Upper Swell.* Refreshments 6 Apr only. **Adm £5, chd free. Sun 6 Apr (1.30-6); Sun 26 Oct (12.30-4).**

Massed plantings of spring bulbs, heathers, flowering shrubs and rhododendrons in dramatic, landscaped hillside stream gardens; fine herbaceous planting in elegant formal gardens with lily pond, terraced lawn and fountain created by Sir Edwin Lutyens. Acers giving good autumn colour later in year. Wheelchair access to main parts of garden.

2 ALDERLEY GRANGE

Alderley GL12 7QT. The Hon Mrs Acloque, 01453 842161. *2m S of Wotton-under-Edge. Turn NW off A46 Bath to Stroud rd at Dunkirk. L signed Hawkesbury Upton & Hillesley. In Hillesley follow sign to Alderley.* **Adm £4, chd free. Visitors welcome by appt June, max 40.**

Walled garden with fine trees, old fashioned roses, herb garden and aromatic plants. A garden of character, charm and historical interest. Some gravel paths.

3 NEW AMPNEY BROOK HOUSE

Ampney Crucis, Cirencester GL7 5RT. Allan and Louise Hirst, 01285 851098, allan.hirst@clmail.co.uk. *From Cirencester go E on A417 toward Fairford. After passing the Crown of Crucis take 1st L and follow yellow arrows.* Home-made teas. **Adm £5, chd free. Sun 6 July (12.30-5); Sun 7 Sept (11.30-4). Visitors also welcome by appt Apr to Oct.**

Striking Grade II Cotswold country house on 4.3 acres fronting Ampney Brook. The gardens are 2 yrs into a 5 year project to create a haven for wildlife with fun and stimulating spaces yr-round. Includes woodland, kitchen garden, herbaceous borders, meadows, lawns for picnicking (encouraged). Limited wheelchair access; no access to kitchen garden and greenhouse.

Stanton Village Gardens

4 ASHLEY GRANGE

Ashley, Tetbury GL8 8SX. Mr & Mrs Richard Atkinson. *Centre of hamlet of Ashley. Ashley has no signage. Ashley Grange is opp entrance to C12 church (indicated).* Home-made teas. **Adm £5, chd free. Sun 8 June (2-6).**

The original garden was designed by the late Miss Avice Pearson and was opened in the 1990s through the NGS. The current owners have extended the garden and added a number of new borders. The peonies and iris borders are a feature of the garden in late May and June. A number of gardens in the village will also be open and C12 church. Wheelchair access to refreshment areas will require some assistance.

5 ATCOMBE COURT

South Woodchester GL5 5ER. John & Josephine Peach. *2m S of Stroud. Take turning off A46 signed South Woodchester, Frogmarsh Mill (NOT turning signed South Woodchester, The Ram).* Home-made teas. **Adm £3.50, chd free. Sat 7 June (2-6).**

12-acre grounds around C17 house (not open) with later Regency front. Delightful views over valley with lakes, mature trees and paddocks. Terraced herbaceous borders, lawns, extensive shrubberies, cutting garden mostly annuals. Long peony border. Woodland walk through beechwood. Display of work by the Minchinhampton Botanical Art Group. Wheelchair access to most of garden.

6 BARN HOUSE

Brockweir Common, Chepstow NP16 7PH. Mrs Kate Patel, 01291 680041, kate.patel@btinternet.com, thegardenbarnhouse.com. *10m S of Monmouth, 8m N of Chepstow. From Chepstow A466 to Monmouth. 2m past Tintern Abbey R across Brockweir Bridge then up Mill Hill ½ m, turn L at The Rock, signed to Cold Harbour. Narrow lane no large coaches.* Home-made teas. **Adm £3.50, chd free. Suns 20 July; 14 Sept (2-5.30). Visitors also welcome by appt June to Sept.**

Boldly and generously planted garden of an acre. Wealth of ornamental grasses plus long, late flowering perennials. Stunning mass plantings include 70m miscanthus hedge. Imaginatively designed contrasting areas include a tranquil sunken terrace with lush Asian grasses, hot border of potted tender perennials, orchard & exuberantly planted vegetable garden screened by bamboos.

7 BARNSLEY HOUSE

Barnsley, Cirencester GL7 5EE. Calcot Health & Leisure Ltd, 01285 740000, reception@barnsleyhouse.com, www.barnsleyhouse.com. *4m NE of Cirencester. From Cirencester, take B4425 to Barnsley. House entrance on R as you enter village.* **Adm £6. Thur 3 Apr (10.30-5). Groups of 10+ also welcome by appt, adm £18.**

The beautiful garden at Barnsley House, created by Rosemary Verey, is one of England's finest and most famous gardens incl knot garden, potager garden and mixed borders in Rosemary Verey's successional planting style. The House also has an extensive kitchen garden which will be open with plants and vegetables available for purchase. Narrow paths mean restricted wheelchair access but happy to provide assistance.

8 ◆ BATSFORD ARBORETUM AND GARDEN CENTRE

Batsford, Moreton-In-Marsh GL56 9AB. Batsford Foundation, 01386 701441, www.batsarb.co.uk. *1½ m W of Moreton-in-Marsh on A44.* **Adm £7, chd £3. For NGS: Sun 2 Mar (10-5). For other opening times and information, please phone or see garden website.**

Batsford is home to one of the country's largest private tree collections providing year-round colour. Wander through 56 acres of wild gardens, paths and streams, enjoy breathtaking views across the Evenlode Valley and discover the oriental-inspired statues. Famous for autumn colour, Batsford is equally beautiful in spring thanks to snowdrops, aconites, daffodils and flowering cherries. Home baked lunches, cakes and afternoon teas available in Garden Terrace Café. Featured on Gardeners' World. Visitor Centre accessible by wheelchair. 2 trampers available for members of the SW Countryside Mobility Scheme. Please book in advance.

9 BERKELEY CASTLE

Berkeley GL13 9PJ. Mr & Mrs J R G Berkeley, www.berkeley-castle.com. *Half-way between Bristol & Gloucester 10 mins from J14 of M5. From M5 follow signs to Berkeley on A38 & B4066. Visitors' entrance is on L of Canonbury St, just before town centre.* **Adm £5, chd £2. Sun 15 June (12-6).**

Unique terraced garden of a plantsman, with far-reaching views across R Severn. Designed with advice from Gertrude Jekyll, the gardens contain many rare plants which thrive in the warm micro-climate against the stone walls of the mediaeval castle. Woodland, historic trees and stunning summer borders. Butterfly House open: walk amongst free-flying butterflies. Cakes for sale in yurt near butterfly house and kitchen garden.

10 BERRYS PLACE FARM

Bulley Lane, Churcham, Gloucester GL2 8AS. Anne Thomas, 07950 808022, g.j.thomas@btconnect.com. *6m W of Gloucester. A40 towards Ross. Turning R into Bulley Lane at Birdwood.* Home-made teas and ploughmans lunches. **Adm £3, chd free. Sat 21, Sun 22, Wed 25, Thur 26 June (11-5).**

Country garden, approx 1 acre, surrounded by farmland and old orchards. Lawns and large sweeping mixed herbaceous borders with over 100 roses. Formal kitchen garden and beautiful rose arbour leading to lake and summerhouse with a variety of water lilies and carp. All shared with peacocks and ducks. Featured in Gloucestershire Echo and on Gloucestershire radio.

11 BEVERSTON CASTLE

nr Tetbury GL8 8TU. Mrs A L Rook, 07876 452645, sjspangles@hotmail.co.uk. *2m W of Tetbury. On A4135 to Dursley between Tetbury & Calcot X-rds.* **Adm £4, chd free. Sun 20, Mon 21 Apr, Sun 13 July (2-5.30). Visitors also welcome by appt Apr to Sept.**

Overlooked by romantic C12-C17 castle ruin (not open), copiously-planted paved terrace leads from C18 house (not open) across moat to sloping lawn with spring bulbs in abundance, and full herbaceous and shrub borders. Large walled kitchen garden and greenhouses. Partial wheelchair access.

BLICKS HILL HOUSE
See Wiltshire

Trench Hill

The NGS: Macmillan Cancer Support's largest ever benefactor

GROUP OPENING

12 BLOCKLEY GARDENS

Blockley GL56 9DB. *3m NW of Moreton-in-Marsh. Just off the Morton-in-Marsh to Evesham Rd A44.* Homemade teas 27 April at Milldene and St George's Hall. **Combined adm £6, chd free. Suns 27 Apr; 8 June (2-6).**

NEW CHURCH GATES
High Street. Mrs Brenda Salmon.
April 27 and June 8

4 THE CLEMENTINES
Kathy Illingworth.
June 8 only

COLEBROOK HOUSE
Richard & Melanie Slimmon.
April 27 only

HOLLYROSE HOUSE
Mr & Mrs Peter Saunders.
June 8 only

NEW LANGATE
Draycott. Mrs Hilary Sutton.
June 8 only

MALVERN MILL
Mr & Mrs J Bourne.
April 27 and June 8

THE MANOR HOUSE
George & Zoe Thompson.
April 27 and June 8

◆ MILL DENE GARDEN
Mr & Mrs B S Dare.
April 27 only
(See separate entry)

THE OLD CHEQUER
Mr & Mrs H Linley.
April 27 and June 8
(See separate entry)

PORCH HOUSE
Mr & Mrs Johnson
April 27 only

SNUGBOROUGH MILL
Mr Rupert Williams-Ellis.
June 8 only

WOODRUFF
Mr Paul & Mrs Maggie Adams.
April 27 and June 8

This popular historic hillside village has a great variety of high quality, well-stocked gardens - large and small, old and new. Blockley Brook, an attractive stream which flows right through the village, graces some of the gardens; these incl gardens of former water mills, with millponds attached. From some gardens there are wonderful rural views. Shuttle coach service provided. Small children welcome but close supervision required. Access to some gardens quite steep and allowances should be made.

13 ◆ BOURTON HOUSE GARDEN

Bourton-on-the-Hill GL56 9AE. Mr & Mrs R Quintus, 01386 700754, www.bourtonhouse.com. *2m W of Moreton-in-Marsh. On A44.* **Adm £6, chd free. For NGS: Sun 17 Aug (10-5). For other opening times and information, please phone or see garden website.**
Award-winning 3-acre garden featuring imaginative topiary, wide herbaceous borders with many rare, unusual and exotic plants, water features, unique shade house and many creatively planted pots. Fabulous at any time of year but magnificent in the summer months. Home-made teas served in Grade I listed C16 Tithe Barn. Cards and gifts available. Featured in international publications. 70% access for wheelchairs.

14 25 BOWLING GREEN ROAD

Cirencester GL7 2HD. Fr John & Susan Beck, 01285 653778, sjb@beck-hems.org.uk. *On NW edge of Cirencester. Take A435 to Spitalgate/Whiteway T-lights, turn into The Whiteway [Chedworth turn], then 1st L into Bowling Green Road.* **Adm £3, chd free. Suns, Mons 6 July (2-5); 7 July (11-4); 13 July (2-5); 14 July (11-4); 20 July (2-5); 21 July (11-4). Visitors also welcome by appt June to July max group size 40.**
Wander at will through our Wow Factor jungle of colour, rated by visitors as a wonderful hidden gem and even as 'cool' by the young, to glimpse a graceful giraffe and friendly frogs sharing their space with hosts of hemerocallis and hostas, graceful grasses, precious perennials, romantic roses and curvaceous clematis in the biggest small garden ever.

BRETFORTON MANOR

See Worcestershire

15 BROCKWORTH COURT

Court Road, Brockworth GL3 4QU. Tim & Bridget Wiltshire, 01452 862938, timwiltshire@hotmail.co.uk. *6m E of Gloucester. 6m W of Cheltenham. Adjacent St Georges Church on Court Rd. From A46 turn into Mill Lane, turn R, L, R. From Ermin St, turn into Ermin Park, then R at r'about then L at next r'about.* Home-made teas in Tithe Barn. **Adm £5, chd free. Sun 21 Sept (2-5). Visitors also welcome by appt May to Oct, house tour available for groups of 10+.**
This intense yet informal tapestry style garden beautifully complements the period Manor House which it surrounds. Organic, with distinct cottage-style planting areas that seamlessly blend together. Natural pond, which is home to moorhens, with Monet bridge leading to small island with thatched Fiji house. Kitchen garden once cultivated by the monks. Historic tithe barn. Views to Crickly and Coopers Hill. Adjacent Norman Church (open). Vintage Tractors. Featured in Country Life, Citizen and on Cotswold TV. Partial wheelchair access.

16 CAMPDEN HOUSE

Chipping Campden GL55 6UP. The Hon Philip & Mrs Smith. *Entrance on Chipping Campden to Weston Subedge Rd (Dyers Lane), approx 1/4 m SW of Campden, 1 1/4 m drive.* Home-made teas. **Combined adm £5, chd free. Wed 11, Wed 18 June (2-6); Thur 4 Sept (2-5). Combined with The Ernest Wilson Memorial Garden.**
2 acres featuring mixed borders of plant and colour interest around house and C17 tithe barn (neither open). Set in fine parkland in hidden valley with lakes and ponds. Woodland walk, vegetable garden. Gravel paths, steep slopes.

17 ◆ CERNEY HOUSE GARDENS
North Cerney GL7 7BX. Lady Angus, 01285 831300, www.cerneygardens.com. *4m NW of Cirencester. On A435 Cheltenham rd. Turn L opp Bathurst Arms, past church up hill, pillared gates on R.* Home-made teas. **Adm £5, chd £1.** **For NGS: Sun 1 June (10-5). For other opening times and information, please phone or see garden website.**
Romantic walled garden filled with old-fashioned roses and herbaceous borders. Working kitchen garden, scented garden, well-labelled herb garden, Who's Who beds and genera borders. Spring bulbs in abundance all around the wooded grounds. Bothy pottery.

Gloucestershire Plant Heritage plant sale at Eastcombe Village Hall . . .

GROUP OPENING

18 CHARFIELD VILLAGE GARDENS
Charfield GL12 8TG. *3m S of Wotton-under-Edge on B4058. From M5 take J14 towards Wotton-Under-Edge. At r'about turn L for 2 of the gardens into village or take 2nd exit into Churchend Lane.* Light refreshments At Warners Court and Pemberley Lodge. **Combined adm £6, chd free. Sun 25, Mon 26 May (1-6).**

PEMBERLEY LODGE
Old Charfield. Rob & Yvette Andrewartha.
From M5 take J14 towards Wotton-under-Edge. At r'about take 2nd exit on to Churchend Lane. Garden approx 600 metres on R
Visitors also welcome by appt prior notice required, groups of 10+.
01454 260885
www.gryfindor.info/ourgarden.html

10 STATION ROAD
Charfield. Mrs Sue Laing.
From M5 take J14 to Wotton-under-Edge. At r'about turn L onto B4058, through village, over bridge then R into Station Rd. No 10 is on L

WARNERS COURT
Wotton Road, Charfield. Barbara & Mike Adams.
From M5 take J14 to Wotton-under-Edge. At r'about turn L onto B4058. Through village opp Memorial Hall on L

Three charming gardens open in Charfield village. Warners Court, the largest with formal garden, shrubbery, wildlife area with large pool, vine house and productive vegetable garden to explore. 10 Station Road is a beautifully planted garden in country cottage style, packed full of delightful plants and with successful vegetable and fruit garden and lovely front garden. Pemberley Lodge is a modern garden, which wraps round the house, professionally designed to provide all yr round interest with low maintenance. It has an unusual roof garden that gives a great view. Light refreshments and delicious cakes and plentiful parking for all the gardens or the more adventurous can walk around the village to visit them all. For all visiting plantaholics there will be plenty to buy as you visit the different gardens. Have lunch in one of our three village pubs. Nearby is Charfield Meadow, an Avon Wildlife Trust site and the C15 St James Church. All gardens have good wheelchair access although some areas may be inaccessible.

19 CHARINGWORTH COURT
Broadway Road, Winchcombe GL54 5JN. Susan & Richard Wakeford, 01242 603033, susanwakeford@googlemail.com, www.charingworthcourtcotswoldsgarden.com/. *In Winchcombe, 8m NE of Cheltenham. 400 metres N of Winchcombe town centre car park in Bull Lane; walk down Chandos St, L onto Broadway Rd. Garden is on L or park along Broadway Rd.* Home-made teas. **Adm £4, chd free.** **Sat 17, Sun 18 May (11-6). Visitors also welcome by appt May to June including evenings.**
Artistically and lovingly created 1½ -acre gardens surrounding restored Georgian/Tudor house (not open). Relaxed country style, with Japanese influences, lily pond and productive walled vegetable garden. Mature copper beech trees, Cedar of Lebanon and Wellingtonia; and younger trees replacing an earlier excess of cupressus leylandii. Garden will be backdrop for garden sculpture selling exhibition.

20 ◆ THE COACH HOUSE GARDEN
Ampney Crucis, Cirencester GL7 5RY. Mr & Mrs Nicholas Tanner, 01285 850256, mel@thetanners.co.uk, www.thecoachhousegarden.co.uk. *3m E of Cirencester. Turn into village from A417, immed before Crown of Crucis Inn. Over hump-back bridge, parking immed to R on cricket field (weather permitting).* Cream teas. **Adm £5, chd free. For NGS: Sun 18 May (2-5). For other opening times and information, please phone or see garden website.**
Approximately 1½ acres and full of structure and design. This garden is divided into rooms which incl gravel garden, rose garden, herbaceous borders, green garden with pleached lime allee, potager and rill. Created over last 25yrs by present owners. Rare plant sales and garden lecture days. Featured in Cotswold Life and The English Garden. Limited wheelchair access. We can install a ramp to enable access to main body of the garden but some other areas are reached via short flights of steps.

CONDERTON MANOR
See Worcestershire

21 COTSWOLD FARM
Duntisbourne Abbots, Cirencester GL7 7JS. Mrs Mark Birchall, 01285 821857, iona@cotswoldfarmgardens.org.uk www.cotswoldfarmgardens.org.uk. *5m NW of Cirencester off old A417. From Cirencester L sign Duntisbourne Abbots Services, R and R underpass. Drive ahead. From Gloucester L signed Duntisbourne Abbots Services. Pass Services. Drive L.* Cream teas. **Adm £5, chd free (share to A Rocha).**

Sat 14, Sun 15 June (2-5). **Visitors also welcome by appt.**
Arts and Crafts garden in lovely position overlooking quiet valley on descending levels with terrace designed by Norman Jewson in 1930s. White border overflowing with flowers, texture and scent. Shrubs, trees, shrub roses, bog garden, snowdrops named and naturalised. Allotments in old walled garden, 8 native orchids, 100's of wild flowers and Roman snails. Family day out. Croquet and toys on lawn. Picnics welcome. Featured in Cotswold Essence, Gardens Illustrated, Gloucestershire Citizen & Echo and on Radio Gloucestershire. Partial wheelchair access.

22 NEW DAGLINGWORTH HOUSE

Daglingworth, nr Cirencester GL7 7AG. David & Henrietta Howard, 01285 885626, daglingworthhse@aol.com. *2m from Cirencester off A417/419. House beside church in Daglingworth.* **Adm £6, chd free.** Visitors welcome by appt **Apr to Sept.**
Walled garden, water features, temple and grotto. Classical garden of views and vistas with humorous contemporary twist. Good planting, hedges, Topiary and herbaceous borders. Pergolas, woodland and pool. Lovely Cotswold village setting beside church.

23 DAYLESFORD HOUSE

Daylesford GL56 0YG. Lord Bamford & Lady Bamford. *5m W of Chipping Norton. Off A436. Between Stow-on-the-Wold & Chipping Norton.* Light refreshments. **Adm £5, chd free.** Wed 14 May (2-5).
Magnificent C18 landscape grounds created 1790 for Warren Hastings, greatly restored and enhanced by present owners. Lakeside and woodland walks within natural wild flower meadows. Large walled garden planted formally, centred around orchid, peach and working glasshouses. Trellised rose garden. Collection of citrus within period orangery. Secret Garden with pavilion and formal pools. Very large garden with substantial distances to be walked.

24 ◆ DR JENNER'S HOUSE & GARDEN

Church Lane, Berkeley GL13 9BN. The Jenner Trust, 01453 810631, www.jennermuseum.com. *Midway between Bristol & Gloucester just off A38. Follow signs to Berkeley, then brown tourist signs to Jenner Museum.* Home-made teas. **Adm £3.50, chd free.** For NGS: Sun 23 Feb 2014; Sun 22 Feb 2015 (11-4). **For other opening times and information, please phone or see garden website.**
Informal woodland garden at the former home of Dr Edward Jenner. Snowdrops and wild garlic guide you around, past the herb garden to the Grade II* listed Temple of Vaccinia, the 200yr old plane tree and into the vinery where Jenner's Hampton Court Palace vine grows. House not open for NGS. Information sheets and children's trail. Gravel paths.

GROUP OPENING

25 EASTCOMBE, BUSSAGE AND BROWNSHILL GARDENS

Eastcombe GL6 7DS. *3m E of Stroud. 2m N of A419 Stroud to Cirencester rd on turning signed to Bisley & Eastcombe. Please park considerately in villages.* Home-made teas at Eastcombe Village Hall. **Combined adm £5, chd free (share to Cotswold Care Hospice; Acorns Children's Hospice; Hope for Tomorrow).** Sun 4, Mon 5 May (2-6).

NEW BADGER'S BROOK
Bismore, Eastcombe, Stroud. Mr & Mrs Peter Zanatta

CADSONBURY
The Ridge, Bussage. Natalie & Glen Beswetherick

NEW THE CHALFONT
St. Mary's Way, Brownshill, Stroud. Mr & Mrs I Lambert

HAMPTON VIEW
The Ridge, Bussage. Geraldine & Mike Carter

1 HIDCOTE CLOSE
Eastcombe. Mr & Mrs J Southall

12 HIDCOTE CLOSE
Eastcombe. Mr & Mrs K Walker

HIGHLANDS
Dr Crouch's Road, Eastcombe. Helen & Bob Watkinson

MARYFIELD AND MARYFIELD COTTAGE
Cowswell Lane, Bussage. Mrs M. Brown

MIDDLEGARTH
Bussage Hill, Bussage. Helen & Peter Walker

NEW THE OLD COACH HOUSE
Dr Crouchs Road, Eastcombe, Stroud. Mr & Mrs Stephen Wright
01452 771196
admin@oldcoachhousebandb.co.uk
www.oldcoachhousebandb.co.uk

REDWOOD
Bussage. Rita Collins

ROSE COTTAGE
The Street, Eastcombe. Mrs Juliet Shipman

VATCH RISE
Eastcombe, Stroud. Peggy Abbott

YEW TREE COTTAGE
Bussage Hill, Bussage. Andy & Sue Green

A group of gardens, medium and small, set in picturesque hilltop location. Some approachable only by foot. (Exhibitions may be on view in Eastcombe village hall). Gloucestershire Plant Heritage plant sale at Eastcombe Village Hall on Sunday afternoon only.

Moor Wood

26 EASTLEACH HOUSE
Eastleach Martin, Cirencester GL7 3NW. Mrs David Richards, garden@eastleachhouse.com, www.eastleachhouse.com. *5m NE of Fairford, 6m S of Burford. Entrance opp church gates in Eastleach Martin. Lodge at gate and driveway is quite steep up to house.* Refreshments at The Victoria Inn, 01367 850277. **Adm £8, chd free. Individuals and groups welcome by appt May to Oct.**
Large traditional all-yr-round garden. Wooded hilltop position with long views S and W. New parkland, lime avenue and arboretum. Wild flower walk, wildlife pond, lawns, walled and rill gardens, with modern herbaceous borders, yew and box hedges, iris and paeony borders, lily ponds, formal herb garden and topiary. Rambling roses into trees. Featured in Country Life, The English Garden Magazine, Cotswold Life, Daily Telegraph and other publications. GGG * rating, RHS garden guide. Features in Tony Russell's book The Cotswolds' Finest Gardens. Gravel paths and some steep slopes.

27 ERNEST WILSON MEMORIAL GARDEN
Leysbourne, Chipping Campden GL55 6DL. EWMG Trust. *High St. Chipping Campden, at Leysbourne below church.* **Combined adm £5, chd free. Wed 11, Wed 18 June (2-6); Thur 4 Sept (2-5). Combined with Campden House.**
The Ernest Wilson Memorial Garden was created in 1984 in memory of Ernest Wilson the celebrated plant hunter who was born in Chipping Campden in 1816. This small tranquil walled garden in the centre of the town features entirely plants, shrubs and trees introduced by Ernest Wilson.

28 EYFORD HOUSE
Upper Slaughter, Nr Cheltenham GL54 2JN. Mrs C Heber-Percy. *2½ m from Stow on the Wold on B4068 Stow to Andoversford Rd.* Cream teas. **Adm £4, chd free. Wed 25 June, Wed 23 July (11-4). Also open Rockliffe 25 June.**
1½ -acre sloping N facing garden, ornamental shrubs and trees. Laid out originally by Graham Stuart Thomas, 1976. West garden and terrace, red border, walled kitchen garden, two lakes with pleasant walks and views, boots recommended! Holy well. Walled garden now open after reconstruction.

29 NEW FORTHAMPTON COURT
Forthampton, Tewkesbury GL19 4RD. John Yorke. *W of Tewkesbury. From Tewkesbury A438 to Ledbury. After 2m turn L to Forthampton. At Xrds go L towards Chaceley. Go 1m turn L at Xrds.* Home-made teas. **Adm £4.50, chd free. Sat 26 Apr, Sat 5 July (12-4).**
Charming and varied garden surrounding a North Gloucestershire Medieval Manor house (not open) within sight of Tewkesbury Abbey. Incl borders, lawns, roses and magnificent Victorian vegetable garden.

30 THE GABLES
Riverside Lane, Broadoak, Newnham on Severn GL14 1JE. Bryan Bamber, bryanbamber@sky.com. *1m NE of Newnham on Severn. Park in White Hart PH unsurfaced car park, to R when facing river. Walk 250 metres along rd past PH to The Gables. Access through marked field gate.* Home-made teas. **Adm £3, chd free. Suns 29 June; 31 Aug (11-5). Groups of 10+ also welcome by appt June to Aug.**
Garden was started in 2006 from a blank canvas. Large flat garden with formal lawns, colourful herbaceous borders and shrubberies. Incl wild flower meadow incorporating soft fruits and fruit trees, an allotment-size productive vegetable plot, greenhouse and composting area. Featured in Gloucestershire Echo/Gloucester Citizen Weekend magazine and on Radio Gloucestershire. All areas of garden visible for wheelchair users but with limited access.

31 NEW GREENACRES
Hay Lane, Bibury, Cirencester GL7 5LZ. Alan & Liz Franklin, www.greenacrescl.co.uk/NGS. *0.5m W of Bibury. From Cirencester, take B4425 to Bibury. Take L turn 50 yards before entering Bibury signed Fosse Cross/Chedworth. House on R.* Home-made teas. **Adm £4, chd free. Sun 1 June (2-6).**
1-acre level garden developed by present owners over 16 yrs. Trees, shrubs, perennials and bulbs to create large informal borders providing variety with yr-round interest. Focus garden areas include: courtyard, pump, gazebo, wild garden/orchard, heather garden and vegetables/herbs with raised beds, polytunnel and greenhouses. Seating integrated in garden design. 9 hole putting course.

32 ◆ HERBS FOR HEALING
Claptons Lane (behind Barnsley House Hotel), Barnsley GL7 5EE. Davina Wynne-Jones, 07773 687493, www.herbsforhealing.net. *4m NE of Cirencester. Coming into Barnsley from Cirencester - turn R after Barnsley House Hotel and R again at the dairy barn. Follow signs.* Home-made teas. **Adm £4, chd free. For NGS: Suns 6 July; 17 Aug (2-5). For other opening times and information, please phone or see garden website.**
Not a typical NGS garden, rural and naturalistic. Davina, the daughter of Rosemary Verey, has created a unique nursery, specialising in medicinal herbs and a tranquil organic garden in a secluded field where visitors can enjoy the beauty of the plants and learn more about the properties and uses of medicinal herbs. Tours of the garden explaining current and historical uses of the plants. Access to WC is difficult for wheelchair users.

33 ◆ HIDCOTE MANOR GARDEN
Hidcote Bartrim, Chipping Campden, nr Mickleton GL55 6LR. National Trust, 01386 438333, www.nationaltrust.org.uk/hidcote. *4m NE of Chipping Campden. Off B4081.* **Adm £11, chd £5.50. For NGS: Sat 5 July (10-6). For other opening times and information, please phone or see garden website.**
One of England's great gardens. A 10½ -acre Arts and Crafts masterpiece created by Major Lawrence Johnston. Series of outdoor rooms, each with a different character, separated by walls and hedges of many different species. Rare trees, shrubs, outstanding herbaceous borders, and unusual plant species from all over the world. Motorised buggies are available to borrow. One or two areas are not completely accessible to wheelchairs.

Wild flower meadow with soft fruits and fruit trees . . .

34 HIGHNAM COURT
Highnam, Gloucester GL2 8DP. Mr and Mrs R J Head, 01684 292875, jane.highnamcourt@gmail.com, www.HighnamCourt.co.uk. *2m W of Gloucester. On A40/A48 from Gloucester.* Light refreshments In the Orangery. **Adm £5, chd free. Suns 6 Apr; 4 May; 1 June; 6 July; 3 Aug; 7 Sept (11-5).**
40 acres of Victorian landscaped gardens surrounding magnificent Grade I house (not open), set out by the artist Thomas Gambier Parry. Lakes, shrubberies and listed Pulhamite water gardens with grottos and fernery. Exciting ornamental lakes, and woodland areas. Extensive 1-acre rose garden and many features, incl numerous wood carvings around the site. Some gravel paths and steps to refreshment area. Disabled WC.

35 HODGES BARN
Shipton Moyne, Tetbury GL8 8PR. Mr & Mrs N Hornby. *3m S of Tetbury. On Malmesbury side of village.* **Adm £5, chd free. Sun 8, Mon 9 June (2-6).**
Very unusual C15 dovecote converted into family home. Cotswold stone walls host climbing and rambling roses, clematis, vines, hydrangeas and together with yew, rose and tapestry hedges create formality around house. Mixed shrub and herbaceous borders, shrub roses, water garden, woodland garden planted with cherries, magnolia and spring bulbs. Some gravel, mostly grass.

36 HOME FARM
Newent Lane, Huntley GL19 3HQ. Mrs T Freeman, 01452 830210, torill@ukgateway.net. *4m S of Newent. On B4216 ½ m off A40 in Huntley travelling towards Newent.* **Adm £3, chd free. Suns 2, 16 Feb; 16 Mar; 13, 27 Apr 2014; Suns 1, 15 Feb 2015 (11-4). Visitors also welcome by appt Jan to Apr.**
Set in elevated position with exceptional views. 1m walk through woods and fields to show carpets of spring flowers. Enclosed garden with fern border, sundial and heather bed. White and mixed shrub borders. Stout footwear advisable in winter.

37 HOOKSHOUSE POTTERY
Hookshouse Lane, Tetbury GL8 8TZ. Lise & Christopher White, hookshousepottery.co.uk. *2½ m SW of Tetbury. From Tetbury take A4135 towards Dursley, then take 2nd L. Pottery 1½ m on R.* Home-made teas. **Adm £3, chd free. Sat 24, Sun 25, Mon 26, Tue 27, Wed 28, Thur 29, Fri 30, Sat 31 May, Sun 1 June (11-6).**
A combination of dramatic open perspectives and intimate corners. Borders, shrubs, woodland glade, water garden containing treatment ponds (unfenced) and flowform cascades. Kitchen garden with raised beds, orchard. Sculptural features. Run on organic principles. Pottery showroom with hand-thrown wood-fired pots incl frostproof garden pots. Art & craft exhibition incl garden furniture and sculptures. Featured on Radio Gloucestershire.

GROUP OPENING

38 ICOMB GARDENS
Icomb, Stow-on-the-Wold GL54 1JL. *3m S of Stow-on-the-Wold. Take Icomb Rd off A424 Burford-Stow Rd. After 1m turn R signed Icomb. Parking near gardens as directed by stewards. No parking on street.* Home-made teas in village hall. **Combined adm £5, chd free. Sun 29 June (1.30-5).**

NEW **CORNER COTTAGE**
Church Road. Jean Hartley

GUYS FARM
Vanda Palmer

HOME FARM
Miss Ellen Fisher

NEW **THE LAWNS**
Church Road. Rachel & Michael Stone

NEW **LITTLE DORMERS**
Church Road. Vanessa & Jonathan Curry

MANOR FARM
Eleanor & Hugh Paget

NEW **1 ORCHARD ROW**
Church Road. John & Janet Bauser

2 PARK VIEW COTTAGES
David Cowdery

Small pretty village with glorious views and early C13 church. Manor Farm: Well laid out large garden with unusual plants, orchard and ornamental vegetable plot and exceptional views. 2 Park View Cottages: Pretty well-stocked small front garden with courtyard at back acting as outdoor room. Guy's Farm: Peaceful cottage garden with terrace and herbaceous border. Home Farm: Extensive well-stocked cottage garden with fruit and vegetables and lovely views. Corner Cottage: Small courtyard garden with pots and climbers. The Lawns: Cottage garden enclosed in Cotswold stone walling with mature and young trees, raised fish pond and borders with all-year round interest featuring pastel colours. Little Dormers: Terraced cottage garden with dry stone walls. 1 Orchard Row: Well-stocked small cottage garden. 2 ParkView Cottages and Little Dormers have no wheelchair access. Dogs on leads welcome except at Home Farm where only guide dogs are allowed.

39 ◆ KEMPSFORD MANOR
High Street, Kempsford GL7 4EQ. Mrs Z I Williamson, 01285 810131, www.kempsfordmanor.com. *3m S of Fairford. Take A419 from Cirencester or Swindon. Kempsford is signed 10m (approx) from each. The Manor is in the centre of village.* Home-made teas. **Adm £4. For NGS: Suns 9, 16 Feb; 13, 20 Apr; 11, 18 May (2-5). For other opening times and information, please phone or see garden website.**
Early spring garden with variety of bulbs incl snowdrop walk along old canal. Occasional musical events, art exhibitions, occasional talks on gardening. Frequently mentioned in local press. Also in Tony Russell's book Finest Gardens of the Cotswolds. Canal path unsuitable for wheelchairs. Disabled parking at garden entrance.

40 ◆ KIFTSGATE COURT
Nr Chipping Campden GL55 6LN. Mr & Mrs J G Chambers, 01386 438777, www.kiftsgate.co.uk. *4m NE of Chipping Campden. Adjacent to Hidcote NT Garden. 3m NE of Chipping Campden.* Home-made teas. **Adm £7.50, chd £2.50. For NGS: Mon 14 Apr, Mon 11 Aug (2-6). For other opening times and information, please phone or see garden website.**
Magnificent situation and views, many unusual plants and shrubs, tree peonies, hydrangeas, abutilons, species and old-fashioned roses incl largest rose in England, Rosa filipes 'Kiftsgate'. Steep slopes and uneven surfaces.

9 hole putting course . . .

41 LITTLEFIELD GARDEN
Hawling, Cheltenham GL54 5SZ. Mr & Mrs George Wilk. *From A40 Cheltenham to Oxford at Andoversford turn onto A436 towards Stow-On-The-Wold. Take 2nd signed rd to Hawling.* Home-made teas. **Adm £4, chd free. Sun 13, Sun 20 July (11-5).**
Surrounded by idyllic countryside with fine views over small valley, site of old medieval village of Hawling, Littlefield Garden was originally designed by Jane Fearnley-Whittingstall. More recently the planting in the yew walk was created by Sherborne Gardens. Rose garden, mixed borders, lily pond, wildflower meadow and lavender borders. Visitors can stroll 200yds across meadow to natural pond or have tea and relax under the pergola. Featured in the Gloucestershire Echo. Mostly wheelchair access. Gravel path and paved terraces.

GROUP OPENING

42 LONGHOPE GARDENS
Station Lane, Longhope GL17 0NA, 01452 830406/ 07918 741297, sally.j.gibson@btinternet.com. *10m W of Gloucester. 6m E of Ross on Wye. A40 take Longhope turn off to Church Rd. From A4136 follow Longhope signs and turn onto Church Rd. Parking on Church Rd, limited parking at Springfield House.* Home-made teas. **Combined adm £4, chd free. Sat 31 May (12-5); Sun 1 June (2-6); Sat 14 June**

Upton Wold

(12-5); Sun 15 June (2-6). **Groups of 5+ also welcome by appt May to July.**

3 CHURCH ROAD
Rev Clive & Mrs Linda Edmonds

SPRINGFIELD HOUSE
Sally & Martin Gibson

Sited in the valley of Longhope with glorious views, this small village offers two well-planted gardens to view. 3 Church Road: long garden divided into rooms with large collection of hardy geraniums, many of them unusual varieties with some new planting for 2014 in silver and grey colours. Springfield House: large enclosed terraced garden with wide variety of shrubs and trees mingling with sweeping borders. Woodland area leading to tranquil wildlife pond.

43 **LOWER FARM HOUSE**

Cliffords Mesne, Newent GL18 1JT. Gareth & Sarah Williams. *2m S of Newent. From Newent, follow signs to Cliffords Mesne and Birds of Prey Centre (1½ m). Approx ½ m beyond Centre, turn L at Xrds (before church).* Home-made teas. **Adm £3.50, chd free.** Wed 21, Mon 26 May (2-6).

2-acre garden, incl woodland, stream and large natural lily pond with rockery and bog garden. Herbaceous borders, pergola walk, terrace with ornamental fishpond, kitchen and herb garden; many interesting and unusual trees and shrubs incl collections of magnolia and cornus. Recently featured in ITV's Love Your Garden. Some gravel paths.

44 ◆ **LYDNEY PARK SPRING GARDEN**

Lydney GL15 6BU. The Viscount Bledisloe, 01594 842844/842922, www.lydneyparkestate.co.uk. *½ m SW of Lydney. On A48 Gloucester to Chepstow rd between Lydney & Aylburton. Drive is directly off A48.* Light refreshments. **Adm £4, chd £0.50.** For NGS: Wed 14 May (10-5). **For other opening times and information, please phone or see garden website.**

Spring garden in 8-acre woodland valley with lakes, profusion of rhododendrons, azaleas and other flowering shrubs. Formal garden; magnolias and daffodils (April). Picnics in deer park which has fine trees. Important Roman Temple site and museum.

45 ◆ MATARA GARDENS OF WELLBEING
Kingscote, Tetbury GL8 8YA. Herons Mead Ltd, 01453 861050, www.mataragardens.com. *5½ m NW of Tetbury. The Matara Centre is located approximately 20 minutes from either J18 of M4 (12m) or J13 of M5 (8.5m).* Home-made teas. **Adm £5, chd £3. For NGS: Sun 15 June (1-5). For other opening times and information, please phone or see garden website.**
Trees of life - enjoy the tranquil beauty of Matara's Gardens of Wellbeing and its dedication to the symbolic, spiritual and cultural role of trees. What makes us special are our Chinese Scholar Garden, Japanese Tea Garden, Shinto Woodland, a Celtic wishing tree, labyrinth, healing spiral, Field of Dreams and ornamental herb and flower gardens. Woodland Walk, Chinese Cloistered Courtyard, ponds. Featured in The Cotswolds' Finest Gardens. Limited wheelchair access. Some steps around house area. Some grass paths.

46 MEADOW COTTAGE
59 Coalway Road, Coalway, nr Coleford GL16 7HL. Mrs Pamela Buckland, 01594 833444. *1m SE of Coleford. From Coleford take Lydney & Chepstow Rd at T-lights in town. Turn L after police stn, signed Coalway & Parkend. Garden on L ½ m up hill opp layby.* **Adm £3, chd free. Tue 22 Apr (11-4); Sun 25 May (2-6); Tues 24 June; 29 July; 26 Aug (11-4). Visitors also welcome by appt 17 April - 30 Sept max 25.**
⅓ -acre cottage garden with modern elements. Interest from early spring to autumn. Gravelled entry, borders with shrubs, large-leaf plants, pots and unusual recycled items. A corner area with Japanese influences leading to colourful perennial-filled borders and interlinking garden rooms. Small pond with waterfall. Vegetable garden in raised beds. Bamboos and grasses. Containers in abundance.

47 THE MEETING HOUSE
New Road, Flaxley, Newnham GL14 1JS. Chris & Sally Parsons, 01452 760733. *Off A48, close to Westbury-on-Severn. S from Westbury-on-Severn, turn R signed Flaxley. Take 2nd L. Parking for coaches 500yds away (drop off at garden).* **Adm £5, chd free. Visitors welcome by appt Apr to Sept please leave clear message on answering machine.**
Cottage with 2 acres developed by owners over last 19yrs. Hedges, lawns, herbaceous borders, organic fruit trees, soft fruit and vegetables, greenhouse, orchard with wild flowers, reed bed sewage system and summerhouse. Also open, are the surrounding 17 acres of wild flower meadows, old and new orchards and ponds, managed for conservation. Featured on BBC Radio Gloucestershire.

48 9 MEREVALE ROAD
Gloucester GL2 0QX. P & J Wilcox. *Off Gloucester Ring Rd (A38) 2m E of City Centre. From Gloucester, follow Ring Rd to Cheltenham Rd r'about. Go straight ahead, take 1st L (Kenilworth Ave). At small Xrds continue into Merevale Rd.* **Adm £3, chd free. Sun 25 May (2-6).**
Medium sized suburban garden including small front garden with gravel area and borders. Collection of acers, patio area with ornamental pots, clematis arch leading to lawn and well stocked herbaceous borders, partially replanted recently (many hardy geraniums and heucheras). New rose arch and small soft fruit area. Wildlife pond within gravel area planted with grasses. Display stand for the Friends of Barnwood Arboretum in support of a local nature reserve and park. Featured in Amateur Gardening and Gloucester Citizen newspaper and on BBC Radio Gloucestershire. Visited by Heart of England in Bloom committee as part of Gloucester in Bloom's gold award. Small step to negotiate and gravel areas.

49 ◆ MILL DENE GARDEN
School Lane, Blockley, Moreton-in-Marsh GL56 9HU. Mr & Mrs B S Dare 01386 700457 www.milldenegarden.co.uk. *3m NW of Moreton-in-Marsh. From A44 follow brown signs from Bourton-on-the-Hill to Blockley. Approx 1¼m down hill turn L behind village gates. Limited parking. Coaches by appt.* Tea. **Adm £5.50, chd £3. For NGS: Sun 18 May (2-5). For other opening times and information, please phone or see garden website.**
50 shades of green (!) at least are in this 2½ acre garden hidden in the Cotswolds. Its centrepiece is a water mill dating from C10 (probably), with its mill-pond and stream. The owners have had fun creating a varied garden, from informal woodland full of bulbs, to rose walk, cricket lawn, then herb garden looking out over the hills with church as backdrop. Garden trail for children. Featured on Love your Garden and in Gardening Which?, Gardens of the Cotswolds and Dream Gardens of England. Half of garden wheelchair accessible. Please ring for reserved parking/ramps. Garden in a valley but sides have slope or step alternatives.

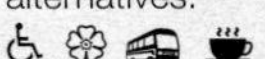

Designed for atmosphere and all year interest . . .

50 ◆ MISARDEN PARK
Miserden, Stroud GL6 7JA. Major M T N H Wills, 01285 821303, www.misardenpark.co.uk. *6m NW of Cirencester. Follow signs off A417 or B4070 from Stroud.* Home-made teas. **Adm £5, chd free. For NGS: Sun 20 Apr, Sun 22 June (2-6). For other opening times and information, please phone or see garden website.**
This lovely, unspoilt garden, positioned high on the Wolds and commanding spectacular views across Misarden deer park to extensive woodland beyond, was created in C17 and still retains a wonderful sense of timeless peace and tranquillity. Much of the original garden is found within ancient Cotswold stone walls. Limited access for wheelchairs.

51 MOOR WOOD
Woodmancote GL7 7EB. Mr & Mrs Henry Robinson, 01285 831692, susie@moorwoodhouse.co.uk. *3½ m NW of Cirencester. Turn L off A435 to Cheltenham at North Cerney, signed Woodmancote 1¼ m; entrance in village on L beside lodge with white gates.* Home-made teas. **Adm £4, chd free.** Sun 29 June (2-6). **Visitors also welcome by appt.**
2 acres of shrub, orchard and wild flower gardens in beautiful isolated valley setting. Holder of the National Collection of rambler roses.
NCH

GROUP OPENING

52 OAKRIDGE LYNCH OPEN GARDENS
Oakridge Lynch, Stroud GL6 7NS. *2m S of Bisley, off Bisley to Eastcombe rd. From Bisley, turn L on leaving village. From Stroud, A419, turn L to Chalford Hill, follow signs to Bisley. Turn R before entering Bisley.* Home-made teas at Edgehill. **Combined adm £4, chd free.** Sun 15 June (2-6).

HILLSIDE COTTAGE
Mrs Elizabeth White

HOPE COTTAGE
Peter & Gillian Wimperis

OLD COTTAGE
Richard & Judy Mackie

OLD POST OFFICE COTTAGE
Eileen Herbert

SWEETBRIAR COTTAGE
David & Caroline Cook

Beautiful hillside village of pretty cottages and stunning views. Selection of small to medium sized lovely gardens packed with interesting plants: herbaceous borders, roses, herbs, climbers, vines, fruit and vegetables, chickens. Featured in Amateur Gardening. Limited wheelchair access at most gardens.

53 THE OLD CHEQUER
Draycott, Moreton in Marsh GL56 9LB. Mr & Mrs H Linley, 01386 700647, g.f.linley1@btinternet.com. *3m NW of Moreton-in-Marsh. Just off Moreton-in-Marsh to Evesham Rd A44.* Home-made teas. **Adm £3, chd free.** Sun 13 Apr (1.30-5). **Also open with Blockley Gardens on 27 April and 8 June. Visitors also welcome by appt Apr to July for groups of 10+.**
A cottage garden, created by owner, set in 2 acres of old orchard with original ridge and furrow. Emphasis on spring planting but still maintaining yr-round interest. Kitchen garden/soft fruit, herbaceous, shrubs, Croquet lawn, unusual plants, alpines and dry gravel borders.

54 THE OLD RECTORY, AVENING
60 High Street, Avening GL8 8NF. Mrs Anthea Beszant, anthea@avening.eclipse.co.uk. *3m W of Tetbury. 2m N of Nailsworth. On B4014 in High St close to Avening Church. Opp Woodstock Lane, on corner of Rectory Lane.* Home-made teas at Avening Social Club, Woodstock Lane. **Adm £4, chd free.** Sun 15 June (2-6). **Also open 18 Star Lane, combined entry £6.**
3-acre garden around C17 Cotswold Rectory (not open). Walks through mature woodland. Paddock with stream and Japanese Bridge. Italianate terrace, steep steps and banks. Supported in places by ancient megaliths transported here in the 1800s. Shady planting, rose and mixed borders, wild garden, sculptures by Darren Yeadon. Limited wheelchair access, gravel paths, steep slopes & steps.

55 THE OLD RECTORY, DUNTISBOURNE ROUS
Cirencester GL7 7AP. Charles & Mary Keen, mary@keengardener.com. *4m NW of Cirencester. From Daglingworth take rd to Duntisbournes. Or from A417 from Gloucester take Duntisbourne Leer turning, follow signs for Daglingworth.* Light refreshments DIY teas are free in schoolroom. **Adm £5, chd free.** Mon 17 Feb, Mon 14 Apr, Mon 15 Sept (12-5.30). **Visitors also welcome by appt Feb to Sept groups of 10 or more and short talk from Mary Keen, adm £10.**
Garden in an exceptional setting made by designer and writer Mary Keen. Subject of many articles and Telegraph column. Designed for atmosphere and all yr interest, but collections of galanthus, hellebores, auriculas and half hardies - especially dahlias - are all features in their season. Plants for sale very occasionally.

OVERBURY COURT
See Worcestershire

56 ◆ PAINSWICK ROCOCO GARDEN
Painswick GL6 6TH. Painswick Rococo Garden Trust, 01452 813204, www.rococogarden.org.uk. *½ m N of Painswick. ½ m outside village on B4073, follow brown tourism signs.* **For opening times and information, please phone or see garden website.**
Unique C18 garden from the brief Rococo period, combining contemporary buildings, vistas, ponds, kitchen garden and winding woodland walks. Anniversary maze, plant nursery. Snowdrop display late winter.

Sandywell. Barn House

© Mandy Bradshaw

57 NEW PASTURE FARM
Upper Oddington, Moreton-In-Marsh GL56 0XG. Mr & Mrs John LLoyd. *Mid-way between Upper and Lower Oddington. Oddington lies about 3m from Stow-on-the-Wold just off A436.* Home-made teas. **Adm £4, chd free. Sun 25, Mon 26 May, Sun 13 July (11-5).**
Medium-sized informal country garden that has evolved over 30yrs by the current owners. It has all-yr interest with mixed borders, topiary, hedging both formal and informal and a wealth of garden trees. In rural setting with very large spring fed pond inhabited by a collection of ducks. Public footpath across 2 small fields arrives at C11 church, St. Nicolas, with doom paintings, set in ancient woodlands. Truly worth a visit. See Simon Jenkins' Book of Churches.

Very large spring-fed pond inhabited by a collection of ducks . . .

58 PAULMEAD
Bisley GL6 7AG. Judy & Philip Howard. *5m E of Stroud. S edge of Bisley at head of Toadsmoor Valley on top of Cotswolds. Signed from Bisley village. Disabled visitors can be dropped off at garden.* **Adm £6, chd free. Sun 22 June (2-6). Combined with Wells Cottage.**
Approx 1-acre landscaped garden constructed in stages over last 25yrs. Terraced in 3 main levels: natural stream garden; formal herbaceous and shrub borders; yew and beech hedges; formal vegetable garden; lawns; summerhouse with exterior wooden decking by pond and thatched roof over well head. Unusual tree house.

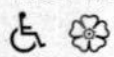

59 PEAR TREE COTTAGE
58 Malleson Road, Gotherington GL52 9EX. Mr & Mrs E Manders-Trett, 01242 674592, edandmary@talktalk.net. *4m N of Cheltenham. From A435, travelling N, turn R into Gotherington 1m after end of Bishop's Cleeve bypass at garage. Garden on L approx 100yds past Shutter Inn.* Light refreshments. **Adm £4, chd free. Visitors welcome by appt Feb to June max 30.**
Mainly informal country garden of approx ½ acre with pond and gravel garden, grasses and herbaceous borders, trees and shrubs surrounding lawns. Wild garden and orchard lead to greenhouses, herb and vegetable gardens. Spring bulbs, early summer perennials and shrubs particularly colourful.

GROUP OPENING

60 QUENINGTON GARDENS
nr Fairford GL7 5BW. *8m NE of Cirencester. Gardens well signed once in village.* Home-made teas at The Old Rectory. **Combined adm £5, chd free. Sun 22 June (2-5.30).**

BANK VIEW
Victoria Rd. Mrs J A Moulden

THE OLD POST HOUSE
Mrs D Blackwood

THE OLD RECTORY, QUENINGTON
Mr & Mrs David Abel Smith www.freshair2013.com

POOL HAY
Mrs E A Morris

YEW TREE COTTAGES
Mr J Lindon

A rarely visited Coln Valley village delighting its infrequent visitors with C12 Norman church and C17 stone cottages (not open). An opportunity to discover the horticultural treasures behind those Cotswold stone walls and visit 5 very different but charming gardens incorporating everything from the exotic and the organic to the simple cottage garden; a range of vistas from riverside to seclusion.

61 RAMBLERS
Lower Common, Aylburton, nr Lydney GL15 6DS. Jane & Leslie Hale. *1½ m W of Lydney. Off A48 Gloucester to Chepstow Rd. From Lydney through Aylburton, out of de-limit turn R signed Aylburton Common, ¾ m along lane.* Home-made teas. **Adm £3.50, chd free. Sun 4 May, Sun 8 June (2-6).**
Peaceful medium-sized country garden with informal cottage planting, herbaceous borders and small pond looking through hedge windows onto wild flower meadow. Front woodland garden with shade-loving plants and topiary. Large productive vegetable garden. Apple orchard. Runner up in the English Garden Magazine's competition 'Gardeners Garden for 2013'.

RIVER BARN
See Wiltshire

62 ROCKCLIFFE HOUSE
Upper Slaughter, Cheltenham GL54 2JW. Mr & Mrs Simon Keswick. *2m SW of Stow-on-the-Wold. 1½ m from Lower Swell on B4068 towards Cheltenham. Leave Stow on the Wold on B4068 through Lower Swell. Continue on B4068 for 1½ m. Rockcliffe is well signposted on L.* Home-made teas. **Adm £5, chd free (share to Kates Home Nursing). Wed 11, Wed 25 June (11-6). Also open Eyford House 25 June.**
Large traditional English garden of 8 acres incl pink garden, white and blue garden, herbaceous border, rose terrace, large walled kitchen garden and orchard. Greenhouses and pathway of topiary birds leading up through orchard to stone dovecot. Dramatic pond surrounded by 6 large Cornus contraversa variegata. Featured in several magazines. 2 wide stone steps through gate, otherwise good wheelchair access.

63 ◆ RODMARTON MANOR
Cirencester GL7 6PF. Mr Simon Biddulph, 01285 841442, www.rodmarton-manor.co.uk. *5m NE of Tetbury. Off A433. Between Cirencester & Tetbury.* Home-made teas. **Adm £5, chd £1. For NGS: Sun 18 May (2-5). For other opening times and information, please phone or see garden website.**
The 8-acre garden of this fine Arts and Crafts house (not open on NGS day) is a series of outdoor rooms each with its own distinctive character. Leisure garden, winter garden, troughery, topiary, hedges, lawns, rockery, containers, wild garden, kitchen garden, magnificent herbaceous borders. Snowdrop collection. Wheelchair access to most of garden.

64 ROOKWOODS

Waterlane, nr Bisley GL6 7PN. Mr & Mrs Des Althorp. *5m E of Stroud. Between Sapperton & Bisley. Turn down no through rd in Waterlane then follow signs.* Home-made teas. **Adm £4, chd free. Sat 28 June (2-6).**
Stunning 3-acre garden set in private secluded valley. Over 100 varieties of old-fashioned and modern climbing and shrub roses laid out by Rosemary Verey. Beautiful herbaceous borders surround traditional Cotswold farmhouse (not open), smothered in a variety of climbers. Stream-fed lake with pleasant walks and outstanding views. Limited wheelchair access.

65 ROSE COTTAGE

Kempley, Nr Dymock GL18 2BN. Naomi Cryer. *3m from Newent towards Dymock. From Newent on B4221 take turning just after PH, on R from Gloucester direction, signed Kempley. Follow rd for approx 3m.* Home-made teas. **Adm £3.50, chd free. Sat 14, Sun 15 June (11-5).**
Open for only the second time. About 1 acre of flat garden, put mostly to herbaceous borders. Hot bed and long border leading to borrowed view, small parterre in the orchard area, grass bed and pond. Small wild flower pasture which is at its best in June. Rose garden, iris bed, vegetable plot, nursery bed and cutting garden. Home made cakes and plants for sale. Featured in the Citizen & Echo Weekend Magazine. Although quite flat, access is mostly across lawn and grass which may make wheelchair use difficult.

66 SANDYWELL. BARN HOUSE

Sandywell Park, Whittington, Cheltenham GL54 4HF. Shirley & Gordon Sills, 01242 820606, shirleysills@btinternet.com. *4m E of Cheltenham on A40. 1m from Andoversford, 300 yds from turning to Whittington village on opp side of rd.* Home-made teas. **Adm £4.50, chd £2. Sun 25, Mon 26 May; Mon 9 June; Sun 20 July (11-5). Groups of 10+ welcome by appt from 26 May to 22 July.**
2½ -acre plantaholic's garden inside weathered walls of former Victorian kitchen garden. Designed, created and maintained by the owners as a series of exhuberantly planted enclosures both formal and informal, sometimes quirky. Herbaceous, climbers, roses, shrubs, trees, lawns, hedges, structures, vistas, water features, spring-fed stream and small pond.

67 NEW SCATTERFORD

Newland, Coleford GL16 8NG. Sean Swallow, 07765 395379, callingcard@seanswallow.com, www.seanswallow.com. *1m S of Newland and just N of Clearwell, opp junction to Coleford. From Monmouth take A466/Redbrook Rd to Redbrook. From Chepstow take B4228 turn off to Clearwell. From Coleford take Newland Street.* Home-made teas. **Adm £5, chd free. Sun 10 Aug (2-7). Groups of 10+ also welcome by appt Aug to Oct.**
2-acre garden set in rolling hills between Wye valley and Forest of Dean. A contemporary take on a country garden: formal pond, walled garden, sculpted terraces, courtyards, haha and natural pond. Home of designer Sean Swallow, the garden steps aside for the beautiful house and setting. Tranquil atmosphere and softly layered planting are best enjoyed towards sunset. Wheelchair access is possible to part of the garden.

A romantic plant lover's paradise grown over time on a limited budget . . .

68 SCHOFIELDS

30 Ford House Road, Newent GL18 1LQ. John & Linda Schofield, 01531 820370, linda@hazelschofield.co.uk. *1½ m NE of Newent off Tewkesbury Rd. At Newent take B4215 N. Pass Fire Station and turn R into Tewkesbury Rd. After approx 1m turn L into Ford House Rd (signed) and L again onto private rd.* Home-made teas. **Adm £3.75. Groups of 10+ welcome by appt Apr to Sept.**
Tranquil 5 acres developed from 1970s providing 2½ -acre spring woodland garden, plantsman's ¾ acres with mature trees, shrub, bulb, herbaceous and hot borders, autumn colour, berries, lily ponds. 1000sq m glasshouse garden of palms, tender and fruiting trees, shrubs, bulbs, climbers and succulents. Seating throughout. Regret garden unsuitable for children. Gravel paths, moderate slopes in woodland.

69 ◆ SEZINCOTE

nr Moreton-in-Marsh GL56 9AW. Mr & Mrs D Peake, 01386 700444, www.sezincote.co.uk. *3m SW of Moreton-in-Marsh. From Moreton-in-Marsh turn W along A44 towards Evesham; after 1½ m (just before Bourton-on-the-Hill) take turn L, by stone lodge with white gate.* Home-made teas. **Adm £5, chd £2. For NGS: Sun 29 June (2-5.30). For other opening times and information, please phone or see garden website.**
Exotic oriental water garden by Repton and Daniell with lake, pools and meandering stream, banked with massed perennials. Large semi-circular orangery, formal Indian garden, fountain, temple and unusual trees of vast size in lawn and wooded park setting. House in Indian manner designed by Samuel Pepys Cockerell. Garden on slope with gravel paths, so not all areas wheelchair accessible.

70 NEW SLAD VALLEY HOUSE

203 Slad Road, Stroud GL5 1RJ. Mr & Mrs Michael Grey. *Situated in Slad Valley 1m W of Stroud on rd to Slad. On to B4070 through Slad along valley towards Stroud. Situated on R through gates beside the Lodge or follow B4070 on Slad Rd leaving Stroud. No Parking on site but parking available on access rd.* Home-made teas. **Adm £3.50, chd free. Sat 14 June (12-4).**
Informal steep garden and woodland areas of approx 1 acre around C18 Manor house (not open). Garden restoration work in progress in all areas. Numerous trees (incl 2 magnificent magnolia trees), shrubs, flowers and borders. N.B. lots of steps and uneven paths, no handrails. The garden is a chosen site for local art exhibitions. Unsuitable for wheelchairs.

71 ◆ SNOWSHILL MANOR & GARDEN

Snowshill, nr Broadway WR12 7JU. National Trust, 01386 842810, www.nationaltrust.org.uk. *2½ m SW of Broadway. Off A44 bypass into Broadway village.* Light refreshments. **Adm £5.80, chd £3. For NGS: Fri 27 June (11-5). For other opening times and information, please phone or see garden website.**

Delightful hillside garden surrounding beautiful Cotswold manor, designed in Arts & Crafts style. Garden consists of a series of contrasting outdoor rooms. Simple, colourful plantings tumble and scramble down the terraces and around byres and ponds. Enjoy produce from the kitchen garden in the restaurant. Garden produce and plants for sale (when available). Garden is terraced with many steps.

72 SOUTH LODGE

Church Road, Clearwell, Coleford GL16 8LG. Andrew & Jane MacBean, 01594 837769, southlodgegarden@btinternet.com, www.southlodgegarden.co.uk. *2m S of Coleford. Off B4228. Follow signs to Clearwell. Garden on L of castle driveway. Please park on rd in front of church or in village.* Home-made teas. **Adm £3, chd free. Sun 6 Apr; Sat 3, Sat 17 May; Sun 22 June (1-5). Groups of 15+ also welcome by appt Apr to June.**

Peaceful country garden in 2 acres with stunning views of surrounding countryside. High walls provide a backdrop for rambling roses, clematis, and honeysuckles. An organic garden with a large variety of perennials, annuals, grasses, shrubs and specimen trees with yr-round colour. Vegetable garden, wildlife and formal ponds. Rustic pergola planted with English climbing roses and willow arbour amongst wildflowers. Gravel paths and steep slopes.

73 STANTON VILLAGE GARDENS

Stanton, nr Broadway WR12 7NE. *3m SW of Broadway. Off B4632, between Broadway (3m) & Winchcombe (6m).* Home-made teas In Burland Hall in centre of village. **Adm £6, chd free (share to local charities). Sun 15 June (2-6).**

Extensive group of over 20 gardens set in this picturesque C17 Cotswold village. Many houses border the street with gardens stretching out behind, hidden from general view. Gardens range from large houses with colourful herbaceous borders, established trees, shrubs and formal vegetable gardens, to tiny cottage gardens packed with interest. Popular plant stall and legendary homemade teas. Featured in Cotswold Life Magazine & Sunday Times. Regret not all gardens suitable for wheelchair users.

74 ◆ STANWAY FOUNTAIN & WATER GARDEN

nr Winchcombe GL54 5PQ. The Earl of Wemyss & March, 01386 584528, www.stanwayfountain.co.uk. *9m NE of Cheltenham. 1m E of B4632 Cheltenham to Broadway rd or B4077 Toddington to Stow-on-the-Wold rd.* Home-made teas. **Adm £4, chd £1.50. For NGS: Sun 11 May, Sun 14 Sept (2-5). For other opening times and information, please phone or see garden website.**

20 acres of planted landscape in early C18 formal setting. The restored canal, upper pond and 165ft high fountain have re-created one of the most interesting Baroque water gardens in Britain. Striking C16 manor with gatehouse, tithe barn and church. Britain's highest fountain at 300ft, the world's highest gravity fountain which runs at 2.45 & 4.00pm for 30 mins each time.

75 NEW 18 STAR LANE

Avening, Tetbury GL8 8NT. Anita Collins, 07769 974849, caravancollins@aol.com. *3m NW of Tetbury off B4014. SE on B4014 from Nailsworth 3m. NW on B4014 from Tetbury 3m. A419 from Cirencester 6.5m. 1st exit at r'about. L at Ragged Cot, L at junction.* Home-made teas at Avening Social Club. **Adm £4, chd free. Sun 15 June (2-6). Also open The Old Rectory, Avening, combined entry £6. Visitors also welcome by appt June to July Mondays only.**

Hillside garden overflowing with cottage garden plants in calming pastel colours. Steps lead up the garden from a cosy seating area and winding paths and borders draw visitors to different areas of the garden including a rose circle, pond, hotbed and wooded area with lovely views across the valley. A romantic plant lover's paradise grown over time on a limited budget.

A contemporary take on a country garden . . .

76 STOWELL PARK

Yanworth, Northleach, Cheltenham GL54 3LE. The Lord & Lady Vestey, www.stowellpark.co.uk. *8m NE of Cirencester. Off Fosseway A429 2m SW of Northleach.* Home-made teas. **Adm £6, chd free. Sun 18 May, Sun 22 June (2-5).**

Magnificent lawned terraces with stunning views over Coln Valley. Fine collection of old-fashioned roses and herbaceous plants, with pleached lime approach to C14 house (not open). Two large walled gardens containing vegetables, fruit, cut flowers and range of greenhouses. Long rose pergola and wide, plant-filled borders divided into colour sections. New water features and hazel arch at the bottom of the garden. Open continuously for 50 years. Plant Sale 18 May only.

77 NEW THREE SALMONS HOUSE

Beachley Road, Beachley, Chepstow NP16 7HG. Mr Christopher & Deirdre Wilson. *2m E of Chepstow. Off A48 signed Sedbury/Beachley, through Sedbury following signs for Beachley Barracks. Reach 30mph limit, garden located 150m on L next to layby.* Home-made teas. **Adm £3, chd £1. Sun 8 June (2-5).**

Interesting garden entirely built, planned and planted by current owners behind former C19 inn. Colourful well-stocked herbaceous borders filled with wide range of plants and curiosities with an Italianate feel. Different areas incl pond, rill garden, rose bed, shady gravel garden, Italian fountain, small sunken garden, Italianate Caseta and iron Gazebo. Short paved ramp in garden and one step otherwise flat.

78 TRENCH HILL
Sheepscombe GL6 6TZ. Celia & Dave Hargrave, 01452 814306, celia.hargrave@btconnect.com. *1½ m E of Painswick. From Cheltenham A46 take 1st turn signed Sheepscombe and follow lane towards Sheepscombe for about 1¼ m. Garden on L opp lane.* Home-made teas. **Adm £3, chd free. Suns 16, 23 Feb (11-5); Sun 20, Mon 21 Apr (11-6); Weds 4, 11, 18, 25 June (2-6); Suns 20 July; 24 Aug; 14 Sept (11-6); Suns 15, 22 Feb 2015 (11-5). Visitors also welcome by appt Feb to Sept not suitable for large coaches max 42 seater.**
Approx 3 acres set in small woodland with panoramic views. Variety of herbaceous and mixed borders, rose garden, extensive vegetable plots, wild flower areas, plantings of spring bulbs with thousands of snowdrops and hellebores, woodland walk, 2 small ponds, waterfall and larger conservation pond. Many interesting wooden sculptures within the garden. Run on organic principles. Mostly wheelchair access but some steps and slopes.

79 UPTON WOLD
Moreton-in-Marsh GL56 9TR. Mr & Mrs I R S Bond, www.uptonwoldgarden.co.uk. *4½ m W of Moreton-in-Marsh. On A44 1m past A424 junction at Troopers Lodge Garage, on R. Look out for marker posts.* Home-made teas. **Adm £10, chd free. Sun 20 Apr (11-5).**
Ever-developing and changing garden, architecturally and imaginatively laid out around C17 house (not open) with commanding views. Yew hedges; herbaceous walk; some unusual plants and trees; vegetables; pond and woodland gardens. National Collections of Juglans and Pterocarya. 2 Star award from GGG.

NCH

80 WELLS COTTAGE
Wells Road, Bisley GL6 7AG. Mr & Mrs Michael Flint, 01452 770289, flint_bisley@talktalk.net. *5m E of Stroud. Garden & car park well signed in Bisley village. Garden lies on S edge of village at head of Toadsmoor Valley, N of A419.* **Adm £6, chd free. Sun 22 June (2-6). Combined with Paulmead. Visitors also welcome by appt June/July.**
Just under an acre. Terraced on several levels with beautiful views over valley. Much informal planting of trees and shrubs to give colour and texture. Lawns and herbaceous borders. Collection of grasses. Formal pond area. Rambling roses on rope pergola. Vegetable garden with raised beds. No access to upper terraces for wheelchair users.

81 ◆ WESTBURY COURT GARDEN
Westbury-on-Severn GL14 1PD. National Trust, 01452 760461, www.nationaltrust.org.uk. *11m SW of Gloucester. on A48.* **Adm £5, chd £2.50. For NGS: Sun 14 Sept (10-5.30). For other opening times and information, please phone or see garden website.**
The finest example of a Dutch water garden in the country. Wheelchair access to most of garden.

82 ◆ WESTONBIRT SCHOOL GARDENS
Tetbury GL8 8QG. Holfords of Westonbirt Trust, 01666 880333, www.holfordtrust.com. *3m SW of Tetbury. Opp Westonbirt Arboretum, on A433. Enter via Holford wrought iron gates to Westonbirt House.* Light refreshments Camellia House in Italianate walled gardens. **Adm £5, chd free. For NGS: Sun 20 July (11-5). For other opening times and information, please phone or see garden website.**
22 acres. Former private garden of Robert Holford, founder of Westonbirt Arboretum. Formal Victorian gardens incl walled Italian garden now restored with early herbaceous borders and exotic border. Rustic walks, lake, statuary and grotto. Rare, exotic trees and shrubs. Beautiful views of Westonbirt House, open with guided tours to see fascinating Victorian interior on designated days of the year. Tea, coffee and refreshments available in the restored Camellia House of the walled Italianate gardens.

WHATLEY MANOR
See Wiltshire

WHITCOMBE HOUSE
See Worcestershire

83 WOODLANDS FARM
Rushley Lane, Winchcombe GL54 5JE. Mrs Morag Dobbin. *On outskirts of Winchcombe, 5mins walk from town centre. Rushley Lane comes off B4632 through Winchcombe, at Footbridge. Proceed up Rushley Lane for 50 yd, gate is behind the Stancombe Lane sign.* **Adm £4, chd free. Fri 13, Sat 14 June (10-4).**
Set against the backdrop of the beautiful Cotswold Hills, this garden has many different areas of interest. Formal double borders frame an ornamental pond. A long hornbeam hedge divides the garden, and encloses an impressive stone monolith. The planting schemes are varied and colourful throughout, with many interesting and unusual plants. Assistance needed with one steepish slope to access the garden.

84 WORTLEY FARM HOUSE
Wortley, Wotton-Under-Edge GL12 7QP. Sean and Annabel Mills. *1m out of Wotton Under Edge, 15 mins from M5 J14 and from M4 J18. From A46: Take left turn to Hawkesbury Upton, continue through Hillesley & Alderley towards Wotton into Wortley. From Wotton head to Wortley & Alderley.* Home-made teas. **Adm £3.50, chd free. Sat 7 June (2-6); Sun 8 June (12-6).**
1½ acres on different levels with wild area, pond, herbaceous borders, textural planting, vegetable garden and disabled garden. Sean is a garden designer. Plant sales. There will be help for wheel chair users on gravel drive. Thereafter the entire garden is accessible via ramps.

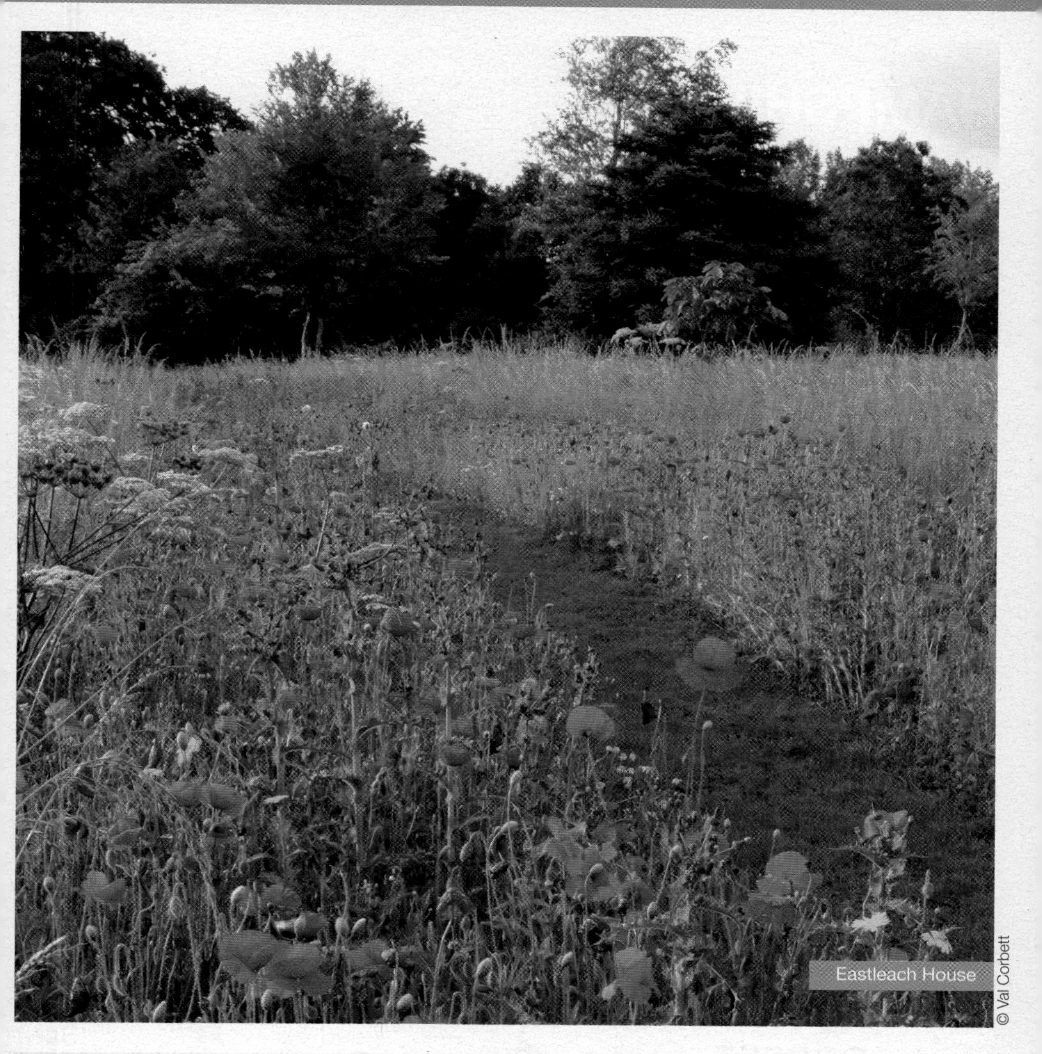

Eastleach House

© Val Corbett

Gloucestershire County Volunteers

County Organiser

Norman Jeffery, 28 Shrivenham Road, Highworth, Swindon SN6 7BZ, 01793 762805, normjeffery28@btinternet.com

County Treasurer

Graham Baber, 11 Corinium Gate, Cirencester GL7 2PX, 01285 650961, grayanjen@onetel.com

Booklet Coordinator

Nick Kane, Church Farm, Goosey, Faringdon SN7 8PA, nick@kanes.org, 07768 478668.

Assistant County Organisers

Sue Hunt, 5 Oatground, Synwell, Wotton-under-Edge GL12 7HX, 01453 521263, suehunt2@btinternet.com

Trish Jeffery, 28 Shrivenham Road, Highworth, Swindon SN6 7BZ, 01793 762805, trishjeffery@btinternet.com

Valerie Kent, 9 Acer Close, Bradwell Grove, Nr Burford, Oxon OX18 4XE, 01993 823294

Shirley & Gordon Sills, Barn House, Sandywell Park, Whittington, Cheltenham GL54 4HF, 01242 820606, shirleysills@btinternet.com

Pat Willey, Edgehill, The Broadway, Oakridge Lynch, Stroud GL6 7NY, 01285 762946, patwilley1@gmail.com

Gareth & Sarah Williams, Lower Farm House, Cliffords Mesne, Newent GL18 1JT, 01531 821654, dgwilliams84@hotmail.com

HAMPSHIRE

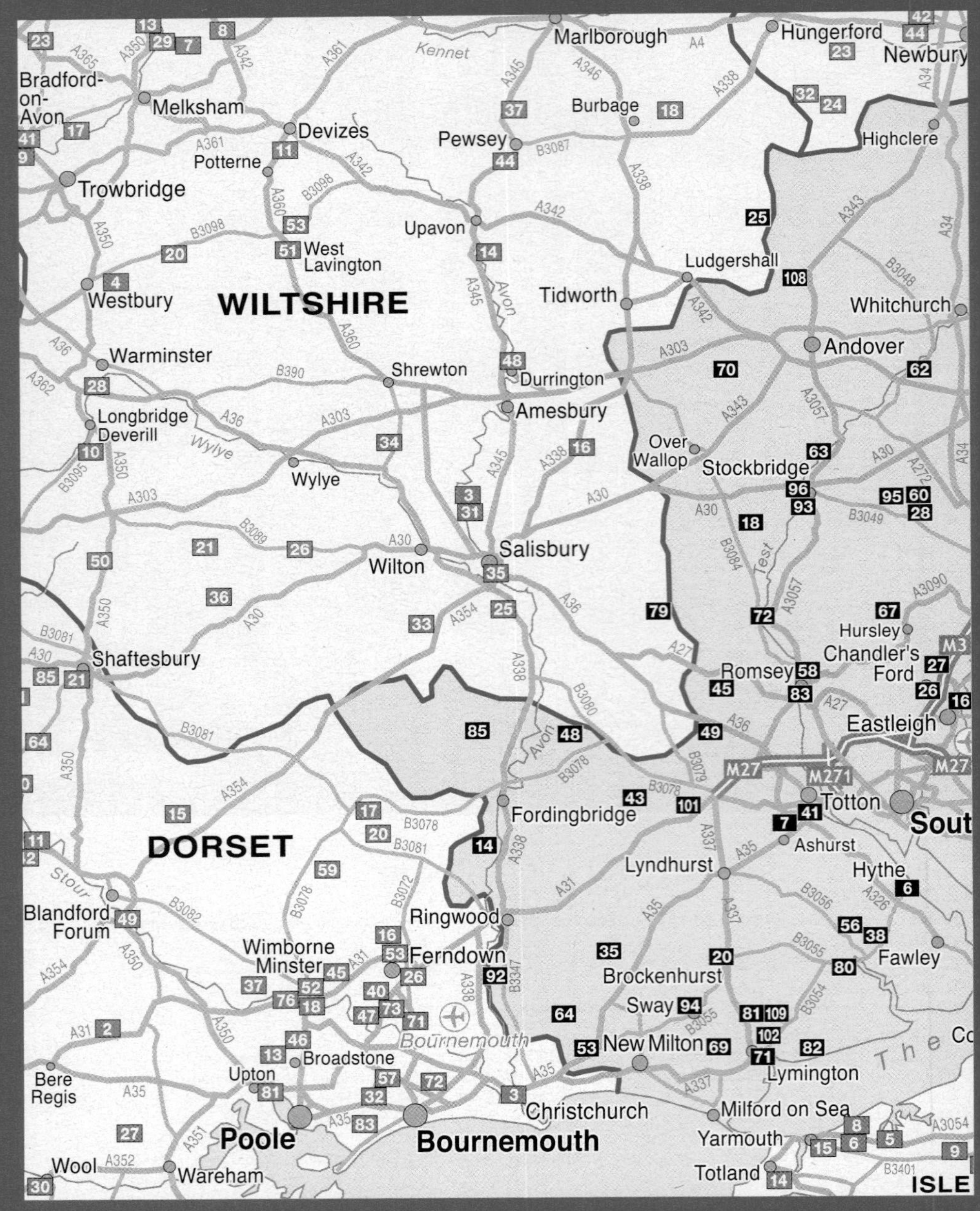

WILTSHIRE
DORSET
Marlborough
Hungerford
Newbury
Bradford-on-Avon
Melksham
Devizes
Pewsey
Burbage
Highclere
Potterne
Trowbridge
Upavon
West Lavington
Ludgershall
Westbury
Tidworth
Whitchurch
Andover
Warminster
Shrewton
Durrington
Amesbury
Longbridge Deverill
Over Wallop
Stockbridge
Wylye
Salisbury
Wilton
Hursley
Chandler's Ford
Shaftesbury
Romsey
Eastleigh
Fordingbridge
Totton
Ashurst
Lyndhurst
Hythe
Blandford Forum
Ringwood
Wimborne Minster
Ferndown
Fawley
Brockenhurst
Sway
New Milton
Bournemouth
Broadstone
Lymington
Upton
Bere Regis
Christchurch
Milford on Sea
Poole
Yarmouth
Wool
Wareham
Totland
ISLE
Kennet
Avon
Wylye
Test
Stour

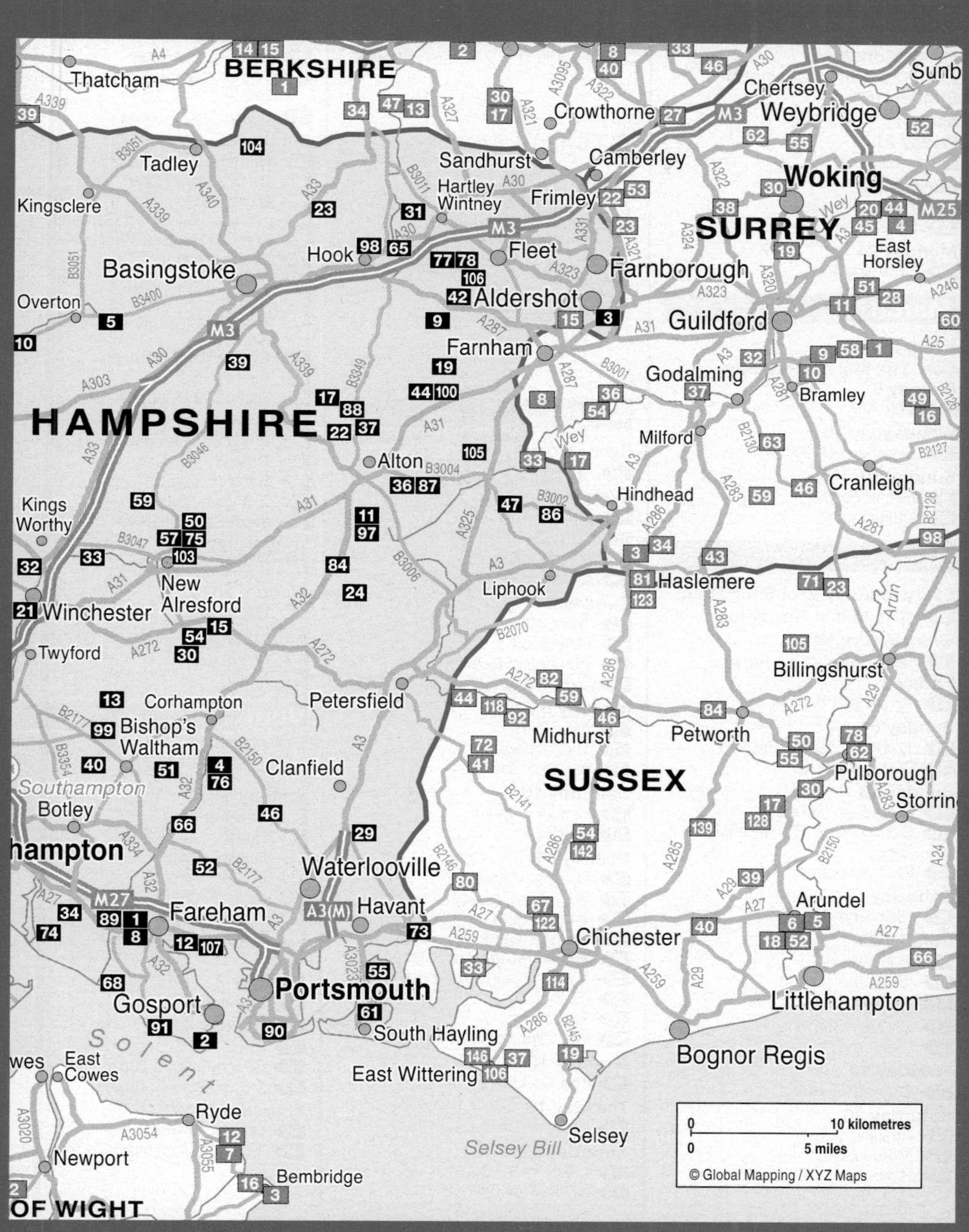
BERKSHIRE
HAMPSHIRE
SURREY
SUSSEX
OF WIGHT
Thatcham
Tadley
Kingsclere
Basingstoke
Overton
Sandhurst
Hartley Wintney
Hook
Fleet
Crowthorne
Camberley
Frimley
Farnborough
Aldershot
Farnham
Chertsey
Weybridge
Woking
East Horsley
Guildford
Godalming
Bramley
Milford
Hindhead
Cranleigh
Alton
Kings Worthy
New Alresford
Winchester
Twyford
Liphook
Haslemere
Billingshurst
Petersfield
Corhampton
Bishop's Waltham
Clanfield
Midhurst
Petworth
Pulborough
Southampton
Botley
Waterlooville
Fareham
Havant
Chichester
Arundel
Portsmouth
Gosport
South Hayling
East Wittering
Littlehampton
Bognor Regis
Selsey
Selsey Bill
Solent
East Cowes
Ryde
Newport
Bembridge
10 kilometres
5 miles
© Global Mapping / XYZ Maps

Opening Dates

All entries subject to change.
For latest information check
www.ngs.org.uk

February

Every Monday
69 **The Mill at Gordleton**

Sunday 16
15 Bramdean House

Friday 21
60 Little Court

Sunday 23
33 The Down House
60 Little Court

Monday 24
60 Little Court

March

Every Monday
69 **The Mill at Gordleton**

Sunday 9
10 Bere Mill

Wednesday 26
9 Beechenwood Farm

Sunday 30
40 Flintstones
60 Little Court

April

Every Monday excl Bank Hols
69 **The Mill at Gordleton**

Every Wednesday
9 **Beechenwood Farm**

Friday 4
21 12 Christchurch Road

Sunday 6
21 12 Christchurch Road
35 Durmast House

Sunday 13
15 Bramdean House
78 Old Thatch & The Millennium Barn
85 St Christopher's

Saturday 19
87 'Selborne'

Sunday 20
82 Pylewell Park
87 'Selborne'

Monday 21
28 Crawley Gardens
87 'Selborne'

Tuesday 22
28 Crawley Gardens

Saturday 26
6 Atheling Villas
71 Moore Blatch
100 Walbury

Sunday 27
6 Atheling Villas
71 Moore Blatch
85 St Christopher's
98 Tylney Hall Hotel
100 Walbury

A plant lovers dream where both colour and scent dictate . . .

May

Every Monday excl Bank Hols
69 **The Mill at Gordleton**

Every Wednesday
9 **Beechenwood Farm**

Saturday 3
61 Littlewood
94 Sway Village Gardens

Sunday 4
26 The Cottage
61 Littlewood
84 Rotherfield Park
94 Sway Village Gardens

Monday 5
5 Ashe Park
26 The Cottage
86 Sandy Slopes

Saturday 10
54 Hinton Ampner
87 'Selborne'

Sunday 11
1 80 Abbey Road
17 Brick Kiln Cottage
26 The Cottage
28 Crawley Gardens
48 NEW Heathermoor House
56 The House in the Wood
87 'Selborne'
96 Terstan
102 Walhampton

Monday 12
26 The Cottage

Tuesday 13
28 Crawley Gardens

Saturday 17
16 6 Breamore Close
74 67 Newtown Road

Sunday 18
16 6 Breamore Close
29 Crookley Pool
48 NEW Heathermoor House
53 Hinton Admiral
74 67 Newtown Road

Saturday 24
2 Alverstoke Crescent Garden
20 21 Chestnut Road
92 The Stable Family Home Trust Garden
94 Sway Village Gardens

Sunday 25
11 Berry Cottage
20 21 Chestnut Road
31 Dipley Mill
70 Monxton & Amport Gardens
77 The Old Rectory, Winchfield
79 Ordnance House
82 Pylewell Park
83 Romsey Gardens
92 The Stable Family Home Trust Garden
94 Sway Village Gardens
103 Weir House
104 West Silchester Hall

Monday 26
70 Monxton & Amport Gardens
83 Romsey Gardens
86 Sandy Slopes
89 2 Shenley Close
104 West Silchester Hall

Tuesday 27
89 2 Shenley Close

Wednesday 28
30 Dean House

Saturday 31
6 Atheling Villas
7 Barhi

June

Every Monday
69 **The Mill at Gordleton**

Sunday 1
6 Atheling Villas
7 Barhi
11 Berry Cottage
40 Flintstones
66 Meon Orchard
88 Shalden Park House
97 NEW The Thatched Cottage

Monday 2
40 Flintstones

Wednesday 4
4 Appletree House
9 Beechenwood Farm
65 1 & 2 Maple Cottage

Thursday 5
29 Crookley Pool
65 1 & 2 Maple Cottage

Festival Weekend

Saturday 7
- 10 Bere Mill
- 44 Froyle Gardens
- 54 Hinton Ampner

Sunday 8
- 10 Bere Mill
- 13 Blackdown House
- 25 Conholt Park
- 31 Dipley Mill
- 44 Froyle Gardens
- 62 Longparish Gardens
- 65 1 & 2 Maple Cottage
- 98 Tylney Hall Hotel

Monday 9
- 62 Longparish Gardens

Tuesday 10
- 40 Flintstones (Evening)

Wednesday 11
- 65 1 & 2 Maple Cottage

Thursday 12
- 28 Crawley Gardens
- 59 Lake House
- 65 1 & 2 Maple Cottage
- 93 Stockbridge Gardens

Saturday 14
- 20 21 Chestnut Road
- 108 NEW Wildhern Gardens

Sunday 15
- 15 Bramdean House
- 20 21 Chestnut Road
- 27 Cranbury Park
- 28 Crawley Gardens
- 59 Lake House
- 63 Longstock Park
- 67 Merdon Manor
- 93 Stockbridge Gardens
- 96 Terstan
- 108 NEW Wildhern Gardens

Wednesday 18
- 4 Appletree House
- 30 Dean House

Saturday 21
- 91 Spindles

Sunday 22
- 11 Berry Cottage
- 22 NEW Clover Farm
- 31 Dipley Mill
- 39 Farleigh House
- 75 Old Alresford House
- 79 Ordnance House
- 97 NEW The Thatched Cottage
- 107 Wicor Primary School Community Garden

Tuesday 24
- 3 23 Anglesey Road

Wednesday 25
- 5 Ashe Park
- 75 Old Alresford House

Friday 27
- 73 23 New Brighton Road

Lower Mill, Longparish Gardens

Saturday 28
- 36 East Worldham Gardens

Sunday 29
- 5 Ashe Park
- 8 19 Barnwood Road
- 24 Colemore House Gardens
- 25 Conholt Park
- 33 The Down House
- 35 Durmast House
- 36 East Worldham Gardens
- 43 Fritham Lodge
- 101 Waldrons

Monday 30
- 24 Colemore House Gardens

July

Every Monday
- 69 **The Mill at Gordleton**

Tuesday 1
- 42 NEW Four Seasons Hotel

Wednesday 2
- 11 Berry Cottage
- 30 Dean House
- 33 The Down House

Thursday 3
- 100 Walbury

Saturday 5
- 23 The Coach House
- 78 Old Thatch & The Millennium Barn (Evening)
- 107 Wicor Primary School Community Garden

Sunday 6
- 14 Braemoor
- 90 Southsea Gardens
- 96 Terstan

Monday 7
- 47 Hanging Hosta Garden

Tuesday 8
- 47 Hanging Hosta Garden

Wednesday 9
- 4 Appletree House
- 47 Hanging Hosta Garden

Thursday 10
- 28 Crawley Gardens
- 47 Hanging Hosta Garden

Friday 11
- 47 Hanging Hosta Garden

Saturday 12
- 54 Hinton Ampner
- 76 NEW Old Droxford Station

Sunday 13
- 17 Brick Kiln Cottage
- 28 Crawley Gardens
- 30 Dean House
- 32 The Dower House
- 68 Michaelmas
- 76 NEW Old Droxford Station
- 104 West Silchester Hall
- 106 Whispers
- 110 1 Wogsbarne Cottages

Monday 14
- 47 Hanging Hosta Garden
- 68 Michaelmas
- 110 1 Wogsbarne Cottages

Tuesday 15
- 3 23 Anglesey Road
- 42 NEW Four Seasons Hotel
- 47 Hanging Hosta Garden

Wednesday 16
- 47 Hanging Hosta Garden

Look out for exciting Designer Gardens D

Thursday 17
47 Hanging Hosta Garden

Friday 18
47 Hanging Hosta Garden

Saturday 19
58 The Island
91 Spindles
108 NEW Wildhern Gardens

Sunday 20
11 Berry Cottage
14 Braemoor
15 Bramdean House
31 Dipley Mill
58 The Island
97 NEW The Thatched Cottage

Thursday 24
95 Tanglefoot

Saturday 26
12 8 Birdwood Grove
36 East Worldham Gardens
109 Willows

Sunday 27
36 East Worldham Gardens
66 Meon Orchard
95 Tanglefoot
109 Willows

Tuesday 29
42 NEW Four Seasons Hotel

August

Every Monday excl Bank Hols
69 **The Mill at Gordleton**

Saturday 2
38 Fairweather's Nursery
87 'Selborne'

Sunday 3
14 Braemoor
30 Dean House
38 Fairweather's Nursery
55 The Homestead
87 'Selborne'
96 Terstan
104 West Silchester Hall

Monday 4
87 'Selborne'

Tuesday 5
50 Hill House

Thursday 7
19 Bury Court

Saturday 9
18 The Buildings
20 21 Chestnut Road
109 Willows

Sunday 10
11 Berry Cottage
18 The Buildings
20 21 Chestnut Road
50 Hill House
109 Willows

Tuesday 12
42 NEW Four Seasons Hotel

Wednesday 13
30 Dean House

Thursday 14
50 Hill House

Saturday 16
74 67 Newtown Road
105 Wheatley House

Sunday 17
15 Bramdean House
74 67 Newtown Road
105 Wheatley House

Saturday 23
57 The Hyde

Sunday 24
57 The Hyde
109 Willows

Monday 25
46 Hambledon House
57 The Hyde
109 Willows

Tuesday 26
42 NEW Four Seasons Hotel

Saturday 30
109 Willows

Sunday 31
13 Blackdown House
45 Gilberts Nursery
99 Upham Farm
109 Willows

September

Every Monday
69 **The Mill at Gordleton**

Wednesday 3
11 Berry Cottage

Saturday 6
18 The Buildings
54 Hinton Ampner
90 Southsea Gardens (Evening)

Sunday 7
18 The Buildings
66 Meon Orchard
78 Old Thatch & The Millennium Barn

Tuesday 9
42 NEW Four Seasons Hotel

Sunday 14
10 Bere Mill
31 Dipley Mill
103 Weir House

Saturday 20
51 Hill Top

Sunday 21
15 Bramdean House
39 Farleigh House
51 Hill Top

Tuesday 23
3 23 Anglesey Road
42 NEW Four Seasons Hotel

October

Every Monday
69 **The Mill at Gordleton**

Sunday 5
98 Tylney Hall Hotel

November

Every Monday
69 **The Mill at Gordleton**

Sunday 2
75 Old Alresford House

Wednesday 5
75 Old Alresford House

December

Monday 1
69 The Mill at Gordleton

February 2015

Friday 20
60 Little Court

Sunday 22
60 Little Court

Tuesday 24
60 Little Court

Gardens open to the public

2 Alverstoke Crescent Garden
54 Hinton Ampner
64 Macpennys Woodland Garden & Nurseries
72 Mottisfont Abbey & Garden
80 Patrick's Patch

By appointment only

34 7 Downland Close
37 NEW Fairbank
41 The Fountains
49 Hideaway
52 2 Hillside Cottages
81 Pilley Hill Cottage

Also open by appointment

- 1 80 Abbey Road
- 3 23 Anglesey Road
- 4 Appletree House
- 6 Atheling Villas
- 7 Barhi
- 8 19 Barnwood Road
- 9 Beechenwood Farm
- 10 Bere Mill
- 11 Berry Cottage
- 12 8 Birdwood Grove
- 14 Braemoor
- 15 Bramdean House
- 16 6 Breamore Close
- 18 The Buildings
- 19 Bury Court
- 20 21 Chestnut Road
- 21 12 Christchurch Road
- 23 The Coach House
- 25 Conholt Park
- 26 The Cottage
- 29 Crookley Pool
- 31 Dipley Mill
- 32 The Dower House
- 33 The Down House
- 35 Durmast House
- 36 Wyck House, East Worldham Gardens
- 40 Flintstones
- 42 NEW Four Seasons Hotel
- 43 Fritham Lodge
- 46 Hambledon House
- 47 Hanging Hosta Garden
- 48 NEW Heathermoor House
- 50 Hill House
- 51 Hill Top
- 55 The Homestead
- 58 The Island
- 59 Lake House
- 60 Little Court
- 67 Merdon Manor
- 68 Michaelmas
- 73 23 New Brighton Road
- 74 67 Newtown Road
- 79 Ordnance House
- 83 4 Mill Lane, Romsey Gardens
- 85 St Christopher's
- 87 'Selborne'
- 91 Spindles
- 92 The Stable Family Home Trust Garden
- 94 12 Gilpin Hill, Sway Village Gardens
- 95 Tanglefoot
- 96 Terstan
- 97 NEW The Thatched Cottage
- 100 Walbury
- 101 Waldrons
- 102 Walhampton
- 103 Weir House
- 104 West Silchester Hall
- 105 Wheatley House
- 109 Willows

The Gardens

1 80 ABBEY ROAD

Fareham PO15 5HW. Brian & Vivienne Garford, 01329 843939, vgarford@aol.com. *1m W of Fareham. From M27 J9 take A27 E to Fareham for approx 2m. At top of hill, turn L at lights into Highlands Rd. Turn 4th R into Blackbrook Rd. Abbey Rd is 4th L.* Home-made teas. **Adm £3, chd free. Sun 11 May (11-5). Visitors also welcome by appt Apr to Aug. Adm £5 incl refreshments, chd free.**

Unusual small garden with large collection of herbs and plants of botanical and historical interest, many for sale. Box hedging provides structure for relaxed planting. Interesting use of containers, and ideas for small gardens. Two ponds and tiny meadow for wildlife. Trails for children. Living willow seat, summerhouse, trained grapevine. Garden trail for children. Art exhibition and sale by local artist.

Winding paths lead to different views across the garden and of the meadows beyond. Lots of ideas for the smaller garden . . .

2 ◆ ALVERSTOKE CRESCENT GARDEN

Crescent Road, Gosport PO12 2DH. Gosport Borough Council, 02392 313359, www.angleseyville.co.uk. *1m S of Gosport. From A32 and Gosport follow signs for Stokes Bay. Continue alongside bay to small r'about, turn L into Anglesey Rd. Crescent Garden signed 50yds on R.* Home-made teas. **Adm by donation. For NGS: Sat 24 May (10-4). For other opening times and information, please phone or see garden website.**

Restored Regency ornamental garden, designed to enhance fine crescent (Thomas Ellis Owen 1828). Trees, walks and flowers lovingly maintained by community/council partnership. Garden's considerable local historic interest highlighted by impressive restoration and creative planting of adjacent St Mark's churchyard. Worth seeing together. Heritage, history and horticulture: a fascinating package. Green Flag Award.

3 23 ANGLESEY ROAD

Aldershot GU12 4RF. Adrian & Elizabeth Whiteley, 01252 677623. *On E edge of Aldershot. Off A331 take A323 Aldershot. In quick succession, R at T-light, 1st R, L bend, immed R Newport Rd, 1st R Wilson Rd, L bend, 1st R Roberts Rd. Anglesey Rd 1st L.* Home-made teas. **Adm £2.50, chd free. Tue 24 June, Tue 15 July, Tue 23 Sept (2-5). Visitors also welcome by appt Apr to Oct for groups of 15 max.**

This very small plot holds much to intrigue the curious visitor, richly rewarding leisurely close inspection. A strong geometric design is abundantly softened with rare and interesting flowering and foliage plants in pleasing harmony with cottage-garden stalwarts. Linger over tea and a chat, maybe leave with something a bit different to grow at home.

4 APPLETREE HOUSE

Station Road, Soberton SO32 3QU. Mrs J Dover, 01489 877333, jennie.dover@yahoo.co.uk. *10m N of Fareham. A32 N to Droxford, at Xrds turn R B2150. Turn R under bridge into Station Rd, garden 1m. Parking in lay-by 300yds or on the road.* Light refreshments. **Adm £3, chd free. Wed 4, Wed 18 June, Wed 9 July (12-4). Visitors also welcome by appt June to Aug with lunches by arrangement.**

Designed to look larger than its 40ft x 90ft, this garden has both shady and sunny areas allowing a variety of planting, incl a large collection of clematis viticella. Winding paths lead to different views across the garden and of the meadows beyond. Lots of ideas for the smaller garden. Featured on Radio Solent.

Ordnance House

5 ASHE PARK

nr Ashe, Overton RG25 3AF. Graham & Laura Hazell. *2m E of Overton. Entrance on B3400, approx 500yds W of Deane Gate Inn.* Home-made teas. **Adm £5, chd free. Mon 5 May, Wed 25, Sun 29 June (2-6).**
Extensive new gardens within the grounds of a Georgian Country House and Estate, with further development in progress. Parkland and specimen trees, woodland and bluebell walks, large contemporary potager, lime avenue and several newly planted areas.

6 ATHELING VILLAS

16 Atheling Road, Hythe, Southampton SO45 6BR. Mary & Peter York, 02380 849349, athelingvillas@gmail.com. *W side of Southampton Water. At M27 J2, take A326 for Hythe/Fawley. Cross all r'abouts until Dibden r'about. L to Hythe. After Shell garage take 2nd L and immed R.* Home-made teas. **Adm £3, chd free (share to The Children's Society). Sat 26, Sun 27 Apr, Sat 31 May, Sun 1 June (2-5). Visitors also welcome by appt Apr to June for groups of 20+.**
Inspirational, imaginatively designed and comprehensively planted 1/3 -acre Victorian villa garden with many rare plants. In spring enjoy bulbs, hellebores and pulmonarias as you explore meandering paths set amongst structural planting. At later openings delight in the flowering trees, shrubs, bulbs and herbaceous planting of this tranquil and welcoming garden. Several seating areas throughout garden. Teas in Old Laundry (log fire at early openings). Self-guide leaflet and children's quiz. Display of original art in Garden Room.

7 BARHI

27 Reynolds Dale, Ashurst SO40 7PS. Mrs Finuala Barnes, 02380 860046, fbarnes@barhi.net, www.barhi.net/garden. *3m W of Southampton. From M27 J2 take A326 to Fawley. At 4th r'about, L into Cocklydown Lane. At mini r'about, L into Ibbotson Way. 1st L into Reynolds Dale and follow signs.* **Adm £2.50, chd free. Sat 31 May, Sun 1 June (2-5). Visitors also welcome by appt.**
Small, compact 'modern cottage' garden shared with lively Springer Spaniels, designed around a chambered nautilus spiral. No lawn, so lots of space for plants. The dense planting, meandering paths, secluded pergola, raised formal pond and feature patio have led visitors to describe the garden as 'Tardis-like'.

8 19 BARNWOOD ROAD

Fareham PO15 5LA. Jill & Michael Hill, 01329 842156, thegarden19@gmail.com. *1m W of Fareham. M27 J9, A27 towards Fareham. At top of Titchfield Hill, L at T-lights, 4th R Blackbrook Rd, 4th R Meadow Bank. Barnwood Rd is off Meadow Bank. Please consider neighbours when parking.* Home-made teas. **Adm £3, chd free. Sun 29 June (11-4). Visitors also welcome by appt May to Aug with wine by arrangement.**
Step through the gate to an enchanting garden designed for peace with an abundance of floral colour and delightful features. Greek-style courtyard leads to natural pond with bridge and bog garden, complemented by a thatched summerhouse and jetty, designed and built by owners. Secret pathways, hexagonal greenhouse and new mosaic seating area. Featured in Beautiful Homes and Gardeners' World magazines.

9 BEECHENWOOD FARM

Hillside, Odiham RG29 1JA. Mr & Mrs M Heber-Percy, 01256 702300, beechenwood@totalise.co.uk. *5m SE of Hook. Turn S into King St from Odiham High St. Turn L after cricket ground for Hillside. Take 2nd turn R after 1 1/2 m, modern house 1/2 m.* Home-made teas. **Adm £4, chd free. Every Wed 26 Mar to 4 June (2-5). Visitors also welcome by appt Mar to June.**
2-acre garden in many parts. Lawn meandering through woodland with drifts of spring bulbs. Rose pergola with steps, pots with spring bulbs and later aeoniums. Fritillary and cowslip meadow. Walled herb garden with pool and exuberant planting. Orchard incl white garden and hot border. Greenhouse and vegetable garden. Rock garden extending to grasses, ferns and bamboos. Shady walk to belvedere. 8-acre copse of native species with grassed rides.

Featured in Homes & Gardens (Apr 2013) and Hampshire Life (Mar 2013). Gravel drive and some shallow steps (avoidable).

10 BERE MILL

London Road, Whitchurch RG28 7NH. Rupert & Elizabeth Nabarro, 01256 892210, rnabarro@aol.com. *9m E of Andover, 12m N of Winchester. In centre of Whitchurch, take London Rd at r'about. Up hill 1m, turn R 50yds beyond The Gables on R. Drop-off point for disabled at garden.* Home-made teas. **Adm £5, chd free (share to Smile Train). Sun 9 Mar, Sat 7, Sun 8 June, Sun 14 Sept (1.30-5). Visitors also welcome by appt Feb to Oct for groups of 10+ with a talk about the garden.**

In a beautiful setting beside the R Test, with carriers and large lake next to restored SSSI water meadow, grazed by Welsh Mountain sheep, lambs and Belted Galloway cattle. Riverside walks, species tulips, Japanese prunus, peonies, wisteria collection, roses, bog garden at its best in autumn. Double perennial beds and swamp cypress avenue. Eastern influence incl Japanese Tea House, many different riverside irises and unique bridges. The working mill was where Portals first made paper for the Bank of England in 1716. Unfenced and unguarded rivers and streams. Restricted wheelchair access if very wet.

11 BERRY COTTAGE

Church Road, Upper Farringdon, nr Alton GU34 3EG. Mrs P Watts, 01420 588318. *3m S of Alton off A32. Turn L at Xrds, 1st L into Church Rd. Follow road past Massey's Folly, 2nd house on R opp church.* Home-made teas. **Adm £2.50, chd free. Sun 25 May, Sun 1, Sun 22 June, Wed 2, Sun 20 July, Sun 10 Aug, Wed 3 Sept (2.30-5). Also open with The Thatched Cottage (next door) on 1, 22 June; 20 July. Visitors also welcome by appt May to Sept.**

Small organic cottage garden with all-yr interest. Spring bulbs, roses, clematis and herbaceous borders. Pond and bog garden. Shrubbery and small kitchen garden. The owner-designed and maintained garden surrounds C16 house. The borders are colour-themed and contain many unusual plants. Close to Massey's Folly built by the Victorian rector incl 80ft tower with unique handmade floral bricks, C11 church and some of the oldest yew trees in the county.

Influenced by the flora of Australia and New Zealand including many indigenous species and plants that are widely grown 'down under' . . .

12 8 BIRDWOOD GROVE

Downend, Fareham PO16 8AF. Jayne & Eddie McBride, 01329 280838, jayne.mcbride@ntlworld.com. *½ m E of Fareham. M27 J11 L lane slip to Delme r'about, L on A27 to Portchester over 2 T-lights, completely around small r'about Birdwood Grove first L.* Home-made teas. **Adm £2.50, chd free. Sat 26 July (1-5). Visitors also welcome by appt July to Aug.**

The sub-tropics in Fareham! This small garden is influenced by the flora of Australia and New Zealand and incl many indigenous species and plants that are widely grown 'down under'. The 4 climate zones - arid, medium, lush fertile and a shady fernery - are all densely planted to make the most of dramatic foliage, from huge bananas to towering cordylines. Gold and overall winner Fareham in Bloom small plantsman's back garden. Short gravel path not suitable for mobility scooters.

13 BLACKDOWN HOUSE

Blackdown Lane, Upham SO32 1HS. Mr & Mrs Tom Sweet-Escott. *5m SE of Winchester, 5m N of Bishops Waltham. 1m N of Upham, best accessed off Morestead Rd Xrds with Longwood Dean Lane from Winchester or through the village of Upham from Bishops Waltham.* Cream teas 8 June, and home-made teas at Upham Farm on 31 Aug. **Adm £4, chd free. Sun 8 June, Sun 31 Aug (2-6). Also open with Upham Farm on 31 Aug only.**

A 5-acre family garden. 100m long colourful successional herbaceous border set against a flint wall. Well established wild flower meadow with orchids and butterflies. Part-walled working kitchen garden with new summerhouse and resident call ducks, orchard with free range hens and sunny terrace. Alpacas and Jacob sheep roam the parkland.

14 BRAEMOOR

Bleak Hill, Harbridge, Ringwood BH24 3PX. Tracy & John Netherway & Judy Spratt, 01425 652983, jnetherway@btinternet.com. *2½ m S of Fordingbridge. Turn off A338 at Ibsley. Go through Harbridge Village to T-junction at top of hill, turn R for ¼ m.* Home-made teas. **Adm £3, chd free. Sun 6, Sun 20 July, Sun 3 Aug (2-5.30). Visitors also welcome by appt June to Aug.**

¾ -acre garden brimming with bold, colourful planting and interest. One of our moongates leads to a seaside haven of painted beach huts and driftwood gems. Another enters the cottage garden with overflowing herbaceous borders, stream and pond. Greenhouse with cacti and carnivorous plants. Vegetable area with bantam chickens. Small adjacent nursery. Some gravel paths.

15 BRAMDEAN HOUSE

Bramdean SO24 0JU. Mr & Mrs H Wakefield, 01962 771214, victoria@bramdeanhouse.com. *4m S of Alresford. In centre of village on A272.* Home-made teas. **Adm £5, chd free. Sun 16 Feb (2-4), Sun 13 Apr, Sun 15 June, Sun 20 July, Sun 17 Aug, Sun 21 Sept (2-4.30). Visitors also welcome by appt Oct to Dec.**

Beautiful 5-acre garden famous for its mirror-image herbaceous borders. Carpets of spring bulbs especially snowdrops. A large and unusual collection of plants and shrubs giving yr-round interest. 1-acre walled garden featuring prize-winning vegetables, fruit and flowers. Small arboretum. Trial of hardy Nerine cultivars in association with RHS. Boxwood Castle. Wild flower meadow. Large collection of old-fashioned sweet peas. Featured in The Gardens of England and Country Life.

16 6 BREAMORE CLOSE
Eastleigh SO50 4QB. Mr & Mrs R Trenchard, 02380 611230, dawndavina6@yahoo.co.uk. *1m N of Eastleigh. M3 J12, follow signs to Eastleigh. Turn R at r'about into Woodside Ave, then 1st L into Broadlands Ave (park here). Breamore Close 3rd on L.* Home-made teas. **Adm £3, chd free. Sat 17, Sun 18 May (1.30-5). Visitors also welcome by appt May to July for groups of 10+.**
Delightful plant lover's garden with coloured foliage and unusual plants, giving a tapestry effect of texture and colour. Many hostas displayed in pots. The garden is laid out in distinctive planting themes with seating areas to sit and contemplate. In May, magnificent wisteria over a pergola with flowers 3ft-4ft long; in June many clematis scramble through roses followed by phlox in July. Small gravel area wheelchairs may find hard to negotiate.

17 BRICK KILN COTTAGE
The Avenue, Herriard, Near Alton RG25 2PR. Barbara Jeremiah, 01256 381301. *4m NE of Alton. A339 Basingstoke to Alton, L along The Avenue, past Lasham Gliding Club on R then past Back Lane on L and take next track on L.* **Adm £3.50, chd free. Sun 11 May, Sun 13 July (12.30-5).**
Cottage garden in a bluebell wood. Woodland garden in 2-acres incl natural water feature, billabong, stumpery and ferny hollow. Tree house (children must be accompanied by an adult). Woodland walk. Tea pavilion. Croquet and boules, weather permitting.

18 THE BUILDINGS
Broughton, Stockbridge SO20 8BH. Dick & Gillian Pugh, 01794 301424, richard260@btinternet.com. *3m W of Stockbridge. NGS yellow signs 2m W of Stockbridge off A30, or 6m N of Romsey off B3084.* Home-made teas. **Adm £4, chd free (share to Friends of St Mary's Broughton and St James' Bossington). Sat 9, Sun 10 Aug, Sat 6, Sun 7 Sept (2-5). Visitors also welcome by appt July to Sept for groups of 10+.**
High on the Hampshire Downs, with wonderful views, our 1-acre offers modern planting in gravel, borders and an exuberant pergola all on thin chalk soil. At its best in late summer, it is often described as 'inspirational', the planting and layout widely admired. Many unusual plants and varieties especially in the Salvia, Viticella Clematis, and Pelargonium families. Featured in Country Living (Autumn 2013).

Kitchen garden with area for children to 'have a go to grow and sow' . . .

19 BURY COURT
Bentley GU10 5LZ. John Coke, Jcoke46@gmail.com, www.burycourtbarn.com. *5m NE of Alton. 1m N of Bentley. Take Hole Lane, then follow signs towards Crondall.* Home-made teas. **Adm £5, chd free. Thur 7 Aug (2-6). Visitors also welcome by appt Apr to Oct.**
Designed in cooperation with Piet Oudolf, created from old farmyard, in the continental 'naturalistic' style, making heavy use of grasses in association with perennials selected for an extended season of interest. Area designed by Christopher Bradley-Hole in minimalist style, featuring grid of gravel paths bisecting chequerboard of naturalistically planted raised squares edged in rusted steel.

20 21 CHESTNUT ROAD
Brockenhurst SO42 7RF. Iain & Mary Hayter, 01590 622009, maryiain.hayter@gmail.com, www.21-chestnut-rdgardens.co.uk. *New Forest, 4M S of Lyndhurst. At Brockenhurst turn R B3055 Grigg Lane. Limited parking, village car park nearby. Leave M27 J2, follow 'Heavy Lorry Route'. Mainline station less than 10 mins walk.* Home-made teas. **Adm £3.50, chd free. Sat 24 (11-5); Sun 25 May (1-5); Sat 14 June (11-5); Sun 15 June (1-5); Sat 9 Aug (11-5); Sun 10 Aug (1-5). Visitors also welcome by appt May to Sept for groups of 10+.**
A well tended highly productive garden with vegetables, fruit trees and wild flower area. Voluptuous perennial shrub and rose borders, wildlife pond with summer house, a plant lovers dream where both colour and scent dictate. From flag irises in May, scented roses in June to spicy hot borders in August, take away inspirational planting ideas for different growing conditions. Photo and painting exhibition in summerhouse. Visit Brockenhurst Village and enjoy seeing the ponies, donkeys and cattle roam freely. Visit St Nicholas Church home to New Zealand War Graves. No wheelchair access to raised deck or some parts of the garden if wet.

21 12 CHRISTCHURCH ROAD
Winchester SO23 9SR. Iain & Penny Patton, 01962 854272, pjspatton@yahoo.co.uk, For B&B info www.visitwinchester.com. *S side of city. Leave centre of Winchester by Southgate St, 1st R into St James Lane, 3rd L into Christchurch Rd.* **Adm £3, chd free. Fri 4, Sun 6 Apr (2-5.30). Visitors also welcome by appt Mar to Oct.**
Small town garden with strong design enhanced by exuberant and vertical planting. All-yr interest incl winter-flowering shrubs, bulbs and hellebores. Two water features, incl slate-edged rill, and pergolas provide structure. Small front garden designed to be viewed from the house with bulbs, roses and herbaceous planting. Cover of and featured in The English Garden and in Amateur Gardener.

22 NEW CLOVER FARM
Shalden Lane, Shalden, Alton GU34 4DU. Mrs Sarah Floyd, 01420 86294. *Approx 3m N of Alton in the village of Shalden. Take A339 out of Alton. After approx 2m turn R up lane. At top turn sharp R next to church sign.* Home-made teas. **Adm £4, chd free. Sun 22 June (2-5.30).**
3-acre garden with views to die for! Herbaceous borders and sloping lawns down to reflection pond, wild flower meadow, lime avenue and rose garden. Kitchen garden with area for children to 'have a go to grow and sow'. Car park open for picnics from 12 noon.

23 THE COACH HOUSE
Reading Road, Sherfield on Loddon RG27 0EX. Jane & Peter Jordan, 01256 880852, jane@janejordangardens.co.uk. *5m N of Basingstoke. Follow A33 and signs to Sherfield on Lodden. Follow*

signs to free car parks. Some on-road parking. Drop off only at house. Home-made teas. **Adm £3.50, chd free. Sat 5 July (2-5). Visitors also welcome by appt May to Oct.**
A hidden gem, this 510-sq-metre walled garden has been replanted extensively over the past 7yrs. Includes mature trees, a wide range of unusual plants and grasses chosen for texture and colour, herb garden, formal pond and sunken brick terrace. The style is relaxed, the content stimulating and the tea fresh, so come and enjoy!. Couple of low steps in garden.

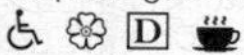

24 COLEMORE HOUSE GARDENS

Colemore, Alton GU34 3RX. Mr & Mrs Simon de Zoete. *4m S of Alton (off A32). Approach from N on A32, take L turn (Shell Lane), ¼ m S of East Tisted. Go under bridge, keep L until you see Colemore Church. Park on verge of church.* Home-made teas. **Adm £4.50, chd free. Sun 29, Mon 30 June (2-6).**
4-acres in lovely unspoilt country, featuring rooms containing many unusual plants and different aspects - a spectacular arched rose walk, water rill, mirror pond, herbaceous and shrub borders and a new woodland walk. Many admire the lawns, new grass gardens and thatched pavilion (built by students from the Prince's Trust). A small arboretum is being planted. Change and development is ongoing, and increasing the diversity of interesting plants is a prime motivation.

25 CONHOLT PARK

Hungerford Lane, Andover SP11 9HA. Conholt Park Estate, 07917 796826, conholt.garden@hotmail.com. *7m N of Andover. Turn N off A342 at Weyhill Church, 5m N through Clanville. L at T-junction, Conholt ½ m on R. A343 to Hurstbourne Tarrant, turn to and through Vernham Dean, L signed Conholt.* Home-made teas. **Adm £5, chd free. Sun 8, Sun 29 June (11-5). Visitors also welcome by appt May to July on weekdays.**
10-acres surrounding Regency House (not open), with mature cedars. Rose, sensory, winter and secret gardens, fern dell and poppy garden. Glasshouses, flower cartwheel, berry wall and orchard

The Down House

© Leigh Clapp

occupy the walled garden. New summer border and gravel garden. Ladies Walk. Large laurel maze with viewing platform. Visitors welcome to picnic.

26 THE COTTAGE

16 Lakewood Road, Chandler's Ford SO53 1ES. Hugh & Barbara Sykes, 02380 254521, barandhugh@aol.com. *2m NW of Eastleigh. Leave M3 J12, follow signs to Chandler's Ford. At King Rufus on Winchester Rd, turn R into Merdon Ave, then 3rd road on L.* Home-made teas. **Adm £3.50, chd free. Sun 4, Mon 5, Sun 11, Mon 12 May (2-6). Visitors also welcome by appt Apr to May.**
¾-acre. Azaleas, bog garden, camellias, dogwoods, erythroniums, free-range bantams, geraniums, hostas, irises, jasmines, kitchen garden, landscaping began in 1950, maintained by owners, new planting, osmunda, ponds, quiz for children, rhododendrons, sun and shade, trilliums, unusual plants, viburnums, wildlife areas, eXuberant foliage, yr-round interest, zantedeschia. 'A lovely tranquil garden' - Anne Swithinbank.

Hampshire Wildlife Trust Wildlife Garden Award. Honey from our garden hives for sale.

COTTAGE IN THE TREES

See Wiltshire

27 CRANBURY PARK

Otterbourne, nr Winchester SO21 2HL. Mrs Chamberlayne-Macdonald. *3m NW of Eastleigh. Main entrance on old A33 at top of Otterbourne Hill. Entrances also in Hocombe Rd, Chandlers Ford and next to Otterbourne Church.* Home-made teas. **Adm £4, chd free (share to St Matthew's Church, Otterbourne). Sun 15 June (2-6).**
Extensive pleasure grounds laid out in late C18 and early C19 by Papworth; fountains, rose garden, specimen trees and pinetum, lakeside walk and fern walk. Family carriages and collection of prams will be on view, also photos of King George VI, Eisenhower and Montgomery reviewing Canadian troops at Cranbury before D-Day. All dogs on leads please. Disabled WC.

Evening primroses obstruct the way to the door to wisteria-shaded terraces . . .

GROUP OPENING

28 CRAWLEY GARDENS

Crawley, nr Winchester SO21 2PR, 01962 776243. *5m NW of Winchester. Between B3049 (Winchester - Stockbridge) and A272 (Winchester - Andover). Parking throughout village.* Home-made teas in the village hall. **Combined adm £6, chd free. Mon 21, Tue 22 Apr, Sun 11, Tue 13 May (2-5.30); Thur 12, Sun 15 June, Thur 10, Sun 13 July (2-6).**

BAY TREE HOUSE D
Julia & Charles Whiteaway.
Open June & July dates

GABLE COTTAGE
Patrick Hendra & Ken Jones.
Open April dates only

LITTLE COURT
Prof & Mrs A R Elkington.
Open April, May, June & July dates
(See separate entry)

PAIGE COTTAGE
Mr & Mrs T W Parker.
Open April & July dates

TANGLEFOOT
Mr & Mrs F J Fratter.
Open May, June & July dates
(See separate entry)

Crawley is an exceptionally pretty village nestling in chalk downland with thatched houses, C14 church and delightful village pond with ducks. A different combination of gardens opens each month providing seasonal interest with varied character, and with traditional and contemporary approaches to landscape and planting. Most of the gardens have beautiful country views and there are other excellent gardens to be seen from the road. The spring gardens are Paige Cottage, Gable Cottage and the 3-acre traditional English country garden at Little Court with carpets of spring bulbs. In summer, other gardens open. At Bay Tree House there are pleached limes, a rill and contemporary borders; while at Tanglefoot there are colour-themed borders, herb wheel, exceptional kitchen garden and a traditional Victorian boundary wall supporting trained fruit incl apricots. Also in the summer, Little Court has a mass of colourful herbaceous planting while Paige Cottage is a typical mixed cottage garden.

29 CROOKLEY POOL

Blendworth Lane, Horndean PO8 0AB. Mr & Mrs Simon Privett, 02392 592662, simon.privett123@btinternet.com. *5m S of Petersfield. 2m E of Waterlooville, off A3. From Horndean up Blendworth Lane between bakery and hairdresser. Entrance 200yds before church on L with white railings.* Home-made teas. **Adm £3.50, chd free. Sun 18 May, Thur 5 June (2-5). Visitors also welcome by appt Mar to Oct with teas by arrangement.**

Here the plants decide where to grow. Californian tree poppies elbow valerian aside to crowd round the pool. Evening primroses obstruct the way to the door and the steps to wisteria-shaded terraces. Hellebores bloom under the trees. Salvias, pandorea jasminoides, justicia, pachystachys lutea and passion flowers riot quietly with tomatoes in the greenhouse. Not a garden for the neat or tidy minded, although this is a plantsman's garden full of unusual plants and a lot of tender perennials. Bantams stroll throughout. Display of watercolour paintings of flowers found in the garden.

30 DEAN HOUSE

Kilmeston Road, Kilmeston SO24 0NL. Mr P H R Gwyn, www.deanhousegardens.co.uk. *5m S of Alresford. Via village of Cheriton or off A272 signed at Cheriton Xrds. Follow signs for Kilmeston, through village and turn L at Dean House sign.* Cream teas in The Orangery. **Adm £5, chd free. Wed 28 May, Wed 18 June, Wed 2 July (10-4); Sun 13 July, Sun 3 Aug (12-4.30); Wed 13 Aug (10-4).**

The 7-acres have been described as 'a well-kept secret hidden behind the elegant facade of its Georgian centrepiece'. Sweeping lawns, York stone paths, gravel pathways, many young and mature trees and hedges, mixed and herbaceous borders, symmetrical rose garden, pond garden, working walled garden, with 125 different varieties of vegetable, and glasshouses all help to create a diverse and compact sliver of Eden. Over 1700 individually documented plant species and cultivars in our collection. Gravel paths.

31 DIPLEY MILL

Dipley Road, Hartley Wintney, Hook RG27 8JP. Miss Rose McMonigall, rose@rosemcm.demon.co.uk, www.dipley-mill.co.uk. *2m NE of Hook. Turn E off B3349 at Mattingley (1½ m N of Hook) signed Hartley Wintney, West Green and Dipley. Dipley Mill ½ m on L just over bridge.* Home-made teas. **Adm £5, chd free. Sun 25 May, Sun 8, Sun 22 June, Sun 20 July, Sun 14 Sept (2-5.30). Visitors also welcome by appt May to Sept.**

A romantic adventure awaits as you wander by the meandering streams surrounding this Domesday Book listed mill! Explore many magical areas, such as the Rust garden, the pill-box grotto or the ornamental courtyard. Or just escape into wild meadows. 'One of the most beautiful gardens in Hampshire' according to Alan Titchmarsh in his TV programme 'Love Your Garden'. Animals. Local fruit stalls (depending on availability).

32 THE DOWER HOUSE

Springvale Road, Headbourne Worthy, Winchester SO23 7LD. Mrs Judith Lywood, 01962 882848, lisawood@thedowerhousewinchester.co.uk, www.thedowerhousewinchester.co.uk. *2m N of Winchester. Entrance is directly opp watercress beds in Springvale Rd and near Goodlife Farm Shop.* Home-made teas. **Adm £3.50, chd free. Sun 13 July (2.30-5.30). Visitors also welcome by appt Mar to Sept for groups of 20-30.**

5½ -acres with easy paths, numerous seats, good views, colourful perennials, shrubs and mature trees (incl large Indian bean tree and cercis 'Forest Pansy'). Large Geranium border overlooking grounds, bog garden, good pond with fish and water lilies, newly installed scented garden at entrance, small secret courtyard garden and excellent container planting on residents' patios. Parking at main entrance to house, following path to garden.

Lemon drizzle cake, Victoria sponge ... yummy!

33 THE DOWN HOUSE
Itchen Abbas SO21 1AX. Jackie & Mark Porter, 01962 791054, markstephenporter@gmail.com, www.thedownhouse.co.uk. *5m E of Winchester on B3047. 5th house on R after the Itchen Abbas Village sign.* Home-made teas. **Adm £4, chd free (share to PCaSO, Prostate Cancer Support). Sun 23 Feb (12-4); Sun 29 June, Wed 2 July (2-6). Visitors also welcome by appt Feb to July for groups of 10+.**
3-acre garden developed by owners since 2001, laid out in rooms overlooking Itchen Valley, adjoining the Pilgrim's Way, with walks through a meadow to the river. Carpet of snowdrops and crocus, plus borders of coloured stems in winter. Roped fountain garden, hot borders, wildlife pond and shady places in summer. Pleached hornbeams, yew-lined avenues, woodland nut and orchard walk. Working vineyard and potager. **Live jazz on 29 June.** The garden in winter has been featured in Country Homes & Interiors and the Potager in Countryside magazine.

34 7 DOWNLAND CLOSE
Locks Heath, nr Fareham SO31 6WB. Roy Dorland, 07768 107779, roydorland@hotmail.co.uk. *3m W of Fareham. M27 J9 follow A27 on Southampton Rd to Park Gate. Past Kams Palace Restaurant, L into Locks Rd, 3rd R into Meadow Ave. 2nd L into Downland Close.* Home-made teas. **Adm £3, chd free. Visitors welcome by appt May to July for groups of 10-20.**
Visit this prizewinning, beautiful, restful and inspirational 50ft x 45ft plantsman's garden, packed with ideas for the 'modest-sized' plot. Many varieties of hardy geraniums, hostas, heucheras, shrubs, ferns and other unusual perennials, weaving a tapestry of harmonious colour. Attractive water feature, plenty of seating areas and charming summerhouse. A garden to fall in love with!.

35 DURMAST HOUSE
Bennetts Lane, Burley BH24 4AT. Mr & Mrs P E G Daubeney, 01425 402132, philip@daubeney.co.uk, www.durmasthouse.co.uk. *5m SE of Ringwood. Off Burley to Lyndhurst Rd, nr White Buck Hotel.* Cream teas. **Adm £4, chd free (share to Delhi Commonwealth Women's Assn Medical Clinic). Sun 6 Apr, Sun 29 June (2-5). Visitors also welcome by appt Apr to Sept with talk and teas incl in adm price.**
Designed by Gertrude Jekyll, Durmast has contrasting hot and cool colour borders, formal rose garden edged with lavender and a long herbaceous border. Many old trees, Victorian rockery and orchard with beautiful spring bulbs. Rare azaleas: Fama, Princeps and Gloria Mundi from Ghent. New rose bowers with rare French roses Eleanor Berkeley and Euphrosyne. New Jekyll border, blue, yellow and white scheme. Featured in Discover Britain Magazine Aug/Sept 2013 and Five of the Finest English Country Gardens created by Edwardian horticulturalist Gertrude Jekyll. Many stone paths, some gravel paths.

GROUP OPENING

36 EAST WORLDHAM GARDENS
East Worldham, Alton GU34 3AE, 01420 83389, www.worldham.org. *2m SE of Alton on B3004. Gardens and car parking (off B3004) signed in village. Tickets and maps available in gardens.* Home-made teas at East Worldham Manor and 'Selborne' (28-29 June) and at 'Selborne' and Three Horseshoes PH (26-27 July). **Combined adm £5, chd free. Sat 28, Sun 29 June, Sat 26, Sun 27 July (2-5.30).**

EAST WORLDHAM MANOR
Worldham Hill. Mrs H V Wood.
Open June dates only

NEW HILLSEYE
Old House Gardens. Mrs Carolyn Goodrham.
Open July dates only

THE OLD HOP KILN
Blanket Street. John & Kate Denyer.
Open June dates only

'SELBORNE'
Brian & Mary Jones.
Open June and July dates
(See separate entry)

SILVER BIRCHES
Old House Gardens. Jenny & Roger Bateman.
Open July dates only

WYCK HOUSE
Chris & Penny Kehoe.
Open July dates only. Coming from Alton, take 2nd turning L after Three Horseshoes PH, signed Wyck and Binsted. Wyck House is 100yds on R
Visitors also welcome by appt Apr to Sept for individuals and groups.
01420 84695
candpkehoe@aol.com

A honey-pot of gardens. East Worldham Gardens offers a different combination of gardens with varied characters and styles and far-reaching views on each of the two openings. East Worldham Manor is a walled Victorian garden with restored greenhouses and rose garden. Gravel paths, wind through the garden. The Old Hop Kiln's terraced garden has free-flowing planting which complements the hard landscaping. A waterfall links the upper and lower levels. 'Selborne' has an old orchard providing dappled shade, metal and stone sculptures and mixed borders with a range of hardy geraniums. The garden at Silver Birches, redesigned from an overgrown jungle, offers mixed borders, fishpond, stream, rockery and rose garden. Wyck House's mature garden contains interesting shrubs and trees, roses, perennials, shady area and features a large collection of clematis. Hillseye, opening for the first time, is a mature garden with terrace, coloured themed borders, pergola, pond with fountain and knot garden. Garden quizzes, sandpit and bookstall at 'Selborne'. C13 church with newly installed stained glass windows. Very limited access for wheelchairs to the Old Hop Kiln.

Pilley Hill Cottage

© Leigh Clapp

37 NEW FAIRBANK

Old Odiham Road, Alton GU34 4BU. Mr & Mrs Robin Lees, 01420 86665, j.lees558@btinternet.com. *1½ m N of Alton. From S, past Sixth Form College, then 1½ m beyond road junction on R. From N, turn L at Golden Pot and then 50yds turn R. Garden 1m on L before road junction.* Home-made teas for additional charge. **Adm £3, chd free. Visitors welcome by appt July to Sept for groups of 30 max. Parking for small coaches only.**

A young garden, begun in 2006, planted for all yr-round interest. Features incl roses, herbaceous borders, a wide variety of trees and shrubs, an orchard and a large vegetable garden. Second prize in 2012 Hampshire Federation Garden competition. Rough surfaces in places.

38 FAIRWEATHER'S NURSERY

Hilltop, Beaulieu, Brockenhurst SO42 7YR. Patrick & Aline Fairweather, www.fairweathers.co.uk. *1½ m NE of Beaulieu Village. Signed Beacon Gate on B3054 between Heath r'about (A326) and Beaulieu Village.* Cream teas. **Adm £2.50, chd free. Sat 2, Sun 3 Aug (11-4).**

Fairweather's holds a specialist collection of 300 Agapanthus grown in pots and display beds. The collection should be looking at its best. Visitors can join a demonstration of how to get the best from Agapanthus and there will be nursery tours during the day. Aline Fairweather's garden (adjacent to the nursery) will also be open; it has mixed shrub and perennial borders containing many unusual plants. Agapanthus and a range of other traditional and new perennials for sale. Guided tours 11.30am and 2.30pm.

39 FARLEIGH HOUSE

Farleigh Wallop, nr Basingstoke RG25 2HT. The Earl & Countess of Portsmouth. *3m SE of Basingstoke. Off B3046 Basingstoke to Preston Candover road.* Home-made teas. **Adm £5, chd free. Sun 22 June, Sun 21 Sept (2-5).**

Contemporary garden of great tranquillity designed by Georgia Langton, surrounded by wonderful views. 3-acre walled garden in 3 sections: ornamental potager, formal rose garden and wild rose garden. Greenhouse full of exotics, serpentine yew walk, contemplative pond garden and lake with planting for wildlife. Approx 10-acres and 1 hour to walk around.

40 FLINTSTONES

Sciviers Lane, Durley SO32 2AG. June & Bill Butler, 01489 860880, j.b.butler@hotmail.co.uk. *5m E of Eastleigh. M3 J11 towards Marwell Zoo. On B2177 turn R opp Woodman PH. M27 J7 follow signs for Fair Oak then Durley turn L at Robin Hood PH.* Home-made teas. **Adm £3.50, chd free. Sun 30 Mar (2-5); Sun 1, Mon 2 June (2-6). Evening Opening £5, chd free, with wine available on Tue 10 June (6.30-8.30). Visitors also welcome by appt May to Sept for groups of 10+.**

Garden of great tranquillity. All yr pleasing tapestry effect of contrasting and blending foliage and flowers. Plantswoman's garden developed from a field on fertile acid clay. Large perennial plant collections, especially hardy geraniums. Interesting island beds to wander round and explore. Plants for sale (June only). Wheelchair access only when dry, please telephone prior to visit.

41 THE FOUNTAINS

34 Frampton Way, Totton SO40 9AE. Jean Abel, 02380 865939. *1m W of Southampton. From Southampton, A35 W for 1m to r'about. U-turn and return towards Southampton on A35. Immed L into Rushington Avenue, L again into Frampton Way.* Home-made teas. **Adm £2.50, chd free. Visitors welcome by appt Apr to Sept for small groups.**

A garden of several 'rooms', each with hedges and connecting rose-covered arches. Filled with a variety of fruit trees, soft fruit cordons and espaliers. Trellis covered in rambling roses, with flowers for every season. Plantswoman's garden designed for yr-round interest with vegetable plot, wildlife ponds and chickens. 'Cottage garden meets the Good Life' - a garden to relax in and enjoy.

42 NEW FOUR SEASONS HOTEL
Chalky Lane, Dogmersfield, Hook RG27 8TD. Darren Moakes, 01252 853010, reservations.ham@fourseasons.com, www.fourseasons.com/hampshire. *3m from M3 J5. Follow A287 towards Farnham for approx 3m. Follow signs for the Four Seasons Hotel.* **Adm £4, chd free. Tue 1, Tue 15, Tue 29 July, Tue 12, Tue 26 Aug, Tue 9, Tue 23 Sept (9-4.30). Visitors also welcome by appt July to Sept for groups of 10+.**
Steeped in nearly 1000-yrs of history, Dogmersfield Park was first mentioned in the Domesday book of 1086. Let us welcome you to explore the country estate where Henry VIII met Catherine of Aragon. Walk through the splendour of the walled garden, rose walk and apple orchard before relaxing with an afternoon tea in the Grade II listed Manor House (reservations required). Set in 500-acres of English heritage parkland, see the largest dovecote in Hampshire built in 1570. Walk in the footsteps of Earls, Lords and Kings through an historic estate and enjoy the peace, serenity, flowers and birdsong.

43 FRITHAM LODGE
Fritham SO43 7HH. Sir Chris & Lady Powell, 02380 812650, chris.powell@ddblondon.com. *6m N of Lyndhurst. 3m NW of M27 J1 (Cadnam). Follow signs to Fritham.* Home-made teas. **Adm £3.50, chd free. Sun 29 June (2-5). Visitors also welcome by appt May to July.**
Set in the heart of the New Forest in 18-acres; with 1-acre old walled garden round Grade II listed C17 house (not open), originally one of Charles II hunting lodges. Parterre of old roses, potager with wide variety of vegetables, herbs and fruit trees, pergola, herbaceous and blue and white mixed borders, ponds, walk across hay meadows to woodland and stream, with ponies, donkeys, sheep and rare breed hens.

GROUP OPENING

44 FROYLE GARDENS
Walbury, Lower Froyle, Froyle GU34 4LJ. Ernie & Brenda Milam. *5m NE of Alton. Access to Lower Froyle from A31 between Alton and Farnham, at Bentley. Follow signs from Lower Froyle to Upper Froyle. Maps given to all visitors.* Home-made teas at Froyle Village Hall. **Combined adm £5, chd free. Sat 7, Sun 8 June (2-6).**

DAY COTTAGE
Mr Nick Whines & Ms Corinna Furse
www.daycottage.co.uk

FORDS COTTAGE
Mr & Mrs M Carr

GLEBE COTTAGE
Barbara & Michael Starbuck

LONG BARLANDS
Maureen Allan

THE OLD SCHOOL
Nigel & Linda Bulpitt

WALBURY
Ernie & Brenda Milam
(See separate entry)

Visitors have been returning to Froyle (The Village of Saints) for 15-yrs to enjoy the wonderful variety of gardens on offer, the warm welcome and the excellent home-made teas in the village hall. The gardens harmonise gently with their surroundings, many with lovely views of beautiful countryside. Six gardens will open their gates this year, not only providing plant interest, colour and scent, but animals frequently associated with a true cottage garden - as well as vegetables, orchards, greenhouses and wild-flower meadows. Large display of richly decorated C18 church vestments in St Mary's Church Upper Froyle - separate donation. No wheelchair access to Glebe Cottage.

45 GILBERTS NURSERY
Dandysford Lane, Sherfield English, nr Romsey SO51 6DT. Nick & Helen Gilbert, gilbertsdahlias.co.uk. *Midway between Romsey and Whiteparish on A27, in Sherfield English Village. From Romsey 4th turn on L, just before small petrol stn on R, visible from main road.* Light refreshments. **Adm £3, chd free. Sun 31 Aug (10-4).**
This may not be a garden but do come and be amazed by the sight of over 300 varieties of dahlias in our dedicated 1½-acre field. The blooms are in all colours, shapes and sizes and can be closely inspected from wheelchair-friendly hard grass paths. An inspiration for all gardeners.

MANOR HOUSE
See Wiltshire

Walk in the footsteps of Earls, Lords and Kings through an historic estate and enjoy the peace, serenity, flowers and birdsong . . .

46 HAMBLEDON HOUSE
Hambledon PO7 4RU. Capt & Mrs David Hart Dyke, 02392 632380, dhartdyke@tiscali.co.uk. *8m SW of Petersfield, 5m NW of Waterlooville. In village centre, driveway leading to house in East St. Do not go up Speltham Hill even if advised by SatNav.* Home-made teas. **Adm £4, chd free. Mon 25 Aug (2-5). Visitors also welcome by appt Mar to Oct with refreshments by prior arrangement.**
3-acre partly walled plantsman's garden for all seasons. Large borders filled with a wide variety of unusual shrubs and perennials with imaginative plant combinations culminating in a profusion of colour in late summer. Hidden, secluded areas reveal surprise views of garden and village rooftops. Planting a large central area, started in 2011, has given the garden an exciting new dimension. Exhibition of watercolours. Limited wheelchair access as garden is on several levels.

47 HANGING HOSTA GARDEN
Narra, Frensham Lane, Lindford, Bordon GU35 0QJ. June Colley & John Baker, 01420 489186, hanginghostas@btinternet.com. *Approx 1m E of Bordon. From the A325 at Bordon take the B3002, then B3004 to Lindford. Turn L into Frensham Lane, 3rd house on L.* **Adm £3.50, chd free. Mon 7 to Fri 11, Mon 14 to Fri 18 July (10-4). Visitors also welcome by appt in July.**
This garden is packed with almost 2000 plants. The collection of over 1300 hosta cultivars is one of the largest in England. Hostas are displayed at eye level to give a wonderful tapestry of foliage and colour. Islamic garden, waterfall and stream garden, cottage garden. Talks given to garden clubs.

48 NEW HEATHERMOOR HOUSE
Hale Purlieu, Fordingbridge SP6 2NN. Andrew & Judy Pownall-Gray, 01725 513033, judypg@btinternet.com. *11m S of Salisbury, 5m NE of Fordingbridge. Yellow NGS signs at Downton and Breamore on A338 Salisbury/ Fordingbridge and at Cadnam M27 J1/B3078 to Downton.* Home-made teas. **Adm £3.50, chd free (share to Wilton Group Riding for the Disabled (RDA)). Sun 11, Sun 18 May (2-5.30). Visitors also welcome by appt Apr to Sept for groups of 10+.**
Our tranquil 4-acre garden leads directly on to the New Forest and abounds with azaleas, camellias, rhododendrons, magnolias and acers, filling the garden with colour and fragrance. Large lawns, surrounded by herbaceous borders, are the perfect setting for tea and cake. The raised bed vegetable garden leads to the cabin in the woods - a joy for wildlife enthusiasts. No wheelchair access to cabin in woods.

49 HIDEAWAY
Hamdown Crescent, East Wellow, Romsey SO51 6BJ. Caroline & Colin Hart, 01794 322445, hart.caroline@yahoo.com. *3m W of Romsey. From M27 J2 take A36 NW towards Salisbury. After 2m, turn R by speed camera into Whinwhistle Rd. Hamdown Crescent is 3rd L.* Home-made teas. **Adm £3, chd free. Visitors welcome by appt June to Aug.**
'So much colour', 'such variety of interesting plants', 'so many bees and butterflies', 'inspirational', 'did you really propagate all those plants yourself?' Visitors to our newly-opened garden in 2013 were very appreciative. Come and enjoy our peaceful ½ -acre garden, close to the New Forest.

50 HILL HOUSE
Old Alresford SO24 9DY. Mrs W F Richardson, 01962 732720, hillhouseolda@yahoo.co.uk. *1m W of Alresford. From Alresford 1m along B3046 towards Basingstoke, then R by church.* Home-made teas. **Adm £3.50, chd free. Tue 5, Sun 10, Thur 14 Aug (1.30-5). Visitors also welcome by appt July to Aug for groups of 10+.**
Traditional English 2-acre garden, established 1938, divided by yew hedge. Large croquet lawn framing the star of the garden, the huge multi-coloured herbaceous border. Impressive dahlia bed and butterfly-attracting sunken garden in lavender shades. Prolific old-fashioned kitchen garden with hens and bantams both fluffy and large. Small Dexter cows, possibly with calves. Dried flowers.

51 HILL TOP
Damson Hill, Upper Swanmore SO32 2QR. David Green, 01489 892653, tricia1960@btinternet.com. *1m NE of Swanmore. Junction of Swanmore Rd and Church Rd, up Hampton Hill, sharp L bend. After 300yds junction with Damson Hill, house on L. Disabled parking by house.* Home-made teas. **Adm £3.50, chd free. Sat 20, Sun 21 Sept (2-5). Visitors also welcome by appt June to Sept.**
2-acres with extensive colourful borders and wide lawns, this garden has stunning views to the Isle of Wight. The glasshouses produce unusual fruit and vegetables from around the world. The outdoor vegetable plots bulge with well-grown produce, much for sale on the day. Potted specimen plants and interesting annuals.

52 2 HILLSIDE COTTAGES
Trampers Lane, North Boarhunt PO17 6DA. John & Lynsey Pink, 01329 832786, landjpink@tiscali.co.uk. *5m N of Fareham. 3m E of Wickham. From A32 at Wickham take B2177 E. Trampers Lane 2nd on L (approx 2m). Hillside Cottages approx ½ m on L.* **Adm £2.50, chd free. Visitors welcome by appt.**
This 1-acre garden, on gently rising ground, contains so much of interest for plantspeople. Many rare and unusual specimens are shown off in sweeping borders in a tranquil setting. The National Collection of salvias is well displayed, all colours, sizes and growing habits. Something for everyone and an ideal venue for a group visit from spring through to autumn.

NCH

53 HINTON ADMIRAL
Christchurch BH23 7DY. Robin Mason, MEM Ltd. *4m NE of Christchurch. On N side of A35, ¾ m E of Cat & Fiddle PH.* **Adm £6, chd free (share to Julia's House Childrens Hospice). Sun 18 May (1-4.30).**
Magnificent 20-acre garden (within a much larger estate) now being restored and developed. Mature plantings of deciduous azaleas and rhododendrons amidst a sea of bluebells. Wandering paths lead through rockeries and beside ponds and a stream with many cascades. Orchids appear in the large lawns. The 2 walled gardens are devoted to herbs and wild flowers and a very large greenhouse. The terrace and rock garden were designed by Harold Peto. No refreshments, but picnics may be taken in the orchard. Some gravel paths.

54 ◆ HINTON AMPNER
Alresford SO24 0LA. National Trust, 01962 771305, www.nationaltrust.org.uk/hinton-ampner. *3½ m S of Alresford. S on A272 Petersfield to Winchester road.* Light refreshments. **Adm £9.35, chd £4.50. For NGS: Sat 10 May, Sat 7 June, Sat 12 July, Sat 6 Sept (10-6). For other opening times and information, please phone or see garden website.**
12-acres. C20 garden created by Ralph Dutton. Manicured lawns and topiary combine with unusual shrubs, climbers and herbaceous plants. Vibrant dahlias alternate in spring with tulips. Rose border incorporates over 45 old and new rose varieties. Dramatic foliage planting in the Dell; orchard with spring bulbs; magnolia and philadelphus walks; restored walled garden. Wheelchair access maps available from visitor reception.

55 THE HOMESTEAD
Northney Road, Hayling Island PO11 0NF. Stan & Mary Pike, 02392 464888, jhomestead@aol.com, www.homesteadhayling.co.uk. *3m S of Havant. From A27 Havant/ Hayling Island r'about, travel S over Langstone Bridge and turn immed L into Northney Rd. Car park entrance on R after Langstone Hotel.* Home-made teas. **Adm £3, chd free. Sun 3 Aug (2-5.30). Visitors also welcome by appt June to Sept for groups of 10+.**
1¼ -acre garden surrounded by working farmland with views to Butser Hill and boats in Chichester Harbour. Trees, shrubs, colourful herbaceous borders and small walled garden with herbs, vegetables and trained fruit trees. A quiet and peaceful atmosphere with plenty of seats to enjoy the vistas within the garden and beyond.

56 THE HOUSE IN THE WOOD
Beaulieu SO42 7YN. Victoria Roberts. *New Forest. 8m NE of Lymington. Leaving the entrance to Beaulieu Motor Museum on R (B3056) take next R turn signed Ipley Cross. Take 2nd gravel drive on RH-bend, approx ½ m.* Cream teas. **Adm £4, chd free. Sun 11 May (2-6).**
Peaceful 12-acre woodland garden with continuing progress and improvement. New areas and streams have been developed and good acers planted among mature azaleas and rhododendrons. Used in the war to train the Special Operations Executive. 'A magical garden to get lost in' and popular with bird-watchers.

57 THE HYDE
Old Alresford SO24 9DH. Sue Alexander. *1m W of Alresford. From Alresford 1m along B3046 towards Basingstoke. House in centre of village, opp village green.* Home-made teas. **Adm £4, chd free. Sat 23, Sun 24, Mon 25 Aug (1.30-5).**
Tucked behind an old field hedge, a delightful ¾ -acre garden created by the owner to attract wildlife and reflect her flower arranging passion for colour and texture. Flowing borders contain an abundant mixture of perennials, half-hardies, annuals, grasses and shrubs. Wonderful ideas for late summer colour. National collection of Patrinia. Short gravel drive at entrance.

NCH

58 THE ISLAND
Greatbridge, Romsey SO51 0HP. Mr & Mrs Christopher Saunders-Davies, 01794 512100, ssd@littleroundtop.co.uk. *1m N of Romsey on A3057. Entrance alongside Greatbridge (1st bridge Xing the R Test), flanked by row of cottages on roadside.* Home-made teas. **Adm £4, chd free. Sat 19, Sun 20 July (2-5). Visitors also welcome by appt Apr to Sept for groups of 15-30 max.**
6-acres either side of the R Test. Fine display of daffodils and spring-flowering trees. Main garden has herbaceous and annual borders, fruit trees, rose pergola, lavender walk and extensive lawns. An arboretum planted in the 1930s by Sir Harold Hillier contains trees and shrubs providing interest throughout the yr. Bring your own picnic.

59 LAKE HOUSE
Northington SO24 9TG. Lord Ashburton, 07795 364539, lukeroeder@hotmail.com. *4m N of Alresford. Off B3046. Follow English Heritage signs to The Grange, then directions.* Home-made teas. **Adm £4.50, chd free. Thur 12, Sun 15 June (12.30-5). Visitors also welcome by appt June to Sept for groups of 10+.**
2 large lakes in Candover Valley set off by mature woodland with waterfalls, abundant bird life, long landscaped vistas and folly. 1½ -acre walled garden, with rose parterre, mixed borders, long herbaceous border, rose pergola leading to moon gate. Formal kitchen garden, flowering pots, conservatory and greenhouses. Picnicking by lakes. Grass paths and slopes to some areas of the garden.

Hidden, secluded areas reveal surprise views of garden and village rooftops . . .

60 LITTLE COURT
Crawley, nr Winchester SO21 2PU. Prof & Mrs A R Elkington, 01962 776365, elkslc@tiscali.co.uk. *5m NW of Winchester. Between B3049 (Winchester - Stockbridge) and A272 (Winchester - Andover).* Home-made teas in village hall or garden for groups. **Adm £3 (Feb), £4 (Mar), chd free. Fri 21, Sun 23, Mon 24 Feb (2-5); Sun 30 Mar (2-5.30); Fri 20, Sun 22, Tue 24 Feb 2015 (2-5). Also open with Crawley Gardens on 21, 22 Apr; 11, 13 May; 12, 15 June; 10, 13 July. Visitors also welcome by appt Feb to Sept.**
A traditional walled country garden, spectacular in spring, with thousands of bulbs, hellebores and snowdrops, and cowslips in the labyrinth. Large beds of perennials in harmonious colours, good lawn. 3-acres incl paddock. Fun for children: tree house, several swings. The Garden is sheltered, has many seats and beautiful views. Field with butterflies. Classic kitchen garden. In a very pretty, small village of thatched cottages.

61 LITTLEWOOD
West Lane, Hayling Island PO11 0JW. Mr & Mrs Steven Schrier. *3m S of Havant. From A27 Havant/Hayling Island junction, travel S for 2m, turn R into West Lane and continue 1m. House set back from road in wood.* Home-made teas. **Adm £3, chd free. Sat 3, Sun 4 May (11-5).**
2½ -acre bluebell wood and spring-flowering garden surrounded by fields and near sea, protected from sea winds by multi-barrier hedge. Rhododendrons, azaleas, camellias and many other shrubs. Woodland walk to full-size tree house. Features incl pond, bog garden, house plants, summerhouse, conservatory and many places to sit outside and under cover. Dogs on leads and picnickers welcome. Close to Hayling Billy coastal trail.

GROUP OPENING

62 LONGPARISH GARDENS
nr Andover SP11 6PS. *7m E of Andover. Off A303. To village centre on B3048. Parking at Lower Mill only, except for disabled.* Home-made teas at Longmead House. **Combined adm £7, chd free. Sun 8, Mon 9 June (2-6).**

LONGMEAD HOUSE
John & Wendy Ellicock

LOWER MILL
Mill Lane. Mrs K-M Dinesen

Longparish is a small beautiful village on R Test with many thatched cottages. Two gardens offer a wide variety of interest. The 2-acre organic and wildlife garden at Longmead House is full of interest with a large, hedged vegetable garden with deep beds, polytunnel, greenhouse, fruit cage and composting area. There are two wildlife ponds and a wild-flower meadow, as well as herbaceous and shrub borders and a woodland walk. Magnificent trees and water are the keys at Lower Mill, a mainly informally planted 15-acre garden on the R Test which delights at every turn. Teardrop-shaped beds are boldly planted with shrubs and underplanted with swathes of grasses and perennials. Harmonious borders around the house lead to a hidden sunken garden and an immaculate water garden. Riverside walks, vegetable garden and wildlife lake await your discovery. Limited wheelchair access at Lower Mill.

63 LONGSTOCK PARK
Leckford, Stockbridge SO20 6EH. Leckford Estate Ltd, part of John Lewis Partnership, www.longstockpark.co.uk. *4m S of Andover. From A30 turn N on to A3057; follow signs to Longstock.* Home-made teas at Longstock Park Nursery. **Adm £5, chd £1. Sun 15 June (2-5).**
Famous water garden with extensive collection of aquatic and bog plants set in 7-acres of woodland with rhododendrons and azaleas. A walk through park leads to National Collections of *Buddleja* and *Clematis viticella*; arboretum, herbaceous border. Assistance dogs only.

NCH

64 ◆ MACPENNYS WOODLAND GARDEN & NURSERIES
Burley Road, Bransgore, Christchurch BH23 8DB. Mr & Mrs T M Lowndes, 01425 672348, www.macpennys.co.uk. *6m S of Ringwood, 5m NE of Christchurch. From Crown PH Xrds in Bransgore take Burley Rd. Entrance ¼ m on R.* **For opening times and information, please phone or see garden website.**
12-acres of nursery with 4-acre gravel pit converted into woodland garden planted with many unusual plants. Offering interest yr-round, but particularly in spring and autumn. Large nursery displaying a wide selection of trees, shrubs, conifers, perennials, hedging plants, fruit trees and bushes. Partial wheelchair access.

65 1 & 2 MAPLE COTTAGE
Searles Lane, off London Road (A30), Hook RG27 9EQ. John & Pat Beagley. *A30: Hartley Wintney side of Hook opp Hampshire Prestige Cars. Use Hook House overflow car park, immed on L. ¼ m up lane to entrance and parking for those with walking difficulties. Follow yellow ribbons.* Home-made teas. **Adm £3, chd free. Wed 4, Thur 5, Sun 8, Wed 11, Thur 12 June (2-5).**
1-acre offering 2 differing established gardens; views towards R Whitewater. Mature fruit trees and shrubs, vegetable plots, cottage-style herbaceous borders, courtyard garden, small wildlife pond named hostas. 'Tree cave' for children. Relax with tea and home-made cakes, listen for call of buzzards soaring overhead. Good selection of birds, including nest box with camera - residents may be home. Some paved paths, mainly grassed areas.

66 MEON ORCHARD
Kingsmead, N of Wickham PO17 5AU. Doug & Linda Smith. *5m N of Fareham. From Wickham take A32 N for 1½ m. Turn L at Roebuck Inn. Continue ½ m. Park on verge.* Home-made teas. **Adm £3.50, chd free. Sun 1 June, Sun 27 July, Sun 7 Sept (2-6).**
1½ -acre garden designed and constructed by current owners. An exceptional range of rare, unusual and architectural plants incl National Collections of Eucalyptus. Dramatic foliage plants from around the world, both hardy and tender. Big bananas, huge taros, tree ferns, cannas, gingers and palms dominate in Sept, flowering shrubs in May/June and perennials in July. Streams and ponds plus an extensive range of planters complete the display. See plants you have never seen before. Plant sale of the exotic and rare Sun 7 Sept. Garden fully accessible by wheelchair, reserved parking.

NCH

67 MERDON MANOR
Merdon Castle Lane, Hursley SO21 2JJ. Mr & Mrs J C Smith, 01962 775215 or 775281, vronk@bluebottle.com. *5m SW of Winchester. From A3090 Winchester to Romsey road, turn R at Standon, Merdon Castle Lane, proceed 1½ m. Entrance on R between two curving brick walls.* Home-made teas. **Adm £4, chd free. Sun 15 June (2-6).**

Visitors also welcome by appt May to Sept.
5-acre country garden surrounded by spectacular views with ha-ha to keep the black sheep in their field. Roses, shrub walk, container plants, wild pond, with special secret walled garden. Wonderfully tranquil and quiet.

68 MICHAELMAS

2 Old Street, Hill Head, Fareham PO14 3HU. Ros & Jack Wilson, 01329 662593, jazzjack00@gmail.com. *4½ m S of Fareham. From Fareham follow signs to Stubbington, then Hill Head. Turn R into Bells Lane. After 1m pass Osborne View PH on L, next R is Old St.* Home-made teas. **Adm £3, chd free. Sun 13, Mon 14 July (2-5). Visitors also welcome by appt July to Aug for groups of 10-20.**
Very cheerful, colourful small garden with the 'wow' factor. A variety of tall plants for a tall lady! Many are grown from seed or cuttings. Small vegetable garden, greenhouse, garden room, pot-grown vegetables and flowers. Styled in the fashion of a country garden with a wide range of plants with the emphasis on perennials. As pictured in preface of The Gardens of England book. 1-min walk from beach, 5-mins walk from Titchfield Haven Nature Reserve.

69 THE MILL AT GORDLETON

Silver Street, Sway, Lymington SO41 6DJ. Mrs Liz Cottingham, 01590 682219, info@themillatgordleton.co.uk, www.themillatgordleton.co.uk. *2m W of Lymington. From Lymington town centre head N on A337, in 500yds turn L after The Toll House PH, for Sway and Hordle. Garden is 2m. Tickets available from Reception Desk.* Light refreshments. **Adm £3. Every Mon 6 Jan to 1 Dec (11-4) excl Bank Hols.**
This old mill is now a small country hotel. The meandering stream which bisects the garden has many areas of different character. The Mill Art Walk is a fascinating display of metal, glass and wooden sculptures created by local artists. Salmon, trout and duck are abundant in the river. Plentiful seating.

21 Chestnut Road

GROUP OPENING

70 MONXTON & AMPORT GARDENS

Amport SP11 8AY. *3m SW of Andover. Turn off A303 signed to East Cholderton from E or Thruxton Village from W. Follow signs to Amport. Parking in field next to village green.* Refreshments at Monxton and Amport Village Hall. **Combined adm £5, chd free. Sun 25, Mon 26 May (2-5.30).**

AMPORT PARK MEWS
Amport Park Mews Ltd

BRIDGE COTTAGE
Jenny Burroughs

NEW **FLEUR DE LYS**
Ian & Jane Morrison

WHITE GABLES
Mr & Mrs D Eaglesham

Monxton and Amport are two pretty villages linked by Pill Hill Brook. Visitors have four gardens to enjoy. **Bridge Cottage** is a 2-acre haven for wildlife, with the banks of the trout stream and lake planted informally with drifts of colour, a large vegetable garden (not suitable for wheelchairs), fruit cage, small mixed orchard and arboretum with specimen trees. **Amport Park Mews** has 11 borders arranged around a communal space surrounded by converted stable/carriage blocks in historic mews. New for 2014, the garden at **Fleur de Lys** is in five parts separated by mixed borders, yew and thuja hedges and has many amusing features. These lead onto the orchard which until 6-yrs-ago was part of the adjacent farm. This consists of symmetrical groups of English ornamental trees. **White Gables** has a collection of interesting trees, incl a young giant redwood - an unexpected feature in a cottage-style garden, along with old roses and herbaceous plants. The 1/6 -acre garden leads down to Pill Hill Brook. No wheelchair access to White Gables.

The Hyde

© Leigh Clapp

71 MOORE BLATCH

48 High Street, Lymington SO41 9ZQ. *Top end of Lymington High St, on S side. Follow signs for Lymington town centre and use High St car parks.* Home-made teas. **Adm £3.50, chd free. Sat 26 Apr (9-1), Sun 27 Apr (2-5).**

Situated behind this elegant Georgian town house lies a surprising S-facing walled garden of 1-acre. From the raised terrace, enjoy the long vista across the croquet lawn to mature gardens beyond and then over to the Isle of Wight. Amusing and varied topiary interplanted with stunning tulips and forget-me-nots. Lymington Saturday Market and lively waterfront at bottom of High St.

72 ◆ MOTTISFONT ABBEY & GARDEN

Romsey SO51 0LP. National Trust, 01794 340757, www.nationaltrust.org.uk. *4 1/2 m NW of Romsey. From A3057 Romsey to Stockbridge road, turn W at sign to Mottisfont.* **For opening times and information, please phone or see garden website.**

Built C12 as Augustinian priory, now house of some note. 30-acre landscaped garden incl spring or 'font', from which house derives its name, magnificent ancient trees and walled gardens with National Collection of over 300 varieties of old roses. Tranquil walks in grounds, along the R Test and in the glorious countryside of the estate. Large developing Winter Garden, and thousands more spring bulbs.

NCH

73 23 NEW BRIGHTON ROAD

Emsworth PO10 7PR. Lucy Watson & Mike Rogers, 01243 699669, lucywatson100@hotmail.com. *N of Emsworth. From main Emsworth r'about head N. Underneath railway bridge and flyover. Garden immed on L up the slope. Park at recreation ground if no room on road.* **Adm £5, chd free, incl wine and nibbles. Fri 27 June (4.30-8.30). Visitors also welcome by appt June to Aug.**

Wide range of plants and ornaments in 250ft long, narrow garden. Ranging from full sun to full shade, the informal planting maximises the available space. A large number of containers, several ponds, greenhouse, shady reading area and mixed borders give yr-round interest. Unusual plants and unusual garden for the plantsperson. Library/summerhouse, wildlife pond and display of old garden tools. New gravel garden and formal pond area. Opening will incl classical guitar music by local musician Peter Rogers.

74 67 NEWTOWN ROAD

Warsash, Southampton SO31 9GA. Pauline & Simon, 01489 600534, gardensweekly@hotmail.co.uk, www.gardensweekly.co.uk. *5m W of Fareham. M27 J8 or J9, head for Maritime College in Warsash.* Home-made teas. **Adm £3, chd free. Sat 17, Sun 18 May, Sat 16, Sun 17 Aug (11-5). Visitors also welcome by appt May to Sept.**

Cross a bridge to a small secret sloping garden with 'a little bit of everything'. Pond, raised beds, perennials, an old Bramley Seedling under planted with ferns, clay snail, greenhouse, pots and a green-roof on the shed. We use every corner! An artist's garden with art work on display. Coastal walks along the Hamble path with D-Day Memorial. Best garden in the Peter Maunder Hampshire Federation of Horticultural Societies garden competition.

D

75 OLD ALRESFORD HOUSE

Colden Lane, Old Alresford, Alresford SO24 9DY. Mike Hall & Shuna MacKillop, www.oldalresfordhouse.com. *7m E of Winchester. Turn down Broad St in centre of Alresford; as you arrive at Old Alresford church is on R with car park opp.* Home-made teas and wine. Soup served in Nov. **Adm £6, chd free. Sun 22, Wed 25 June, Sun 2, Wed 5 Nov (10-5).**

C18 landscape garden (Grade II listed) restored from original plans. 22-acre parkland with rare breeds, wild flowers and vineyard surrounded by 13-acre gardens and perimeter woodland walk (30 mins) featuring ha-ha, immaculate lawns, shrubberies, wildlife ponds, chalk stream with bog garden and boardwalk. Views and vistas. Also, contemporary Mediterranean walled garden and fern garden. Illustrated talk by owner at 11am & 2pm (40 mins). Awarded Commendation for Best restoration of a Georgian garden by the Georgian Group 2012. Perimeter walk bumpy in places. Chalk stream not wheelchair accessible but beautiful views from coach road above. **NB: Dogs welcome Weds only.**

76 NEW OLD DROXFORD STATION

Station Road, Soberton, Southampton SO32 3QU. Jo & Tony Williams, 01489 878271. *12m E of Winchester, 12m SW of Petersfield. A32 N through Droxford. After ½ m turn R (opp petrol station), under bridge, turn R, property first on R, park in road.* **Adm £3.50, chd free. Sat 12, Sun 13 July (11-5).**

A sympathetically restored railway station with wild flower garden in the former track. Established specimen trees, perennials, annuals and bulbs. Raised vegetable beds, greenhouse and a new orchard. Winston Churchill was based here before D Day. Please call to arrange disability parking.

77 THE OLD RECTORY, WINCHFIELD

Bagwell Lane, Winchfield, Hook RG27 8DB. George & Sarah Adams. *4m S of M3 J5. A287 towards Farnham. At dual carriageway L into London Rd. 1st R into Bagwell Lane to St Mary's Church. Entrance on R, drive approx 500yds.* Home-made teas. **Adm £3.50, chd free. Sun 25 May (2-6).**

The Old Rectory Winchfield is adjacent to Grade I Norman church. 3-acres plus extensive woodland walks. Formal topiary with areas of different character to explore. Wild flowers with formal close-mown paths in grid pattern. Swimming pool is now a handsome pond. Broad views to surrounding fields with lambs and woodland.

GROUP OPENING

78 OLD THATCH & THE MILLENNIUM BARN

Sprats Hatch Lane, Winchfield, Hook RG27 8DD. *3m W of Fleet. From A287 Odiham to Farnham turn N to Dogmersfield, L by Queens Head PH and L at Barley Mow. From Winchfield to Dogmersfield, R after 1.3m at Barley Mow.* Light refreshments, music and pimms on Sat 5 Jul. **Combined adm £3, chd free. Sun 13 Apr (2-6). Evening Opening £5, chd free, wine, Sat 5 July (7-10); Sun 7 Sept (2-6).**

THE MILLENNIUM BARN
Mr & Mrs S White

OLD THATCH
Jill Ede
www.old-thatch.co.uk

Two gardens in one! A small secluded haven sits under the old oak tree next to the pond, surrounded by yr-round colour and seasonal fragrance from roses and honeysuckle. You can listen to birdsong, wind-chimes and the trickling of a small waterfall whilst enjoying views of Old Thatch and the cottage garden beyond. Who could resist visiting Old Thatch, a 'chocolate box' thatched cottage, featured on film and TV, and evolving smallholding with 5-acres garden and woodland alongside the Basingstoke Canal (unfenced). A succession of spring bulbs, a profusion of wild flowers, perennials and home-grown annuals pollinated by our own bees and fertilised by the donkeys, who await your visit. Over 30 named clematis and rose cultivars. Lambs in April, donkey foals in summer. Children: enjoy our quiz on Sundays and look-out in a tree (supervised, please). Dads love the cakes. Mums enjoy the music and candlelight in the evening. Arrive by boat! Slipway opp Barley Mow PH. Basingstoke Canal Society may have boat trips to coincide with Sunday openings. Featured in local paper and magazines. Wheelchair access by grass slopes and paths. Limited disabled parking on site (ask at car park entrance).

79 ORDNANCE HOUSE

West Dean, Salisbury SP5 1JE. Terry & Vanessa Winters, 01794 341797, terry.winters@ordnancehouse.com, www.ordnancehouse.com. *7m W of Romsey. Park at West Dean Recreation Ground, 350 yds away. Disability parking only at garden.* **Adm £3.50, chd free. Suns 25 May, 22 June (1-5). Visitors also welcome by appt May to July.**

A ¾ -acre garden designed and planted by owners from 2011. Herbaceous beds, orchard, soft fruit and vegetable gardens. Formal parterre and spectacular alliums and foxgloves. Use of unusual varieties of lavender. Seating areas with garden views of surrounding countryside and walks to Dean Hill. Featured on Wiltshire Society Magazine.

80 ◆ PATRICK'S PATCH

Fairweather's Garden Centre, High Street, Beaulieu SO42 7YB. Mr P Fairweather, 01590 612307, www.fairweathers.co.uk. *SE of New Forest at head of Beaulieu River. Leave M27 at J2 and follow signs for Beaulieu Motor Museum. Go up High St and park in Fairweathers on LH-side.* **Adm by donation, suggested donation £2.50, chd free. For opening times and information, please phone or see garden website.**

Model kitchen garden with a full range of vegetables, trained top and soft fruit and herbs. Salads in succession used as an educational project for all ages. Maintained by volunteers, primary school children and a part-time gardener. A very productive garden enclosed by walls built from New Forest heather bales and local softwood.

A sympathetically restored railway station with wild flower garden in the former track . . .

81 PILLEY HILL COTTAGE

Pilley Hill, Pilley, Lymington SO41 5QF. Steph & Sandy Glen, 01590 677844, stephglen@hotmail.co.uk, www.pilleyhillcottage.com. *New Forest. 2m N of Lymington off A337. To avoid traffic delays in Lyndhurst leave M27 at J2.* Cream teas. **Adm £6, chd free. Visitors welcome by appt Apr to July for groups of 20+ (adm incl cream teas).**

Naturalistic, wildlife-friendly garden of surprises around every corner. Enter through the rose-covered lych-gate, to a spectacle of colour. Wild flowers rub shoulders with perennials among quaint objects and oak structures. Meander through the wild old orchard through willow walks and oak archways, on to the shady pond garden. Take tea on the front lawn surrounded by herbaceous borders. Raffle and children's quiz.

82 PYLEWELL PARK

South Baddesley, Lymington SO41 5SJ. Lord Teynham. *Coast road 2m E of Lymington. From Lymington follow signs for Car Ferry to Isle of Wight, continue for 2m to South Baddesley.* Home-made teas. **Adm £3.50, chd free (share to St Mary's Church). Sun 20 Apr, Sun 25 May (2-5).**

A large parkland garden, laid out in 1890. Enjoy a walk along the extensive grass paths, bordered by rhododendrons, magnolias, embothriums and cornus. Wild daffodils in bloom at Easter and bluebells in May. Large lakes are bordered by giant gunnera - on to magnificent views of the Solent. Lovely for families and dogs. Wear suitable footwear for muddy areas.

GROUP OPENING

83 ROMSEY GARDENS

Romsey SO51 8EQ. *Town centre, all gardens within walking distance of Romsey Abbey, clearly signed. Car parking by King John's Garden.* Home-made teas at King John's House. **Combined adm £6, chd free. Sun 25, Mon 26 May (11-5.30).**

KING JOHN'S GARDEN
Friends of King John's Garden & Test Valley Borough

THE LAKE HOUSE
64 Mill Lane. David & Lorraine Henley

4 MILL LANE
Miss J Flindall
Visitors also welcome by appt Mar to Oct with coaches by prior arrangement.
01794 513926

Romsey is a small, unspoilt, historic market town with the majestic C12 Norman Abbey as a backdrop to **4 Mill Lane**, a garden described by Joe Swift as 'the best solution for a long thin garden with a view'. **King John's Garden**, with its fascinating listed C13 house, has all period plants that were available before 1700. It also has an award-winning Victorian garden with a courtyard where tea is served (no dogs here, please). **The Lake House** has 4½-acres and a large meadow, lake to walk round and a pastoral view. It is a very tranquil place, yet is only 5 mins from the centre of Romsey. Spot the kingfishers if you're lucky!. No wheelchair access at 4 Mill Lane.

84 ROTHERFIELD PARK

East Tisted, Alton GU34 3QE. Sir James & Lady Scott. *4m S of Alton on A32.* Home-made teas. **Adm £4, chd free. Sun 4 May (2-5).**

Take some ancient ingredients: ice house, ha-ha, lime avenue; add a walled garden, fruit and vegetables, trees and hedges; set this 12-acre plot in an early C19 park (picnic here from noon) with views to coin clichés about. Mix in a bluebell wood and Kim Wilkie's modern take on an amphitheatre by the stable block. Good disabled access to walled garden.

85 ST CHRISTOPHER'S

Whitsbury, Fordingbridge SP6 3PZ. Christine Southey & David Mussell, 01725 518404, chrismarysouthey@gmail.com. *3½ m NW of Fordingbridge. In village centre, 200yds down from Cartwheel PH.* Home-made teas in village hall 120yds away. **Adm £3.50, chd free. Sun 13, Sun 27 Apr (2-5). Visitors also welcome by appt Mar to June for groups of 20+.**

Tranquil, ¾ -acre, long sloping garden with superb views. Alpines in S-facing scree bed with unusual beds, incl dwarf iris, tulips and narcissi, and alpine troughs. In spring, wild banks of bluebells and primroses, fern bed with erythroniums, hellebores, anemone blanda and many shrubs. Pond and bog gardens full of primula. In summer, 25ft rambling roses, beds of delphiniums, eremurus and many herbaceous treasures. Fruit and vegetable garden.

86 SANDY SLOPES

Honeysuckle Lane, Headley Down, Bordon GU35 8EH. Mr & Mrs R Thornton, 01428 717604. *6m S of Farnham. Off B3004 and W of A3 Hindhead tunnel, via Grayshott.* **Adm £3, chd free. Mon 5, Mon 26 May (2-5).**

A plantsman's garden with a remarkable collection of mature plants from China and other parts of the world. Many of these are rare and exciting. Some are naturalised and many are shade lovers such as trilliums, areseamas, primulas and rare blue meconopsis growing beneath mature rhododendrons, magnolias and rare trees. Rising terraced ground with a stream and wildlife pond. Steep slopes and steps, unsuitable for pushchairs and very young children.

87 'SELBORNE'

Caker Lane, East Worldham GU34 3AE. Brian & Mary Jones, 01420 83389, mary.trigwell-jones@virgin.net. *2m SE of Alton. On B3004 at Alton end of East Worldham opp The Three Horseshoes PH (please note, NOT in the village of Selborne). Parking signed.* Home-made teas. **Adm £3, chd free (share to East Worldham Church Fabric Fund in Apr and Tafara Mission Zimbabwe in Aug). Sat 19, Sun 20, Mon 21 Apr, Sat 10, Sun 11 May, Sat 2, Sun 3, Mon 4 Aug (2-5). Also open with East Worldham Gardens on 28, 29 June; 26, 27 July. Visitors also welcome by appt Apr to Aug for individuals and groups.**

Full of surprises, this ½ -acre mature garden features an old established orchard of named varieties. Meandering paths provide views across farmland. Mixed borders of hardy geraniums and other herbaceous plants and shrubs. Soft fruit garden, containers, metal and stone sculpture. A garden to relax in. Enjoy tea sitting in the dappled shade of the orchard. Summerhouses and conservatory provide shelter. Book stall, garden quizzes for children, sandpit. Some gravel paths.

88 SHALDEN PARK HOUSE

The Avenue, Shalden, Alton GU34 4DS. Mr & Mrs Michael Campbell. *4½ m NW of Alton. B3349 from Alton or J5 M3 onto B3349. Turn W at Golden Pot PH*

marked Herriard, Lasham, Shalden. Entrance 1/4 m on L. Home-made teas. **Adm £4, chd free. Sun 1 June (2-5).**
Large 4-acre garden to stroll round, with beautiful views. Herbaceous borders incl kitchen walk and rose garden, all with large-scale planting and foliage interest. Pond, pool, arboretum, perfect kitchen garden and garden statuary.

89 2 SHENLEY CLOSE

Fareham PO15 5PL. Sue Withecombe. *1m W of Fareham. M27 J9 A27 to Fareham. At top of Titchfield Hill L at T-lights into Highlands Rd. 4th L into Greyfriars Rd, L into Abbeyfield, R into Shenley Close.* Home-made teas. **Adm £3, chd free. Mon 26, Tue 27 May (11-4).**
Small, interesting peaceful garden. Sweeping rockeries with alpines, azaleas, acers, firs and heathers. Clematis and wisteria cover archways and seating areas. Water features incl large koi pond and a wildlife pond with frogs. Borders with striking perennials, troughs, tubs, baskets and window boxes fill the garden with colour and fragrance. Gold and overall winner large back garden Fareham in Bloom. Limited wheelchair access, assistance available where necessary.

GROUP OPENING

90 SOUTHSEA GARDENS

Southsea, Portsmouth PO4 0PR. *St Ronan's Rd can be found off Albert Rd, Southsea.* Home-made teas in July, and wine in Sept, at 87 St Ronan's Road. **Combined adm £3 (July), £5 (Sept), chd free. Sun 6 July (2-6); Sat 6 Sept (4-8).**

85 ST RONAN'S ROAD
Mr Mike Hodges

87 ST RONAN'S ROAD
Miss Judy Walker

Two town gardens conveniently next door to each other. Each has a distinctive style, with different designs showing what can be achieved in an urban setting. **85 St Ronan's Road** is a city garden with a classical twist, featuring a Neptune water feature in a pool of smoke. The 'inside-out' garden at **87 St Ronan's Road** captures busy urban living at its best, with an impressive dining area and sitting room with a permanent outside fireplace. Clever evergreen planting has been used to create privacy in a city setting. Garden lighting gives these gardens a magical feeling at night and can been seen on our second opening. Both gardens have won national landscape design awards and have been featured on TV. Inside Outside garden featured in Woman & Home (Summer 2013).

91 SPINDLES

24 Wootton Road, Lee-on-the-Solent, Portsmouth PO13 9HB. Peter & Angela Arnold, 02393 115181, elijahblew22@sky.com. *Approx 6m S of Fareham. Exit A27, turn L Gosport Rd A32. At r'about 2nd exit Newgate Lane B3385. Through 3 r'abouts, turn L Marine Parade B3333 onto Wootton Rd.* Home-made teas. **Adm £3, chd free. Sat 21 June, Sat 19 July (2-6). Visitors also welcome by appt May to July for groups of 30 max.**
An exciting and constantly changing garden, cottage style planting alongside exotic and tropicals. Creative use of every available space, fine display of roses and clematis, tiny pond and bog garden. Hostas, ferns, herbs, grasses, succulents, grapes, fig and olive.

92 THE STABLE FAMILY HOME TRUST GARDEN

The Stables, Bisterne, Ringwood BH24 3BN. Mrs Marion Davies, 01425 485090, mariondavies@sfht.org.uk. *3 1/2 m S of Ringwood. Follow B3347 through Bisterne Village from Ringwood. Past Manor House, entrance on L.* Cream teas. **Adm £3.50, chd free (share to SFHT). Sat 24, Sun 25 May (2-5.30). Visitors also welcome by appt May to June.**
3 walled gardens lovingly tended by our head gardener and some of the 100 adults with learning difficulties in our care. Gravel garden a riot of colour with flowers, shrubs and herbs and adorned with pottery objects made here. Kitchen garden with polytunnels, greenhouse and raised vegetable beds. The small rose garden is a place of peace, leading to main lawn with pond and dragon-head fountain, also made in our pottery.

GROUP OPENING

93 STOCKBRIDGE GARDENS

Stockbridge SO20 6EX. *9m W of Winchester. On A30, at junction of A3057 and B3049. Parking on High St. All gardens on High St/Winton Hill.* Tea on St Peter's Church Lawn. **Combined adm £6, chd free (share to St Peter's Church). Thur 12, Sun 15 June (2-5.30).**

LITTLE WYKE
High Street. Mrs Mary Matthews

THE OLD RECTORY
High Street. Mr Robin Colenso

SHEPHERDS HOUSE
Winton Hill. Kim & Frances Candler

TROUT COTTAGE
High Street. Mrs Sally Milligan

Stockbridge with its many listed houses, excellent shops and pubs is on the famous R Test. Four gardens are open this year offering a variety of styles and character. Tucked in behind the High Street, **Trout Cottage's** small walled garden flowers for almost 10 months of the year. **Little Wyke**, also on the High Street next to the Town Hall, has a long mature town garden with curved mixed borders and fruit trees. **The Old Rectory** is a mature garden with formal pond and planting near the house and woodland and bog areas bounded by a carrier stream of the R Test. **Shepherds House**, 50yds E of the White Hart r'about, is a S-facing, 3/4-acre garden on rising ground around a Georgian house. Continuing renovation incl lawns and terraces, mixed borders, ponds, small orchard and viewpoint overlooking the village. Many excellent small shops in the village.

Clever evergreen planting has been used to create privacy in a city setting . . .

Explore contrasting areas, linked by vistas, with a theme of circles and ovals . . .

GROUP OPENING

94 SWAY VILLAGE GARDENS

Sway SO41 6DT. *8m S of Lyndhurst, 4m NW of Lymington. From A337 Lyndhurst to Lymington Rd take B3055 signposted to Sway at Brockenhurst and turn R into Sway Village. Follow NGS signs.* Home-made teas at Ashen Bank and 12 Gilpin Hill only. **Combined adm £5, chd free. Sat 3, Sun 4, Sat 24, Sun 25 May (12-5).**

ASHEN BANK
Adlams Lane. Richard & Deborah Walker
01590 681014
ashenbank@yahoo.co.uk
www.ashenbank.com

12 GILPIN HILL
Jack & Sonia McPhie.
Visitors also welcome by appt Apr to Sept.
01590 682312
jack.mcphie@tiscali.co.uk

HIGH FOREST
Manchester Road. David & Karen Ball

Sway Village lies deep in the heart of the New Forest National Park, with its roaming cattle and ponies along with miles of lowland heath. Three complementary gardens are located within easy walking distance of each other close to Sway Village centre. **Ashen Bank** is a mature haven of trees and shrubs set in a ½ -acre tranquil setting. Beautiful old apple trees are underplanted with azaleas, hellebores and spring bulbs. Mature shrubs provide a wonderful background for the spring flowers. **12 Gilpin Hill** has a small garden packed with a wide variety of unusual plants and trees. A wooded area and a bog area planted with candelabra primulas surround a pond which is a haven for dragonflies, frogs and newts. **High Forest** is a 1½ -acre mature woodland garden with a mind of its own. Colourful rhododendrons, camellias, shrubs, perennials, roses, lawns and pools are contained within a peaceful setting. Large terrace with space for picnics with partial wheelchair access. All three gardens have good wheelchair access but with some areas restricted.

95 TANGLEFOOT

Crawley, Winchester SO21 2QB. Mr & Mrs F J Fratter, 01962 776243, fred@tanglefoot-house.demon.co.uk. *5m NW of Winchester. Between B3049 (Winchester - Stockbridge) and A272 (Winchester - Andover). Lane beside Crawley Court (Arqiva). Drop-off at house; parking in field 50yds.* **Adm £3.50, chd free. Thur 24, Sun 27 July (2-5.30). Also open with Crawley Gardens 11, 13 May; 12, 15 June; 10, 13 July. Visitors also welcome by appt May to July.**

Designed and developed by owners since 1976, Tanglefoot's ½ -acre garden is a blend of influences, from Monet-inspired rose arch and small wildlife pond to Victorian boundary wall with trained fruit trees. Highlights include a raised lily pond, wild-flower meadow, herbaceous bed (a riot of colour later in the summer), herb wheel, large productive kitchen garden and unusual flowering plants. Plants from the garden for sale.

96 TERSTAN

Longstock, Stockbridge SO20 6DW. Alexander & Penny Burnfield, penny.burnfield@andover.co.uk, www.pennyburnfield.wordpress.com. *½ m N of Stockbridge. From Stockbridge (A30) turn N to Longstock at bridge. Garden ½ m on R.* Home-made teas. **Adm £4, chd free. Sun 11 May, Sun 15 June, Sun 6 July, Sun 3 Aug (2-6). Visitors also welcome by appt May to Aug. Coaches by prior arrangement only.**

A country garden for the C21. Unusual plants, an ever-changing display of half-hardy specimens in pots, and an artist's eye for colour. Secluded and peaceful, with views to the R Test and the Hampshire Downs. Explore contrasting areas, linked by vistas, with a theme of circles and ovals. Featured in Countryside magazine. Some gravel paths and steps.

97 NEW THE THATCHED COTTAGE

Church Road, Upper Farringdon, Alton GU34 3EG. Mr & Mrs David & Cally Horton, 01420 587922. *3m S of Alton off A32. At S end of Lower Farringdon take road to Upper Farringdon. At top of hill turn L into Church Rd, follow road to cottage on right opp church.* **Adm £3.50, chd free. Sun 1, Sun 22 June, Sun 20 July (2.30-5). Also open with Berry Cottage (next door). Visitors also welcome by appt Mar to Sept for groups of 10+.**

A once neglected 1½ -acre garden that has been lovingly restored over the last 2-yrs. Running south from a beautiful C16 thatched cottage the formal lawn and packed borders blend into more informal areas of perennial and shrub planting, to vegetables, fruit and wild flowers surrounding a gypsy caravan. Chickens ducks and guinea fowl. Fully accessible by wheelchair after a short gravel drive.

TRANTOR HOUSE

See Wiltshire

98 TYLNEY HALL HOTEL

Ridge Lane, Rotherwick RG27 9AZ. Elite Hotels, 01256 764881, sales@tylneyhall.com, www.tylneyhall.com. *3m NW of Hook. From M3 J5 via A287 and Newnham, M4 J11 via B3349 and Rotherwick.* Light refreshments. **Adm £4, chd free. Sun 27 Apr, Sun 8 June, Sun 5 Oct (10-4).**

Large garden of 66-acres with extensive woodlands and fine vista being restored with new planting. Fine avenues of wellingtonias; rhododendrons and azaleas, Italian garden, lakes, large water and rock garden, dry-stone walls originally designed with assistance of Gertrude Jekyll.

Gilberts Nursery

© Leigh Clapp

99 UPHAM FARM

Upham SO32 1JD. Penny Walker. *2m NW of Bishop's Waltham. Turn into Upham St from B2177, then ½ m on R just past post box turn R into farmyard*. Home-made teas. **Adm £3.50, chd free. Sun 31 Aug (2-6). Also open with Blackdown House.**

Established 1½ -acre garden with mature trees and shrubs. Borders recently renovated with new plantings of perennials. Features incl a 'hot' border, a new woodland garden and an exciting extension to the wild-flower meadow with mass plantings of ornamental grasses leading down to a lake. Together with a traditional orchard, rose garden and productive kitchen garden, Upham Farm is well worth a visit. Gravel drive and path to garden.

100 WALBURY

Lower Froyle, Alton GU34 4LJ. Ernie & Brenda Milam, 01420 22216, walbury@uwclub.net. *5m NE of Alton. Access to Lower Froyle from A31 between Alton and Farnham at Bentley. Parking available nr Walbury, at village hall*. Home-made teas. **Adm £3, chd free. Sat 26, Sun 27 Apr, Thur 3 July (2-5). Also open with Froyle Gardens on 7, 8 June. Visitors also welcome by appt Apr to June.**

One garden (⅓-acre) in 3 sections. All sections have a cottage-garden atmosphere in different styles. Each one is packed with plants in colour-themed borders incl many unusual plants. There are water features, an alpine house and fern walk. Featured in Hampshire Life April 2013. Suitable for wheel chairs in 2 of the 3 sections of the garden.

101 WALDRONS

Brook, Bramshaw SO43 7HE. Major & Mrs J Robinson, 02380 813367, jrobinson08@btinternet.com. *4m N of Lyndhurst. On B3079 1m W from J1 M27. 1st house L past Green Dragon PH and directly opp Bell PH*. Home-made teas. **Adm £3, chd free. Sun 29 June (2-5). Visitors also welcome by appt June to July for groups of 20 max.**

Come and be suprised by our 1-acre garden hidden behind a high hedge on the edge of the New Forest. The garden contains a raised alpine garden, raised vegetable beds, fruit cage, a fern and hosta wooded area, a green house and large herbaceous beds with shrubs and unusual plants giving yr-round colour.

102 WALHAMPTON

Beaulieu Road, Walhampton, Lymington SO41 5ZG. Walhampton School Trust Ltd, 01590 677246, d.hill@walhampton.com. *1m E of Lymington. From Lymington follow signs to Beaulieu (B3054) for 1m and turn R into main entrance at 1st school sign 200yds after top of hill*. **Adm £4.50, chd free (share to St John's Church, Boldre). Sun 11 May (2-5). Visitors also welcome by appt Mar to May for groups of 10-20.**

Glorious walks through large C18 landscape garden surrounding magnificent mansion (not open). Visitors discover 3 lakes, serpentine canal, climbable prospect mount, period former banana house/orangery, fascinating shell grotto, glade and terrace by Peto (c1907), drives and colonnade by Mawson (c1914). Seating, guided tours with garden history. Gravel paths, some slopes.

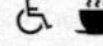

103 WEIR HOUSE

Abbotstone Road, Old Alresford SO24 9DG. Mr & Mrs G Hollingbery, 01962 735549, jhollingbery@me.com. *½ m N of Alresford. From Alresford down Broad St (B3046) past Globe PH. Take 1st L, signed Abbotstone. Park in signed field*. **Adm £5, chd free. Sun 25 May, Sun 14 Sept (2-5). Visitors also welcome by appt May to Sept for groups of 10+.**

Spectacular riverside garden with sweeping lawn backed by old walls, yew buttresses and mixed perennial beds. Contemporary vegetable and cut flower garden at its height in Sept. Also incl newly designed garden around pool area, bog garden (at best in May) and wilder walkways through wooded areas. Children can use the playground at their own risk. Wheelchair access to most of garden.

Conhholt Park

104 WEST SILCHESTER HALL
Silchester RG7 2LX. Mrs Jenny Jowett, 0118 970 0278, www.jennyjowett.com. *9m N of Basingstoke. 9m S of Reading, off A340 (signed from centre of village).* Home-made teas. **Adm £3.50, chd free. Sun 25, Mon 26 May, Sun 13 July, Sun 3 Aug (2-6). Visitors also welcome by appt May to Sept for groups of 10+, coaches welcome.**
This much loved 2-acre garden has fascinating colour combinations inspired by the artist owners with many spectacular herbaceous borders filled with rare and unusual plants flowering over a long period. Many pots filled with half hardies, a wild garden surrounding a natural pond, banks of rhododendron, a self supporting kitchen garden with lovely views across a field of grazing cattle. Dig during August at nearby Roman site of Silchester. Large studio with exhibition of the owners botanical, landscape and portrait paintings. Gravel drive, most of the garden suitable for wheelchairs.

105 WHEATLEY HOUSE
between Binsted and Kingsley GU35 9PA. Mr & Mrs Michael Adlington, 01420 23113, susannah@westcove.ie. *4m E of Alton, 5m SW of Farnham. Take A31 to Bentley, follow sign to Bordon. After 2m, R at Jolly Farmer PH towards Binsted, 1m L and follow signs to Wheatley.* Home-made teas. **Adm £4, chd free. Sat 16, Sun 17 Aug (1.30-5.30). Visitors also welcome by appt Apr to Oct with refreshments by arrangement.**
Magnificent setting with panoramic views over fields and forests. Sweeping mixed borders, shrubberies and grasses. 1½ acres, designed by artist-owner. The colours are spectacular. Striking 'white & black' border, now with deep red accents. Local crafts and paintings in Old Barn. Wheelchair access with care on lawns, good views of garden and beyond from terrace.

106 WHISPERS
Chatter Alley, Dogmersfield RG27 8SS. Mr & Mrs John Selfe. *3m W of Fleet. Turn N to Dogmersfield off A287 Odiham to Farnham Rd. Turn L by Queen's Head PH.* Home-made teas. **Adm £4.50, chd free (share to Samantha Dickson Brain Tumour Trust). Sun 13 July (12-5).**
Visitors say you could spend all day discovering new plants in these 2-acres of manicured lawns surrounded by large borders of colourful shrubs, trees and long-flowering perennials. Alstromerias and salvias a speciality. Wild flower area, water storage system, greenhouse, kitchen garden and living sculptures. Spectacular waterfall cascades over large rock slabs and magically disappears below the terrace. A garden not to be missed. Assistance available on request over gravel entrance.

107 WICOR PRIMARY SCHOOL COMMUNITY GARDEN
Portchester, Fareham PO16 9DL. Louise Bryant. *Halfway between Portsmouth and Fareham on A27. Turn S at Seagull PH r'about into Cornaway Lane, 1st R into Hatherley Drive. Entrance to school is almost opp.* Home-made teas. **Adm £3.50, chd free. Sun 22 June, Sat 5 July (10-2).**
Beautiful school gardens tended by pupils, staff and community gardeners. Wander along the new Darwin path to see a lush orchard, tropical bed, stumpery, wildlife areas and allotment featuring Camera Obscura, one of only 12 in the south of England. The gardens are situated in historic Portchester with views of Portsdown Hill. The planting has been chosen to provide nectar and habitat for Wicor's rich wildlife. Flat ground, wheelchair access to all areas.

GROUP OPENING

108 NEW WILDHERN GARDENS

Andover SP11 0JE. *From Andover or Newbury A343. After Enham Alamein or Hurstbourne turn at Xrd to Penton Mewsey. Wildhern is 3/4 m on R. Parking at village hall.* Home-made teas in village hall. **Combined adm £5 (June), £4 (July), chd free. Sat 14, Sun 15 June, Sat 19 July (2-6).**

NEW **ELM TREE COTTAGE**
Ian & Rosie Swayne.
Open June & July dates

NEW **FINCH COTTAGE**
Ray Curtis.
Open June & July dates

NEW **OAKWOOD**
Jean Pittfield.
Open June dates only

NEW **SALTERTON COTTAGE**
Jacqueline Waller.
Open June dates only

NEW **STARLINGS**
Annie Bullen & Roy Wardale.
Open June & July dates

NEW **WALNUT COTTAGE**
Tym Paige-Dickins.
Open June dates only

NEW **WILTON COTTAGE**
Primrose Pitt.
Open June dates only

There is wonderful variety in seven different gardening styles, from the mature yr-round planting at **Oakwood** to the delightful country garden feel at **Salterton Cottage**, whose boundary is shaded by a 200-yr-old beech tree. At nearby **Elm Tree Cottage** the garden, wrapping round the old building, looks established, although it has been just 2 yrs in the making. In the centre of the village, mature lawns, beds and borders are full of interest at **Finch Cottage** and **Walnut Cottage**, with a wonderful vegetable garden at the former and fruit trees, including a peach, a pear - and a walnut at the latter. **Starlings** is newly planted with a sunken gravel garden full of nectar-bearing plants and grasses, shady lawns, enclosed vegetable beds shared by chickens and a tortoise, while meticulous attention to detail makes the beautiful part-walled garden at **Wilton Cottage** with its rose and clematis filled pergola, pond and well-planted borders a delight. No wheelchair access to sunken gravel garden at Starlings which may be viewed from pathway.

109 WILLOWS

Pilley Hill, Boldre, Lymington SO41 5QF. Elizabeth & Martin Walker, 01590 677415, elizabethwalker13@gmail.com, www.willowsgarden.co.uk. *New Forest. 2m N Lymington off A337. To avoid traffic in Lyndhust, leave M27 at J2 and follow 'Heavy Lorry Route'.* Cream teas. **Adm £3.50, chd free. Sat 26, Sun 27 July, Sat 9, Sun 10, Sun 24, Mon 25, Sat 30, Sun 31 Aug (2-5). Visitors also welcome by appt July to Sept for groups of 20+.**
Vibrant late summer borders of colour-themed dahlias, zinnias, cannas and contrasting miscanthus frame Willows front lawn. Statuesque bamboos, giant gunnera manicata, reed grass and hostas surround the pond and bogs. Hidden paths through the fernery lead to the upper lawn - surrounded by colourful coleus, dark-leaved dahlias and flowing grasses. Plant Sale Sun 24 Aug. Four of the best New Forest Nurseries attending, incl Chelsea Gold medal winners Heucheraholics.

110 1 WOGSBARNE COTTAGES

Rotherwick RG27 9BL. Miss S & Mr R Whistler. *2 1/2 m N of Hook. M3 J5, M4 J11, A30 or A33 via B3349.* Home-made teas. **Adm £3, chd free. Sun 13, Mon 14 July (2-5).**
Small traditional cottage garden with a 'roses around the door' look, much photographed, seen on calendars, jigsaws and in magazines. Mixed flower beds and borders. Vegetables grown in abundance. Ornamental pond and alpine garden. Views over open countryside to be enjoyed whilst you take afternoon tea on the lawn. The garden has been open for NGS for 30-yrs this yr. Small vintage motorcycle display (weather permitting). Some gravel paths.

Enjoy tea sitting in the dappled shade of the orchard . . .

Hampshire County Volunteers

County Organiser
Publicity and Central Winchester Mark Porter, The Down House, Main Road, Itchen Abbas, Winchester SO21 1AX, 01962 791054, markstephenporter@gmail.com

County Treasurer
Fred Fratter, Tanglefoot, Crawley, Winchester SO21 2QB, 01962 776243, fred@tanglefoot-house.demon.co.uk

Assistant County Organisers
Central East Sue Alexander, The Hyde, Old Alresford, Alresford SO24 9DH, 01962 732043, suealex13@gmail.com
Central West Patricia Elkington, Little Court, Crawley, Winchester SO21 2PU, 01962 776365, elkslc@tiscali.co.uk
East Linda Smith, Meon Orchard, Kingsmead, Wickham PO17 5AU, 01329 833253, linda.ngs@btinternet.com
North Cynthia Oldale, Yew Tree Cottage, School Lane, Bentley, Farnham GU10 5JP, 01420 520438, c.k.oldale@btinternet.com
North East Mary Trigwell-Jones, 'Selborne', Caker Lane, East Worldham, Alton GU34 3AE, 01420 83389, mary.trigwell-jones@virgin.net
North West Carol Pratt, 10 Catherine's Walk, Abbotts Ann, Andover SP11 7AS, 01264 710305, carolacap@yahoo.co.uk
South Barbara Sykes, The Cottage, 16 Lakewood Road, Chandler's Ford SO53 1ES, 02380 254521, barandhugh@aol.com
South West Elizabeth Walker, Willows, Pilley Hill, Boldre, Lymington SO41 5QF, 01590 677415, elizabethwalker13@gmail.com
West Christopher Stanford, Oakdene, Sandleheath, Fordingbridge SP6 1TD, 01425 652133, stanfordsnr@gmail.com

HEREFORDSHIRE

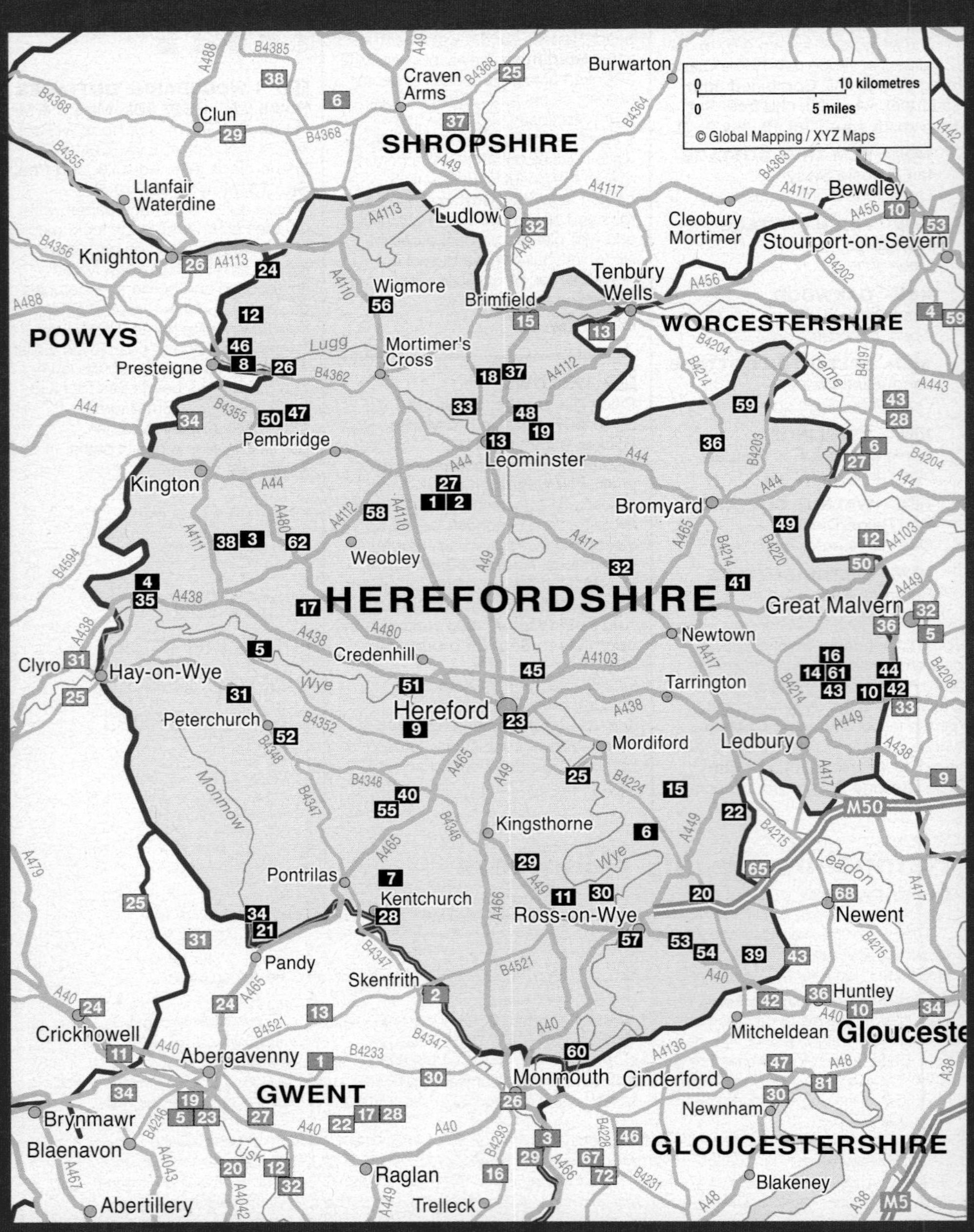

Opening Dates

All entries subject to change. For latest information check www.ngs.org.uk

February

27 Ivy Croft (Every Thursday)

Wednesday 19
51 The Weir

March

Sunday 23
55 Whitfield

Saturday 29
14 NEW Coddington Vineyard
61 Woofields Farm

Sunday 30
14 NEW Coddington Vineyard
39 The Old Corn Mill
61 Woofields Farm

April

Wednesday 2
48 Stockton Bury Gardens Ltd

Monday 7
36 Moors Meadow Gardens & Nursery

Sunday 13
32 Lower Hope
42 Perrycroft

Sunday 20
2 Aulden Farm
27 Ivy Croft
39 The Old Corn Mill

Monday 21
39 The Old Corn Mill

Sunday 27
56 NEW Wigmore Gardens

May

Sunday 11
3 Batch Cottage
5 Brobury House Gardens

Monday 12
8 Bryan's Ground
36 Moors Meadow Gardens & Nursery

Thursday 15
47 Staunton Park

Sunday 18
2 Aulden Farm
27 Ivy Croft

Wednesday 21
11 Church Cottage
22 Hellens

Thursday 22
22 Hellens
47 Staunton Park

Saturday 24
37 The Nest

Sunday 25
25 Holme Lacy House Hotel
32 Lower Hope
37 The Nest
39 The Old Corn Mill

Monday 26
37 The Nest
39 The Old Corn Mill

Tuesday 27
58 NEW Windsor Cottage

Thursday 29
47 Staunton Park
58 NEW Windsor Cottage

Saturday 31
40 The Old Rectory
43 Phelps Cottage Garden

June

47 Staunton Park (Every Thursday)
58 NEW Windsor Cottage (Every Tuesday & Thursday)

Sunday 1
28 Kentchurch Gardens
40 The Old Rectory
43 Phelps Cottage Garden
53 Weston Hall

Festival Weekend

Sunday 8
3 Batch Cottage
7 The Brooks
9 NEW The Carpenters
57 Wilton Castle on the Wye

Monday 9
36 Moors Meadow Gardens & Nursery
38 Newport House

Tuesday 10
38 Newport House

Wednesday 11
38 Newport House

Thursday 12
38 Newport House

Friday 13
38 Newport House

Saturday 14
54 Weston Mews

Sunday 15
10 Caves Folly Nurseries
17 Darkley
35 Montpelier Cottage
41 The Orchards
54 Weston Mews
55 Whitfield

Friday 20
23 Hereford Cathedral Gardens

Saturday 21
46 Stapleton Castle Court Garden

Sunday 22
33 The Marsh
42 Perrycroft
46 Stapleton Castle Court Garden
62 NEW Woonton & Almeley Gardens

Wednesday 25
5 Brobury House Gardens

Saturday 28
21 Grove Farm (cellar gallery)
34 Middle Hunt House
52 Wellbrook Manor

Sunday 29
9 NEW The Carpenters
21 Grove Farm (cellar gallery)
25 Holme Lacy House Hotel
33 The Marsh
34 Middle Hunt House
52 Wellbrook Manor

July

11 Church Cottage (Every Tuesday & Wednesday)
47 Staunton Park (Every Thursday)
58 NEW Windsor Cottage (Every Tuesday & Thursday)

Saturday 5
15 NEW Croose Farm
59 Wolferlow House

Sunday 6
16 The Cross
40 The Old Rectory

Monday 7
36 Moors Meadow Gardens & Nursery

Wednesday 9
40 The Old Rectory

Saturday 12
24 Hill House Farm

Sunday 13
24 Hill House Farm
32 Lower Hope
60 Woodview

Saturday 19
49 NEW Stone House

Sunday 20
9 NEW The Carpenters
41 The Orchards
57 Wilton Castle on the Wye
60 Woodview

Tuesday 22
49 NEW Stone House

Wednesday 23
49 NEW Stone House

Sunday 27
25 Holme Lacy House Hotel
28 Kentchurch Gardens

Tuesday 29
49 NEW Stone House

Wednesday 30
49 NEW Stone House

August

47 **Staunton Park (Every Thursday)**
58 NEW **Windsor Cottage (Every Tuesday & Thursday)**

Saturday 2
1 Aulden Arts and Gardens (Evening)
44 The Picton Garden

Sunday 3
1 Aulden Arts and Gardens
27 Ivy Croft

Tuesday 5
11 Church Cottage
49 NEW Stone House

Wednesday 6
11 Church Cottage
49 NEW Stone House

Sunday 10
44 The Picton Garden

Monday 11
36 Moors Meadow Gardens & Nursery

Tuesday 12
11 Church Cottage

Wednesday 13
11 Church Cottage

Sunday 17
44 The Picton Garden

Thursday 21
44 The Picton Garden

Sunday 24
40 The Old Rectory
41 The Orchards
46 Stapleton Castle Court Garden

Monday 25
44 The Picton Garden
46 Stapleton Castle Court Garden

Saturday 30
34 Middle Hunt House

Sunday 31
25 Holme Lacy House Hotel
34 Middle Hunt House

September

Tuesday 2
44 The Picton Garden

Thursday 4
47 Staunton Park

Sunday 7
2 Aulden Farm
27 Ivy Croft
29 NEW The Laskett Gardens

Thursday 11
47 Staunton Park

Friday 12
44 The Picton Garden

Sunday 14
56 NEW Wigmore Gardens

Sunday 21
6 Brockhampton Cottage
7 The Brooks
20 Grendon Court

Sunday 28
32 Lower Hope
42 Perrycroft

October

Wednesday 1
5 Brobury House Gardens

Tuesday 7
44 The Picton Garden

Wednesday 8
51 The Weir

Monday 13
38 Newport House

Tuesday 14
38 Newport House

Wednesday 15
38 Newport House

Thursday 16
38 Newport House

Friday 17
38 Newport House

Sunday 19
44 The Picton Garden

January 2015

Wednesday 21
51 The Weir

February 2015

27 **Ivy Croft (Every Thursday)**

Gardens open to the public

2 Aulden Farm
5 Brobury House Gardens
8 Bryan's Ground
10 Caves Folly Nurseries
22 Hellens
23 Hereford Cathedral Gardens
27 Ivy Croft
34 Middle Hunt House
36 Moors Meadow Gardens & Nursery
44 The Picton Garden
47 Staunton Park
48 Stockton Bury Gardens Ltd
51 The Weir

By appointment only

4 Brilley Court
12 Cloister Garden
13 Coach House
19 Grantsfield
26 Ivy Cottage
30 Lawless Hill
31 Little Llanavon
45 The Rambles
50 Upper Tan House

Also open by appointment

3 Batch Cottage
9 The Carpenters
11 Church Cottage
14 Coddington Vineyard
20 Grendon Court
21 Grove Farm (cellar gallery)
24 Hill House Farm
32 Lower Hope
38 Newport House
39 The Old Corn Mill
40 The Old Rectory
42 Perrycroft
43 Phelps Cottage Garden
46 Stapleton Castle Court Garden
53 Weston Hall
54 Weston Mews
55 Whitfield
56 Bury Court Farmhouse, Wigmore Gardens
59 Wolferlow House
60 Woodview

amateur gardener's obsession always changing and developing . . .

The Gardens

GROUP OPENING

1 AULDEN ARTS AND GARDENS

Aulden, Leominster HR6 0JT, www.auldenfarm.co.uk. *4m SW of Leominster. From Leominster, take Ivington/Upper Hill rd, 3/4 m after Ivington church turn R signed Aulden. From A4110 signed Ivington, take 2nd R signed Aulden*. Home-made teas (Sun). **Combined adm £6. Evening Opening wine, Sat 2 Aug (5-8); Sun 3 Aug (11-3.30).**

◆ **AULDEN FARM** NCH
Alun & Jill Whitehead
(See separate entry)

HILL VIEW
Aulden. Tricia & Andy Mitchell.
On L opp Aulden farm

HONEYLAKE COTTAGE
Jennie & Jack Hughes

Is gardening an art form? We are a group of neighbours who share an active interest in art and gardens, and believe that gardens give ever-changing colour and composition in 3 dimensions. Art, in a variety of forms, will be on display. Come and see the art, explore the gardens and decide for yourself. Aulden Farm art will be on display in the barn, alias the potting shed! At Hill View, prints, paintings and drawings will be on display. This garden is about green spaces and mature trees with minimal planting. There is plenty of seating from which to enjoy the view and a glass of wine. Honeylake Cottage has views over the wonderful Herefordshire countryside. The garden emphasis on traditional cottage flowers is reflected in the art work. The garden also incl a productive vegetable patch.

2 ◆ AULDEN FARM

Aulden, Leominster HR6 0JT. Alun & Jill Whitehead, 01568 720129, www.auldenfarm.co.uk. *4m SW of Leominster. From Leominster take Ivington/Upper Hill rd, ¾ m after Ivington church turn R signed Aulden. From A4110 signed Ivington, take 2nd R signed Aulden.* Home-made teas and ice cream. **Adm £3.50, chd free. Combined with Ivy Croft adm £6, except Aug. For NGS: Suns 20 Apr; 18 May; 7 Sept (2-5.30). For other opening times and information, please phone or see garden website.**

Informal country garden surrounding old farmhouse. 3 acres planted with wildlife in mind. Emphasis on structure and form with hint of quirkiness, a garden to explore. Irises thrive around the natural pond, Hemerocallis intermingle with sculpture, grasses and kniphofias for added zing. Shady areas, places to sit, feels mature but still evolving. Homemade ice cream and yummy cakes! National Collection of Siberian Iris and plant nursery.

THE BARTON

See Worcestershire

3 BATCH COTTAGE

Almeley HR3 6PT. Jeremy & Elizabeth Russell, 01544 327469. *16m NW of Hereford. 2m off A438-A4111 to Kington, turn R at Eardisley.* Cream teas. **Adm £4, chd free. Suns 11 May; 8 June (2-5.30). Visitors also welcome by appt Apr to Sept, individuals and groups.**

Established unregimented, conservation-oriented garden of some 2½ acres with streams and large pond, set in a natural valley, surrounded by woodland and orchard. Over 360 labelled trees and shrubs, mixed borders, fern and bog beds, wild flower bank, stumpery, woodland walk. Fritillaries and spotted orchids abound in season. Some gravel paths and steep slopes.

Stapleton Castle Court Garden

BIRTSMORTON COURT

See Worcestershire

BRIDGES STONE MILL

See Worcestershire

4 BRILLEY COURT

Whitney-on-Wye HR3 6JF. Mr & Mrs David Bulmer, 01497 831467, rosebulmer@hotmail.com. *6m NE of Hay-on-Wye. 5m SW of Kington. 1½ m off A438 Hereford to Brecon rd signed to Brilley.* Home-made teas. **Adm £4, chd free. Visitors welcome by appt Apr to Sept, individuals and groups.**

3-acre garden, walled ornamental kitchen garden. Spring tulip collection, summer rose and herbaceous borders. 7-acre arboretum/wild stream garden, wild flowers and rhododendron collection. Limited wheelchair access.

5 ◆ BROBURY HOUSE GARDENS

Brobury by Bredwardine HR3 6BS. Keith & Pru Cartwright, 01981 500229, www.broburyhouse.co.uk. *10m W of Hereford. S off A438 signed Bredwardine & Brobury. Garden 1m on L (before bridge).* Tea. **Adm £4, chd £1. For NGS: Sun 11 May (11-5); Weds 25 June; 1 Oct (2-5). For other opening times and information, please phone or see garden website.**

9 acres of gardens, set on the banks of an exquisitely beautiful section of the R Wye, offer the visitor a delightful combination of Victorian terraces with mature specimen trees, inspiring water features, architectural planting and woodland areas. Redesign and development is ongoing. Bring a picnic, your paint brushes, binoculars and linger awhile. Wheelchair users, strong able-bodied assistant advisable.

6 BROCKHAMPTON COTTAGE

Brockhampton HR1 4TQ. Peter & Ravida Clay. *8m SW of Hereford;. 5m N of Ross-on-Wye on B4224. In Brockhampton take rd signed to church, cont up hill for ½ m, after set of farm buildings, driveway on L, over cattle grid. Car park 500yds from garden.* **Adm £5, chd free. Sun 21 Sept (10.30-2). Combined with Grendon Court 2-5, adm £8.**

Created from scratch in 1999 by the owners and Tom Stuart-Smith, this beautiful hilltop garden looks S and W over miles of unspoilt countryside. On one side a woodland garden and wild flower meadow, on the other side a Perry pear orchard and in valley below: lake, stream and arboretum. Picnic parties welcome by lake until 2pm. Visit Grendon Court (2-5) after your visit to us.

7 THE BROOKS
Pontrilas HR2 0BL. Marion & Clive Stainton, www.marionet.co.uk/the_brooks. *12m SW of Hereford. From the A465 Hereford to Abergavenny rd, turn L at Pontrilas onto B4347, take 2nd L signed Orcop & Garway Hill. Garden 1¾ m on L.* Home-made teas. **Adm £3.50, chd free. Suns 8 June; 21 Sept (2-5.30).**
This 2½ -acre Golden Valley garden incl part-walled enclosed vegetable garden and greenhouse (wind/solar-powered), orchard, ornamental, perennial, shade and shrub borders, wildlife pond, evolving arboretum cum coppice, and meadow with stunning views. Surrounding a stone 1684 farmhouse (not open), the garden has mature elements, but much has been created since 2006, with future development plans.

8 ◆ BRYAN'S GROUND
Letchmoor Lane, nr Stapleton, Presteigne LD8 2LP. David Wheeler & Simon Dorrell, 01544 260001, www.bryansground.co.uk. *12m NW of Leominster. Between Kinsham & Stapleton. At Mortimer's Cross take B4362 signed Presteigne. At Combe, follow signs. SATNAV is misleading.* Tea. **Adm £6, chd £2. For NGS: Mon 12 May (2-5). For other opening times and information, please phone or see garden website.**
8-acre internationally renowned contemporary reinterpretation of an Arts and Crafts garden dating from 1912, conceived as series of rooms with yew and box topiary, parterres, colour-themed flower and shrub borders, reflecting pools, potager, Edwardian greenhouse, heritage apple orchard, follies. Arboretum planted mainly for autumn colour with wildlife pool beside R Lugg. Home of Hortus, garden journal. The majority of the garden is accessible by wheelchair, though there are some steps adjoining the terrace.

9 NEW THE CARPENTERS
Eaton Bishop, Hereford HR2 9QD. Christine & Alan Morris, 01981 250143, chrisalmo@hotmail.co.uk. *4m SW Hereford. A465 towards Abergavenny. After 2½ m turn R on B4349, after Clehonger turn R to Eaton Bishop. Park at village hall continue on foot 100yds.* Home-made teas. **Adm £3.50, chd free. Suns 8, 29 June; 20 July (2-6). Visitors also welcome by appt May to Sept.**
2 acre amateur gardener's obsession always changing and developing with over 25 planted areas incl herbaceous and mixed borders, ditch border, shrubberies, trees and pond. 2 summerhouses and plenty of other seats. Wildlife area, nest boxes and resident owls. Mainly flat with no significant slopes but all paths grass. You can get 'lost' in this garden. Suitable for disability scooters but not wheelchairs.

10 ◆ CAVES FOLLY NURSERIES
Evendine Lane, Colwall WR13 6DX. Wil Leaper & Bridget Evans, 01684 540631, www.cavesfolly.com. *1¼ m NE of Ledbury. B4218. Between Malvern & Ledbury. Evendine Lane, off Colwall Green.* Tea. **Adm £3, chd free. For NGS: Sun 15 June (2-5). For other opening times and information, please phone or see garden website.**
Organic nursery and display gardens. Specialist growers of herbaceous, alpines, grasses, vegetable and herb plants, all grown organically. This is not a manicured garden! It is full of drifts of colour and wild flowers and a haven for wildlife.

11 CHURCH COTTAGE
Hentland, Ross-on-Wye HR9 6LP. Sue Emms & Pete Weller, 01989 730222, sue.emms@mac.com. *6m from Ross-on-Wye. A49 from Ross. R turn to Hentland/Kynaston. At bottom of hill sharp R to St.Dubricius Church. Narrow lane - please take care.* Tea. **Adm £3, chd free. Every Tue & Wed 21 May to 13 Aug (2-5). Visitors also welcome by appt May to Sept, groups welcome.**
Garden designer and plantswoman's new ½ -acre evolving garden packed with plants, many unusual varieties mixed with old favourites providing interest over a long period. Wildlife pond, rose garden, potager, mixed borders, white terrace, gravel garden. Interesting plant combinations and design ideas to inspire.

12 CLOISTER GARDEN
Pant Hall, Willey, Presteigne LD8 2LY. Malcolm Temple & Karen Roberts, 01544 260066, karmal@live.co.uk, www.karenontheborders.wordpress.com. *3m N of Presteigne. 3m from Presteigne Bridge follow rd from bridge, signed to Willey. Past Stapleton Castle on R. Pant Hall on L.* Home-made teas. **Adm £3.50, chd free. Visitors welcome by appt May to Sept, groups or individuals - please ring.**
The ½ -acre garden incl terraced lawns, flower beds and shrubberies leading down to a wildlife pond and bog garden. Bordering one side is a tumbling stream over which a bridge leads to a steep bank cut through with paths rising to a recently terraced area which will be planted as an ancient orchard. Beyond this a 3 acre recently planted woodland with avenues and coppice.

13 NEW COACH HOUSE
The Grange off Church Street, Pinsley Road, Leominster HR6 8NP. John & Rosemary Verity, 01568 615200, verity200@btinternet.com. *Nr Priory Church. Last R turn top of Church Street. 30 metres straight ahead on R.* Home-made teas. **Adm £3, chd free. Visitors welcome by appt Apr to Sept, small groups max 12.**
Plantsman's walled town garden of approx. ⅓ acre planted for year round interest with shrubs, small specimen trees and interspersed with bulbs and perennials. Formal and woodland areas. Usually good display of irises May/June. Close proximity to ancient Priory dating from 670AD, C17 Grange Court (newly restored) and historic market town with small privately owned shops and antique markets.

14 NEW CODDINGTON VINEYARD

Coddington HR8 1JJ. Sharon & Peter Maiden, 01531 641817. *4m NE of Ledbury. From Ledbury to Malvern rd A449, follow brown signs to Coddington Vineyard.* Home-made teas. **Adm £3.50, chd free. Sat 29, Sun 30 Mar (12.30-4). Combined with Woofields, adm £5. Visitors also welcome by appt Mar to Sept, groups of 10+.**

5 acres incl 2-acre vineyard, listed farmhouse, threshing barn and cider mill. Garden with terraces,wild flower meadow, woodland with masses of spring bulbs, pond and stream. Unusual perennials, trees and shrubs.

15 NEW CROOSE FARM

Woolhope HR1 4RD. Mr & Mrs R Malim. *5m N of Ross-on-Wye. Woolhope signed off the B4224 Ross to Hereford rd. From Woolhope take rd opp the Church signed Sollars Hope & The Hyde. Follow garden signs.* Home-made teas. **Adm £4, chd free. Sat 5 July (12-5).**

3-acre country garden, set in middle of lovely Woolhope dome, created from original farmyard in 1987. Now well established it has as its theme a number of separate small gardens. These incl a 'hot bed', rose garden, white garden, courtyards, knot garden, water garden and wild flower meadow. The garden is stocked with a great variety of shrubs, trees and herbaceous plants.

16 THE CROSS

Coddington, Ledbury HR8 1JL. Brian & Megan Taylor. *4m N of Ledbury. From Colwall take Mill Lane to Coddington for 3m, then follow signs for garden & parking. From Bosbury, take B4220 (to Cradley), turn R signed Colwall & Coddington; after 2m follow signs to garden & parking.* Home-made teas. **Adm £3, chd free. Sun 6 July (2-5).**

1-acre informal country garden. Generous mixed borders lavishly planted with shrubs, roses, perennials and bulbs. Wildlife pond and native flower patch. Gravel area and kitchen garden. Pleasant walk through paddock leads to a tranquil path through 5 acres of mature woodland. Lovely views of the Malvern Hills. All paths are gravel.

17 DARKLEY

Norton Canon, Hereford HR4 7BT. Mr & Mrs Robert Maskery. *10m NW of Hereford. On A480 towards Kington. Take 1st L after Norton Canon sign. Towards Norton Wood. 1¼ m from the turning on L.* Light refreshments. **Adm £4, chd free. Sun 15 June (12-5).**

Beautiful 3½ acre garden with stunning views over countryside. Large collection of clematis and roses. Wide herbaceous borders incl specimen trees and shrubs. Decorative walled, gravel, herb and kitchen gardens. Wildlife pond and flower meadows. Some gravel paths.

19 GRANTSFIELD

nr Kimbolton, Leominster HR6 0ET. Colonel & Mrs J G T Polley, 01568 613338. *3m NE of Leominster. A49 N from Leominster, at A4112 turn R, then immed R (signed Hamnish), 1st L, then R at Xds. Garden on R after ½ m.* Home-made teas. **Adm £3.50, chd free. Visitors welcome by appt Apr to Sept, for individuals and groups.**

Contrasting styles in gardens of old stone farmhouse; wide variety of unusual plants, trees and shrubs, old roses, climbers, herbaceous borders, superb views. 1½ -acre orchard and kitchen garden with flowering and specimen trees and shrubs. Spring bulbs. Comma butterfly saved from extinction here by Emma Hutchinson in 1890s.

20 GRENDON COURT

Upton Bishop, Ross on Wye, Herefordshire HR9 7QP. Mark & Kate Edwards, 7971339126, kate@grendoncourt.co.uk. *3m NE of Ross-on-Wye. M50, J3. Hereford B4224 Moody Cow PH, 1m open gate on R. From Ross. A40, B449, Xrds R Upton Bishop. 100yds on L by cream cottage.* Home-made teas will be outdoors, weather permitting, as the barn is being renovated. **Adm £4, chd free. Sun 21 Sept (2-5). Combined with Brockhampton Cottage (morning opening 10.30-2) adm £8. Visitors also welcome by appt June to Oct (can do lunch up to 50 people).**

A contemporary garden designed by Tom Stuart-Smith. Planted on 2 levels, a clever collection of mass-planted perennials and grasses of different heights, textures and colour give all-yr round interest. The upper walled garden with a sea of flowering grasses makes a highlight. Views of pond and valley walk. Visit Brockhampton Cottage (10.30-2) before you visit us (picnic by the lake).

21 GROVE FARM (CELLAR GALLERY)

Walterstone HR2 0DX. David & Christine Hunt, 01873 890293, davidbhunt@tiscali.co.uk. *On the A465 at Pandy, turn L at the Pandy Inn, follow signs to Cellar Gallery, close to the Carpenters Arms PH.* Tea. **Adm £3.50, chd free. Sat 28, Sun 29 June (11-5). Visitors also welcome by appt June to Aug.**

Large tranquil courtyard with ponds, shrubs, specimen trees, greenhouse and gallery created from the old cattle yard and parlour. Banks of herbaceous borders, shrubberies and rose-covered pergolas leading to vegetable and herb garden, wild pond and orchard. Christine's art gallery (Cellar Gallery) is also open.

3-acre garden, set in middle of lovely Woolhope dome, created from original farmyard . . .

22 ◆ HELLENS

Much Marcle, Ledbury HR8 2LY. PMMCT, 01531 660504, www.hellensmanor.com. *6m from Ross-on-Wye. 4m SW of Ledbury, off A449.* Light refreshments. **Adm £2.50, chd free. For NGS: Wed 21, Thur 22 May (10-5). For other opening times and information, please phone or see garden website.**

In the grounds of Hellens manor house, the gardens are being gently redeveloped to reflect the C17 ambience of the house. Incl a rare octagonal dovecote, 2 knot gardens and yew labyrinth, lawns, herb and kitchen gardens, short woodlands and pond walk. Longer walk to Hall Wood, SSSI. Gardens are fairly level but pathways are gravel.

Staunton Park

23 ◆ HEREFORD CATHEDRAL GARDENS

Hereford HR1 2NG. Dean of Hereford Cathedral, 01432 374202, www.herefordcathedral.org. *Centre of Hereford. Approach roads to the Cathedral are signed. Tours leave from information desk in the cathedral building*. Light refreshments in Cathedral's Cloister Café. **Adm £5, chd free (share to Homeless Charity). For NGS: Fri 20 June (11-4). For other opening times and information, please phone or see garden website.**

Guided tours of historic gardens which won 2 top awards in 'It's Your Neighbourhood 2012'. The tour incl: a courtyard garden; an atmospheric cloisters garden enclosed by C15 buildings; the Vicar's Choral garden; the Dean's own garden; and 2 acre Bishop's garden with fine trees, vegetable and cutting garden, outdoor chapel for meditation in a floral setting, all sloping to the Wye. Collection of plants with ecclesiastical connections in College Garden. In 2013 awarded the outstanding certificate and special award to gardeners for excellence in gardening in the RHS 'It's Your Neighbourhood Campaign'. Limited wheelchair access.

HIGH VIEW

See Worcestershire

HIGHFIELD COTTAGE

See Worcestershire

24 HILL HOUSE FARM

Knighton LD7 1NA. Simon & Caroline Gourlay, 01547 528542, simongourlay@btinternet.com. *4m SE of Knighton. S of A4113 via Knighton (Llanshay Lane, 3m) or Bucknell (Reeves Lane, 3m)*. Cream teas. **Adm £4, chd free. Sat 12, Sun 13 July (2-5). Visitors also welcome by appt May to Aug.**

5-acre south facing hillside garden developed over past 40 years with magnificent views over unspoilt countryside. Some herbaceous around the house with extensive lawns and mown paths surrounded by roses, shrubs and specimen trees leading to the half acre Oak Pool 200ft below house. Transport available from bottom of garden if required.

25 HOLME LACY HOUSE HOTEL

Holme Lacy HR2 6LP. Warner Leisure Hotels, 01432 870870, www.holmelacyhouse.co.uk. *5m SE of Hereford. From Hereford B4399, from Gloucester B4215, then B4224, from Ledbury A438 signed from Holme Lacy village*. Light refreshments in Terrace Bar. **Adm £5. Suns 25 May; 29 June; 27 July; 31 Aug (10-4).**

The gardens were conceived on a very bold scale in 'The Grand Manner' and is Herefordshire's only surviving example of such gardens. Battlement gardens, ancient yew hedging, formal Italian gardens with ponds. Herbaceous borders, walled garden and orchard with historic pear trees. The gardens are going through phases of renovation and replanting, in keeping with the historical period of the house and existing garden features. Children not permitted. Gravel paths, some steep slopes, unfenced pond.

26 IVY COTTAGE

Kinsham LD8 2HN. Jane & Richard Barton, 01544 267154, rjjebarton@btinternet.com. *12m NW of Leominster. From Mortimer's Cross take B4362 towards Presteigne. Turn R at Combe towards Lingen for 1m. Easy parking*. **Adm £3.50, chd free. Visitors welcome by appt May to Aug, refreshments by arrangement.**

A mature ½ -acre garden 'divided' into distinct areas for long season interest and colour co-ordination.

Mixed borders with roses, shrubs, clematis, hardy and half-hardy perennials. Ancient apple trees create a tranquil, shady area with bulbs and foliage plants. Small areas of wild flower meadow. Vegetable and fruit area with raised beds. A true cottage garden for the traditionalist and the plantaholic. Featured in the Daily Mail On-line Weekend Magazine.

Tea and cake in the round house and magical views overlooking waterfall and the river valley . . .

27 ◆ IVY CROFT
Ivington Green, Leominster HR6 0JN. Sue & Roger Norman, 01568 720344, www.ivycroftgarden.co.uk. *3m SW of Leominster. From Leominster take Ryelands Rd to Ivington. Turn R at church, garden ¾ m on R. From A4110 signed Ivington, garden 1¾ m on L.* **Adm £3.50, chd free. Combined with Aulden Farm, adm £6, except Feb & 6 Aug. For NGS: Every Thur 6 Feb to 27 Feb (9-4); Suns 20 Apr; 18 May; 3 Aug; 7 Sept (2-5.30); Every Thur 5 to 26 Feb 2015. For other opening times and information, please phone or see garden website.**
A maturing rural garden with areas of meadow, wood and orchard, blending with countryside and providing habitat for wildlife. The cottage is surrounded by borders, raised beds, trained pears and containers giving all year interest. Paths lead to the wider garden including herbaceous borders, vegetable garden framed with espalier apples and seasonal pond with willows, ferns and grasses. Snowdrops. Featured in Herefordshire Life. Partial wheelchair access.

GROUP OPENING

28 KENTCHURCH GARDENS
Pontrilas HR2 0DB. *12m SW of Hereford. From Hereford A465 to Abergavanny, at Pontrilas turn L signed Kentchurch. After 2m fork L, after Bridge Inn. Drive opp church.* Home-made teas. **Combined adm £5, chd free. Suns 1 June; 27 July (11-5).**

KENTCHURCH COURT
Mrs Jan Lucas-Scudamore
01981 240228
jan@kentchurchcourt.co.uk
www.kentchurchcourt.co.uk

UPPER LODGE
Jo Gregory

Kentchurch Court is sited close to the Welsh border. The large stately home dates to C11 and has been in the Scudamore family for over 1000yrs The deer-park surrounding the house dates back to the Knights Hospitallers of Dinmore and lies at the heart of an estate of over 5000 acres. Historical characters associated with the house incl Welsh hero Owain Glendower, whose daughter married Sir John Scudamore. The house was modernised by John Nash in 1795. First opened for NGS in 1927. Formal rose garden, traditional vegetable garden redesigned with colour, scent and easy access. Walled garden and herbaceous borders, rhododendrons and wild flower walk. Deer-park and ancient woodland. Extensive collection of mature trees and shrubs. Stream with habitat for spawning trout. Upper Lodge is a tranquil and well-established walled cottage garden situated at the centre of the main garden. Incl a wide variety of herbaceous plants, bulbs and shrubs ranging from traditional favourites to the rare and unusual. Most of the garden can be accessed by wheelchairs.

29 NEW THE LASKETT GARDENS
Much Birch, Hereford HR2 8HZ. Sir Roy Strong, www.thelaskettgardens.co.uk. *Approx 7m from Hereford; 7m from Ross. On A49, midway between Ross-on-Wye & Hereford, turn into Laskett Lane towards Hoarwithy. The drive is approx 350yds on L.* **Adm £10, chd free. Sun 7 Sept (10-4).**
The Laskett Gardens are the largest private formal gardens to be created in England since 1945 consisting of 4 acres of stunning garden rooms incl rose and knot garden, fountains, statuary and topiary. Featured in national and international press. Limited wheelchair access.

30 LAWLESS HILL
Sellack, Ross-on-Wye HR9 6QP. Keith Meehan & Katalin Andras, 07595 678837, info@lawlesshill.com, www.lawlesshill.com. *4m NW of Ross-on-Wye/western end of M50. On A49 towards Hereford take 2nd R signed to Sellack. After approx 2m at junction (White House on R), turn R towards Sellack church. Turn L onto narrow lane at next Sellack church sign. Garden halfway down lane, before the church.* Home-made teas. **Adm £3, chd free. Visitors welcome by appt Mar to Nov, for individuals and small groups.**
Modernist, Japanese-influenced garden with dramatic views over R Wye. Collection of 'rooms' sculpted from the steep hillside using network of natural stone walls and huge rocks. Among exotic and unusual plantings, natural ponds are held within the terracing forming waterfalls between them. Due to steep steps and stepping stones open by water, the garden is unsuitable for the less mobile and young children. Tea and cake in the round house and magical views overlooking waterfall and the river valley.

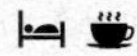

31 LITTLE LLANAVON
Dorstone, Hereford HR3 6AT. Jenny Chippindale, 01981 550984, jennichip@hotmail.co.uk, www.goldenvalleybandb.co.uk. *2m W of Peterchurch. In the Golden Valley, 15m W of Hereford on B4348, ½ m towards Peterchurch from Dorstone.* Tea. **Adm £3, chd free. Visitors welcome by appt May to Sept.**
½ -acre S-facing cottage-style walled garden in lovely rural location. Meandering paths among shrubs in shady spring garden. Hot gravel area and herbaceous borders closely planted with select perennials and grasses, many unusual. Good late colour.

LITTLE MALVERN COURT
See Worcestershire

32 LOWER HOPE
Ullingswick, Hereford HR1 3JF. Mr & Mrs Clive Richards, 01432 820557, cliverichards@crco.co.uk. *5m S of Bromyard. A465 N from Hereford, after 6m turn L at Burley Gate onto A417 towards Leominster. After approx 2m turn R to Lower Hope. After 1/2 m garden on L.* Home-made teas. **Adm £5, chd £1. Suns 13 Apr; 25 May; 13 July; 28 Sept (2-5). Visitors also welcome by appt, visits within 5 days after each open day.**
5-acre garden facing S and W. Herbaceous borders, rose walks and gardens, laburnum tunnel, Mediterranean garden, new Italian garden, bog gardens. Lime tree walk, lake landscaped with wild flowers, streams, ponds. Conservatories and large glasshouse with exotic species incl orchids, colourful butterflies, bougainvilleas. Prizewinning herd of pedigree Hereford cattle, flock of pedigree Suffolk sheep.

33 THE MARSH
Eyton HR6 0AG. Peter & Jane Ramsey, 01568 620211. *2m N of Leominster off B4361. Take B4361 to Ludlow, after 1/2 m turn L to Eyton, garden 1 1/2 m on R.* Home-made teas. **Adm £3, chd free. Suns 22, 29 June (2-5).**
A developing garden based on strong formal design. Main feature is a box parterre based on the roof timbers of the medieval hall. The garden is bisected by a small stream, planted either side with marginal and herbaceous plants. Small orchard, productive vegetable plot, reed bed, new gazebo and borders.

34 ◆ MIDDLE HUNT HOUSE
Walterstone, Hereford HR2 0DY. Trustees of Monnow Valley Arts & Rupert & Antoinetta Otten, 01873 860529, www.monnowvalleyarts.org. *4m W of Pandy, 17m S of Hereford, 10m N of Abergavenny. A465 to Pandy, L towards Longtown, turn R at Clodock Church, 1m on R. Disabled parking available.* Home-made teas. **Adm £5, chd free. For NGS: Sats, Suns 28, 29 June; 30, 31 Aug (2-5). For other opening times and information, please phone or see garden website.**
A modern garden using swathes of herbaceous plants and grasses, surrounding a stone built farmhouse and barns with stunning views of the Black Mountains. Special features: Rose borders, hornbeam alley, formal parterre garden with sensory plants, fountain courts with Wlliam Pye water feature, architecturally designed greenhouse complex, vegetable gardens and carved lettering and sculpture throughout, covering about 4 acres. During June opening, gallery exhibition of the Ken Stradling collection of post war modern design through ceramics, glass and furniture. In August, Edgar Holloway, a centenary exhibition of watercolours drawings and prints. Partial wheelchair access.

MODEL FARM
See Worcestershire

35 MONTPELIER COTTAGE
Brilley, Whitney-on-Wye, Hereford HR3 6HF. Dr Noel Kingsbury & Ms Jo Eliot, www.noelkingsbury.com. *Between Hay-on-Wye and Kington. From A438 1/2 m E of Rhydspence Inn, take road signed Brilley, then 0.9m. From Kington, follow road to Brilley, then 0.6m from Brilley Church.* Home-made teas. **Adm £5, chd free. Sun 15 June (2-6).**
Exuberant wild-style garden created by well-known garden writer. Approx 1 acre of garden and trial beds where English cottage style meets German parks and American prairie. Wide range of perennials, plus ponds, vegetable garden and fruit. A further 3 acres incl hay meadow habitat and unusual wild flower-rich wet meadow. Children's playground.

36 ◆ MOORS MEADOW GARDENS & NURSERY
Collington, Bromyard HR7 4LZ. Ros Bissell, 01885 410318, www.moorsmeadow.co.uk. *4m N of Bromyard, on B4214. 1/2 m up lane follow yellow arrows.* **Adm £5, chd £1. For NGS: Mons 7 Apr; 12 May; 9 June; 7 July; 11 Aug (11-5). For other opening times and information, please phone or see garden website.**
Gaining international recognition for its phenomenal range of wildlife and rarely seen plant species, this inspirational 7-acre organic hillside garden is a 'must see'. Full of peace, secret corners and intriguing features and sculptures with fernery, grass garden, extensive shrubberies, herbaceous beds, meadow, dingle, pools and kitchen garden. Resident Artist Blacksmith.

C12 castle, home to the Mortimer family and now a 'romantic ruin'. . .

37 THE NEST
Moreton, Eye HR6 0DP. Sue Evans & Guy Poulton. *5m N of Leominster. 1m W of A49 at Ashton, 4m N of Leominster, last driveway on L.* Home-made teas. **Adm £4, chd free. Sat 24, Sun 25, Mon 26 May (2-5).**
Classic cottage garden, 1 acre surrounding 1530s timber-framed house (not open). Summer garden with water features, pond, waterfall, Mediterranean plants, ferns, potager, scree and gravel gardens. Canal remnant and wild-flower meadow with rare orchids. Guided wildlife walks through meadow. Featured in Herefordshire & Wye Valley Life magazine and The English Garden and on Radio Hereford & Worcester. Some gravel, assistance available, otherwise good wheelchair access.

38 NEWPORT HOUSE
Almeley HR3 6LL. David & Jenny Watt, 07754 234903, david.gray510@btinternet.com. *5m S of Kington. 1m from Almeley Church, on rd to Kington. From Kington take A4111 to Hereford. After 4m turn L to Almeley, continue 2m, garden on L.* Light refreshments. **Adm £5, chd free. Mons, Tues, Weds, Thurs, Fris 9, 10, 11, 12, 13 June (11-6); 13, 14, 15, 16, 17 Oct (11-5). Visitors also welcome by appt May to Oct.**
20 acres of garden, woods and lake (with walks). Formal garden set on 3 terraces with large mixed borders framed by formal hedges, in front of Georgian House (not open). 2 1/2 -acre walled organic garden in restoration since 2009.

39 THE OLD CORN MILL

Aston Crews, Ross-on-Wye HR9 7LW. Mrs Jill Hunter, 01989 750059. *5m E of Ross-on-Wye. A40 Ross to Gloucester. Turn L at T-lights at Lea Xrds onto B4222 signed Newent, Garden ½ m on L. Parking for disabled down drive. DO NOT USE THE ABOVE POSTCODE IN YOUR SAT NAV - try HR9 7LA.* Home-made teas. **Adm £3, chd free. Suns, Mons 30 Mar; 20, 21 Apr; 25, 26 May (11-5). Visitors also welcome by appt Jan to Oct, max 50+.**

Surrounding the award-winning converted C18 Mill (not open), this valley garden has been designed to merge into the surrounding fields. Massed banks and borders provide colour all yr while streams, ponds, meadows and native trees support a variety of wildlife. Wild daffodils, common spotted orchids and tulips are spring highlights. Quirky garden sculptures. Children's trail. Peace and tranquillity. Unusual perennials for sale. Natural country garden in a peaceful setting.

40 THE OLD RECTORY, THRUXTON

Thruxton HR2 9AX. Mr & Mrs Andrew Hallett, 01981 570401, ar.hallett@gmail.com. *6m SW of Hereford. A465 to Allensmore. At Locks (Shell) garage take B4348 towards Hay-on-Wye. After 1½ m turn L towards Abbey Dore & Cockyard. Car park 150yds on L.* Home-made teas. **Adm £3.50, chd free. Sat 31 May; Sun 1 June; Sun 6, Wed 9 July; Sun 24 Aug (2-5.30). Visitors also welcome by appt May to Sept.**

2 acre plantsman's garden with stunning panoramic views. Extensive borders stocked with shrubs, unusual perennials and old shrub roses, formal gazebo, large glasshouse and vegetable parterre. Most of our plants are labelled. Additional 2 acre paddock with young ornamental trees, old varieties of fruit trees, wild life pond, chickens and rare breed bantams. Children very welcome. Featured in Hereford and Wye Valley Life and on Hereford and Worcester Radio.

41 THE ORCHARDS

Golden Valley, Bishops Frome, nr Bromyard WR6 5BN. Mr & Mrs Robert Humphries. *14m E of Hereford. A4103 turn L at bottom of Fromes Hill, through Bishops Frome on B4214. Turn R immediately after de-regulation signs. Follow NGS signs to car park.* Home-made teas. **Adm £3, chd free. Suns 15 June; 20 July; 24 Aug (2-6).**

1-acre garden designed in areas on various levels. 15 water features incl Japanese water garden and tea house, Mediterranean area, rose garden with rill, aviary. Large rose, clematis, fuchsia and dahlia collections. Seating areas on all levels. New projects every year.

PEAR TREE COTTAGE
See Worcestershire

42 PERRYCROFT

Jubilee Drive, Upper Colwall, Malvern WR13 6DN. Gillian & Mark Archer, 07858 393767, gillianarcher@live.co.uk. *Between Malvern & Ledbury. Situated on B4232 between British Camp & Wyche cutting. Park in Gardiners Quarry pay & display car park, short walk to garden. No parking at house.* Home-made teas. **Adm £5, chd free. Suns 13 Apr; 22 June; 28 Sept (2-5). Visitors also welcome by appt all year.**

10-acre garden and woodland on upper slopes of Malvern Hills with magnificent views. Arts and Crafts house (not open), garden partly designed by CFA Voysey. Walled garden, mixed and herbaceous borders, yew and box hedges and topiary, old roses, natural wild flower meadows, ponds (unfenced), bog garden, gravel and grass walks. Some steep and uneven paths. Ongoing restoration. Featured in House and Garden, Country Life and Gardens Illustrated. Garden not suitable for wheelchairs.

43 PHELPS COTTAGE GARDEN

Coddington, Ledbury HR8 1JH. David & Diane Hodgson, 01531 640622, dhodgson363@btinternet.com. *From Ledbury take the Bromyard road, 1st R to T junction turn R, 1st L for Coddington. From Worcester to Colwall signed for Coddington.* Home-made teas. **Adm £3.50, chd free. Sat 31 May (1.30-5.30); Sun 1 June (1.30-3.30). Visitors also welcome by appt June to July.**

Plantsmans ¾ -acre cottage garden on different levels (some steps), mixed borders, terrace, wild areas, stream and bog garden, large fruit and vegetable potager with poly tunnel. 2013 Featured in Herefordshire and Wye Valley Life and BBC Hereford and Worcester.

44 ◆ THE PICTON GARDEN

Old Court Nurseries, Colwall WR13 6QE. Mr & Mrs Paul Picton, 01684 540416, www.autumnasters.co.uk. *3m W of Malvern. On B4218 (Walwyn Rd) N of Colwall Stone. Turn off A449 from Ledbury or Malvern onto the B4218 for Colwall.* **Adm £3.50, chd free. For NGS: Sat 2, Sun 10, Sun 17, Thur 21, Mon 25 Aug; Tue 2, Fri 12 Sept; Tue 7, Sun 19 Oct (11-5). For other opening times and information, please phone or see garden website.**

1½ acres W of Malvern Hills. Interesting perennials and shrubs in Aug. In Sept and Oct colourful borders display the National Plant Collection of Michaelmas daisies, backed by autumn colouring trees and shrubs. Many unusual plants to be seen, incl bamboos, ferns and acers. Features raised beds and silver garden. National Plant Collection of autumn-flowering asters and an extensive nursery that has been growing them since 1906. Featured on BBC2 Great British Garden Revival and in Countrylife, Amateur Gardening, Garden Answers, The English Garden.

NCH

45 THE RAMBLES

Shelwick, Hereford HR1 3AL. Shirley & Joe Fleming, 01432 357056, joe.eff@live.co.uk. *2m E of Hereford. A465/ A4103 roundabout take the Sutton St Nicholas Rd, turn L signed Shelwick, under railway bridge, The Rambles is behind 1st house on the L. Car parking on drive by house.* Tea. **Adm £3, chd free. Visitors welcome by appt June to Sept.**

Colourful plantaholics 1/3acre garden packed with a wide range of interesting plants, colour-themed borders, large covered shade area and water feature. Many pots with tender plants.

SHUTTIFIELD COTTAGE
See Worcestershire

46 STAPLETON CASTLE COURT GARDEN

Stapleton, Presteigne LD8 2LS. Margaret & Trefor Griffiths, 01544 267327. *2m N of Presteigne. From Presteigne cross Lugg Bridge at bottom of Broad St. and continue to Stapleton. Do not turn into Stapleton but follow signs to garden on R.* Home-made teas. **Adm £4, chd free. Sat 21, Sun 22 June; Sun 24, Mon 25 Aug (2-5.30). Visitors also welcome by appt May to Sept.**

Situated on a gentle slope overlooked by the ruins of Stapleton Castle. The garden developed over the past 6 yrs by an enthusiastic plantswoman and benefits from considered and colour-themed borders. Guided tour of the castle ruins at 2.30 and 3.30 each day. Site history display including: castle site, C17 house ruin, mill pond, mill pit, disused turbine etc. Wheelchairs not suitable for castle tour.

47 ◆ STAUNTON PARK

Staunton-on-Arrow, Leominster HR6 9LE. Susan Fode, 01544 388556, www.stauntonpark.co.uk. *3m N of Pembridge. From Pembridge (on A44) take Presteigne rd, after 3m look for red phone box on R, Staunton Pk is 150yds on L. Do not go to Staunton-on-Arrow.* Light refreshments. **Adm £4, chd free. For NGS: Every Thur 15 May to 11 Sept (11-5). For other opening times and information, please phone or see garden website.**

10-acre garden and grounds, drive with wellingtonias, box and lavender knot garden, kitchen garden, colourful mixed borders flowering well into September, Victorian rock garden, lake and lakeside walk with views. Specimen trees incl mature monkey puzzle, gigantic liriodendron, *Davidia involucrata*, *Ginkgo bilobas* and ancient oaks. A garden much enjoyed for its peace and tranquillity. Yew hedges, hostas, dahlias, early C18 dovecote under restoration. 2 steps to WC.

Many plants grown from seed with lilies and sweet peas a speciality . . .

48 ◆ STOCKTON BURY GARDENS LTD

Kimbolton HR6 0HB. Raymond G Treasure, 01568 613432, www.stocktonbury.co.uk. *2m NE of Leominster. On A49 turn R onto A4112 Kimbolton rd. Gardens 300yds on R.* Light refreshments. **Adm £6. For NGS: Wed 2 Apr (12-5). For other opening times and information, please phone or see garden website.**

Superb, sheltered 4-acre garden with a very long growing season giving colour and interest all yr. Extensive collection of plants, many rare and unusual set amongst medieval buildings, a real kitchen garden. Pigeon house, tithe barn, grotto, cider press, pools, ruined chapel and rill, all surrounded by unspoilt countryside. Unsuitable for children. (This is no ordinary garden). Featured in The English Garden. Partial wheelchair access.

49 NEW STONE HOUSE

Linley Green, Whitbourne, Worcester WR6 5RG. Bill & Jill Cartlidge. *12m W of Worcester. A44 W from Worcester.After approx 12m turn L into B4220 Malvern Road, after 1m fork L to Linley Green, cottage on R after 1/2 m.* Light refreshments. **Adm £3, chd free (share to The Firefighters Charity). Sat 19, Tue 22, Wed 23, Tues, Weds 29, 30 July; 5, 6 Aug (2-5.30).**

The garden mixes the traditional features of the timeless cottage garden with innovative contemporary elements. Alongside glorious floral planting, orchard, herb terrace and abundant vegetable plot stand a wall mosaic, bell sculpture, living willow boat, iridescent sofa and crossword. Many plants grown from seed with lilies and sweet peas a speciality. Generally level garden. Beware molehills and tunnels in grass areas. One set of steps with alternative grass ramp access.

50 UPPER TAN HOUSE

Stansbatch, Leominster HR6 9LJ. James & Caroline Weymouth, 01544 260574, james@dipperdesign.com, www.uppertanhouse.com. *4m W of Pembridge. From A44 in Pembridge take turn signed Shobdon & Presteigne. After exactly 4m & at Stansbatch Nursery turn L down hill. Gdn on L 100yds after chapel.* Tea. **Adm £4, chd free. Visitors welcome by appt May to Sept, for individuals and groups.**

S-facing garden sloping down to Stansbatch brook in idyllic spot. Deep herbaceous borders with informal and unusual planting, pond and bog garden, formal vegetable garden framed by yew hedges and espaliered pears. Reed beds, wild-flower meadow with orchids in June. Good late summer colour and diverse wildlife.

51 ◆ THE WEIR

Swainshill, Hereford HR4 7QF. National Trust, 01981 590509, www.nationaltrust.org.uk/weir. *5m W of Hereford. On A438, signed The Weir Garden.* Tea. **Adm £5, chd free. For NGS: Weds 19 Feb; 8 Oct (11-4) 21 Jan 2015. For other opening times and information, please phone or see garden website.**

Stunning riverside gardens with sweeping views along the R Wye and Herefordshire countryside. Drifts of snowdrops and spring bulbs give way to summer wild flowers in the woodland garden and in autumn the walled garden is full of fruit and vegetables. Snowdrops in full bloom in February. Very limited wheelchair access.

52 WELLBROOK MANOR

Peterchurch, Hereford HR2 0SS. The Vivat Trust, 01981 550753, bronwyn@vivat-trust.org. *11m W of Hereford. Going towards Hay on Wye on the B4348 turn R when entering Peterchurch (signed Stockley Hill). Wellbrook Manor is on L before you leave the village.* Home-made teas. **Adm £4, chd free. Sat 28, Sun 29 June (1-5).**

The garden was created by the late Mrs Joan Griffith. Noted for its structural topiary, potager garden, rare variety orchard and soft succulent atmosphere. Over the weekend the roses will thrill and, weather permitting, the fragrant peonies will delight. Works are in progress to lay out the paddock area. The Grade I-listed Wellbrook Manor (not open) sits in the centre of the garden. Tea/coffee and home-made cakes stall, plus the Vivat Trust's apple juice and cider made from our own orchard produce is on sale.

53 WESTON HALL

Weston-under-Penyard, Ross-on-Wye HR9 7NS. Mr P & Miss L Aldrich-Blake, 01989 562597, aldrichblake@btinternet.com. *1m E of Ross-on-Wye. On A40 towards Gloucester.* Light refreshments. **Adm £4, chd free. Sun 1 June (11-5). Visitors also welcome by appt May to July, groups of 10+.**

6 acres surrounding Elizabethan house (not open). Large walled garden with herbaceous borders, vegetables and fruit, overlooked by Millennium folly. Lawns with both mature and recently planted trees, shrubs with many unusual varieties. Ornamental ponds and lake.
4 generations in the family, but still evolving year on year.

54 WESTON MEWS

Weston-under-Penyard HR9 7NZ. Ann Rothwell & John Hercock, 01989 563823. *2m E of Ross-on-Wye. Going towards Gloucester on A40, continue approx 100yds past the Weston Cross PH and turn R into grey brick-paved courtyard.* Light refreshments. **Adm £3, chd free. Sat 14, Sun 15 June (11-5). Visitors also welcome by appt May to Sept, wine.**

Walled ex-kitchen garden divided by yew and box hedges. Traditional in style and planting with large herbaceous beds and borders at different levels. Broad range of plants incl roses. Enclosed garden with sundial. Large vine house.

Upper Tan House

© Carole Drake

55 WHITFIELD

Wormbridge HR2 9BA. Mr & Mrs Edward Clive, 01981 570202, tclive@whitfield-hereford.com, www.whitfield-hereford.com. *8m SW of Hereford. The entrance gates are off the A465 Hereford to Abergavenny rd, ½ m N of Wormbridge.* Home-made teas. **Adm £4, chd free. Suns 23 Mar; 15 June (2-5.30). Visitors also welcome by appt Mar to Nov, tour & refreshments available for groups 15+.**

Parkland, wild flowers, ponds, walled garden, many flowering magnolias (species and hybrids), 1780 ginkgo tree, 1½ m woodland walk with 1851 redwood grove. Picnic parties welcome. Partial access to wheelchair users, some gravel paths and steep slopes.

GROUP OPENING

56 NEW WIGMORE GARDENS

Wigmore, Leominster HR6 9UP. *10m from Leominster, 10m from Knighton. On A4110 from Leominster, at Wigmore turn R just after shop & garage into Ford St.Follow signs to parking & gardens.* Home-made teas at Bury Court Farmhouse. **Combined adm £5, chd free. Suns 27 Apr; 14 Sept (2-5).**

NEW BURY COURT FARMHOUSE
Margaret & Les Barclay
Visitors also welcome by appt Mar to Sept, individuals and groups 20+.
01568 770618

NEW CLAREMONT COTTAGE
Ford Street. Myra & Iain Field

The ancient village of Wigmore is known for its C12 castle, home to the Mortimer family and now a 'romantic ruin', and its medieval church. The two gardens are both within 300yds of the parking area. Bury Court Farmhouse has a ¾ -acre garden, 'rescued' since 1997, surrounding an 1840's stone farmhouse (not open). The courtyard contains a pond, mixed borders, fruit trees and shrubs, with steps up to a terrace which leads to lawn and vegetable plots. The main garden (semi-walled) is on 2 levels with mixed borders greenhouse, pond, mini-orchard with daffs in spring and wildlife area. The garden is designed for yr-round interest and colour. Claremont Cottage is a miniature gem, developed from scratch over 10yrs. Small but with an emphasis on colourful and fragrant plants, shrubs and lilies, the garden incl 4 vegetable plots and a selection of acers in pots. Interesting trees and variety of clematis also feature.

57 WILTON CASTLE ON THE WYE

Wilton, Ross-on-Wye HR9 6AD. Alan & Suzie Parslow, www.wiltoncastle.co.uk. *1/2 m NW of Ross on R Wye. Sgnd at Wilton r'about on M50/A40/A449 trunk rd. Imm turn L opp garage. Castle entrance behind Castle Lodge Hotel. DO NOT cross bridge into Ross.* Tea. **Adm £4, chd £2. Suns 8 June; 20 July (12-5).**

The romantic ruins of a restored C12 castle and C16 manor house (ruin) form the perfect backdrop for herbaceous borders, roses entwined around mullioned windows, an abundance of sweetly scented old-fashioned roses, gravel gardens and shrubberies. The 2-acre gardens are surrounded by a dry moat which leads down to the R Wye with swans, ducks, kingfishers etc. No disabled access into dry moat area, or inside towers; disabled WC.

58 NEW WINDSOR COTTAGE

Dilwyn, Hereford HR4 8HJ. Jim & Brenda Collins. *6m W of Leominster off A4112. Turn L off A4112 into Dilwyn. From centre of village, with PH on L, turn L. After 100y turn R. Cottage 400yds on L. Limited parking.* Home-made teas. **Adm £3, chd free. Every Tue & Thur 27 May to 28 Aug (2-5.30).**

1/2 -acre wildlife friendly garden redesigned over the last 3yrs by present owners. Herbaceous borders, shrub bed, rose garden, wildlife ponds, fruit and vegetables in raised beds. Extensive use of gravel beds. Wide selection of plants for all year interest including peonies, irises, hostas and clematis. Exhibition of watercolour and oil paintings. Wildlife friendly garden. Plants chosen to encourage bees, birds, and butterflies. Gravelled drive giving access to level, lawned garden.

59 WOLFERLOW HOUSE

Wolferlow, nr Upper Sapey HR7 4QA. Stuart & Jill Smith, 01886 853311, hillheadfm@aol.com, www.theretreatholidaylettings.co.uk. *5m N of Bromyard. Off B4203 or B4214 between Upper Sapey & Stoke Bliss. Disabled parking at the house.* Home-made teas. **Adm £3.50, chd free. Sat 5 July (10-5). Visitors also welcome by appt, groups up to 20+, one week either side of 5 July.**

Surrounded by farmland this former Victorian rectory is set within formal and informal gardens with planting to attract wildlife. Walks through the old orchard and ponds to sit by, space to relax and reflect taking in the views of borrowed landscape. Fruit, vegetable and cutting garden and wild-flower meadow. Gravel paths.

♿ ❀ 🛏 ☕

Wildlife friendly garden. Plants chosen to encourage bees, birds, and butterflies . . .

60 WOODVIEW

Great Doward, Whitchurch, Ross-on-Wye HR9 6DZ. Janet & Clive Townsend, 01600 890477, clive.townsend5@homecall.co.uk. *6m SW of Ross-on-Wye, 4m NE of Monmouth. A40 Ross/Mon At Whitchurch follow signs to Symonds Yat west. Then to Doward Park campsite. Take forestry rd 1st L garden 2nd L follow NGS signs.* Home-made teas. **Adm £4, chd free. Suns 13, 20 July (1-6). Visitors also welcome by appt June to Sept, please telephone for details.**

Formal and informal gardens approx 4 acres in woodland setting. Herbaceous borders, hosta collection, mature trees, shrubs and seasonal bedding. Gently sloping lawns. Statuary and found sculpture, local limestone, rockwork and pools. Woodland garden, wild-flower meadow and indigenous orchids. Collection of vintage tools and memorabilia, garden games. Croquet, clock golf and garden games.

61 WOOFIELDS FARM

Coddington, Ledbury HR8 1JJ. Mrs Rosemary Simcock. *3m N of Ledbury. From Ledbury to Malvern rd A449, follow brown signs to Coddington Vineyard.* **Adm £3.50, chd free. Sat 29, Sun 30 Mar (12.30-4). Combined with Coddington Vineyard, adm £5.**

2-acre garden on working farm: an eclectic mixture of planting, colour all yr round. Variety in shape and texture. Spring bulbs and shrubs. Borders planted with roses, clematis, wide range of herbaceous plants, many alstromeria, gravel garden, ornamental pond. Natural pond recently re-landscaped and planted by Peter Dowle.

GROUP OPENING

62 NEW WOONTON & ALMELEY GARDENS

Woonton, Hereford HR3 6QN. *12m W of Leominster. From Leominster follow A44 & then A4112, turn R after 10 metres onto A480 at Sarnesfield to Woonton & Almeley by following yellow signs.* Home-made teas at The Old Villa. **Combined adm £5, chd free. Sun 22 June (2-5.30).**

NEW THE BRIARY
Roger & Ruth Wardle

NEW OAK HALL
Tessa & Jeremy Plummer

NEW THE OLD VILLA
Almeley. Mrs Caryl Mead

3 small but very different gardens. The Briary is a small informal country garden designed in an old farmyard, created since 2003. Specimen trees, shrubs, perennials and grasses, plus over 30 varieties of clematis, with many inspiring combinations. Rose and clematis pergola with rill. 'Hot' gravel garden, raised vegetable beds and fruit trees. Oak Hall is an enchanting 3/4 -acre walled cottage garden surrounding a C15 open-hall house (not open); herbaceous borders, herb garden, romantic rose garden with fountain, soft fruit and vegetables and lovely views over the countryside. The Old Villa is a small garden of informal design with gravel paths and some steps. Borders are packed with plants, some old favourites like roses, iris and aster, some unusual like arisaema, climbing codonopsis and veratrum. Small raised pond, vegetable and fruit area, greenhouse, small collection of ferns and views to Hay Bluff. Homemade tea and cakes, plants for sale. All 3 are accessible to wheelchairs users, although some areas of each would be restricted.

♿ ❀ ☕

Hill House Farm

Herefordshire County Volunteers

County Organiser
Rowena Gale, Bachefield House, Kimbolton, Leominster HR6 0EP, 01568 615855, rowena.jimgale@btinternet.com

County Treasurer
Michael Robins, Newsholme, 77 Bridge Street, Ledbury HR8 2AN, 01531 632232, mrobins101@btinternet.com

Publicity
Sue Evans, The Nest, Moreton, Eye, nr Leominster HR6 0DP, 01568 614501, s.evans.gp@btinternet.com
Gill Mullin, The White House, Lea, Ross-on-Wye HR9 7LQ, 01989 750593, gill@longorchard.plus.com

County Booklet
Chris Meakins, Yew Tree Cottage, Huntington, Kington HR5 3PF, 01544 370215, christine.meakins@btinternet.com

Assistant County Organisers
Andy Hallett, The Old Rectory, Thruxton, Hereford HR2 9AX, 01981 570401, ar.hallett@gmail.com
David Hodgson, Phelps Cottage, Coddington, nr Ledbury HR8 1JH, 01531 640622, dhodgson363@btinternet.com
Sue Londesborough, Brighton House, Newton St Margarets, Vowchurch HR2 0JU, 01981 510148, slondesborough138@btinternet.com
Penny Usher, Old Chapel House, Kimbolton, Leominster HR6 0HF, 01568 611688, pennyusher@btinternet.com

HERTFORDSHIRE

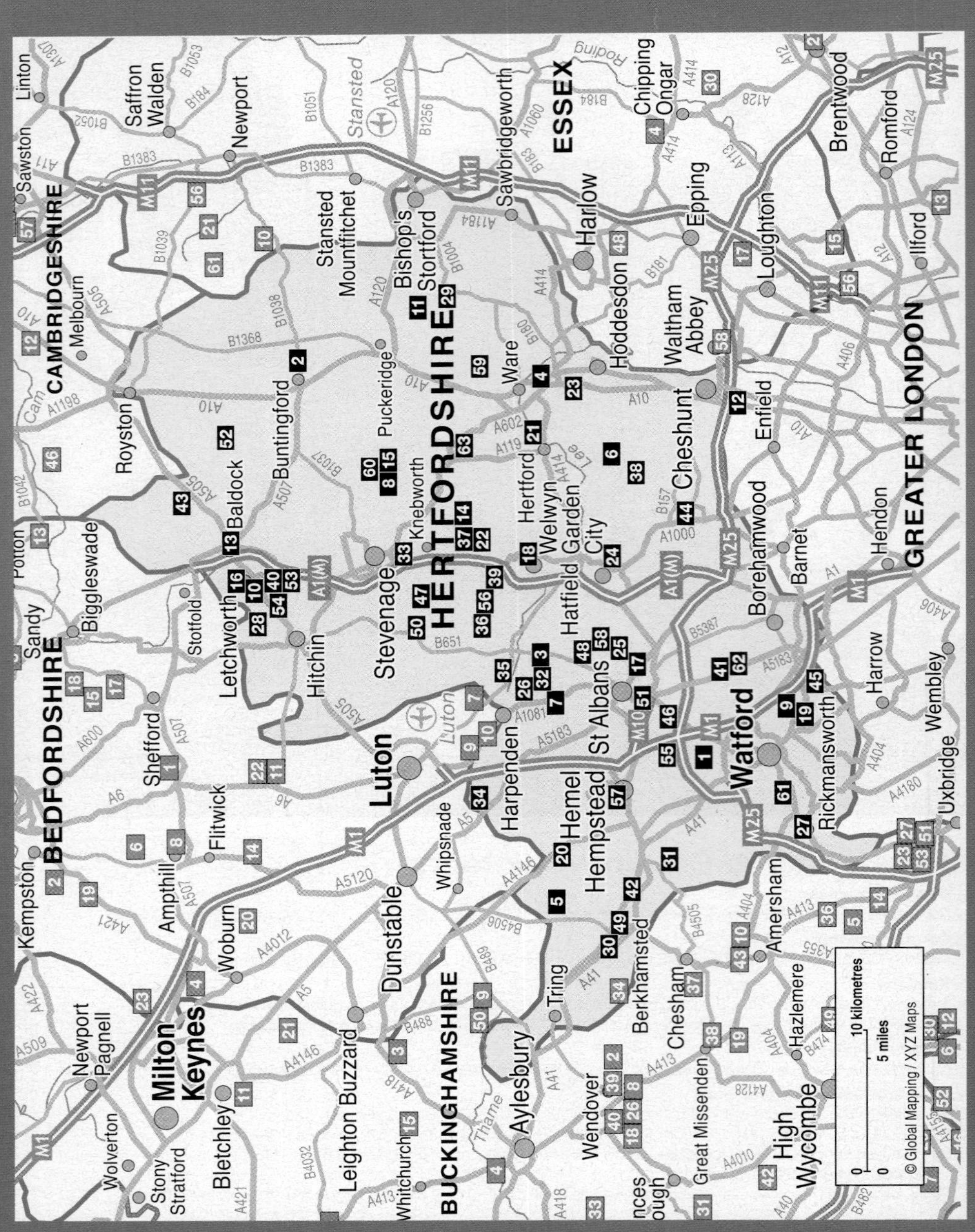

Opening Dates

All entries subject to change. For latest information check www.ngs.org.uk

February

Saturday 22
60 Walkern Hall

Sunday 23
60 Walkern Hall

March

Saturday 8
12 Capel Manor Gardens

Sunday 9
12 Capel Manor Gardens

Saturday 29
24 Hatfield House West Garden

April

Sunday 13
50 St Paul's Walden Bury

Saturday 19
39 The Mill House

Monday 21
39 The Mill House

Sunday 27
2 NEW Alswick Hall
31 Huntsmoor
40 324 Norton Way South

May

9 **47 Bournehall Avenue (Every Wednesday & Thursday)**

Friday 2
32 NEW 8 Kingcroft Road (Evening)

Sunday 4
32 NEW 8 Kingcroft Road
42 Patchwork

Friday 9
47 Rustling End Cottage

Sunday 11
47 Rustling End Cottage
50 St Paul's Walden Bury

Friday 16
13 NEW 42 Church Street (Evening)
16 10 Cross Street (Evening)

Saturday 17
4 NEW Amwellbury
16 10 Cross Street
25 NEW 122 Hazelwood Drive

Sunday 18
13 NEW 42 Church Street
16 10 Cross Street
36 The Manor House, Ayot St Lawrence
37 43 Mardley Hill

Sunday 25
17 NEW 25 Cunningham Hill Road
20 15 Gade Valley Cottages
44 Queenswood School
59 Thundridge Hill House

Friday 30
35 Mackerye End House (Evening)

June

9 **47 Bournehall Avenue (Every Wednesday & Thursday)**

Sunday 1
43 Pembroke Farm

Festival Weekend

Saturday 7
11 Bromley Hall
27 NEW 124 Highfield Way

Sunday 8
5 Ashridge House
11 Bromley Hall
50 St Paul's Walden Bury
56 Shaw's Corner

Saturday 14
25 NEW 122 Hazelwood Drive
34 NEW The Lodge

Sunday 15
3 Amwell Cottage
26 NEW 3 Highfield Avenue
34 NEW The Lodge

Friday 20
54 NEW Serendi (Evening)

Saturday 21
52 NEW Sandon Bury

Sunday 22
6 Bayford Musical Gardens Day
15 Croft Cottage
49 St Michael's Croft
52 NEW Sandon Bury
54 NEW Serendi
55 Serge Hill Gardens

Sunday 29
8 Benington Lordship
35 Mackerye End House
38 Michaels Folly
51 St Stephens Avenue Gardens
63 Woodhall Park

July

9 **47 Bournehall Avenue (Every Wednesday & Thursday)**

Tuesday 1
28 Hitchin Lavender (Evening)

Saturday 5
23 NEW Haileybury

Sunday 6
22 NEW Greenwood House
23 NEW Haileybury
43 Pembroke Farm

Wednesday 9
58 217 The Ridgeway

Friday 11
22 NEW Greenwood House (Evening)
53 Scudamore (Evening)

Sunday 13
14 NEW The Cottage
37 43 Mardley Hill
58 217 The Ridgeway

Friday 18
46 The Royal National Rose Society (Evening)

Sunday 20
7 Beesonend Gardens
17 NEW 25 Cunningham Hill Road
27 NEW 124 Highfield Way
57 9 Tannsfield Drive

Monday 21
28 Hitchin Lavender (Evening)

Saturday 26
19 42 Falconer Road

Sunday 27
18 35 Digswell Road
19 42 Falconer Road
20 15 Gade Valley Cottages
41 Oakridge Avenue Gardens

Surrounded by woods with thousands of spring bulbs . . .

August

9 **47 Bournehall Avenue (Every Wednesday & Thursday)**

Friday 1
10 44 Broadwater Avenue (Evening)
28 Hitchin Lavender (Evening)

Saturday 2
19 42 Falconer Road

Sunday 3
10 44 Broadwater Avenue
19 42 Falconer Road
43 Pembroke Farm

Sunday 10
57 9 Tannsfield Drive

Friday 15
48 3 St Marys Walk (Evening)

Sunday 17
42 Patchwork
48 3 St Marys Walk

Thursday 21
28 Hitchin Lavender (Evening)

Monday 25
15 Croft Cottage

Sunday 31
62 3 Watford Road

September

9 47 Bournehall Avenue (Every Wednesday & Thursday)

Sunday 7
30 NEW Hospice of St Francis Garden

Sunday 14
45 Reveley Lodge

Sunday 21
31 Huntsmoor

October

Sunday 12
21 8 Gosselin Road

Saturday 18
12 Capel Manor Gardens

Sunday 19
12 Capel Manor Gardens

November

Saturday 8
19 42 Falconer Road (Evening)

Gardens open to the public

5 Ashridge House
8 Benington Lordship
12 Capel Manor Gardens
24 Hatfield House West Garden
28 Hitchin Lavender
29 Hopleys
33 Knebworth House Gardens
43 Pembroke Farm
46 The Royal National Rose Society
50 St Paul's Walden Bury
56 Shaw's Corner

By appointment only

1 The Abbots House
61 Waterdell House

Also open by appointment

9 47 Bournehall Avenue
11 Bromley Hall
18 35 Digswell Road
19 42 Falconer Road
31 Huntsmoor
32 8 Kingcroft Road
41 45 Oakridge Avenue, Oakridge Avenue Gardens
42 Patchwork
48 3 St Marys Walk
51 20 St Stephens Avenue, St Stephens Avenue Gardens
57 9 Tannsfield Drive
59 Thundridge Hill House
62 3 Watford Road

Look out for exciting Designer Gardens D

The Gardens

1 THE ABBOTS HOUSE

10 High Street, Abbots Langley WD5 0AR. Peter & Sue Tomson, 01923 264946, peter.tomson@btinternet.com. *5m NW of Watford. M25, J20, take A4251 signed Kings Langley. R at r'about, R at T-junction, under railway bridge and follow yellow signs. Park in free village car park.* Home-made teas. **Adm £4.50, chd free (share to Friends of St Lawrence Church). Visitors welcome by appt Mar to Sept, groups of 10 - 30.**

1¾ -acre garden with unusual trees, shrubs, mixed borders with interesting colour combinations, scented garden, sunken garden, pond, conservatory and a bed with many Himalayan plants. A garden of 'rooms' with different styles and moods. Many half-hardy plants. Pea shingle path.

2 NEW ALSWICK HALL

Hare Street Road, Buntingford SG9 0AA. Mike & Annie Johnson, www.alswickhall.co.uk. *1m from Buntingford on B1038. From the South take the A10 to Buntingford, drive into the town and take B1038 E towards Hare Street Village. Alswick Hall is 1m on R.* **Adm £5, chd free. Sun 27 Apr (12-4).**

Listed Tudor House with 5 acres of landscaped gardens set in unspoiled farmland. Two well established natural ponds with rockeries. Herbaceous borders, shrubs, roses, woodland walk and wild flower meadow with a beautiful selection of daffodils and tulips. Spring blossom, formal beds, orchard and glasshouses. Good access for disabled with lawns and wood chip paths. Slight undulations.

3 AMWELL COTTAGE

Amwell Lane, Wheathampstead AL4 8EA. Colin & Kate Birss. *½ m S of Wheathampstead. From St Helen's Church, Wheathampstead turn up Brewhouse Hill. At top L fork (Amwell Lane), 300yds down lane, park in field opp.* Home-made teas. **Adm £3.50, chd free. Sun 15 June (2-5).**

Informal garden of approx 2½ acres around C17 cottage (not open). Large orchard of mature apples, plums and pear laid out with paths. Extensive lawns with borders, framed by tall yew hedges and old brick walls. A large variety of roses, stone seats with views, woodland pond, greenhouse and recently designed fire-pit area. Gravel drive.

4 NEW AMWELLBURY

Walnut Tree Walk, Great Amwell, Ware SG12 9RD. David & Antonia Preston. *1½ m S of Ware. From Amwell r'dabout proceed towards Ware. Just past Van Hage's Garden Centre turn L up Walnut Tree Walk. After 250yds turn R through woods.* Home-made teas. **Adm £3.50, chd free. Sat 17 May (1.30-4.30).**

Woodland garden created originally by Sir John Hanbury, who was a lover of rhododendrons. The garden has acid soil, which is unusual in this area. With few herbaceous borders the garden was planted predominantly with azaleas, rhododendrons and flowering trees such as Prunus and cherry. The garden is surrounded by woods with thousands of spring bulbs. Woods are not accessible by wheelchair.

Woodland walk and wild flower meadow with a beautiful selection of daffodils and tulips. Spring blossom . . .

5 ◆ ASHRIDGE HOUSE

Berkhamsted HP4 1NS. Ashridge (Bonar Law Memorial) Trust, 01442 843491, www.ashridge.org.uk. *3m N of Berkhamsted. A4251, 1m S of Little Gaddesden.* Cream teas. **Adm £4.50, chd £2.50. For NGS: Sun 8 June (12-6). For other opening times and information, please phone or see garden website.**

The gardens cover 190-acres forming part of the Grade II Registered Landscape of Ashridge Park. Based on designs by Humphry Repton in 1813 modified by Jeffry Wyatville. Small secluded gardens, as well as a large lawn area leading to avenues of trees. 2013 marks the 200th anniversary of Repton presenting Ashridge with the Red Book, detailing his designs for the estate.

6 BAYFORD MUSICAL GARDENS DAY
Bayford SG13 8PX, www.bayfordgardensday.org. *3m S of Hertford. Off B158 between Hatfield and Hertford.* Light refreshments. **Combined adm £8, chd free. Sun 22 June (11.30-5).**
A popular biennial event held for over 20yrs. More than a dozen gardens from large, long established formal layouts to pretty cottage gardens. 5 live bands incl, jazz, steel and brass add a festive backdrop, while visitors can enjoy a variety of ploughman's lunches, cream teas and licensed bars. Stalls sell plants, local produce, cakes and ice-cream. For the more active there are a number of signposted walks, complementary transport around the village is also provided and there is ample car parking. Bayford itself remains an oasis of countryside even though it is just 3m S of Hertford, and 10mins from Potters Bar. Mentioned in the Doomsday book of 1086 as Begesford, the village today is fortunate to retain much of its old world charm, incl a fine church with C15 font. Please see website for more details. Dogs welcome in some gardens.

GROUP OPENING

7 BEESONEND GARDENS
Harpenden AL5 2AN. *1m S of Harpenden. Take A1081 S from Harpenden, after 1m turn R into Beesonend Lane, bear R into Burywick to T-junction. Follow signs to Barlings Road & The Deerings.* Home-made teas at 17 The Deerings. **Combined adm £5, chd free. Sun 20 July (2-5.30).**

2 BARLINGS ROAD
Liz & Jim Machin

17 THE DEERINGS
Mr & Mrs Phillip Thompson

38 THE DEERINGS
Christine Viollet

Set in a mature development these gardens reflect their owners individual interests and needs. 2 Barlings Road is packed with unusual plants, shrubs and climbers to provide yr-round structure. The colourful courtyard garden with water feature and secluded shade garden add extra interest. 17 The Deerings offers specimen trees, architectural plants,

Woodhall Park

ornamental grasses, herbaceous borders as well as a compact kitchen garden and herb bed.
38 The Deerings is a generous ½ acre of mature enclosed formal and informal garden rooms. A sunny sunken garden with ornamental fish pond, colour themed herbaceous borders and a large wildlife pond all invite closer inspection.

8 ◆ BENINGTON LORDSHIP
nr Stevenage SG2 7BS. Mr & Mrs R R A Bott, 01438 869668, www.beningtonlordship.co.uk. *4m E of Stevenage. In Benington Village, next to church. Signs off A602.* Light refreshments and home made teas in the parish hall next to garden entrance. **Adm £5, chd free. For NGS: Sun 29 June (12-5). For other opening times and information, please phone or see garden website.**
7-acre garden incl historic buildings, kitchen garden, lakes, roses. Spectacular herbaceous borders, unspoilt panoramic views.

9 47 BOURNEHALL AVENUE
Bushey WD23 3AU. Caroline & Jim Fox, 0208 950 0727, carolinefox@f2s.com. *1m S of Watford. Bushey Village A411, Falconer Rd, Herkomer Rd, 2nd on L is Bournehall Ave. Map on www.jamespfox.co.uk.* Light refreshments. **Adm £4, chd free. Every Wed & Thur 4 May to 28 Sept (10.30-7). Visitors also welcome by appt May to Sept, for groups of 4+.**
Medium sized village garden on 3 levels, designed by owners. Garlanded planters overlook sunken garden with acers and pond. Wisteria and vine covered pergola leads to fruited potager. Step up to sculpted lawn edged with small trees, shrubs and sumptuous perennials. Featured in the Daily Express and on The One Show.

10 44 BROADWATER AVENUE
Letchworth Garden City SG6 3HJ. Karen & Ian Smith. *½ m SW Letchworth town centre. A1(M) J9 signed Letchworth. Straight on at 1st three r'abouts, 4th r'about take 4th exit then R into Broadwater Ave.* Home-made teas. **Adm £4, chd free. Evening Opening wine, Fri 1 Aug (6-9); Sun 3 Aug (10-4).**
Town garden in the Letchworth Garden City conservation area that successfully combines a family garden with a plantswoman's garden. Out of the ordinary, unusual herbaceous plants and shrubs. Attractive front garden designed for yr-round interest. Featured in Amateur Gardening and Garden Answers. Winner of best front and back garden Letchworth in bloom.

11 BROMLEY HALL
Standon, Ware SG11 1NY. Julian & Edwina Robarts, 01279 842 422, edwina.robarts@gmail.com, www.bromley-hall.co.uk. *6m W of Bishop's Stortford. From A120 turn into Standon High St. Follow rd for 1½ m towards Much Hadham.* Home-made teas. **Adm £5, chd free. Sat 7 June (11-5); Sun 8 June (2-5.30). Visitors also welcome by appt May to Sept, groups of 10+.**
4½ acres surrounding C16 farmhouse. Some elements are traditional - formal hedging, Irish yews, and mixed borders, vegetables, mown paths through long grass. Others are modern, a grove of white poplars surrounding cranes and a modern formal garden on the site of the old tennis court. Everywhere there are places to sit, view and contemplate. Home made marmalade, jams and chutneys for sale.

12 ◆ CAPEL MANOR GARDENS
Bullsmoor Lane, Enfield EN1 4RQ. Capel Manor Charitable Corporation, 08456 122 122, www.capelmanorgardens.co.uk. *2m from Cheshunt. 3 mins from J25 of M25/A10. Nearest train station is Turkey Street, then 20 mins walk.* Light refreshments. **Adm £5.50, chd £2.50. For NGS: Sat 8, Sun 9 Mar (10-5); Sat 18, Sun 19 Oct (10-5.30). For other opening times and information, please phone or see garden website.**
A beautiful 30-acre estate providing a colourful and scented oasis surrounding a Georgian Manor House and Victorian Stables. Be inspired by prize winning themed, model and historical gardens incl the latest additions the Old Manor House Garden and the Australian Garden (Chelsea Gold Medal winner). Wheelchair loan available and free with advanced booking.

13 NEW 42 CHURCH STREET
Baldock SG7 5AF. Leila Shafarenko. *Baldock town centre. 3m N of A1M J9 in the center of Baldock. 2m S of A1M J10. At the end of High St turn R at r'about, soon L into Sun St, continue Church St.* Home-made teas. **Adm £3, chd free. Evening Opening wine, Fri 16 May (6-8.30); Sun 18 May (1-5).**
Secluded walled garden hidden behind a C16 house in the heart of Baldock's conservation area. Mature trees, incl a magnificent magnolia, wisteria-clad walls and wide herbaceous borders. Cottage-style planting featuring species peonies, and many varieties of thornless roses.

14 NEW THE COTTAGE
Datchworth Green, Datchworth, Knebworth SG3 6TL. James & Anne Halliday. *5m N of Welwyn Garden City. From J6 A1 take B197 to Knebworth. In centre of Woolmer Green opp Chequers PH turn R to Datchworth. Follow rd to The Green.* **Adm £3.50, chd free. Sun 13 July (2-5).**
A country style village garden of ½ acre developed over last 15yrs. The space is divided into distinctive areas to explore with contrasting atmosphere and plantings; a garden full of surprises and interesting focal points incl wildlife pond. The dominant feel is soft, romantic and relaxed, modern perennials and grasses enliven the planting palette Teashop in village.

15 CROFT COTTAGE
9 Church Green, Benington SG2 7LH. Richard Arnold-Roberts & Julie Haire. *4m E of Stevenage. A1 J7 onto A602 to Hertford. Onto single carridgeway. Next r'about L down hill to mini r'about. Up hill through Aston. 1½ m to Xrd. Then 1½ m. Park on road opp cottage.* Home-made teas (June), teas in village hall (Aug). **Adm £3.50, chd free. Sun 22 June (1-5); Mon 25 Aug (10-4).**
C16 cottage with small, extensively planted garden divided into several areas. Many variegated and colourful-leafed shrubs and perennials. Mixed border in pastel shades. Euphorbia and hosta collection. Pool with fish, waterspout and seat. Rose and clematis shaded arbour with view over fields. Japanese maple garden with pool overlooking C13 church. Gravel paths. Featured in Garden News.

16 10 CROSS STREET
Letchworth Garden City SG6 4UD. Renata Hume, www.cyclamengardens.com. *Nr town centre. From A1(M) J9 signed Letchworth, across 2 r'abouts, R at 3rd, across next 3 r'abouts L into Nevells Rd, 1st R into Cross St.* Teas. **Adm £3.50, chd free. Evening Opening wine, Fri 16 May (5-8); Sat 17 May (9-12); Sun 18 May (2-5).**
A cottage garden fronts a Letchworth Garden City exhibition cottage of 1905. The back garden contains informal planting dictated by the gently sloping plot and three formal circular lawns. Trees, shrubs, grasses and herbaceous perennials combine to create interest in the different areas. The garden also contains a lily pond, small pond for wildlife, well-stocked greenhouse and an apple walk with a selection of old varieties.

17 NEW 25 CUNNINGHAM HILL ROAD
St. Albans AL1 5BX. David & Anne Myles. *1m S of St Albans City Centre. At A414 London Colney r'about turn onto London Road (City Centre). Turn R at sign 30mph.* Home-made teas. **Adm £4, chd free. Suns 25 May; 20 July (2-5.30).**
½ acre gardens with mature trees and shrubs, developed for all round colour. Wildlife ponds are linked to a fish pond. Wrought iron arches of roses, lonicera and clematis, are flanked by double herbaceous borders. A lawn, bordered by woodland planting beneath a beech tree, ends in a conifer and heather bed; behind which a sunny trellis separates the fruit and kitchen garden.

18 35 DIGSWELL ROAD
Welwyn Garden City AL8 7PB. Adrian & Clare de Baat, 01707 324074, adrian.debaat@ntlworld.com, www.adriansgarden.org. *½ m N of Welwyn Garden City centre. From the Campus r'about in city centre take N exit just past the Public Library into Digswell Rd. Over the White Bridge, 300yds on L.* Home-made teas. **Adm £4, chd free. Sun 27 July (2-5.30). Visitors also welcome by appt June to Oct, groups up to 20, adm incl tea & cake.**
Town garden of around a third of an acre with naturalistic planting inspired by the Dutch garden designer, Piet Oudolf. The garden is full of perennial borders and island beds packed with herbaceous plants and grasses. The contemporary planting gives way to the exotic, incl a succulent bed and, under mature trees, a lush jungle garden incl bamboos, bananas and tree ferns. Featured in Homes and Gardens and Country Homes and Interiors magazines and on BBC Gardeners World. Grass paths and gentle slopes to all areas of the garden.

19 42 FALCONER ROAD
Bushey, Watford WD23 3AD. Mrs Suzette Fuller, 07714 294170, suzettesdesign@btconnect.com. *M1 J 5 follow signs for Bushey From London A40 via Stanmore towards Watford. From Watford via Bushey Arches, through to Bushey High St turn L into Falconer Rd, opp St James church.* Light refreshments. **Adm £3, chd free. Sats, Suns 26, 27 July, 2, 3 Aug (12-6); Evening Opening wine, Sat 8 Nov (5-7). Visitors also welcome by appt July.**
Enchanting magical unusual Victorian style space. Children so very welcome. Winter viewing for fairyland lighting, for all ages, bring a torch. Bird cages and chimneys a feature, plus a walk through conservatory with orchids. Featured in Amateur Gardening and Hertfordshire Life.

20 15 GADE VALLEY COTTAGES
Dagnall Road, Great Gaddesden, Hemel Hempstead HP1 3BW. Bryan Trueman. *3m N of Hemel Hempstead. Follow A4146 N from Hemel Hempstead. Past Water End. Go past turning for Great Gaddesden. Gade Valley Cottages on R. Park in village hall car park.* Tea. **Adm £3, chd free. Suns 25 May; 27 July (1.30-5).**
165ft x 30ft sloping rural garden. Patio, lawn, borders and pond. Paths lead through a woodland area emerging by wildlife pond and sunny border. A choice of seating offers sunny rural views or quiet shady contemplation with sounds of rustling bamboos and bubbling water. Featured in Garden News. Gravel paths and some steps.

Secluded garden of ⅓ acre surrounds our contemporary home and backs on to a beautiful ancient woodland . . .

21 8 GOSSELIN ROAD
Bengeo, Hertford SG14 3LG. Annie Godfrey & Steve Machin, anne@daisyroots.com, www.daisyroots.com. *Take B158 from Hertford signed to Bengeo. Gosselin Rd 2nd R after White Lion PH (phone box on corner).* **Adm £3.50, chd free. Sun 12 Oct (12-5).**
Owners of Daisy Roots nursery, garden acts as trial ground and show case for perennials and ornamental grasses grown there. Lawn replaced in 2010 by a wide gravel path, flanked by deep borders packed with perennials and grasses. Sunken area surrounded by plants chosen for scent. Small front garden with lots of foliage interest. Featured in House Beautiful.

22 NEW GREENWOOD HOUSE
2a Lanercost Close, Welwyn AL6 0RW. David & Cheryl Chalk. *1½ m E of Welwyn village, close to J6 on A1(M). Off B197 in Oaklands. Opp North Star PH turn into Lower Mardley Hill. Park here as limited at house (5min walk). Take Oaklands Rise to top of the hill & take L fork.* Home-made teas. **Adm £3, chd free. Sun 6 July (1-5). Evening Opening wine, Fri 11 July (6-9).**
Secluded garden of ⅓ acre surrounds our contemporary home and backs on to a beautiful ancient woodland. Garden has been transformed in last 6 years, with mature trees providing a natural backdrop to the many shrubs and perennials which provide interest and colour throughout the seasons. Access to rear garden across pebble paths and some steps.

23 NEW HAILEYBURY
Haileybury and Imperial Service College, Hertford SG13 7NU. Sarah Carthew, www.haileybury.com. *Close to A10 and easily accessible via M25, A1(M) & A414. From A414 at Hertford, take the B1197 (London Rd) to Hertford Heath. Drive through the village and turn L into Haileybury estate main entrance.* Light refreshments & cream teas in the dining hall, Costa coffee cafe will be open. **Adm £5, chd free. Sat 5, Sun 6 July (10-4).**
Opening for the first time to the public, Haileybury is a 500 acre site with Grade I listed buildings, designed by William Wilkins, made up of small gardens, unusual specimen trees and grand landscapes including one of the largest quads in Europe. The Humphry Repton 1809 garden scheme still remains with plans to develop a restoration project. Guided tours given by Garden staff and the Archivist.

24 ◆ HATFIELD HOUSE WEST GARDEN
Hatfield AL9 5NQ. The Marquess of Salisbury, 01707 287010, www.hatfield-house.co.uk. *Opp Hatfield Stn, 21m N of London, M25 J23. 7m A1(M) J4 signed off A414 & A1000. Free parking.* Light refreshments. **Adm £6, chd free. For NGS: Sat 29 Mar (11-5). For other opening times and information, please phone or see garden website.**
Visitors can enjoy the spring bulbs in the lime walk, sundial garden and view the famous Old Palace garden, childhood home of Queen Elizabeth I. The adjoining woodland garden is at its best in spring with masses of naturalised daffodils and bluebells. Restaurant open. Exclusive shopping in Stable Yard.

The Mill House

25 NEW 122 HAZELWOOD DRIVE

St. Albans AL4 0UZ. Phil & Becky Leach. *3/4 m NE of St Albans city centre. From city centre take A1057 (Hatfield Rd). After 3/4 m turn L into Beechwood Ave. Take 2nd R into Central Drive, then 2nd L into Hazelwood Drive*. Home-made teas. **Adm £3, chd free. Sats 17 May; 14 June (2.30-5.30).**

A densely and informally planted small town garden divided into sections, with an emphasis on foliage and structure. Large-leaved plants incl foxglove tree (paulownia), giant rhubarb (gunnera) and rice-paper plant (tetrapanax). Structural plants incl onopordum, acanthus, cynara and eryngium. Many plants grown from seed: echinops, echium, teasel and melianthus. Access is via small section of gravel drive.

26 NEW 3 HIGHFIELD AVENUE

Harpenden AL5 5UB. Sue Gudgin. *2/3 m from Harpenden Railway Stn. Station Rd, R into Milton Rd, over r'about, L into Fairmead Ave then Highfield Ave. No 3 on L*. Home-made teas. **Adm £3, chd free. Sun 15 June (2-6).**

Romantic, peaceful, garden (80' x 30', N-facing), designed over 10yrs for all-year colour. Informal garden rooms interlinked by winding grass paths and wide traditional borders creating seating areas with different atmospheres. Arches with wisteria, rose and lonicera. Trees incl silver birch, ash, rowan and acers. Small raised herb patch, sedum roof on garden shed.

27 NEW 124 HIGHFIELD WAY

Rickmansworth WD3 7PH. Mrs Barbara Grant. *1m E of J18 M25, 1m NW of Rickmansworth. Easily accessible from J18 M25 follow yellow arrows*. Home-made teas. **Adm £4, chd free. Sat 7 June; Sun 20 July (2-6.30).**

Gently sloping from terrace at the top down to deck at the bottom the plethora of plants and trees provide an ever-changing burst of colour and interest throughout the year. Clipped yew and bamboo hedging, together with mixed shrub and perennial borders seamlessly surround mixed grasses, woodland area, bog garden, fruit and vegetable patches, greenhouse and an enormous pond packed with fish.

28 ◆ HITCHIN LAVENDER

Cadwell Farm, Ickleford, Hitchin SG5 3UA. Mr Tim Hunter, 01462 434343, www.hitchinlavender.com. *2m N of Hitchin. From Hitchin take A600 N. At r'about R into Turnpike Lane. Continue into Arley Rd, garden on R after railway Xing*. **For NGS: Evening Openings adm £4, chd £1, light refreshments, Tue 1, Mon 21 July, Fri 1, Thur 21 Aug (5-9). For other opening times and information, please phone or see garden website.**

Visitors are encouraged to walk through the miles of lavender rows at Hitchin Lavender. As well as taking home some great photos you can also pick a bunch of lavender. The fields are a great spot for photographers, artists or those just wanting to take life a little slower. Entrance incl pick your own bunch of lavender - please bring your own scissors!.

29 ◆ HOPLEYS

High Street, Much Hadham SG10 6BU. Aubrey & Jan Barker, 01279 842509, www.hopleys.co.uk. *5m W of Bishop's Stortford. On B1004. M11 (J8) 7m or A10 (Puckeridge) 5m via A120. 50yds N of Bull PH in centre of Much Hadham*. **For opening times and information, please phone or see garden website.**

4 acres laid out in informal style with island beds. The garden has become a useful collection of stock plants and trial ground for many new plants collected over the years, and features a wide selection of trees, shrubs, perennials and grasses. The nursery production area is hidden by an avenue of fastigiate hornbeams.

30 NEW HOSPICE OF ST FRANCIS GARDEN

Spring Garden Lane, Berkhamsted HP4 3GW. Hospice of St Francis. *1½ m W of Berkhamsted town centre. Leave A41 at A416 Chesham exit. Follow signs for Berkhamsted, When rd bends R go straight on into Shootersway, signed Northchurch, for 1¼ m.* Cream teas. **Adm £4, chd free. Sun 7 Sept (2-5.30).**

The hospice was built in 2006 on seven acres of previously damaged land and designed to resemble a farmhouse, barns and outbuildings. The garden has native woodland at the boundaries and pergolas, paved terraces, lawns, ponds, and flower and shrub beds visible and accessible from patients' bedrooms; a peaceful oriental healing garden; and a sensory garden with views across to Ashridge. Parts of woodland not suitable for wheelchairs.

31 HUNTSMOOR

Stoney Lane, Bovingdon, Hemel Hempstead HP3 0DP. Mr Brian Bradnock & Ms Jane Meir, 01442 832014, b.bradnock@btinternet.com. *Between Bovingdon & Hemel Hempstead. Do not follow sat nav directions along Stoney Lane. Huge pot holes and ruts in lane. Approach from Bushfield Rd.* Home-made teas. **Adm £4, chd free. Sun 27 Apr, Sun 21 Sept (2-5). Visitors also welcome by appt Apr to Sept 10+.**

Rose garden, rhododendron border, arboretum, Koi pond, nature pond, shrub and herbaceous borders. Also has a 'cave', and lots of places to sit. Full access to garden including easy access to WC.

32 NEW 8 KINGCROFT ROAD

8 Kingcroft Road, Southdown, Harpenden AL5 1EJ. Zia Allaway, 07770 780 231, zia.allaway@ntlworld.com, ziaallaway.com. *1½ m S of Harpenden town centre. From Harpenden take the St Albans Rd A1081 S. At 1st r'about turn L onto Southdown Rd. Continue straight over 3 r'abouts to Grove Rd.* Home-made teas. **Adm £3.50, chd free. Evening Opening wine, Fri 2 May (5.30-8); Sun 4 May (2-6). Visitors also welcome by appt Apr to Oct for small groups.**

Beautiful mature town garden designed by garden writer and designer in a contemporary informal style, with pool and pebbled beach area, gravel garden, a wide range of tulips and spring bulbs, herbaceous perennials and shrubs, mature trees, shady borders, greenhouse, and inspirational container displays. Small courtyard features flower-filled window boxes and vegetables in pots.

33 ◆ KNEBWORTH HOUSE GARDENS

Knebworth SG1 2AX. The Hon Henry Lytton Cobbold, 01438 812661, www.knebworthhouse.com. *28m N of London. Direct access from A1(M) J7 at Stevenage. Stn, Stevenage 3m.* **For opening times and information, please phone or see garden website.**

Knebworth's magnificent gardens were laid out by Lutyens in 1910. Lutyens' pollarded lime avenues, Gertrude Jekyll's herb garden, the restored maze, yew hedges, roses and herbaceous borders are key features of the formal gardens with peaceful woodland walks beyond. Gold garden, green garden, brick garden and walled kitchen garden.

34 NEW THE LODGE

Luton Road, Markyate, St Albans AL3 8QA. Jan & John Paul. *2m N of M1 J9. Turn off the A5 to Luton on the B4540. The garden is between the villages of Markyate & Slip End.* Light refreshments. **Adm £4, chd free. Sat 14 June (11-5); Sun 15 June (11-4.30).**

The garden, of nearly 3 acres, has evolved over 46 years, partly through our own efforts and partly through nature growing plants wherever it chooses. The garden, mainly informal with a series of rooms, with small wooded area, a wild flower meadow, remains of an orchard which is full of common spotted orchids and other lovely wild flowers all of which arrived by themselves. Come and see for yourself. Main entrance gravel. Garden mostly flat.

35 MACKERYE END HOUSE

Mackerye End, Harpenden AL5 5DR. Mr & Mrs G Penn. *3m E of Harpenden. A1 J4 follow signs Wheathampstead. then turn R Marshalls Heath Lane. M1 J10 follow Lower Luton Road B653. Turn L Marshalls Heath Lane. Follow signs.* Home-made teas. **Adm £5, chd free. Evening Opening wine, Fri 30 May (6-9); Sun 29 June (2-5).**

C16 (Grade 1 listed) Manor House (not open) set in 15 acres of formal gardens, parkland and woodland, front garden set in framework of formal yew hedges. Victorian walled garden with extensive box hedging and box maze, cutting garden, kitchen garden and lily pond. Courtyard garden with extensive yew and box borders. West garden enclosed by pergola walk of old English roses. Plants for sale (Sun). Walled garden access by gravel paths.

Remains of an orchard which is full of common spotted orchids and other lovely wild flowers all of which arrived by themselves . . .

36 THE MANOR HOUSE, AYOT ST LAWRENCE

Welwyn AL6 9BP. Rob & Sara Lucas. *4m W of Welwyn. 20 mins J4 A1M. Take B653 Wheathampstead. Turn into Codicote Rd follow signs to Shaws Corner. Parking in field short walk to garden.* Home-made teas. **Adm £5, chd free. Sun 18 May (11-5).**

A 6-acre garden set in mature landscape around Elizabethan Manor House (not open). 1-acre walled garden incl glasshouses, fruit and vegetables, double herbaceous borders, rose and herb beds. Herbaceous perennial island beds, topiary specimens. Parterre and temple pond garden surround the house. Gates and water features by Arc Angel. Garden designed by Julie Toll.

37 **43 MARDLEY HILL**
Welwyn AL6 0TT. Kerrie & Pete. *5m N of Welwyn Garden City. On B197 between Welwyn & Woolmer Green, on crest of Mardley Hill by bus stop for Arriva 300/301.* Cream teas. **Adm £3, chd free. Suns 18 May; 13 July (12-5).**
There is much to discover in this garden designed and created by plantaholics and filled with lots of unusual plants, focusing on interesting foliage with splashes of flower colour. Dense planting of perennials and bulbs on varied levels provides ever-changing interest. There are several seating areas with different views. Features incl an outdoor lounge and pond fed by naturalistic cascade.

A peaceful oriental healing garden; and a sensory garden with views across to Ashridge . . .

38 **MICHAELS FOLLY**
Henderson Place, Epping Green, nr Hertford SG1 38NE. Fabrizia Verrecchia, Tessa Verrecchia & Tim Metcalfe, www.bitzia.co.uk. *4m SW of Hertford. A414 follow signs to Berkhamsted. L at war memorial to Epping Green. Turn R into Henderson Place. Garden 100yds on L.* Home-made teas. **Adm £3.50, chd free. Sun 29 June (2-5.30).**
Something different! Forget your busy life and enter this atmospheric naturalistic garden. Meander the woodland walk and visit the earth labyrinth. Sit and reflect by the large natural pond and enjoy the abundant organic kitchen garden festooned with roses. Interesting structures abound a straw bale studio for yoga and dance and a Mongolian Yurt where tea will be served. Artist Tessa Verrechia's Stained glass studio fusingglass.co.uk.

39 **THE MILL HOUSE**
31 Mill Lane, Welwyn AL6 9EU. Sarah & Ian. *Old Welwyn. J6 A1M approx 3/4 m to garden, follow yellow arrows to Welwyn Village.* Home-made teas. **Adm £3.50, chd free. Sat 19 Apr (2-5); Mon 21 Apr (2-5).**
Listed millhouse (not open) with semi-walled garden bordered by a bridged millstream and mill race. This romantic garden has ancient apple trees underplanted with an abundant display of tulips and white narcissi. These set off a garden full of perennial promise, within nestles a stylish summerhouse, a hidden parterre and productive potager.

40 **324 NORTON WAY SOUTH**
Letchworth Garden City SG6 1TA. Roger & Jill Thomson. *Just off the A505, E of town centre. From the A1M leave at J 9 (A505) to Letchworth. At 2nd r'about turn L. to Hitchin, still on A505. At T-lights turn L into Norton Way South.* Light refreshments. **Adm £3.50, chd free. Sun 27 Apr (2-5).**
1/5 acre organic garden of a sympathetically extended Garden City house (1906). Features incl an informal knot garden, a bespoke David Harber armillary sphere as focal point of a lawn surrounded by a rockery, scree garden, borders, summerhouse and pond. Mature shrubs and mixed planting in beds and containers, sculptures, greenhouse and kitchen garden. Good in most areas of the garden.

GROUP OPENING

41 **OAKRIDGE AVENUE GARDENS**
Radlett WD7 8EW. *Radlett. 1m N of Radlett off A5183, Watling St. From S, through Radlett Village last turning on L.* Cream teas. **Combined adm £4, chd free. Sun 27 July (2-5.30).**

45 OAKRIDGE AVENUE
Radlett. Mr & Mrs Vaughan.
Follow yellow arrows
Visitors also welcome by appt Apr to Sept.
01923 854650
ekvaughan@btinternet.com

47 OAKRIDGE AVENUE
Scott Vincent

Two varied interconnecting gardens in attractive village near St Albans. Both on the edge of a working farm. The main features of no. 45 are the plants carefully chosen to combine the use of colour throughout the year. The garden is in two halves approx 150ft x 60ft on 3 levels of terracing, looping around to a garden of vegetables and soft fruit. Beds divided by sleepers. Plants for sale are propagated from the garden. No. 47 is a spacious and mature garden, approx 1 acre with a large pond, an impressive Victorian wall & small orchard. A local brook runs alongside. Featured in Garden News.

42 **PATCHWORK**
22 Hall Park Gate, Berkhamsted HP4 2NJ. Jean & Peter Block, 01442 864731. *3m W of Hemel Hempstead. Entering E side of Berkhamsted on A4251, turn L 200yds after 40mph sign.* Light refreshments. **Adm £3, chd free. Suns 4 May; 17 Aug (2-5). Visitors also welcome by appt Mar to Oct.**
1/4 -acre garden with lots of yr-round colour, interest and perfume, particularly on opening days. Sloping site with background of colourful trees, rockeries, two small ponds, patios, shrubs and trees, spring bulbs, herbaceous border, roses, bedding, fuchsias, dahlias, patio pots and tubs galore and hanging baskets. Seating and cover from the elements. Summer garden featured in Garden News.

43 **◆ PEMBROKE FARM**
Slip End, nr Ashwell, Baldock SG7 6SQ. Krysia Selwyn-Gotha, 01462 743100, pembrokefarmgarden.co.uk. *1/2 m S of Ashwell. Off A505 Ashwell turn opp Wallington junction. Under railway bridge garden 1/8 m on R.* Home-made teas. **Adm £3.50, chd free. For NGS: Suns 1 June; 6 July; 3 Aug (12-5). For other opening times and information, please phone or see garden website.**
A country house garden with a wildlife walk and formal surprises. You are invited to meander through changing spaces creating a palimpsest of nature and structure. Car park close to garden entry.

44 QUEENSWOOD SCHOOL
Shepherds Way, Brookmans Park, Hatfield AL9 6NS. Queenswood School. *3m N of Potters Bar. M25 J24 signed Potters Bar at T-lights turn R onto A1000 signed Hatfield. 2m turn R onto B157. School ½ m on R. From N A1000 from Hatfield turn L B157.* Light refreshments. **Adm £4, chd free.** **Sun 25 May (11-5).**
120 acres of informal gardens and woodlands. Rhododendrons, fine specimen trees, shrubs and herbaceous borders. Glasshouses. Fine views to Chiltern Hills. Picnic area. Full Sunday Roast served alongside Scampi and Chips, also a vegetarian option. Muffins, strawberries and cream teas. Some gravel areas.

45 REVELEY LODGE
88 Elstree Road, Bushey Heath WD23 4GL. Bushey Museum Property Trust. *3½ m E of Watford and 1½ m E of Bushey Village. From A41 take A411 signed Bushey & Harrow. At mini-r'about 2nd exit into Elstree Rd. Garden ½ m on L.* Home-made teas. **Adm £4, chd free.** **Sun 14 Sept (2-6).**
2½ -acre garden surrounding a Victorian house bequeathed to Bushey Museum in 2003 and in process of re-planting and renovation. Featuring colourful annual, tender perennial and medicinal planting in beds surrounding a mulberry tree. Conservatory, lean-to greenhouse, vegetable garden and beehive. Analemmatic (human) sundial constructed in stone believed unique to Hertfordshire. Limited wheelchair access. Disabled parking only onsite.

46 ◆ THE ROYAL NATIONAL ROSE SOCIETY
Chiswell Green Lane, St Albans AL2 3NR. The Secretary, 0845 833 4344, www.rnrs.org.uk. *M25 J21a M1 J6. Follow brown signs, Gardens of the Rose off A405 Noke Lane 1st R Miriam Lane as you enter Butterfly World Ltd. For Satnav use postcode AL2 3NY.* **For NGS: Evening Opening £6, chd free, Cream teas, Fri 18 July (6-8). For other opening times and information, please phone or see garden website.**
The gardens were completely rebuilt to a design by Michael Balston & Co in 2007, in the winter of 2009 the garden design was further enhanced by the introduction of additional grass paths enabling visitors more access to the roses. Also at this time a decision was taken to support general gardening trends by the introduction of many more companion plants. The garden showcases over 15,000 roses old and new, fragrant and colourful, displaying the stunning heritage of our favorite flower in a beautiful setting.

Croft Cottage

© Mike Howes

47 RUSTLING END COTTAGE
Rustling End, nr Codicote SG4 8TD. Julie & Tim Wise, www.rustlingend.com. *1m N of Codicote. From B656 turn L into '3 Houses Lane' then R to Rustling End. House 2nd on L.* Home-made teas. **Adm £4.50, chd free.** **Fri 9 May (4-8); Sun 11 May (1-5).**
Meander through our wild flower meadow to a cottage garden with contemporary planting. Behind lumpy hedges explore a simple box parterre, topiary, reflecting pool and abundant planting. Late flowering borders feature blue Camassia in late spring. Naturalistic planting includes the use of wildflowers with perennials and grasses. Hens in residence. View the bluebell woods en route to garden. Featured on BBC Gardeners World, BBC The One Show and in Garden Answers magazine.

48 3 ST MARYS WALK
St. Albans AL4 9PD. Mrs Rosemary Coldstream, 01727 860092, rose@rosemarycoldstream.com, www.rosemarycoldstream.com. *Marshalswick, North St Albans. Located off Pondfield Crescent or via walkway from The Ridgeway, follow yellow NGS signs.* Home-made teas. **Adm £3.50, chd free.** **Evening Opening wine, Fri 15 Aug (6-9); Sun 17 Aug (2-5.30).** **Visitors also welcome by appt.**
This contemporary and late-summer garden features an unusual collection of antipodean and English plants. A garden designer's own family garden, pathways lead off in all directions from a central oval-shaped lawn. The borders are packed with grasses, perennials, ferns, tree ferns, exotic trees and shrubs and some quirky topiary. The garden also houses Rosemary's design studio.

D

Hitchin Lavender

49 ST MICHAEL'S CROFT

Woodcock Hill, Durrants Lane, Berkhamsted HP4 3TR. Sue & Alan O'Neill, 01442 872770. *1¼ m W of Berkhamsted town centre. Leave A41 signed A416 Chesham. Follow sign to Berkhamsted, after 500 metres straight on to Shootersway. 1m on turn R into Durrants Lane. Garden 1st on L.* Home-made teas. **Adm £4, chd free. Sun 22 June (2-6).**

1-acre S-facing garden with variety of densely planted borders surrounded by mature trees. Rhododendrons, azaleas, hostas, ferns, alliums, palms and bananas. Water features and waterfall from lock gate. Pergolas with clematis and climbers, vegetable beds, 2 greenhouses. Working beehives. Seating and cover. Home produced honey and plants for sale. Featured in Garden News. Easy access for wheelchairs.

50 ◆ ST PAUL'S WALDEN BURY

Whitwell, Hitchin SG4 8BP. Simon & Caroline Bowes Lyon, 01438 871218, www.stpaulswaldenbury.co.uk. *5m S of Hitchin. On B651; ½ m N of Whitwell village. From London leave A1(M) J6 for Welwyn (not Welwyn Garden City). Pick up signs to Codicote, then Whitwell.* Home-made teas. **Adm £5, chd £1. For NGS: Suns 13 Apr; 11 May; 8 June (2-7). For other opening times and information, please phone or see garden website.**

Spectacular formal woodland garden, Grade 1 listed, laid out 1720. Long rides lined with clipped beech hedges lead to temples, statues, lake and a terraced theatre. Seasonal displays of snowdrops, daffodils, cowslips, irises, magnolias, rhododendrons, lilies. Wild flowers are encouraged. This was the childhood home of the late Queen Mother. Children welcome. Open Garden combined with Open Farm Sunday 8 June. Performances of 'The Tempest' 25-27 July. Suitable for wheel chairs in part of the garden. Steep grass slopes in places.

GROUP OPENING

51 ST STEPHENS AVENUE GARDENS

St Albans AL3 4AD. *1m S of St Albans City Centre. From A414 take A5183 Watling St. At double mini-r'bout by St Stephens Church/King Harry PH take B4630 Watford Rd. St Stephens Ave is 1st R.* Home-made teas at no. 20. **Combined adm £5, chd free. Sun 29 June (2-6).**

20 ST STEPHENS AVENUE
Heather & Peter Osborne
Visitors also welcome by appt, home made teas available. 01727 856354 heather.osborne20@btinternet.com

30 ST STEPHENS AVENUE
Carol & Roger Harlow

Two gardens of similar size and aspect, developed in different ways. Hostas, ferns and seasonal containers surround the patio of No. 20. Densely planted colour themed mixed borders encircle a wildlife pond. Fences clothed with honeysuckle, clematis and roses provide perfume and privacy. Winding paths lead to a white border, the 'St Albans' bed and gravel areas of grasses and architectural plants. Through the arch are displays of late summer perennials and tender succulents. No. 30 has an informal gravel front garden; the Mediterranean style planting is tolerant of very dry conditions and poor soil. Clipped box, beech and hornbeam provide a framework for herbaceous planting and lawns in the back garden. Different sections incl a sunken garden, black garden and productive greenhouse.

52 NEW SANDON BURY

Sandon, Buntingford SG9 0QY. Teddy & Louise Faure Walker. *5m N of Buntingford. A10 N of Buntingford. L at Buckland. Follow signs to Sandon. A1 N of Stevenage, A505 towards Royston. R after 2½ m to Sandon.* Tea at Sandon Village Hall. **Adm £5, chd free. Sat 21, Sun 22 June (2-5).**

1640 Manor House in 2 acre garden.The highest point in Hertfordshire with views over countryside. Large herbaceous borders, walled vegetable garden, parterre, dovehouse, mature trees. ART EXHIBITION in recently restored 1250 Saxon Barn one of the oldest in Europe. C13 Church, Village Hall Teas, Easy Parking, all adjacent to the garden. Disabled Parking and WC at village hall. Mown lawns and gentle slopes. Access to church and barn up gentle slopes.

53 SCUDAMORE

1 Baldock Road, Letchworth Garden City SG6 3LB. Michael & Sheryl Hann. *Opposite Spring Road, between Muddy Lane & Letchworth Lane. Junction 9 A1 directions to Letchworth. Hitchin A505. House on L opposite corner shop. Parking in Muddy Lane & Spring Rd.* **Adm £3, chd free (share to Garden House Hospice). Evening Opening wine, Fri 11 July (6-9).**

½ acre garden surrounding early C17 cottages that were converted and extended in 1920s to form current house (not open). Family garden of mature trees, mixed herbaceous borders with shrubs, pond and stream, wet bed, wild garden and orchard/vegetable area. Many sculptures add interest to the garden.

54 NEW SERENDI

Hitchin Road, Letchworth Garden City SG6 3LT. Valerie Aitken. *1m from city centre. A1 M J9 signed Letchworth on A505. At 2nd r'about turn L to Hitchin on A505. Straight over T-lights on to Hitchin Rd. Serendi 400yds.* Home-made teas. **Adm £4, chd free. Evening Opening wine, Fri 20 June (6-9); Sun 22 June (1-5).**

⅓ acre plot comprising several different areas. Front garden - wonderful wisteria, an 'S' loop of lavender, blue and pink bed. A 'back yard' of hostas, memento wall, formal planting and exuberant cottage style planting with roses and magnolias in larger beds. Greenhouse and contemporary knot garden. Gravel entrance driveway.

GROUP OPENING

55 SERGE HILL GARDENS

Serge Hill Lane, Bedmond, Watford WD5 0RT. *½ m E of Bedmond. Go to Bedmond & take Serge Hill Lane, where you will be directed past the lodge & down the drive.* Home-made teas at Serge Hill. **Combined adm £7, chd free. Sun 22 June (2-5).**

THE BARN D
Sue & Tom Stuart-Smith

SERGE HILL
Kate Stuart-Smith

Two very diverse gardens. At its entrance The Barn has an enclosed courtyard, with tanks of water, herbaceous perennials and shrubs tolerant of generally dry conditions. To the N there are views over the 5-acre wild flower meadow, and the West Garden is a series of different gardens overflowing with bulbs, herbaceous perennials and shrubs. Serge Hill is originally a Queen Anne House (not open), beautifully remodelled by Busby (architect of Brighton and Hove) in 1811. It has wonderful views over the ha-ha to the park; a walled vegetable garden with a large greenhouse, roses, shrubs and perennials leading to a long mixed border. At the front of the house there is an outside stage used for family plays, and a ship.

56 ◆ SHAW'S CORNER

Ayot St Lawrence, nr Welwyn AL6 9BX. National Trust, 01438 820307, www.nationaltrust.org.uk/shawscorner. *2m NE of Wheathampstead. At SW end of village, approx 2m from B653 (A1 J4, M1 J10). Signed from B653 (Shaw's Corner/The Ayots).* **Adm £6.30, chd free. For NGS: Sun 8 June (12-5.30). For other opening times and information, please phone or see garden website.**

Approx 3½ acres with richly planted borders, orchard, small meadow, wooded areas and views over the Hertfordshire countryside. Historical garden, belonging to George Bernard Shaw from 1906 until his death in 1950. Hidden among the trees is the revolving writing hut where Shaw retreated to write his plays. Ionian Singers will perform in the garden on NGS open day. No wheelchair accessible WC.

57 9 TANNSFIELD DRIVE

Hemel Hempstead HP2 5LG. Peter & Gaynor Barrett, 01442 393508, tterrabjp@ntlworld.com, www.peteslittlepatch.co.uk. *Approx. 1m NE of Hemel Hempstead town centre. Approx 2m W of J8 on M1. From J8 straight across r'about onto A414 dual carriageway to Hemel Hemstead. Pass under footbridge and straight across r'about, then 1st R across the dual carriageway into Leverstock Green Rd. Continue straight on into High St Green, then L into Ellingham Rd. R into Orchard Close, L into Tannsmore Close which leads into Tannsfield Drive.* Home-made teas. **Adm £3, chd free. Suns 20 July; 10 Aug (1.30-5). Visitors also welcome by appt June to Sept, tea and coffee available.**
This small, town garden is decorated with over 400 plants creating a welcoming oasis of calm. The owners love to experiment with the garden planting schemes which ensure the look of the garden alters from year to year. Narrow paths divide, leading the visitor on a discovery of the garden's many features. The sound of water is ever-present. Water features, metal sculptures, wall art and mirrors run throughout the garden. As a time and cost saving experiment all hanging baskets are planted with hardy perennials most of which are normally used for ground cover.

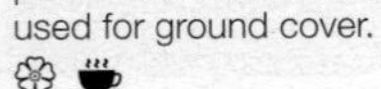

The owners love to experiment with the garden planting schemes which ensure the look of the garden alters from year to year . . .

58 217 THE RIDGEWAY

Marshalswick, St. Albans AL4 9XG. Kathy & Keith Caddy. *1½ m NE of St Albans city centre. A1081 towards Harpenden. B561 towards Sandridge. At 0.7m R at T-lights. At 0.6m L at 2nd r'about to The Ridgeway. 217 is 0.2m on R behind the green.* Home-made teas. **Adm £3.50, chd free. Wed 9, Sun 13 July (2-6).**
2/3 acre divided into different areas full of colour and interest. Sunken central patio with pond and fountain. Summer house surrounded by gravel garden. Box hedge parterre, many flower beds with acers, shrubs and perennials. Patio with hanging baskets and pots. Greenhouse, rose arches, water features and ponds. Garden begun from scratch 18 years ago. Featured in Garden News.

59 THUNDRIDGE HILL HOUSE

Cold Christmas Lane, Ware SG12 0UE. Christopher & Susie Melluish, 01920 462500, c.melluish@btopenworld.com. *2m NE of Ware. ¾ m from The Sow & Pigs PH off the A10 down Cold Christmas Lane, crossing new bypass.* Cream teas. **Adm £4.50, chd free. Sun 25 May (2-5.30). Visitors also welcome by appt Apr to Aug.**
Well-established garden of approx 2½ acres; good variety of plants, shrubs and roses, attractive hedges. We are at present creating an unusual yellow-only bed. Several delightful places to sit. Wonderful views in and out of the garden especially down to the Rib Valley. 'A most popular garden to visit'.

60 WALKERN HALL

Walkern, Stevenage SG2 7JA. Mrs Kate de Boinville. *4m E of Stevenage. Turn L at War Memorial as you leave Walkern, heading for Benington (immed after small bridge). Garden 1m up hill on R.* Home-made soup and teas. **Adm £3.50, chd free. Sat 22, Sun 23 Feb (12-4.30).**
Walkern Hall is essentially a winter woodland garden. Set in 8 acres, the carpet of snowdrops and aconites is a constant source of wonder in Jan/Feb. This medieval hunting park is known more for its established trees such as the tulip trees and a magnificent London plane tree which dominates the garden. There is wheelchair access but no WC.

61 WATERDELL HOUSE

Little Green Lane, Croxley Green, Rickmansworth WD3 3JH. Mr & Mrs Peter Ward, 01923 772775, peterward31@yahoo.com. *1½ m NE of Rickmansworth. M25 J18 to Rickmansworth & join A412 to Watford From A412 turn L to Sarrett along Croxley Green R past 2nd PH cross Baldwins Lane to Little Green Lane L at top.* **Adm £5, chd free. Visitors welcome by appt Apr to Sept, afternoon & evenings.**
1½ -acre walled garden systematically developed over 60yrs by present owner/gardener. Mature and young trees, topiary holly hedge, herbaceous borders, modern island beds of shrubs, old-fashioned roses, grasses and pond garden.

62 3 WATFORD ROAD

Radlett WD7 8LA. Mr & Mrs Wisenfeld Paine, 01923 859560, alison.wisenfeld@live.co.uk. *5m S of St Albans. Situated W of Watling Street, Follow yellow signs. Watford Rd is continuation of Aldenham Rd off A5183 Watling St. Main garden entrance in Barn Close.* Home-made teas. **Adm £4, chd free. Sun 31 Aug (11-6). Visitors also welcome by appt July to Sept.**
An Edwardian Arts and Crafts house (not open) with a garden on several levels. Specimen trees and steep weathered limestone rockery, hidden paths and grottoes forming a natural amphitheatre. This garden has architectural features and a wide range of plants and trees. The flint walled, stone flagged upper Italian garden has tree ferns, olive trees and herbs in formal beds and terracotta pots.

63 WOODHALL PARK

Watton-at-Stone, Hertford SG14 3NF. Mr & Mrs Ralph Abel Smith, www.woodhallestate.co.uk. *4m N of Hertford. 6m S of Stevenage, 4m NW of Ware, Main lodge entrance to Woodhall Park on A119.* Home-made teas. **Adm £5, chd free. Sun 29 June (12-5).**
Mature 4-acre garden created out of surrounding park in 1957 when C18 stable block was converted into a dwelling house (not open). Special features: courtyard, rose borders, rose arbours, herbaceous and mixed borders, swimming pool garden, kitchen garden and areas to sit with unspoilt views. Grassland park full of mature and ancient trees traversed by the R Beane and lake. Homemade teas served from pavilion in the swimming pool garden. After seeing the gardens visitors are welcome to walk in C18 park. Long and short routes clearly marked.

20 St Stephens Avenue, St Stephens Avenue Gardens

Hertfordshire County Volunteers

County Organiser

Julie Wise, Rustling End Cottage, Rustling End, Nr Hitchin SG4 8TD, 01438 821509, juliewise@f2s.com

County Treasurer

Peter Barrett, 9 Tannsfield Drive, Hemel Hempstead HP2 5LG, 01442 393508, tterrabjp@ntworld.com

Publicity

Julie Knight, 27 Glenferrie Road, St Albans AL1 4JT, 01727 752375, jknight21@gmail.com
Chris Roper 12 Twynham Road, Maidenhead SL6 5AS, 07793 739732, chris.roper@talktalk.net

Booklet co-ordinator

Edwina Robarts, Bromley Hall, Standon, Ware SG11 1NY, 01279 842422, edwina.robarts@gmail.com

Assistant County Organisers

Marion Jay, 84 Valley Road, Welwyn Garden City AL8 7DP, marion@garden84.net
Julie Loughlin, 3 Dalton Way, Whitewell SG4 8BG, 01438 871488, jloughlin11@gmail.com
Sarah Marsh, The Mill House, 31 Mill Lane, Welwyn AL6 9EU, 078130 83126, sarahkmarsh@hotmail.co.uk
Christopher Melluish, Thundridge Hill House, Cold Christmas Lane, Ware SG12 0UF, 01920 462500, c.melluish@btinternet.com
Virginia Newton, South Barn, Kettle Green, Much Hadham SG10 6AE, 01279 843232, vnewton@southbarn.net
Karen Smith, 44 Broadwater Avenue, Letchworth Garden City SG6 3HJ, 01462 673133, hertsgardeningangel@googlemail.com

ISLE OF WIGHT

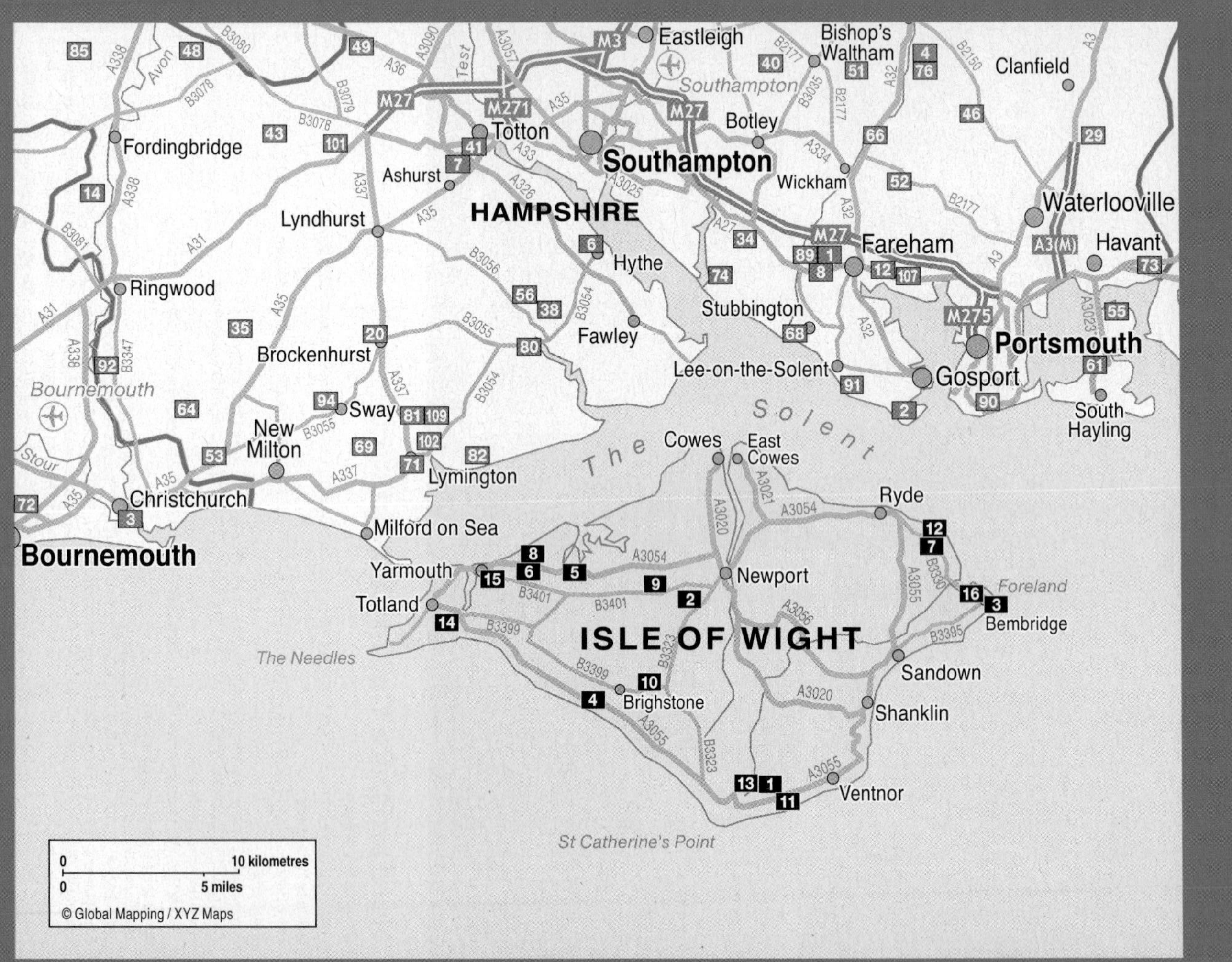

Opening Dates

All entries subject to change. For latest information check **www.ngs.org.uk**

May

Friday 2
14 NEW Sunny Patch

Saturday 3
14 NEW Sunny Patch

Sunday 18
2 Badminton

Sunday 25
9 Meadowsweet

Saturday 31
3 Blue Haze
16 1 White Cottages

June

Sunday 1
13 NEW Saxons

Festival Weekend

Sunday 8
10 Northcourt Manor Gardens

Saturday 14
12 Salterns Cottage (Evening)

Sunday 15
15 Thorley Manor

Sunday 29
4 Brighstone Village Gardens

July

Saturday 5
1 Ashknowle House

Sunday 6
1 Ashknowle House

Sunday 13
3 Blue Haze
16 1 White Cottages

Sunday 20
7 NEW High Vista

Sunday 27
11 Pelham House

August

Sunday 17
5 Crab Cottage

Friday 22
14 NEW Sunny Patch

By appointment only

6 Funakoshi
8 Highwood

Pelham House

Also open by appointment

10 Northcourt Manor Gardens

The Gardens

1 ASHKNOWLE HOUSE

Ashknowle Lane, Whitwell, Ventnor PO38 2PP. Mr & Mrs K Fradgley. *4m W of Ventnor. Take the Whitwell Rd from Ventnor or Godshill. Turn into unmade lane next to Old Rectory. Field parking and disabled parking at house.* Home-made teas. **Adm £4, chd free. Sat 5, Sun 6 July (11.30-4.30).**

A variety of features to explore in the grounds of this Victorian house. Informative woodland walks, borders, wildlife pond and other water features. Ongoing development of ornamental areas. The well-maintained kitchen garden is highly productive and boasts a wide range of fruit and vegetables grown in cages, tunnels, glasshouses and raised beds. New orchard including protected cropping. Display and video of resident red squirrel. Featured in the Daily Telegraph gardening supplement.

2 BADMINTON

Clatterford Shute, Carisbrooke, Newport PO30 1PD. Mr & Mrs G S Montrose. *1½ m SW of Newport. Free parking in Carisbrooke Castle car park. Garden signposted approx 200yds. Parking for disabled can be arranged, please phone prior to opening.* **Adm £3, chd free. Sun 18 May (2-5).**

1-acre garden on sheltered S-and-W-facing site with good vistas. Planted for all-yr interest with many different shrubs, trees and perennials to give variety, structure and colour. Natural stream and pond being developed alongside kitchen garden.

3 BLUE HAZE

24 Beachfield Road, Bembridge PO35 5TN. Gerry Price, www.thecoastalgardener.co.uk. *Take B3395 for Bembridge. At Windmill Inn turn into Lane End, 2nd R into Egerton Rd, L into Howgate Rd, then 1st R onto unmade road.* Home-made teas. **Combined Adm £3, chd free with 1 White Cottages. Sat 31 May, Sun 13 July (11-4).**

A passion for plants, art and the coast inspired the creation of this small coastal garden which wraps around Blue Haze. Native coastal plants thrive alongside more cultivated species whilst sculptures made from objects washed ashore augment the theme. Fruit, vegetables and a small nursery are integrated into the garden making it productive as well as attractive. Garden will be featured in Coast during 2014. Flat gravel garden, wheelchair access to some areas may be difficult.

GROUP OPENING

4 BRIGHSTONE VILLAGE GARDENS

Brighstone PO30 4BP. *7m from both Newport and Freshwater. Follow signs for Brighstone from Military Rd or from the B3399. Tickets to all gardens available at both village stores.* Home-made teas at the Brighstone Scout Hut. **Combined adm £4.50, chd free. Sun 29 June (11-4).**

BRIGHSTONE PRIMARY SCHOOL
Isle of Wight Council

NEW **GILLMANS**
Upper Lane. Julia Bery & Boni Reeks

KIPLINGS
David & Margaret Williamson

LITTLE ORCHARD
Elaine & Tom Boyer

NEW **RED GABLES**
Moortown Lane. Mr & Mrs Peter and Shirley Cornelius

NEW **STONERIDGE**
Moortown Lane. Mrs Sheila Easby & Mrs Sandra Dickie

NEW **TRALEE**
Main Road. Mr & Mrs Mike and Joan Kirby

Brighstone is an attractive large village with an interesting C12 church. A collection of very varied village gardens will be on show, including gardens established on challenging sites. The gardens vary in size and setting and are full of bright ideas as well as traditional planting and design. Among them the cleverly designed school gardens that will make you wish that you were back at school. The gardens are within a fairly concise area of the village and so walking distances are comfortable. Partial wheelchair access.

5 CRAB COTTAGE

Mill Road, Shalfleet PO30 4NE. Mr & Mrs Peter Scott. *4½ m E of Yarmouth. Turn past New Inn into Mill Rd. Please park before going through NT gates. Entrance 1st on L, less than 5 mins walk.* Home-made teas. **Adm £3.50, chd free. Sun 17 Aug (11.30-5).**

1¼-acres on gravelly soil. Part glorious views across croquet lawn over Newtown Creek and Solent leading to wild flower meadow, woodland walk and hidden water lily pond. Part walled garden protected from westerlies, with mixed borders, leading to terraced sunken garden with ornamental pool and pavilion; planted with exotics, tender shrubs and herbaceous perennials. Gravel path, uneven grass paths.

A small garden which defies its size with immense variety and riot of colour . . .

6 FUNAKOSHI

Cranmore Avenue, Yarmouth PO41 0XR. Mrs Helen Mount, 01983 761321. *2m E of Yarmouth off the Newport Yarmouth Rd. There is a bus shelter opp the entrance to Cranmore Avenue from the main road.* Light refreshments. **Adm £3, chd free. Visitors welcome by appt Mar to Sept for groups of 50 max.**

Approx 1-acre of mixed planting designed for yr-round interest on heavy clay. Garden developed over last 5-yrs after being retrieved from yrs of neglect. Particular interest in growing South African plants and growing cultivated plants that are good for pollinating insects. Involved in plant conservation scheme with the Hardy Plant Society and grow some less common or hard to find perennial plants. Partial wheelchair access.

7 NEW HIGH VISTA

Seaview Lane, Seaview PO34 5DJ. Mrs Linda Bush. *Location is at the top of Seaview Lane, just outside Nettlestone. Please park on main and side roads only.* Home-made teas. **Adm £3, chd free. Sun 20 July (10.30-5).**

A small, new garden by a new gardener which defies its size with immense variety and riot of colour. Sit under a vine covered pergola and enjoy the feeling of the Mediterranean. Sloping driveway from main road.

8 HIGHWOOD

Cranmore Avenue, Cranmore PO41 0XS. Mr & Mrs Cooper, 01983 760550, ross.cooper@virgin.net. *2m E of Yarmouth on Yarmouth to Newport Rd. Bus shelter opp entrance to Cranmore Avenue.* **Adm £3.50, chd free. Visitors welcome by appt.**

A garden for all seasons. In spring, snowdrops, hepaticas and hellebores. In summer, perennials, grasses, ferns, wild flowers, and orchids particularly. In autumn, asters, berries and much colour. A wonderful contrast of sunny borders & shady woodland garden. S-facing slope leads to an oak copse. Clay soil, so good footwear needed if inclement weather.

9 MEADOWSWEET

5 Great Park Cottages, off Betty-Haunt Lane, Carisbrooke PO30 4HR. Gunda Cross. *4m SW of Newport. From A3054 Newport/Yarmouth Rd turn L at Xrd Porchfield-Calbourne, over bridge into 1st lane on R. Parking along 1-side, on grass verge past house.* Home-made teas. **Adm £3, chd free. Sun 25 May (11.30-4.30).**

From windswept barren 2-acre cattle field to developing tranquil country garden. Natural, mainly native, planting and wild flowers. Cottagey front garden, herb garden, orchard, fruit cage and large pond. The good life and a haven for wildlife! Flat level garden with grass paths.

10 NORTHCOURT MANOR GARDENS

Main Road, Shorwell PO30 3JG. Mr & Mrs J Harrison, 01983 740415, www.northcourt.info. *4m SW of Newport. On entering Shorwell from Newport, entrance at bottom of hill on R. If entering from other directions head through village in direction of Newport.* Home-made teas. **Adm £4.50, chd free. Sun 8 June (12-5). Visitors also welcome by appt Apr to Aug for groups of 8+.**

15-acre garden surrounding large C17 Manor House (not open), incl walled kitchen garden, chalk stream, terraces, magnolias and camellias. Subtropical planting. Boardwalk along jungle garden. Very large range of plants enjoying the different microclimates. There are roses, primulas by the stream and hardy geraniums in profusion. Picturesque wooded valley around the stone manor house. Bath house and snail mount leading to terraces. 200yd chalk stream bordered with primulas. 1-acre walled garden. Wheelchair access only on main paths.

A garden of an eccentric plantaholic and ornament collector . . .

11 PELHAM HOUSE

Seven Sisters Road, St Lawrence, Ventnor PO38 1UY. Steve & Dee Jaggers. *1½ m W of Ventnor. A3055 Undercliff Drive from Ventnor to Niton, ½ m past botanical gardens, on R Seven Sisters Rd & village hall (free parking opp).* Home-made teas at St Lawrence Village Hall. **Adm £3, chd free. Sun 27 July (11-5).**
Interesting 1-acre garden hidden away in the heart of the Undercliff. Stunning sea views and access into Pelham Woods. Planted for yr-round interest with trees, shrubs, perennials and unusual palms. Fish pond and sloping lawns lead to tropical hut and swimming pool surrounded by exotic plants and tree ferns. Vegetable garden with raised beds and greenhouse. New woodland area and echium walk. Wheelchair access, although some steep slopes and steps.

12 SALTERNS COTTAGE

Salterns Road, Seaview PO34 5AH. Susan & Noël Dobbs. *Enter Seaview from W via Springvale, Salterns Rd links the Duver Rd with Bluett Avenue.* **Evening Opening, Adm £10 (incl refreshments), chd free on Sat 14 June (6-8.30).**
A glasshouse, a potager, exotic borders & fruit trees are some of the many attractions in this 33ft x 131ft plot. Salterns Cottage was built in 1640 and is listed. The cottage was bought in 1927 by Noel's grandmother Florence, married to Bram Stoker the author of Dracula. The garden was created by Susan in 2005. Come and join this lovely summers evening opening and enjoy a glass of wine or elderflower fizz and some delicious canapes. There will also be a small Dracula exhibition. Featured in the English Garden Magazine and Isle of Wight County Press.

13 NEW SAXONS

Kemming Road, Whitwell, Ventnor PO38 2QT. Rhys & Nicola Nigh. *Road from Whitwell towards Niton. The last property on the RH-side that has a pavement outside. Coming from the village church, this is about 300yds.* Home-made teas. **Adm £3, chd free. Sun 1 June (11-5).**
Created over 19yrs on sloping ground, spread over 3 terraced levels, this ½ -acre garden has 3 ponds, unusual and rare trees and shrubs in borders, providing yr-round interest and attracting much wildlife. A stream is an attractive feature within the garden, together with several modern sculptures for added interest. Wheelchair access is not possible to the patio area due to steps.

14 NEW SUNNY PATCH

Victoria Road, Freshwater PO40 9PP. Mrs Eileen Pryer. *½ -way between Freshwater Village and Freshwater Bay. Down Afton Rd, L at garage up Stroud Rd. Keep L just up from Parish Hall on same side. Parking in road outside house.* Teas and cakes. **Adm £3, chd free. Fri 2, Sat 3 May, Fri 22 Aug (10.30-4.30).**
A garden of an eccentric plantaholic and ornament collector. A light hearted garden of 'rooms' which incl acers, magnolias and many herbaceous plants and shrubs, 2 ponds, a fairy wood, and a folly. Each season brings another treasure to the fore and the borders continue to grow. There are no paths and numerous years of moles has made the ground very uneven.

15 THORLEY MANOR

Thorley, Yarmouth PO41 0SJ. Mr & Mrs Anthony Blest. *1m E of Yarmouth. From Bouldnor take Wilmingham Lane. House ½ m on L.* Home-made teas. **Adm £3.50, chd free. Sun 15 June (2.30-5).**
Delightful informal gardens of over 3-acres surrounding Manor House (not open). Garden set out in a number of walled rooms incl herb garden, colourful perennial and self seeding borders, sweeping lawn and shrub borders, plus unusual island croquet lawn. Venue renowned for excellent home-made teas and the eccentric head gardener.

16 1 WHITE COTTAGES

109 High Street, Bembridge PO35 5SF. Mr Nick Inigo Peirce, whitecottagedaylilies.com. *B3395 for Bembridge. The 'Old' High St is straight on through village or past the NT Windmill if coming from Sandown or Brading.* Home-made teas. **Combined Adm £3, chd free with Blue Haze. Sat 31 May, Sun 13 July (11-4).**
A dry gravel garden, mainly used to grow and breed daylilies (Hemerocallis). They are in full bloom at the end of June and at the beginning of July. The garden is predominantly herbaceous mixed with grasses and thus the garden changes dramatically over the year. Spring flowers provide interest before the daylilies and grasses, and the late perennials. The garden is long and narrow with narrow winding paths. 100 registered daylilie varieties and seedlings in garden setting with seedling borders.

Isle of Wight County Volunteers

County Organiser
Jennie Fradgley, Ashknowle House, Ashknowle Lane, Whitwell, Ventnor, Isle of Wight PO38 2PP, 01983 730805, jenniemf805@yahoo.co.uk

Assistant County Organisers
Sukie Hillyard, Spithead House, Seaview Lane, Seaview, Isle of Wight PO34 5DG, 01983 565093 robin@robinandsukie.plus.com
Sally Parker, Beach House, The Duver, Seaview, Isle of Wight PO34 5AJ, 01983 612495, sallyparkeriow@btinternet.com

KENT

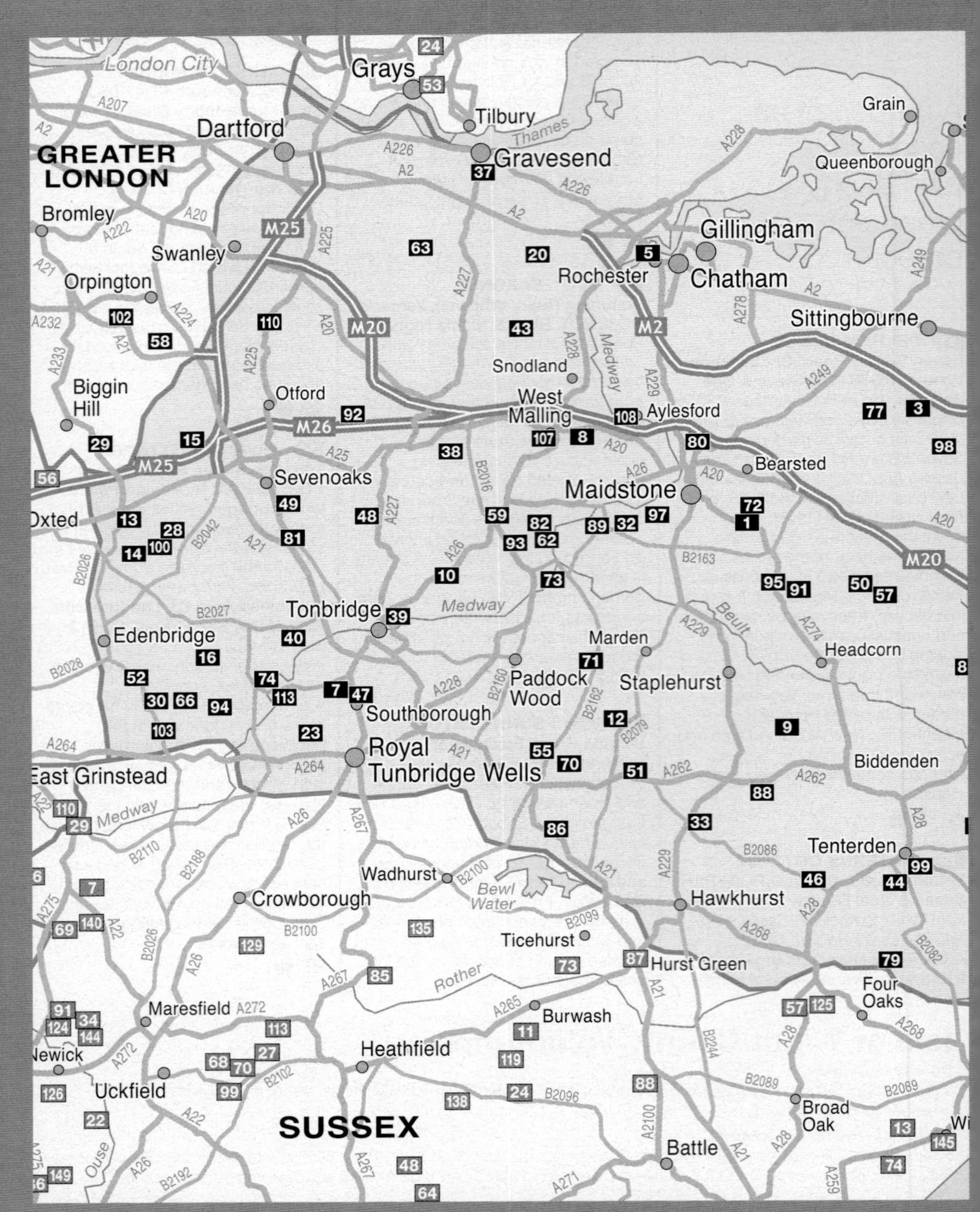

GREATER LONDON
Grays
Tilbury
Dartford
Gravesend
Grain
Queenborough
Bromley
Swanley
Orpington
Gillingham
Rochester
Chatham
Sittingbourne
Snodland
Biggin Hill
Otford
West Malling
Aylesford
Bearsted
Sevenoaks
Maidstone
Oxted
Tonbridge
Edenbridge
Marden
Headcorn
Paddock Wood
Staplehurst
Southborough
Royal Tunbridge Wells
Biddenden
East Grinstead
Tenterden
Wadhurst
Crowborough
Hawkhurst
Ticehurst
Hurst Green
Four Oaks
Maresfield
Burwash
Newick
Heathfield
Uckfield
Broad Oak
SUSSEX
Battle

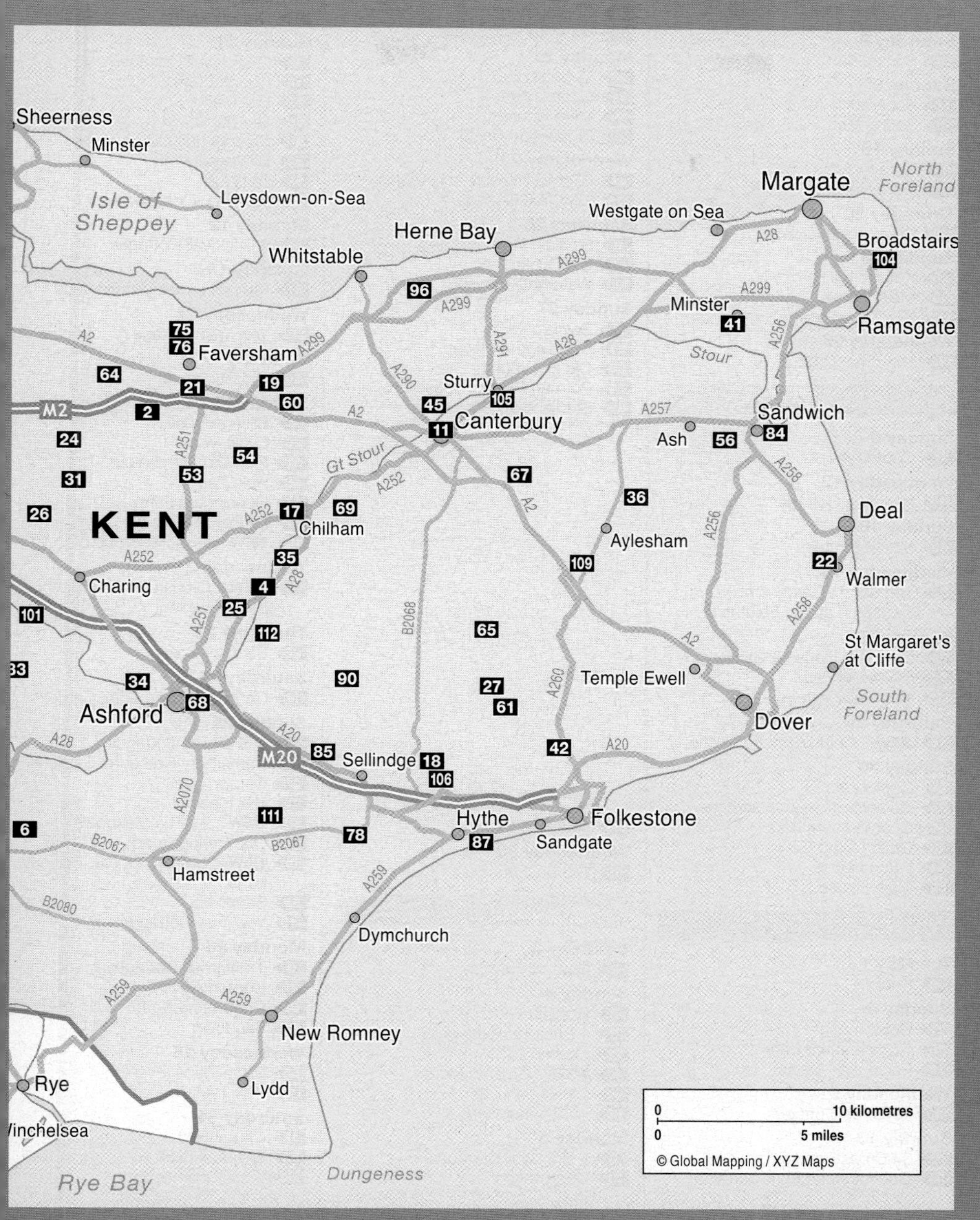
Sheerness
Minster
Isle of Sheppey
Leysdown-on-Sea
Margate
North Foreland
Westgate on Sea
Herne Bay
Whitstable
Broadstairs
104
96
A299
A28
Minster
41
Ramsgate
75
76
Faversham
Stour
A2
64
21
19
Sturry
105
60
A291
A290
M2
2
45
Canterbury
11
Sandwich
84
A257
Ash
56
24
54
A251
53
Gt Stour
A252
67
A258
31
36
26
KENT
17
69
Chilham
A2
A256
Deal
Aylesham
A252
35
109
22
Walmer
Charing
4
A28
25
A251
101
112
B2068
65
St Margaret's at Cliffe
33
90
A260
Temple Ewell
34
27
61
South Foreland
Ashford
68
Dover
A28
A20
85
M20
Sellindge
18
106
42
A20
A2070
111
Hythe
Folkestone
6
B2067
78
87
Sandgate
Hamstreet
A259
B2080
Dymchurch
A259
New Romney
Rye
Lydd
Winchelsea
Rye Bay
Dungeness
0
10 kilometres
0
5 miles
© Global Mapping / XYZ Maps

Opening Dates

All entries subject to change. For latest information check www.ngs.org.uk

February

Saturday 8
91 Spring Platt

Sunday 9
50 Knowle Hill Farm
91 Spring Platt

Sunday 16
21 Copton Ash
59 Mere House

Thursday 20
10 Broadview Gardens

Sunday 23
50 Knowle Hill Farm
59 Mere House
113 Yew Tree Cottage

Wednesday 26
113 Yew Tree Cottage

March

Sunday 9
21 Copton Ash

Wednesday 12
113 Yew Tree Cottage

Sunday 16
60 Mount Ephraim

Wednesday 19
84 The Secret Gardens of Sandwich at The Salutation

Sunday 23
34 Godinton House & Gardens
94 Stonewall Park
113 Yew Tree Cottage

Saturday 29
16 NEW Chiddingstone Castle

Sunday 30
21 Copton Ash
34 Godinton House & Gardens
35 Godmersham Park
38 Great Comp Garden
54 Luton House
59 Mere House

April

Tuesday 1
49 Knole

Sunday 6
21 Copton Ash
35 Godmersham Park
73 Parsonage Oasts

Wednesday 9
113 Yew Tree Cottage

Sunday 13
22 34 Cross Road
36 Goodnestone Park Gardens
70 Orchard End
113 Yew Tree Cottage

Wednesday 16
46 Hole Park

Sunday 20
4 Bilting House
21 Copton Ash
31 Frith Old Farmhouse

Monday 21
20 Cobham Hall
21 Copton Ash
59 Mere House
73 Parsonage Oasts

Wednesday 23
81 Riverhill Himalayan Gardens
113 Yew Tree Cottage

Saturday 26
2 Bayfield Farm
66 Old Buckhurst
105 Watergate House

Sunday 27
2 Bayfield Farm
24 Doddington Place
66 Old Buckhurst
79 Potmans Heath House
93 St Michael's Gardens

Look for the plant symbol and purchase a plant . . .

113 Yew Tree Cottage

Wednesday 30
66 Old Buckhurst

May

Saturday 3
2 Bayfield Farm

Sunday 4
2 Bayfield Farm
9 1 Brickwall Cottages
21 Copton Ash
32 NEW Gallants Manor
66 Old Buckhurst
80 11 Raymer Road

Monday 5
9 1 Brickwall Cottages
21 Copton Ash
32 NEW Gallants Manor

Tuesday 6
49 Knole

Wednesday 7
66 Old Buckhurst

Saturday 10
66 Old Buckhurst

Sunday 11
9 1 Brickwall Cottages
13 Charts Edge
40 Hall Place
66 Old Buckhurst
88 Sissinghurst Castle
94 Stonewall Park
98 Torry Hill
113 Yew Tree Cottage

Monday 12
9 1 Brickwall Cottages

Tuesday 13
81 Riverhill Himalayan Gardens

Wednesday 14
113 Yew Tree Cottage

Saturday 17
66 Old Buckhurst

Sunday 18
4 Bilting House
26 Eagleswood
31 Frith Old Farmhouse
46 Hole Park
47 Honnington Farm
51 Ladham House
100 NEW Toys Hill Group

Wednesday 21
71 NEW Orchard House, Spenny Lane (Evening)

Thursday 22
86 Scotney Castle

Saturday 24
11 Canterbury Cathedral Gardens

Sunday 25
9 1 Brickwall Cottages
11 Canterbury Cathedral Gardens
21 Copton Ash
40 Hall Place
58 NEW 12 The Meadows
68 One Dering Road
71 NEW Orchard House, Spenny Lane
85 Sandown
113 Yew Tree Cottage

Monday 26
9 1 Brickwall Cottages
21 Copton Ash
68 One Dering Road
85 Sandown

Wednesday 28
55 Marle Place (Evening)
113 Yew Tree Cottage

Saturday 31
18 Churchfield
66 Old Buckhurst
106 West Court Lodge

June

Sunday 1
- 9 1 Brickwall Cottages
- 18 Churchfield
- 26 Eagleswood
- 31 Frith Old Farmhouse
- 65 Old Bladbean Stud
- 89 Smiths Hall
- 93 St Michael's Gardens
- 106 West Court Lodge

Monday 2
- 9 1 Brickwall Cottages

Tuesday 3
- 49 Knole

Wednesday 4
- 66 Old Buckhurst

Festival Weekend

Saturday 7
- 36 Goodnestone Park Gardens
- 44 Heronden
- 66 Old Buckhurst
- 76 Pheasant Farm
- 85 Sandown
- 111 Wyckhurst

Sunday 8
- 21 Copton Ash
- 24 Doddington Place
- 44 Heronden
- 68 One Dering Road
- 76 Pheasant Farm
- 85 Sandown
- 99 Townland
- 102 223 Tubbenden Lane
- 111 Wyckhurst
- 113 Yew Tree Cottage

Monday 9
- 28 Emmetts Garden
- 64 Norton Court

Tuesday 10
- 64 Norton Court

Wednesday 11
- 55 Marle Place (Evening)
- 113 Yew Tree Cottage

Thursday 12
- 60 Mount Ephraim

Saturday 14
- 27 Elham Gardens
- 63 NEW New Barn Gardens
- 70 Orchard End
- 105 Watergate House
- 111 Wyckhurst

Sunday 15
- 6 Boldshaves
- 27 Elham Gardens
- 40 Hall Place
- 47 Honnington Farm
- 58 NEW 12 The Meadows
- 65 Old Bladbean Stud
- 68 One Dering Road
- 69 The Orangery

Cutlass Cottage © Leigh Clapp

- 70 Orchard End
- 92 St Clere
- 98 Torry Hill
- 101 Tram Hatch
- 107 West Malling June Gardens
- 110 The World Garden at Lullingstone Castle
- 111 Wyckhurst

Wednesday 18
- 12 Capel Manor Estate Gardens
- 46 Hole Park
- 103 Upper Pryors

Thursday 19
- 63 NEW New Barn Gardens

Saturday 21
- 5 Bishopscourt
- 50 Knowle Hill Farm (Evening)
- 57 Masons Farm
- 66 Old Buckhurst
- 75 Pheasant Barn
- 85 Sandown
- 108 Wickham Lodge

Sunday 22
- 5 Bishopscourt
- 12 Capel Manor Estate Gardens
- 15 Chevening
- 35 Godmersham Park
- 57 Masons Farm
- 62 Nettlestead Place
- 68 One Dering Road
- 79 Potmans Heath House
- 85 Sandown
- 112 Wye Gardens
- 113 Yew Tree Cottage

Wednesday 25
- 14 Chartwell
- 82 Rock Farm
- 113 Yew Tree Cottage

Thursday 26
- 53 Lords
- 84 The Secret Gardens of Sandwich at The Salutation

Friday 27
- 34 Godinton House & Gardens

Saturday 28
- 19 NEW The Coach House
- 67 NEW The Old Palace
- 82 Rock Farm
- 109 Womenswold Gardens

Sunday 29
- 1 Ashley
- 7 Boundes End
- 19 NEW The Coach House
- 20 Cobham Hall
- 22 34 Cross Road
- 30 NEW Falconhurst
- 33 Goddards Green
- 35 Godmersham Park
- 39 115 Hadlow Road
- 53 Lords
- 65 Old Bladbean Stud
- 67 NEW The Old Palace
- 72 Otham Gardens
- 109 Womenswold Gardens

Mare Curie is the leader in end of life care research

July

Tuesday 1
49 Knole
95 NEW Sutton Valence School

Sunday 6
54 Luton House
89 Smiths Hall

Wednesday 9
66 Old Buckhurst
113 Yew Tree Cottage

Thursday 10
48 Ightham Mote

Saturday 12
66 Old Buckhurst
75 Pheasant Barn
85 Sandown

Sunday 13
65 Old Bladbean Stud
68 One Dering Road
85 Sandown
98 Torry Hill
99 Townland
101 Tram Hatch
113 Yew Tree Cottage

Wednesday 16
66 Old Buckhurst

Saturday 19
37 Gravesend Gardens Group
42 NEW Hawkinge Allotments
61 Mounts Court Farmhouse
70 Orchard End

Sunday 20
37 Gravesend Gardens Group
42 NEW Hawkinge Allotments
45 Highlands
61 Mounts Court Farmhouse
70 Orchard End
96 43 The Ridings
99 Townland

Wednesday 23
24 Doddington Place
113 Yew Tree Cottage

Saturday 26
23 Cutlass Cottage (Evening)
66 Old Buckhurst
85 Sandown

Sunday 27
3 Bexon Manor
23 Cutlass Cottage
30 NEW Falconhurst
33 Goddards Green
65 Old Bladbean Stud
68 One Dering Road
69 The Orangery
85 Sandown
113 Yew Tree Cottage

August

Saturday 2
29 NEW Eureka
83 Rose Farm Studio
104 NEW The Watch House

Sunday 3
3 Bexon Manor
29 NEW Eureka
50 Knowle Hill Farm
52 Leydens
66 Old Buckhurst
83 Rose Farm Studio
104 NEW The Watch House

Tuesday 5
49 Knole

Saturday 9
29 NEW Eureka
85 Sandown

Sunday 10
3 Bexon Manor
29 NEW Eureka
68 One Dering Road
85 Sandown
113 Yew Tree Cottage

Wednesday 13
55 Marle Place (Evening)
71 NEW Orchard House, Spenny Lane (Evening)
113 Yew Tree Cottage

Sunday 17
71 NEW Orchard House, Spenny Lane
101 Tram Hatch

Friday 22
17 Chilham Castle (Evening)

Saturday 23
17 Chilham Castle

Sunday 24
39 115 Hadlow Road
65 Old Bladbean Stud
68 One Dering Road
113 Yew Tree Cottage

Monday 25
68 One Dering Road

Wednesday 27
113 Yew Tree Cottage

Saturday 30
29 NEW Eureka
70 Orchard End
85 Sandown

Sunday 31
29 NEW Eureka
70 Orchard End
85 Sandown

September

Wednesday 3
66 Old Buckhurst

Saturday 6
5 Bishopscourt
66 Old Buckhurst
85 Sandown

Sunday 7
5 Bishopscourt
13 Charts Edge
65 Old Bladbean Stud
66 Old Buckhurst
85 Sandown
96 43 The Ridings

Tuesday 9
74 Penshurst Place

Wednesday 10
113 Yew Tree Cottage

Thursday 11
29 NEW Eureka

Friday 12
78 NEW Port Lympne, The Aspinall Foundation

Saturday 13
66 Old Buckhurst

Sunday 14
29 NEW Eureka
66 Old Buckhurst
78 NEW Port Lympne, The Aspinall Foundation
113 Yew Tree Cottage

Monday 15
88 Sissinghurst Castle

Sunday 21
8 Bradbourne House and Gardens
62 Nettlestead Place
65 Old Bladbean Stud

Friday 26
34 Godinton House & Gardens

Sunday 28
24 Doddington Place
60 Mount Ephraim

October

Sunday 5
36 Goodnestone Park Gardens
65 Old Bladbean Stud

Monday 6
84 The Secret Gardens of Sandwich at The Salutation

Sunday 12
46 Hole Park

Sunday 19
26 Eagleswood
38 Great Comp Garden

Sunday 26

- 38 Great Comp Garden
- 59 Mere House

February 2015

Saturday 7

- 91 Spring Platt

Sunday 8

- 50 Knowle Hill Farm
- 91 Spring Platt

Sunday 15

- 21 Copton Ash

Sunday 22

- 50 Knowle Hill Farm
- 59 Mere House

Gardens open to the public

- 10 Broadview Gardens
- 13 Charts Edge
- 14 Chartwell
- 16 Chiddingstone Castle
- 17 Chilham Castle
- 17 Chilham Castle
- 20 Cobham Hall
- 24 Doddington Place
- 28 Emmetts Garden
- 34 Godinton House & Gardens
- 36 Goodnestone Park Gardens
- 38 Great Comp Garden
- 46 Hole Park
- 48 Ightham Mote
- 49 Knole
- 55 Marle Place
- 60 Mount Ephraim
- 74 Penshurst Place
- 81 Riverhill Himalayan Gardens
- 84 The Secret Gardens of Sandwich at The Salutation
- 86 Scotney Castle
- 88 Sissinghurst Castle
- 110 The World Garden at Lullingstone Castle

By appointment only

- 25 Downs Court
- 41 Haven
- 43 Haydown
- 56 Marshborough Farmhouse
- 77 Placketts Hole
- 87 Sea Close
- 90 South Hill Farm
- 97 Timbers

Also open by appointment

- 1 Ashley
- 4 Bilting House
- 7 Boundes End
- 9 1 Brickwall Cottages
- 18 Churchfield
- 19 The Coach House
- 21 Copton Ash
- 26 Eagleswood
- 31 Frith Old Farmhouse
- 33 Goddards Green
- 35 Godmersham Park
- 39 115 Hadlow Road
- 45 Highlands
- 47 Honnington Farm
- 50 Knowle Hill Farm
- 53 Lords
- 61 Mounts Court Farmhouse
- 64 Norton Court
- 67 The Old Palace
- 68 One Dering Road
- 69 The Orangery
- 70 Orchard End
- 73 Parsonage Oasts
- 75 Pheasant Barn
- 76 Pheasant Farm
- 79 Potmans Heath House
- 82 Rock Farm
- 85 Sandown
- 91 Spring Platt
- 98 Torry Hill
- 99 Townland
- 106 West Court Lodge
- 111 Wyckhurst

The Gardens

1 ASHLEY

White Horse Lane, Otham, Maidstone ME15 8RQ. Susan & Roger Chartier, 01622 861333, susanchartier@hotmail.com. *4m SE of Maidstone. From A20 or A274 follow signs for Otham or Stoneacre, garden located between White Horse PH & Simmonds Lane.* Home-made teas. **Combined adm £5, chd free (share to Kent Autistic Trust).** **Sun 29 June (11-5.30)** **as part of Otham Gardens. Visitors also welcome by appt May to Sept. Adm £5, chd free. Max 20 visitors.**

Front garden developed into a parterre, leading to surprisingly large rear garden with many unusual perennials. Pond with bridge, kitchen garden, dry garden and scented leaf pelargonium collection. Two beehives, one handmade in an original design following the principles of natural beekeeping. G Scale garden railway layout with working model trains. Limited wheelchair access.

2 BAYFIELD FARM

Painters Forstal, Faversham ME13 0EG. Mr & Mrs John Moor. *W of Painters Forstal. S on Brogdale Rd from A2 at Faversham signed Painters Forstal. Signed at Xrds in village.* **Adm £3.50, chd free.** **Sat 26, Sun 27 Apr, Sat 3, Sun 4 May (11-6).**

¾-acre garden developed over 50yrs from an open site to a densely planted open woodland, informal, romantic garden! A mix of trees, shrubs, herbaceous and annuals and recently established grass garden.

Plenty of places to sit and enjoy the garden . . . and maybe a home-made tea . . .

3 BEXON MANOR

Hawks Hill Lane, Bredgar ME9 8HE. Mr & Mrs Robert Reeves. *3m S of Sittingbourne. B2163 at Bredgar, turn into Bexon Lane at church. Approx 1m turn R into Hawks Hill Lane.* Delicious home-made teas. **Adm £4.50, chd free.** **Sun 27 July, Sun 3, Sun 10 Aug (1.30-5).**

2 acre garden, divided into a series of rooms. Clipped yew hedges, topiary, borders with a wide variety of unusual annuals grown from seed, perennials, roses, many colourful shrubs. Terrace overlooking walled kitchen garden with dwarf yew squares filled with organic vegetables, flowers, roses, herbs and bamboo. Rose-covered gazebo, water feature. 5-acre woodland walk. Display of vintage Bentleys (weather permitting). Limited wheelchair access to certain areas.

4 BILTING HOUSE

nr Ashford TN25 4HA. Mr John Erle-Drax, 07764 580011, jdrax@marlboroughfineart.com. *5m NE of Ashford. A28, 9m S from Canterbury. Wye 1½ m.* Home-made teas. **Adm £4, chd free.** **Sun 20 Apr, Sun 18 May (2-6). Visitors also welcome by appt Apr to Sept.**

6-acre garden with ha-ha set in beautiful part of Stour Valley. Wide variety of rhododendrons, azaleas and ornamental shrubs. Woodland walk with spring bulbs. Mature arboretum with recent planting of specimen trees. Rose garden and herbaceous borders. Conservatory.

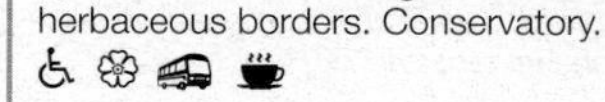

Church View, Capel Manor Estate Gardens

© Leigh Clapp

5 BISHOPSCOURT

24 St Margarets Street, Rochester ME1 1TS. Mrs Bridget Langstaff. *Central Rochester, nr castle & cathedral. On St Margaret's Street at junction with Vines Lane. Rochester rail station 10 mins walk. Disabled parking only, many car parks within 5-7 mins walk.* Home-made teas. **Adm £3, chd free.** **Sat 21, Sun 22 June, Sat 6, Sun 7 Sept (1-5).**

The residence of the Bishop of Rochester, a peaceful 1-acre garden in the heart of Rochester with views of the castle from a raised 'lookout'. Yew hedges, sculpture, rose garden, gravel garden, wild flowers and mixed borders with a variety of shrubs perennials and grasses. Greenhouse and small vegetable garden. Most of garden is accessible by wheelchair. Disabled WC.

6 BOLDSHAVES

Woodchurch, nr Ashford TN26 3RA. Mr & Mrs Peregrine Massey, 01233 860302, masseypd@hotmail.co.uk, www.boldshaves.co.uk. *Between Woodchurch & High Halden off Redbrook St. From A28 towards Ashford, turn R at village green in High Halden. 2nd R, Redbrook St, towards Woodchurch, before R on unmarked lane after ½ m. After ½ m, R through brick entrance. Ignore oast house on L, follow signs to car park. If approaching through Woodchurch, past church, L on Susan's Hill, next R, then L through brick entrance (as above).* Home-made teas in C18 barn. **Adm £5, chd free (share to Kent Minds).** **Sun 15 June (2-6).**

7-acre garden, partly terraced, S-facing, with ornamental trees and shrubs, walled garden, Italian Garden, Diamond Jubilee Garden, Camellia dell, herbaceous borders (including flame bed and red borders), bluebell walks in April, woodland and ponds. For other opening times please see website. Grass paths.

7 BOUNDES END

2 St Lawrence Avenue, Bidborough, Tunbridge Wells TN4 0XB. Carole & Mike Marks, 01892 542233, carole.marks@btinternet.com, www.boundesendgarden.co.uk. *Between Tonbridge & Tunbridge Wells off A26. Take B2176 Bidborough Ridge signed to Penshurst. Take 1st L into Darnley Drive, then 1st R into St Lawrence Ave.* Home-made teas. **Adm £3, chd free (share to Hospice in the Weald).** **Sun 29 June (11-5).** **Visitors also welcome by appt July to Aug for groups max 20.**

Garden, designed by owners, on an unusually-shaped ⅓ acre plot formed from 2 triangles of land. Front garden features raised beds, and the main garden divided into a formal area with terrace, pebble bed and 2 pergolas, an informal area in woodland setting with interesting features and specimen trees. Plenty of places to sit and enjoy the garden. Some uneven ground in lower garden.

8 BRADBOURNE HOUSE AND GARDENS

New Road, East Malling ME19 6DZ. East Malling Trust, www.bradbournehouse.org.uk. *4m NW of Maidstone. Entrance is E of New Rd, which runs from Larkfield on A20 S to E Malling.* Light refreshments. **Adm £3.50, chd free.** **Sun 21 Sept (2-5).**

Demonstration fruit plantings within a walled former kitchen garden. Apple and pear trees pruned into 25 different forms incl pyramid, goblet, le bateau, fan, arch, arcure, espalier, table, vase etc. Examples of 47 varieties of apple, 28 varieties of pear and individuals of medlar, nectarine, peach and fig. Queen Anne period house, science exhibits, music, beekeeping exhibits, produce and plant sales.

9 1 BRICKWALL COTTAGES

Frittenden, Cranbrook TN17 2DH. Mrs Sue Martin, 01580 852425, sue.martin@talktalk.net, www.geumcollection.co.uk. *6m NW of Tenterden. E of A229 between Cranbrook & Staplehurst & W of A274 between Biddenden & Headcorn. Park in village & walk along footpath opp school.* Home-made teas. **Adm £3.50, chd free. Sun 4, Mon 5, Sun 11, Mon 12, Sun 25, Mon 26 May, Sun 1, Mon 2 June (2-5.30). Visitors also welcome by appt May to June.**

Although less than 1/4 acre, the garden gives the impression of being much larger as it is made up of several 'rooms' all intensively planted with a wide range of hardy perennials, bulbs and shrubs, with about 100 geums which comprise the National Collection planted throughout the garden. Pergolas provide supports for climbing plants and there is a small formal pond. Featured in RHS The Garden, Country Life, Gardens Illustrated and The English Garden and on BBC Gardener's World. Some paths are narrow and wheelchairs may not be able to reach far end of the garden.

NCH

10 ◆ BROADVIEW GARDENS

Hadlow College, Hadlow TN11 0AL www.broadviewgardens.co.uk. *4m NE of Tonbridge. On A26, 2 1/2 m NE of Tonbridge on L, 200metres before village of Hadlow, via Main Hadlow College entrance.* **Adm £3, chd free. For NGS: Thur 20 Feb (10-5). For other opening times and information, please see garden website.**

10 acres of ornamental planting in attractive landscape setting; 100m double mixed border, island beds with mixed plantings, lakes and water gardens; series of demonstration gardens incl Italian, Oriental and Sutton's vegetable garden. National Collections of Anemone japonica and Helleborus. Light refreshments. Wheelchair access limited in wet weather.

Beds showing the origin of plants from around the world . . .

GROUP OPENING

11 CANTERBURY CATHEDRAL GARDENS

Canterbury CT1 2EP, 01227 865350, www.canterbury-cathedral.org. *Canterbury Cathedral Precincts.* ***Enter precincts via main Christchurch gate***. No access for cars, use park & ride or public car parks. Home-made teas on Green Court. **Sat 24 May (11-5) Normal precinct charges apply plus £5 adm to Open Gardens Event per adult, chd free; Sun 25 May (2-5) No precinct charges apply today, £5 adm to Open Gardens Event per adult, chd free.**

ARCHDEACONRY
The Archdeacon, Sheila Watson

THE DEANERY
The Dean

15 THE PRECINCTS
Canon Papadapulos

19 THE PRECINCTS
Canon Irvine

22 THE PRECINCTS
Canon Clare Edwards

A wonderful opportunity to visit and enjoy five Canonical gardens within the historic precincts of Canterbury Cathedral: the Deanery Garden with wonderful roses, wildflower planting and orchard, unusual medlar tree, vegetable garden and wild fowl enclosure; the Archdeaconry incl the ancient mulberry tree, contrasting traditional and modern planting and a Japanese influence; the three further precinct gardens, varied in style, offer sweeping herbaceous banks, delightful enclosed spaces, and areas planted to attract and support birds, insects and wildlife. All the gardens now incl vegetable plots personal to each house. Step back in time and see the herb garden, which show the use of herbs for medicinal purposes in the Middle Ages. The walled Memorial Garden has wonderful wisteria, formal roses, mixed borders and the stone war memorial at its centre, and hidden Bastion Chapel in the city wall. Gardeners' plant stall and home-made refreshments. Dover Beekeepers Association, up close and personal opportunity with Birds of Prey and unique access to Bastion Chapel. Classic cars on Green Court. Wheelchair access to all gardens but Archdeaconry has separate entrance for wheelchair access.

GROUP OPENING

12 CAPEL MANOR ESTATE GARDENS

Grovehurst Lane, Horsmonden TN12 8BG. *Approx 8m SE of Tonbridge, 10 m E of Tunbridge Wells. From Horsmonden village, follow yellow NGS signs towards Goudhurst, leaving the Gun & Spitroast PH on R.* Home-made teas Capel Manor Courtyard. **Combined adm £5, chd free. Wed 18, Sun 22 June (12-5).**

CHURCH VIEW
Mr & Mrs H Tangen

THE COURTYARD
Mr & Mrs Iain Stewart

The two gardens form a substantial part of the former Capel Manor estate built for the Austen family (relatives of the renowned Jane Austen). The Courtyard gardens cover several acres of formal gardens and woodland incl a stunning Mediterranean courtyard garden using tranquil-coloured planting with a fountain at its centre. Church View is a lovely one-acre S-facing sloping garden with spectacular countryside views. Featured in Kent Life and one of 5 finalists in Kent Garden of the Year. Amazing tea-room situated in the Courtyard with plenty of seating and a delicious selection of cakes and scones. Most of the gardens can be seen by wheelchair users but some gravel paths and steep slopes may prove difficult to negotiate.

13 ◆ CHARTS EDGE

Westerham TN16 1PL. Mr & Mrs J Bigwood, 07833 385169, www.chartsedgegardens.co.uk. *1/2 m S of Westerham, 4m N of Edenbridge. On B2026 towards Chartwell*. Home-made teas. **Adm £4.50, chd free. For NGS: Sun 11 May, Sun 7 Sept (2-5). For other opening times and information, please phone or see garden website.**

8-acre hillside garden being updated by present owners. Large collection of rhododendrons, azaleas and magnolias; among specimen trees, 2 copper beech recorded as the tallest in UK. Majority of plants labelled, rock garden, water gardens, rainbow borders and rill. Beds showing the origin of plants from around the world. Fine views over N Downs. Partial access for wheelchair users.

14 ◆ CHARTWELL

Mapleton Road, nr Westerham TN16 1PS. National Trust, 01732 868381, www.nationaltrust.org.uk. *4m N of Edenbridge. 2m S of Westerham. Fork L off B2026 after 1 1/2 m*. **Adm £6.25, chd £3.10. For NGS: Wed 25 June (10-4). For other opening times and information, please phone or see garden website.**

Informal gardens on hillside with glorious views over Weald of Kent. Water garden and lakes together with red-brick wall built by Sir Winston Churchill, former owner of Chartwell. Lady Churchill's rose garden. Avenue of golden roses runs down the centre of a must-see productive kitchen garden. Hard paths to Lady Churchill's rose garden and the terrace. Some steep slopes and steps.

15 CHEVENING

Chevening Nr Sevenoaks TN14 6HG. The Board of Trustees of the Chevening Estate, www.cheveninghouse.com. *4m NW of Sevenoaks. Turn N off A25 at Sundridge T-lights on to B2211; at Chevening Xrds 1 1/2 m turn L*. Home-made teas. **Adm £5, chd £2. Sun 22 June (2-5).**

27 acres with lawns, woodland, lake, maze and parterre. Gentle slopes, gravel paths throughout.

Designed with outdoor entertaining very much in mind, there are plenty of social as well as intimate seating areas . . .

16 NEW ◆ CHIDDINGSTONE CASTLE

Hill Hoath Road, Chiddingstone, Edenbridge TN8 7AD. Trustees of the Denys Eyre Bower Bequest, 01892 870347, www.chiddingstonecastle.org.uk. *Chiddingstone Castle. From B2027 in village of Bough Beech follow signs to Castle via Mill Lane. Entrance is on Hill Hoath Rd*. **Garden adm £4.50, chd free (house open, normal entry charges apply). Sat 29 Mar (11-4.30). For other opening times and information, please phone or see garden website.**

Chiddingstone Castle, a historic garden, is surrounded by 35 acres of unspoilt informal gardens including a large fishing lake, waterfall and woodland. During spring, the East Meadow is a riot of golden daffodils and cherry trees blossom in the Japanese Earthquake Memorial Orchard. Beautiful views from the North Lawn, and the South Lawn leads to the restored Grade II* Victorian Orangery. Free garden tours. Chiddingstone Castle's history can be traced to C16. It now houses the remarkable collections of the late antiquarian, Denys Eyre Bower - featuring Japanese Samurai armour and lacquerware, antiquities from Ancient Egypt and rare paintings and memorabilia of the Stuarts and Jacobites. Tea rooms serving cream teas and gift shop also open. The path to the village across the lake is suitable for wheelchairs, although steep in places. All other paths are either grass or gravel.

17 ◆ CHILHAM CASTLE

Chilham CT4 8DB. Mr & Mrs Wheeler, 01227 733100, www.chilham-castle.co.uk. *6m SW of Canterbury, 7 m NE of Ashford, centre of Chilham Village. Follow NGS signs for garden open day from A28 or A252 up to Chilham village square & through main gates of Chilham Castle*. Home-made teas. **Adm £5, chd free. For NGS: Evening Opening, light refreshments, Fri 22 Aug (5-8); Sat 23 Aug (2-5). For other opening times and information, please phone or see garden website.**

The garden surrounds Jacobean house 1616 (not open). C17 terraces with herbaceous borders. Topiary frames the magnificent views with lake walk below. Extensive kitchen and cutting garden beyond spring bulb filled Quiet Garden. Established trees and ha-ha lead onto park. Restricted wheelchair access.

18 CHURCHFIELD

Pilgrims Way, Postling, Hythe CT21 4EY. Mr & Mrs C Clark, 01303 863558, coulclark@hotmail.com. *2m NW of Hythe. From M20 J11 turn S onto A20. 1st L after 1/2 m on bend take rd signed Lyminge. 1st L into Postling*. Home-made teas in the Village hall. **Adm £3, chd free. Sat 31 May, Sun 1 June (1-5). Combined with West Court Lodge adm £5, chd free. Visitors also welcome by appt May to Sept up to 20.**

At the base of the Downs springs rising in this garden form the source of the East Stour. Two large areas are home to wildfowl and fish and the banks have been planted with drifts of primula and large leaved herbaceous. The rest of the 5-acre garden is a Kent cobnut platt and vegetable garden, large grass areas and naturally planted borders with an area under development as a prairie garden. Postling Church open for visitors. Areas around water may be slippery. Children must be carefully supervised.

19 NEW THE COACH HOUSE

Kemsdale Road, Hernhill, Faversham ME13 9JP. Alison & Philip West, 07801 824867. *3m E of Faversham. At J7 of M2 take A299, signed Margate. After 600 metres take 1st exit signed Hernhill, take 1st L over dual carriageway to T-junction,*

turn R & follow yellow NGS signs. Cream teas. **Adm £3.50, chd free. Sat 28, Sun 29 June (1-6). Also open Lords, Sun 29 June. Visitors also welcome by appt.**
The ½ acre garden has views over surrounding fruit producing farmland. Sloping terraced site, and island beds with yr round interest, a pond 'room', herbaceous borders containing bulbs, shrubs, and perennials, and a developing tropical bed.The different areas are connected by flowing curved paths. Unusual planting on light sandy soil where wildlife is encouraged. Most of the garden is accessible to wheelchairs and seating is available in all parts.

20 ◆ COBHAM HALL
Cobham DA12 3BL. Mr D Standen (Bursar), 01474 823371, bracej@cobhamhall.com, www.cobhamhall.com. *3m W of Rochester, 8m E of M25 J2. Ignore satnav directions to Lodge Lane. The entrance drive is off Brewers Rd, 50 metres E from Cobham/Shorne A2 junction*. Home-made teas in the Gilt Hall. **Adm £2.50, chd free. For NGS: Mon 21 Apr, Sun 29 June (2-5). For other opening times and information, please phone or see garden website.**
1584 brick mansion (open for tours) and parkland of historical importance, now a boarding and day school for girls. Some herbaceous borders, formal parterres, drifts of daffodils, C17 garden walls, yew hedges and lime avenue. Humphry Repton designed 50 hectares of park, most garden follies restored in 2009. Film location for BBC's 'Bleak House' series and films by MGM and Universal. Gravel and slab paths through gardens. Land uneven, many slopes to contend with. Many stairs and steps within Main Hall. Disabled visitors should telephone in advance to ensure they are assisted.

21 COPTON ASH
105 Ashford Road, Faversham ME13 8XW. Drs Tim & Gillian Ingram, 01795 535919, coptonash@yahoo.co.uk, www.coptonash.plus.com. *½ m S of Faversham. On A251 Faversham to Ashford rd. opp. E-bound J6 with M2*. Home-made teas. **Adm £3, chd free. Sun 16 Feb (12-4); Suns 9, 30 Mar; Suns 6, 20, Mon 21 Apr; Sun 4, Mon 5, Sun 25, Mon 26 May; Sun 8 June (2-5.30); Sun 15 Feb 2015. Visitors also welcome by appt Feb to Oct.**
Garden grown out of a love and fascination with plants from an early age. Contains very wide collection incl many rarities and newly introduced species raised from wild seed. Special interest in woodland flowers, snowdrops and hellebores with flowering trees and shrubs of spring. Wide range of drought-tolerant plants. Raised beds with choice alpines and bulbs. Small alpine nursery. Gravel drive and some narrow grass paths.

22 34 CROSS ROAD
Walmer, CT14 9LB CT14 9LB. Mr Peter Jacob & Mrs Margaret Wilson. *A258 Dover to Deal. In Upper Walmer turn L into Station Rd. Under railway bridge, Cross Rd is 2nd R. DO NOT approach from Ringwould as SatNav suggests*. **Adm £3.50, chd free. Sun 13 Apr, Sun 29 June (11-5).**
An exciting and lovely garden combining great artistic sensibility with an extensive and fascinating variety of plants. ⅓ acre plantsman garden. Collection of Daphnes, hardy Geraniums, herbaceous beds, unusual trees, shrubs and alpines.

23 CUTLASS COTTAGE
Langton Road, Speldhurst, Tunbridge Wells TN3 0NR. Stephen & Christine Lee, www.vistasltd.com. *3m W of Tunbridge Wells. From Tunbridge Wells go to Langton Green, take turning to Speldhurst at Hare PH. Cutlass Cottage 1¾ m on R opposite rd called Ferbies*. Home-made teas. **Adm £4, chd free. Evening Opening, wine, Sat 26 July (5-8.30); Sun 27 July (12-5).**
Private garden of garden designer and landscaper of approx. 1 acre in an AONB with fine views. Designed with outdoor entertaining very much in mind, there are plenty of social as well as intimate seating areas, a cutting garden, kitchen/herb garden, sunken 'cosy-up' terrace with Kadai, formal and informal ponds. Planting is designed for maximum yr round interest. Access for wheelchairs to most parts of garden.

24 ◆ DODDINGTON PLACE
Church Lane, Doddington, nr Sittingbourne ME9 0BB. Mr & Mrs Richard Oldfield, 01795 886101, www.doddingtonplacegardens.co.uk. *6m SE of Sittingbourne. From A20 turn N opp Lenham or from A2 turn S at Teynham or Ospringe (Faversham), all 4m*. Home-made teas. **Adm £6, chd £2. For NGS: Sun 27 Apr (11-5); Sun 8 June (6.30am-5pm); Wed 23 July, Sun 28 Sept (11-5). For other opening times and information, please phone or see garden website.**
10-acre garden, landscaped with wide views; trees and cloud clipped yew hedges; woodland garden with azaleas and rhododendrons; Edwardian rock garden recently renovated (not wheelchair accessible); formal garden with mixed borders. Gothic folly. Wheelchair access possible to majority of the gardens but not the Rock Garden.

25 DOWNS COURT
Church Lane, Boughton Aluph, Ashford TN25 4EU. Mr & Mrs Bay Green, 07984 558945, bay@baygee.com. *4m NE of Ashford. From A28 Ashford or Canterbury, after Wye Xrds take next turn NW to Boughton Aluph Church. Fork R at pillar box, garden only drive on R*. **Adm £5, chd free. Visitors welcome by appt May to July.**
Three-acre downland plantsman's garden on alkaline soil with fine trees, mature yew and box hedges, mixed borders with many unusual plants. Shrub roses and rose arch pathway, small parterre. Sweeping lawns and lovely views over surrounding countryside.

26 EAGLESWOOD

Slade Road, Warren Street, Lenham ME17 2EG. Mike & Edith Darvill, 01622 858702, mike.darvill@btinternet.com. *Going E on A20 nr Lenham, L into Hubbards Hill for approx 1m then 2nd L into Slade Rd. Garden 150yds on R. Coaches permitted.* **Adm £3.50, chd free (share to Demelza House Hospice). Sun 18 May, Sun 1 June, Sun 19 Oct (11-5). Also open Frith Old Farmhouse, Suns 18 May, 1 June. Visitors also welcome by appt Apr to Nov.**

2-acre plantsman's garden situated high on N Downs, developed over the past 26yrs. Wide range of trees and shrubs (many unusual), herbaceous material and woodland plants grown to give yr-round interest, particularly in spring and for autumn colour. Some gravel areas, grass paths may be slippery when wet.

27 ELHAM GARDENS

Elham CT4 6TU. *10m S of Canterbury, 6m N of Hythe. Enter Elham from Lyminge (off A20) or Barham (off A2). Car parking in village square. Tickets & maps from gazebo on main rd opp Browns estate agents.* Home-made teas off village square. **Adm £5, chd free. Sat 14, Sun 15 June (2-5).**

Elham boasts a thriving community of amateur gardeners, many of whom will open their gardens in this idyllic setting. Wide range of styles of garden all within easy walking distance of each other. Owners on hand to ensure you make the most of your visit to the picturesque Elham valley. Old market town in middle of Elham Valley. Unspoilt countryside. Special offer Ploughman's Lunch for just £5 at The King's Arms, in village square.

28 ◆ EMMETTS GARDEN

Ide Hill, Sevenoaks TN14 6BA. National Trust, 01732 750367, www.nationaltrust.org.uk. *5m SW of Sevenoaks. 1½ m S of A25 on Sundridge-Ide Hill Rd. 1½ m N of Ide Hill off B2042.* Cream teas in Stable Tea-room. **Adm £7.60, chd £3.80. For NGS: Mon 9 June (10-4). For other opening times and information, please phone or see garden website.**

5-acre hillside garden, with the highest tree top in Kent, noted for its fine collection of rare trees and flowering shrubs. The garden is particularly fine in spring, while a rose garden, rock garden and extensive planting of acers for autumn colour extend the interest throughout the season. Hard paths to the Stable tea-room and WC. Some steep slopes. Volunteer driven buggy available for lifts up the steepest hill.

A riot of plants growing together as if in the wild . . .

29 NEW EUREKA

Buckhurst Road, Westerham Hill TN16 2HR. Mr & Mrs Gordon & Suzanne Wright. *1½ m N of Westerham, 1m S from centre of Biggin Hill. 5m from J5 & J6 of M25, parking at Westerham Heights Garden Centre on A233. Limited disabled parking at house.* Home-made teas. **Adm £4, chd free. Sat 2, Sun 3, Sat 9, Sun 10, Sat 30, Sun 31 Aug, Thur 11, Sun 14 Sept (2-5.30).**

A blaze of colourful displays in perennial borders and the cartwheel centre beds, with hanging baskets, tubs, troughs and garden art. Hidden areas to be discovered, chickens, lots of seating, plus a children's Treasure Trail and viewing platform. Rabbit proof fencing around all borders. Garden art incl a 12ft red dragon, a horse's head carved out of a 200 yr old Yew tree stump and a 9ft dragon fly on a reed.

30 NEW FALCONHURST

Cowden Pound Road, Mark Beech, Edenbridge TN8 5NR. Mr & Mrs Charles Talbot, www.falconhurst.co.uk. *3m SE of Edenbridge. B2026 at Queens Arms PH turn E to Markbeech. 2nd drive on R before Markbeech village. Parking 1st L in paddock if dry.* Home-made teas. **Adm £4.50, chd free. Sun 29 June, Sun 27 July (12-5).**

4 acre garden with fabulous views devised and cared for by the same family for 160 yrs. Wide mixed borders with old roses, peonies, shrubs and a wide variety of herbaceous and annual plants; ruin garden; walled garden; interesting mature trees and shrubs; kitchen garden; wild flower meadows with woodland and pond walks. Woodland pigs; orchard chickens; lambs in the paddocks.

31 FRITH OLD FARMHOUSE

Frith Road, Otterden, Faversham ME13 0DD. Drs Gillian & Peter Regan, 01795 890556, peter.regan@cantab.net. *½ m off Lenham to Faversham rd. From A20 E of Lenham turn up Hubbards Hill, follow signs to Eastling. After 4m turn L signed Newnham, Doddington. From A2 in Faversham, turn S towards Brogdale & continue through Painters Forstal & Eastling. Turn R 1½ m beyond Eastling.* Home-made teas. **Adm £4, chd free. Sun 20 Apr, Sun 18 May, Sun 1 June (11-5). Also open Eagleswood, Suns 18 May, 1 June. Visitors also welcome by appt Apr to Sept for groups max 50. Please call in advance.**

A riot of plants growing together as if in the wild, developed over 30yrs. No neat edges or formal beds, but a very wide range of unusual and interesting plants, together with trees and shrubs chosen for yr-round appeal. Special interest in bulbs and woodland plants. Visitor comments - 'a plethora of plants', 'inspirational', 'a hidden gem'. Featured in Kent Life and RHS 'The Garden'.

32 NEW GALLANTS MANOR

Gallants Lane, East Farleigh, Maidstone ME15 0LF. Michael & Barbara Bartlett. *From E Farleigh Church continue in direction of W Farleigh/Yalding. Take 1st turning on L into Gallants Lane. Entrance & parking about 400m on L.* Home-made teas. **Adm £5, chd free (share to Canine Partners). Sun 4, Mon 5 May (11-5).**

A 10 acre country garden surrounding C14 house (not open) designed for ease of maintenance. Formal rose garden, pond with stream leading into small lake. Spring bulbs. Azaleas, rhododendrons, japanese maples, herbaceous and shrub borders. Lawns, paved courtyard. Views of North Downs. Wheelchair access on grass.

Pheasant Barn

© Leigh Clapp

33 GODDARDS GREEN
Angley Road, Cranbrook TN17 3LR. John & Linde Wotton, 01580 715507, jpwotton@gmail.com. *1/2 m SW of Cranbrook. On W of Angley Rd. (A229) at junction with High St, opposite War Memorial.* **Adm £5, chd free.** **Sun 29 June, Sun 27 July (12-4.30). Visitors also welcome by appt Apr to Sept.**
Garden of about 2 acres, surrounding beautiful 500yr-old clothier's hall (not open), laid out in 1920s and redesigned over past 20yrs to combine traditional and modern planting schemes. Fountain, rill and water garden, borders with bulbs, herbaceous plants, flowering shrubs and exotics, birch grove, grass border, pond, kitchen garden and mature mixed orchard.

34 ◆ GODINTON HOUSE & GARDENS
Godinton Lane, Ashford TN23 3BP. Godinton House Preservation Trust, 01233 643854, info@godintonhouse.co.uk, www.godintonhouse.co.uk. *11/2 m W of Ashford. M20 J9 to Ashford. Take A20 towards Charing & Lenham, then follow brown tourist signs.* **Adm £5, chd free. For NGS: Sun 23, Sun 30 Mar, Fri 27 June (1-6); Fri 26 Sept (10.30-12.30). For other opening times and information, please phone or see garden website.**
12 acres complement the magnificent Jacobean house. Terraced lawns lead through herbaceous borders, rose garden and formal lily pond to intimate Italian garden and large walled garden with delphiniums, potager, cut flowers and iris border. March/April the wild garden is a mass of daffodils, fritillaries, other spring flowers. March 23rd and 30th, Daffodil Meadow; June 27th Delphinium Festival; September 26th Macmillan Coffee Morning. Home-made teas available. RHS Partner Garden. Partial wheelchair access to ground floor of house and most of gardens.

35 GODMERSHAM PARK
Godmersham CT4 7DT. Mrs Fiona Sunley, 01227 730293. *5m NE of Ashford. Off A28, midway between Canterbury & Ashford.* Home-made teas. **Adm £5, chd free (share to Godmersham Church). Sun 30 Mar, Sun 6 Apr, Sun 22, Sun 29 June (1-5). Visitors also welcome by appt, min 3 visitors.**
24 acres restored wilderness and formal gardens set around C18 mansion (not open). Topiary, rose garden, herbaceous borders, walled kitchen garden and recently restored Italian garden. Superb daffodils in spring and roses in June. Historical association with Jane Austen. Also visit the Heritage Centre. Deep gravel paths.

36 ◆ GOODNESTONE PARK GARDENS
Wingham, Canterbury CT3 1PL. Margaret, Lady FitzWalter, 01304 840107, www.goodnestoneparkgardens.co.uk. *6m SE of Canterbury. Village lies S of B2046 from A2 to Wingham. Brown tourist signs off B2046.* Light refreshments. **Adm £6, chd £2 (no concessions on NGS open days). For NGS: Sun 13 Apr, Sat 7 June, Sun 5 Oct (12-5). For other opening times and information, please phone or see garden website.**
10-12 acres with good trees, woodland garden, snowdrops, spring bulbs and walled garden with old-fashioned roses. Connections with Jane Austen who stayed here.
2 arboretums planted in 1984 and 2001, gravel garden. Picnics allowed.

GROUP OPENING

37 GRAVESEND GARDENS GROUP

Gravesend DA12 1JZ. *Approx ½ m from Gravesend town centre. From A2 take A227 towards Gravesend. At T-lights with Cross Lane West turn R then L at next T-lights following yellow NGS signs. Park in Sandy Bank Rd.* Home-made teas. **Combined adm £3.50, chd free.** Sat 19, Sun 20 July (12-5).

58A PARROCK ROAD
Mr Barry Bowen

68 SOUTH HILL ROAD
Judith Hathrill

Enjoy two lovely gardens, very different in character, close to Windmill Hill which has extensive views over the Thames estuary. 58A Parrock Road is a beautiful, well-established town garden, approx 120ft x 40ft, nurtured by owner for 50yrs. There is a stream running down to a pond, luscious planting along the rocky banks, fascinating water features, mature trees and shrubs, magnificent display of hostas and succulents. 68 South Hill Road is an award-winning wildlife garden, showing that wildlife friendly gardens need not be 'wild'. Colourful herbaceous borders, flowers, herbs and salads in the potager, raised vegetable and herb beds, ferns, grasses and colourful containers. Mediterranean vegetables thrive in the greenhouse, two ponds planted with native species. Jazz Trio at 58A Parrock Road.

38 ◆ GREAT COMP GARDEN

Comp Lane, Platt, nr Borough Green, Sevenoaks TN15 8QS. Great Comp Charitable Trust, 01732 885094, www.greatcompgarden.co.uk. *7m E of Sevenoaks. A20 at Wrotham Heath, take Seven Mile Lane, B2016; at 1st Xrds turn R; garden on L ½ m.* Home-made teas. **Adm £6, chd £2.50.** For NGS: Sun 30 Mar, Suns 19, 26 Oct (11-4.30). **For other opening times and information, please phone or see garden website.**

Skilfully designed 7-acre garden of exceptional beauty. Spacious setting of well-maintained lawns and paths lead visitors through plantsman's collection of trees, shrubs, heathers and herbaceous plants. Good autumn colour. Early C17 house (not open). Magnolias, hellebores and snowflakes (leucojum), hamamellis and winter flowering heathers are great feature in spring. A great variety of perennials in summer incl salvias, dahlias and crocosmias. Featured in Gardens Illustrated.

39 115 HADLOW ROAD

Tonbridge TN9 1QE. Mr & Mrs Richard Esdale, 01732 353738. *1½ m N of Tonbridge stn. Take A26 from N end of High St signed Maidstone, house 1m on L in service rd.* **Adm £3.50, chd free.** Sun 29 June, Sun 24 Aug (2-5). **Visitors also welcome by appt June to Aug.**

Almost ½ -acre unusual terraced garden with large collection of modern roses, island herbaceous border, many clematis, hardy fuchsias, heathers, grasses, hostas, phormiums, and ferns, shrub borders, alpines, annuals, kitchen garden and pond; well labelled.

40 HALL PLACE

Leigh TN11 8HH. The Lady Hollenden. *4m W of Tonbridge. From A21 Sevenoaks to Tonbridge, B245 to Hildenborough, then R onto B2027 through Leigh & on R.* **Adm £6, chd £2.50.** Suns 11, 25 May, Sun 15 June (2-6).

Large outstanding garden with 11-acre lake, lakeside walk crossing over picturesque bridges. Many rare and interesting trees and shrubs.

41 HAVEN

22 Station Road, Minster, Ramsgate CT12 4BZ. Robin Roose-Beresford, 01843 822594, robin.roose@hotmail.co.uk. *Off A299 Ramsgate Rd, take Minster exit from Manston r-bout, straight rd, R fork at church is Station Rd.* **Adm £3, chd free.** Visitors welcome by appt **Feb to Nov, please phone or email. Small groups only, coach max 20.**

A smallish (300ft x 30ft) garden, designed with wildlife in mind, devised and maintained by the owner, densely planted in a natural style with meandering stepping stone paths. Two ponds (one for wildlife), gravel garden, rock garden, bog areas, fernery, Japanese garden, hostas and carnivorous plant beds, many exotic and unusual trees, shrubs and plants, colourful in leaf and flower. Featured in Kent Life, one of five finalists in Kent Garden of the Year and Gold Award from Kent Wildlife Trust.

42 NEW HAWKINGE ALLOTMENTS

Stombers Lane, Hawkinge, Folkestone CT18 7QX. Mr Nick Lord, www.hawkingeallotments.org.uk. *E side of Hawkinge village. From village centre, turn off Canterbury Rd along The Street, follow to end & take next L into Stombers Lane, entrance 200m on L.* Home-made teas. **Adm £3, chd free.** Sat 19, Sun 20 July (1-5). **Also open Mounts Court Farmhouse, Acrise.**

An allotment site with over 60 families having plots of varying sizes, incl raised beds for those less able. A diverse range of vegetables and flowers are grown and the site is self-managed by plot-holders. The site which includes a compostable toilet and its own club house has only existed for 5yrs and has already won many awards. No specific disabled parking area, please make marshals aware if you need assistance on arrival, area is mostly flat rough or grass terrain.

43 HAYDOWN

Great Buckland, nr Cobham DA13 0XF. Dr & Mrs I D Edeleanu, 01474 814329, ion-danedeleanu@fsmail.net. *6m W of Rochester. 4m S of A2. Turn for Cobham. At war memorial straight down hill under rail bridge to T-*

junction. Turn R. In 200yds take L fork. Narrow lane. Gdn on L. **Adm £5, chd free. Visitors welcome by appt June to Aug for garden tours, Haydown wine available.**
9-acre garden on North Downs created over nearly 40yrs. Formerly scrubland, it now incl woodland of indigenous and unusual trees, orchard, ponds and vineyard. Meadowland with many varieties of wild orchids in June, and abundant wild flowers in August. A haven for wildlife, incl badgers.

44 HERONDEN

Smallhythe Road, Tenterden TN30 7LR. Peter & Vicky Costain. *From Tenterden High St, take B2082 Rye rd. Leave Tesco on L & take next R, lane marked to potato shop, Morghew. Entrance 1st R in lane.* Cream teas. **Adm £4, chd free (share to Tenterden & District Day Centre). Sat 7, Sun 8 June (2-5).**
Old walled garden consisting of spring, summer herbaceous and autumn borders. Centre of walled garden redesigned and prairie planted in April 2009 with mixed grasses and flowers. Remaining garden mixed shrubs incl peonies and hydrangeas. House and garden set in park. Featured in Kent Life. Grass paths, ramp to walled garden.

45 HIGHLANDS

Hackington Close, St Stephen's, Canterbury CT2 7BB. Dr & Mrs B T Grayson, 01227 765066, terrygrayson@supanet.com. *1m N of Canterbury. At the foot of St Stephen's Hill, 200m N of Archbishops School, on rd to Tyler Hill/Chestfield. Car parking in Downs Rd, opp Hackington Close.* Home-made teas. **Adm £5, chd free. Sun 20 July (1-5). Also open 43 The Ridings. Visitors also welcome by appt Apr to Aug.**
2-acre peaceful garden, set in S-facing bowl, with sweeps of narcissus in spring and island beds of herbaceous perennials, roses, azaleas, acers, hydrangeas, hebes and other shrubs. Many conifer and broad-leafed trees, incl plantation of ornamental trees. Two ponds, small alpine bed and novel hanging gardens feature. Also includes carved features from trees grown in the garden.

46 ◆ HOLE PARK

Benenden Road, Rolvenden, Cranbrook TN17 4JB. Mr & Mrs E G Barham, 01580 241344, www.holepark.com. *4m SW of Tenterden. Midway between Rolvenden & Benenden on B2086.* **Adm £6, chd £1. For NGS: Wed 16 Apr, Sun 18 May, Wed 18 June, Sun 12 Oct (11-6). For other opening times and information, please phone or see garden website.**
Hole Park is proud to stand amongst the group of gardens which first opened in 1927 soon after it was laid out by my great grandfather. Our 15-acre garden is surrounded by parkland with beautiful views and contains fine yew hedges, large lawns with specimen trees,walled gardens, pools and mixed borders combined with bulbs, rhododendrons and azaleas. Massed bluebells in woodland walk, standard wisterias, orchids in flower meadow and glorious autumn colours make this a garden for all seasons. The Sundial Garden was redesigned and planted in 2013. Light refreshments and home-made cream teas. Improved wheelchair provision for 2014. Wheelchairs available for free hire, may be booked.

47 HONNINGTON FARM

Vauxhall Lane, Southborough, Tunbridge Wells TN4 0XD. Mrs Ann Tyler, 01892 536990, ann.honnington@btinternet.com, www.honningtonfarmgardens.co.uk. *Between Tonbridge & Tunbridge Wells. A21 to A26. Signed Honnington Equestrian Centre. Enter at Honnington & cottages.* Home-made teas. **Adm £5, chd free. Sun 18 May, Sun 15 June (11-4). Visitors also welcome by appt Apr to Oct, groups of 10+. Coaches not exceeding 54 seats.**
6-acre garden, with heavy clay soil enriched yearly and producing a wide range of habitats, incl water and bog gardens, primrose and bluebell walks. Wildlife promotion a priority. Natural pool in wild flower meadow. Rose walkways, rockery, lakes and water features. Large herbaceous beds, some with New Zealand influence. Wonderful views. Sculptures exhibited by our local sculptor. Large plant sale on occasions. Newly renovated Kent Barn which holds 60 for teas/lunches. Steep slopes and gravel drives.

48 ◆ IGHTHAM MOTE

Ivy Hatch, Sevenoaks TN15 0NT. National Trust, 01732 810378, www.nationaltrust.org.uk. *6m E of Sevenoaks. Off A25, 2½ m S of Ightham. Buses from rail stns Sevenoaks or Borough Green to Ivy Hatch, ½ m walk to Ightham Mote.* **Adm £11.50, chd £5.75. For NGS: Thur 10 July (10.30-5). For other opening times and information, please phone or see garden website.**
14-acre garden and moated medieval manor c1320, first opened for NGS in 1927. North lake and pleasure gardens, ornamental pond and cascade created in early C18. Orchard, enclosed, formal, vegetable and cutting gardens all contribute to the famous sense of tranquillity. Free guided tours of garden (donations to NGS welcome). Garden team on hand for tips and advice.

A haven for wildlife . . .

49 ◆ KNOLE

Knole, Sevenoaks TN15 0RP. Lord Sackville, 01732 462100, www.nationaltrust.org.uk. *1½ m SE of Sevenoaks. Leave M25 J5 (A21). Park entrance S of Sevenoaks town centre off A225 Tonbridge Road (opposite St Nicholas church). Sat Nav: use TN13 1HU.* **Adm £5, chd £2.50. For NGS: Tue 1 Apr, Tue 6 May, Tue 3 June, Tue 1 July, Tue 5 Aug (11-4). Last entry 3.30pm. For other opening times and information, please phone or see garden website.**
Lord Sackville's private garden at Knole commands the most beautiful view of the house. An impressive display of bluebells can be seen in April and May. Towards the end of May and throughout June, the magnificent wisteria wall provides the most glorious and delicately scented backdrop to the garden. The Brewhouse Café is closed for refurbishment during 2014, but limited refreshments will be served outdoors. Picnics are welcome in Green Court (on blankets) or in the park at our picnic tables. Wheelchair access limited in wet weather.

Haven

© Leigh Clapp

50 KNOWLE HILL FARM

Ulcombe, Maidstone ME17 1ES. The Hon Andrew & Mrs Cairns, 01622 850240, elizabeth.cairns@btinternet.com, www.knowlehillfarmgarden.co.uk. *7m SE of Maidstone. From M20 J8 follow A20 towards Lenham for 2m. Turn R to Ulcombe. After 1½ m, L at crossroad, ½ m 2nd R Windmill Hill. Past Pepper Box PH, ½ m 1st L.* Light refreshments. **Adm £4, chd free. Sun 9, Sun 23 Feb (11-3). Evening Opening £4, chd free, wine, Sat 21 June (5-8); Sun 3 Aug (2-6); Sun 8, Sun 22 Feb 2015. Visitors also welcome by appt May to Sept, access for 25/30 seater coaches.**

1½ -acre garden, created over 30yrs, on S-facing slope of N Downs with spectacular views. Mixed borders: Mediterranean and tender plants, roses, agapanthus, verbenas, salvias and grasses, flourish on the light soil. Many unusual plants. Evolving topiary. Lavender ribbons are magnets for bees. Pool and rill enclosed in small walled garden planted mainly with white flowers. New green garden is being developed. Featured in Period Homes and Interiors. Some steep slopes.

51 LADHAM HOUSE

Goudhurst TN17 1DB. Mr Guy Johnson. *8m E of Tunbridge Wells. On NE of village, off A262. Through village towards Cranbrook, turn L at The Chequers PH. 2nd R into Ladham Rd, main gates approx 500yds on L.* Light refreshments. **Adm £4, chd £1. Sun 18 May (2-5).**

Large garden and parkland with rhododendrons, camellias, azaleas and magnolias. Spectacular twin borders, a rose garden and an arboretum containing some fine specimens. Also, an Edwardian sunken rockery (inaccessible to wheelchairs), woodland walk, ha-ha and vegetable garden.

52 LEYDENS

Hartfield Road, Edenbridge TN8 5NH. Roger Platts, 01732 863318, info@rogerplatts.com, www.rogerplatts.com. *1m S of Edenbridge. On B2026 towards Hartfield (use Nursery entrance & car park).* Home-made teas. **Adm £4, chd free. Sun 3 Aug (12-5). Also open Old Buckhurst.**

Small private garden of garden designer, nursery owner and author who created NGS Garden at Chelsea in 2002, winning Gold and Best in Show, and in 2010 Gold and People's Choice for the M&G Garden. Constant development with wide range of shrubs and perennials incl late summer flowering perennial border adjoining wild flower hay meadow. Kitchen garden. Plants clearly labelled and fact sheet available.

53 LORDS

Sheldwich, Faversham ME13 0NJ. Jane Wade, 01795 536900, jane@sellwade.co.uk. *4m S of Faversham. From A2 or M2 take A251 towards Ashford. ½ m S of Sheldwich church find entrance lane on R adjacent to wood. (3½ m N of Challock Xrds).* Lemon Barley water and shortbread biscuits served. **Adm £4.50, chd free. Thur 26 June (2-5); Sun 29 June (2-5.30). Also open The Coach House Sun 29 June. Visitors also welcome by appt in July.**

C18 canted walled garden and greenhouse. A herb terrace overlooks a citrus standing and beyond is a flowery mead beneath medlar and quince trees. Across a grass tennis court is a cherry orchard grazed by Jacob sheep. A shady fernery leads to lawns, ponds and wild area. Old specimen trees include redwoods, planes, copper beech, yew hedges and 120ft tulip tree. Some gravel paths.

54 LUTON HOUSE

Selling ME13 9RQ. Sir John & Lady Swire. *4m SE of Faversham. From A2 (M2) or A251 make for White Lion, entrance 30yds E on same side of rd.* **Adm £4, chd free. Sun 30 Mar, Sun 6 July (2-5).**

6 acres; C19 landscaped garden; ornamental ponds; trees underplanted with azaleas, camellias, woodland plants. Hellebores, spring bulbs, magnolias, cherries, daphnes, halesias, maples, Judas trees and cyclamen. Depending on the weather, those interested in camellias, early trees and bulbs may like to visit in late Mar/early April. For private visits please apply in writing, or by email to moiraswire@aol.com

55 ◆ MARLE PLACE

Marle Place Road, Brenchley TN12 7HS. Mr & Mrs Gerald Williams, 01892 722304, www.marleplace.co.uk. *8m SE of*

Tonbridge. At Forstal Farm r'about N of Lamberhurst bypass on A21 take B2162 Horsmonden direction about 3m. From Brenchley brown/white tourism signs 1½ m. **For NGS: Evening Openings £6, chd £2, Light refreshments, Wed 28 May, Wed 11 June, Wed 13 Aug (5-8). For other opening times and information, please phone or see garden website.**
Victorian gazebo, plantsman's shrub borders, walled scented garden, Edwardian rockery, herbaceous borders, bog and kitchen gardens. Woodland walks, mosaic terrace, artists' studios and gallery with contemporary art. Autumn colour. Restored Victorian 40ft greenhouse with orchids. C17 listed house (not open). Collection of interesting chickens. Nature trail, Art exhibition. Guided tour at 6pm. Tea room with homemade cakes. Ramps in place for stepped areas. Access incl some sloping lawns and gravel paths. Wheelchair users enter free of charge.

56 MARSHBOROUGH FARMHOUSE

Farm Lane, Marshborough, Sandwich CT13 0PJ. David & Sarah Ash, 01304 813679. *1½ m W of Sandwich, ½ m S of Ash. From Ash take R fork to Woodnesborough. After 1m Marshborough sign. Turn L into Farm Lane at white thatched cottage, garden 100yds on L. Coaches must phone for access information.* **Adm £4, chd free. Visitors welcome by appt 11 May - 22 June and 16 Aug - 7 Sept. For other dates please phone. Coaches phone for access information.**
Fascinating 2½ -acre plantsman's garden, developed enthusiastically over 16yrs. Original lawns are rapidly shrinking, giving way to meandering paths around informal island beds with many unusual shrubs, trees and perennials creating yr-round colour and interest. Herbaceous borders, pond, rockery, raised dry garden, vegetables and tender pot plants.

57 MASONS FARM

Headcorn Road, Grafty Green, Maidstone ME17 2AP. Paul & Sharon Jennings. *3.8m E of Headcorn. Follow A274 towards Maidstone. Leaving Headcorn village turn R into Lenham Rd. Follow for 3.8m to Grafty Green. Masons Farm approx 300 yards on R.* Home-made teas. **Adm £4, chd free (share to St Nicholas Church). Sat 21, Sun 22 June (1-5). Also open Knowle Hill Farm**, Sat 21 June (5-8).
1-acre garden designed by local landscape architect, Tom La Dell. Constructed and extensively planted over past 5yrs around C16 farmhouse. Shrubs, grasses and perennials hedged with box and yew. Rose garden, herb parterre, Mediterranean courtyard. Beautiful views in an area of outstanding natural beauty. Please take care around swimming pool.

Tree house in the Sequoia . . .

58 NEW 12 THE MEADOWS

12 The Meadows, Chelsfield, Orpington BR6 6HS. Mr & Mrs Roger & Jean Pemberton. *3m from J4 on M25. Exit M25 at J4 r'about, 3rd exit - A224, ½ m, take 2nd L, Warren Rd. Bear L into Windsor Drive. 1st L The Meadway, follow signs to garden.* Light refreshments. **Adm £4, chd free. Sun 25 May, Sun 15 June (1-5.30).**
Front garden Mediterranean style gravel with sun loving plants. Rear ¾ acre garden in 2 parts. Semi formal area with two ponds, one Koi and one natural (lots of Spring interest). Mature bamboos, acers, grasses etc and semi wooded area, children's path with 13ft high giraffe and lots of points of interest. Designated children's area. Children only allowed access! London Gardens Society award winners. Wheelchair access to all parts except small area at very bottom of garden due to steps.

59 MERE HOUSE

Mereworth ME18 5NB. Mr & Mrs Andrew Wells, www.mere-house.co.uk. *7m E of Tonbridge. From A26 turn N on to B2016 & then into Mereworth village. 3½ m S of M20/M26 junction, take A20, then B2016 to Mereworth.* **Adm £4, chd free. Suns 16, 23 Feb, Sun 30 Mar, Mon 21 Apr, Sun 26 Oct (2-5); Sun 22 Feb 2015.**
6 acre garden with C18 lake. Snowdrops, daffodils, lawns, herbaceous borders, ornamental shrubs and trees with foliage contrast and striking autumn colour. Woodland walk and major tree planting and landscaping since 1990. Park and lake walks.

60 ◆ MOUNT EPHRAIM

Hernhill, Faversham ME13 9TX. Mr & Mrs E S Dawes & Mr W Dawes, 01227 751496, www.mountephraimgardens.co.uk. *3m E of Faversham. From end of M2, then A299 take slip rd 1st L to Hernhill, signed to gardens.* **Adm £6, chd £2.50, under 3's free. For NGS: Sun 16 March, Thur 12 June, Sun 28 Sept (11-5). For other opening times and information, please phone or see garden website.**
Herbaceous border, topiary, daffodils and rhododendrons, rose terraces leading to small lake. Rock garden with pools, water garden, young arboretum. Rose garden with arches and pergola planted to celebrate the Millennium. Magnificent trees. Grass maze. Superb views over fruit farms to Swale estuary. Village craft centre. Teas and lunches available. ATAK leaflet. Featured in various articles, Faversham Times and News.

61 MOUNTS COURT FARMHOUSE

Acrise, nr Folkestone CT18 8LQ. Graham & Geraldine Fish, 01303 840598, geraldine_fish@btinternet.com. *6m NW of Folkestone. From A260 Folkestone to Canterbury rd, turn L at Densole opp Black Horse Inn, 1½ m towards Elham & Lyminge, on N side.* Home-made teas. **Adm £5, chd free. Sat 19, Sun 20 July (1-5). Also open Hawkinge Allotment Society. Visitors also welcome by appt June to Aug, coaches permitted.**
Developed from a 1½ -acre horse paddock over 30yrs in surroundings designated as an Area of Outstanding Natural Beauty at a height of 150 metres. Variety of trees, shrubs and grasses and herbaceous plants. Wide winding paths flow through deep, densely planted mixed borders varying from cottage to woodland in character, with an eye to foliage pattern and changing colour mixes. Pond and bog garden.

62 NETTLESTEAD PLACE

Nettlestead ME18 5HA. Mr & Mrs Roy Tucker, www.nettlesteadplace.co.uk. *6m W/SW of Maidstone. Turn S off A26 onto B2015 then 1m on L, next to Nettlestead Church.* **Adm £5, chd free. Sun 22 June, Sun 21 Sept (2-5).**

C13 manor house in 10-acre plantsman's garden. Large formal rose garden. Large herbaceous garden of island beds with rose and clematis walkway leading to garden of China roses. Fine collection of trees and shrubs; sunken pond garden, terraces, bamboos, glen garden, acer lawn. Young pinetum adjacent to garden. Sculptures. Wonderful open country views. Gravel paths, sunken pond garden. New large steep bank and lower area in development - regret not wheelchair accessible.

GROUP OPENING

63 NEW NEW BARN GARDENS

Longfield DA3 7NA. *1m E of Longfield. From Longfield towards Meopham on B260, turn L, New Barn Rd. From A2, Longfield exit take New Barn Rd towards Longfield. Then follow yellow NGS arrows.* Home-made teas. **Combined adm £3.50, chd free. Sat 14, Thur 19 June (2-5).**

NEW FOXBERRY
Pam & Dave Towler

NEW LYNDHURST
Richard & Eve Falconer

Enjoy two lovely gardens, within minutes walk of each other, but very different in character and style. Foxberry is an award-winning 1/3 acre garden designed and developed by the present owners over 20 years. It has an unusual cottage style front garden and from the rear terrace you can enjoy the view over the country style garden with sloping lawns surrounded by flower beds and backed by woodland. Linger by the pond, relax in the oriental arbour, lounge in a deck chair in the seaside area or explore the jungle. The delightful garden at Lyndhurst is bordered by mature trees and has a mixture of established shrubs, perennials, grasses and ferns. The garden borders are interspersed with interesting water and other garden features. Colourfully planted containers abound. Refreshments will be served in seating areas dotted around the garden and in the conservatory.

64 NORTON COURT

Teynham, Sittingbourne ME9 9JU. Tim & Sophia Steel, 01795 522941, sophia@nortoncourt.net. *Off A2 between Teynham & Faversham. L off A2 at Texaco garage into Norton Lane; next L into Provender Lane; L signed Church for car park.* Home-made teas. **Adm £5, chd free. Mon 9, Tue 10 June (2-5). Visitors also welcome by appt June to July.**

10-acre garden within parkland setting. Mature trees, topiary, wide lawns and clipped yew hedges. Orchard with mown paths through wild flowers. Walled garden with mixed borders and climbing roses. Pine tree walk. Formal box and lavender parterre. Tree house in the Sequoia. Church open, adjacent to garden. Gravel paths.

Linger by the pond, relax . . . explore the jungle . . .

65 OLD BLADBEAN STUD

Bladbean, Canterbury CT4 6NA. Carol Bruce, oldbladbeanstud@sky.com, www.oldbladbeanstud.co.uk. *6m S of Canterbury. From B2068, follow signs into Stelling Minnis, turn R onto Bossingham Rd, then follow yellow NGS signs through single track lanes.* Home-made teas. **Adm £5.50, chd free. Suns 1, 15, 29 June, Suns 13, 27 July, Sun 24 Aug, Suns 7, 21 Sept, Sun 5 Oct (2-6).**

Five interlinked gardens all designed and created from scratch by the garden owner on 3 acres of rough grassland between 2003 and 2011. Romantic walled rose garden with over 90 labelled old fashioned rose varieties, tranquil yellow and white garden, square garden with blended pastels borders and Victorian style greenhouse, 300ft long colour-schemed symmetrical double borders. An experimental self-sufficiency project comprises a wind turbine, rain water collection, solar panels and a ground source heat pump, an organic fruit and vegetable garden. The gardens are maintained entirely by the owner and were designed to be managed as an ornamental ecosystem with a large number of perennial species encouraged to set seed, and with staking, irrigation, mulching and chemical use kept an absolute minimum. Each garden has a different season of interest - please see the garden website for more information. Featured in Mail on Sunday and The Telegraph.

66 OLD BUCKHURST

Markbeech, nr Edenbridge TN8 5PH. Mr & Mrs J Gladstone, 01342 850825, www.oldbuckhurst.co.uk. *4m SE of Edenbridge. B2026, at Queens Arms PH turn E to Markbeech. In approx 1½ m, 1st house on R* ***after*** *leaving Markbeech. Parking in paddock if dry.* **Adm £4, chd free. Sat 26, Sun 27, Wed 30 Apr, Sun 4, Wed 7, Sat 10, Sun 11, Sat 17, Sat 31 May, Wed 4, Sat 7, Sat 21 June, Wed 9, Sat 12, Wed 16, Sat 26 July, Sun 3 Aug, Wed 3, Sat 6, Sun 7, Sat 13, Sun 14 Sept (11-5). Also open Leydens (Sun 3 Aug).**

1-acre partly-walled cottage garden around C15 Grade II Listed farmhouse with catslip roof (not open). Comments from Visitors' Book: 'perfect harmony of vistas, contrasts and proportions. Everything that makes an English garden the envy of the world'. 'The design and planting is sublime, a garden I doubt anyone could forget'. Mixed borders with roses, clematis, wisteria, poppies, iris, peonies, lavender, July/Aug a wide range of day lilies.

67 NEW THE OLD PALACE

Old Palace Road, Bekesbourne, Canterbury CT4 5ES. Mrs Nicky Fry, 01227 830319, nicolafry@cscope.co.uk. *2m S of Canterbury. A2 towards Dover take Bridge/Bekesbourne exit. Turn R into School Lane, in 500 yds turn R into Old Palace Rd. Parking for small coaches only.* Home-made teas. **Adm £5, chd free. Sat 28, Sun 29 June (1.30-5.30). Visitors also**

welcome by appt May to July.
The site of Thomas Cranmer's Old Palace and home of Ian Fleming. 4 acre garden created by present owner with many interesting features. A natural pond, planted to encourage wildlife. 100 year old Scots pines, other specimen trees including large flowering tulip tree. Walled potager with rose pergola and espaliered fruit trees. New allium walkway and herbaceous border planted in 2013.

68 ONE DERING ROAD

Ashford TN24 8DB. Mrs Claire de Sousa Barry, 07979 816104, nazgulnota-bene@ntlworld.com. *Town centre. Off Hythe Rd, nr Henwood r'about. Short walk from pay & display car park located just past Fire Station. Please no parking in Dering Rd.* Home-made teas. **Adm £3.50 (regret no children). Sun 25, Mon 26 May, Suns 8, 15, 22 June, Suns 13, 27 July, Sun 10, Sun 24, Mon 25 Aug (2-5). Visitors also welcome by appt May to Aug. Home-made cakes and teas by prior agreement.**
Plantsperson's romantic small town garden. Optimum use of space with yr-round interest. Successional planting. Vitex, crinodendron, acer, cardiocrinum, buddlia, roses, honeysuckle, lilies, delphiniums, clematis, dahlias, fuchsias, azaleas, trillium, arisaema, rhododendrons plus a host of other plants, trees and shrubs. Ever-changing canvas of colour, scent and form: 'wonderful, inspirational'. Featured in numerous publications and filmed for Secret Garden Section of Hampton Court and Chelsea Flower Show.

69 THE ORANGERY

Mystole, Chartham, Canterbury CT4 7DB. Rex Stickland & Anne Prasse, 01227 738348, rex@mystole.fsnet.co.uk. *5m SW of Canterbury. Turn off A28 through Shalmsford St. After 1½ m at Xrds turn R downhill. Continue on, ignoring rds on L (Pennypot Lane) & R. Ignore drive on L signed 'Mystole House only', at sharp bend in 600yds turn L into private drive signed Mystole Farm.* Home-made teas. **Adm £3.50, chd free. Sun 15 June, Sun 27 July (1-6). Visitors also welcome by appt Apr to Sept. Coaches welcome, please contact owner for parking information.**
1½ -acre gardens around C18 orangery, now a house (not open). Front gardens, established well-stocked herbaceous border and large walled garden with a wide variety of shrubs and mixed borders. Splendid views from terraces over ha-ha and paddocks to the lovely Chartham Downs. Water features and very interesting collection of modern sculptures set in natural surroundings. Ramps to garden.

70 ORCHARD END

Cock Lane, Spelmonden Road, Horsmonden TN12 8EQ. Mr Hugh Nye, 01892 723118, hughnye@aol.com. *8m E of Tunbridge Wells. From A21 going S turn L at r'bout onto B2162 to Horsmonden. After 2m turn R onto Spelmonden Rd. Affter ½ m turn R into Cock Lane. Garden on R.* Home-made teas. **Adm £3.50, chd free (share to The Amyloidosis Foundation). Sun 13 Apr (11-4); Sat 14, Sun 15 June, Sat 19, Sun 20 July, Sat 30, Sun 31 Aug (11-5). Visitors also welcome by appt June to Sept, max group 40.**
Contemporary classical garden within a 4-acre site. Made over 15yrs by resident landscape designer. Divided into rooms with linking vistas. Incl hot borders, white garden, exotics, oak and glass summerhouse amongst magnolias. Dramatic changes in level. Formal pool with damp garden, ornamental vegetable potager. Wildlife orchards and woodland walks.

71 NEW ORCHARD HOUSE, SPENNY LANE

Claygate, Marden, Tonbridge TN12 9PJ. Mr & Mrs Lerwill. *Just off B2162 between Collier St & Horsmonden. Spenny Lane is adjacent to the White Hart PH. Orchard House is 1st house on R about 400m from PH. Please park in Lane.* Home-made teas. **Adm £3.50, chd free. Evening Opening, wine, Wed 21 May (5-8); Sun 25 May (11-4). Evening Opening, wine, Wed 13 Aug (5-8); Sun 17 Aug (11-4).**
A relatively new garden created within the last 8yrs. Gravel garden with potted tender perennials, cottage garden and herbaceous borders. Potager with vegetables, fruit and flowers for cutting. Bee friendly borders. Hornbeam avenue underplanted with camassia. Small nursery on site specialising in herbaceous perennials and ornamental grasses. Access for wheelchairs but some pathways are gravel and grassed areas are uneven in places.

72 OTHAM GARDENS

Otham, nr Maidstone ME15 8RQ, 01622 861333. *4m SE of Maidstone. From A20 or A274 follow signs to Otham and brown NT signs for Stoneacre to take you to Village Green.* Light refreshments at Otham Village Hall. **Combined adm £5, chd free. Sun 29 June (11-5.30).**
Otham is a small village near Maidstone with 7 open gardens offering a mixture of styles and sizes, full of variety and interest, with Stoneacre's National Trust garden completing the picturesque ensemble. With lovely countryside views, enjoy established rose gardens, water features, a pond with bridge, a wild meadow area, beehives and productive kitchen gardens. There is a collection of pelargoniums, as well as a wealth of unusual perennials, an artist's garden and even a garden railway. There is something for everyone, and a warm welcome awaits. This year there are 2 additional new gardens. Parking in official car parks (except for disabled visitors at Stoneacre) and in drives of other gardens. Roads are narrow so please avoid parking on bends or causing an obstruction. Start at Otham Village Hall, next to the Green, where garden map available and teas being served. Limited wheelchair access.

73 PARSONAGE OASTS
Hampstead Lane, Yalding ME18 6HG. Edward & Jennifer Raikes, 01622 814272. *6m SW of Maidstone. On B2162 between Yalding village & stn, turn off at Anchor PH over canal bridge, continue 150yds up lane. House & car park on L.* Cream teas. **Adm £3, chd free.** Sun 6, Mon 21 Apr (2-5.30). **Visitors also welcome by appt Apr to Aug.**
Our garden has a lovely position on the bank of the river Medway. Typical Oast House (not open) often featured on calendars and picture books of Kent. 60yr old garden now looked after by grandchildren of its creator. 3/4 acre garden with walls, daffodils, crown imperials, shrubs and a spectacular magnolia. Exhibition and sale of pottery in barn. Unfenced river bank. Gravel paths.

74 ◆ PENSHURST PLACE
Penshurst TN11 8DG. Lord & Lady De L'Isle, 01892 870307, www.penshurstplace.com. *6m NW of Tunbridge Wells. SW of Tonbridge on B2176, signed from A26 N of Tunbridge Wells.* **Adm £8, chd £6.** For NGS: Tue 9 Sept (10.30-6). **For other opening times and information, please phone or see garden website.**
11 acres of garden dating back to C14; garden divided into series of rooms by over a mile of yew hedge; profusion of spring bulbs; formal rose garden; famous peony border. Woodland trail and arboretum. All-yr interest. Toy museum. Cream teas. Garden is wheelchair accessible.

75 PHEASANT BARN
Church Road, Oare ME13 0QB. Paul & Su Vaight, 01795 591654, paul.vaight@btinternet.com. *2m NW of Faversham. Entering Oare from Faversham, turn R at Three Mariners PH towards Harty Ferry. Garden 400yds on R, before church. Parking on roadside.* Home-made teas. **Adm £4, chd free.** Sat 21 June, Sat 12 July (1-5). **Visitors also welcome by appt Apr to July, refreshments by prior request.**
Series of smallish gardens around award-winning converted farm buildings in beautiful situation overlooking Oare Creek. Main area is nectar-rich planting in formal design with a contemporary twist inspired by local landscape. Also vegetable garden, parterre, water features, wild flower meadow and labyrinth. July optimum for wild flowers. Spring blossom. Kent Wildlife Trust Oare Marshes Bird Reserve within 1m. Two village inns serving lunches/dinners.

Ever-changing canvas of colour, scent and form: 'wonderful, inspirational' . . .

76 PHEASANT FARM
Church Road, Oare, Faversham ME13 0QB. Jonathan & Lucie Neame, 01795 535366. *2m NW of Faversham. Enter Oare from Faversham. R at 3 Mariners PH towards Harty Ferry. Garden 450yds on R, beyond Pheasant Barn, before church. Parking on roadside.* Home-made teas. **Adm £3.50, chd free.** Sat 7, Sun 8 June (12-5). **Visitors also welcome by appt May to June, adm incl refreshments for groups 20 max.**
Redesigned in 2008, a walled garden surrounding C17 farmhouse with outstanding views over Oare marshes and creek. Main garden with shrubs and herbaceous plants. Infinity lawn overlooking creek, orchard and circular walk through adjoining churchyard. 2 local Public Houses serving lunches. Wheelchair access in main garden only.

77 PLACKETTS HOLE
Bicknor, nr Sittingbourne ME9 8BA. Allison & David Wainman, 01622 884258, aj@aj-wainman.demon.co.uk. *5m S of Sittingbourne. W of B2163. Bicknor is signed from Hollingbourne Hill & from A249 at Stockbury Valley. Placketts Hole is midway between Bicknor & Deans Hill.* Light refreshments. **Adm £5, chd free.** Visitors welcome by appt **May to July.**
Mature 3-acre garden in Kent Downland valley incl herbaceous borders, rose and formal herb garden, small, walled kitchen garden and informal pond intersected by walls, hedges and paths. Many unusual plants, trees and shrubs and small wildflower calcareous meadow. Most of garden is accessible by wheelchair users.

78 NEW PORT LYMPNE, THE ASPINALL FOUNDATION
Aldington Road, Lympne, Hythe CT21 4PD. The Aspinall Foundation, info@aspinallfoundation.org. *Follow signs from M20, J11, to Port Lympne Wild Animal Park.* Home-made teas available from the Mansion. **Adm £6, chd £4. Howletts/Port Lympne passport holders half-price.** Fri 12, Sun 14 Sept (10-4).
Port Lympne Mansion and Gardens. 15 acres of beautiful landscaped grounds cut out of the old sea cliffs overlooking Romney Marsh and out to the English Channel. Features incl formal ponds, chessboard and striped gardens with an outdoor staircase - Italian inspired. Partial wheelchair access. Historical site with steps and terraces.

79 POTMANS HEATH HOUSE
Wittersham TN30 7PU. Dr Alan & Dr Wilma Lloyd Smith, 01797 270221, potmansheath@hotmail.com. *1½ m W of Wittersham. Between Wittersham & Rolvenden, 1m from junction with B2082. 200yds E of bridge over Potmans Heath Channel. Nearest public WC at Wittersham Church.* Home-made teas. **Adm £5, chd free.** Sun 27 Apr, Sun 22 June (2-6). **Visitors also welcome by appt for Autumn and Winter visits.**
Large compartmentalised country garden. Our specialities are widespread naturalised bulbs and spectacular blossom in spring, followed by a variety of climbing roses and mixed borders in summer. Part walled vegetable garden, greenhouses. Specimen trees, some unusual. Orchards. Adjoining parkland with duck ponds. Rich variety of garden birds. Wheelchair users welcome. Some awkward slopes but generally good.

Norton Court

© Leigh Clapp

Leydens

80 11 RAYMER ROAD
Penenden Heath, Maidstone ME14 2JQ. Mrs Barbara Badham. *1m from J6 M20. At M20, J6 at Running Horse r'about take Penenden Heath exit along Sandling Lane towards Bearsted. At T-lights turn into Downsview Rd & yellow NGS follow signs*. Home-made teas. **Adm £3, chd free.** **Sun 4 May (11-4).**
An average sized garden with lovely views of the Downs, divided into different areas and intensely planted for year round interest. Cottage garden border, oriental themed pond, secret woodland garden and a selection of ferns and hostas arranged under the canopy of a strawberry tree. Organic fruit and vegetables in raised beds and containers, minarette fruit trees underplanted with wild flowers.

81 ◆ RIVERHILL HIMALAYAN GARDENS
Riverhill, Sevenoaks TN15 0RR. The Rogers Family, 01732 459777, www.riverhillgardens.co.uk. *2m S of Sevenoaks on A225. Leave A21 at A225 & follow signs for Riverhill Himalayan Gardens*. **Adm £7.50, chd £5.25. For NGS: Wed 23 Apr, Tue 13 May (10.30-5). For other opening times and information, please phone or see garden website.**
Beautiful hillside garden, privately owned by the Rogers family since 1840. Extensive views across the Weald of Kent. Spectacular rhododendrons, azaleas and fine specimen trees. Bluebell and natural woodland walks. Walled Garden has extensive new planting, terracing and water feature. Children's adventure playground, den-building trail, hedge maze and 'Yeti Spotting'. Cafe open all day serving freshly ground coffee, speciality teas, light lunches and homemade cream teas and cakes. Wheelchair access only to Walled Garden, free access to cafe, shop and tea terrace.

82 ROCK FARM
Gibbs Hill, Nettlestead ME18 5HT. Mrs S E Corfe, 01622 812244. *6m SW of Maidstone. Turn S off A26 onto B2015, then 1m S of Wateringbury turn R up Gibbs Hill*. **Adm £4, chd free (share to Nettlestead Church). Wed 25, Sat 28 June (11-6). Visitors also welcome by appt.**
2-acre garden set around old Kentish farmhouse (not open) in beautiful setting; created with emphasis on all-yr interest and ease of maintenance. Plantsman's collection of shrubs, trees and perennials for alkaline soil; extensive herbaceous border, vegetable area, bog garden and plantings around two large natural ponds.

83 ROSE FARM STUDIO
Rose Farm Road, Pluckley, Ashford TN27 0RG. Mel & Lizzi Smith. *4m W of Ashford. 1m S of Pluckley village, turn off Smarden rd into Rose Farm Rd*. Cream teas. **Adm £4, chd free. Sat 2, Sun 3 Aug (12.30-6.30).**
An artist's garden within the grounds of our home and studio, completely organic, built using reclaimed materials. Incl many potted plants, roof meadow, wild flower meadow surrounding the fire pit, raised vegetable beds, herbaceous beds, greenhouses and a pebble-dashed Morris Minor! Featured in Gardens Illustrated.

84 ◆ THE SECRET GARDENS OF SANDWICH AT THE SALUTATION
Knightrider Street, Sandwich CT13 9EW. Mr & Mrs Dominic Parker, 01304 619919, www.the-secretgardens.co.uk. *In the heart of Sandwich. Turn L at Bell Hotel & into Quayside car park. Entrance in far R-hand corner of car park*. **Adm £6.50, chd £3. For NGS: Wed 19 Mar (10-4); Thur 26 June (10-5); Mon 6 Oct (10-4). For other opening times and information, please phone or see garden website.**
3½ acres of ornamental and formal gardens designed by Sir Edwin Lutyens and Gertrude Jekyll in 1911 surrounding Grade I listed house. Designated historic park and garden, lake. White, yellow, spring, woodland, rose, kitchen, vegetable and herbaceous gardens. Designed to provide yr-round changing colour. Unusual plants for sale. Tea Rooms open offering cream teas and light lunches. Gardens, tearoom and shop are wheelchair friendly.

85 SANDOWN

Plain Road, Smeeth, nr Ashford TN25 6QX. Malcolm & Pamela Woodcock, 01303 813478, pmw@woodcock.mail1.co.uk. *4m SE of Ashford. Exit M20 at J10 onto A20 take the 3rd L at Smeeth xrds. At Woolpack PH turn R, past garage on L, past next L, garden on L. Park in lay-by on R up hill.* Cream teas. **Adm £3. Sun 25, Mon 26 May, Sat 7, Sun 8, Sat 21, Sun 22 June, Sat 12, Sun 13, Sat 26, Sun 27 July, Sat 9, Sun 10, Sat 30, Sun 31 Aug, Sat 6, Sun 7 Sept (1-5). Visitors also welcome by appt May to Sept 20 max.**

Our small and compact Japanese-style garden and Koi pond has a Japanese arbour, tea house/veranda, waterfall and stream. Acers, bamboos, ilex crenata, ginkgo, gunnera magellanica, fatsia japonica, equisetum, ferns, akebia quinatas, clerodendrum trichotomum, pinus mugos, wisterias, hostas, daturas, agapanthus and 'mind your own business' for ground cover. WC available. Regret no children owing to deep pond. Mentioned on Radio Kent.

86 ◆ SCOTNEY CASTLE

Lamberhurst TN3 8JN. National Trust, 01892 893819, www.nationaltrust.org.uk. *6m SE of Tunbridge Wells. On A21 London-Hastings, brown tourist signs. Bus: (Mon to Sat) Tunbridge Wells-Wadhurst, alight Lamberhurst Green.* **Adm £8.20, chd £4.10. For NGS: Thur 22 May (10-5). For other opening times and information, please phone or see garden website.**

Scotney Castle's garden has seen many changes since the 1920s when it first opened as part of the NGS open days. You could say it has been a true survivor - from bombs in WW2 to the great storm of 1987 which brought down over 90 substantial trees. Its doors however are still proudly open and the full glory of this romantic setting still encapsulates the original picturesque inspiration. March is all about atmosphere, with low mists across the moat and the first signs of spring to come. With over 20 acres of garden to explore it is a great time to get back out into the garden after the winter. Wheelchairs available for loan.

87 SEA CLOSE

Cannongate Road, Hythe CT21 5PX. Major & Mrs R H Blizard, 01303 266093. *1/2 m from Hythe. Towards Folkestone (A259), on L, signed.* **Adm £3, chd free (share to Royal Signals). Visitors welcome by appt Apr to Oct (between 10-5 only).**

With sea views, a 1-acre garden on steep hill allows growing of tender plants and shrubs collected by Old Knowledgeable Plantsman with his supportive wife. The unusual plants still flourish and visitors are very welcome. Indigofera; Crinodendron pategue, Banksia rose; Diarama; Eucryphia; Hibiscus; Campsis; Clerodendron bungei and fargesii; Hedychium (ginger); Fascicularia.

88 ◆ SISSINGHURST CASTLE

Sissinghurst TN17 2AB. National Trust, 01580 710700, www.nationaltrust.org.uk. *On A262 1m E of Sissinghurst. Bus: Arriva Maidstone-Hastings, alight Sissinghurst 1 1/4 m. Approx 30 mins walk from village.* **Adm £12.40, chd £6. For NGS: Sun 11 May (6am-10.30am); Mon 15 Sept (11-4.30). For other opening times and information, please phone or see garden website.**

Garden created by Vita Sackville-West and Sir Harold Nicolson. Spring garden, herb garden, cottage garden, white garden, rose garden. Tudor building and tower, partly open to public. Moat. Vegetable garden and estate walks. On Sunday 11 May for NGS visitors only, a very special and first ever opportunity to visit this world famous garden in the beauty of dawn light. The Head gardener (Troy Scott Smith) will be present to answer questions. Breakfast available from 6.45am. Free welcome talks and estate walks leaflets. Cafe. Some areas unsuitable for wheelchair access due to narrow paths and steps.

89 SMITHS HALL

Lower Road, West Farleigh ME15 0PE. Mr S Norman, www.smithshall.com. *3m W of Maidstone. A26 towards Tonbridge, turn L into Teston Lane B2163. At T-junction turn R onto Lower Rd B2010. Opp Tickled Trout PH.* Home-made cakes and quiche. **Adm £4.50, chd free (share to Dandelion Time). Sun 1 June, Sun 6 July (11-5).**

Delightful 3-acre gardens surrounding a beautiful 1719 Queen Anne House (not open). Lose yourself in numerous themed rooms: sunken water garden, iris beds, scented old fashioned rose walk, formal rose garden, intense wild flowers, peonies, deep herbaceous borders and specimen trees. Walk, 9 acres of park and woodland with great variety of young native and American trees and fine views of the Medway valley. Gravel paths.

90 SOUTH HILL FARM

Tamley Lane, Hastingleigh, Ashford TN25 5HL. Sir Charles Jessel, 01233 750325, sircjj@btinternet.com. *4 1/2 m E of Ashford. Turn off A28 to Wye, through village & ascend Wye Downs. 2m turn R at Xrds, Brabourne & South Hill, then 1st L. From Stone St (B2068) turn W opp Stelling Minnis, follow signs to Hastingleigh. Continue towards Wye, turn L at Xrds marked Brabourne & South Hill, then 1st L.* Tea, coffee and homemade biscuits. **Adm £4.50, chd free. Groups welcome by appt Sun 15 June to Tue 1 July. Refreshments available on request.**

2 acres high up on N Downs, C17/18 house (not open). Old walls, ha-ha, formal water garden; old and new roses, unusual shrubs, perennials and coloured foliage plants.

91 SPRING PLATT

Boyton Court Road, Sutton Valence, Maidstone ME17 3BY. Mr & Mrs John Millen, 01622 843383, carolyn.millen@virginmedia.com, www.kentsnowdrops.com. *5m SE of Maidstone. From Sutton Valence follow yellow NGS signs. Limited parking but large groups by coach welcome.* Light refreshments. **Adm £4, chd free.** Sat 8, Sun 9 Feb (11-3) Sat 7, Sun 8 Feb 2015. **Visitors also welcome by appt Feb only.**

1-acre garden under continual development with panoramic views of the Weald. Over 350 varieties of snowdrop grown in tiered display beds with spring flowers in borders. An extensive collection of alpine plants in rockeries and a large greenhouse. Vegetable garden.

92 ST CLERE

Kemsing, Sevenoaks TN15 6NL. Mr & Mrs Simon & Eliza Ecclestone, www.stclere.com. *6m NE of Sevenoaks. 1m E of Seal on A25, turn L signed Heaverham. In Heaverham turn R signed Wrotham. In 75yds straight ahead marked private rd; 1st L to house.* Home-made teas in the Garden Room. **Adm £5, chd £1.** Sun 15 June (2-5).

4-acre garden, full of interest. Formal terraces surrounding C17 mansion (not open), with beautiful views of the Kent countryside. Herbaceous and shrub borders, productive kitchen and herb gardens, lawns and rare trees. Garden tours with Head Gardener at 2.30 & 3.45 (£1 per head). Some gravel paths and small steps.

GROUP OPENING

93 ST MICHAEL'S GARDENS

Roydon Hall Road, East Peckham TN12 5NH. *5m NE of Tonbridge, 5m SW of Maidstone. Turn off A228 between Mereworth & Paddock Wood into Roydon Hall Rd. Gardens ½ m up hill on L.* Home-made teas. **Combined adm £5, chd free (share to Friends of St Michael's Church, Roydon).** Sun 27 Apr, Sun 1 June (2-5).

ST MICHAEL'S COTTAGE
Mr Peter & Mrs Pauline Fox

ST MICHAEL'S HOUSE
The Magan family

A Victorian house and cottage garden come together to provide colour, scent and inspiration in April and June in this rural village. The year unfolds at the grey stone old vicarage with a lovely display of tulips in spring, followed by irises, then a mass of roses from red hot to old soft colours, all complemented by yew topiary hedges and wonderful views from the meadow. The traditional cottage garden, with a wildlife area, was designed so it cannot be seen all at once. Explore and enjoy the collection of lavenders, hostas, clematis, ferns, heathers and heucheras. Southdown sheep and lambs, chickens. Carp lake. Limited wheelchair access to St Michael's Cottage.

Unusual plants still flourish and visitors are very welcome . . .

94 STONEWALL PARK

Chiddingstone Hoath, nr Edenbridge TN8 7DG. The Fleming Family. *4m SE of Edenbridge,. via B2026. Halfway between Markbeech & Penshurst.* Home-made teas in Conservatory. **Adm £5, chd free (share to Sarah Matheson Trust & St Mary's Church).** Sun 23 Mar (2-5); Sun 11 May (1.30-5).

Romantic woodland garden in historic setting featuring species rhododendrons, magnolias, azaleas, bluebells, a range of interesting trees and shrubs, wandering paths and lakes. Historic parkland with cricket ground, Although undergoing changes, there is a Victorian walled garden with herbaceous borders and vegetable garden backed by 100 yr-old espalier pear trees. Sea of wild daffodils in March.

95 NEW SUTTON VALENCE SCHOOL

North Street, Sutton Valence, Maidstone ME17 3HL. Sutton Valence School, 01622 845271, knotth@svs.org.uk, www.svs.org.uk. *Approx 6m S of Maidstone on A274. M20, J8. Turn L A20, Lenham. 2nd r'about, B2163, Sutton Valence. Xrds A274, Sutton Valence. School on L after 1m.* Cream teas. **Adm £4, chd free.** Tue 1 July (11-3).

Sutton Valence School garden surrounds the main buildings with a mixture of formal and more naturalistic planting. The borders reflect the style of the older buildings, with the newer areas having a gravel garden and a Mediterranean border. There are steps and gradients to contend with as the gardens are built around a sloping site with several changes of level. A shorter tour can be taken comprising some of the highlights. Few areas are accessible by wheelchair. Tours by School gardeners.

96 43 THE RIDINGS

Whitstable CT5 3QE. David & Sylvie Sayers. *From r'about on A2990 at Chestfield, turn onto Chestfield Rd, 5th turning on L onto Polo Way which leads into The Ridings.* Home-made teas. **Adm £3.50, chd free.** Sun 20 July, Sun 7 Sept (1-5). **Also open Highlands, Sun 20 July (1-5).**

Delightful small garden brimming with interesting plants both in the front and behind the house. Many different areas. Dry gravel garden in front, raised beds with Alpines and bulbs and borders with many unusual perennials and shrubs.

97 TIMBERS

Dean Street, East Farleigh, nr Maidstone ME15 0HS. Mrs Sue Robinson, 01622 729568, suerobinson.timbers@gmail.com, www.timbersgardenkent.co.uk. *2m S of Maidstone. From Maidstone take B2010 to East Farleigh. After Tesco's on R follow Dean St for ½ m. Timbers on L behind 8ft beech hedge. Parking through gates.* Home-made teas. **Adm £4.50, chd free. Visitors welcome by appt Apr to July, evening openings. Refreshments available on request.**

5-acre garden, well stocked with unusual hardy plants, annuals and shrubs designed with flower arranger's eye. Formal areas comprising parterre, pergola, herbaceous, vegetables, fruit, lawns and mature specimen trees surrounded by 100 yr-old Kentish cobnut plat, wild flower meadows and woodland. Natural rock pool with waterfalls. Valley views. Plant list. Access for 54 seater coaches. Featured in Kent Life as finalist in Kent's Best Amateur Gardens. Most of garden is flat, some steep slopes to rear.

98 TORRY HILL

Frinsted/Milstead, Sittingbourne ME9 0SP. Lady Kingsdown, 01795 830258, lady.kingsdown@btinternet.com. *5m S of Sittingbourne. From M20 J8 take A20 (Lenham). At r'about by Ramada Inn turn L Hollingbourne (B2163). Turn R at X'rds at top of hill (Ringlestone Rd). Thereafter Frinsted-Doddington (not suitable for coaches), then Torry Hill/NGS signs. From M2 J5 take A249 towards Maidstone, then 1st L (Bredgar), L again (follow Bredgar signs), R at War Memorial (T-junction), 1st L (Milstead), Torry Hill/NGS signs from Milstead.* Home-made teas. **Adm £4, chd free (share to St Dunstans Church May/June, The Caldecott Association).** Sun 11 May, Sun 15 June, Sun 13 July (2-5). **Visitors also welcome by appt April - August (weekdays only). Tea, coffee and biscuits available.**

8 acres; large lawns, specimen trees, flowering cherries, rhododendrons, azaleas and naturalised daffodils; walled gardens with lawns, shrubs, herbaceous borders, rose garden incl shrub roses, wild flower areas and vegetables. Extensive views to Medway and Thames estuaries. Some shallow steps. No wheelchair access to rose garden but can be viewed from pathway. Please use entrance marked D on a red background for parking.

99 TOWNLAND

Sixfields, Tenterden TN30 6EX. Alan & Lindy Bates, 01580 764505, alanandlindybates@yahoo.co.uk. *From centre of Tenterden High St, turn into Jackson's Lane next to Webbs Ironmongers. Follow lane to end (400m). Townland at end on R.* Home-made teas. **Adm £4, chd free (share to Pilgrims Hospice 8 June, 20 July; and ShelterBox 13 July).** Sun 8 June, Suns 13, 20 July (2-5.30). **Visitors also welcome by appt June to July for groups of 6+, adm £5, please phone or email for bookings.**

A 1.8 acre family garden in a unique position. Landscaped features incl a rose garden, Mediterranean gravel garden and shrubbery. Wander around and discover the meadow areas, stunning mixed borders and herbaceous beds providing a riot of colours and textures, wide range of fruit and vegetables. Also wild flowers grown specially to attract bees. Featured in Kent Life.

Potmans Heath House

© Leigh Clapp

GROUP OPENING

100 NEW TOYS HILL GROUP

Scords Lane, Toys Hill, Westerham TN16 1QE. Mrs Jeremy Seddon. *4m from J5 of M25 & 8m from J6. In Brasted (on A25) turn into Chart Lane signed Toys Hill. Turn E at X'rds in Toys Hill into Scords Lane. Parking adjacent to Meadow House.* Home-made teas. **Combined adm £5.** Sun 18 May (1.30-5).

NEW THE MEADOW HOUSE
Mrs Jeremy Seddon

NEW OLD FARM COTTAGE
The Lady Nolan

NEW THE RUSHES
Mr & Mrs Howard Jarvis

Three gardens (a short walk apart) brimming with colourful acid loving plants, waterbirds and livestock, surrounded by farmland with truly exceptional panoramic views to the South, bordering 450 acres of NT woodland and a short distance from Emmetts NT garden.

101 TRAM HATCH

Charing Heath, Ashford TN27 0BN. Mrs P Scrivens, www.tramhatchgardens.co.uk. *10m NW of Ashford. A20 towards Charing Railway Stn on Pluckley Rd, over motorway then 1st L signed Barnfield to end, turn L carry on past Barnfield, Tram Hatch ahead.* Home-made teas. **Adm £5, chd free.** Sun 15 June, Sun 13 July, Sun 17 Aug (12.30-5.30).

Meander your way off the beaten track to a mature and extensive garden changing through the seasons. You will enjoy a garden laid out in rooms - what surprises are round the corner: large selection of trees (some unusual), vegetable, rose and gravel gardens, colourful containers. The Great River Stour and the Angel of the South enhance your visit. Please come and enjoy. The garden is totally flat, apart from a very small area which can be viewed from the lane.

Townland

© Leigh Clapp

Treat yourself to a plant from the plant stall

102 223 TUBBENDEN LANE

Orpington BR6 9NN. Jo & Disha Sehmi. *1m SW of Orpington. Off A21 into Tubbenden Lane. Turn 1st R into Beechcroft Rd, entrance is through garage between 1A & 3 Beechcroft Rd.* Home-made teas. **Adm £5, chd free.** Sun 8 June (2-5).
A small plantsman's garden with lots of interest created by exotic planting. The emphasis is on foliage provided by ferns, bamboos and hostas. These are set off by topiary, sculpture and water features.

103 UPPER PRYORS

Butterwell Hill, Cowden TN8 7HB. Mr & Mrs S G Smith. *4½ m SE of Edenbridge. From B2026 Edenbridge-Hartfield, turn R at Cowden Xrds & take 1st drive on R.* Home-made teas. **Adm £5, chd free.** Wed 18 June (12-6).
Ten acres of English country garden surrounding C16 house - a garden of many parts; colourful profusion, interesting planting arrangements, immaculate lawns, mature woodland, water and a terrace on which to appreciate the view, and tea!

104 NEW THE WATCH HOUSE

7, Thanet Road, Broadstairs CT10 1LF. Dan Cooper & Alex Dawson, www.frustratedgardener.com. *Off Broadstairs High St on narrow side rd. At Broadstairs station, continue along High St (A255) towards sea front. Turn L between Lloyds Bank & Estate Agent then immed turn R.* Light refreshments. **Adm £3, chd free.** Sat 2, Sun 3 Aug (12-4).
Adjoining an historic fishermen's cottage in the town centre, this tiny garden measures just 20ft x 30ft. Sheltered, and enjoying a unique microclimate, the garden is home to an array of exotic and unusual plants and trees. A constantly changing display of tender plants in containers demonstrates how yr-round interest can be achieved in the smallest of spaces. Within a few minutes walk of Viking Bay, The Dickens Museum and Bleak House.

105 WATERGATE HOUSE

King Street, Fordwich, Canterbury CT2 0DB. Fiona Cadwallader, www.cadwallader.co.uk. *2m E of Canterbury. From Canterbury A257 direction, Sandwich, 1m L to Fordwich. 1m L on Moat Lane, direct to Watergate House bottom of High St. Follow parking instructions.* Home-made teas. **Adm £4, chd free.** Sat 26 Apr, Sat 14 June (2-6).
Magical walled garden by the River Stour: defined areas of formal, spring, woodland, vegetable and secret garden reveal themselves in a naturally harmonious flow, each with its own colour combinations. Ancient walls provide the garden's basic structure, while a green oak pergola echoes a monastic cloister. Featured in Country Homes and Interiors and The English Garden. The garden is mainly on one level, but there is one raised walkway under the pergola.

D

The garden is home to an array of exotic and unusual plants and trees . . .

106 WEST COURT LODGE

Postling Court, The Street, Postling, nr Hythe CT21 4EX. Mr & Mrs John Pattrick, 01303 863285, malliet@hotmail.co.uk. *2m NW of Hythe. From M20 J11 turn S onto A20. Immed 1st L. After ½ m on bend take rd signed Lyminge. 1st L into Postling.* Cream teas in village hall. **Adm £3, chd free.** Sat 31 May, Sun 1 June (1-5). **Combined with Churchfield, combined adm £5.00, chd free. Visitors also welcome by appt Apr to Aug, max 20 visitors.**
S-facing 1-acre walled garden at the foot of the N Downs, designed in 2 parts: main lawn with large sunny borders and a romantic woodland glade planted with shadow loving plants and spring bulbs. Lovely C11 church will be open next to the gardens.

GROUP OPENING

107 WEST MALLING JUNE GARDENS

West Malling ME19 6LW. *On A20, nr J4 of M20. Park in West Malling for Little Went & Went House where maps, directions & combined tickets available for other gardens. No disabled parking at Little Went.* Home-made teas New Barns Cottages and 2 New Barns Oast only. **Combined adm £6, chd free (share to St Mary's Church, W Malling).** Sun 15 June (12-5).

LITTLE WENT
Anne Baring

NEW BARNS COTTAGES
Mr & Mrs Anthony Drake

2 NEW BARNS OAST
Nick Robinson & Becky Robinson Hugill

TOWN HILL COTTAGE
Mr & Mrs P Cosier

WENT HOUSE
Alan & Mary Gibbins

West Malling is an attractive small market town with some fine buildings. Enjoy five lovely gardens that are entirely different from each other and cannot be seen from the road. In the middle of the town, Little Went's long narrow secret garden has fish ponds, an aviary with love birds, conservatory, gravel garden and parterre, lavender garden and statues, as well as an exhibition of paintings. Went House is a Queen Anne house surrounded by a secret garden with a stream, specimen trees, old roses, mixed borders, attractive large kitchen garden, fountain and parterre. Approx ½m S of the town, New Barns Cottages, developed over 30yrs from a blank site, is a 2½ -acre garden and paddock surrounded by orchards and woodland. From the parking area, the garden is approached via a meadowed pathway leading to a romantic roomed garden explored via serpentine paths inviting surprise and discovery. 2 New Barns Oast is a child-friendly garden with interesting hard landscaping features and raised vegetable garden. Town Hill Cottage is a part walled garden with mature and interesting planting but difficult wheelchair access. All other gardens have good wheelchair access.

108 WICKHAM LODGE

The Quay, High Street, Aylesford ME20 7AY. Cherith & Richard Bourne, 01622 717267, wickhamlodge@aol.com, www.wickhamlodge.co.uk. *3m NW of Maidstone. Off High St on riverbank, turning into The Quay by Chequers PH. Park in village car park.* Light refreshments. **Adm £4.50, chd free (share to St Peter and St Paul Church Aylesford). Sat 21 June (11-5).**

There is a sense of romance, peace and tranquillity in these 14 small and varied inspirational gardens. Every corner of this walled and terraced ½ -acre plot has been used to create gardens that could be picked up and recreated anywhere. Journey from productive kitchen garden to formal Tudor, from Japanese to funky banana foliage. Endless surprises are here in abundance. Aylesford's Community Choir (Aylesford Village Voices) singing Garden and River songs. Genuine Cornish Pasties delivered from Chough Bakeries Padstow for people to take away. Selected by Alan Titchmarsh as the 'Inspirational Garden' for his new series of 'Love your Garden'. Selected by Sawday's for Country Living Magazine.

Endless surprises are here in abundance . . .

109 WOMENSWOLD GARDENS

Womenswold, Canterbury CT4 6HE. *6m S of Canterbury, midway between Canterbury & Dover. Take B2046 for Wingham at Barham Xover. Turn 1st R, following signs.* Home-made teas. **Adm £4, chd free. Sat 28, Sun 29 June (1-5.30).**

Several colourful and diverse gardens in a picturesque C18 hamlet, situated mostly around the C13 church. These incl an established traditional country garden with unusual and interesting plants incl many clematis, pergola and large pond; a cottage garden with a selection of climbing and shrub roses and a beehive; a 2-acre plantsman's garden with many unusual features; a large display of perennials inc kniphofias and hemerocalis; colourful garden with ponds and other interesting features; a traditional thatched cottage garden; a walled garden with countryside views. Produce stall; exhibition in Church.

110 ◆ THE WORLD GARDEN AT LULLINGSTONE CASTLE

Eynsford DA4 0JA. Guy Hart Dyke, 01322 862114, www.lullingstonecastle.co.uk. *1m from Eynsford. Over Ford Bridge in Eynsford Village. Follow signs to Roman Villa. Keep Roman Villa immed on R then follow Private Rd to Gatehouse.* **Adm £7, chd £4. For NGS: Sun 15 June (12-5). For other opening times and information, please phone or see garden website.**

Interactive world map of plants laid out as a map of the world within a walled garden. The oceans are your pathways as you navigate the world in 1 acre. You can see Ayers Rock and walk alongside the Andes whilst reading intrepid tales of plant hunters. Discover the origins of some 6,000 different plants - you'll be amazed where they come from! Plant nursery and Lullingstone World Garden seeds for sale. Refreshments. Wheelchairs available upon request.

NCH

111 WYCKHURST

Mill Road, Aldington, Ashford, Kent TN25 7AJ. Mr & Mrs Chris Older, 01233 720395, cdo@rmfarms.co.uk. *4m SE of Ashford. Leave M20 at J10 onto A20 travel E 2m to Aldington turning; turn R at Xrds; proceed 1½ m to Aldington village hall. Turn R & immed L by Walnut Tree Inn. Take rd down Forge Hill signed to Dymchurch, after ¼ m take 1st turn R into Mill Rd.* Home-made teas. **Adm £4, chd free. Sat 7, Sun 8, Sat 14, Sun 15 June (11-6). Visitors also welcome by appt June.**

C16 cottage (not open) nestles in romantic seclusion at the end of a drive. This enchanting garden is a mixture of small mixed herbaceous borders, roses and unusual topiary, plenty of seating to enjoy the garden and the extensive views across Romney Marsh towards the sea. Some gentle slopes, limited wheelchair access.

GROUP OPENING

112 WYE GARDENS

Wye TN25 5BJ. *3m NE of Ashford. From A28 take turning signed Wye. Bus: Ashford to Canterbury via Wye. Train: Wye. Collect map of gardens at the Church.* Home-made teas at Wye Church. **Combined adm £5, chd free. Sun 22 June (2-6).**

3 BRAMBLE CLOSE
Dr M Copland

CUMBERLAND COURT D
Mr & Mrs F Huntington

MISTRAL
Dr & Mrs G Chapman
01233 813011
geoff@chapman.invictanet.co.uk

NEW **SPRING GROVE FARM HOUSE**
Heather Van den Bergh

YEW TREES
Ian & Elizabeth Coulson

Start at the centre of this historic village to visit five unusual gardens. 3 Bramble Close is a unique experience, a very wild garden with meadow, pond and ditches, mown paths and hedges buzzing with wildlife. A water feature and unusual artefacts complement the exciting courtyard garden at Cumberland Court, once an asphalt car park now densely planted with a wide range of unusual plants, pots and recently added secret garden. 250 species of botanical interest (all labelled) flourish at Mistral, once part of an old tennis court, incl white and alpine gardens and centre stage, a mini outdoor theatre! New this year, Spring Grove Farm House a country garden full of colour and interest with stream, lily pond and gravel garden. Yew Trees is a traditional garden divided into 3 distinct, secluded areas with lawns, naturalised wildlife area, pond, mature trees, wide borders planted with shrubs, grasses and herbaceous perennials and enclosed potager. Wye Gardens opening coincides with Stour Music Festival and Wye Food Festival.

113 YEW TREE COTTAGE

Tonbridge TN11 8AD. Mrs Pam Tuppen, 01892 870689. *4m SW of Tonbridge. From A26 Tonbridge to Tunbridge Wells, join B2176 Bidborough to Penshurst rd. 2m W of Bidborough, 1m before Penshurst. Please phone if needing advice for directions. Unsuitable for coaches.* Light refreshments. **Adm £2.50, chd free. Sun 23, Wed 26 Feb, Wed 12, Sun 23 Mar, Wed 9, Sun 13, Wed 23, Sun 27 Apr, Sun 11, Wed 14, Sun 25, Wed 28 May, Sun 8, Wed 11, Sun 22, Wed 25 June, Wed 9, Sun 13, Wed 23, Sun 27 July, Sun 10, Wed 13, Sun 24, Wed 27 Aug, Wed 10, Sun 14 Sept (12-5).** Small, romantic, hillside cottage garden with steep entrance. Lots of seats and secret corners, many unusual plants - hellebores, spring bulbs, old roses, many special perennials. Small pond; something to see in all seasons. Created and maintained by owner, a natural garden full of plants. Garden filmed for Japanese TV.

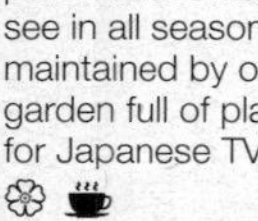

Hole Park

© Harpur GL

Kent County Volunteers

Joint County Organisers

Jacqueline Anthony, 44 Cambridge Street, Tunbridge Wells TN2 4SJ, 01892 518879, jacquelineanthony7@googlemail.com

Jane Streatfeild, The Bungalow, Hoath House, Chiddingstone Hoath, Edenbridge TN8 7DB, 01342 850362/07531 001277, jane@hoath-house.freeserve.co.uk

Acting County Treasurer

Nicholas Ward, Hookwood House, Shipbourne TN11 9RJ, 01732 810525, hookwood1@yahoo.co.uk

Radio

Jane Streatfeild (as above)

Advertising

Marylyn Bacon, Ramsden Farm, Stone-cum-Ebony, Tenterden TN30 7JB, 01797 270300, ngsbacon@ramsdenfarm.co.uk

Booklet distribution

Diana Morrish, Cacketts Farmhouse, Haymans Hill, Horsmonden, Tonbridge TN12 8BX, 01892 723905, diana.morrish@hotmail.co.uk

Assistant County Organisers

Marylyn Bacon (as above)

Clare Barham, Hole Park, Rolvenden, Cranbrook TN17 4JB, 01580 241386, clarebarham@holepark.com

Virginia Latham, Stowting Hill House, Ashford TN25 6BE, 01303 862881, lathamvj@gmail.com

Caroline Loder-Symonds, Denne Hill Farm, Womenswold, Canterbury CT4 6HD, 01227 831203, cloder_symonds@hotmail.co.uk

Susan Moir, Little Worge Barn, Willingford Lane, Brightling TN32 5HN, 01892 722223, moirconsultant@btinternet.com

Ingrid Morgan Hitchcock, 6 Brookhurst Gardens, Southborough, Tunbridge Wells TN4 0UA, 01892 528341, ingrid@morganhitchcock.co.uk

Diana Morrish (as above)

Julia Stanton, Mill House Farm, Waltham, Canterbury CT4 5SL, 01227 700421, familystanton@hotmail.com

Felicity Ward, Hookwood House, Shipbourne TN11 9RJ, 01732 810525, hookwood1@yahoo.co.uk

LANCASHIRE

Merseyside, Greater Manchester and Isle of Man

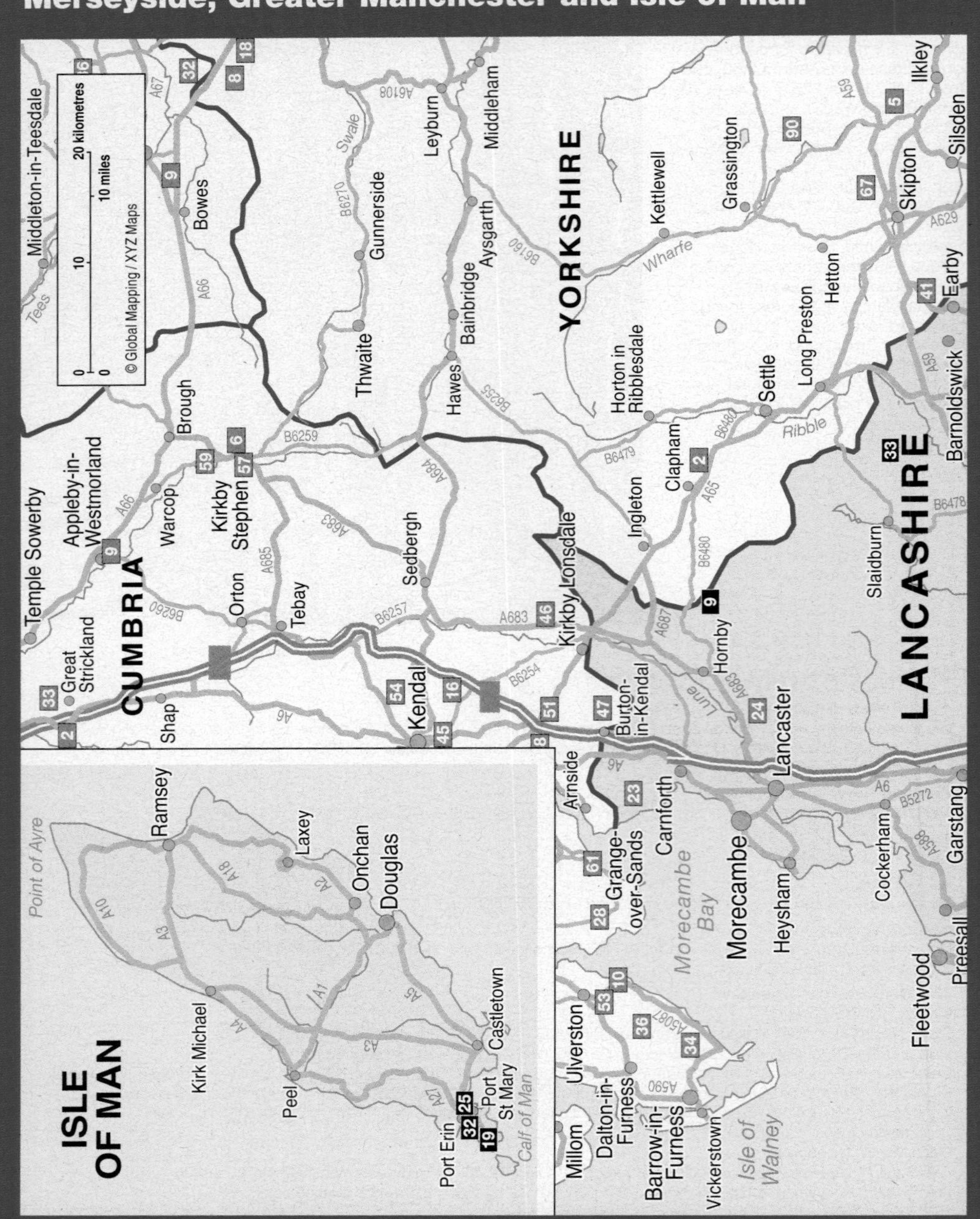

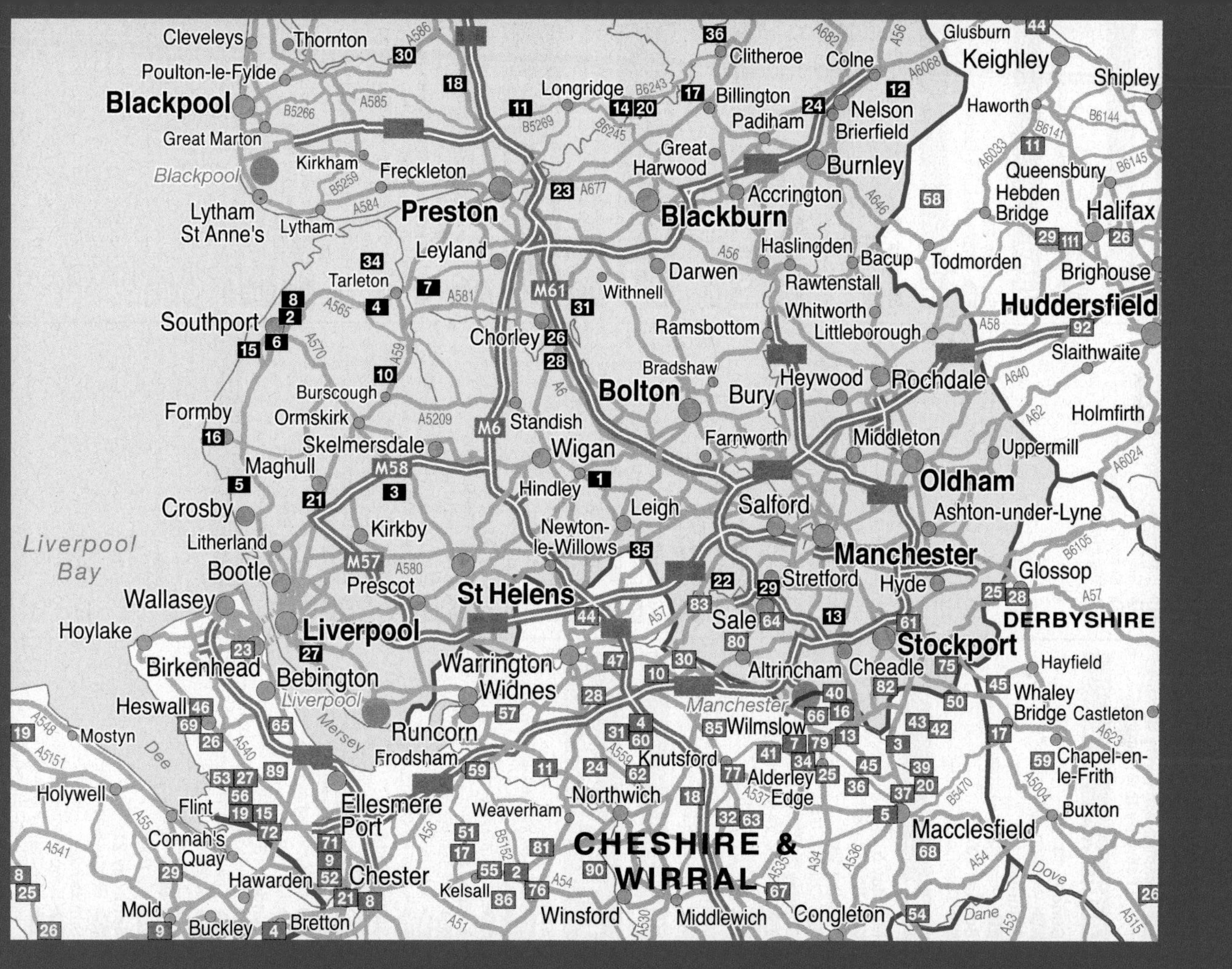

Cleveleys
Thornton
Poulton-le-Fylde
Blackpool
Great Marton
Kirkham
Freckleton
Lytham St Anne's
Lytham
Preston
Leyland
Tarleton
Southport
Burscough
Formby
Ormskirk
Skelmersdale
Maghull
Crosby
Litherland
Liverpool Bay
Bootle
Wallasey
Hoylake
Birkenhead
Liverpool
Bebington
Heswall
Mostyn
Holywell
Flint
Connah's Quay
Hawarden
Mold
Buckley
Bretton
Chester
Ellesmere Port
Frodsham
Runcorn
Widnes
Warrington
St Helens
Prescot
Kirkby
Newton-le-Willows
Hindley
Wigan
Standish
Chorley
Withnell
Bolton
Bradshaw
Farnworth
Leigh
Salford
Manchester
Stretford
Sale
Altrincham
Cheadle
Stockport
Hyde
Glossop
DERBYSHIRE
Hayfield
Whaley Bridge
Castleton
Chapel-en-le-Frith
Buxton
Macclesfield
Wilmslow
Alderley Edge
Knutsford
Northwich
Weaverham
Kelsall
Winsford
Middlewich
Congleton
CHESHIRE & WIRRAL
Longridge
Billington
Clitheroe
Colne
Nelson
Brierfield
Padiham
Great Harwood
Burnley
Accrington
Blackburn
Darwen
Haslingden
Rawtenstall
Bacup
Whitworth
Ramsbottom
Bury
Heywood
Rochdale
Littleborough
Middleton
Oldham
Ashton-under-Lyne
Uppermill
Holmfirth
Slaithwaite
Huddersfield
Brighouse
Halifax
Todmorden
Hebden Bridge
Queensbury
Haworth
Keighley
Glusburn
Shipley

Opening Dates

All entries subject to change. For latest information check www.ngs.org.uk

February & March

35 Weeping Ash (every Sunday 9 February to 2 March)

April

Sunday 13
35 Weeping Ash

Saturday 19
11 Dale House Gardens

Sunday 20
11 Dale House Gardens

May

Monday 5
26 The Ridges

Sunday 18
10 Crabtree Lane Gardens

Sunday 25
6 Birkdale Village Gardens
7 Bretherton Gardens
9 Clearbeck House

Monday 26
9 Clearbeck House

June

Festival Weekend

Saturday 7
6 Birkdale Village Gardens
23 Mill Barn
24 Montford Cottage

Sunday 8
6 Birkdale Village Gardens
23 Mill Barn
24 Montford Cottage

Saturday 14
2 NEW 15 Allerton Road
5 NEW Beechcroft
12 NEW Dent Hall
21 NEW Maghull Gardens
23 Mill Barn

Sunday 15
7 Bretherton Gardens
10 Crabtree Lane Gardens
12 NEW Dent Hall
13 Didsbury Village Gardens
21 NEW Maghull Gardens
23 Mill Barn

Saturday 21
3 Barrow Nook Gardens

Sunday 22
3 Barrow Nook Gardens
9 Clearbeck House
14 Dutton Hall

Saturday 28
11 Dale House Gardens
30 St Michael's Gardens

Sunday 29
1 NEW 40 Acreswood Avenue
9 Clearbeck House
11 Dale House Gardens
27 Sefton Park Gardens
30 St Michael's Gardens
34 Wedgwood

It uses planting to bring privacy to an overlooked space . . .

July

Saturday 5
17 Great Mitton Hall

Sunday 6
17 Great Mitton Hall

Saturday 12
29 Southlands

Sunday 13
16 Freshfield Gardens
25 NEW Primrose Lodge
29 Southlands
31 The Stones & Roses Garden

Saturday 19
8 4 Brocklebank Road
33 Varley Farm

Sunday 20
7 Bretherton Gardens
8 4 Brocklebank Road
22 Marlborough Road Allotments
33 Varley Farm

Saturday 26
4 NEW Becconsall
18 NEW Hallidays Farm
28 Silver Birches

Sunday 27
4 NEW Becconsall
28 Silver Birches

August

Sunday 3
6 Birkdale Village Gardens

Saturday 9
20 Lower Dutton Farm

Sunday 10
20 Lower Dutton Farm

Monday 25
26 The Ridges

September

Sunday 7
7 Bretherton Gardens

Isle of Man Gardens

May

Sunday 18
19 NEW Kentraugh House

June

Sunday 22
32 NEW Thie-ny-Chibbyr

July

Sunday 13
25 NEW Primrose Lodge

August

Sunday 24
25 NEW Primrose Lodge

February 2015

35 Weeping Ash (every Sunday)

Gardens open to the public

9 Clearbeck House
26 The Ridges

Also open by appointment

4 Becconsall
6 71 Dunbar Crescent, Birkdale Village Gardens
6 Maple Tree Cottage, Birkdale Village Gardens
6 14 Saxon Road, Birkdale Village Gardens
7 Hazel Cottage, Bretherton Gardens
7 Owl Barn, Bretherton Gardens
8 4 Brocklebank Road
10 Crabtree Lane Gardens
11 Dale House Gardens
13 3 The Drive, Didsbury Village Gardens
15 Foxbury
22 Marlborough Road Allotments
23 Mill Barn
25 Primrose Lodge
28 Silver Birches
29 Southlands
31 The Stones & Roses Garden
34 Wedgwood

The Gardens

1 NEW 40 ACRESWOOD AVENUE
Hindley Green, Wigan WN2 4NJ. Angie Barker, www.angiebarker.co.uk. *4m E of Wigan. Take A577 from Wigan to Manchester, L at Victoria Hotel, at T junction L for parking on Dray King car park. Walk back to T junction and take 1st L.* Home-made teas. **Adm £3.50, chd free. Sun 29 June (11-4).**
This small garden in the middle of a modern housing estate, has been created from scratch over the last 8 years. It uses planting to bring privacy to an overlooked space and has a mix of contemporary and cottage garden styles. It features a formal decked pond area and a small wildlife pond and manages to squeeze in a small vegetable garden.

2 NEW 15 ALLERTON ROAD
Southport PR9 9NJ. Peter & Liz Downham. *1 ¼ m N of Southport. From Liverpool take A565, Southport to Preston Rd. 1st turn R after r'about at Hesketh Park.* Home-made teas. **Adm £3, chd free (share to Queenscourt Hospice). Sat 14 June (1-5).**
Medium size suburban corner house garden. Selection of herbaceous beds and borders. Perennials and shrubs planned for year round effect. Hot bed with variety of grasses. Patio with small water feature, containers and raised beds. Small vegetable and fruit area. Wheelchair access limited to front garden.

GROUP OPENING

3 BARROW NOOK GARDENS
Bickerstaffe L39 0ET. *5m SW of Ormskirk. From M58 J3 Southport A570, L Stanley Gate T lights, Liverpool Rd 1st L Church Rd, then Hall Lane, approx 1m into Barrow Nook Lane.* Cream teas at Barrow Nook Farm. **Combined adm £4, chd free. Sat 21, Sun 22 June (1-5).**

BARROW NOOK FARM
Cynthia & Keith Moakes

18 BARROW NOOK LANE
Paul & Sheila Davies

Glynwood House, Bretherton Gardens

26 BARROW NOOK LANE
Gary Jones

Barrow Nook Gardens are 3 neighbouring gardens of very different styles within a short walking distance, set in rural surroundings. Barrow Nook Farm is a peaceful country garden planted in cottage garden style to attract birds, bees, butterflies and much more. The large wildlife pond is an attractive feature. Pergola leads to orchard with soft and stoned fruit. Home-made jams for sale. 18 Barrow Nook Lane is a small diverse garden with herbaceous borders, pergola, gravel paths, rockery, herbs, island beds, fruit trees and raised vegetable beds.
26 Barrow Nook Lane is a low maintenance garden for people with limited time and budget who appreciate outdoor living, dining and relaxing.

4 NEW BECCONSALL
Hunters Lane, Holmes,Tarleton, Preston PR4 6JL. John & Elizabeth Caunce, 07739 297 248, johnelizabeth.caunce@yahoo.co.uk. *11m S of Preston. From Preston, take A565 to Southport. After 3m at r'about turn back on yourself. Garden 1m on L. Parking in nearby field.* Tea. **Adm £3, chd free. Sat 26 (10.30-5.30); Sun 27 July (10.30-7.30). Visitors also welcome by appt May to Sept.**
1 acre sympathetically combining different areas lawn, rill, arboretum, herbaceous border, wild flower area and raised vegetable beds. Featured in Lancashire Magazine. Wheelchair access to most of the garden.

5 NEW BEECHCROFT
Thirlmere Road, Hightown, Liverpool L38 3RQ. Mr & Mrs M Williams. *9m N of Liverpool. On coast via A565 follow Hightown signs & keep L before railway. On R immed after Windermere Rd. Park before reaching house.* Home-made teas. **Adm £3.50, chd free. Sat 14 June (11.30-4.30).**
Garden recently created around new house. Front garden has shrubs bordering a slate garden with perennial planting around 2 sunken trees. The main garden has a background of mature trees, a large pergola under-planted with azaleas, rhododendrons, acers, tree ferns and paved water feature. Beautiful lawn bordered by herbaceous and shrub beds. Patio has oval fish pond.

The Ridges

GROUP OPENING

6 BIRKDALE VILLAGE GARDENS
Birkdale, Southport PR8 2AX. *1m S of Southport. Off A565 Southport to Liverpool rd. 4th on L after r'about, opp St James Church. Maps available at each location.* Home-made teas at Saxon Rd, bacon sandwiches at Maple Tree Cottage May & Aug, at Meadow Ave June. **Combined adm £4.50, chd free (share to Riding for the Disabled). Sun 25 May; Sat 7, Sun 8 June; Sun 3 Aug (11-5).**

71 DUNBAR CRESCENT
PR8 3AA. Mrs Kimberley Gittins.
Open 7 & 8 June. S along A565 from town centre, over railway bridge at Hillside. Dunbar Crescent is 3rd rd on L
Visitors also welcome by appt May to July, refreshments on request for group bookings.
01704 579325
kgo611@ymail.com

MAPLE TREE COTTAGE
22 Hartley Crescent. PR8 4SG. Sandra & Keith Birks.
Open 25 May, 3 August. ½ m from village, S along Liverpool Rd, turn R into Richmond Rd, 1st R Hartley Rd, then 1st R Hartley Crescent
Visitors also welcome by appt May to Aug groups of 10+.
01704 567182
sandie.b@talktalk.net

10 MEADOW AVENUE
PR8 5HF. John & Jenny Smith.
Open 25 May, 7 & 8 June. S on A5267 through Birkdale Village, L at T-lights, continue past 1 zebra Xing, just before next turn R into Warwick St, then 2nd L

14 SAXON ROAD
Margaret & Geoff Fletcher.
Open all 4 dates
Visitors also welcome by appt May to Aug, for groups of 10+.
01704 567742
geoffwfletcher@hotmail.co.uk

An established group of gardens encircling the attractive, bustling Victorian village of Birkdale, some within easy walking distance, others reached by a short car journey. 1 garden opening on all 4 dates, others less, please see below for details.Gardens feature a ½ -acre inspirational cottage garden, a quirky large family garden full of reclaimed materials and surprises, a walled garden with an array of tender plants amongst informal island beds and a developing family garden with pond, mini orchard, reclaimed materials and lots of good ideas. Refreshments available 2 gardens.

GROUP OPENING

7 BRETHERTON GARDENS
North Road, Bretherton, nr Leyland PR26 9AY. *8m SW of Preston. Between Southport & Preston, from A59, take B5247 towards Chorley for 1m. Gardens off North Rd (B5248) & South Rd (B5247).* Home-made teas at Bretherton Congregational Church. **Combined adm £5, chd free (share to St Catherine's Hospice). Suns 25 May; 15 June; 20 July; 7 Sept (12-5).**

GLYNWOOD HOUSE
Eyes Lane, PR26 9AS.
Terry & Sue Riding

HAZEL COTTAGE
PR26 9AN. John & Kris Jolley
Visitors also welcome by appt.
01772 600896
jolley@johnjolley.plus.com

◆ HAZELWOOD
North Road, PR26 9AY.
Jacqueline Iddon & Thompson Dagnall
For other opening times and information, please phone or see garden website.
01772 601433
www.jacquelineiddonhardyplants.co.uk

OWL BARN
PR26 9AD. Richard & Barbara Farbon.
From Croston, after Rampers Shetland Ponies ignore your SAT NAV. After a double bend Owl Barn can be seen behind the modern bungalow on R
Visitors also welcome by appt May to Aug, small groups only max 10.
01772 600750
farbonb@btinternet.com

PEAR TREE COTTAGE

Eyes Lane, PR26 9AS. John & Gwenifer Jackson.
In Bretherton turn into Eyes Lane at the War Memorial

Five contrasting gardens spaced across 2m in an attractive village with conservation area. Glynwood House has $\frac{3}{4}$ -acre mixed borders, pond with drystone-wall water feature, woodland walk, patio garden with pergola and raised beds, all in a peaceful location with spectacular open aspects. Pear Tree Cottage garden blends seamlessly into its rural setting with informal displays of ornamental and edible crops, water and mature trees, against a backdrop of open views to the West Pennine Moors. Owl Barn has a model kitchen garden and harmonious formal borders with exuberant planting to complement an historic C18 listed building (not open). Hazelwood Garden, Nursery and Sculpture Gallery cover $1\frac{1}{2}$ acres of mature orchard, with a wide range of habitats showing the finest plants for every situation, from moist shade to well-drained sun, including new beach area for 2014. Hazel Cottage garden has evolved from a Victorian subsistence plot to encompass a series of themed spaces packed with plants to engage the senses and the mind. Sculpture demonstration 2pm at Hazelwood, live music at Hazelwood and Glynwood. Home-made preserves for sale at Pear Tree Cottage. Hazel Cottage featured in Garden News.

8 4 BROCKLEBANK ROAD

Southport PR9 9LP. Alan & Heather Sidebotham, 01704 543389, alansidebotham@yahoo.co.uk. *$1\frac{1}{4}$ m N of Southport. Off A565 Southport to Preston Rd, opp North entrance to Hesketh Park.* Home-made teas. **Adm £3, chd free. Sat 19, Sun 20 July (11-5). Visitors also welcome by appt May to Aug, groups of 8+.**

A walled garden incorporating a church folly. Landscaped with reclaimed materials from historic sites in the Southport area. There are several water features, an extensive herbaceous border and various areas of differing planting, thus creating a garden with much interest. Featured in Lancashire Life and Amateur Gardening.

9 ◆ CLEARBECK HOUSE

Mewith Lane, Higher Tatham via Lancaster LA2 8PJ. Peter & Bronwen Osborne, 01524 261029, www.clearbeckgarden.org.uk. *13m NE of Lancaster. Signed from Wray (M6 J34, A683, B6480) & Low Bentham.* Light refreshments. **Adm £3, chd free. For NGS: Sun 25, Mon 26 May; Suns 22, 29 June (11-5). For other opening times and information, please phone or see garden website.**

'A surprise round every corner' is the most common response as visitors encounter fountains, streams, ponds, sculptures, boathouses and follies: Rapunzel's tower, temple, turf maze, giant fish made of CDs, walk-through pyramid. 2-acre wildlife lake attracts many species of insects and birds. Planting incl herbaceous borders, grasses, bog plants and many roses. Vegetable and fruit garden. Painting studio open. Children- friendly incl quiz. Artists and photographers welcome by arrangement. New features incl a silver rill for the 25th year of opening. Many grass paths, some sloped. Tramper disability electric chair available by prior arrangement.

GROUP OPENING

10 CRABTREE LANE GARDENS

Burscough L40 0RW, 01704 893713, peter.curl@btinternet.com, www.youtube.com/watch?v=TqpxW7_8HT4. *3m NE of Ormskirk. A59 Preston - Liverpool Rd. From N before bridge R into Redcat Lane signed Martin Mere. From S over 2nd bridge L into Redcat Lane after $\frac{3}{4}$ m L into Crabtree Lane.* Home-made teas at no.79. **Combined adm £3.50, chd free. Sun 18 May, Sun 15 June (11-4). Visitors also welcome by appt May to July.**

79 CRABTREE LANE
Burscough. Sandra & Peter Curl

81 CRABTREE LANE
Prue & Barry Cooper

2 very diverse gardens looked after by avid plants persons 79 Crabtree Lane is a $\frac{3}{4}$ -acre garden that over recent yrs has been changed and replanted but still has many established and contrasting hidden areas. Colour themed herbaceous beds. Rose garden recently replanted, fishpond surrounded by a large rockery and a koi pond with waterfall and shallow area for wildlife. Spring and woodland garden, pergola, alpine garden and late summer hot bed. Hosta and fern walk. A derelict, dry stone bothy and stone potting shed with a garden of unusual plants surrounded by stone walls. 81 Crabtree Lane has water features, old fashioned rockery, vine and rose covered pergola, trompe l'oeils. Central gazebo with climbers. Herbaceous plants. Arches with clematis and roses. Featured in Lancashire Home & Gardens. Wheelchair access at no. 79.

11 DALE HOUSE GARDENS

off Church Lane, Goosnargh, Preston PR3 2BE. Caroline & Tom Luke, 01772 862464, tomlukebudgerigars@hotmail.com. *$2\frac{1}{2}$ m E of Broughton. M6 J32 signed Garstang Broughton, T-lights R at Whittingham Lane, $2\frac{1}{2}$ m to Whittingham at r'about turn L at Church Lane garden between nos 17 & 19.* Home-made teas. **Adm £3.50, chd free (share to Goosnargh Scout Group). Sats, Suns 19, 20 Apr; 28, 29 June (10-4). Visitors also welcome by appt Apr to Oct.**

$\frac{1}{2}$ -acre tastefully landscaped gardens comprising of limestone rockeries, well stocked herbaceous borders, raised alpine beds, well stocked koi pond, lawn areas, greenhouse and polytunnel, patio areas, specialising in alpines rare shrubs and trees, large collection unusual bulbs. All year round interest. Large indoor budgerigar aviary. 300+ budgies to view. Gravel path, lawn areas.

12 NEW DENT HALL
Colne Road, Trawden, Colne BB8 8NX. Mr Chris Whitaker-Webb. *Turn L at end of M65. Follow A6068 for 2m, after 3rd r'about turn R down B6250. After 1½ m turn R, signed Carry Bridge. Parking on R 200yds in village 5 mins walk on public footpaths*. Home-made teas. **Adm £3.50, chd free (share to Pendleside Hospice). Sat 14, Sun 15 June (12-5).**
Country garden surrounding 400 year old grade II listed hall (not open). Garden reflects nature of house and surrounding countryside. Parterre, lawns, herbaceous borders, shrubbery, wildlife pond with bridge to seating area, hidden summerhouse in woodland area. Plentiful seating. Some uneven paths and gradients.

Wildlife pond with bridge to seating area, hidden summerhouse in woodland area . . .

GROUP OPENING

13 DIDSBURY VILLAGE GARDENS
Didsbury, South Manchester M20 3GZ. *5m S of Manchester. From M60 J5 follow signs to Northenden. Turn R at T-lights onto Barlow Moor Rd to Didsbury. From M56 follow A34 to Didsbury*. Home-made teas at Moor Cottage and 68 Brooklawn Drive. **Combined adm £6, chd free. Sun 15 June (12-5).**

68 BROOKLAWN DRIVE
Mrs Anne Britt. M20 3GZ.

23 CRANMER ROAD
Christine Clarke. M20 6AW. Off Wilmslow Rd, then Fog Lane

NEW 3 THE DRIVE
Peter & Sarah Clare. M20 6HZ
Off Fog Lane
Visitors also welcome by appt Mar to Oct. peter_clare@ntlworld.com

ESTHWAITE, 52 BARLOW MOOR ROAD
M20 2TR. Margaret & Derek Crowther.
500 metres W along B5127 from T-lights junction with B5093. House 400 metres on R. Park in Linden Rd

6 GRENFELL ROAD
M20 6TQ. Malcolm Allum

NEW 30 LIDGATE GROVE
M20 6TS. Mary Powell.
From Didsbury village take the rd by Oxfam into Grove Lane, which then becomes Lidgate Grove. Follow NGS sign into garden

MOOR COTTAGE
Grange Lane. William Godfrey. M20 6RW. Off Wilmslow Rd

NEW 2 PARKFIELD ROAD SOUTH
Conrad & Kate Jacobson. M20 6DA

NEW 38 WILLOUGHBY AVENUE
M20 6AS. Mr Simon Hickey.
Garden at closed end of cul-de-sac; some may prefer to park further up & walk a short distance

Didsbury is an attractive South Manchester suburb which retains its village atmosphere. There are interesting shops, cafes and restaurants, well worth a visit in themselves! This year we have nine gardens, three of which are new. One is a large family garden divided into several interesting areas including pretty courtyard and Jewel garden, another is an enchantingly planted shade garden with many rarities, whilst the third reflects the charm of the cottage garden ethos with rose covered pergola, old fashioned perennials and tranquil raised pool. Our smaller gardens demonstrate beautifully how suburban plots, with limited space, can be packed full of interesting features and a range of planting styles. Dogs allowed at some gardens. Wheelchair access to some gardens.

14 DUTTON HALL
Gallows Lane, Ribchester PR3 3XX. Mr & Mrs A H Penny, www.duttonhall.co.uk. *2m NE of Ribchester. Signed from B6243 & B6245*. Home-made teas. **Adm £4, chd free. Sun 22 June (1-5).**
Formal garden at front with backdrop of C17 house (not open). 2 acres at rear which incl large collection of old fashioned roses, water feature, wild orchid meadow and viewing platforms with extensive views over the Ribble Valley. Visitors requested to keep to mown paths in meadow areas. Also Orangery and collection of Pemberton roses. Due to being on a hillside, with many steps between different levels the garden is not easily accessible by wheelchair.

GROUP OPENING

16 FRESHFIELD GARDENS
Freshfield L37 1PB. *6m S of Southport. From A565 (Crosby to S'port rd) take B5424 to Formby. Cross mini r'about, turn R, then L down Victoria Rd. After 600 yds turn L. Park in Harington Rd*. Home-made teas. **Combined adm £4, chd free. Sun 13 July (10.30-4.30).**

37 BREWERY LANE
L37 7DY. Mr & Mrs P Thornton.
Off cont. of Green Lane

2 GORSE WAY
L37 1PB. Brenda & Ray Doldon.
Off Harington Rd, through Squirrel Green. (parking is much easier early in the day)

THE SQUIRRELS
67 Victoria Road, L37 1LN. Kathleen & Andrew Train.
Near corner with Harington Rd

6 WEST LANE
Formby, L37 7BA. Laurie & Sue Lissett.
Off cont. of Green Lane

WOODLANDS
46 Green Lane, L37 7BH. Ken & Rita Carlin.
From B5424 turn R at mini r'about

5 suburban gardens on sandy soil near to Formby sand dunes and NT nature reserve, home to the red squirrel. 2 Gorse Way is a S facing garden on several levels, featuring a sunken garden, pergola, and pond with beach area. The emphasis is on colour themed beds. The Squirrels is a plant collector's well-stocked garden, primarily to attract wildlife. Unusual tender plants in containers and interesting collection of cacti. 37 Brewery Lane. A compact garden with grasses, pergola, dry-stone wall and interesting conifers. 'Twenty shades of green' contrast with bright summer bedding and architectural plants. 6 West Lane is a child friendly garden with pergola and arches, mixed planting and rockery. Baskets and containers. Woodlands a leafy suburban, shady front garden with mature trees under preservation leading to oblong rear garden, with cottage style colourful borders, small pond and plenty of seating areas to relax and view. 37 Brewery Lane featured in Autumn Lancashire Life and 2 Gorse Way Lancashire Life.

An attractive South Manchester suburb which retains its village atmosphere . . .

17 GREAT MITTON HALL

Mitton Road, Mitton, nr Clitheroe BB7 9PQ. Jean & Ken Kay. *2m W of Whalley. Take Mitton Rd out of Whalley pass Mitton Hall on L, Aspinall Arms on R over bridge. Hall is on R next to Hillcrest tearooms.* Home-made teas. **Adm £3.50, chd free (share to Help for Heroes). Sat 5, Sun 6 July (1-5).**
Overlooked by C12 Allhallows Church, with stunning views to the river and Pendle Hill the terraced gardens with herbaceous borders, lawn, topiary and raised lily pond, sympathetically surround the medieval hall (not open). Stalls on village green at side of Hall.

18 NEW HALLIDAYS FARM

Moss Lane, Bilsborrow, Preston PR3 0RU. Lisa Walling. *4m S of Garstang. Leave M6 at J32. Follow signs for Garstang 4m, turn R onto St Michaels Rd, take your 1st R onto Moss Lane, 1st Farm on R.* Home-made teas. **Adm £3.50, chd free. Sat 26 July (10.30-4.30).**
A relatively new garden, designed as the golf garden consisting of 3 fairways and greens, wildlife pond with waterfall and a log water feature on the patio with a settee to sit on and relax and listen to the sound of trickling water. The garden is planted with lots of colour and planting combinations with shrubs perennials, bulbs climbers and roses. Raised bed vegetable patch.

19 NEW KENTRAUGH HOUSE

Kentraugh, Port St. Mary, Isle Of Man IM9 5NA. David & Gill Gawne. *2½ m S of Castletown on A5 coast road. Kentraugh is situated in the S of the Island about half way between Castletown & Port St Mary. Enter (east) lodge gates at junction Colby Rd.* Tea. **Adm £5, chd free. Sun 18 May (11-5).**
Large walled sunken garden laid to lawns and shrubs with mature specimen trees, orchard, vegetable garden, substantial greenhouse, Victorian orangery. Take a relaxing stroll through the woodland walk amongst the bluebells and in the gardens of historic Kentraugh. Partial wheelchair access to orangery and parts of the sunken garden.

20 LOWER DUTTON FARM

Gallows Lane, Ribchester PR3 3XX. Mr R Robinson. *1½ m NE of Ribchester. Leave M6 J31. Take A59 towards Clitheroe, turn L at T-lights towards Ribchester. Signed from B6243 & B6245. Ample car parking.* Tea and wine. **Adm £3.50, chd free. Sat 9, Sun 10 Aug (1-5).**
Traditional long Lancashire farmhouse and barn (not open), with 1½ acre garden. Formal gardens nr house with mixed herbaceous beds, wild flower beds and shrubs, sweeping lawns leading to wildlife area and established large pond and small woodland with mix of trees and plants. Ample parking on adjacent field. Lawns may be difficult in very wet weather.

GROUP OPENING

21 NEW MAGHULL GARDENS

Maghull, Liverpool L31 7DR. *7m N of Liverpool. End of M57/M58/A59 take A59 towards O/skirk after 1½ m take next slip rd on L, L at bridge onto Liverpool Rd Sth, L Balmoral Rd, R Buckingham Rd.* Home-made teas. **Combined adm £3.50, chd free (share to Maghull Station Volunteers). Sat 14, Sun 15 June (1-5).**

NEW 136 BUCKINGHAM ROAD
L31 7DR. Debbie & Mark Jackson

NEW 46 BUCKINGHAM ROAD
L31 7DP. Mr & Mrs W A Rawlinson

NEW 294 LIVERPOOL ROAD SOUTH
L31 7DH. Eileen & Alan Pritchard

NEW MAGHULL STATION
Station Road, L31 3DE. Merseyrail.
Turn R at Town Hall over canal bridge. Follow signs to Maghull Station

NEW 43 SEFTON LANE
L31 8AE. Mr Norman Conway.
Cross mini r'about L next set T- lights into Sefton Lane

4 gardens and an award winning station offering different planting styles, 46 Buckingham Rd is a diverse ¼ acre garden, mainly herbaceous with mature trees. 136 Buckingham Road is planted with herbaceous and bedding to attract wildlife. 294 Liverpool Rd has a colourful display of bedding alongside herbaceous. 43 Sefton Lane is a semi tropical delight offering an array of unusual plants. All gardens are within walking distance or a few minutes drive. Refreshments at 3 gardens.

ALLOTMENTS

22 MARLBOROUGH ROAD ALLOTMENTS

Marlborough Road, Flixton, Manchester M41 5QP. Lesley Pye, 07879 715634, mraa.m415qp@gmail.com, https://sites.google.com/site/marlboroughroadallotmentsm41/. *2½ m SW of Urmston. J10 M60 go S through 2 r'abouts to T-lights turn R into Moorside Rd, Next r'about 2nd exit (Lymm) Take 5th rd on R (Irlam Rd) & 1st R (Marlborough Rd).* Cream teas. **Adm £3, chd free. Sun 20 July (1-5). Visitors also welcome by appt July to Sept, not Wednesdays.**

109 allotment plots over 4 acres containing a large variety of fruit and vegetables. A mini orchard plus 500yds of grassed walkways with colourful perennial and annual flower borders. Borough of Trafford award-winning allotments. Many areas to sit and relax with a wide range of plants, baskets, containers and other garden items for sale. Wheelchair access to most areas.

23 MILL BARN

Goosefoot Close, Samlesbury, Preston PR5 0SS. Chris Mortimer, 01254 853300, chris@millbarn.net. *6m E of Preston. From M6 J31 2½ m on A59/A677 B/burn. Turn S. Nabs Head Lane, then Goosefoot Lane.* Cream teas. **Adm £4, chd free. Sats, Suns 7, 8, 14, 15 June (1-5). Visitors also welcome by appt Apr to July, min Group Donation £40.**

Tranquil terraced garden along the banks of R Darwen. A garden on many levels, both physical and psychological. A sense of fun and mystique is present and an adventurous spirit may be needed to negotiate the various parts. Flowers, follies and sculptures engage the senses, moving up from the semi formal to the semi wild where nature is only just under control. A grotto dedicated to alchemy, a suspension bridge over the R Darwen 20 metres wide at this point, and a tower on the far bank above the 'Lorelei' rocks where a princess might wait for her lover. Partial wheelchair access, visitors have not been disappointed in the past.

24 MONTFORD COTTAGE

Cuckstool Lane, Fence-in-Pendle BB12 9NZ. Craig Bullock & Tony Morris, www.craigbullock.net. *4m N of Burnley. From J13 M65, take A6068, in 2m turn L onto B6248. Go down hill for ½ m. Garden on L, with parking further down hill on L.* Light refreshments. **Adm £3.50, chd free. Sat 7, Sun 8 June (11-5).**

In this last year of opening (30 years in the making, 21 years of opening), the garden takes its last chance to share its magic with you. Growing from a blank canvas, varying rooms have been created to imbue atmosphere. A plantsman's garden, an artist's garden but moreover a place to relax.

25 NEW PRIMROSE LODGE

Athol Park, Port Erin, Isle Of Man IM9 6ES. Caroline Couch, 01624 832266, carolinecouch@manx.net. *Centre of Port Erin village. From Castletown A5, R to Port Erin village. L into Droghadfayle Rd, cross railway lines then R into Athol Park. On L on junction with Sunnydale Ave.* **Adm £3, chd free. Suns 13 July; 24 Aug (11-4). Visitors also welcome by appt July to Aug.**

A delightful cottage garden packed with shrubs and perennials designed to give interest and colour all year round. In addition to the lawns and flower beds there are espalier fruit trees, a greenhouse and vegetable and fruit garden.

26 ◆ THE RIDGES

Weavers Brow (cont. of Cowling Rd), Limbrick, Chorley PR6 9EB. Mr & Mrs J M Barlow, 01257 279981, www.bedbreakfast-gardenvisits.com. *2m SE of Chorley town centre. From M6 J27, M61 J8. Follow signs for Chorley A6 then signs for Cowling & Rivington. Passing Morrison's up Brooke St, mini r'about 2nd exit.* Home-made teas. **Adm £4, chd free. For NGS: Mon 5 May, Mon 25 Aug (11-5). For other opening times and information, please phone or see garden website.**

3 acres, incl old walled orchard garden, cottage-style herbaceous borders, and perfumed rambling roses through the trees Arch leads to formal lawn, surrounded by natural woodland, shrub borders and trees with contrasting foliage. Woodland walks and dell. Natural looking stream, wildlife ponds. Walled water feature with Italian influence, and walled herb garden. Classical music played. Home made cakes, baked and served by ladies of St James Church, Chorley. Featured in Lancashire Telegraph garden supplement, Lancashire evening post colour supplement. Some gravel paths and woodland walks not accessible.

GROUP OPENING

27 SEFTON PARK GARDENS

Liverpool L8 3SL. *1m S of Liverpool city centre. From end of M62 take A5058 Queens Drive ring rd S through Allerton to Sefton Park Parking roadside in Sefton Park. Maps & tickets at all gardens.* Light refreshments. **Combined adm £5, chd free. Sun 29 June (12-5).**

NEW THE BLOOMIN' GREEN TRIANGLE
Wild Flower Meadow, Ducie Street, L8 2XA. Mrs Helen Hebden.
Ducie St runs between Granby St & Kingsley Rd, at the end of Princes Rd nr the Sunburst Gates in Liverpool 8. Guided tours 1pm and 3pm

PARKMOUNT
38 Ullet Road. Jeremy Nicholls. L17 3BP

SEFTON PARK ALLOTMENTS
Greenbank Drive. Sefton Park Allotments Society. L17 1AS *Next door to Sefton Park cricket club*

SEFTON VILLA
14 Sefton Drive.
Patricia Williams.
L8 3SD
0151 281 3687
seftonvilla@live.co.uk

Marlborough Road Allotments

VICE CHANCELLOR'S GARDEN
12 Sefton Park Road. University of Liverpool, Vice-Chancellor Sir Howard & Lady Sheila Newby.
L8 3SL.

YORK HOUSE GARDENS
Croxteth Drive. Jean Niblock & Arena Holmes.
L17 3AQ.

A varied group showing a range of city gardening, from the shrub roses of the 1-acre Vice-Chancellor's lodge garden. A new 'Alice in Wonderland' themed section of this large garden has been developed in time for this year's garden opening. The garden features a statue and pool of Alice's tears,. A trail around the garden will lead to important features related to Alice's adventures in Wonderland, her meetings with the White Rabbit, the Cheshire Cat and the Mad Hatter's Tea Party, all within a newly planted garden area, to the 6 acres of vegetables and flowers of the allotments. The Bloomin' Green Triangle in Toxteth is the latest addition, with a wild flower meadow on derelict land, and the beautified front gardens of boarded up houses. It started as Guerilla Gardening and it has taken off. An inspirational garden surrounds a tower block with herbaceous borders and colourful containers. Surprises and rare and unusual plants at Park Mount as well as Paddy Christian's special plants for sale and refreshments. The small walled garden at Sefton Villa is secluded and tranquil, with rare plants and an enclosed Japanese garden. Gardening advice from Ness Gardens experts and a string quartet at the vice-chancellor's lodge. Guided tours of The Bloomin' Green Triangle, Wild Flower Meadow awarded Outstanding Britain in Bloom, 1pm and 3pm. Wheelchair access at York House and Sefton Park Allotments. Limited access at the Vice-Chancellor's Lodge. Wheelchair access WC at the allotments.

28 SILVER BIRCHES

Rawlinson Lane, Heath Charnock, Chorley PR7 4DE. Margaret & John Hobbiss, 01257 480411. *2½ m S of Chorley. From the A6 turn into Wigan Lane (A5106). After 0.4m turn L into Rawlinson Lane. Silver Birches is 0.2m on L. Disabled parking only next to the house.* Home-made teas. **Adm £3, chd free (share to St George's Church, Chorley). Sat 26, Sun 27 July (1-5). Visitors also welcome by appt July to Aug.**

The garden has evolved from a family garden into one with a variety of features. There are herbaceous borders, sunken shaded dell, an African hut, lawns, 2 ponds, polytunnel, vegetable plot and orchard. The embankment of a disused railway has been turned into rockeries with a wood of native trees. There are paths for exploring which lead to the nearby Leeds-Liverpool canal. Wheelchair access is possible to many areas of the garden.

29 SOUTHLANDS

12 Sandy Lane, Stretford M32 9DA. Maureen Sawyer & Duncan Watmough, 0161 283 9425, moe@southlands12.com, www.southlands12.com. *3m S of Manchester. Sandy Lane (B5213) is situated off A5181 (A56) ¼ m from M60 J7.* Tea, cake-away (take a slice of your favourite cake home). **Adm £3.50, chd free. Sat 12, Sun 13 July (1-6). Visitors also welcome by appt June to Aug, guided tours for groups 10+.**

Artist's multi-award winning, inspirational s facing garden unfolding into a series of beautiful garden 'rooms' each with its own theme incl courtyard, Mediterranean, ornamental and woodland garden. Organic kitchen garden with large glasshouse containing vines and tomatoes. Extensive herbaceous borders, stunning containers of exotics, succulents and annuals, 2 ponds and water feature. Live jazz. Featured in Garden News magazine.

79 Crabtree Lane, Crabtree Lane Gardens

GROUP OPENING

30 ST MICHAEL'S GARDENS

Preston PR3 0UE. *9m N of Preston. Head N on the A6. Turn L onto the A586 for 2½ m into St Michael's Village*. Light refreshments at Catterall Farm. **Combined adm £5, chd free. Sat 28, Sun 29 June (10.30-4.30).**

1 ASH GROVE
PR3 0TP. Mrs Dawn Gerrard.
From St Michaels village, turn into Rawcliffe Rd, 1st turning on L, 2nd corner house on L

CATTERALLS FARM
Rawcliffe Road, PR3 0UE. Anika & Andy Gibbons.
Turn R onto Rawcliffe Rd 0.3m Catteralls Farm on R

THE CROFT
Garstang Road, PR3 0TE. Mr Bill Patterson.
The Croft is on R as you drive into the village

MALLARD COTTAGE
1a Post Office Row, Garstang Road, PR3 0TE. Ms Jeanette Martin.
Garden to rear of Post Office Row on A586 Garstang Rd. Pedestrian access only via driveway between terraced cottages & The Coach House

NEW 7 RAWCLIFFE ROAD
PR3 0UD. Mr & Mrs Tony & Karen Ball.
50 yds down Rawcliffe Rd

11 RAWCLIFFE ROAD
PR3 0UD. John & Christine Holmes.
Next Door to St Kilda's garden

ST. KILDA
Rawcliffe Road, PR3 0UD. Mrs Pat Kaylor.
Turn R on to Rawcliffe Rd & St Kilda is on the LH side 0.1m. No parking at the property

NEW 1 STONE COTTAGE
Blackpool Road, PR3 0UA. Mr & Mrs Christine & Graham Fleet.
From Garstang, over mini r'about, approx 100yds on L, a pair of Stone Cottages just before the village hall, where parking is available

St Michael's is a village on the R Wyre surrounded by farmland. North West In Bloom last year we were awarded a Gold. 8 open gardens. 1 Ash Grove has a pond, greenhouse and well planted borders. Catteralls Farm is a dairy farm with an range of planting and structures incl parterre, rill and archways, watched by Pygmy goats. The Croft is a mature garden in which a display of acers and ferns lead into a secret area. Mallard Cottage is a compact garden which boasts a variety of shrubs, plants and attractive planting of clipped Box. 11 Rawcliffe Road has a colourful display in well filled borders leading to a bespoke patio. St Kilda, a large cottage garden planted in different styles with a continuous tapestry of colours. 1 Stone Cottage is a mix of old and new and the planting complements the cottage. 7 Rawcliffe Road garden is an inspiration to the small gardener with trees and lots of perennials. Featured in the Lancashire Magazine. Disabled parking at Catteralls Farm.

31 THE STONES & ROSES GARDEN

White Coppice Farm, White Coppice, Chorley PR6 9DF. Raymond & Linda Smith, 01257 277633, stonesandroses@btinternet.com, www.stonesandroses.org. *3m NE of Chorley. J8 M61 (next to the Mormon Temple & Botany Bay) take A674 to Blackburn, 3rd R to Heapey & White Coppice. Parking up hill next to the garden*. Home-made teas. **Adm £3.50, chd free. Sun 13 July (10.30-4.30). Visitors also welcome by appt July, individuals may be added to groups 7-25 July.**

The garden where the cows used to

live set in the beautiful hamlet of White Coppice with wonderful views. Sunken rose garden, fountains, waterfalls, herbaceous borders, all with colour themed planting and formal kitchen garden. Fruit tree walk down to the Gentleman's Lodge with wild flower planting. Wonderful walking area with beautiful cricket field. Gravel paths ¾ of garden accessible by wheelchair and entrance into the house.

32 NEW THIE-NY-CHIBBYR
Surby Road, Surby, Port Erin, Isle Of Man IM9 6TA. Mike & Wendy Ingram. *1m from Port Erin. From Douglas, take A7 through Colby to Ballachurry. Turn R take B47 to Fleshwick. 1st R up hill, fork L, 2nd house on L.* Home-made teas. **Adm £3, chd free. Sun 22 June (12-5).**
Hillside cottage garden which has evolved from three long, narrow gardens. Small lawns, a variety of mixed colourful borders, patios and interesting nooks and crannies. Small pond, stone troughs and containers. Shrubs maintained to enjoy the superb views over the south of the Island. Gravel drive.

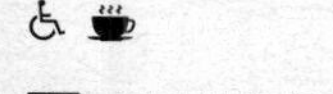

33 VARLEY FARM
Anna Lane, Forest Becks, Bolton-by-Bowland, Clitheroe BB7 4NZ. Mr & Mrs B Farmer. *7m N of Clitheroe. A59 off at Sawley follow Settle 2nd L after Copy Nook onto Settle Rd turn L at road sign on L. Follow lane 1m to a sharp R hand bend garden on L.* Home-made teas. **Adm £4, chd free. Sat 19, Sun 20 July (11-4.30).**
1½ -acre garden that's been developing from 2004. Varley Farm is 700ft above sea level with views across the Forest of Bowland and Pendle. Herbaceous lawned cottage garden, flagged herb garden and walled gravel garden, steps to orchard and organic kitchen garden. Stream and pond area planted in 2009 still maturing with a grassed walk through natural meadow and wild flower meadow.

Shrubs maintained to enjoy the superb views over the south of the Island . . .

34 WEDGWOOD
Shore Road, Hesketh Bank, Preston PR4 6XP. Denis & Susan Watson, 01772 816509, heskethbank@aol.com, www.wedgwoodgarden.com. *10m SW of Preston & 8m E of Southport. From Preston: A59. Turn R at Tarleton T-lights, Turn R onto Hesketh Lane for 2½ m onto Shore Rd. Garden 1.3 metres on L. Park on road.* Home-made teas. **Adm £3, chd free. Sun 29 June (11-5). Visitors also welcome by appt June to July, adm £5 incl light refreshments.**
1-acre country garden containing gravel garden with pots, formal pond, 2 lawns surrounded by extensive herbaceous borders in sun or shade, with mature trees, 50ft square glasshouse, 50ft x 30ft sheltered patio, leading to 90ft parterre with colour themed beds, archways, pergolas and rose covered gazebo, wild flower meadow, fruit trees. Listed in Lancashire Life's 10 glorious gardens in Lancashire. Wood chip paths in parterre.

35 WEEPING ASH
Bents Garden & Home, Warrington Road, Glazebury WA3 5NS. John Bent, www.bents.co.uk. *15m W of Manchester. Located next to Bents Garden & Home, just off the East Lancs Rd A580 at Greyhound r'about near Leigh. Follow brown 'Garden Centre' signs.* **Adm £3, chd free. Every Sun 9 Feb to 2 Mar; Sun 13 Apr (11-4); Suns Feb 2015.**
Created by retired nurseryman and photographer John Bent, Weeping Ash is a garden of all-yr interest with beautiful display of early snowdrops. Broad sweeps of colour lend elegance to this beautiful garden, which is currently undergoing an extensive re-design. Weeping Ash Garden is located immediately adjacent to Bents Garden & Home with its award winning Fresh Approach Restaurant and children's adventure play area. Featured in Warrington Guardian.

Lancashire, Merseyside, Greater Manchester and Isle of Man County Volunteers

County Organisers
Brenda Doldon, 2 Gorse Way, Formby, Merseyside L37 1PB, 01704 834253, doldon@btinternet.com
Margaret Fletcher, 14 Saxon Road, Birkdale, Southport, Merseyside PR8 2AX, 01704 567742, geoffwfletcher@hotmail.co.uk

County Treasurer
Geoff Fletcher, 14 Saxon Road, Birkdale, Southport, Merseyside PR8 2AX, 01704 567742, geoffwfletcher@hotmail.co.uk

Publicity
Christine Ruth, 15 Princes Park Mansions, Croxteth Road, Liverpool L8 3SA, 0151 727 4877, caruthchris@aol.com
Lynn Kelly, 48 Bedford Road, Birkdale PR8 4HJ, 01704 563740, lynn-kelly@hotmail.co.uk

Booklet coordinator
Brenda Doldon, 2 Gorse Way, Formby, Merseyside L37 1PB, 01704 834253, doldon@btinternet.com

Assistant County Organisers
Anne Britt, 68 Brooklawn Drive, Didsbury, Manchester M20 3GZ, 0161 445 8100, annebritt@btinternet.com
Ray Doldon, 2 Gorse Way, Formby, Merseyside L37 1PB, 01704 834253, doldon@btinternet.com

Isle of Man
Caroline Couch, Primrose Lodge, Athol Park, Isle of Man IM9 6ES, 01624 832266, carolinecouch@manx.net

LEICESTERSHIRE & RUTLAND

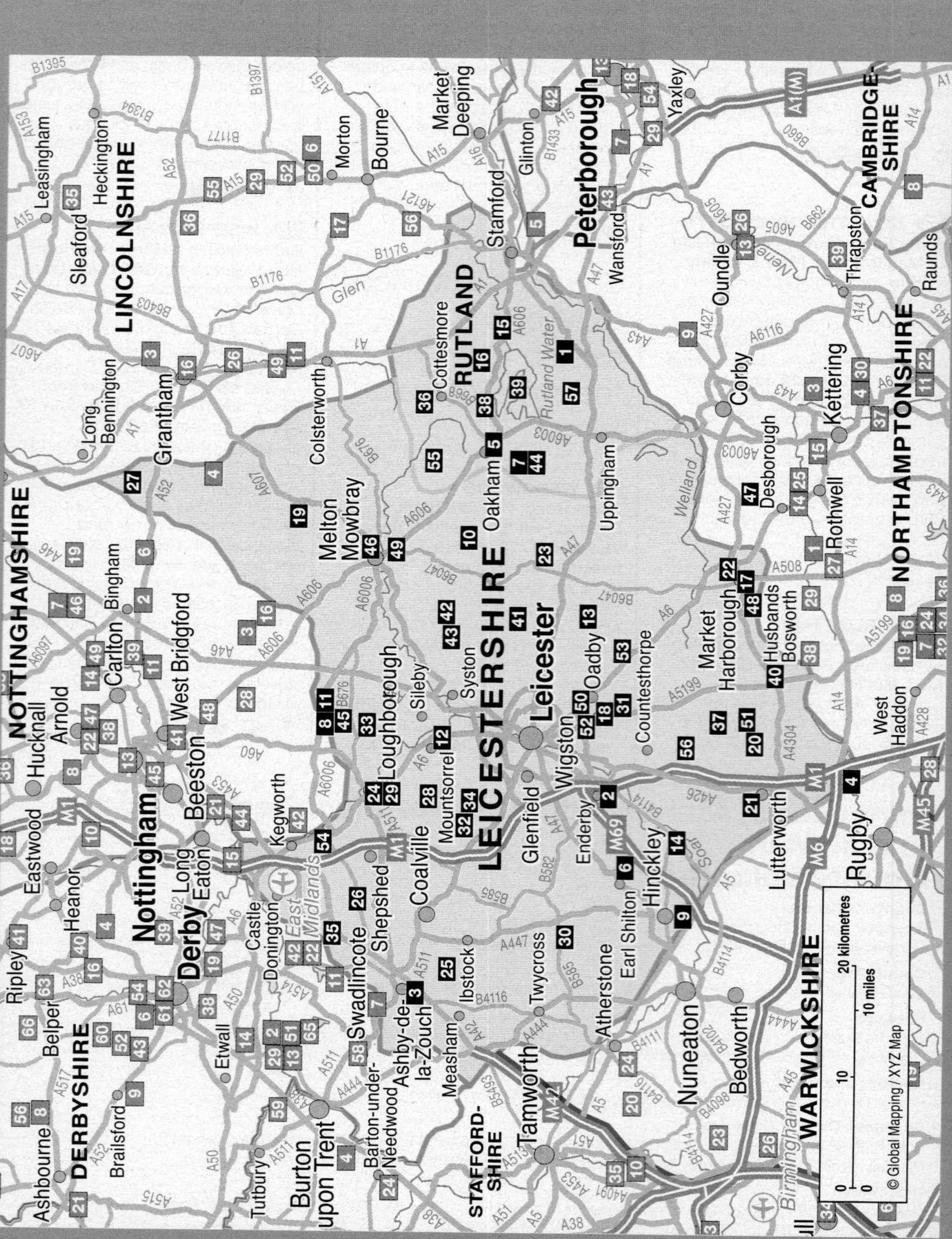

Opening Dates

All entries subject to change. For latest information check www.ngs.org.uk

February

Sunday 23
9 Burbage Gardens

March

Sunday 2
27 The Homestead
53 Westview

Sunday 23
22 Hammond Arboretum

April

28 Long Close (Open daily)

All organically managed to encourage wildlife . . .

May

28 Long Close (Open daily)

Sunday 4
5 Barleythorpe Gardens
23 Hedgehog Hall
49 Tresillian House

Monday 5
23 Hedgehog Hall

Sunday 11
7 NEW Braunston & Withcote Gardens

Sunday 18
2 NEW 12 Alexander Avenue
8 88 Brook Street
11 Cradock Cottage
36 The Old Hall
53 Westview

Tuesday 20
48 Thorpe Lubenham Hall

Saturday 24
19 Goadby Marwood Hall

Sunday 25
14 Dairy Cottage
31 Mill House
55 NEW Whissendine Gardens

Monday 26
34 NEW Newtown Linford Gardens

June

28 Long Close (Open daily)

Wednesday 4
47 Stoke Albany House

Festival Weekend

Saturday 7
24 134 Herrick Road
41 The Paddocks
54 Whatton Gardens

Sunday 8
29 NEW Loughborough Gardens
37 The Old Stables
38 The Old Vicarage, Burley
41 The Paddocks

Wednesday 11
47 Stoke Albany House

Saturday 14
18 28 Gladstone Street

Sunday 15
10 NEW Burrough Gardens
18 28 Gladstone Street
23 Hedgehog Hall

Wednesday 18
31 Mill House
47 Stoke Albany House

Thursday 19
29 NEW Loughborough Gardens (Evening)

Sunday 22
15 NEW Empingham Gardens
20 The Grange
33 NEW 14 New Lane
51 Walton Gardens

Wednesday 25
20 The Grange
47 Stoke Albany House
51 Walton Gardens

Saturday 28
6 Barracca

Sunday 29
6 Barracca
17 NEW 2 Fairway
25 Highfield House
39 NEW Orchard House

July

28 Long Close (Open daily)

Wednesday 2
47 Stoke Albany House

Sunday 6
14 Dairy Cottage
17 NEW 2 Fairway
32 Mountain Ash
49 Tresillian House
53 Westview
57 Wing Gardens

Wednesday 9
47 Stoke Albany House

Saturday 12
18 28 Gladstone Street

Sunday 13
1 Acre End
18 28 Gladstone Street
31 Mill House
32 Mountain Ash
37 The Old Stables

Wednesday 16
21 Green Wicket Farm

Sunday 20
16 NEW Exton Gardens
21 Green Wicket Farm
26 Hill Park Farm
56 Willoughby Gardens

Sunday 27
2 NEW 12 Alexander Avenue
30 Market Bosworth Gardens
46 NEW 119 Scalford Road

August

28 Long Close (Open daily)

Sunday 10
3 NEW Ashby-de-la-Zouch Gardens
40 Orchard House
50 University of Leicester Botanic Garden

Sunday 17
44 Quaintree Hall

Sunday 24
4 Avon House
26 Hill Park Farm
49 Tresillian House

September

28 Long Close (Open daily)

Sunday 7
52 NEW Washbrook Allotments
53 Westview

October

28 Long Close (Open daily until Monday 20)

Sunday 12
22 Hammond Arboretum

Sunday 26
49 Tresillian House

Gardens open to the public

54 Whatton Gardens

By appointment only

12 7 The Crescent
13 Cupplesfield
35 The Old Chapel
42 Parkside
43 Pine House
45 Ridgewold Farm

Also open by appointment

The Gardens

1 ACRE END

The Jetties, North Luffenham LE15 8JX. Jim & Mima Bolton, 01780 720906, mmkb@mac.com. *7m SE of Oakham. Via Manton & Edith Weston, 7m SW of Stamford via Ketton. 2m off A47 through Morcott village.* Light refreshments at North Luffenham Community Centre. **Adm £5, chd free.** Sun 13 July (11-5). **Visitors also welcome by appt June to Aug.**

1-acre garden, imaginatively designed, intensively planted, incl knot garden, oriental courtyard garden, mixed borders, circular lawn with island beds, herb and scented garden. Working fruit and vegetable garden, long herbaceous borders, woodland garden. Many unusual trees, shrubs, herbaceous perennials, tender exotics in containers. All organically managed to encourage wildlife. Paintings, cards, crafts. Wildlife wood carvings display. Challenging Quiz. GGG. Mainly grass paths and lawns, some gravel.

2 NEW 12 ALEXANDER AVENUE

Enderby, Leicester LE19 4NA. Mr & Mrs J Beeson. *4m S of Leicester. From M1 J21 take A5460 to Fosse Park, turn R on B4114. Turn R to Enderby at next r'about, straight on to church then follow yellow NGS signs.* Home-made teas. **Adm £2, chd free.** Sun 18 May, Sun 27 July (11-5).

We have creatively designed our small town garden to provide interest all yr-round. There is a wide variety of plants in the garden chosen for both colour and to attract wildlife. The garden has been carefully planned to make full use of the space available. The garden is mostly paved with some gravel areas.

GROUP OPENING

3 NEW ASHBY-DE-LA-ZOUCH GARDENS

Ashby-De-La-Zouch LE65 2FA. *10 mins walk from town centre. 1m from A42 J12. From end of High Street, bear L at mini r'about. Pass Royal Hotel, under railway bridge & follow yellow NGS signs.* Cream teas and home-made cakes. **Combined adm £3, chd free.** Sun 10 Aug (11-5).

NEW 27 AVENUE ROAD
Annie & Steve Mills

NEW 7 AVENUE ROAD
Mrs Jane Sheffield

NEW 72 TAMWORTH ROAD
Mike & Jane Plackett

Set in the historic market town in the heart of the national forest, three gardens in close walking distance are opening for the first time to NGS visitors. All set behind Victorian town-houses, are three very different approaches to similar spaces. **72 Tamworth Road** - A relatively new garden bordered by a wall and a hedge which we've tried to make seem less narrow with the use of circular lawns. Plenty of seating areas for enjoying the view! Featured in 'The Gardener's World' magazine. **7 Avenue Road** - With a high 'Jungle' feel, as the seasons pass, it has herbaceous plants, shrubs and trees with an emphasis on texture. Planting and water features encourage wildlife. **27 Avenue Road** - A constantly evolving plant addicts garden with many unusual specimen plants. A 15ft curved rose tunnel is at the core of the garden. Christopher Lloyd inspiration evident in the late summer planting. Choice perennials, annuals and exotic plants for sale from my private nursery.

4 AVON HOUSE

4 Rugby Road, Catthorpe, Lutterworth LE17 6DA. David & Julia King, 01788 860346, avonhouse4@btinternet.com. *3m NE Rugby 3m S Lutterworth. 1m SW M1 J19, A14, M6 Junctions. 1/2 m NE A5. Park at Manor Farm Shop (200yds).* Light refreshments at Manor Farm shop. **Adm £2.50, chd free.** Sun 24 Aug (11-5). **Groups welcome by appt Mar to Sept, refreshments by prior arrangement.**

A surprising 1/2 -acre garden in the heart of the village with varied interest. Large vegetable plot, mixed borders of late season interest, fruit trees, hens, bees and garden ponds all tucked away behind a country cottage. Featured in Garden Answers. Some gravelled areas.

GROUP OPENING

5 BARLEYTHORPE GARDENS

Barleythorpe, nr Oakham LE15 7EQ. *1m from Oakham on A6006 towards Melton Mowbray. Car park in Pasture Lane 1st L in Barleythorpe by post box. Please park in field on L not on lane.* Home-made teas at Dairy Cottage. **Combined adm £5, chd free (share to East Midlands Immediate Care Scheme).** Sun 4 May (2-5).

BARLEYTHORPE HOUSE
Richard Turner

DAIRY COTTAGE
Mr & Mrs W Smith

THE LODGE
Dr & Mrs T J Gray

Visit 3 beautiful gardens in this Rutland village. Dairy Cottage (opp car park), is a cottage-style garden at rear with interesting and unusual shrubs and spring bulbs. Paved/walled garden to front (with pond) and lime hedge. Orchard with spring bulbs and unusual shrubs and trees. The Lodge (next door), with mixed flowers within walled garden, ½ lawn and part-walled kitchen garden small stretch of gravel path between lawned area and vegetable garden. Follow path alongside Dairy Cottage, turn left into Barleythorpe House, 8 Manor Lane - offering both water and woodland. Flowering shrubs, large weeping trees, small lake and woodland walk.

6 BARRACCA

Ivydene Close, Earl Shilton LE9 7NR. Mr & Mrs John & Sue Osborn, 01455 842609, susan.osborn1@btinternet.com. *10m W of Leicester. From A47 after entering Earl Shilton, Ivydene Close is 4th on L from Leicester side of A47.* Home-made teas. **Adm £3, chd free.** Sat 28 June (11-9.30); Sun 29 June (11-5). **Visitors also welcome by appt June to July for groups 10+.**
1-acre garden with lots of different areas, a silver birch walk, wildlife pond with seating, apple tree garden, Mediterranean planted area and lawns surrounded with herbaceous plants and shrubs. Patio area with climbing roses and wisteria. There is also a utility garden with greenhouse, vegetables in beds, herbs and perennial flower beds, lawn and fruit cage. Part of the old gardens owned by the Cotton family who used to open approx 9 acres to the public in the 1920's. Partial wheelchair access.

GROUP OPENING

7 NEW BRAUNSTON & WITHCOTE GARDENS

Braunston & Withcote, nr.Oakham LE15 8QS. *Villages of Braunston & Withcote. Quaintree Hall is located in Braunston, 2m S of Oakham, and Preston Lodge in Withcote, 2m W of Braunston.* Home-made teas Preston Lodge, Withcote. **Combined adm £5, chd free.** Sun 11 May (2-6).

NEW PRESTON LODGE, WITHCOTE
Mr & Mrs John & Sophie Weatherby

Dairy Cottage

QUAINTREE HALL
Mrs Caroline Lomas
(See separate entry)

Start your visit at Quaintree Hall in Braunston, an established garden surrounding the medieval hall house (not open) incl a formal box parterre to the front of the house, a woodland walk, formal walled garden with yew hedges, a small picking garden and a terraced courtyard garden with conservatory. A wide selection of interesting plants can be enjoyed here, each carefully selected for it's specific site by the knowledgeable garden owner. Continue on to Preston Lodge, at the nearby village of Withcote. Here you will find an extensive garden surrounding a beautiful ironstone Lodge in a picturesque country setting. With dramatic views across a small valley to mature woodland beyond, this garden features small formal gardens surrounding the house, sweeping lawns planted with spring bulbs and mown walkways into the woodland through ornate wrought iron gates in the red brick walls which enclose the garden.

8 88 BROOK STREET

Wymeswold LE12 6TU. Adrian & Ita Cooke, 01509 880155, itacooke@btinternet.com. *4m NE of Loughborough. From A6006 Wymeswold turn S by church onto Stockwell, then E along Brook St. Roadside parking on Brook St.* **Combined adm £3, chd free.** Sun 18 May (2-5). **Combined with Craddock Cottage. Visitors also welcome by appt May to June.**
The ½ acre garden is set on a hillside, which provides lovely views across the village, and comprises 3 distinct areas: firstly, a 'cottage-style' garden; then a water garden with a stream and 'champagne' pond; and finally at the top there is a vegetable plot, small orchard and wild flower meadow.

GROUP OPENING

9 BURBAGE GARDENS

Sketchley Manor Estate, Burbage LE10 2LR. *1m S of Hinckley. From M69 J1, take B4109 signed Hinckley, at 2nd r'about follow NGS signs.* Light refreshments at 7 Hall Rd (lunchtime) and 6 Denis Rd (afternoon). **Combined adm £3.50, chd free.** Sun 23 Feb (11-4).

6 DENIS ROAD
Mr & Mrs D A Dawkins

7 HALL ROAD
Don & Mary Baker

A pleasant West Leicestershire village. **6 Denis Road** small garden redesigned to look much larger. Wide range of snowdrops, spring bulbs and hellebores. **7 Hall Road** medium sized garden with good mix of shrubs, spring bulbs, hellebores and unusual perennials.

GROUP OPENING

10 NEW BURROUGH GARDENS

Burrough on the Hill, Nr Melton Mowbray LE14 2QZ. *In the village of Burrough on the Hill. Close to B6047. 10 mins from A606. 20 mins from Melton Mowbray*. Teas at Burrough Hall. **Combined adm £5, chd free.** **Sun 15 June (2-5).**

BURROUGH HALL
Richard & Alice Cunningham

BURROUGH HOUSE
Roger & Sam Weatherby

2 Large gardens, both with magnificent views over High Leicestershire. Burrough House, in the middle of the village, has an extensive garden surrounding a former stone farmhouse with stunning views over the surrounding countryside. The current owners are adding to the former established garden to create a series of vistas and spaces and maximise the views in and out of the garden with the use of clipped hedges and avenues. Burrough Hall, outside the village between Somerby and Burrough, was built in 1867 as a classic Leicestershire hunting lodge. The garden, framed by mature trees and shrubs, was extensively redesigned by garden designer George Carter in 2007. This family garden, which continues to develop for the enjoyment of all generations, consists of extensive lawns, mixed borders, a vegetable garden and woodland walks. There will be a small collection of vintage and classic cars on display at Burrough Hall.

11 CRADOCK COTTAGE

74 Brook St, Wymeswold LE12 6TU. Mike & Carol Robinson. *4m NE of Loughborough. From A6006 Wymeswold turn S by church onto Stockwell, then E along Brook St. Roadside parking on Brook St.* Home-made teas. **Combined adm £3, chd free.** **Sun 18 May (2-5).** **Combined with 88 Brook Street.**

3/4 acre S-facing country garden developed over the last 12yrs. 3/4 acre meadow beyond with attractive views of the village and countryside. Colour themed borders with alliums. Small bluebell woodland with mature trees. Formal vegetable garden. Also hosting The Worm That Turned, a garden retailer, displaying and selling goods to revitalise your outdoor space.

12 7 THE CRESCENT

Rothley LE7 7RW. Mrs Fiona Dunkley, 01162 376301, fiona.dunkley@btinternet.com. *Off Montsorrel Lane, Rothley. Parking on Montsorrel Lane*. Home-made teas. **Adm £2, chd free. Visitors welcome by appt May to Oct.**

Small, well designed garden with interesting and unusual plants. Good display of bulbs in spring, especially alliums. Many diverse grasses and bamboos combined with verbena bonariensis create a very special effect in late summer and autumn.

13 CUPPLESFIELD

2 Stoughton Road, Gaulby LE7 9BB. Roger & Ruth Harris, Ruth@cupplesfield.co.uk. *6m E of Leicester. Garden is one of two properties on Stoughton Rd, Gaulby. Follow NGS yellow arrows.* **Adm £6 (incl tea/coffee and cake), chd free. Visitors welcome by appt July for groups 12 - 20.**

One acre garden packed full of surprises! Themes range from a contemporary Japanese style area to a long informal herbaceous border and Piet Oudolf inspired prairie beds. Interesting borders incl a hidden 'jungle', a small wild life pond and low walled potager. The garden is alive with sculptures and 'hedge art' which add that extra interest. Such a lot in so little. Most parts accessible by wheelchair in dry conditions. Reduced when wet due to grass paths.

14 DAIRY COTTAGE

15 Sharnford Road, Sapcote LE9 4JN. Mrs Norah Robinson-Smith. *9m SW of Leicester. Sharnford Rd joins Leicester Rd in Sapcote to B4114 Coventry Rd. Follow NGS signs at both ends.* Home-made teas. **Adm £3, chd free.** **Sun 25 May, Sun 6 July (11-4).**

From a walled garden with colourful mixed borders to a potager approached along a woodland path, this mature cottage garden combines extensive perennial planting with many unusual shrubs and specimen trees, incl a variegated Cornus controversa (Wedding Cake Tree). More than 80 clematis and climbing roses are trained up pergolas, arches and into trees 50' high - so don't forget to look up!

GROUP OPENING

15 NEW EMPINGHAM GARDENS

Empingham LE15 8PS. *Empingham Village. 5m E of Oakham, 5m W of Stamford on A606.* Home-made teas at Prebendal House. **Combined adm £5, chd free.** **Sun 22 June (2-5.30).**

NEW HOME FARM HOUSE
Mr & Mrs David & Susan Painter

NEW LAVANDER COTTAGE
Virginia Todd

PREBENDAL HOUSE
Mr J Partridge

3 very different gardens in a lovely Rutland village. Park and start your visit at Prebendal House, next door to the Church and explore the 4 acres surrounding the house (not open), built in 1688 as a summer palace for the Bishop of Lincoln. Incl are extensive herbaceous borders, topiary and a water garden. In complete contrast is the tiny garden of Lavander Cottage in Nook Lane, opposite the White Horse Inn. Developed over 10yrs into a series of rooms linked by rose and honeysuckle arches and packed with climbing, shrub and standard roses, richly underplanted with lavender, alliums and clematis and full of surprises. Between the two in scale is Home Farm House at 4 Main Street, a contemporary family garden with wrought ironwork, sunken garden with pool, and paved terrace surrounded by aromatic plants. Wheelchair access at Home Farm House and Prebendal House only.

GROUP OPENING

16 NEW EXTON GARDENS

Exton, Nr Oakham LE15 8BH. *Village of Exton. 5m E of Oakham, 3m N of Rutland Water, turn off A606 between Oakham & Stamford at Barnsdale Lodge Hotel & follow signs to village.* Home-made teas at Exton Village Hall. **Combined adm £5, chd free.** **Sun 20 July (2-5).**

NEW FAIRVIEW
Marian Foers

NEW NO 7 THE GREEN
Chris Eaglesham & Bobby Smith

NEW 12 PUDDING BAG LANE
Meryl Hart

NEW 14 PUDDING BAG LANE
Nick Fisher & Tamsin Summers

NEW 3 TOP STREET
Sheila Flawn

5 gardens will open in this very picturesque Rutland village. Start your visit at the Village Hall for map and directions. Part of the joy of this village tour is the sight of the many beautiful buildings and front gardens seen en route. The first open garden is off The Village Green, also the location of The Fox and Hounds PH. 2 more are located behind the terrace of pretty thatched cottages in Pudding Bag Lane and the 4th off High Street. All 4 of these are small country cottage gardens, imaginatively planted for maximum yr-round interest and a riot of colour and scents. The 5th garden, on Stamford Rd, is the largest and has been developed over 10yrs on a very low budget to maximise wildlife and create a peaceful haven. Plants for sale at Fair View.

17 NEW 2 FAIRWAY

Market Harborough LE16 9QL. Mr & Mrs J Coombs. *3/4 m N of Harborough, L off Leicester Rd. Follow yellow NGS arrows.* Home-made teas. **Adm £2, chd free.** **Sun 29 June, Sun 6 July (10.30-4.30).**
A small plantwomans garden started 2 yrs ago, planting had to be rare, unusual, a touch of normal but only plants we really love, come and see just what can be done in a short time. There are lots of plants and grasses, some trees, some exotics, a real mix of old and new ideas and some very interesting climbers. Small in size but planted with big ideas.

18 28 GLADSTONE STREET

Wigston Magna LE18 1AE. Chris & Janet Huscroft, 01162 886014, chris.huscroft@tiscali.co.uk. *4m S of Leicester. Off Wigston by-pass (A5199) follow signs off r'about.* Home-made teas. **Adm £2, chd free.** **Sat 14 June (11-5); Sun 15 June (12-5); Sat 12 July (11-5); Sun 13 July (12-5).** **Visitors also welcome by appt June to July, max 20.**
Our small town garden is divided into rooms and bisected by a pond with a bridge. It is brimming with unusual hardy perennials, incl collections of ferns and hostas. David Austin roses chosen for their scent feature throughout, incl a 30' rose arch. An unusual shade house with rare plants, incl hardy orchids and arisaemas. Come and see how many plants you can get into a small garden. Frameworks Knitters Museum nearby - open Sundays.

19 GOADBY MARWOOD HALL

Goadby Marwood LE14 4LN. Mr & Mrs Westropp, 01664 464202. *4m NW of Melton Mowbray. Between Waltham on the Wolds & Eastwell.* Teas in Village Hall. **Adm £5, chd free.** **Sat 24 May (11-4).** **Visitors also welcome by appt.**
Redesigned in 2000 by the owner based on C18 plans. A chain of 5 lakes (covering 5 acres) and several ironstone walled gardens all interconnected. Lakeside woodland walk. Planting for yr-round interest. Landscaper trained under plantswoman Rosemary Verey at Barnsley House. Beautiful C13 church open. Swans on lake. Gravel paths and lawns.

20 THE GRANGE

Kimcote, Lutterworth LE17 5RU. Shaun & Mary Mackaness, www.thegrangekimcote.co.uk. *12m S of Leicester. 4m from J20 of M1. Follow rd signs to Kimcote.* Teas in All Saints Church (Sun only). **Adm £2, chd free (share to LOROS).** **Sun 22, Wed 25 June (11-5).**
Recently designed and renovated English country garden hidden behind original brick walls of beautiful Grade II listed Queen Anne house. 3/4 -acre garden, immaculate expanses of lawn, parterre, pond, croquet lawn and stone terraces. Herbaceous borders with collection of Old English roses. Green oak structures and hand-forged gazebo and rose arches. Walkways with mature trees, pleached hornbeams and naturalised bulbs.

Small in size but planted with big ideas . . .

21 GREEN WICKET FARM

Ullesthorpe Road, Bitteswell, Lutterworth LE17 4LR. Mrs Anna Smith. *2m NW of Lutterworth J20 M1. From Lutterworth follow signs through Bitteswell towards Ullesthorpe. Farm is situated behind Bitteswell Cricket Club. Parking in field.* Home-made teas. **Adm £3, chd free.** **Wed 16, Sun 20 July (2-5.30).**
A developing garden created in 2008 on a working farm. Clay soil and very exposed but beginning to look established. Many unusual hardy plants along with a lot of old favourites have been used to provide a long season of colour and interest. Formal pond and water features. Some gravel paths.

22 HAMMOND ARBORETUM

Burnmill Road, Market Harborough LE16 7JG. The Robert Smyth Academy. *15m S of Leicester on A6. From High St, follow signs to The Robert Smyth Academy via Bowden Lane to Burnmill Rd. Park in 1st entrance on L.* Home-made teas. **Adm £3, chd free.** **Sun 23 Mar, Sun 12 Oct (2-5).**
A site of just under 2½ -acres containing an unusual collection of trees and shrubs, many from Francis Hammond's original planting dating from 1913 to 1936 whilst headmaster of the school. Species from America, China and Japan with malus and philadelphus walks and a moat. Proud owners of 4 'champion' trees identified by national specialist. Guided walks and walk plans available. Some steep slopes.

Farmway, Willoughby Gardens

23 HEDGEHOG HALL

Loddington Road, Tilton on the Hill LE7 9DE. Janet & Andrew Rowe, 01162 597339, janetnandrew@btinternet.com. *8m W of Oakham. 2m N of A47 on B6047 between Melton & Market Harborough. Follow yellow NGS signs in Tilton towards Loddington.* Cream teas. **Adm £3, chd free.** **Sun 4, Mon 5 May, Sun 15 June (11-5).**

½ -acre organically managed plant lover's garden. Steps leading to three stone-walled terraced borders filled with shrubs, perennials and bulbs. Lavender walk, herb border, spring garden, colour themed long border and serpentine island bed packed with campanulas, astrantias, sanguisorbas, roses, clematis and many more. Sheltered walled courtyard filled with hostas, ferns and wisteria. Hot terraced borders. Cake stall. No wheelchair access to terraced borders- but all can be seen from the level.

24 134 HERRICK ROAD

LE11 2BU. Janet Currie & Pete Mosley, 01509 212191, janet.currie@me.com, www.thesecateur.com. *1m SW of Loughborough. From M1 J23 take A512 Ashby Rd to Loughborogh. At r'about R onto A6004 Epinal Way. At Beacon Rd r'about L, Herrick Rd 1st on R.* Home-made teas. **Adm £2, chd free.** **Sat 7 June (12-4).** **Combined with Loughborough Gardens Sun 8 June (12-4). Thurs 19 June (5-9), combined adm £3, chd free. Visitors also welcome by appt June to Oct.**

A small garden brimming with texture, colour and creative flair. Trees, shrubs and climbers give structure. A sitting area surrounded by lilies, raised staging for herbs and alpines. A lawn flanked with deeply curving and gracefully planted beds of perennials growing through hand-made willow structures. A shaded area under the Bramley apple tree, raised vegetable beds and potting area. The owners have a great reputation for the contemporary art and crafts events often held at the same time as Open Gardens. Secret Craft Fair on the 7th and 8th June during National Gardens Festival Weekend. Specially selected high quality contemporary crafts, many with garden themes, will be on sale and displayed amongst the plants.

25 HIGHFIELD HOUSE

1 Highfield Close, Normanton Le Heath, Coalville LE67 2TN. Mr & Mrs T Ikin, 01530 260375, maryikin@aol.com. *3m E of A42 at Ashby-de-la-Zouch. On minor rd midway between Ashby de la Zouch & Ibstock. Highfield Close is off Main Street, opp church.* Home-made teas. **Adm £3, chd free.** **Sun 29 June (2-6).** **Visitors also welcome by appt June to July.**

This garden was established in 2004 on a farmyard site. SW facing with views over the Mease Valley, it comprises of gardens within a garden. The courtyard is a cottage garden with trellises, roses, water feature and tubs with small raised bed. Vegetable patch. Terraced lawns with herbaceous borders. A wild area with shrubs and trees, and two large ponds. Koi carp are fed late afternoon.

26 HILL PARK FARM

Dodgeford Lane, Belton LE12 9TE. John & Jean Adkin. *6m W of Loughborough. Dodgeford Lane off B5324 between Belton & Osgathorpe.* Home-made teas. **Adm £3, chd free.** **Sun 20 July, Sun 24 Aug (2-6).**

Beautiful medium sized garden to a working farm. Shrubs, fruit trees and vegetable garden. Rock garden and herbaceous borders brimming with colour. Pergola with clematis and roses, water features, and many planted stone troughs and window boxes.

27 THE HOMESTEAD

Normanton-by-Bottesford NG13 0EP. John & Shirley Palmer, 01949 842745. *8m W of Grantham. From A52, turn N in Bottesford, signed Normanton; last house on R. From A1, 1st house on L.* Home-made teas. **Adm £2.50, chd free.** **Sun 2 Mar (2-5).** **Visitors also welcome by appt Feb to May and Aug to early Sep for National collection of Heliotropes.**

¾ -acre informal plant lover's garden. Vegetable garden, small orchard, woodland area, many hellebores, growing collection (over 100) of snowdrops and some single peonies and salvias. Collections of hostas and sempervivums. National Collection of heliotropes. A garden where plants (incl vegetables) come first to produce a peaceful and relaxed overall effect.

NCH

28 LONG CLOSE
Main St, Woodhouse Eaves LE12 8RZ. John Oakland, 01509 890376. *4m S of Loughborough. Nr M1 J23. From A6, W in Quorn.* Home-made teas (18 May only). **Adm £4, chd 50p.** For NGS: Open daily Apr - Oct incl Bank Hols (10-5). Also special open day Sun 18 May (11-4). **Visitors also welcome by appt Apr to mid Oct. Tea and biscuits by prior arrangement.**
5 acres spring bulbs, rhododendrons, azaleas, camellias, magnolias, many rare shrubs, mature trees, lily ponds; terraced lawns, herbaceous borders, potager in walled kitchen garden, wild flower meadow walk. Winter, spring, summer and autumn colour, a garden for all seasons. Orchid Meadow guided walks from 10th June to mid July. Small collection of Penstemons. Partial wheelchair access. Slopes and some uneven paths.

GROUP OPENING

29 NEW LOUGHBOROUGH GARDENS
Herrick Road, Loughborough LE11 2BU, www.thesecateur.com. *1m SW Loughborough. From M1 J23 take A512 Ashby Rd to Loughborough. At r'about R onto A6004 Epinal Way. At Beacon Rd r'about L, Herrick Rd 1st on R.* Home-made teas at 134 Herrick Road. **Combined adm £3, chd free.** Sun 8 June (12-4). Evening Opening £3, chd free, wine, Thur 19 June (5-9).

NEW **80 HERRICK ROAD**
Sarah Fazakerly
Visitors also welcome by appt May to July for small groups only.
01509 211476
sarahfazpianos@btopenworld.com

134 HERRICK ROAD
Janet Currie & Pete Mosley
(See separate entry)

Herrick Road is a quiet leafy area with a mix of Victorian and mid century homes. The two gardens in this group contain plenty of horticultural and creative interest. 134 Herrick Road is a small garden brimming with texture, colour and creative flair. Trees, shrubs and climbers give structure. A sitting area surrounded by lilies, raised staging for herbs and alpines. A lawn flanked with deeply curving and gracefully planted beds of perennials growing through hand-made willow structures. A shaded area under the Bramley apple tree, raised vegetable beds and potting area. The owners have a great reputation for the contemporary art and crafts events often held at the same time as Open Gardens. 80 Herrick Road, is an intriguing small suburban garden, which is constantly developing. The garden is laid out in several sections linked by a winding path, with evergreens, dwarf conifers, herbaceous borders and climbers. Of particular interest are the owner's eight elderly tortoises - seen in various areas of the garden. 134 Herrick Rd is holding an Open Garden & Secret Craft Fair (7 & 8 June) and is home to a Clandestine Cake Club organiser, so the cakes are often scrummy!

It is full of surprises with memorabilia and bygones a reminder of our past . . .

GROUP OPENING

30 MARKET BOSWORTH GARDENS
Market Bosworth CV13 0LE. *13m W of Leicester; 8m N of Hinckley. 1m off A447 Coalville to Hinckley Rd, 3m off A444. Burton to Nuneaton Rd.* Light refreshments at 13 Spinney Hill and 15 York Close. **Combined adm £5, chd free (share to Bosworth in Bloom).** Sun 27 July (1-6).

GLEBE FARM HOUSE
Mr Peter Ellis & Ms Ginny Broad

4 LANCASTER AVENUE
Mr Peter Bailiss

NEW **26 NORTHUMBERLAND AVENUE**
Mrs Kathy Boot

30 PARK STREET
Lesley Best

4 PRIORY ROAD
Mr & Mrs Stan Barrett

5 PRIORY ROAD
David & Linda Chevell

RAINBOW COTTAGE
Mr David Harrison

13 SPINNEY HILL
Mrs J Buckell

NEW **3 WARWICK CLOSE**
Mrs Margaret Birch

NEW **6 WARWICK CLOSE**
Mrs Betty Zuger

15 YORK CLOSE
Mrs G M Clinton

Market Bosworth is an attractive market town, with an enviable record for the quality of its regular entry in the annual East Midlands in Bloom competition. There are a number of gardens open, some for the first time, and all within walking distance of the Market Square. The gardens show various planting styles and different approaches to small and intimate spaces in the historic town centre, as well as larger plots in more recent developments. Tickets and descriptive maps obtainable in the Market Place, with refreshments available there and at two of the gardens. Plants will be on sale at a number of gardens. A proportion of the proceeds from the Gardens Open Day will be used to support Bosworth in Bloom, the voluntary group responsible for the town's floral displays; see www.bosworthinbloom.co.uk. Farmers' Market in town centre (9-2) local produce, hot and cold food.

31 MILL HOUSE
118 Welford Road, Wigston LE18 3SN. Mr & Mrs P Measures, 01162 885409, petemeasures@hotmail.co.uk. *4m S of Leicester. From Leicester, follow A5199 S, up hill past Mercers Newsagents, 100yds on L.* Home-made teas. **Adm £2.50, chd free.** Sun 25 May (12-5); Wed 18 June (2.30-8); Sun 13 July (12-5).
Visitors also welcome by appt May to Aug.
Walled town garden with extensive plant variety, many rare and unusual. A plant lovers garden, with interesting designs incorporated in the borders, rockery and scree. It is full of surprises with memorabilia and bygones a reminder of our past.

32 MOUNTAIN ASH

140 Ulverscroft Lane, Newtown Linford LE6 0AJ. Mike & Liz Newcombe, 01530 242178, mjnew12@gmail.com. *7m SW of Loughborough, 7m NW of Leicester, 1m NW of Newtown Linford. Head ½ m N along Main St towards Sharpley Hill, fork L into Ulverscroft Lane.* Light refreshments. **Adm £3.50, chd free. Sun 6, Sun 13 July (11-5). Visitors also welcome by appt May to Aug for groups of 10+ afternoon or evening.**

2-acre SW facing garden with stunning views across Charnwood countryside. Near the house are patios, lawns, water features, flower and shrub beds, fruit trees, greenhouses and vegetable gardens. Lawns then slope down to a gravel garden, a large wildlife pond with waterfall and three areas of woodland, with pleasant walks though many species of trees. Several places to sit and relax around the garden.

Take a walk on mown paths around the grass meadow . . .

33 NEW 14 NEW LANE

Walton on the Wolds, Loughborough LE12 8HY. Mr & Mrs G Jones. *4m E of Loughborough. 25 mins from M1, J23 via Loughborough & 10 mins from A46 Sixhills. Exit B676 between Barrow on Soar & Burton on the Wolds.* Cream teas. **Adm £3, chd free. Sun 22 June (11-5).**

A country garden laid out in 2004 with formal herbaceous borders, Yew hedges and David Austin roses. Set in a two acre plot with a productive vegetable garden. Take a walk on mown paths around the grass meadow and enjoy outstanding views of the Leicestershire Wolds. Parking and wheelchair access on grass, some slopes and gravel paths.

GROUP OPENING

34 NEW NEWTOWN LINFORD GARDENS

Main Street, Newtown Linford, Leicester LE6 0AF. Mr & Mrs R Howard. *6m NW Leicester. 2½ m from M1 J22. ½ m W of main Bradgate Park Entrance.* Home-made teas. **Combined adm £4, chd free. Mon 26 May (11-5).**

NEW APPLETREE COTTAGE
Katherine Duffy Anthony

NEW BANK COTTAGE
Jan Croft

NEW DELL COTTAGE
Maureen Sutton

NEW DINGLE HOUSE
Mr & Mrs R Howard

NEW LINCROFT
Stan Clarke

NEW WOODLANDS
Mary Husseini

Newtown Linford is a historic village bordering Bradgate Park and is part of Charnwood Forest. Through the village runs the R. Lin, and four of these adjacent properties have river banks from where you can see brown trout or the occasional kingfisher. All of the neighbours share a passion for their very different gardens. **Appletree Cottage** Charming enclosed garden surrounding C17 thatched cottage, interesting paths leading to lawns, borders, sun terrace and small lily pond. **Bank Cottage** is set on different levels and is a typical cottage garden providing yr-round colour but is prettiest in spring. **Dell Cottage** is a small sheltered garden where azaleas and rhododendrons grow well. The R. Lin runs through **Woodlands** where there are many varied shrubs and spring flowers and there is work in progress around the mature trees. **Dingle House** has a small garden on many levels with yr-round colour. **Lincroft** is noted for spectacular displays of rhododendrons and azaleas. Not to be missed.

35 THE OLD CHAPEL

Main Street, Breedon on the Hill, Derby DE73 8AN. Mr & Mrs S Jones, 01332 865460, vanessajjones@hotmail.co.uk. *Just off A453 between East Midlands Airport & Ashby de la Zouch. Parking available at Priory Garden Centre, by village green or on rd outside.* **Adm £3, chd free. Visitors welcome by appt May to Sept. Teas/coffees by prior arrangement.**

In the shadows of Breedon Hill lies The Old Chapel garden. With the brook running through the centre, two bridges lead to the other side which rises steeply through terraces to a pond and patios. The garden, more cottage than formal, contains mixed shrubs and small trees. There is a formal lawn surrounded by borders consisting of herbaceous plants, roses, perennials and vegetables. Featured in Amateur Gardening magazine. Limited room for wheelchair viewing on lower level. Regret no wheelchair access to high garden.

♿

36 THE OLD HALL

Main Street, Market Overton LE15 7PL. Mr & Mrs Timothy Hart, 01572 767145, stefahart@hambletondecorating.co.uk. *6m N of Oakham. Beyond Cottesmore; 5m from A1 via Thistleton. 10m E from Melton Mowbray via Wymondham.* Home-made teas. **Adm £4.50, chd free (share to Rutland Macmillan Cancer Support). Sun 18 May (2-6). Visitors also welcome by appt Apr to Sept weekdays only.**

Set on a southerly ridge overlooking Catmose Vale, the garden is now on 4 levels. Stone walls and yew hedges divide the garden into enclosed areas with herbaceous borders, shrubs, and young and mature trees. In 2006 the lower part of garden was planted with new shrubs to create a walk with mown paths. Terrace and lawn give a great sense of space, enhancing the view. Neil Hewertson has been involved in the gardens design since 1990s.

♿ 🐕 ✿ 🚌 ☕

37 THE OLD STABLES

Bruntingthorpe LE17 5QL. Gordon & Hilary Roberts, 01162 478713, gordon.hilary.1943@btinternet.com. *10m S of Leicester. Leicester A5199, R at Arnesby to Bruntingthorpe; R towards Peatling Parva. M1, J20 for Lutterworth; R in front of police station to Bruntingthorpe.* Home-made teas. **Adm £3, chd free. Sun 8 June, Sun 13 July (11-5). Visitors also welcome by appt June to July for groups 15-35.**

Plant-lovers' delightful 1-acre country

garden. A range of individual but interconnecting areas give a feeling of spaciousness and tranquillity. Wide grass walks set off the large herbaceous borders packed with a collection of interesting perennials, shrubs and climbers. Many mature trees, wild-life area with pond; striking views to Leicester. Rockery and raised alpine beds, tender plants in containers.

38 THE OLD VICARAGE, BURLEY

Church Road, Burley, Nr Oakham LE15 7SU. Jonathan & Sandra Blaza, 01572 770588, sandra.blaza@btinternet.com. *1m NE of Oakham. In Burley just off B668 between Oakham & Cottesmore. Church Rd is opposite the village green, the Old Vicarage 1st L off Church Rd.* Home-made teas. **Adm £4, chd free (share to Eden Valley Hospice). Sun 8 June (1.30-5). Visitors also welcome by appt June only.**

3-acre country garden, planted for yr-round interest, incl walled garden (with vine-house) producing fruit, herbs, vegetables and cut flowers. Formal lawns and borders, lime walk, rose gardens and a rill through an avenue of standard wisteria. Wildlife garden with pond, 2 orchards and beech woodland. Featured in Country Homes and Interiors and Winner, Country Living Kitchen Table Talent Awards. Some gravel and steps.

39 NEW ORCHARD HOUSE

Lyndon Road, Hambleton, Nr Oakham LE15 8TJ. Richard & Celia Foulkes. *Next to Rutland Water, 400 yds from centre of Hambleton. Enter village, turn R at church, down hill, only house at bottom on R.* Light refreshments. Teas will be served in village hall, 400yds up steep hill, in the event of bad weather. **Adm £3.50, chd free. Sun 29 June (10-5).**

Beautifully situated partly bordering Rutland Water. Series of garden rooms incl formal, Japanese and vegetable gardens; newly planted orchard; and large informal garden with rose pergola and copses.

40 ORCHARD HOUSE

14 Mowsley Rd, Husbands Bosworth, Lutterworth LE17 6LR. David & Ros Dunmore. *6m W of Market Harborough. A4304 from Market Harborough enter village. Mowsley Rd is 3rd R. A4304 from Lutterworth/ M1, enter village. Mowsley Rd is 3rd L.* Home-made teas. **Adm £2.50, chd free (share to Rainbows children's hospice). Sun 10 Aug (11-5).**

A hidden gem. Small enclosed cottage garden with elements of surprise around each corner. Five 'garden rooms' shaded by mature trees and linked by Victorian gravel paths. Patio area with summer planting, small pond and other water features. Alpine bed and varied use of container planting. Wheelchair access to main features of the garden. Some gravel paths.

41 THE PADDOCKS

Main Street, Hungarton, Leicester LE7 9JY. Michael & Helen Martin. *8m E of Leicester. Follow NGS signs.* Light refreshments in local village hall. **Adm £3.50, chd free. Sat 7, Sun 8 June (11-5).**

2-acre garden with mature and specimen trees, rhododendrons, azaleas, magnolia grandiflora, wisterias. Two lily ponds and stream. Three lawn areas surrounded by herbaceous and shrub borders. Woodland walk. Pergola with clematis and roses, hosta collection and two rockeries. Large well established semi-permanent plant stall in aid of Local Charities. Featured in Leicester Mercury, Whats On in Leicester and on Radio Leicester. Limited wheelchair access due to steep slopes at the rear of garden. Flat terrace by main lawn provides good viewing area.

42 PARKSIDE

6 Park Hill, Gaddesby LE7 4WH. Mr & Mrs D Wyrko, 01664 840385, david.wyrko1@btopenworld.com. *8m NE of Leicester. From A607 Rearsby bypass turn off for Gaddesby. L at Cheney Arms. Garden 400yds on R.* Home-made teas. **Adm £6 (inc tea and cake), chd free. Visitors welcome by appt Mar to July.**

Woodland garden of approx 1¼ acres containing many spring flowers and bulbs. Vegetable garden with cordon fruit trees and soft fruit. Greenhouse, cold frame and pond. New bog garden and other features. Informal mixed borders planted to encourage wildlife and to provide a family friendly environment.

43 PINE HOUSE

Gaddesby LE7 4XE. Mr & Mrs T Milward, 01664 840213, suemilward@googlemail.com. *8m NE of Leicester. From A607, turn off for Gaddesby.* Home-made teas. **Adm £4, chd free. Visitors welcome by appt Apr to Oct for groups 10+.**

2-acre garden with fine mature trees, woodland walk, and water garden. Herb and potager garden and wisteria archway to Victorian vinery. Pleached lime trees, mixed borders with rare and unusual plants. Wide variety of tender plants in gravel garden and terracotta pot garden. Interesting topiary hedges and box trees. Grass Tennis Court and Dragon Hedge.

> Cottage garden with elements of surprise around each corner . . .

44 QUAINTREE HALL

Braunston, Nr Oakham LE15 8QS. Mrs Caroline Lomas. *Braunston, nr Oakham. 1st house on L in Cedar St, off High St. past village green in centre of village. Park in Cedar St & around church.* Light refreshments. **Adm £3.50, chd free. Sun 17 Aug (2-6). Combined with Braunston & Withcote Gardens (Preston Lodge) Sun 11 May (2-6), combined adm £5, chd free.**

An established garden surrounding the medieval hall house (not open) incl a formal box parterre to the front of the house, a woodland walk, formal walled garden with yew hedges, a small picking garden and terraced courtyard garden with conservatory. A wide selection of interesting plants can be enjoyed, each carefully selected for its specific site by the knowledgeable garden owner.

Hedgehog Hall

45 RIDGEWOLD FARM
Burton Lane, Wymeswold LE12 6UN. Robert & Ann Waterfall, 01509 881689, robert.waterfall@yahoo.co.uk. *5m SE of Loughborough. Off Burton Lane between A6006 & B676.* Home-made teas. **Adm £3.50, chd free. Visitors welcome by appt May to July, max 45.**
2½ -acre rural garden in the Leicestershire Wolds. Conducted tours of the garden start at the sweeping drive through specimen trees. Beech, Laurel and Saxon hedges divide different areas. Lawn, rill, water feature, summer house, shrubs, rose fence, clematis arch, wisteria, ivy tunnel, rose garden, herbaceous, orchard, vegetable patch. Birch avenue gives view of the village. Woodland walk. Natural fish pond. Escorted tours.

46 NEW 119 SCALFORD ROAD
Melton Mowbray LE13 1JZ. Richard & Hilary Lawrence, 01664 562821, randh1954@me.com. *½ m N of Melton Mowbray. Take Scalford Rd from town centre past Cattle Market. Garden 100yds after 1st turning on L (The Crescent).* Home-made teas. **Adm £2.50, chd free. Sun 27 July (11-5). Visitors also welcome by appt June to Aug.**
Larger than average town garden which has evolved over the last 24 yrs. Mixed borders with traditional and exotic plants, enhanced by container planting particularly begonias. Vegetable parterre and greenhouse. Various seating areas for viewing different aspects of the garden. Water features incl ponds. Limited wheelchair access. Gravelled drive, ramp provided up to lawn but paths not accessible.

47 STOKE ALBANY HOUSE
Desborough Road, Stoke Albany LE16 8PT. Mr & Mrs A M Vinton, 01858 535227, del.jones7@googlemail.com, www.stokealbanyhouse.co.uk. *4m E of Market Harborough. Via A427 to Corby, turn to Stoke Albany, R at the White Horse (B669) garden ½ m on L.* **Adm £3.50, chd free (share to Marie Curie Cancer Care). Weds 4, 11, 18, 25 June; Weds 2, 9 July (2-4.30). Groups welcome by appointment (preferably Weds) June and July of 10+.**
4-acre country-house garden; fine trees and shrubs with wide herbaceous borders and sweeping striped lawn. Good display of bulbs in spring, roses June and July. Walled grey garden; nepeta walk arched with roses, parterre with box and roses. Mediterranean garden. Heated greenhouse, potager with topiary, water feature garden and sculptures.

48 THORPE LUBENHAM HALL
Lubenham LE16 9TR. Sir Bruce & Lady MacPhail. *2m W of Market Harborough. From Market Harborough take 3rd L off main rd, down Rushes Lane, past church on L, under old railway bridge & straight on up private drive.* Cream teas. **Adm £3.50, chd free. Tue 20 May (10-4).**
15 acres of formal and informal garden surrounded by parkland and arable. Many mature trees. Traditional herbaceous borders and various water features. Walled pool garden with raised beds. Ancient moat area along driveway. Gravel paths, some steep slopes and steps.

49 TRESILLIAN HOUSE
67 Dalby Road, Melton Mowbray LE13 0BQ. Mrs Alison Blythe, 01664 481997, studentsint@aol.com, www.studentsint.com. *S of Melton Mowbray. Follow signs B6047 (Dalby Rd) S. Parking on site or opposite in slip rd.* Ploughman's lunches and Cream teas. Soup (Oct only). **Adm £2.50, chd free. Sun 4 May, Sun 6 July, Sun 24 Aug, Sun 26 Oct (11-5). Visitors also welcome by appt Mar to Oct max 20.**
3/4 acre garden re-established by new owner between 2009 and 2012. Beautiful blue cedar trees, excellent specimen tulip tree. Parts of garden original, others reinstated with variety of plants and bushes. Original bog garden and pond. Vegetable plot. Parts left uncultivated with wild cowslips and grasses. Quiet oasis. Slate paths, steep in places.

50 UNIVERSITY OF LEICESTER BOTANIC GARDEN
'The Knoll' entrance, Glebe Road, Oadby LE2 2LD, 01162 712933, www.le.ac.uk/botanicgarden. *2m SE of Leicester off A6. On outskirts of city opp race course.* Light refreshments. **Adm by donation. Sun 10 Aug (10-4).**
16-acre garden, whose formal planting centres around a restored Edwardian garden. Plantings originate from around the world and include an arboretum, a herb garden, woodland and herbaceous borders, rock gardens, a water garden, special collections of skimmia, aubretia and hardy fuchsia, and a series of glasshouses displaying temperate and tropical plants, alpines and succulents. Guide dogs allowed. Open daily; phone or see website for details.

Handmade sculptures and artefacts made from recycled materials on display . . .

GROUP OPENING

51 WALTON GARDENS
Walton LE17 5RP. *4m NE of Lutterworth. M1 J20, via Lutterworth follow signs for Kimcote & Walton, or from Leicester take A5199. After Shearsby turn R signed Bruntingthorpe. Follow signs.* Cream teas at The Dog and Gun with all proceeds to NGS. **Combined adm £4, chd free. Sun 22, Wed 25 June (11-5).**

THE MEADOWS
Mr & Mrs Falkner

MULBERRY HOUSE
Mr & Mrs Karl & Hazel Busch

ORCHARDS
Mr & Mrs G Cousins
Visitors also welcome by appt June to July.
01455 556958
jennyandgraham@talktalk.net
www.grahamsgreens.com

NEW RYLANDS FARMHOUSE
Mark & Sonya Raybould

TOAD HALL
Sue Beardmore

Small village set in beautiful south Leicestershire countryside. The five gardens at Walton are in such contrasting sizes and styles that, together, they make the perfect garden visit. There is a plantsman's garden filled with gorgeous rare plants; a Modernist garden where all the leaves are green (no variegated, gold or purple foliage) featuring the extensive use of grasses and a lovely view across the surrounding landscape; a traditional garden featuring serpentine hedging and another which is walled and has a unique water feature; last but not least, a really delightful enclosed cottage garden. Some wood chip and cobbled paths that can be accessed by wheelchairs but may prove difficult.

ALLOTMENTS

52 NEW WASHBROOK ALLOTMENTS
Welford Road, Leicester LE2 6FP. Sharon Maher. *Approx 2½ m S of Leicester, 1½ m N of Wigston. Regret no onsite parking. Welford Rd is difficult to park on. Please use nearby side rds & Pendlebury Drive (LE2 6GY).* **Adm £3, chd free. Sun 7 Sept (11-3).**
Our allotment gardens have been described as a hidden oasis off the main Welford Road. There are over 100 whole and half plots growing a wide variety of fruit and vegetables. We have a fledgling wildflower meadow, a composting toilet and a shop. Keep a look out for the remains of Anderson Shelters, and see how woodchip is put to good use! Circular access route around the site is uneven in places but is usable for people in wheelchairs.

53 WESTVIEW
1 St Thomas' Road, Great Glen LE8 9EH. Gill & John Hadland, 01162 592170, gill@hadland.wanadoo.co.uk. *7m S of Leicester. Take either r'about from A6 into village. At centre (War Memorial) follow NGS signs.* Home-made teas. **Adm £2, chd free. Sun 2 Mar (12-4); Sun 18 May, Sun 6 July, Sun 7 Sept (12-5). Visitors also welcome by appt Mar to Sept.**
Organically managed small walled cottage-style garden with yr-round interest. Interesting and unusual plants, many grown from seed. Formal box parterre herb garden, courtyard, herbaceous borders, small wildlife pond, greenhouse, beehives, vegetable and fruit area. Auricula display. Handmade sculptures and artefacts made from recycled materials on display. Collection of Galanthus (snowdrops). Featured in Garden Answers.

Lemon drizzle cake, Victoria sponge ... yummy!

54 ◆ WHATTON GARDENS

nr Kegworth LE12 5BG. Lord & Lady Crawshaw, 01509 842225, whattonhouse@gmail.com, www.whattonhouseandgardens.co.uk. *4m NE of Loughborough. On A6 between Hathern & Kegworth; 2½ m SE of M1J24.* **Adm £4, chd free. For NGS: Sat 7 June (11-6). For other opening times and information, please phone or see garden website.**

A wonderful extensive 15 acre C19 country house garden. Open daily March to Oct except Sat. Arboretum with many fine trees, large herbaceous borders, traditional rose garden, ornamental ponds, flowering shrubs and many spring bulbs. Nooks and crannies to explore. A hidden treasure and a truly relaxing experience for all the family. Home-made teas. Also available for group bookings. Gravel paths.

GROUP OPENING

55 NEW WHISSENDINE GARDENS

Whissendine, Nr Oakham LE15 7HG. *5m N of Oakham. Whissendine is signed from A606 between Melton Mowbray & Oakham.* Home-made teas St Andrew's Church, Whissendine. **Combined adm £5, chd free. Sun 25 May (2-5).**

THE OLD VICARAGE
Prof Peter & Dr Sarah Furness

NEW **WHISSENDINE COTTAGE**
Mr & Mrs C Davies

2 beautiful gardens in this Rutland village. The Old Vicarage, next door to the church, up the hill: ⅔ -acre packed with variety. Terrace with topiary, a formal fountain courtyard and raised beds backed by small gothic orangery burgeoning with tender plants. Herbaceous borders surround main lawn. Wisteria tunnel leads to orchard filled with naturalised bulbs, home to four beehives, Gothic hen house plus six rare breed hens. Hidden 'white walk', unusual plants and much, much more! Off the village green, at the bottom of the hill, Whissendine Cottage: A large family garden surrounded by mature trees, with countryside views. The house is surrounded by formal topiary gardens, raised beds and planted pots on the stone terraces. Steps lead to lawns with mixed borders, filled with unusual plants, a woodland walk, meandering mown grass paths between fruit and ornamental trees and shrub roses and a wonderful vegetable garden. The Old Vicarage featured in GGG. Limited wheelchair access due to gravel paths, slopes and steps.

♿ ✿ ☕

GROUP OPENING

56 WILLOUGHBY GARDENS

Willoughby Waterleys LE8 6UD. Eileen Spencer, 01162 478321, eileenfarmway9@msn.com. *9m S of Leicester. Follow Yellow NGS road arrows.* Teas in village hall. **Combined adm £3, chd free. Sun 20 July (11-5). Visitors also welcome by appt July to Aug, max group 25.**

FARMWAY
Eileen Spencer

JOHN'S WOOD
John & Jill Harris

Willoughby Waterleys lies in the South Leicestershire countryside. Willoughby's name comes from springs which are near the surface. The church dates from Norman times. **Farmway** in Willoughby is a ¼ acre garden on a gentle slope with views across Leicestershire. This is a plant lovers garden closely planted with shrubs, perennials, lavender, roses and clematis. Two ponds, vegetable garden and many containers. **John's Wood** is a 1½ -acre nature reserve planted in 2006 with 80cm native trees. The site incl a pond, wildflower meadow strip where butterflies are a feature in July. Mown paths through 18 feet high trees. Elevated viewing platform in place, further extension planned.

✿ ☕

GROUP OPENING

57 WING GARDENS

Wing, Nr Oakham LE15 8SA. *2m S of Rutland Water. Off A6003 between Oakham & Uppingham.* Home-made teas in Wing Village Hall. **Combined adm £5, chd free. Sun 6 July (11-5).**

NEW **16 CHURCH STREET**
Mr & Mrs Mick & Mary Rodgers

NEW **DOVE COTTAGE**
Mr & Mrs David & Alison Seviour

NEW **GREYSTONES**
Mr & Mrs Alisdair & Jane Alexander-Orr

HOME CLOSE
Joanne Beaver

TOWNSEND HOUSE
David & Jeffy Wood

WINGWELL
John & Rose Dejardin

6 very different gardens in pretty stone village of Wing with medieval church and turf maze. For map and directions start visit at Wingwell, halfway along Top St: bold use of plants, stone, water and sculpture. Paths lead around the C17 house, cutting and salad garden, woodland and meadow walk, main garden dominated by a rolling serpentine yew hedge. Dove Cottage, on Middle St: hidden walled garden with converted stone dovecote c1759. Rose arch walk, mature fruit trees, wild life pond and mixed borders. Artists studio open. 16,Church St: small cottage garden with beautiful views over countryside. Artists studio open. Home Close: small 'secret garden' in traditional cottage garden style. roses, fruit tree arch, pond & Hosta bed. Greystones: small enclosed cottage garden, creating outdoor living space with all year round planting. Vegetable plot and fruit. Townsend House: cottage garden with mixed borders and roses. Walled gravel garden with swimming pool, vegetable garden. Limited wheelchair access to some of the gardens.

Mountain Ash

Leicestershire & Rutland County Volunteers

County Organiser Leicestershire
Colin Olle, Croft Acre, The Belt, South Kilworth, Lutterworth LE17 6DX, 01858 575791, colin.olle@tiscali.co.uk

County Treasurer Leicestershire
Martin Shave, Oak Tree House, North Road, South Kilworth, Lutterworth, LE17 6DU, 01455 556633, martinshave@kilworthaccountancy.co.uk

Publicity Leicestershire
Janet Currie, 134 Herrick Road, Loughborough, LE11 2BU, 07929 710045, janet.currie@me.com

Publicity Rutland
Jane Aleander-Orr, Greystones, The Jetty, Wing LE15 8RX, 01572 737368, janealexanderorr@hotmail.com

Booklet co-ordinator
Mary Hayward, 1 Wellhouse Close, Wigston LE18 2RQ, 07545 817664, maryehayward@googlemail.com

Assistant County Organisers Leicestershire
Mary Hayward, 1 Wellhouse Close, Wigston LE18 2RQ, 01162 884018, maryehayward@googlemail.com
Pete Measures, Mill House, 118 Welford Road, Leicester LE18 3SN, 01162 885409
Verena Olle, Croft Acre, The Belt, South Kilworth, Lutterworth LE17 6DX, 01858 575791
David & Beryl Wyrko, Parkside, 6 Park Hill, Gaddesby, Leicester LE7 4WH, 01664 840385, david.wyrko1@btinternet.com

County Organiser/Publicity Rutland
Rose Dejardin, 5 Top Street, Wing, Nr Oakham LE15 8SE, 01572 737557, rosedejardin@btopenworld.com, twitter @RutlandNGS

County Treasurer Rutland
David Wood, Townsend House, Morcott Road, Wing, nr Oakham LE15 8SA, 01572 737465, rdavidwood@easynet.co.uk

LINCOLNSHIRE

Opening Dates

All entries subject to change. For latest information check **www.ngs.org.uk**

February

Saturday 15
26 Little Ponton Hall

Sunday 16
26 Little Ponton Hall

Saturday 22
6 21 Chapel Street

Sunday 23
6 21 Chapel Street

March

Saturday 1
50 Walters Cottage

Sunday 2
50 Walters Cottage

Sunday 16
8 Doddington Hall Gardens

Sunday 30
6 21 Chapel Street

Dutch gardens with lavender and timeless topiary . . .

April

Saturday 12
5 Burghley House Private South Gardens

Sunday 13
5 Burghley House Private South Gardens
17 Grimsthorpe Castle

Friday 18
11 Easton Walled Gardens
54 Willow Cottage

Sunday 20
57 Woodlands

Monday 21
54 Willow Cottage

Saturday 26
32 Marigold Cottage

Sunday 27
15 Goltho House
32 Marigold Cottage
39 The Old Rectory

May

Sunday 4
16 Grantham House

Sunday 11
1 Ashfield House
9 Dunholme Lodge
40 The Old Vicarage
41 Old White House

Sunday 18
4 Belvoir Castle
47 Shepherds Hey
57 Woodlands

Friday 23
54 Willow Cottage

Saturday 24
3 Belton House
32 Marigold Cottage
52 10 Wendover Close

Sunday 25
30 Manor House
32 Marigold Cottage
52 10 Wendover Close

Monday 26
54 Willow Cottage

June

Sunday 1
39 The Old Rectory

Festival Weekend

Saturday 7
13 Frog Hall Cottage
44 Pottertons Nursery
48 Sir Joseph Banks Tribute Garden

Sunday 8
2 Aubourn Hall
13 Frog Hall Cottage
18 Guanock House
23 Holly House
44 Pottertons Nursery
48 Sir Joseph Banks Tribute Garden

Thursday 12
17 Grimsthorpe Castle

Friday 13
54 Willow Cottage

Saturday 14
50 Walters Cottage

Sunday 15
20 Hackthorn Hall
25 Horncastle Gardens
28 NEW Manor Farm
50 Walters Cottage
54 Willow Cottage
57 Woodlands

Saturday 21
12 Fen View

Sunday 22
12 Fen View
36 The Moat
37 Nova Lodge
56 Witham Hall School

Saturday 28
21 Hall Farm
32 Marigold Cottage

Sunday 29
10 East Mere House
21 Hall Farm
22 The Hawthorns
24 Hope House
29 NEW Manor House
31 March House
32 Marigold Cottage
45 Ramada
55 NEW Willow Holt

July

Friday 4
54 Willow Cottage

Saturday 5
34 Mill Farm
35 NEW 11 Millfield Terrace

Sunday 6
4 Belvoir Castle
34 Mill Farm
35 NEW 11 Millfield Terrace
37 Nova Lodge
54 Willow Cottage

Wednesday 9
8 Doddington Hall Gardens

Saturday 12
33 2 Mill Cottage
42 Overbeck

Sunday 13
7 NEW Courtlands
9 Dunholme Lodge
22 The Hawthorns
46 73 Saxilby Road
48 Sir Joseph Banks Tribute Garden

Sunday 20
38 Nut Tree Farm
43 NEW Pear Tree Cottage
57 Woodlands

Sunday 27
49 Stoke Rochford Hall

August

Sunday 3
19 Gunby Hall & Gardens
31 March House
51 68 Watts Lane

Sunday 10
48 Sir Joseph Banks Tribute Garden
51 68 Watts Lane

Sunday 17
30 Manor House
38 Nut Tree Farm

You are always welcome at an NGS garden!

47 Shepherds Hey
51 68 Watts Lane
57 Woodlands

Sunday 24
51 68 Watts Lane

Saturday 30
32 Marigold Cottage

Sunday 31
32 Marigold Cottage
51 68 Watts Lane

Early spring is a great time to visit by appointment to see the masses of bulbs . . .

September

Sunday 7
21 Hall Farm

Sunday 14
14 The Garden House
48 Sir Joseph Banks Tribute Garden
53 West Barn

Saturday 20
3 Belton House

Sunday 28
15 Goltho House

October

Sunday 5
46 73 Saxilby Road

Sunday 19
1 Ashfield House

February 2015

Saturday 14
26 Little Ponton Hall

Sunday 15
26 Little Ponton Hall

Saturday 21
6 21 Chapel Street

Sunday 22
6 21 Chapel Street

Gardens open to the public

3 Belton House
4 Belvoir Castle
5 Burghley House Private South Gardens
8 Doddington Hall Gardens
11 Easton Walled Gardens
14 The Garden House
15 Goltho House
16 Grantham House
17 Grimsthorpe Castle
19 Gunby Hall & Gardens
21 Hall Farm

By appointment only

27 1 Lomond Grove

Also open by appointment

1 Ashfield House
6 21 Chapel Street
7 Courtlands
20 Hackthorn Hall
22 The Hawthorns
23 Holly House
25 15 Elmhirst Road, Horncastle Gardens
26 Little Ponton Hall
30 Manor House
31 March House
32 Marigold Cottage
34 Mill Farm
36 The Moat
37 Nova Lodge
38 Nut Tree Farm
39 The Old Rectory
40 The Old Vicarage
42 Overbeck
43 Pear Tree Cottage
46 73 Saxilby Road
51 68 Watts Lane
54 Willow Cottage
55 Willow Holt
57 Woodlands

The Gardens

1 ASHFIELD HOUSE

Lincoln Road, Branston, Lincoln LN4 1NS. John & Judy Tinsley, 07977 505682, jmt@ashtreedevelopments.co.uk. *3m S of Lincoln. From Branston off B1188 Lincoln Rd on L; 1m from Branston Hall Hotel signed Ashfield Farms.* Home-made teas. **Adm £3.50, chd free. Sun 11 May (11-4.30); Sun 19 Oct (11-4). Visitors also welcome by appt Feb to Oct.**

10 acre garden constructed around a planting of trees and shrubs. The main feature in the spring is the collection of some 110 flowering cherries of 40 different varieties. Sweeping lawns with massed plantings of spring flowering bulbs around a large pond. In the autumn the colours can be amazing. A recently planted magnolia collection in a newly constructed woodland garden. Early spring is a great time to visit by appointment to see the masses of bulbs. Fairly level garden. Grass paths.

2 AUBOURN HALL

Harmston Road, Aubourn, nr Lincoln LN5 9DZ. Mr & Mrs Christopher Nevile, www.aubournhall.co.uk. *7m SW of Lincoln. Signed off A607 at Harmston & off A46 at Thorpe on the Hill.* Light refreshments. **Adm £4.50, chd free. Sun 8 June (2-5).**

Approx 8 acres. Lawns, mature trees, shrubs, roses, mixed borders, new rose garden, large prairie and topiary garden, spring bulbs and ponds. C11 church adjoining. House featured in Country Life magazine. Access to garden is fairly flat and smooth. Depending on weather some areas may be inaccessible for wheelchairs. Parking in field not on tarmac.

3 ◆ BELTON HOUSE

Grantham NG32 2LS. National Trust, 01476 566116, www.nationaltrust.org.uk. *3m NE of Grantham. On A607 Grantham to Lincoln rd. Easily reached & signed from A1 (Grantham N junction).* **Adm £10.60, chd £7. For NGS: Sat 24 May, Sat 20 Sept (9.30-5.30). For other opening times and information, please phone or see garden website.**

The 35-acre gardens at Belton House are a yr-round delight. Italian gardens with orangery and picturesque fountain, Dutch gardens with lavender and timeless topiary lead on to woodland paths, boathouse and tranquil lakeshore. C17 Country House, stone temple and mirror pond fountain. Quiet lakeside area. Several seats in sun or shade. Light refreshments in Stables Restaurant. Gravel paths, cobbled driveway, some steps. Please ask at Visitor Reception for wheelchair access advice or phone in advance.

4 ◆ BELVOIR CASTLE

Belvoir, Nr Grantham, Lincolnshire NG32 1PE. The Duke & Duchess of Rutland, www.belvoircastle.com. *9m W of Grantham. Follow brown heritage signs for Belvoir Castle on A52, A1, A607.* **Adm £8, chd £5. For NGS: Sun 18 May, Sun 6 July**

(2-5.30). For other opening times and information, please see garden website.
English Heritage Grade 2 gardens. Formal garden designed by Harold Peto and replanted with roses by the present Duchess; bandstand, formal parterres, Caius Gabriel Cibber statue garden and pet cemetery. Japanese garden with camellias, magnolias and hydrangeas set in a natural amphitheatre The spring gardens house a spectacular collection of acers, magnolias, rhododendrons and azaleas and a magnificent Davidia involucrata. Flat shoes essential. Light refreshments available at entrance next to car park. Only rose garden accessible by wheelchair, steep slopes and steps in other areas.

5 ◆ BURGHLEY HOUSE PRIVATE SOUTH GARDENS
Stamford PE9 3JY. Burghley House Preservation Trust, 01780 752451, www.burghley.co.uk. *1m E of Stamford. From Stamford follow signs to Burghley via B1443.* **Adm £3.50, chd £2. For NGS: Sat 12, Sun 13 Apr (11-4). For other opening times and information, please phone or see garden website.**
On 12 and 13 April the Private South Gardens at Burghley House will open for the NGS with spectacular spring bulbs in park like setting with magnificent trees and the opportunity to enjoy Capability Brown's famous lake and summerhouse. Entry to the Private South Gardens via orangery. The Garden of Surprises, Sculpture Garden and house are open as normal. Regular admission prices apply. Light refreshments. Gravel paths.

6 21 CHAPEL STREET
Hacconby, Bourne PE10 0UL. Cliff & Joan Curtis, 01778 570314, cliffordcurtis@btinternet.com. *3m N of Bourne. A15, turn E at Xrds into Hacconby, L at village green.* Home-made teas. **Adm £2.50, chd free. Sat 22, Sun 23 Feb, Sun 30 Mar (11-5), Sat 21, Sun 22 Feb 2015. Visitors also welcome by appt Jan to Oct.**
A cottage garden behind a 300yr old cottage. Snowdrops, primroses, hellebores and many different spring flowering bulbs. Colour with bulbs and herbaceous plants through the yr, autumn with asters, dahlias, salvias and many of the autumn flowering yellow daises.

Grimsthorpe Castle

7 NEW COURTLANDS
Tattershall Road, Kirkby-on-Bain, Woodhall Spa LN10 6YN. Peter & Jill Hilton, 01526 353115, peter@courtlandshilton.co.uk. *Kirkby on Bain. Garden located on S edge of village, on rd leading to Recycling Centre, gravel pits & Coningsby.* Home-made teas. **Adm £3, chd free. Sun 13 July (2-5). Visitors also welcome by appt May to Oct.**
Enjoy the peace and quiet of this lovely 3½ acre garden and 'paddock'. A flat established garden with large trees (60 mature Scots Pines), open lawn, herbaceous borders, island beds, folly area, water feature, newly developed Japanese garden, and a large vegetable garden with raised beds. Full wheelchair access but regret no WC.

8 ◆ DODDINGTON HALL GARDENS
Doddington, Lincoln LN6 4RU. Claire & James Birch, 01522 812510, www.doddingtonhall.com. *5m W of Lincoln. Signed clearly from A46 Lincoln bypass & A57, 3m.* **Adm £5, chd £2.75. For NGS: Sun 16 Mar (11-4); Wed 9 July (11-5). For other opening times and information, please phone or see garden website.**
5 acres of romantic walled and wild gardens. Naturalised spring bulbs and scented shrubs from Feb to May. Spectacular iris display late May/early June in box-edged parterres of West Garden. Sumptuous herbaceous borders throughout summer; ancient chestnut trees; turf maze; Temple of the Winds. Fully productive, walled kitchen garden. Wheelchair access possible via gravel paths. Ramps also in use. Access map available from Gatehouse Shop.

♿ 🚌 ☕

9 DUNHOLME LODGE
Dunholme, Lincoln LN2 3QA. Hugh & Lesley Wykes. *4m NE of Lincoln. Turn off A46 towards Welton at Hand Car Wash garage. After ½ m turn L up long concrete rd. Garden at top.* Cream teas. **Adm £2.50, chd free. Sun 11 May, Sun 13 July (11-5).**
3 acre garden. Spring bulb area, shrub border, fern garden, topiary, large natural pond, wild flower area, orchard and vegetable garden. Crafts and stalls. Plant sales (July only), private RAF Dunholme Lodge Museum and War Memorial. Most areas wheelchair accessible but some loose stone and gravel.

10 EAST MERE HOUSE

Bracebridge Heath, Lincoln LN4 2JB. Mr & Mrs James Dean. *Turn off A15 to Bardney & Mere on B1178. After 1m turn R on LH bend. Garden 100yds on R.* Home-made teas. **Adm £3, chd free. Sun 29 June (11.30-5).**

2 acre formal country garden, recently redesigned by Angel Collins, surrounding a stone farmhouse. Box-edged borders planted with grasses, perennials and seasonal bedding. Lawns, ornamental trees, crab apple avenue and small rose garden. Parterre planted with rosemary, lavender, santolina and alliums. Large kitchen garden with raised vegetable beds and young fruit trees on the farm-yard walls. Wild flower meadow.

11 ◆ EASTON WALLED GARDENS

Easton NG33 5AP. Sir Fred & Lady Cholmeley, 01476 530063, www.eastonwalledgardens.co.uk. *7m S of Grantham. 1m off A1. Follow village signposts via B6403.* **Adm £6.75, chd £2.50. For NGS: Fri 18 Apr (11-4). For other opening times and information, please phone or see garden website.**

12 acres of 400yr old forgotten gardens undergoing extensive renovation. Set in parkland with dramatic views. C16 garden with Victorian embellishments. Italianate terraces; yew tunnel; snowdrops and cut flower garden. David Austin roses, meadows and sweet pea collections. Cottage and vegetable gardens. Please wear sensible shoes suitable for country walking. Childrens' Trail. Light refreshments. Regret no wheelchair access to lower gardens but tearoom, shop and upper gardens all accessible.

12 FEN VIEW

Fen Lane, East Keal PE23 4AY. Mr & Mrs Geoffrey Wheatley. *2m SW of Spilsby. Car parking - Church Lane, in field opp church. 200yds to garden. Disabled parking at garden.* Home-made teas. **Adm £2.50, chd free. Sat 21, Sun 22 June (2-5.30).**

Sloping secluded 1/2 -acre garden planted to reflect the owners interest in gardening for wildlife. Designed around a number of different themed areas, ponds, vistas, sculptures and plenty of seating.

13 FROG HALL COTTAGE

Langrick Road, New York LN4 4XH. Kathy Wright. *B1192, 2m S of New York Xrds. 3m N of Langrick Bridge.* Home-made teas. **Adm £2.50, chd free. Sat 7, Sun 8 June (2-5).**

3/4 -acre plantswoman's garden designed by the owner. Courtyard style patio, stream, and small terraced area. Large gravel area with raised beds planted with many unusual plants and a thatched summerhouse. A path leads to a lawn with island beds and a pond. There is a classic style garden planted with roses and perennials, many unusual. Some new features have been added. Small plant centre attached.

A country garden in an attractive historic town in the heart of the Lincolnshire Wolds . . .

14 ◆ THE GARDEN HOUSE

Saxby, Market Rasen, Lincoln LN8 2DQ. Chris Neave & Jonathan Cartwright, 01673 878820, www.thegardenhousesaxby.co.uk. *8m N of Lincoln; 2 1/4 m E of A15. Turn off A15 signed Saxby.* **Combined adm £4, chd free. For NGS: Sun 14 Sept (11-4). Combined with West Barn. For other opening times and information, please phone or see garden website.**

8-acre landscaped garden packed with interest. Yew hedging and walls enclose magical garden rooms full of roses and herbaceous plants. Long terrace, Dutch, pergola and obelisk gardens link to a lavender walk. Large natural damp garden. Dry garden leading onto hillside planted with rarer trees overlooking a large reflective pond. Native woodland areas, prairie and wild flower meadow planted with massed bulbs. Wonderful views. Adjacent to C18 classical church. Home-made teas. Gravel paths, steep slopes.

15 ◆ GOLTHO HOUSE

Lincoln Road, Goltho, Nr Wragby, Market Rasen LN8 5NF. Mr & Mrs S Hollingworth, 01673 857768, www.golthogardens.com. *10m E of Lincoln. On A158, 1m before Wragby. Garden on L (not in Goltho Village).* **Adm £5, chd free. For NGS: Sun 27 Apr, Sun 28 Sept (10-4). For other opening times and information, please phone or see garden website.**

4 1/2 -acre garden started in 1998 but looking established with long grass walk flanked by abundantly planted herbaceous borders forming a focal point. Paths and walkway span out to other features incl nut walk, prairie border, wild flower meadow, rose garden and large pond area. Snowdrops, hellebores and shrubs for winter interest. Light refreshments.

16 ◆ GRANTHAM HOUSE

Castlegate, Grantham NG31 6SS. National Trust, 01476 564705, www.nationaltrust.org.uk. *Centre of Grantham. Follow A607 round one-way system & turn R up Castlegate at T-lights on corner before Jet station. Garden on L opp Church St.* **Adm £3, chd free. For NGS: Sun 4 May (2-5). For other opening times and information, please phone or see garden website.**

A delightful secret garden in a medieval setting. Created by plantswoman Lady Molly Wyldbo re-Smith and in the process of restoration. 5 acres of unusual trees and shrubs with colour themed herbaceous borders. Features incl gravel garden, iris walk and box parterre. Woodland area carpeted with bulbs and in the orchard, a wild flower meadow. Barnsdale plant stall. Home-made teas. Gravel paths.

17 ◆ GRIMSTHORPE CASTLE

Grimsthorpe, Bourne PE10 0LZ. Grimsthorpe & Drummond Castle Trust, 01778 591205, www.grimsthorpe.co.uk. *3m NW of Bourne. 8m E of A1 on A151 from Colsterworth junction.* **Adm £5.50, chd £2. For NGS: Sun 13 Apr, Thur 12 June (11-5). For other opening times and information, please phone or see garden website.**

15 acres of formal and woodland gardens incl bulbs and wildflowers. Formal gardens encompass fine

topiary, roses, herbaceous borders and unusual ornamental kitchen garden. Light refreshments. Gravel paths.

18 GUANOCK HOUSE

Guanock Gate, Sutton St Edmund PE12 0LW. Mr & Mrs Michael Coleman. *16m SE of Spalding. From village church turn R, cross rd, then L Guanock Gate. Garden at end of rd on R.* Tea and cakes. **Adm £3, chd free. Sun 8 June (1.30-5).**
Garden designed by Arne Maynard. 5 acres. Herbaceous border, knot garden, rose garden and lime walk. Orchard, walled kitchen garden, Italian garden. Guanock House is a C16 manor house built in the flat fens of S Lincolnshire. Plant stall. Partial wheelchair access. Garden on different levels.

19 ◆ GUNBY HALL & GARDENS

Spilsby PE23 5SS. National Trust, 01754 890102, www.nationaltrust.org.uk. *2½ m NW of Burgh-le-Marsh. 7m W of Skegness. On A158. Signed off Gunby r'about.* **Adm £4, chd £2. For NGS: Sun 3 Aug (11-5). For other opening times and information, please phone or see garden website.**
8 acres of formal and walled gardens; old roses, herbaceous borders; herb garden; kitchen garden with fruit trees and vegetables. Greenhouses, carp pond and sweeping lawns. Tennyson's 'Haunt of Ancient Peace'. House built by Sir William Massingberd in 1700. Home-made teas at the Old Laundry Tea-room. Wheelchair access in gardens but not the hall.

20 HACKTHORN HALL

Hackthorn, Lincoln LN2 3PQ. Mr & Mrs William Cracroft-Eley, 01673 860423, office@hackthorn.com, www.hackthorn.com. *6m N of Lincoln. Follow signs to Hackthorn. Approx 1m off A15.* Home-made teas at Hackthorn Village Hall. **Adm £3.50, chd free. Sun 15 June (1-5). Visitors also welcome by appt Apr to Oct for groups 10+.**
Formal and woodland garden, productive and ornamental walled gardens surrounding Hackthorn Hall and church extending to approx 15 acres. Parts of the formal gardens designed by Bunny Guinness. The walled garden boasts a magnificent 'Black Hamburg' vine, believed to be second in size to the vine at Hampton Court. Limited wheelchair access, gravel paths, grass drives.

21 ◆ HALL FARM

Harpswell, Gainsborough DN21 5UU. Pam & Mark Tatam, 01427 668412, www.hall-farm.co.uk. *7m E of Gainsborough. On A631, 1½ m W of Caenby Corner.* **Adm £3.50, chd free. For NGS: Sat 28, Sun 29 June, Sun 7 Sept (10-5). For other opening times and information, please phone or see garden website.**
The garden is now about 3 acres, encompassing mature area, formal and informal areas, a parterre filled with salad crops, herbs and annuals. There is also a sunken garden, courtyard with rill, a walled Mediterranean garden, double herbaceous borders for late summer, lawns, pond, giant chess set, and a flower and grass meadow. A short walk to a medieval moat. Free seed collecting on Sun 7 Sept. Light refreshments and lunches. Featured in Landscape magazine. Most of garden is suitable for wheelchairs.

22 THE HAWTHORNS

Bicker Road, Donington PE11 4XP. Colin & Janet Johnson, 01775 822808, colinj04@hotmail.com, www.thehawthornsrarebreeds.co.uk. *½ m NW of Donington. Bicker Rd is directly off A52 opp Church Rd. Parking available in Church Rd or village centre car park.* Home-made teas. **Adm £3.50, chd free. Sun 29 June, Sun 13 July (11-4). Visitors also welcome by appt June to Aug for groups of 12+.**
Traditional garden with extensive herbaceous borders, pond, large old English rose garden, vegetable and fruit areas with feature greenhouse. Cider orchard and area housing rare breed animals incl pigs, sheep and chickens. Featured in Lincolnshire Pride Magazine.

23 HOLLY HOUSE

Fishtoft Drove, Frithville, Boston PE22 7ES. Sally & David Grant, 01205 750486, sallygrant50@btinternet.com. *3m N of Boston. 1m S of Frithville. Unclassified rd. On W side of West Fen Drain. Marked on good maps.* Home-made teas. **Adm £3, chd free. Sun 8 June (12-5). Visitors also welcome by appt May to June for groups 10+.**
Approx 1 acre informal mixed borders, scree beds, steps leading down to pond with cascade and stream. Small woodland area. Quiet garden with water feature. Extra 2½ acres devoted to wildlife, especially bumble bees and butterflies. Partial wheelchair access with some steep slopes and steps.

24 HOPE HOUSE

15 Horsemarket, Caistor LN7 6UP. Sue Neave, www.hopehousegardens.co.uk. *Off A46 Between Lincoln & Grimsby. Centre of town.* Home-made teas at Caistor Arts & Heritage Centre (until 4pm). **Combined adm £3.50, chd free. Sun 29 June (1-5). Combined with Ramada.**
A country garden in an attractive historic town in the heart of the Lincolnshire Wolds. Small walled garden attached to an interesting Georgian house. Roses, perennials, shrubs, trees, fruit and a small raised vegetable area. Wildlife pond and formal water trough in the dining area. Yr-round colour and interest in a tranquil space created by its garden designer owner. New planting planned for 2014. Caistor Arts and Heritage Centre opposite. Gold award Best Front Garden, East Midlands in Bloom.

The Hawthorns

GROUP OPENING

25 HORNCASTLE GARDENS

Horncastle LN9 5AS. *Take A158 from Lincoln. Just inside 40mph turn L into Accommodation Rd. Gardens signed from here. Roadside parking only. Please park sensibly*. Home-made teas at 15 Elmhirst Road. **Combined adm £4, chd free. Sun 15 June (11-4.30).**

40 ACCOMMODATION ROAD
Eddie & Marie Aldridge

15 ELMHIRST ROAD
Sylvia Ravenhall
Visitors also welcome by appt June to July for daytime or evening visits.
01507 526014
sylvan@btinternet.com

1 MAPLE CLOSE
Miss Chrissy Bark

The market town of Horncastle some 20m to the east of Lincoln on the A158 is often called 'The Gateway to the Wolds'. It is well known for its Antique and bric-a-brac shops. These three very different gardens are within easy walking distance of each other, maps provided. 40 Accommodation Road is packed with herbaceous perennials and climbers in a garden which wraps around three sides of a bungalow. The rear garden has suffered from flooding in the past, hence the raised beds. 1 Maple Close has an exposed gravelled front garden with masses of lavender. The sunny and very dry rear garden is densely planted in the cottage garden style with its mix of flowers, herbs, vegetables and fruit. 15 Elmhirst Road is a long and narrow town garden, two thirds walled, winding gravel paths and shallow steps take you around 'secret' corners. It is planted with mixed perennials, shrubs, climbers, small trees and lawn. Many hostas are grown in pots and in the ground. There are plenty of seats. Hand made cards and preserves for sale, percentage of proceeds to NGS. 15 Elmhirst Rd featured in Garden Answers.

26 LITTLE PONTON HALL

Grantham NG33 5BS. Mrs Alastair McCorquodale, 01400 281288, wendy@linkmagazines.co.uk, www.littlepontonhallgardens.org.uk. *2m S of Grantham. ½ m E of A1 at S end of Grantham bypass*. Home-made teas. **Adm £5, chd free. Sat 15, Sun 16 Feb (11-4); Sat 14, Sun 15 Feb 2015. Visitors also welcome by appt Feb to Oct.**

3 to 4-acre garden. Massed snowdrops and aconites in Feb. Stream, spring blossom and hellebores, bulbs and river walk. Spacious lawns with cedar tree over 200yrs old. Formal walled kitchen garden and listed dovecote, with recently developed herb garden. Victorian greenhouses with many plants from exotic locations. Disabled parking. Access on hard surfaces, unsuitable on grass. Disabled WC.

27 1 LOMOND GROVE

Humberston, Grimsby DN36 4BD. Mike & Josie Ireland, 01472 319579, m.ireland1@ntlworld.com, www.alpinegarden.co.uk. *1m S of*

Cleethorpes. From A16 Peaks Parkway turn onto A1098 Hewitts Ave. Turn R at r'about onto A1031, 3rd R into Derwent Drive. 2nd R into Lomond Grove. **Adm £2.50, chd free. Visitors welcome by appt Mar to Aug.**
Small S-facing garden for alpines, bulbs, dwarf conifers and other interesting genera which grow alongside alpines. Acers grown from seed provide shade. Trillium, corydalis, primula, pulsatilla, crocus, fritillaria, anemone and sanguinaria are just some of the species grown. Raised tufa bed in alpine house and new tufa wall in the garden.

The brick east wing is described by Pevsner as 'wild, artisan, mannerism! . . .

28 NEW MANOR FARM
Horkstow Road, South Ferriby, Barton-upon-Humber DN18 6HS. Geoff & Angela Wells. *3m from Barton on A1077, turn L onto B1204, opp Village Hall.* Home-made teas. **Adm £3, chd free. Sun 15 June (11-5).**
A traditional farmhouse set within approx 1 acre with mature shrubberies, herbaceous borders, gravel garden and pergola walk. Many old trees with preservation orders. New rose garden planted 2013. Wildlife lake set within a paddock.

30 MANOR HOUSE
Hagworthingham, Spilsby PE23 4LN. Gill Maxim & David O'Connor, 01507 588530, vcagillmaxim@aol.com. *5m E of Horncastle. S of A158 in Hagworthingham, turn into Bond Hayes Lane downhill, becomes Manor Rd. Please follow signs down gravel track to parking area.* Home-made teas. **Adm £3, chd free (share to Holy Trinity Hagworthingham). Sun 25 May, Sun 17 Aug (2-5). Visitors also welcome by appt May to Sept.**
2-acre garden on S-facing slope, partly terraced and well protected by established trees and shrubs. Redeveloped over 10yrs with natural and formal ponds. Shrub roses, laburnum walk, hosta border, gravel bed and other areas mainly planted with hardy perennials, trees and shrubs.

29 NEW MANOR HOUSE
Aslackby, Sleaford NG34 0HG. Mr Alan Baxter. *6m N of Bourne just off A15.* Home-made teas in adjacent Church. **Adm £4, chd free. Sun 29 June (2-5.30).**
5 acres of gardens, orchards, meadows and woodland surround the Grade 1 Manor House (not open). The brick east wing is described by Pevsner as 'wild, artisan, mannerism!' Now framed by riotous gardens, best described as 'romantic'. Featured in Country Life magazine. With care most areas accessible to wheelchair users.

31 MARCH HOUSE
3 Harmston Park Avenue, Harmston, Lincoln LN5 9GF. Asif & Barbara Kamal, 01522 722554. *7m S of Lincoln. In the village of Harmston, off Church Lane.* Light refreshments. **Adm £2.50, chd free. Sun 29 June, Sun 3 Aug (1-4.30). Visitors also welcome by appt June to Sept for daytime or evening visits.**
The unexpected garden. Beautifully designed, lush with many unusual plants. Bird friendly with a large pond teeming with wildlife. An oasis, verdant with semi tropical colours. Very atmospheric and described by a visitor as a 'piece of paradise'.

32 MARIGOLD COTTAGE
Hotchin Road, Sutton-on-Sea LN12 2NP. Stephanie Lee & John Raby, 01507 442151, marigoldlee@btinternet.com, www.marigoldcottage.webs.com. *16m N of Skegness on A52. 7m E of Alford on A1111. 3m S of Mablethorpe on A52. Turn off A52 on High St at Cornerhouse Cafe. Follow rd past playing field on R. Rd turns away from the dunes. House 2nd on L.* Home-made teas. **Adm £3, chd free. Sats & Suns 26, 27 Apr, 24, 25 May, 28, 29 June, 30, 31 Aug (2-5). Visitors also welcome by appt Apr to Sept for groups. Home-made teas available.**
This is a plantswoman's seaside garden. Look out for oriental influences from years spent working in the Far East. Productive garden and small nursery. Most of the garden is wheelchair accessible along flat, paved paths.

33 2 MILL COTTAGE
Barkwith Road, South Willingham, Market Rasen LN8 6NN. Mrs Jo Rouston, 01673 858656, jo@rouston-gardens.co.uk. *5m E of Wragby. On A157 turn R at PH in East Barkwith then immed L to South Willingham. Cottage 1m on L. Please email or phone for more directions.* Home-made teas. **Adm £2.50, chd free. Sat 12 July (12-5).**
A garden of several defined spaces, packed with interesting features, unusual plants and well placed seating areas, created by garden designer Jo Rouston. Original engine shed, a working well, raised beds using local rock with small pond. Clipped box, alpines, roses, summerhouses and water feature. Box and lavender hedge to greenhouse and herb garden. Late season bed. Woven metal and turf tree seat. Featured in Gardening News. Gravel at far end of garden to new woven seat. Steps down to the main greenhouse.

34 MILL FARM
Brigg Road, Grasby, Caistor DN38 6AQ. Mike & Helen Boothman, 01652 628424, boothmanhelen@gmail.com. *3m NW of Caistor on A1084. Between Brigg & Caistor. From Cross Keys PH towards Caistor for approx 200yds.* Home-made teas. **Adm £3, chd free. Sat 5, Sun 6 July (11-4). Visitors also welcome by appt Apr to Aug.**
3½ -acre hill-top garden with panoramic views. Development began circa 2005. New beds and features still evolving, whilst the older beds are now maturing. Rill, rose and peony beds. Remains of windmill adapted into a fernery. Plantsman's garden with a wealth of shrubs and perennials, wildlife ponds, vegetable beds and woodland area with specimen trees.

35 NEW 11 MILLFIELD TERRACE

Sleaford NG34 7AD. Mrs Weston. *Opp Northgate Sports Hall & Carres Grammer School. Parking available at grammer school.* **Adm £3, chd free. Sat 5, Sun 6 July (12-5).**

11 Millfield Terrace is a charming small town garden. On entry there is an intimate courtyard garden, with an abundance of ferns, hostas and various perennials. Venturing through an ivy arch you enter the main gravel garden which features a large variety of clematis, heucheras and grasses. Also an imaginative planting of pots and finally on to a thoughtfully planted allotment. The garden also backs on to an allotment full of fruit trees, vegetables and flowers.

Kids love exploring winding paths through the wilder areas . . .

36 THE MOAT

Newton NG34 0ED. Mr & Mrs Mike Barnes, 01529 497462, lynnebarnes14@googlemail.com. *Off A52 halfway between Grantham & Sleaford. In Newton village, opp church. Please park sensibly in village.* Home-made teas. **Adm £3.50, chd free. Sun 22 June (11-5). Visitors also welcome by appt May to July.**

Delightful 2½ acre country garden established 12yrs. Created to blend with its country surroundings and featuring island beds planted with a variety of unusual perennials, large natural pond and ha-ha, again imaginatively planted. Topiary, courtyard and orchard. Small vegetable garden. Featured in Lincolnshire Life. Garden on slope but accessible to wheelchair users.

37 NOVA LODGE

150 Horncastle Road, Roughton Moor, Woodhall Spa LN10 6UX. Leo Boshier, 01526 354940, moxons555@btinternet.com. *On B1191. Approx 2m E of centre of Woodhall Spa on Horncastle Rd. Roadside parking.* Home-made teas. **Adm £3, chd free. Sun 22 June, Sun 6 July (12-5). Visitors also welcome by appt June to July for groups 10+.**

⅔-acre traditional garden set within mature trees started 2009. Herbaceous beds and borders, rose and hosta beds, shrubs, ferns and grasses, large lawns 2 ponds, summerhouse, small vegetable and herb areas, 2 greenhouses. Seating to enjoy all areas. Featured in Lincolnshire Today magazine.

38 NUT TREE FARM

Peppin Lane, Fotherby, Louth LN11 0UP. Tim & Judith Hunter, 01507 602208, nuttreefarm@hotmail.com. *2m N of Louth. At end of Peppin Lane. Continue on farm track for ½ m. Transport available for those with mobility problems from Woodlands.* Light refreshments at Woodlands. **Combined adm £3.50 (July), £4 (Aug), chd free. Sun 20 July, Sun 17 Aug (11-5). Combined with Woodlands, Sun 20 July; Shepherds Hey and Woodlands, Sun 17 Aug. Visitors also welcome by appt June to Sept.**

A garden of over an acre recently established with stunning views of the Lincolnshire Wolds. There is a sweeping herbaceous border framing the lawn, double walls planted with pelargoniums surrounding the house and a rill running from the raised terrace to the large pond. There is also an attractive brick potager. Pedigree flock of prize winning Hampshire Down sheep in fields surrounding part of garden. Honey for sale. Some gravel paths.

39 THE OLD RECTORY

East Keal, Spilsby PE23 4AT. Mrs Ruth Ward, 01790 752477, rfjward@btinternet.com. *2m SW of Spilsby. Off A16. Turn into Church Lane by PO.* Home-made teas. **Adm £3, chd free. Sun 27 Apr, Sun 1 June (2-5). Visitors also welcome by appt Feb to Nov with refreshments by arrangement.**

Beautifully situated, with fine views, rambling cottage garden on different levels falling naturally into separate areas, with changing effects and atmosphere. Steps, paths and vistas to lead you on, with seats well placed for appreciating special views or relaxing and enjoying the peace. Dry border, vegetable garden, orchard, woodland walk, wild flower meadow.

40 THE OLD VICARAGE

Low Road, Holbeach Hurn PE12 8JN. Mrs Liz Dixon-Spain, 01406 424148, lizdixonspain@gmail.com. *2m NE of Holbeach. Turn off A17 N to Holbeach Hurn, past post box in middle of village, 1st R into Low Rd. Old Vicarage on R approx 400yds.* Teas at Old White House. **Combined adm £5, chd free. Sun 11 May (1-5). Combined with Old White House. Visitors also welcome by appt Feb to Oct.**

2 acres of garden with 150yr old tulip, plane and beech trees: borders of shrubs, roses, herbaceous plants. Shrub roses and herb garden in old paddock area, surrounded by informal areas with pond and bog garden, wild flowers, grasses and bulbs. Small fruit and vegetable gardens. Kids love exploring winding paths through the wilder areas. Garden is managed environmentally. Lots of areas for kids to explore.

41 OLD WHITE HOUSE

Holbeach Hurn PE12 8JP. Mr & Mrs A Worth. *2m N of Holbeach. Turn off A17 N to Holbeach Hurn, follow signs to village, go straight through, turn R after Rose & Crown at Baileys Lane.* Home-made teas. **Combined adm £5, chd free. Sun 11 May (1-5). Combined with The Old Vicarage.**

1½ acres of mature garden, featuring herbaceous borders, roses, patterned garden, herb garden and walled kitchen garden.

42 OVERBECK

46 Main Street, Scothern LN2 2UW. John & Joyce Good, 01673 862200, jandjgood@btinternet.com. *4m E of Lincoln. Scothern is signed from A46 at Dunholme & A158 at Sudbrooke. Overbeck is at E end of Main St.* Light refreshments. **Adm £3, chd free. Sat 12 July (11-5). Visitors also welcome by appt May to Aug for daytime and evening visits. Coaches welcome.**

Approx ½ -acre garden in quiet village. Long herbaceous borders and colour-themed island beds with some unusual perennials. Hosta border, gravel bed with grasses, fernery, trees, numerous shrubs and climbers and large prolific vegetable and fruit area.

43 NEW PEAR TREE COTTAGE
Butt Lane, Goulceby, Louth LN11 9UP. Jill Mowbray & Miranda Manning Press, 01507 343201, chirpy@theraggedrobin.co.uk, www.theraggedrobin.co.uk. *6m N of Horncastle & 8m SW of Louth. 2m off A153 between Louth & Horncastle. 2m off Caistor High St (B1225).* Home-made teas. **Adm £3, chd free. Sun 20 July (11-4). Visitors also welcome by appt Apr to Aug for groups 6 - 12 max.**
Situated in the heart of the Wolds, the garden which surrounds the house on three sides, is an oasis of bright colour within the delightful village of Goulceby. The balance of perennials and annuals ensure a vibrant display throughout the seasons. Productive fruit and vegetable plots and greenhouses lie alongside the borders which only serves to add to the verdant atmosphere within the garden. Wheelchair access via front gate of house leading to lawn. No solid paths, access on grass only.

44 POTTERTONS NURSERY
Nettleton, Caistor LN7 6HX. Rob & Jackie Potterton, www.pottertons.co.uk. *1m W of Nettleton. From A46 at Nettleton turn onto B1205 (Moortown). Nursery 1¼ m by edge of wood.* Home-made teas. **Adm £3, chd free. Sat 7, Sun 8 June (10-4).**
Large established garden featuring extensive selection of alpines, dwarf bulbs, conifers and woodland plants. Superb landscaped rockery with stream and waterfalls, pool, raised beds, troughs and island beds. Level paths mostly on mixed grass surfaces.

45 RAMADA
17 Horsemarket, Caistor, Market Rasen LN7 6UP. Peter & Gwyneth Thompson. *Caistor is off A46 between Lincoln & Grimsby. Garden off Market Place down Plough Hill on the Horsemarket.* **Combined adm £3.50, chd free. Sun 29 June (1-5). Combined with Hope House.**
Hillside garden with terraced herbaceous borders filled with perennials for yr-round interest. Small pond fed by natural spring and boggy area. Fruit trees and vegetable area. Caistor Arts and Heritage Centre nearby.

46 73 SAXILBY ROAD
Sturton by Stow LN1 2AA. Charles & Tricia Elliott, 01427 788517. *9m NW of Lincoln. On B1241. Halfway between Lincoln & Gainsborough.* **Adm £2.50, chd free. Sun 13 July, Sun 5 Oct (11-4). Visitors also welcome by appt May to Oct.**
Small but extensively planted garden devoted to colourful summer flowering plants and grasses followed in autumn by asters, late season grasses and autumn colouring shrubs. A plant lover's garden. Large display of tender fuchsias in July. Open aspect front and rear, good views. Featured in Country Life magazine.

47 SHEPHERDS HEY
Peppin Lane, Fotherby, Louth LN11 0UW. Roger & Barbara Chester. *2m N of Louth. Leave A16 to Fotherby. Peppin Lane is no-through rd running E from village centre. Please park on RH verge opp allotments.* Home-made teas at Woodlands. **Combined adm £3.50 (May) £4 (Aug), chd free. Sun 18 May, Sun 17 Aug (11-5). Combined with Woodlands, Sun 18 May; Nut Tree Farm and Woodlands, Sun 17 Aug.**
Small garden packed with unusual and interesting perennials. Open frontage gives visitors a warm welcome, with a small pond, terraced border and steep bank side to a small stream. Rear garden takes advantage of the panoramic views over open countryside, with colour themed borders. Featured in Lincolnshire Life. Wheelchair access to rear garden possible with care. Front garden can be viewed from road.

48 SIR JOSEPH BANKS TRIBUTE GARDEN
Bridge Street, Horncastle LN9 5HZ. Sir Joseph Banks Society. *From Horncastle Market Square 100yrds along Bridge St. Garden on L, entrance through shop.* **Adm £2.50, chd free. Sat 7, Sun 8 June, Sun 13 July, Sun 10 Aug, Sun 14 Sept (1.30-4.30).**
Sir Joseph Banks (1743-1820) Tribute Garden is a courtyard providing an attractive oasis in a busy market town. It features 70 different species of plants, many collected on his voyage with Capt. Cook on HMS Endeavour. Interpretation material available. Featured in Lincolnshire Life and local press. Level gravel path.

49 STOKE ROCHFORD HALL
Stoke Rochford, Grantham NG33 5EJ, 01476 530337, enquiries@stokerochfordhall.co.uk, www.stokerochfordhall.co.uk. *6m S of Grantham W off A1. Garden on R before village.* Light refreshments. **Adm £4, chd free. Sun 27 July (10-6).**
Stoke Rochford Hall is a superb Grade II listed Victorian manor house with formal landscaped gardens and surrounded by 28 acres of parkland. The gardens are in the Victorian style, with long herbaceous borders, rose garden, informal paths and a particular feature being the many interesting trees and shrubs, incl the magnificent Cedar of Lebanon and the Gingko Biloba or Maidenhair Tree. Hall, bars and restaurants easily accessible to wheelchair users. Gardens accessible via gravel paths and occasional gentle slope.

This is a beautiful setting for afternoon tea . . .

50 WALTERS COTTAGE
6 Hall Road, Haconby, nr Bourne PE10 0UY. Ivan & Sadie Hall. *3m N of Bourne A15. Turn E at Xrds to Haconby. Turn R at Hare & Hounds PH.* Home-made teas. **Adm £3, chd free. Sat 1, Sun 2 Mar (12-4); Sat 14 June (12-5); Sun 15 June (12-4).**
Country cottage garden of over ¼ acre developed over the past 11yrs. Various themed areas. Walled garden with hornbeam allée, topiary and rill. Woodland area with wildlife pond and plants. Sunken garden. Long herbaceous borders, lawns and collection of hostas. Garden is well-stocked with many interesting and rare plants with added features. Snowdrops, hellebores and spring bulbs. Featured in Stamford Mercury.

51 68 WATTS LANE

Louth LN11 9DG. Jenny & Rodger Grasham, 07977 318145, sallysing@hotmail.co.uk, www.facebook.com/thesecretgardenoflouth. *½ m S of Louth town centre. Watts Lane off Newmarket (on B1200). Turn by pedestrian lights & Londis shop.* Home-made teas. **Adm £2.50, chd free. Sun 3, Sun 10, Sun 17, Sun 24, Sun 31 Aug (11-4). Visitors also welcome by appt July to Sept with teas provided.**

Blank canvas of ⅕ acre in early 90s. Developed into lush, colourful, exotic plant-packed haven. A whole new world on entering from street. Exotic borders, raised island, long hot border, ponds, stumpery, developing prairie style border. Conservatory, grapevine. Intimate seating areas along garden's journey. Facebook page - The Secret Garden of Louth. Children, find where the frogs are hiding! Many butterflies and bees but how many different types? Grass pathways, main garden area accessible by wheelchair.

52 10 WENDOVER CLOSE

Rippingale, Bourne PE10 0TQ. Chris & Tim Bladon. *5½ m N of Bourne. Enter village at Rippingale/Kirby Underwood Xrds on A15. Wendover Close is 1st turning on L. Garden at end of close.* Home-made teas. **Adm £3, chd free. Sat 24, Sun 25 May (11-4.30).**

Tranquil, secluded village garden of approx ½ acre containing usual and unusual herbaceous plants, shrubs and trees of general and specialist interest. Garden accessible to wheelchairs but gravel from main entrance to garden (approx 30yrds).

53 WEST BARN

Saxby, Market Rasen LN8 2DQ. Mrs E Neave. *8m N of Lincoln. 2¼ m E of A15.* Home-made teas. **Combined adm £4, chd free. Sun 14 Sept (11-4). Combined with The Garden House.**

Formal walled courtyard garden with loggia, box hedging, shrub roses, climbers and herbaceous planting. Water feature and pots with seasonal planting. Gravel paths, some steps.

54 WILLOW COTTAGE

Gravel Pit Lane, Burgh-le-Marsh PE24 5DW. Bob & Karen Ward, 01754 811450, robertward055@aol.com, www.willowcottagecl.webs.com. *6m W of Skegness. S of Gunby r'about on A158, take 1st R signed Bratoft & Burgh-le-Marsh. 1st R again onto Bratoft Lane. L at T-junction, parking on R 25yds.* Home-made teas. **Adm £3, chd free. Fri 18, Mon 21 Apr, Fri 23, Mon 26 May, Fri 13, Sun 15 June, Fri 4, Sun 6 July (2-5). Visitors also welcome by appt Apr to July with garden tours and Treasure Hunt.**

A warmly, welcoming English Cottage Garden, painters palette of natural planting. Meandering pathways to discover, tranquil spots where you'll long to linger. This is a beautiful setting for afternoon tea, and a hidden gem not to be missed! Open additional Fridays by appointment. Group tours and treasure hunts Fridays 6.30pm by appointment. Woodland walk and plants for sale. Partial wheelchair access. For assistance please ring ahead of visit.

55 NEW WILLOW HOLT

Sleaford Road, Folkingham, Sleaford NG34 0SA. Simon & Annetta Turner, 01529 497215. *On A15 just N of Folkingham. ½ m S of junction with A52.* Home-made teas. **Adm £3, chd free. Sun 29 June (1-5.30). Visitors also welcome by appt May to July.**

A traditional 1 acre country garden with herbaceous flower beds, roses, vegetable and fruit areas, greenhouse and interesting poultry.

56 WITHAM HALL SCHOOL

Witham-on-the-Hill, Bourne PE10 0JJ. Mr & Mrs C Banks, www.withamhall.com. *7m NNE of Stamford. 4m SW of Bourne. From Stamford take A6121 to Bourne. After approx 7m turn L at Xrds, signed Witham-on-the-Hill. Entrance to Witham Hall after 1m on L.* Home-made teas. **Adm £3.50, chd free. Sun 22 June (2-5).**

One of the first gardens that opened in 1927. Now home of Witham Hall School. Formal garden with ornamental pond and paved rosewalk. Several mature cedar trees, walled garden, pupils' allotment area, herbaceous borders. 20 acres of quality sports grounds. Wheelchair access to garden only, gravel driveway.

57 WOODLANDS

Peppin Lane, Fotherby, Louth LN11 0UW. Ann & Bob Armstrong, 01507 603586, annbobarmstrong@btinternet.com, www.woodlandsplants.co.uk. *2m N of Louth on A16 signposted Fotherby. Please park on RH verge opp allotments & walk approx 350 yds to garden. No parking at garden. Please do not drive beyond designated area.* Home-made teas. **Single garden adm £2.50, 2 gardens £3.50, 3 gardens £4, chd free. Suns 20 Apr, 18 May, 15 June, 20 July, 17 Aug (11-5). Combined with Nut Tree Farm, 20 Jul & 17 Aug & Shepherds Hey, 18 May & 17 Aug. Visitors also welcome by appt Feb to Oct.**

A lovely mature woodland garden with many unusual plants set against a backdrop of an ever changing tapestry of greenery. A peaceful garden where wildlife is given a chance to thrive. The front garden has been developed into a crevice area for alpine plants. The nursery, featured in RHS Plantfinder, gives visitors the opportunity to purchase plants seen in the garden. Award winning professional artist's studio/gallery open to visitors. There is a specialist collection of Codonopsis for which Plant Heritage status has been requested.

Treat yourself to a plant from the plant stall

Hall Farm

© Clive Nicholls

Lincolnshire County Volunteers

County Organiser
Susie Dean, The Orchards, Old Somerby, Grantham NG33 4AG, 01476 565456, susie@dean0.plus.com

County Treasurer
Peter Sandberg, Croft House, Ulceby DN39 6SW, 01469 588330, peter.sandberg@btinternet.com

Publicity
Margaret Mann, Larksfield House, Little Humby, Grantham NG33 4HW, 01476 585905, marg_mann2000@yahoo.com
Erica McGarrigle, Corner House Farm, Little Humby, Grantham NG33 4HW, 01476 585909, ericamcg@hotmail.co.uk

Leaflet Coordinator
Sylvia Ravenhall, 15 Elmhirst Road, Horncastle LN9 5AT, 01507 526014, sylvan@btinternet.com

Assistant County Organisers
Lynne Barnes, The Moat, Newton, Sleaford NG34 0ED, 01529 497462, lynnebarnes14@googlemail.com
Helen Boothman, The Farmhouse, Mill Farm, Grasby, Barnetby DN38 6AQ, 01652 628424, boothmanhelen@gmail.com
Sally Grant, Holly House, Fishtoft Drove, Boston PE22 7ES, 01205 750486. sallygrant50@btinternet.com
Stephanie Lee, Marigold Cottage, 77 Church Lane, Sutton-on-Sea LN12 2JA, 01507 442151, marigoldlee@btinternet.com
Lizzie Milligan-Manby, Wykeham Hall Farm, East Wykeham, Ludford, Market Rasen LN8 6AU, 01507 313286, lizzie@milliganmanby.plus.com
Annetta Turner, Willow Holt, Folkingham, Sleaford NG34 0SA, 01529 497215, annetta.turner@googlemail.com

LONDON

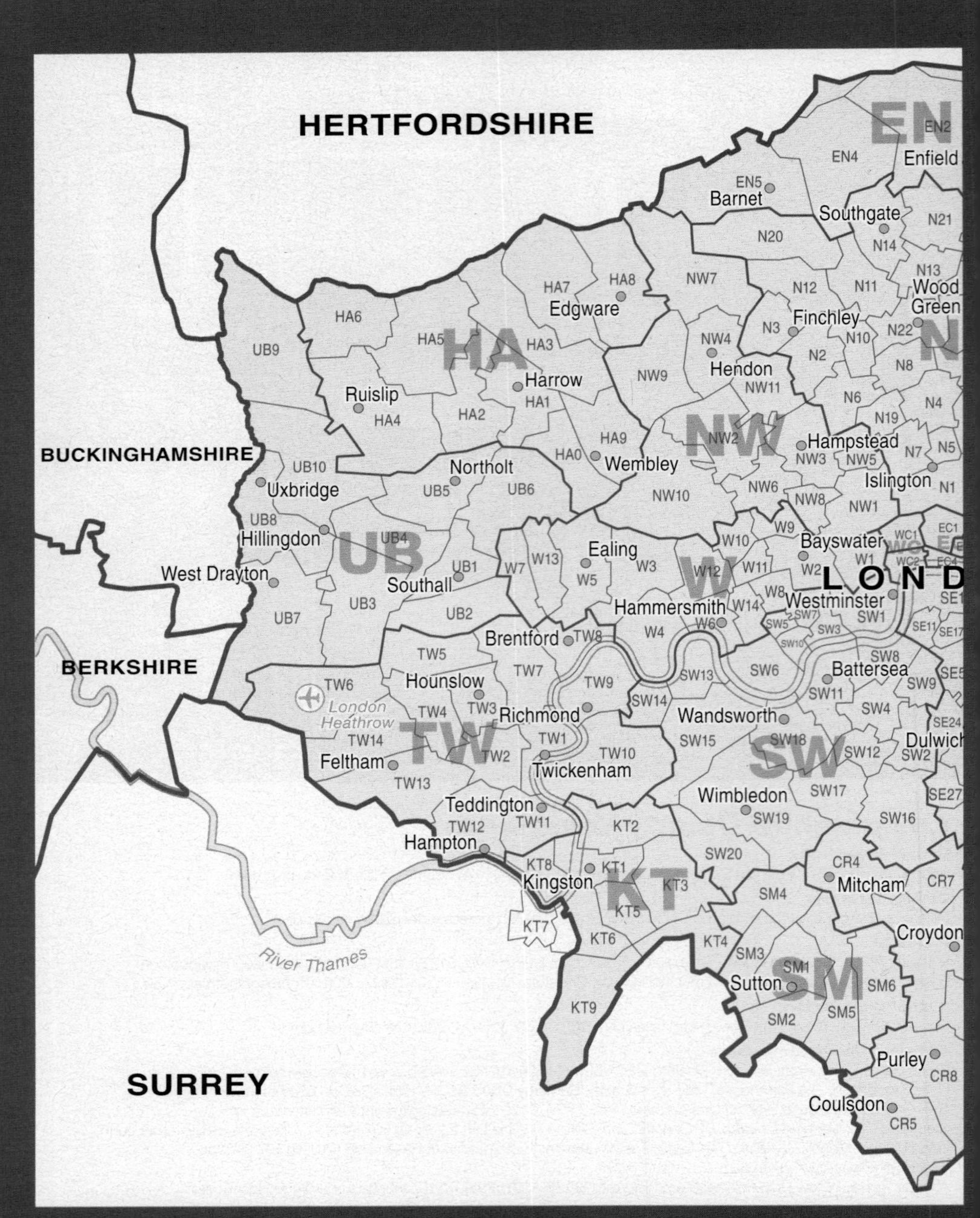

HERTFORDSHIRE
BUCKINGHAMSHIRE
BERKSHIRE
SURREY
River Thames
London Heathrow
EN
EN2
EN4
Enfield
EN5
Barnet
Southgate
N21
N20
N14
N13
Wood Green
NW7
N12
N11
HA7
HA8
Edgware
HA6
N3
Finchley
N22
N
HA5
HA
HA3
NW4
N10
UB9
Hendon
N2
N8
NW9
Harrow
NW11
Ruislip
HA1
N6
N4
HA4
HA2
N19
HA9
NW
NW2
Hampstead
N7
N5
HA0
Wembley
NW3
NW5
UB10
Northolt
Islington
N1
Uxbridge
UB5
UB6
NW6
NW10
NW8
NW1
UB8
W9
EC1
Hillingdon
UB4
W10
Bayswater
WC1
UB
W13
Ealing
W
W12
W11
W2
WC2
EC4
West Drayton
UB1
W7
W3
LONDON
W5
Southall
W8
Westminster
SE1
UB3
Hammersmith
W14
SW5
SW7
SW1
UB7
UB2
W6
SW3
SE11
SE17
W4
SW10
TW8
Brentford
TW5
SW8
SE5
TW7
SW6
Battersea
TW6
Hounslow
SW13
SW11
SW9
TW9
SW14
SW4
TW4
TW3
Richmond
Wandsworth
SE24
TW14
TW
TW1
SW15
SW18
Dulwich
TW2
SW
SW12
SE22
Feltham
TW10
Twickenham
TW13
SW17
SE27
Wimbledon
Teddington
SW19
SW16
TW12
TW11
KT2
Hampton
SW20
CR4
KT8
KT1
Mitcham
CR7
Kingston
KT3
KT
SM4
KT5
KT7
KT6
Croydon
KT4
SM3
SM1
Sutton
SM
SM6
KT9
SM5
SM2
Purley
CR8
Coulsdon
CR5

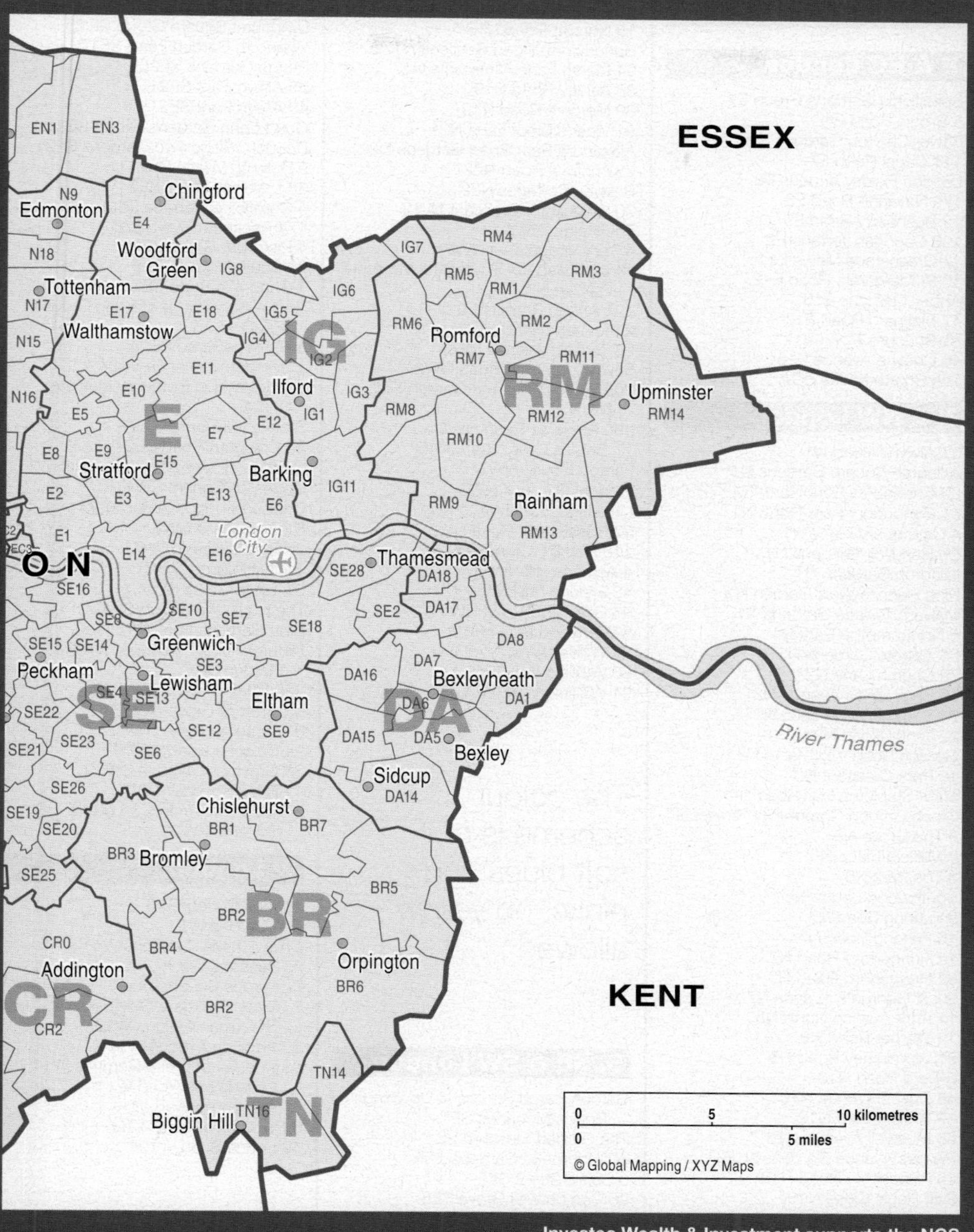
ESSEX
KENT
River Thames
London City
Chingford
Edmonton
Woodford Green
Tottenham
Walthamstow
Ilford
Romford
Upminster
Stratford
Barking
Rainham
Thamesmead
Greenwich
Peckham
Lewisham
Eltham
Bexleyheath
Bexley
Sidcup
Chislehurst
Bromley
Orpington
Addington
Biggin Hill
E
IG
RM
SE
DA
BR
CR
TN
0 5 10 kilometres
0 5 miles
© Global Mapping / XYZ Maps

London gardens listed by postcode

Inner London postcodes

E & EC London

Spitalfields Gardens Group E1
5 Brodie Road E4
Lower Clapton Gardens E5
111 Capel Road E7
London Fields Gardens E8
17a Navarino Road E8
12 Bushberry Road E9
128 Cadogan Terrace E9
17 Greenstone Mews E11
16 St Margarets Road E12
Abbey Gardens E15
47 Maynard Road E17
87 St Johns Road E17
46 Cheyne Avenue E18
The Charterhouse EC1

N & NW London

37 Alwyne Road N1
Arlington Square Gardens N1
29 Canonbury Park North N1
31 Canonbury Park North N1
4 Canonbury Place N1
De Beauvoir Gardens N1
Islington Gardens N1
King Henry's Walk Garden N1
Malvern Terrace Gardens N1
5 Northampton Park N1
66 Abbots Gardens N2
79 Church Lane N2
58 Summerlee Avenue N2
64 Summerlee Avenue N2
22 Trinity Road N2
Gordon Road Allotments N3
18 Park Crescent N3
160a Stapleton Hall Road N4
Olden Garden Community Project N5
7 The Grove N6
2 Millfield Place N6
3 The Park N6
Southwood Lodge N6
9 Furlong Road N7
16 Furlong Road N7
1a Hungerford Road N7
62 Hungerford Road N7
90 St George's Avenue N7
11 Park Avenue North N8
12 Warner Road N8
21 Womersley Road N8
5 Cecil Road N10
48 Dukes Avenue N10
19 Hillfield Park N10
66 Muswell Avenue N10
Princes Avenue Gardens N10
131 Rosebery Road N10
5 St Regis Close N10
94 Brownlow Road N11
Golf Course Allotments N11
The Rose Garden at Golf Course Allotments N11
21 Wroxham Gardens N11
5 Russell Road N13
49 Albion Road N16
51 Albion Road N16
15 Norcott Road N16
Handsworth Road Gardens N17
94 Marsh Lane Allotments N17
36 Ashley Road N19
30 Mercers Road N19
91 Vicar's Moor Lane N21
Alexandra Park Road Gardens N22
23 Imperial Road N22
Railway Cottages N22
70 Gloucester Crescent NW1
The Holme NW1
4 Park Village East NW1
Royal College of Physicians Medicinal Garden NW1
121 Anson Road NW2
27 Menelik Road NW2
93 Tanfield Avenue NW2
58A Teignmouth Road NW2
208 Walm Lane, The Garden Flat NW2
180 Adelaide Road NW3
17 Belsize Lane, NW3 NW3
Fenton House NW3
Frognal Gardens NW3
Little House A NW3
27 Nassington Road NW3
116 Hamilton Terrace NW8
4 Asmuns Hill NW11
48 Erskine Hill NW11
94 Oakwood Road NW11
5 Wildwood Rise NW11
74 Willifield Way NW11
86 Willifield Way NW11
91 Willifield Way NW11

The colour scheme is of soft blues and pinks; no yellow allowed . . . !

S, SE & SW London

Garden Barge Square at Downings Roads Moorings SE1
The Garden Museum SE1
40 Kidbrooke Gardens SE3
8 Calais Street SE5
35 Camberwell Grove SE5
Camberwell Grove Gardens SE5
24 Grove Park SE5
Grove Park Camberwell Group SE5
Roots and Shoots SE11
41 Southbrook Road SE12
Choumert Square SE15
Holly Grove Gardens Group SE15
Lambeth Palace SE1
Lyndhurst Square Group SE15
Walworth Garden Farm SE17
Penge Gardens SE20
25 Alleyn Park SE21
49 Alleyn Park SE21
Court Lane Gardens Group SE21
Dulwich Village Two Gardens SE21
9 Dulwich Village SE21
38 Lovelace Road SE21
4 Cornflower Terrace SE22
174 Peckham Rye SE22
4 Piermont Green SE22
22 Scutari Road SE22
7 Canonbie Road SE23
Tewkesbury Lodge Garden Group SE23
5 Burbage Road SE24
2 Shardcroft Avenue SE24
South London Botanical Institute SE24
Stoney Hill House SE26
24 Chestnut Road SE27
Cadogan Place South Garden SW1
Eccleston Square SW1
Chelsea Physic Garden SW3
51 The Chase SW4
28 Sibella Road SW4
Trinity Hospice SW4
35 Turret Grove SW4
The Hurlingham Club SW6
Bina Gardens East SW7
Natural History Museum Wildlife Garden SW7
225a Brixton Road SW9
6 Cornford Grove SW12
81 Tantallon Road SW12
9a Calonne Road SW19
55 Grasmere Avenue SW19
11 Ernle Road SW20
Paddock Allotments & Leisure Gardens SW20

W London

41 Mill Hill Road W3
Zen Garden W3
Chiswick Mall Gardens W4
All Seasons W5
Edwardes Square W8
7 Upper Phillimore Gardens W8
57 St Quintin Avenue W10
29 Addison Avenue W11
Arundel & Ladbroke Gardens W11
12 Lansdowne Road W11
8 Lansdowne Walk W11
6 Flanchford Road W12
49 Loftus Road W12

Treetops

5 St Regis Close

Outer London postcodes

36 Downs Hill BR3
22 Kelsey Way BR3
109 Addington Road BR4
212 Langley Way BR4
White Cottage BR5
Columcille BR7
Elm Tree Cottage CR2
33a Brookhill Road EN4
207 East Barnet Road EN4
Elm Court Gardens EN4
West Lodge Park EN4
190 Barnet Road EN5
7 Byng Road EN5
53 Brook Drive HA1
54 Ferndown HA6
23 Links Way HA6
Treetops HA6
20 Goldhaze Close IG8
7 Woodbines Avenue KT1
Warren House KT2
The Watergardens KT2
The Circle Garden KT3
65 Farm Way KT4
Berrylands Gardens Group KT5
52A Berrylands Road KT5
Little Lodge KT7
Speer Road Gardens KT7
Hampton Court Palace KT8
61 Wolsey Road KT8
239a Hook Road KT9
18 Pettits Boulevard RM1
7 St George's Road TW1
Osterley Park and House TW7
Kew Gardens Station Group TW9
Kew Green Gardens TW9
Trumpeters House & Sarah's Garden TW9
Ham House and Garden TW10
Ormeley Lodge TW10
Petersham House TW10
St Michael's Convent TW10
Stokes House TW10
Hampton Hill Gardens TW12
30 St James's Road TW12

Opening Dates

All entries subject to change. For latest information check www.ngs.org.uk

January

Wednesday 1
5 Northampton Park, N1 (Evening)

April

Tuesday 1
Chelsea Physic Garden, SW3

Saturday 5
Natural History Museum Wildlife Garden, SW7
Trinity Hospice, SW4

Sunday 6
Trinity Hospice, SW4

Tuesday 8
Fenton House, NW3 (Evening)

Thursday 10
Hampton Court Palace (Evening - **Pre-booking essential**)

Saturday 12
4 Canonbury Place, N1

Sunday 13
Edwardes Square, W8
7 The Grove, N6

Saturday 19
17a Navarino Road, E8

Sunday 27
5 Burbage Road, SE24
51 The Chase, SW4
15 Norcott Road, N16
Petersham House
7 Upper Phillimore Gardens, W8

May

Saturday 3
11 Ernle Road, SW20

Sunday 4
9a Calonne Road, SW19
Elm Tree Cottage
11 Ernle Road, SW20
2 Millfield Place, N6
5 St Regis Close, N10
Southwood Lodge, N6

Wednesday 7
Lambeth Palace SE1
51 The Chase, SW4 (Evening)

Sunday 11
NEW Arundel & Ladbroke Gardens, W11
NEW 53 Brook Drive
Cadogan Place South Garden, SW1
Eccleston Square, SW1
Garden Barge Square at Downings Roads Moorings, SE1
Warren House
The Watergardens

Saturday 17
111 Capel Road, E7
The Hurlingham Club, SW6

Sunday 18
49 Alleyn Park, SE21
111 Capel Road, E7
Kew Green Gardens
27 Nassington Road, NW3
94 Oakwood Road, NW11
Princes Avenue Gardens, N10
22 Scutari Road, SE22
Stoney Hill House, SE26
West Lodge Park

Wednesday 21
Holly Grove Gardens Group, SE15 (Evening)
12 Lansdowne Road, W11

Saturday 24
Hampton Hill Gardens

Sunday 25
36 Ashley Road, N19
Hampton Hill Gardens
Holly Grove Gardens Group, SE15
Penge Gardens, SE20
28 Sibella Road, SW4
Speer Road Gardens
58 Summerlee Avenue, N2
64 Summerlee Avenue, N2
NEW 91 Vicar's Moor Lane, N21

Monday 26
36 Ashley Road, N19

Saturday 31
Tewkesbury Lodge Garden Group, SE23 (Evening)

June

Sunday 1
37 Alwyne Road, N1
190 Barnet Road, EN5
31 Canonbury Park North, N1
Islington Gardens, N1
Kew Gardens Station Group
Little Lodge
Osterley Park and House
3 The Park, N6
90 St George's Avenue, N7
Tewkesbury Lodge Garden Group, SE23

Wednesday 4
Lambeth Palace SE1
Little Lodge

Thursday 5
Hampton Court Palace (Evening - **Pre-booking essential**)

Festival Weekend

Saturday 7
180 Adelaide Road, NW3
Columcille
The Garden Museum, SE1
7 St George's Road (Evening)
Spitalfields Gardens Group, E1
Walworth Garden Farm, SE17
Zen Garden, W3

Sunday 8
66 Abbots Gardens, N2
180 Adelaide Road, NW3
Arlington Square Gardens, N1
17 Belsize Lane, NW3
Berrylands Gardens Group
35 Camberwell Grove, SE5
24 Chestnut Road, SE27
Chiswick Mall Gardens, W4
Choumert Square, SE15
4 Cornflower Terrace, SE22
Dulwich Village Two Gardens, SE21
9 Dulwich Village, SE21
48 Erskine Hill, NW11
9 Furlong Road, N7
16 Furlong Road, N7
7 The Grove, N6
1a Hungerford Road, N7
62 Hungerford Road, N7
22 Kelsey Way
23 Links Way
Lower Clapton Gardens, E5
15 Norcott Road, N16
174 Peckham Rye, SE22
5 Russell Road, N13
NEW 160a Stapleton Hall Road
Walworth Garden Farm, SE17
White Cottage
Zen Garden, W3

Tuesday 10
49 Loftus Road, W12 (Evening)

Wednesday 11
Malvern Terrace Gardens, N1 (Evening)

Saturday 14
49 Albion Road, N16
51 Albion Road, N16
212 Langley Way
NEW 18 Pettits Boulevard

Sunday 15
29 Addison Avenue, W11
94 Brownlow Road, N11
79 Church Lane, N2
De Beauvoir Gardens, N1
Elm Tree Cottage
6 Flanchford Road, W12
55 Grasmere Avenue
NEW Grove Park Camberwell Group, SE5
239a Hook Road
212 Langley Way
8 Lansdowne Walk, W11
London Fields Gardens, E8
17a Navarino Road, E8
Olden Garden Community Project, N5
NEW 18 Pettits Boulevard
St Michael's Convent
2 Shardcroft Avenue, SE24
41 Southbrook Road, SE12
Southwood Lodge, N6
Stokes House
22 Trinity Road, N2
Trumpeters House & Sarah's Garden
NEW 12 Warner Road, N8
NEW 74 Willifield Way, NW11
91 Willifield Way, NW11
61 Wolsey Road
21 Wroxham Gardens, N11

Tuesday 17
The Charterhouse, EC1 (Evening)

Wednesday 18
239a Hook Road (Evening)
2 Millfield Place, N6 (Evening)

Friday 20
Roots and Shoots, SE11

Sunday 22
33a Brookhill Road, EN4
6 Cornford Grove, SW12
Frognal Gardens, NW3
116 Hamilton Terrace, NW8 (Evening)
Little House A, NW3
Lyndhurst Square Group, SE15
Ormeley Lodge
18 Park Crescent, N3
5 St Regis Close, N10
22 Scutari Road, SE22
South London Botanical Institute, SE24

Monday 23
6 Cornford Grove, SW12 (Evening)
Royal College of Physicians Medicinal Garden, NW1

Saturday 28
The Holme, NW1

Sunday 29
NEW 25 Alleyn Park, SE21
12 Bushberry Road, E9
Camberwell Grove Gardens, SE5
5 Cecil Road, N10
The Circle Garden
NEW Court Lane Gardens Group, SE21
36 Downs Hill
48 Dukes Avenue, N10
65 Farm Way
70 Gloucester Crescent, NW1
The Holme, NW1
40 Kidbrooke Gardens, SE3
11 Park Avenue North, N8
4 Park Village East, NW1
The Rose Garden at Golf Course Allotments, N11
NEW 81 Tantallon Road, SW12
208 Walm Lane, The Garden Flat, NW2

Lush country-style garden brimming with colour . . .

July

Tuesday 1
66 Muswell Avenue, N10 (Evening)

Friday 4
225a Brixton Road, SW9 (Evening)

Saturday 5
225a Brixton Road, SW9
38 Lovelace Road, SE21
Zen Garden, W3

Sunday 6
109 Addington Road
NEW 30 Mercers Road, N19
41 Mill Hill Road, W3 (Evening)
131 Rosebery Road, N10
57 St Quintin Avenue, W10
Zen Garden, W3

Tuesday 8
66 Muswell Avenue, N10 (Evening)

Wednesday 9
Ham House and Garden
King Henry's Walk Garden, N1 (Evening)

Thursday 10
Royal College of Physicians Medicinal Garden, NW1

Saturday 12
Paddock Allotments & Leisure Gardens, SW20

Sunday 13
121 Anson Road, NW2
52A Berrylands Road
NEW 7 Canonbie Road, SE23
Elm Court Gardens, EN4
NEW Handsworth Road Gardens, N17
27 Menelik Road, NW2
17a Navarino Road, E8
4 Piermont Green, SE22
Railway Cottages, N22
58A Teignmouth Road, NW2
Treetops
5 Wildwood Rise, NW11

Sunday 20
4 Asmuns Hill, NW11
190 Barnet Road, EN5
128 Cadogan Terrace, E9
29 Canonbury Park North, N1
NEW 46 Cheyne Avenue, E18
20 Goldhaze Close
116 Hamilton Terrace, NW8 (Evening)
19 Hillfield Park, N10
47 Maynard Road E17
Petersham House
35 Turret Grove, SW4
86 Willifield Way, NW11
NEW 21 Womersley Road, N8

Saturday 26
NEW 18 Pettits Boulevard

Sunday 27
29 Addison Avenue, W11
47 Maynard Road E17
18 Park Crescent, N3
NEW 18 Pettits Boulevard
57 St Quintin Avenue, W10
5 St Regis Close, N10

Thursday 31
Hampton Court Palace (Evening)

August

Saturday 2
All Seasons, W5
The Holme, NW1
Trinity Hospice, SW4

Sunday 3
Alexandra Park Road Gardens, N22
All Seasons, W5
70 Gloucester Crescent, NW1
17 Greenstone Mews, E11
The Holme, NW1
47 Maynard Road E17
Trinity Hospice, SW4

Friday 8
41 Mill Hill Road, W3

Sunday 10
5 Brodie Road, E4
Elm Tree Cottage
94 Marsh Lane Allotments, N17
47 Maynard Road E17

Saturday 16
87 St Johns Road, E17

Sunday 17
NEW 46 Cheyne Avenue, E18
54 Ferndown
20 Goldhaze Close
3 Tanfield Avenue, NW2

Saturday 23
212 Langley Way
87 St Johns Road, E17

Sunday 24
5 Brodie Road, E4
212 Langley Way
7 Woodbines Avenue

Thursday 28
Hampton Court Palace (Evening - **Pre-booking essential**)

Sunday 31
NEW 16 St Margarets Road, E12

September

Sunday 7
7 Byng Road, EN5
8 Calais Street, SE5
24 Chestnut Road, SE27 (Evening)
Golf Course Allotments, N11
NEW Gordon Road Allotments, N3
24 Grove Park, SE5
23 Imperial Road, N22
NEW 30 Mercers Road, N19
5 Russell Road, N13

Thursday 11
30 St James's Road (Evening)

Saturday 13
Abbey Gardens, E15

Sunday 21
Bina Gardens East, SW7

October

Sunday 12
Warren House
The Watergardens

Sunday 26
West Lodge Park

Gardens open to the public

Chelsea Physic Garden, SW3
Fenton House, NW3
The Garden Museum, SE1
Ham House and Garden
Hampton Court Palace
Natural History Museum Wildlife Garden, SW7
Osterley Park and House
Roots and Shoots, SE11

By appointment only

207 East Barnet Road

Also open by appointment

180 Adelaide Road, NW3
49 Albion Road, N16
Arundel & Ladbroke Gardens, W11
4 Asmuns Hill, NW11
190 Barnet Road, EN5
17 Belsize Lane, NW3
225a Brixton Road, SW9
5 Burbage Road, SE24
Cadogan Place South Garden, SW1
35 Camberwell Grove, SE5
111 Capel Road, E7
51 The Chase, SW4
16 Eyot Gardens, Chiswick Mall Gardens, W4
Field House, Chiswick Mall Gardens, W4
Columcille
36 Downs Hill
Eccleston Square, SW1
3 Elm Court, Elm Court Gardens, EN4
Elm Tree Cottage
48 Erskine Hill, NW11
54 Ferndown
70 Gloucester Crescent, NW1
20 Goldhaze Close
17 Greenstone Mews, E11
7 The Grove, N6
116 Hamilton Terrace, NW8
1a Hungerford Road, N7
1 Battlebridge Court, Islington Gardens, N1
5 Ennerdale Road, Kew Gardens Station Group
40 Kidbrooke Gardens, SE3
8 Lansdowne Walk, W11
23 Links Way
Little Lodge
49 Loftus Road, W12
53 Mapledene Road, London Fields Gardens, E8
94 Marsh Lane Allotments, N17
30 Mercers Road, N19
41 Mill Hill Road, W3
2 Millfield Place, N6
66 Muswell Avenue, N10

The Gardens

ABBEY GARDENS, E15
Bakers Row, Newnham, East London E15 3NF. The Friends of Abbey Gardens. *Tube: Stratford, West Ham. DLR Abbey Rd stn at end of garden. Short walk along greenway from Olympic Stadium*. Home-made teas. **Adm £2.50, chd free. Sat 13 Sept (10-5).**
This is a unique shared community 'harvest garden' instigated by the local Friends of Abbey Gardens, then designed and developed with artists Nina Pope and Karen Guthrie (see www.somewhere.org.uk). Now up and running for 5yrs, Abbey Gardens host 3 free weekly garden club sessions where volunteers tend all the shared raised beds rather than individual plots. Garden tours, teas, produce and plant sales. Gardens also house the gatehouse ruin of a Cistercian Abbey, one of the few scheduled ancient monuments in this part of London. For more information see www.abbeygardens.org and www.whatwilltheharvestbe.com.

66 ABBOTS GARDENS, N2
East Finchley, London N2 0JH. Stephen & Ruth Kersley. *6 min from rear exit along Causeway (ped) to East End Rd. 2nd L into Abbots Gardens. 143 stops at Abbots Gardens.102, 263 & 234 on East End Rd*. Home-made teas. **Adm £3, chd free. Sun 8 June (2-5.30).**
Combining 'grass and glass'; Stephen studied garden design at Capel Manor and Ruth is a glass artist. Designed for yr round interest, this garden creates a calming yet dramatic environment through plant form, colour, texture and asymmetrical geometry. Glass amphorae and feathers catch the eye among grasses, ornamental shrubs, perennials, vegetable plot and water features.

109 ADDINGTON ROAD
Coney Hall, West Wickham BR4 9BG. Mrs Sheila Chivers. *A2022 Bromley to Croydon rd, between Glebe Way & Corkscrew Hill/Layhams Rd r'abouts. Please park on main rd*. Home-made teas. **Adm £3, chd free. Sun 6 July (1-5).**
An Informal garden, winding paths lead you past hot sunny borders, cool shady areas with contrasting foliage plants, a bog garden and ponds with water lilies. There are shady seating areas surrounded by colourful borders an apple tree with woodland planting. Hanging baskets and various containers adding extra colour and interest throughout the garden.

29 ADDISON AVENUE, W11
London W11 4QS. Shirley Nicholson. *No entry for cars from Holland Park Ave, approach via Queensdale Rd. Tube: Holland Park or Shepherds Bush. Buses: 31, 94, 148, 228, 295, 316*. **Adm £3, chd free. Sun 15 June, Sun 27 July (2-6). Also open with 8 Lansdowne Walk 15 June and 57 St Quintin Ave 27 July.**
The small lawn is dominated by an ancient pear tree and surrounded by shrubs and hardy geraniums. The colour scheme is of soft blues and pinks; no yellow allowed! In June roses and clematis (a speciality here) cover the walls, while in late July phlox, salvias, and monarda make a bright splash in the centre beds. Plenty of ideas for those who think their gardens are finished by the end of June.

180 ADELAIDE ROAD, NW3
Swiss Cottage, London NW3 3PA. Simone Rothman, 07817 060206, rothmansimone@gmail.com. *Tube: Swiss Cottage, 100yds. Buses: 13, 46, 82, 113 on Finchley Rd; 31 & C11 on Adelaide Rd. 50yds from Marriott Hotel, Winchester Rd*. Home-made teas. **Adm £3.50, chd free. Sat 7 June (4-6); Sun 8 June (3-6). Visitors also welcome by appt Apr to Aug.**
A very enchanting S-facing walled garden 25ft x 30ft, with numerous densely planted large containers on gravel, profuse and colourful. Roses, clematis and topiary. Stylish front garden with lawn, shrubs, topiary and many herbaceous plants. Featured in Ham & High and Wood & Vale.

Golf Course Allotments

8 Lansdowne Walk

49 ALBION ROAD, N16
Ground Floor Flat (bottom bell), London N16 9PP. Ms Jane Taylor, 07980 241475, jat102@blueyonder.co.uk. *Tube: Highbury & Islington or Angel. Overground: Canonbury. Buses: 21, 73, 141, 236, 341, 476. 2 mins walk from Newington Green*. Light refreshments. **Combined adm £4, chd free. Sat 14 June (4-7). Combined with 51 Albion Road. Visitors also welcome by appt Apr to Oct.**
Growing pains and pleasures ... this W-facing, approx 70ft N London back garden was transformed from a fox-dwelling bindweed jungle in 2007 by SGD designer Carol Whitehead. Her orderly informality is now being subverted by stroppy adolescent plants and my obsession with propagating stuff. Accessed by unusual metal staircase: high-heeled gardeners beware!

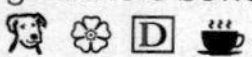

51 ALBION ROAD, N16
London N16 9PP. Mr Roger Tolson. *Tube: Highbury & Islington or Angel. Overground: Canonbury. Buses: 21, 73, 141, 236, 341, 476. 2 mins walk from Newington Green*. **Combined adm £4, chd free. Sat 14 June (4-7). Combined with 49 Albion Road.**
A varied and productive town garden. Fruit trees and plants, vegetables and herbs intertwine with established planting and newly-developed informal flower beds. The front garden features a flourishing British native species hedgerow. Water features incl a rill and pond. A work in progress.

GROUP OPENING

ALEXANDRA PARK ROAD GARDENS, N22
Nos 270, 272, 279, 289 & 300, Alexandra Park Road, London N22 7BG. *Tube: Bounds Green or Wood Green, then bus 10 mins. Buses: 184, W3. Alight at junction of Alexandra Park Rd & Palace Gates Rd*. Home-made teas at No. 272. **Combined adm £4, chd free. Sun 3 Aug (2-6).**

270 ALEXANDRA PARK ROAD
Dan McGiff

272 ALEXANDRA PARK ROAD
Clive Boutle & Kate Tattersall

279 ALEXANDRA PARK ROAD
Gail & Wilf Downing

289 ALEXANDRA PARK ROAD
Julie Littlejohn

300 ALEXANDRA PARK ROAD
Paul Cox & Bee Peak

On the site of the original Alexandra Park estate are five front gardens and a back garden to enjoy: the surprisingly long rear garden of a 1920s house backing onto deer enclosure, and five exuberant contrasting front gardens. The back garden retains many pre-war features incl an Anderson Shelter, rock garden, crazy paving and venerable trees as well as a tree house, greenhouse and wildlife-friendly eclectic planting. The front gardens all provide colour and interest for the community and are inspiring examples of how much can be achieved in a very small space. There is a profusion of colour in pots, while tall plants hide a secret hidden from the street. One steeply-sloping front garden has a semi-tropical theme, with a rill running through a riverbed rockery, disappearing under the path and dropping into a pool surrounded by beautiful stones, another is a modern re-creation of a cottage country garden, another concentrates on scent and screening to hide its roadside location. Winner - London Green Corners Award.

Ferns unfurl fresh, vibrant fronds over a tumbling stream . . .

ALL SEASONS, W5
97 Grange Road, Ealing, London W5 3PH. Dr Benjamin & Mrs Maria Royappa. *Tube: Ealing Broadway/ South Ealing / Ealing Common: 10-15 mins walk*. Light refreshments. **Adm £3, chd free. Sat 2 Aug (1-6); Sun 3 Aug (12.30-6).**
Garden designed and planted by owners, with changes and new interesting planting. Features incl ponds, pergolas, Japanese gardens, tropical house for orchids and exotics, aviaries, recycled features, composting and rain water harvesting, orchard, kiwi, grape vines, architectural and unusual plants, collections incl ferns, bamboos, conifers and cacti. Limited wheelchair access.

NEW **25 ALLEYN PARK, SE21**
Dulwich, London SE21 8AT. Don & Lisa McGown. *Nr W Dulwich & Gipsy Hill train stations. Buses No 3, P13 & P4. 10 mins walk. Street parking*. Home-made teas. **Adm £3, chd free. Sun 29 June (2-5). Also open Camberwell Grove Group and Court Lane Gardens Group.**
Inviting front and rear gardens of Victorian house with mixed beds and borders, planted for sun and shade. Framed by beautiful mature trees. Wide variety of perennials, roses, climbers and shrubs. Also containers, small pond, lawn, terrace, seating areas, conservatory. Jazz band. Most of garden accessible by wheelchair, but note access over a gravel drive.

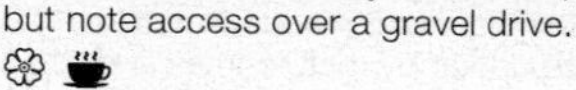

49 ALLEYN PARK, SE21
Dulwich, London SE21 8AT. Celia & Charles Randell. *5 mins walk from W Dulwich stn, 8 mins walk from Gipsy Hill stn. 3 mins from No 3 bus route. Free parking on Alleyn Park & Huntslip Rd*. Home-made teas. **Adm £3.50, chd free. Sun 18 May (2-6). Also open Stoney Hill House and 22 Scutari Road.**
A large family garden of mature and unusual trees and shrubs and carefully sited modern sculptures. Large borders are designed to be low maintenance and wildlife friendly. The formal structure of lawns, hedges, brick paths and topiary contrasts with secret corners and romantic planting. Unfenced pond.

37 ALWYNE ROAD, N1

London N1 2HW. Mr & Mrs J Lambert. *Buses: 38, 56, 73, 341 on Essex Rd; 4, 19, 30, 43 on Upper St, alight at Town Hall; 271 on Canonbury Rd, A1. Tube: Highbury & Islington.* Home-made teas. **Adm £3.50, chd free (share to The Friends of the Rose Bowl). Sun 1 June (2-6).**

The New River curves around the garden, freeing it from the tyranny of a London rectangle and allowing different degrees of formality - topiary, a new urban meadow next to the conservatory, and a bit of wildness at the back where the life of the river is part of the charm. The garden continues to develop, visitors return to see what's new - and to have more Brownies. The New River, the big trees and a big sky all create a remarkably country atmosphere in London. Shelter if it rains. Wheelchair access with own assistant only for 3 entrance steps.

121 ANSON ROAD, NW2

London NW2 4AH. Helen Marcus. *Cricklewood. Tube: Willesden Grn or Kilburn, Thameslink: Cricklewood, Buses: 226, (Dawson Rd stop) 16, 32, 189, 245, 260, 266, 316 to Cricklewood Bdy.* **Adm £2.50, chd free. Sun 13 July (2-5.30). Also opening 27 Menelik Road and 58A Teignmouth Road combined adm (3 gardens), £7, chd free.**

Lush country-style garden brimming with colour and yr-round interest, surrounded by mature trees and shrubs creating a secluded haven. Lawned area with deep flower borders densely planted for sun and shade; wide variety of cottage garden and unusual plants, shrubs, perennials, clematis, roses. Trellises, urns and statues used to create unexpected vistas and focal points. Charming produce garden combining formal features with wild flower area, vegetables and fruit.

GROUP OPENING

ARLINGTON SQUARE GARDENS, N1

London N1 7DP, www.arlingtonassociation.org.uk. *Off New North Rd via Arlington Ave or Linton St. Buses: 271, 141, 21, 76.* Home-made teas at The Vicarage, 1A Arlington Square. **Combined adm £5, chd free. Sun 8 June (2-5.30).**

26 ARLINGTON AVENUE
Mr Thomas Blaikie

21 ARLINGTON SQUARE
Ms Alison Rice

25 ARLINGTON SQUARE
Mr Michael Foley

5 REES STREET
Gordon McArthur & Paul Thompson

NEW ST JAMES' VICARAGE, N1
Fr John Burniston

Five gardens surrounding Arlington Square behind Victorian terrace houses, this yr incl the local vicarage. It is fascinating to see how each garden has used the limited space available and created an inspiring and relaxing space. Arlington Square has been transformed by the Arlington Square Association, a local residents group. Gold Award - Islington in Bloom.

NEW ARUNDEL & LADBROKE GARDENS, W11

Kensington Park Road, Notting Hill, London W11 2LW. Arundel & Ladbroke Gardens Committee, 07957 640816, susan.lynn1@ntlworld.com, www.arundelladbrokegardens.co.uk. *Entrance on Kensington Park Rd, between Ladbroke & Arundel Gardens. Tube: Notting Hill Gate, Buses: 23, 52, 452.* Home-made teas. **Adm £3.50, chd free. Sun 11 May (2-6). Visitors also welcome by appt Apr to Aug, max 10 visitors.**

A private square, of mid-Victorian design, planted as a woodland garden: with massed rhododendrons, camellias, and dogwoods, a glade of tulips, alliums and other spring bulbs: Australasian plants, such as prostanthera, corokia and dicksonias, as well as acers, cercis, birches and a Stachyurus chinensis for foliage interest. Wheelchair access possible but 2 steps and gravel paths to negotiate.

36 ASHLEY ROAD, N19

London N19 3AF. Alan Swann & Ahmed Farooqui. *Underground: Archway or Finsbury Park. Buses: 210 from Archway to Hornsey Rise. W7 from Finsbury Park to Heathville Rd. Free parking in Ashley Rd.* Home-made teas. **Adm £3.50, chd free. Sun 25, Mon 26 May (2-6).**

A lush town garden rich in textures, colour and forms. At its best in late spring as Japanese maple cultivars display great variety of shape and colour, whilst ferns unfurl fresh, vibrant fronds over a tumbling stream and alpines and clematis burst into flower on the rockeries and pergola. Garden also incl a formal lily pond. Ferns, woodland plants and unique, garden-developed aquilegia for sale. Featured in Ham & High.

4 ASMUNS HILL, NW11

Hampstead Garden Suburb, London NW11 6ET. Peter & Yvonne Oliver, 0208 455 8741. *Close to Finchley Rd & N Circular. Tube: Golders Green, then buses 82,102 or 460 to Temple Fortune, then 2 mins walk along Hampstead Way, Asmuns Hill 2nd on L.* **Adm £3.50, chd free. Sun 20 July (1-6). Also open 86 Willifield Way. Visitors also welcome by appt June to Aug.**

Exquisite Arts and Crafts cottage garden in the Artisan's Quarter of Hampstead Garden Suburb. Clematis and other climbers, both front and back. Mid-Summer colour from crocosmias, heleniums, salvias. Succulents, acers and other plants in pots and containers. Pond, patio, herbaceous bed, shade area. Sculptures and objets trouvés. Garden visited by the Duke of Wessex, HRH Prince Edward in 2013. Winner of London Gardens Society Gold Medal and Cup.

190 BARNET ROAD, EN5

Arkley, Barnet EN5 3LF. Hilde & Lionel Wainstein, 020 8441 4041, hildewainstein@hotmail.co.uk. *1m S of A1, 2m N of High Barnet*

tube. A411 Barnet Road. Tube: High Barnet, then 107 bus stops opp house. Home-made teas. **Adm £3, chd free. Sun 1 June, Sun 20 July (2-6). Visitors also welcome by appt May to Sept.**
Garden designer's walled garden, approx 90ft x 36ft. Four years old, modern asymmetric design thickly planted in flowing, natural drifts around trees, shrubs and central pond; a changing array of interesting containers and found objects. Hand-made beaten copper trellis divides the garden. The garden continues to evolve as the lawn shrinks and new planted areas are expanded. National Collection of akebias. Wide range of interesting plants for sale, incl akebia, all propagated from the garden. Single steps within garden.

A labour of love and watering . . . !

17 BELSIZE LANE, NW3

Hampstead NW3 5AD. Maureen Michaelson, 020 7435 0510, mm@maureenmichaelson.com, www.maureenmichaelson.com. *Trains: Belsize Park 5 mins; Hampstead Heath, Finchley Rd, Swiss Cottage 12 mins. Close to Haverstock Hill buses. From Fitzjohns Ave pass shops on Belsize Lane & turn L to stay on Belsize Lane after Village Close. Opp School.* **Adm £3.50, chd free. Sun 8 June (2-6). Visitors also welcome by appt May to Sept.**
Professional garden sculpture gallerist's own lushly planted garden with backdrop of mature trees and evergreens. Flashes of colour from perennials and flowering shrubs. Irregular shaped plot reveals different aspects. Pergolas with many climbers, small pond, deck with large planted pots. Artist made pots and artworks sensitively and discretely displayed provide humour, colour and interest all yr. Works by contemporary artists incl sculptures and installations in ceramic, glass, copper; slate tables and chairs. Unusual plants. Also open in association with Chelsea Fringe. See www.chelseafringe.com for details. Feature in Ham & High Gardening and Art sections; Crafts Magazine; shootgardening.com blog. Access for wheelchair 69cm.

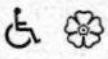

GROUP OPENING

BERRYLANDS GARDENS GROUP

Berrylands, Surbiton KT5 9AF. *2½ m S of Kingston-upon-Thames. From A3 take A240 joining Ewell Rd. Take Hollyfield Rd on R, cross King Charles Rd into Alexandra Drive. Map to other gardens from here.* **Combined adm £5, chd free. Sun 8 June (2-5).**

68 ALEXANDRA DRIVE
Andy Hutchings

1 THE CREST
Robert & Julia Humphries

64 PINE GARDENS
Barbara Hutchings

A selection of three gardens all within 10 mins walk of each other, all owned by different members of the same family. The gardens are all very varied, from country cottage to jungle, chicken runs to quirky, even an enormous giant's head hidden away. Have an enjoyable afternoon being nosey, buying plants and sampling my sister's fantastic cakes. We look forward to seeing you.

52A BERRYLANDS ROAD

Surbiton KT5 8PD. Dr Tim & Mrs Julia Leunig. *2m E of Kingston-upon-Thames. A3 to Tolworth; A240 (towards Kingston) for approx 1m, then R into Berrylands Rd (after Fire Stn). 52A on R after Xrds.* Home-made teas. **Adm £3, chd free. Sun 13 July (2.30-5.30).**
Shapes define this professionally designed garden. The 'bold verticality' of eucalyptus glaucescens, huge leaves of tetrapanex, slender cyresses, clipped hebes, cloud formed bamboo, and an S shaped lawn all in a T shaped garden. Add in a stream, a wooded area and great cakes . . .

BINA GARDENS EAST, SW7

Dove Mews, London SW7 4NH. Alice Ulm. *Pedestrian access through Dove Mews off Old Brompton Rd, or Rosary Gardens, Kensington. Tube: Gloucester Rd - 5 mins away.* **Adm £3, chd free. Sun 21 Sept (12-5).**
A private 'secret' garden of ⅓ of an acre, hidden behind buildings. The original formal layout of 1880 is softened by generous and mature planting. Predominantly in shade there is enough light and warmth to grow unusual and exotic plants. As a winner of many London garden competitions, both plants and sculptures reflect a personal touch. Wonderful in September. Plant list available. Garden team attending opening.

225A BRIXTON ROAD, SW9

London SW9 6LW. Deborah Nagan & Michael Johnson, 020 7633 0247, deborah@uncommonland.co.uk, www.uncommonland.co.uk. *Tube: Oval or Brixton. Bus: 3, 59, 133, 159 (Stop: Groveway), Brixton Rd is the A23; 225a is on E side, next to Mostyn Rd. Parking locally after 6.30pm & weekends.* Cream teas. **Adm £3.50, chd free. Evening Opening £3.50, chd free, wine, Fri 4 July (5.30-9.30); Sat 5 July (2-6.30). Visitors also welcome by appt July to Sept.**
Architects' listed and extended home with productive vegetable garden in modern raised beds in the front garden. To the rear - fruit and mostly perennial flowers in a rusty palette. Lower level calm garden with fish pond. Modern urban oasis with unusual materials. Featured in Gardens Illustrated and The English Garden. Also in The London Garden Guide and RHS Small Garden Book by Andrew Wilson.

5 BRODIE ROAD, E4

Chingford, London E4 7HF. Mr & Mrs N Booth. *From Chingford train station, any bus to Chingford Green (Co-op), turn L at Prezzo, 2nd R (Scholars Rd), then 1st L.* Light refreshments. **Adm £2.50, chd free. Sun 10, Sun 24 Aug (2-5).**
A constantly evolving garden with new plantings annually obtained from specialist nurseries. The gardener's love of butterflies has moulded the planting style over the years, with two wide herbaceous borders packed with stunning colour from heleniums, rudbeckia, hydrangeas and dahlias. The borders are intersected by a narrow path leading to clematis and rose covered arches.

NEW **53 BROOK DRIVE**
Harrow HA1 4RT. Mr Brian Porter, brianpolly@talktalk.net. *1m W of Harrow & Wealdstone stn & H9 bus to Pinner View, or 1m N of Harrow on the Hill stn & H14 bus Hatch End to Headstone Gdns/Drive.* Light refreshments. **Adm £3, chd free. Sun 11 May (2-5).**
Lots of lush colour, especially in spring with a selection of vegetables amongst a variety of perennials, bulbs, shrubs and trees incl two magnificent magnolias in a small suburban garden. Wheelchair access via side passage.

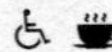

33A BROOKHILL ROAD, EN4
Barnet EN4 8SE. Barbara Perry. *Between E Barnet Rd & Cat Hill. Tube: Cockfosters on Piccadilly line then 384 bus to Brookhill Rd, High Barnet Northern line then 384 bus to Brookhill Rd.* **Adm £2.50, chd free. Sun 22 June (2-5).**
Small, secluded courtyard garden with an interesting collection of shrubs and lots of clematis. A tranquil private space with fences covered in wisteria, roses and clematis, trees and plants in pots. A good example of what can be achieved in a small space over a short time.

94 BROWNLOW ROAD, N11
Bounds Green, London N11 2BS. Spencer Viner, www.northeleven.co.uk. *Close to N Circular. Tube: Bounds Green then 5 mins walk, direction N Circular. Corner of Elvendon Rd & Brownlow Rd.* Light refreshments. **Adm £2.50, chd free. Sun 15 June (2-6).**
'A small courtyard for meditation'. The conception of this garden by a designer has the ability to transport the visitor to a different, foreign place of imagination and tranquillity, far away from the suburbs. Features incl reclaimed materials, trees, water, pergola, pleached limes, seating and a strong theme of pared-back simplicity. Design and horticultural advice. Featured in Gardens Illustrated.

5 BURBAGE ROAD, SE24
Herne Hill, London SE24 9HJ. Crawford & Rosemary Lindsay, 020 7274 5610, rl@rosemarylindsay.com, www.rosemarylindsay.com. *Nr junction with Half Moon Lane. Herne Hill & N Dulwich mainline stns, 5 mins walk. Buses: 3, 37, 40, 68, 196, 468.* Home-made teas. **Adm £3.50, chd free. Sun 27 Apr (2-5). Visitors also welcome by appt Apr to June.**
The garden of a member of The Society of Botanical Artists. 150ft x 40ft with large and varied range of plants. Herb garden, herbaceous borders for sun and shade, climbing plants, pots, terraces, lawns. Gravel areas to reduce watering. See our website for what the papers say. Very popular plant sale.

Have an enjoyable afternoon being nosey, buying plants and sampling my sister's fantastic cakes . . .

12 BUSHBERRY ROAD, E9
Hackney, London E9 5SX. Molly St Hilaire. *Overground stn: Homerton, then 5 mins walk. Buses: 26, 30, 388, alight last stop in Cassland Rd.* Home-made teas. **Adm £3, chd free. Sun 29 June (2-6).**
Petite courtyard garden with water feature. Rambling roses, jasmine, vine and clematis cover the overarching pergola. 'Small but beautifully formed' ... 'a pure joy to see'.

7 BYNG ROAD, EN5
High Barnet EN5 4NW. Mr & Mrs Julian Bishop. *Opp Foulds School - 10 mins walk from tube. Tube: High Barnet. Stn: Hadley Wood or New Barnet. Buses: 107, 263, 384 alight Ravenscroft Park or The Spires.* Home-made teas. **Adm £3, chd free. Sun 7 Sept (2-5).**
Six different borders all in one London garden. One filled with tropical plants, another 'hot' border, two with cooler coloured perennials. Lots of rare and unusual varieties with a modern design twist. Owner a Chelsea Flower Show TV producer for 10 yrs. Emphasis on salvias, rudbeckias, persicarias, unusual half-hardy plants. Also vegetable/cutting garden, series of raised beds and colourful pots. Featured in Hertfordshire Life magazine.

CADOGAN PLACE SOUTH GARDEN, SW1
Sloane Street, London SW1X 9PE. The Cadogan Estate, 07890 452992, Ric.Glenn@cadogan.co.uk. *Entrance to garden opp 97 Sloane St.* **Adm £3.50, chd free. Sun 11 May (11-4.30). Visitors also welcome by appt Apr to Sept.**
Many surprises and unusual trees and shrubs are hidden behind the railings of this large London square. The first square to be developed by architect Henry Holland for Lord Cadogan at the end of C18, it was then called the London Botanic Garden. Mulberry trees planted for silk production at end of C17. Cherry trees, magnolias and bulbs are outstanding in spring, when the fern garden is unfurling. Award winning Hans Sloane Garden exhibited at the Chelsea Flower Show. Ponds. Spring walk on East side of garden. Feel free to bring a picnic to enjoy in the garden.

128 CADOGAN TERRACE, E9
Hackney, London E9 5HP. William Dowden. *Overground stn: Hackney Wick. Cadogan Terrace runs parallel to A102M, along edge of Victoria Park, enter by St Mark's Gate.* **Adm £3, chd free. Sun 20 July (2-6).**
A tranquil yet exotic garden. Your journey begins at the Regent's Canal. You enter the upper level with its gazebo surrounded by roses, hibiscus and lavatera. You move through the middle level with its shrub borders, and finally enter the courtyard with its sunken pool. Journey's end. Adjacent nursery.

8 CALAIS STREET, SE5
Myatts Fields, Camberwell, London SE5 9LP. Mr Patrick de Nangle. *N side of Myatts Fields. Buses 36, 185, 436 along Camberwell New Rd. Get off at Flodden Rd, walk to r'about, turn R Calais Rd. Nearest tube: Oval, stn Denmark Hill.* Home-made teas. **Adm £3.50, chd free. Sun 7 Sept (2-5.30). Also open 24 Grove Park, Camberwell.**

Lemon drizzle cake, Victoria sponge ... yummy! 

An unexpected primeval grove lies behind a traditional Victorian facade offering a host of delights. The dramatic heart of this surprising and totally original garden consists of a grove of 25 tall tree ferns clustered on a carpet of lush, low-level ground cover and surrounded by a host of exotic and dramatic large-leaved plants. A labour of love - and watering! Featured in Garden News. Access is via a side gate with one step.

9A CALONNE ROAD, SW19
London SW19 5HH. Mr & Mrs Neville & Marissa Quie. *Tube & Mainline: Wimbledon 15-20 mins walk. Bus: 93 on Parkside.* Home-made teas. **Adm £3, chd free. Sun 4 May (12-5). Also open 11 Ernle Road.**
Japanese inspired garden with many acers, bamboo, sunken rock pool and Balinese summerhouse. Colourful display of rhododendrons and bulbs. Bird boxes to encourage wildlife.

35 CAMBERWELL GROVE, SE5
London SE5 8JA. Lynette Hemmant & Juri Gabriel, 020 7703 6186, juri@jurigabriel.com. *From Camberwell Green go down Camberwell Church St. Turn R into Camberwell Grove.* **Adm £3.50, chd free (share to St Giles Church). Sun 8 June (12-6). Also open 59, 103, 105 Dulwich Village, Choumert Square and 174 Peckham Rye. Visitors also welcome by appt June to July (£70 minimum charge).**
Plant-packed 120ft x 20ft garden with charming backdrop of St Giles Church. Evolved over 29 yrs into a romantic country-style garden brimming with colour and overflowing with pots. In June, spectacular roses stretch the full length of the garden, both on the artist's studio and festooning an old iron staircase. Artist's studio open. Lynette (who has earned her living by pen and brush throughout her life) has painted the garden obsessively for the past 20yrs; see NGS website. Over the years has featured in numerous magazines and newspapers (and the odd tv programme) in the UK and abroad.

91 Vicar's Moor Lane

GROUP OPENING

CAMBERWELL GROVE GARDENS, SE5
Camberwell, London SE5 8JE. *5 mins from Denmark Hill mainline & overgound stn. Buses: 12, 36, 68, 148, 171, 176, 185, 436. Entrance through garden rooms at rear.* Outstanding tea and cakes at No.81. **Combined adm £5, chd free (share to CJD Support Network). Sun 29 June (2-6). Also open Court Lane Gardens Group.**

81 CAMBERWELL GROVE
Alex & Jane Maitland Hudson

83 CAMBERWELL GROVE
Robert Hirschhorn & John Hall

Neighbouring walled gardens behind C18 houses in this beautiful tree-lined street. At No. 81 a Japanese maple and a tall Trachycarpus palm shade York stone paving and borders filled with herbaceous perennials, roses, clematis and shade-loving ground cover. There is a pond and bog garden. Pots of all sizes line the steps to the kitchen door and the terrace outside the garden room and greenhouse. No. 83 is a 90ft x 18ft beautifully designed plant-lovers' garden developed over the past 14 yrs. The emphasis is on yr-round interest, with abundant unusual planting within a structure of box hedging providing varied and interesting areas of peace and privacy. As trees mature the nature of the garden is changing, and more shade-tolerant perennials are being introduced. Contemporary garden room, gravel and York stone paths and seating areas, calming pool and lovely views of parish church.

NEW 7 CANONBIE ROAD, SE23
London SE23 3AW. Mrs June Wismayer. *Rail: Honor Oak Pk (7 mins walk). Bus: P12, 63 & 363 to Forest Hill Tavern. Unrestricted parking nearby.* Home-made teas. **Adm £3.50, chd free. Sun 13 July (2-5.30). Also open 4 Piermont Green.**
An exuberant, upward-sloping, town garden, 90ft x 30ft. Created on a tight budget (with the aid of a small greenhouse), many plants are propagated from seed and softwood cuttings. In summer, the air is filled with the scent of jasmine and lilies; roses, clematis and vines scramble over shrubs and fences; purple fennel whispers in the wind. A wild, romantic garden in an urban setting.

Look out for the NGS yellow arrows ...

29 CANONBURY PARK NORTH, N1

London N1 2JZ. James Longstaff, www.29cpn.com. *Between Upper St and St Paul's Rd. Tube: Highbury & Islington. Buses: 19, 73, 277.* Light refreshments. **Adm £3, chd free. Sun 20 July (12-4).**
Bold foliage with a tropical flavour fringes sunlit terraces and an ornamental pond to create a stylish urban retreat from the stress of the city. This compact 8 yr-old garden demonstrates that you don't need acres of space to create an oasis in the heart of London.

31 CANONBURY PARK NORTH, N1

London N1 2JU. Mr & Mrs Brian Morris. *Canonbury Park North is between Upper St and St Paul's Rd. Tube: Highbury & Islington. Buses: 19, 73, 277.* Light refreshments. **Adm £3.50, chd free. Sun 1 June (2-6).**
Tranquil, well established, west facing wooded town garden laid down predominately with mature shrubs and plants that attract wildlife with a striking clutch of silver birches, a pond and two fountains.

4 CANONBURY PLACE, N1

London N1 2NQ. Mr & Mrs Jeffrey Tobias. *Tube & Overground: Highbury & Islington. Buses: 271 to Canonbury Square. Located in the old part of Canonbury Place, off Alwyne Villas in a cul de sac.* Home-made teas. **Adm £3.50, chd free. Sat 12 Apr (2-6).**
A paved, 100ft garden behind a 1780 house. Spectacular mature trees enclosed in a walled garden. Mostly pots and also interesting shrubs and climbers. Daffodlils, tulips and bluebells abound for this springtime opening.

111 CAPEL ROAD, E7

London E7 0JS. Jan Tallis & John Lock, 07951 762874, jantallis@btinternet.com. *2m from Stratford City. 10 mins walk from Forest Gate, Manor Park & Wanstead Park Overground stations. Many buses. Easy parking.* Home-made teas. **Adm £3, chd free (share to School-Home-Support). Sat 17 May (12-5); Sun 18 May (12-4). Visitors also welcome by appt (few weeks notice required).**
90ft x 30ft urban villa garden. 7 areas: vibrant; subtle; hot; white; quiet; fernery; woodland. Large ponds - 2 wildlife ponds and 1 formal. Amazing disappearing shed (mirrors, sedum roof). Interesting small trees. Natural sculptures. No lawn! Two patios, scattered fruits. Carnivorous plant collection, lots of pots. Attached to unique modern house with balcony view. Owner's paintings on display.

5 CECIL ROAD, N10

Muswell Hill N10 2BU. Ben Loftus. *Off Alexandra Park Rd. Buses: 102, 299 from E Finchley or Bounds Green, alight St Andrew's Church.* **Adm £2.50, chd free. Sun 29 June (2-5). Also open 48 Dukes Avenue.**
Garden designer's sloping garden featured in several magazines. Spectacular, well planted large pots (irrigated), interesting small raised pond, unusual small trees, shrubs and perennials with much emphasis on foliage and shape. Stylish garden office with green roof of bulbs, thymes etc.

THE CHARTERHOUSE, EC1

Charterhouse Square, London EC1M 6AN. The Governors of Sutton's Hospital, www.thecharterhouse.org. *Buses: 4, 55. Tube: Barbican. Turn L out of stn, L into Carthusian St & into square. Entrance through car park.* **Evening Opening £5, chd free, wine, Tue 17 June (6-9).**
Enclosed courtyard gardens within the grounds of historic Charterhouse, which dates back to 1347. 'English Country Garden' style featuring roses, herbaceous borders, ancient mulberry trees and small pond. Various garden herbs found here are still used in the kitchen today. Buildings not open. A private garden for the Brothers of Charterhouse, not usually open to the public.

51 THE CHASE, SW4

London SW4 0NP. Mr Charles Rutherfoord & Mr Rupert Tyler, 020 7627 0182, www.charlesrutherfoord.net. *Off Clapham Common Northside. Tube: Clapham Common. Buses: 137, 452.* **Adm £3.50, chd free. Sun 27 Apr (2-5). Evening Opening £3.50, chd free, Wed 7 May (6-8). Visitors also welcome by appt Apr to Sept.**
Member of the Society of Garden Designers, Charles has created the garden over 25yrs using 15 different species of trees. Spectacular in spring, when 1500 tulips bloom among irises and tree peonies, and in Sept with dahlias. Narrow paths lead to a mound surrounded by acanthus and topped by a large steel sculpture. Rupert's geodetic dome shelters seedlings, succulents and subtropicals. Featured in 'The Gardens of England - Treasures of the National Gardens Scheme', Sunday Times, Evening Standard, The London Garden Book A-Z and on BBC Gardeners' World.

D

◆ CHELSEA PHYSIC GARDEN, SW3

66 Royal Hospital Road, London SW3 4HS. Chelsea Physic Garden self-funding charity, www.chelseaphysicgarden.co.uk. *Tube: Sloane Square (10 mins). Bus: 170. Parking Battersea Park (charged). Entrance in Swan Walk (except wheelchairs).* Light refreshments. **Adm £9.90, chd £6.60. For NGS: Tue 1 Apr (11-6). For other opening times and information, please phone or see garden website.**
Come feed your senses at London's oldest botanic garden. Four acres with Edible and Useful Gardens, family order beds, historical walk, glasshouses. Also Cool Fernery and Robert Fortune's tank pond. Guided and audio tours. New for 2014 - Garden of Medicinal Plants. Wheelchair access is via 66 Royal Hospital Rd.

24 CHESTNUT ROAD, SE27
West Norwood, London SE27 9LF. Paul Brewer & Anne Rogerson. *Stns: West Norwood or Tulse Hill. Buses: 2, 68, 196, 322, 432, 468. Off S end of Norwood Rd, nr W Norwood Cemetery.* **Adm £2, chd free (share to Sound Minds - the arts for mental health). Sun 8 June (2-5). Evening Opening £3, chd free, wine, Sun 7 Sept (5-9).**
Front garden with borders. Compact rear garden with patios, decking, pond and unusual gazebo, bamboos and bananas. Shed with green roof. Stag beetle habitat. Penguin. Candle lit evening opening. Fire pit ensures a warm welcome for all.

Relax in the Japanese area, stroll through the potager and chat to our suburban hens . . .

NEW **46 CHEYNE AVENUE, E18**
London E18 2DR. Helen Auty. *Nearest tube S. Woodford. Short walk. From station take Clarendon Rd. Cross High Rd into Broadwalk, 3rd on L Bushey Ave. 1st R Cheyne Ave.* Light refreshments. **Adm £3.50, chd free. Sun 20 July, Sun 17 Aug (12-4).**
On site of Lord Cheyne's original market garden, typical suburban garden with lawn and borders of shrubs, climbers and perennials - greenhouse and productive fruit and vegetable garden.

GROUP OPENING

CHISWICK MALL GARDENS, W4
Chiswick, London W6 9TN. *Tube: Stamford Brook or Turnham Green. Buses: 27, 190, 267 & 391 to Young's Corner from Hammersmith, through St Peter's Sq under A4 to river. By Car: Hogarth r'about, A4 (W) turn off at Eyot Grds S, then R into Chiswick Mall.* **Combined adm £2.50, chd free. Sun 8 June (2-6).**

16 EYOT GARDENS
Ms Dianne Farris
Visitors also welcome by appt Apr to Sept.
020 8741 1370
dianefarris@gmail.com

FIELD HOUSE
Rupert King
Visitors also welcome by appt Apr to Oct.
kingrupert@hotmail.com

SWAN HOUSE
Mr & Mrs George Nissen

A unique group of riverside houses and gardens situated in an unspoilt quiet backwater.

CHOUMERT SQUARE, SE15
London SE15 4RE. The Residents. *Off Choumert Grove. Trains from London Bridge, Clapham Junction to Peckham Rye; buses (12, 36, 37, 63, 78, 171, 312, 345). Car park 2 mins.* Refreshments available inside the Square incl a traditional tea and cakes stand. **Adm £4, chd free (share to St Christopher's Hospice). Sun 8 June (1-6). Also open 35 Camberwell Grove and 174 Peckham Rye 103 Dulwich Village Two Gardens.**
About 46 mini gardens with maxi-planting in Shangri-la situation that the media has described as a 'Floral Canyon', which leads to small communal 'secret garden'. This year the popular open gardens will combine with our own take on a village fete! Live music, arts, crafts and entertaining stalls. Highly commended in London Squares Competition. Featured in Sunday Times, Period Living, The Guardian, Evening Standard and other national press.

79 CHURCH LANE, N2
London N2 0TH. Caro & David Broome, carosgarden@virginmedia.com. *Tube: E Finchley, then East End Rd for ¾ m, R into Church Ln. Buses: 143 to Five Bells PH, 3 min walk; 263 to E Finchley Library, 5 min walk.* Home-made teas. **Adm £3.50, chd free. Sun 15 June (2-6). Also open 22 Trinity Road.**
Garden writer's garden with a 'twist'. Enter through 'catatorium', a plant-filled open air conservatory, into the NEW lawn free garden beyond. Shrubs, roses and unusual perennials create a colour coordinated palette, with curved rill, hidden water features and quirky ornamentals! Rustic archway leads to secluded ferny glen, home to David's perfectly appointed Man Shed sanctuary! New for 2014 - The lawn has finally gone and in its place Indian stone setts planted with camomile and thyme. Also find a secluded bubble fountain.

THE CIRCLE GARDEN
33 Cambridge Avenue, New Malden KT3 4LD. Vincent & Heidi Johnson-Paul-McDonnell, www.thecirclegarden.com. *1¼ m N of A3 Malden junction. Bus: 213. 10 mins walk from New Malden railway station; A3 signposted for Kingston; 213 bus stop located a short distance from end of rd; our house is pink!* Home-made teas. **Adm £3, chd free. Sun 29 June (2-6).**
A welcoming front garden with cottage-style planting leading to an 'unexpected' rear garden with intriguing vistas where you will find herbaceous and annuals in mixed borders. Relax in the Japanese area, stroll through the potager and chat to our suburban hens. An ever-evolving garden with plans for further developments.

COLUMCILLE
9 Norlands Crescent, Chislehurst BR7 5RN. Nancy & Jim Pratt, 0208 467 9383, nancyandjim@btinternet.com. *Off A222 turn into Cricket Ground Rd, then 1st R into Norlands Cres, approx ½ m from Chislehurst BR stn. Buses: 162 or 269, Susan Wood stop.* Light refreshments. **Adm £3, chd free (share to St Nicholas Church). Sat 7 June (1-5). Visitors also welcome by appt May to Sept.**
Small garden featuring Japanese sanctuary, influenced by Zen tradition, incl water feature, lanterns, traditional Japanese plants and garden shed transformed into a tea house. Also cottage garden section with colourful display of roses, digitalis, lupins, peonies and delphiniums, especially in June. Wheelchair access will require assistance.

Field House, Chiswick Mall Gardens

4 CORNFLOWER TERRACE, SE22
East Dulwich, London SE22 0HH. Clare Dryhurst. *5 mins walk from 63 bus stop at bottom of Forest Hill Rd. Turn into Dunstans Rd, then 2nd on L. Mainline: Peckham Rye or Honor Oak Park.* Home-made teas. **Adm £3.50, chd free. Sun 8 June (2-5.30). Also open 174 Peckham Rye, Dulwich Village Gardens, Choumert Square and 35 Camberwell Grove.**
A garden Tardis - this pretty, secluded and tiny courtyard cottage garden, in a quiet street in the heart of artistic East Dulwich, is only 50ft x 9ft. Around a sunken patio and solar fountain are clustered climbers, roses, ferns, annuals and herbs in raised beds and pots backed by a charming painted garden shed. Picture perfect.

6 CORNFORD GROVE, SW12
London SW12 9JF. Susan Venner & Richard Glassborow, 020 8675 8574, sv@vennerlucas.co.uk. *Tube & mainline Balham, then 8 mins walk.* Home-made teas. **Adm £3, chd free. Sun 22 June (2-6). Evening Opening £3, chd free, wine, Mon 23 June (6-9).**
This medium sized garden is an integral extension of sustainable low carbon living. The guiding principles within the garden combine aesthetic values with productivity, biodiversity and low maintenance. Technically an orchard, 20 fruiting trees and forest berries merge with herbaceous planting and two working bee hives.

GROUP OPENING

NEW COURT LANE GARDENS GROUP, SE21
Dulwich, London SE21 7EA. *Buses P4, 12 (to Dulwich Library), 37, 176. Mainline: N Dulwich then 20 mins walk. Ample free parking.* Home-made teas. **Combined adm £5, chd free. Sun 29 June (2-5.30). Also open 35 Camberwell Grove.**

122 COURT LANE, SE21
Jean & Charles Cary-Elwes

NEW 125 COURT LANE, SE21
Stephen Henden & Neil Ellis

Two gardens in the same road with very different planting styles which makes for an interesting visit. No 122 is a mature garden with deep herbaceous borders, tender shrubs, a generous lawn and a shady woodland area - agapanthus is a signature plant - as it is, too, at No 125, but here the mood is more of a cottage garden with winding lavender-lined gravel paths, billowing grasses and arching roses. Partial wheelchair access.

GROUP OPENING

DE BEAUVOIR GARDENS, N1
London N1 4HU. *De Beauvoir. Dalston Junction or Haggerton Station, London. Overground (E London line); Highbury & Islington tube then 30 or 277 bus; Angel tube then 38, 56 or 73 bus. Street parking. Gardens within 5 mins walk of each other.* Teas and home-made cakes at 158 Culford Road. **Combined adm £5, chd free. Sun 15 June (11-3).**

158 CULFORD ROAD
Gillian Blachford

114 DE BEAUVOIR ROAD
Nancy & Richard Turnbull

21 NORTHCHURCH TERRACE
Nancy Korman

Three gardens to explore in De Beauvoir, a leafy enclave of Victorian villas near to Islington and Dalston. The area boasts some of Hackney's keenest gardeners and a thriving gardening club. Many gardens have been resuscitated from neglect and sensitively restored to glory.
158 Culford Rd is a long narrow garden with a romantic feel. A path winds through full borders with shrubs, small trees, perennials and many unusual plants. The walled garden at 21 Northchurch Terrace has a more formal feel, with deep herbaceous borders, pond, fruit trees, pergola, patio pots and herb beds. 114 De Beauvoir Rd is wildlife-friendly having decorative borders, a fruit and vegetable garden, many resident birds and beehives on the roof. Visitors can taste the honey and learn about bees. There will be information on bee-keeping and vegetable growing available as well as seed-sowing for children. Honey tasting. Some gardens can be viewed with no steps.

36 DOWNS HILL
Beckenham BR3 5HB. Marc & Janet Berlin, 020 8650 9377, janetberlin@hotmail.com. *1m W of Bromley. 2 mins from Ravensbourne mainline station nr top of Foxgrove Rd*. Home-made teas. **Adm £3, chd free. Sun 29 June (2-5). Visitors also welcome by appt Apr to Oct.**
Long, 2/3 -acre E-facing, award winning garden sloping steeply. Ponds, water courses and several varied patio areas. Many tender unusual plants and hundreds of pots. Wooded paths, dense planting of trees, shrubs and flowers, raised beds and gravel areas. Two alpine houses and greenhouse. Music.

48 DUKES AVENUE, N10
Muswell Hill, London N10 2PU. Margo Buchanan. *Short walk from main Muswell Hill r'about. Tube: Highgate then bus 43 or 134 to Muswell Hill Broadway, then bus 7 from Finsbury Park.* **Adm £3.50, chd free. Sun 29 June (2-6). Also open 5 Cecil Road.**
Garden on 3 levels. DOWN to a secret, hidden retreat with ferns and shade-tolerant flowering climbers. UP to a paved terrace with lawn and flowerbeds beyond. Specimen plants incl forest pansy and established acers. Planting in complementary colour combinations featuring unusual alliums and perennials, creating a relaxing environment for entertaining and contemplation. Music.

GROUP OPENING

DULWICH VILLAGE TWO GARDENS, SE21
London SE21 7BJ. *Rail: N Dulwich or W Dulwich then 10-15 mins walk. Tube: Brixton then P4 bus passes the gardens, alight Dulwich Picture Gallery stop. Street parking*. Home-made teas at No103. **Combined adm £5, chd free (share to Macmillan, local branch). Sun 8 June (2-5). Also open 9 Dulwich Village, 174 Peckham Rye, Choumert Square and 35 Camberwell Grove.**

103 DULWICH VILLAGE
Mr & Mrs N Annesley

105 DULWICH VILLAGE
Mr & Mrs A Rutherford

2 Georgian houses with large gardens, 3 mins walk from Dulwich Picture Gallery and Dulwich Park. 103 Dulwich Village is a 'country garden in London' with a long herbaceous border, lawn, pond, roses and fruit and vegetable gardens. 105 Dulwich Village is a very pretty garden with many unusual plants, lots of old-fashioned roses, fish pond and water garden. Amazing collection of plants for sale.

An old barrel is home to the Goldfish . . .

9 DULWICH VILLAGE, SE21
Fairfield, 9 Dulwich Village, London SE21 7BU. Helen Marsden. *5 mins from N Dulwich Station. Rail: N Dulwich or W Dulwich then 10-15 mins walk. Tube: Brixton then P4 bus passes garden. Street parking.* Home-made teas. **Adm £3.50, chd free. Sun 8 June (2-5). Also open Dulwich Village Two Gardens, 35 Camberwell Grove and Choumert Square.**
This stunning garden in Dulwich is a surprise on many levels; the traditional frontage belies the dramatic contemporary garden behind - almost an acre designed by the master of minimalism, Christopher Bradley-Hole. Designed on a grid, there are huge blocks of yew, gravel and box balls and raised beds for fruit and vegetables. Slate swimming pool, patio with pink walls. Wheelchairs can access the garden through a side gate but will need to be able to go over gravel.

207 EAST BARNET ROAD
New Barnet. EN4 8QS. Margaret Chadwick, 020 8440 0377, magg1ee@hotmail.com. *East Barnet Village. M25 J24 then A111 to Cockfosters. Tube: Northern line to High Barnet or Piccadilly line to Cockfosters. Buses: 184, 307 & 326.* **Adm £3.50. Visitors welcome by appt.**
Delightful example of a minute courtyard garden 25ft x 30ft. High fences are covered with clematis, honeysuckle and passion flowers; roses and vines scramble over an arch above a seat. Small pond sustains frogs and tadpoles and water plants. An old barrel is home to the Goldfish. Many interesting and unusual plants, mainly in pots. Clever use of mirrors lends added dimensions to this pretty garden. Good use of space, packed full of plants and designed not to reveal itself all at once.

ECCLESTON SQUARE, SW1
London SW1V 1NP. Roger Phillips & the Residents, roger.phillips@rogersroses.com, www.rogerstreesandshrubs.com. *Off Belgrave Rd nr Victoria Stn, parking allowed on Suns*. Home-made teas. **Adm £4, chd free. Sun 11 May (2-5). Visitors also welcome by appt Mar to July.**
Planned by Cubitt in 1828, the 3-acre square is subdivided into mini-gardens with camellias, iris, ferns and containers. Dramatic collection of tender climbing roses and 20 different forms of tree peonies. National Collection of ceanothus incl more than 70 species and cultivars. Notable important additions of tender plants being grown and tested. Specialist collection of Ceanothus, Tea Roses and Tree Peonies. Featured in Gardeners World.

NCH

EDWARDES SQUARE, W8
South Edwardes Square, Kensington, London W8 6HL. Edwardes Square Garden Committee. *Tube: Kensington High St & Earls Court. Buses: 9, 10, 27, 28, 31, 49 & 74 to Odeon Cinema. Entrance in South Edwardes Square.* **Adm £4, chd free. Sun 13 Apr (12.30-5).**
One of London's prettiest secluded garden squares. 3½ acres laid out differently from other squares, with serpentine paths by Agostino Agliothe, Italian artist and decorator who lived at no.15 from 1814-1820, and a beautiful Grecian temple which is traditionally the home of the head gardener. Romantic rose tunnel winds through the middle of the garden. Good displays of bulbs and blossom. Very easy wheelchair access.

GROUP OPENING

ELM COURT GARDENS, EN4

Oakhurst Avenue, East Barnet EN4 8HA, 020 8361 2642. *200 yds from Oakleigh Pk Stn on rail line to Welwyn Garden City. M25 J24, then A111 to Cockfosters & A110 down Cat Hill to East Barnet Village.* Home-made teas. **Combined adm £4.50, chd free. Sun 13 July (2-6).**

3 ELM COURT
Mike & Alyne Lidgley
Visitors also welcome by appt July to Aug. No min, max 20 visitors.
020 8361 2642

4 ELM COURT
Simon Moor & Jayne Evans

Many contrasts in these two quite different gardens, both larger than average. Front gardens - one a formal parterre, one natural, with gravel, grasses, conifers and reclaimed materials. Back gardens: one with hot annuals, perennials, shrubs, hanging baskets, water feature, two topiary beds, pink, blue, 'spiky' and heuchera beds, a 'ball' bed, greenhouse, garden and potting sheds, 2 rockeries, alpine troughs, and much more. The other is long and shady, with curving lawns, a gravel area with containers full of colour, a white bed, a rockery and the whole emphasis is on attracting pollinators - blue, pink, purple and yellow shrubs and perennials. Jayne is a successful artist and has her studio in the garden. A developing garden, still evolving and hungrily devouring cuttings, contributions and advice from all sources and gradually triumphing over poor soil, overhanging trees and lack of water. Plant crèche: plants purchased delivered locally after the event, free of charge. Raffle. 3 Elm Court featured in Garden News.

ELM TREE COTTAGE

85 Croham Road, South Croydon CR2 7HJ. Wendy Witherick & Michael Wilkinson, 020 8681 8622, elmtreecottage@sky.com. *2m S of Croydon. Off B275 from Croydon, off A2022 from Selsdon, bus 64. Station: East or South Croydon.* **Adm £3, chd free. Sun 4 May, Sun 15 June, Sun 10 Aug (1-4). Visitors also welcome by appt May to Sept.**
Picture this! Come through the gate of our c1855 flint cottage and welcome to the Mediterranean! Meander up the sloping brick path to the sound of running water, see lemon trees, olives, palms and other drought-tolerant plants. Look inside the glasshouse and you will find agaves, cacti and succulents. Rest before you carry on your journey, past lavender, rosemary and much much more! Steep garden, unsuitable for those unsteady on their feet. Regret no dogs or children.

11 ERNLE ROAD, SW20

Wimbledon, London SW20 0HH. Theresa-Mary Morton. *1/4 m from Wimbledon Village, 200yds from Crooked Billet PH. Exit A3 at A238 to Wimbledon, turning L at Copse Hill. Mainline: Wimbledon or Raynes Park. Tube: Wimbledon; Bus: 200 to Christchurch then 100yds walk.* Home-made teas. **Adm £3.50, chd free. Sat 3, Sun 4 May (2.30-6). Also open 9a Calonne Road, Sun 4 May.**
Established suburban garden of 1/4 acre on sandy acid soil, spatially organised into separate sections: oak pergola framing the main vista, hidden parterre, woodland, pool, winter iris border, flower garden and summerhouse. Featured in Country Life. Beaten gravel paths, one step up to main garden.

48 ERSKINE HILL, NW11

Hampstead Garden Suburb, London NW11 6HG. Marjorie & David Harris, 020 8455 6507. *1m N of Golders Green. Nr A406 & A1. Tube: Golders Green. H2 Hail & Ride bus from Golders Green to garden, or 82, 460, 102 buses to Temple Fortune (10 mins walk).* Light refreshments. **Adm £3.50, chd free. Sun 8 June (2-6). Visitors also welcome by appt May to Sept.**
Bird-friendly garden, wrapped around Arts and Crafts artisan's cottage, featuring perennials, shrubs, roses, clematis, old apple tree and flowering cherry. Terrace with well-planted containers. Intriguing brick-paved area with four raised beds. Greenhouse. London Gardens Society 'highly recommended back garden' visited by LGS patron, HRH Prince Edward, June 2013. Nest boxes, miniature long grass areas, organic and pesticide-free. Featured in Ham & High (Royal visit) and Suburb News. Some single steps and narrow paths. Rail to lawn.

65 FARM WAY

Worcester Park KT4 8SB. Mr & Mrs A Rutherford. *Stn: Worcester Park. Bus: 213.* Cream teas. **Adm £3, chd free. Sun 29 June (1-5).**
Plant lover's 6yr-old garden with wide mixed borders bursting with colour and plants of different textures and interest, incl shrubs, roses and perennials. Assorted pots of vegetables, raised beds. Paving and decking, plenty of seating areas.

◆ FENTON HOUSE, NW3

Hampstead Grove, Hampstead, London NW3 6SP. National Trust, www.nationaltrust.org.uk. *300yds from Hampstead tube. Entrances: Top of Holly Hill & Hampstead Grove.* **For NGS: Tue 8 Apr (6.30-8.30). Pre booking essential for Special Evening Tour, £10 with wine & light refreshments. Please phone 01932 864532. Please note: Payment by cheque only. For other opening times and information, please see garden website.**
Join the Gardener-in-Charge for a special evening tour. Andrew Darragh who brings over 10 yrs' experience from Kew to Fenton House will explore this timeless 1 1/2 -acre walled garden. Laid out over 3 levels, and featuring formal walks and areas, a small sunken rose garden, a 300yr-old orchard and a kitchen garden, Andrew will present the garden and his plans for its future development.

54 FERNDOWN

Northwood Hills HA6 1PH. David Bryson & Ros Preston, 020 8866 3792, davidbryson@sky.com. *Tube: Northwood Hills 5 mins walk. R out of stn, R down Briarwood Dr then 1st R.* Cream teas. **Adm £3, chd free.**

Sun 17 Aug (11-6). Visitors also welcome by appt Aug to Sept.
Subtropical escapism in suburbia. Intensely planted with a shoehorn, the garden incl many rare species of palms, bromeliads, ferns, cacti, succulents and other unusual plants. Of note are large examples of trachycarpus princeps and alcantarea. A raised deck and ponds help create a unique effect. Featured in The Independent Magazine.

> An oasis in Camden's urban density, where challenges of space and shade are met by resourceful planting . . .

6 FLANCHFORD ROAD, W12

London W12 9ND. Mr & Mrs Yadav. *District line to Stamford Brook. Exit L into Goldhawk Rd. Pass petrol station T-junction turn L then 1st R.* Light refreshments. **Adm £3, chd free. Sun 15 June (2-6).**
A family garden designed in such a way as to provide an oasis of peace and calm to adults while providing a spacious secluded play area for children at the back. The planting plan is varied and interesting and provides colour all yr round. Interest is added to the garden with a stone wall and arch with a fountain and stone bird bath. Garden is level so should be accessible to wheelchair users, although side return is narrow in places.

GROUP OPENING

FROGNAL GARDENS, NW3

Hampstead, London NW3 6UY. *Tube: Hampstead. Buses: 46, 268 to Hampstead High St. Frognal Gdns 2nd R off Church Row from Heath St.* Home-made teas. **Combined adm £5, chd free. Sun 22 June (2-5).**

5 FROGNAL GARDENS
Ruth & Brian Levy

5A FROGNAL GARDENS
Ian & Barbara Jackson

2 neighbouring gardens divided by path lined with trellises of cascading roses and clematis, underplanted with carpets of flowers. At No.5, the long narrow structured garden is romantically planted with soft colours and a profusion of unusual climbers and cottage perennials. The small, beautifully landscaped garden at 5A is a garden to enjoy and relax in with lawn, colourful flower beds and containers. 4 inch step from patio doors.

9 FURLONG ROAD, N7

Islington, London N7 8LS. Nigel Watts & Tanuja Pandit. *Tube & Overground: Highbury & Islington, 3 mins walk along Holloway Rd, 2nd L. Furlong Rd joins Holloway Rd & Liverpool Rd. Buses: 43, 271, 393.* Home-made teas. **Adm £2, chd free. Sun 8 June (2-6). Also open 16 Furlong Rd.**
Award-winning small garden designed by Karen Fitzsimon which makes clever use of an awkwardly-shaped plot. Curved lines are used to complement a modern extension. Raised beds contain a mix of tender and hardy plants to give an exotic feel and incl loquat, banana, palm, cycad and tree fern. Contrasting traditional front garden. Featured in 'Small Family Gardens' and 'Modern Family Gardens' by Caroline Tilston.

16 FURLONG ROAD, N7

Islington, London N7 8LS. Charles & Ingrid Maggs. *Tube & Overground: Highbury & Islington, 3mins walk along Holloway Rd, 2nd L. Furlong Rd joins Holloway Rd & Liverpool Rd. Buses: 43, 271, 393.* Home-made teas. **Adm £3, chd free. Sun 8 June (2-6). Also open 9 Furlong Rd.**
Exceptional aspect as garden backs onto churchyard with church tower giving a feeling of being in the country rather than just off the Holloway Rd. Informal flower borders and trellises of roses, surrounding lawn, a pond, pergola and rock garden.

GARDEN BARGE SQUARE AT DOWNINGS ROADS MOORINGS, SE1

31 Mill Street, London SE1 2AX. Mr Nick Lacey. *Close to Tower Bridge & Design Museum. Mill St off Jamaica Rd, between London Bridge & Bermondsey stns, Tower Hill also nearby. Buses: 47, 188, 381, RV1.* **Adm £3.50, chd free (share to RNLI). Sun 11 May (2-5.30).**
Series of 7 floating barge gardens connected by walkways and bridges. Gardens have an eclectic range of plants for yr round seasonal interest. Marine environment: suitable shoes and care needed. Not suitable for small children.

◆ THE GARDEN MUSEUM, SE1

Lambeth Palace Road, London SE1 7LB. The Garden Museum, 020 7401 8865, www.gardenmuseum.org.uk. *E side of Lambeth Bridge. Tube: Lambeth North, Vauxhall, Waterloo. Buses: 507 Red Arrow from Victoria or Waterloo mainline & tube stns, also 3, 77, 344.* **Adm £7.50, chd free (share to Garden Museum). For NGS: Sat 7 June (10.30-4). For other opening times and information, please phone or see garden website.**
Reproduction C17 knot garden with period plants, topiary and box hedging. Wild garden in front of graveyard area; front border designed by Dan Pearson. Temporary exhibitions focusing on leading garden designers or garden related themes, permanent display of tools, paintings and ephemera, shop and café housed in former church of St-Mary-at-Lambeth. Cafe offering delicious home baked menu. The Museum is accessible for wheelchair users via ramps and access lift.

70 GLOUCESTER CRESCENT, NW1

London NW1 7EG. Lucy Gent, 020 7485 6906, gent.lucy@gmail.com. *Tube: Camden Town 2 mins, Mornington Crescent 10 mins. Metered parking in Oval Rd.* **Adm £3.50, chd free. Sun 29 June, Sun 3 Aug (2-5.30). Also open The Holme and 4 Park Village East 29 June and The Holme 3 August. Visitors also welcome by appt Apr to Oct.**
An oasis in Camden's urban density, where challenges of space and shade are met by resourceful planting. In August as well as at midsummer there is a lively play of colour and foliage interest. Notice also the pretty cottage garden at 69 Gloucester Crescent next door where visitors are also welcome.

20 GOLDHAZE CLOSE

Woodford Green IG8 7LE. Jenny Richmond, oscar.singh@ntlworld.com. *Off A1009 Broadmead Rd, Orchard Estate Bus Stop for W14.* Home-made teas. **Adm £3.50, chd free. Sun 20 July, Sun 17 Aug (12-5.30). Visitors also welcome by appt July to Aug.**

100ft L-shaped landscaped garden is bursting with over 100 plants grown in different types of conditions. A huge 29yr-old eucalyptus resembles a mature oak with beautiful bark. Paths lined with plants such as a strawberry tree, roses, campsis, penstemons, crocosmia and vegetables (in pots grown from seed in a greenhouse) lead to a secret decked garden for relaxation.

> An exotic garden full of the exuberance of late summer inspired by travel in Southeast Asia . . .

ALLOTMENTS

GOLF COURSE ALLOTMENTS, N11

Winton Avenue, London N11 2AS. GCAA/Haringey, www.gcaa.pwp.blueyonder.co.uk. *Tube Bounds Green. Buses 102 184 299 to Sunshine Garden Centre, Durnsford Rd. Through park to Bidwell Gdns. Turn L up Winton Ave. No cars on site.* Light home-made lunches. **Adm £3.50, chd free (share to GCAA). Sun 7 Sept (1-4.30).**

Large, long-established allotment with over 200 plots, some organic. Maintained by culturally diverse community growing wide variety of fruit, vegetables and flowers. Picturesque corners and quirky sheds - a visit feels like being in the countryside. Autumn Show on Sun 7 Sept features prize winning horticultural and domestic exhibits. Tours of best plots. Fresh allotment produce, chutneys, jams, cakes and light lunches all available for sale. Award Winning Rose Garden Allotment featured on BBC Gardener's World. Wheelchair access limited to main paths. Gravel and some uneven surfaces. WC, incl disabled.

ALLOTMENTS

NEW GORDON ROAD ALLOTMENTS, N3

Gordon Road, London N3 1EL. Judy Woollett, www.finchleyhorticulturalsociety.org.uk. *Finchley Central. 10 mins walk from Finchley Central tube. 326 bus. Parking in Gordon Rd & adjacent st. No parking on site.* Home-made teas. **Adm £3.50, chd free. Sun 7 Sept (1.30-5.30).**

Founded in 1940 to promote the interests of gardeners throughout Finchley with over 70 plots. Allotments comprise a mixture of traditional plots and raised beds for those with physical disabilities and for children from local schools. Also a wildlife area with slow worms and an area set aside for bee hives. Tours of best plots. Seasonal vegetables on sale incl perennial flowers. Wheelchair access on main paths only. Disabled WC.

55 GRASMERE AVENUE

Merton Park SW19 3DY. Glen Burnell & Roger Blanks. *1m S of Wimbledon. Tube: Morden, 5 mins walk, turn R out off stn. Car: Close to Morden Town Centre, just off one way system.* Home-made teas. **Adm £3, chd free. Sun 15 June (11-3).**

An oasis of calm in suburbia. Rich lush foliage, sculptured with tropical planting, sets off a subtle palette of cooling purple and white in a little haven of tranquillity in this 70ft rear garden of a 1930s London semi. Soft background music and the sound of flowing water add to the tranquil, relaxing ambiance.

17 GREENSTONE MEWS, E11

Wanstead, London E11 2RS. Mr & Mrs S Farnham, 07761 476651, farnhamz@yahoo.co.uk. *Wanstead. Tube: Snaresbrook or Wanstead, 5 mins walk. Bus: 101, 308, W12, W14 to Wanstead High St.* **Adm £12 (incl pre-booked High Tea), regret no children. Sun 3 Aug (2.30-5). Visitors also welcome by appt June to Sept, min 4, max 6 visitors.**

Slate paved garden (20ft x 17ft). Height provided by a mature strawberry tree. A buried bath used as a fishpond is surrounded by climbers clothing fences underplanted with herbs, vegetables, shrubs and perennials grown from cuttings; cultivated with tools stored in a shed on wheels. Ideas aplenty for small space gardening. High Tea with sandwiches, scones, choice of cakes and pot of Tea incl in admission price. Book and plant sale. Featured in Over 50's Olympia Magazine.

7 THE GROVE, N6

Highgate Village, London N6 6JU. Mr Thomas Lyttelton, 07713 638161. *The Grove is between Highgate West Hill & Hampstead Lane. Tube: Archway or Highgate. Buses: 143, 210, 214 and 271.* Home-made teas. **Adm £3.50, chd free (share to The Harington Scheme). Sun 13 Apr, Sun 8 June (2-5.30). Visitors also welcome by appt Mar to Sept.**

½ acre designed for maximum all-yr interest with its variety of conifers and other trees, ground cover, water garden, vistas, 19 paths, surprises. Exceptional camellias and magnolia in April. Wheelchair access to main lawn only; many very narrow paths.

24 GROVE PARK, SE5

Camberwell, London SE5 8LH. Clive Pankhurst, www.alternative-planting.blogspot.com. *Chadwick Rd end of Grove Park. Stns: Peckham Rye or Denmark Hill, both 10 mins walk. Good street parking.* Home-made teas. **Adm £3.50, chd free. Sun 7 Sept (2-5.30). Also open 8 Calais Street.**

An exotic garden full of the exuberance of late summer inspired by travel in Southeast Asia. A jungle of big leafed plants, bold colours and shapes incl bananas, dahlias and tetrapanax. Huge 'secret' garden gives the garden unexpected size with ponds, bee hives, sunken terrace, productive area and greenhouse of carnivorous plants. Featured on BBC Gardeners World and in the Independent.

GROUP OPENING

NEW GROVE PARK CAMBERWELL GROUP, SE5

Camberwell, London SE5 8LH. *Chadwick Rd end of Grove Park. Train: Peckham Rye or Denmark Hill, both 10 mins walk. Good street parking*. Tea available at No. 34. **Combined adm £4, chd free. Sun 15 June (2-5.30).**

NEW 37 GROVE PARK, SE5
Madeleine Aldridge & James La Terriere

34 GROVE PARK
Christopher & Philippa Matthews

Two very different gardens in a leafy part of Camberwell. No.34 is an 80ft x 40ft garden started in 2006, designed for yr-round flowers. Large colour-themed beds with abundant perennials, old English roses, alliums, echiums, cardoons and climbers. Packed 50ft S-facing front garden, best described as organised chaos. No.37 is a creative mix of sub-tropical plants interspersed with walkways made of reclaimed hardwood. Lancewoods compete for attention with muehlenbeckia and Tibetan ferns. Designed by New Zealander James Fraser the garden has had 10yrs to flourish, creating an original presence for this South London location. Both front and rear garden are enclosed with James' signature irregular fencing.

◆ HAM HOUSE AND GARDEN

Ham Street, Ham, Richmond TW10 7RS. National Trust, 020 8940 1950, www.nationaltrust.org.uk. *Mid-way between Richmond & Kingston. W of A307 on Surrey bank of R Thames. Follow NT signs*. **Adm £4.50, chd £2.25. For NGS: Wed 9 July (10-5). For other opening times and information, please phone or see garden website.**

The beautiful C17 gardens incl Cherry Garden, featuring lavender parterres flanked by hornbeam arbours; S terrace with clipped yew cones; eight grass plats; maze-like wilderness; C17 orangery with working kitchen garden and licensed café and terrace. Gravel paths and some cobbles.

36 Ashley Road

116 HAMILTON TERRACE, NW8

London NW8 9UT. Mr & Mrs I B Kathuria, 020 7625 6909, gkathuria@hotmail.co.uk. *Tube: Maida Vale (5 mins) or St.Johns Wood (10 mins) Buses: 16, 98 to Maida Vale, 139, 189 to Abbey Road. Free parking on Sundays*. **(share to St. Mark's Church). Evening Openings £5, chd free, wine, Sun 22 June, Sun 20 July (5-9). Visitors also welcome by appt May to Aug. Refreshments by arrangement for groups only.**

Lush front garden full of dramatic foliage with a water feature and tree ferns. Large back garden of different levels with Yorkshire stone paving, many large terracotta pots and containers, water feature and lawn. Wide variety of perennials and flowering shrubs, many unusual, and subtropical plants, succulents, acers, ferns, hebes, climbers, roses, fuchsias and prizewinning hostas. Packed with colour and rich foliage of varied texture.

◆ HAMPTON COURT PALACE

East Molesey KT8 9AU. Historic Royal Palaces, 0844 482 7777, hamptoncourt@hrp.org.uk, www.hrp.org.uk. *Follow brown tourist signs on all major routes. Junction of A308 with A309 at foot of Hampton Court Bridge*. **Adm £10, wine. For NGS: Pre-booking essential Thur 10 Apr, Thur 5 June, Thur 31 July, Thur 28 Aug (6.30-8). Special evening tours with specialist talks. Please visit www.ngs.org.uk for information & bookings, or phone 01483 211535. For other opening times and information, please phone or see garden website.**

Take the opportunity to join 4 very special NGS private tours - in the evening, after these wonderful historic gardens have closed to the public. 4th April **Tulip Time**, visit the gardens at this special time of year. 5th June **Virtuoso Horticulture** learn how the traditional summer bedding schemes are created. 31st July **The 20th Century Garden** Explore a less well known area of the gardens August 28th **Glass and Grapes** make a behind the scenes visit to the nursery and 246 year old Great Vine. With specialist talks, and the chance to go behind the scenes, come and learn about the 500 year history of these royal gardens and find out what goes into creating and maintaining them. Some un-bound gravel paths.

♿ NCH ☕

GROUP OPENING

HAMPTON HILL GARDENS

Hampton Hill TW12 1DW. *3m from Twickenham/4m from Kingston-upon-Thames. Between A312 (Uxbridge Rd) and A313 (Park Rd). Bus: 285 from Kingston stops on Uxbridge Rd. Stn: Fulwell 15 mins walk.* Home-made teas at 99 Uxbridge Rd. **Combined adm £5, chd free. Sat 24, Sun 25 May (2-5).**

18 CRANMER ROAD
Bernard Wigginton

30 ST JAMES'S ROAD
Jean Burman
(See separate entry)

99 UXBRIDGE ROAD
Anne & Bob Wagner

3 gardens of diverse interest in an attractive West London suburb. With the backdrop of St James's Church spire, 18 Cranmer Rd is a colourful garden with herbaceous and exotic borders and a WW2 air raid shelter transformed as rockery and water garden with azaleas, helianthemums and foliage plants. The SE-facing garden at 30 St James's Rd is subdivided into 5 rooms. Decking with seating leads to ponds surrounded by grasses and shrubs and an African-themed thatched exterior 'sitting room'. 99 Uxbridge Rd is a wildlife-friendly, urban cottage garden. Secluded and peaceful, many pots and containers, lawn, shrubs, flowers, fruit trees, ponds and an organic kitchen garden. Lots of places to sit and relax. Partial wheelchair access at Cranmer Rd and Uxbridge Rd.

Relaxed family garden with a distinct cottage feel to it with arching roses and scrambling clematis . . .

GROUP OPENING

NEW HANDSWORTH ROAD GARDENS, N17

London N17 6DB. *Tube: Seven Sisters (15 min walk). Buses: 341, 230 or W4 (alight Broadwater Lodge). Driving: one-way rd, entry Philip Lane.* Light refreshments at No 47 using produce from the garden. **Combined adm £4.50, chd free. Sun 13 July (2-6).**

NEW 47A HANDSWORTH ROAD
Hazel Griffiths & Andy D'Cruz

NEW 75 HANDSWORTH ROAD
Hilary Adams

NEW 77 HANDSWORTH ROAD
Serge Charles

In a quiet Tottenham street sit these three contrasting gardens, united by their owners' love of plants and creative use of space. At 47a a gravel path leads beneath a vine-covered pergola to emerge into a sunny, Mediterranean-inspired garden. A geometric pattern of paths and trellis provides a framework for the informal planting. Many unusual plants, some propagated for sale. Mature quince tree, rill pool with copper waterfall and sculpture by the resident artist. At 75 the exuberant front garden is packed with colourful flowering plants, pots and found objects, demonstrating how much can be achieved in a tiny space. At 77 a long, narrow front garden is home to bamboos, roses and clematis which screen a secret knot garden of box. Container planted trees include olive and mimosa. A shady path, planted with a wide range of ferns and shade tolerant plants, leads to a small back garden where the bamboos reach 25 ft., underplanted with tree ferns.

19 HILLFIELD PARK, N10

London N10 3QT. Zaki & Ruth Elia. *Off Muswell Hill Broadway, corner HSBC Bank. Buses: W7, 43, 102, 144, 134, 234. Tube: Highgate, E Finchley, Finsbury Park.* **Adm £3, chd free. Sun 20 July (2-6).**
An orientalist garden in Edwardian Muswell Hill. Created by owner/designer, inspired by the original British Raj features within the house. Three tiled terraces with ceramic containers unfold around a traditional fountain. A bespoke Eastern-style shed crowns the top terrace, while dramatic planting by Declan Buckley cocoons visitors in lush seclusion. Featured on ITV's 'Love Your Garden'.

GROUP OPENING

HOLLY GROVE GARDENS GROUP, SE15

Peckham, London SE15 5DF. *Stn: Peckham Rye 3 mins walk. Turn L into Holly Grove & L past Green towards Bellenden Rd. Buses to Rye Lane Peckham 12, 37, 63, 78, 197, 343, 363.* Home-made teas. **Combined adm £5, chd free. Evening Opening £6, chd free, wine, Wed 21 May (6.30-9); Sun 25 May (1-5).**

NEW 19 HOLLY GROVE PECKHAM
Ms Helen Christie & Mr Guy Atkins

18 HOLLY GROVE
David Woodbine

27 HOLLY GROVE
Sally & Kevin O'Brien

29 HOLLY GROVE
Jessica Nicholas

Four distinctively different small gardens in a quiet leafy Peckham cul de sac, benefitting from the shared backdrop of a high wall along their back acting as an elegant buffer and offering wind shelter to create a warm micro-climate. No 18 has a modern feel with waving grasses in the front and steel gabon-lined raised beds. No19 is shady, contemporary and multi-levelled. No 27 neatly lines up on the diagonal with a rectangular wildlife pond, raised beds and standard roses, while at No 29 climbing hydrangeas and camellias lead visitors to an enchanting, informal, relaxed family garden with a distinct cottage feel to it with arching roses and scrambling clematis.

THE HOLME, NW1

Inner Circle, Regents Park, London NW1 4NT. Lessee of The Crown Commission. *In centre of Regents Park on The Inner Circle. Within 10 mins walk from Great Portland St or Baker St Underground Stations, opp*

Regents Park Garden Cafe. **Adm £4, chd free. Sat 28, Sun 29 June, Sat 2, Sun 3 Aug (2.30-5.30).**
4-acre garden filled with interesting and unusual plants. Sweeping lakeside lawns intersected by islands of herbaceous beds. Extensive rock garden with waterfall, stream and pool. Formal flower garden with unusual annual and half hardy plants, sunken lawn, fountain pool and arbour. Gravel paths and some steps which gardeners will help wheelchair users to negotiate.

239A HOOK ROAD
Chessington KT9 1EQ. Mr & Mrs D St Romaine, 020 8397 3761, derek@gardenphotolibrary.com, www.gardenphotolibrary.com. *4m S of Kingston. A3 from London, turn L at Hook underpass onto A243. Gdn. 300yds on L. Parking opp in Park. Buses K4, 71, 465 from Kingston & Surbiton to North Star PH*. Home-made teas. **Adm £3.50, chd free (share to St Catherine of Siena Church). Sun 15 June (2-6). Evening Opening £5, chd free, wine, Wed 18 June (8.30-10.30).**
Garden photographer's garden. Contemporary flower garden with entertaining area, gravel garden, colour-themed herbaceous borders, fernery, pond and rose tunnel. Traditional potager with 20 varieties of fruit and 50+ varieties of vegetables and herbs. Special late night opening to show how over 500 candles and lighting, used in imaginative ways with containers and architectural foliage, can effectively transform areas of a garden at night. Images by Derek St Romaine.

1A HUNGERFORD ROAD, N7
London N7 9LA. David Matzdorf, davidmatzdorf@blueyonder.co.uk, www.growingontheedge.net. *Between Camden Town & Holloway. Caledonian Rd tube. Buses 17, 29, 91, 253, 259 & 393*. **Adm £2, chd free (share to Terrence Higgins Trust). Sun 8 June (12-6). Also open 62 Hungerford Rd. Visitors also welcome by appt Apr to Oct. Please email for visits by appointment.**
Unique eco-house with walled, lush front garden planted in modern-exotic style. Front garden densely planted with palms, acacia, ginger lilies, brugmansias, bananas, euphorbias, yuccas and bamboo. Floriferous 'green roof' resembling scree slope planted with agaves, aloes, yuccas, dasylirions, alpines, sedums, mesembryanthemums, bulbs, grasses, Mediterranean shrubs and aromatic herbs. Access via ladder to roof (can also be seen from below). Garden and roof each 50ft x 18ft. Featured in Small Green Roofs (Timber Press).

62 HUNGERFORD ROAD, N7
London N7 9LP. John Gilbert & Lynne Berry. *Between Camden Town & Holloway. Tube: Caledonian Rd, 6 mins walk. Buses: 29 & 253 to Hillmarton Rd stop in Camden Rd. Also 17, 91, 259, 393 to Hillmarton Rd. 10 to York Way*. **Adm £2.50, chd free. Sun 8 June (2-6). Also open 1A Hungerford Road.**
Densely planted mature town garden at rear of Victorian terrace house which has been designed to maximise space for planting and create several different sitting areas, views and moods. NW facing with considerable shade, it is arranged in a series of paved rooms with a good range of perennials, shrubs and trees. Professional garden designer's own garden. Featured in Garden Answers magazine.

THE HURLINGHAM CLUB, SW6
Ranelagh Gardens, London SW6 3PR. The Members of the Hurlingham Club, www.hurlinghamclub.org.uk. *Main gate at E end of Ranelagh Gardens. Tube: Putney Bridge (110yds)*. Light refreshments available in The Harness Room. The East wing will also be open. **Adm £5, chd free. Sat 17 May (12-4).**
Rare opportunity to visit this 42-acre jewel with many mature trees, 2-acre lake with water fowl, expansive lawns and a river walk. Capability Brown and Humphry Repton were involved with landscaping. The gardens are renowned for their roses, herbaceous and lakeside borders, shrubberies and stunning bedding displays. The riverbank is a haven for wildlife with native trees, shrubs and wild flowers. Garden Tour at 2pm.

23 IMPERIAL ROAD, N22
London N22 8DE. Kate Gadsby. *Off Bounds Green Rd between Bounds Green Tube & Wood Green Tube. 5 mins from Alexandra Palace mainline*. **Adm £2.50, chd free. Sun 7 Sept (2-6). Also open 5 Russell Rd.**
Tiny back garden overflowing with interesting and unusual plants where an inventive and inspiring approach to planting, both in raised borders and containers, has created a surprising number of perspectives. In late summer a tangle of climbers, vegetables, herbs, annuals and perennials, creates a sensational visual treat. Semi-covered deck allows enjoyment in sun and rain.

GROUP OPENING

ISLINGTON GARDENS, N1
London N1 1BE. *Tube: Kings Cross, Caledonian Rd or Angel. Buses: 17, 91, 259 to Caledonian Rd*. Home-made teas at 36 Thornhill Square. **Combined adm £7, chd free. Sun 1 June (2-6).**

BARNSBURY WOOD
London Borough of Islington

1 BATTLEBRIDGE COURT
Visitors also welcome by appt Mar to Oct. Please email for appointments. horticulturist@blueyonder.co.uk

44 HEMINGFORD ROAD
Peter Willis & Haremi Kudo

36 THORNHILL SQUARE
Anna & Christopher McKane

Four contrasting gardens in the Barnsbury conservation area and close to the vibrant new developments at King's Cross.

21 Wilkes Street, Spitalfields Gardens Group

22 KELSEY WAY

Beckenham BR3 3LL. Janet & Steve Wright. *From Beckenham town centre, take Kelsey Park Rd, R into Manor Way. Kelsey Way is turning off this. Bus: 367 Sunday service to Village Way stop.* Home-made teas. **Adm £3, chd free. Sun 8 June (2-5.30).**
Multiple award winning garden. Colourful herbaceous borders with many tropical plants incl bananas, colocasias, alocasias, cannas and several different varieties of brugmansias. Displays of potted plants and a conservatory with a magnificent bougainvillea. Extensive and varied vegetable garden with a large fruit cage.

GROUP OPENING

KEW GARDENS STATION GROUP

Kew TW9 4DA. *Within walking distance of Kew Gardens Station.* **Combined adm £5, chd free. Sun 1 June (2-5).**

5 ENNERDALE ROAD
Jane Tandy & Lawrence Lawson

31 WEST PARK ROAD
Anna Anderson

Enjoy 2 varied gardens near Kew Gardens Station, within walking distance of each other. The S-facing walled garden at 5 Ennerdale Road (approx 30m x 19m) has raised beds, mixed borders, modern sculpture, a scree bed and a large terrace with pots. The modern botanical garden at 31 West Park Road has an oriental twist. Emphasis is on foliage and an eclectic mix of plants, with a reflecting pool and rotating willow screens which provide varying views or privacy. Also a dry bed, shady beds, mature trees and a private paved dining area with dappled light and shade.

GROUP OPENING

KEW GREEN GARDENS

Kew, London TW9 3AH. *Kew Green. NW side of Kew Green. Tube: Kew Gardens. Mainline stn: Kew Bridge. Buses: 65, 391. Entrance via riverside.* Home-made teas at 67 Kew Green. **Combined adm £6, chd free. Sun 18 May (2-6).**

65 KEW GREEN
Giles & Angela Dixon

NEW **67 KEW GREEN**
Lynne & Patrick Lynch

69 KEW GREEN
John & Virginia Godfrey

71 KEW GREEN
Mr & Mrs Jan Pethick

73 KEW GREEN
Sir Donald & Lady Elizabeth Insall

5 long gardens behind a row of C18 houses on the Green, close to the Royal Botanic Gardens. These gardens feature the profusely planted and traditional borders of a mature English country garden, and contrast formal gardens, terraces, lawns, laid out around tall old trees, with wilder areas and woodland and wild flower planting. One has an unusual architect-designed summerhouse, while another offers the surprise of a modern planting of espaliered miniature fruit trees.

40 KIDBROOKE GARDENS, SE3

Blackheath, London SE3 0PD. Mrs Lynne Doughty, 07970 646424, lynne@ski-base.com. *Blackheath BR 10 mins walk, Buses 89,108 202 to Blackheath village, street parking available.* Home-made teas. **Adm £4, chd free. Sun 29 June (2-6.30). Visitors also welcome by appt June to Sept.**
Unusually large, well-stocked, S-facing, formal garden. Beautiful herbaceous borders, summer and winter vegetable gardens, pretty pond and miniature fruit orchard. This is an old garden that was completely replanted during 2011 and has come into its own. Featured in The Guide Resident Amateur Gardener. Few steps to negotiate, alternative slightly sloping access available on request to wheelchair users.

KING HENRY'S WALK GARDEN, N1

11c King Henry's Walk, London N1 4NX. Friends of King Henry's Walk Garden, www.khwgarden.org.uk. *Buses incl: 21, 30, 38, 56, 141, 277. Behind adventure playground on KHW, off Balls Pond Rd.* Light refreshments. **(Share to Friends of KHW Garden. Evening Opening £5, chd free, wine, Wed 9 July (6-9).**
Vibrant ornamental planting welcomes the visitor to this hidden oasis and leads you into a verdant community garden with secluded woodland area, beehives, wildlife pond, wall-trained fruit trees, and plots used by local residents to grow their own fruit and vegetables. Live music. Art exhibition. Disabled WC.

LAMBETH PALACE, SE1

Lambeth Palace Rd, London SE1 7JU. The Church Commissioners www.archbishopofcanterbury.org. *Across R Thames from Houses of Parliament. Station: Waterloo Tube: Westminster, Lambeth North & Vauxhall all 10 mins walk. Buses: 3, C10, 76, 77, 77a, 344, 507.* **Adm £4, chd free. Wed 7 May, Wed 4 June (2-5).**
Lambeth Palace garden is one of the oldest and largest private gardens in London. Site occupied by Archbishops of Canterbury since end C12. Parkland-style garden with mature trees, woodland and native planting, pond, hornbeam allée. Also formal terrace, summer gravel border, scented chapel garden and beehives. Ramped path to rose terrace, disabled WC.

Vibrant ornamental planting welcomes the visitor to this hidden oasis and leads you into a verdant community garden . . .

212 LANGLEY WAY
West Wickham BR4 0DU. Fleur, Cliff & William Wood, 020 8249 7840, fleur.wood@ntlworld.com. *1½ m SW of Bromley. At junction of A232 & B265 T-lights turn N into Baston Rd. Junction with B251 turn L into Pickhurst Ln. Follow rd to Pickhurst PH, then take1st L.* Light refreshments. **Adm £3, chd free (share to National Hospital Development Foundation). Sat 14, Sun 15 June, Sat 23, Sun 24 Aug (11.30-5).**
Not your average suburban back garden! Enter through old oak door under brick arch into cool white courtyard garden. In contrast, fiery Mediterranean terrace with marble fountain, fish, and pergola with vines. Natural cottage garden, tree house in rainforest garden, vegetable area with raised beds, greenhouses, fruit trees and chickens. Everything grown organically with emphasis on wildlife. Kent Wildlife Trust - Gold Award; Bromley in Bloom - Best Garden for Biodiversity; London Garden Society 'The All London Championships', various awards. Narrow paths, rear of garden not wheelchair accessible.

12 LANSDOWNE ROAD, W11
London W11 3LW. The Lady Amabel Lindsay. *Tube: Holland Park. Buses: 12, 88, GL 711, 715 to Holland Park, 4 mins walk up Lansdowne Rd.* **Adm £3, chd free. Wed 21 May (2-6).**
Medium-sized garden with a 200yr-old mulberry tree as a centrepiece. It incl densely planted borders in mostly soft colours. A large terrace with massed pots and a greenhouse of climbing geraniums. Featured in 'The Gardens of England - Treasures of the NGS'. Partial wheelchair access.

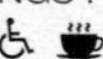

8 LANSDOWNE WALK, W11
London W11 3LN. Nerissa Guest, 020 7727 2660, nmguest@waitrose.com, www.8lansdownewalk.co.uk. *Tube: Holland Park, then 2 mins walk N. Or Notting Hill Gate & 10 mins walk W. Buses: 94, 148.* Home-made teas. **Adm £3.50, chd free. Sun 15 June (2.30-6). Also open 29 Addison Avenue. Visitors also welcome by appt (any date considered).**
Prizewinning garden, Brighter Kensington & Chelsea Scheme and Kensington Gardeners' Club. All-yr interest: specialist collection of species camellias winter and spring; choice salvias and pelargoniums summer and autumn; many clematis. Emphasis in borders and containers on foliage, texture and scent with an unusual mix of exotic and herbaceous.

23 LINKS WAY
Northwood HA6 2XA. Jackie Simmonds, 01923 824180, jackiesdesk@gmail.com, www.jackiesimmonds.com. *5m S of Watford, 15m NW of Central London. Close to A40 & M25 off A404. Tube: Northwood Metropolitan Line, stn 25 mins walk. Ample parking.* Light refreshments. **Adm £3, chd free. Sun 8 June (11-6). Visitors also welcome by appt June to July.**
Two thirds of an acre, artist's garden with rhododendrons and azaleas, sweeping lawn, herbaceous border of perennials, annuals and shrubs; stunning Magnolia grandiflora. 6 ponds, 3 stocked with fish, the others within beautiful rock garden with alpines and acers. Display of award-winning artist's paintings with garden painting demo possible, weather permitting. Sloping path to bottom of garden, then lawn accessible to wheelchair users.

LITTLE HOUSE A, NW3
16A Maresfield Gardens, Hampstead, London NW3 5SU. Linda & Stephen Williams. *5 mins walk Swiss Cottage or Finchley Rd tube. Off Fitzjohn's Ave & 2 doors from Freud Museum (signed).* Home-made teas. **Adm £3.50, chd free. Sun 22 June (2-6).**
1920s Arts and Crafts house (not open) built by Danish artist Arild Rosenkrantz. Award-winning front and rear garden set out formally with water features, stream and sculpture. Unusual shrubs and perennials, many rare, incl *Paeonia rockii* and *Dicksonia fibrosa*. Wide collections of hellebores, roses, hostas, toad lilies, acers, clematis and astrantia.

LITTLE LODGE
Watts Road, Thames Ditton KT7 0BX. Mr & Mrs P Hickman, 020 8339 0931, julia.hickman@virgin.net. *2m SW of Kingston. Mainline St Thames Ditton 5 min walk. House opp Thames Ditton Library after Giggs Hill Green, Parking in Library Car Park.* Home-made teas. **Adm £3.50, chd free (share to Cancer Research UK). Sun 1 June (11.30-5.30); Wed 4 June (2-5.30). Visitors also welcome by appt May to June, 10+ visitors.**
Partly walled ½ -acre informal cottage garden filled with usual and unusual shrubs, perennials, native plants and topiary. Lots of stone sinks, troughs and terracotta pots, plus a Victorian-style glasshouse. Productive hidden parterre vegetable garden edged with espalier apple trees. Garden designed and maintained by owners. Plants for sale, all propagated and grown by owners.

49 LOFTUS ROAD, W12
London W12 7EH. Emma Plunket, emma@plunketgardens.com, www.plunketgardens.com. *Train & tube: Hammersmith. Walk or bus from Shepherds Bush. Free street parking.* **Evening Opening £4, chd free, wine, Tue 10 June (5-8). Visitors also welcome by appt June to Sept.**
Professional garden designer, Emma Plunket, opens her acclaimed walled garden. Richly planted, it is the ultimate 'hard working city garden' with all yr structure and colour; fruit, vegetables and herbs. Set against a backdrop of trees, it is unexpectedly open and peaceful. Garden plan, plant list and advice.

D

GROUP OPENING

LONDON FIELDS GARDENS, E8
Hackney, London E8 3LS. *On W side of London Fields park. Short walk from Haggerston stn, London Overground; or London Fields stn (from Liverpool St) or tube to Bethnal Green then bus towards Hackney.* Home-made teas at 61 Lansdowne Drive and 84 Lavender Grove. **Combined adm £6, chd free. Sun 15 June (2-5).**

61 LANSDOWNE DRIVE
Chris Thow & Graham Hart

84 LAVENDER GROVE
Anne Pauleau

36 MALVERN ROAD
Kath Harris

53 MAPLEDENE ROAD
Tigger Cullinan
Visitors also welcome by appt June to Aug. Max 10 visitors. 020 7249 3754 tiggerine8@blueyonder.co.uk

84 MIDDLETON ROAD
Penny Fowler

A diverse group of 5 gardens in London Fields, an area which takes its name from fields on the London side of the old village of Hackney. They are unexpected havens from the city's hustle and bustle, with an exciting range and variety of colours, scents and design. This year we have a large, long wildlife and sculpture garden, a fascinating plantsman's garden, lush tropical plantings, a scented cottage garden and a serene designer garden filled with the sound of running water. Expect everything from courtyards to areas of banana, from showers of roses to clusters of clematis, ponds with water lilies and giant gunnera.

38 LOVELACE ROAD, SE21
Dulwich, London SE21 8JX. José & Deepti Ramos Turnes. *Midway between West Dulwich & Tulse Hill stations. Buses: 2, 3 & 68.* Home-made teas. **Adm £3, chd free. Sat 5 July (2-6).**
Beautiful all white front garden with stepped path leading to family friendly garden gently sloping up with curving borders, packed with informal mix of roses, perennials and annuals. Grass paths wander past 2 magnificent mature acers and wildlife pond with water lilies. Children's play area, vegetable plot with raised beds and fruit trees. Lovely selection of cakes, scones with cream and jam!

GROUP OPENING

LOWER CLAPTON GARDENS, E5
Hackney, London E5 0RL. *10 mins walk from Hackney Central or Hackney Downs stns. Buses 38, 55, 106, 253, 254 or 425, alight Lower Clapton Rd.* **Combined adm £5, chd free. Sun 8 June (2-6).**

8 ALMACK ROAD
Philip Lightowlers

16 POWERSCROFT ROAD
Elizabeth Welch

99 POWERSCROFT ROAD
Rose Greenwood

Lower Clapton is an area of mid-Victorian terraces sloping down to the R Lea. Dotted with mature trees and all with lawns, this group of gardens reflect their owner's tastes and interests. On Powerscroft Rd, No.16 has sun and space for meditation, while No. 99 has a high level patio looking out across the garden to a thatched gazebo. No. 8 Almack Rd is a long thin garden with two different rooms, one incl a classic blue agave named Audrey.

GROUP OPENING

LYNDHURST SQUARE GROUP, SE15
London SE15 5AR, 7969641955, martin.lawlor@sky.com. *Rail & London Overground orbital network - Clapham Junction to Highbury & Islington; Peckham Rye (check timetables), then 5 mins walk NW. Buses:36 from Oval tube, 171 from Waterloo, 63 from Kings Cross, 12 from oxford Circus. Free parking in Lyndhurst Square.* Home-made teas at No 4. **Combined adm £7, chd free (share to Share to Terrence Higgins Trust & CoolTan Arts). Sun 22 June (1.30-5). Also open Court Lane Gardens and South London Botanical Institute.**

1 LYNDHURST SQUARE
Josephine Pickett-Baker

3 LYNDHURST SQUARE
Stephen Haines

4 LYNDHURST SQUARE
Amelia Thorpe & Adam Russell

5 LYNDHURST SQUARE
Martin Lawlor & Paul Ward

6 LYNDHURST SQUARE
Iain Henderson & Amanda Grygelis

7 LYNDHURST SQUARE
Pernille Ahlström & Barry Joseph

Six very attractive gardens open in this small, elegant square of 1840s listed villas. Each approx 90ft x 50ft has its own shape and style as the Square curves in a U shape. No. 1, Eclectic and comfortable walled garden reflecting the creative background of the gardener. Mostly evergreen foliages of varying colours and textures with surprising details. No. 3 is a pretty, classic English garden with shrubs, fruit trees and sculpted topiary. A delightful greenhouse enhances the impression of peace. No. 4 is for a family, with a generous lawn, vegetables and herbs, and mature fruit trees adding lushness. At No. 5, the design combines Italianate and Gothic themes with roses, lavender, olives, euphorbia and ferns within yew and box parterres. Plants for sale here. No. 6 is an up-to-date family garden given drama with architectural plants. A wisteria pergola frames the vegetables bordered by espaliered apples. Check the treehouse! Simplicity, Swedish style, is key at No. 7, with roses and raised beds, framed by yew hedges. Home-made teas and 'other treats' available on the day.

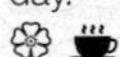

Lovely selection of cakes, scones with cream and jam . . . !

MALVERN TERRACE GARDENS, N1

London N1 1HR. *Malvern Terrace is off Thornhill Rd (nr The Albion) between Hemingford Rd & Liverpool Rd.* **Evening Opening £5, chd free, wine, Wed 11 June (6-8.30).**

Group of unique 1830s London terrace houses built on the site of Thomas Oldfield's dairy and cricket field. Cottage-style gardens in cobbled cul-de-sac.

ALLOTMENTS

94 MARSH LANE ALLOTMENTS, N17

Marsh Lane, Tottenham, London N17 OHY. Chris Achilleos, 07903 211715, a_c_h1964@yahoo.co.uk. *Opp Northumberland Park stn, on the corner of Marsh Lane & Marigold Rd. Buses: W3, 318, 341, 476.* Home-made teas. **Adm £3, chd free. Sun 10 Aug (2-6). Visitors also welcome by appt June to Aug groups welcomed before 6pm.**

An oasis in the city, a unique allotment exuding peace and tranquillity. An exuberant collection of decorative, edible and exotic plants. Gravel plants lined with potted tender specimens. Established herbaceous border, mini orchard of Mediterranean and native fruit trees. Central gazebo, wildlife pond, sculptures - something for everyone. Artwork and mosaics. Featured in My Cool Allotment by Lia Leendertz.

47 MAYNARD ROAD, E17

Walthamstow, London E17 9JE. Don Mapp, www.donsgarden.co.uk. *Tube & mainline Waltham Central. Bus from station to Shernal Rd or 15 minutes walk.* **Adm £3, chd free. Every Sun 20 July to 10 Aug (11-6).**

Plant collector's paradise. An eclectic mix of exotic plants and other ornaments in a 40ft x 16ft space, entered via a densely planted front garden. The front garden will be a mix of 'Food, Fruits and Herbs' showcasing how much can be grown in a small space. Botanical art, photography and sculpture on show. Access for wheelchairs via standard doors.

12 THE MEADOWS

See Kent

27 MENELIK ROAD, NW2

London NW2 3RJ. C Klemera. *E of Shoot up Hill. Kilburn, buses 16,32,189,316,332 to Mill Lane on Shoot up Hill, then Minster Rd/Menelik Rd at end. From W Hampstead, C11 bus to Menelik Rd.* **Adm £3, chd free. Sun 13 July (2-5.30). Also open 58a Teignmouth Rd and 121 Anson Rd, combined adm (3 gardens) £7, chd free.**

A magic oasis of exotic plants created to make you smile. Oriental corner with 'cha shit su' (tea house), large twisted robinia, pagoda and cloud pruned trees. The piazza is enclosed by formal bay trees, lush hostas and banana, often in flower. Topiary pops out of flower crammed borders and a 30yr old Trachycarpus overlooks this garden of strong shapes, textures and colour. Something to see in every corner.

A magic oasis of exotic plants created to make you smile . . .

NEW 30 MERCERS ROAD, N19

London N19 4PJ. Ms Joanne Bernstein, 07939 921068, j@joannebernstein-gardendesign.com, www.joannebernstein-gardendesign.com. *Tufnell Park. Tube: Tufnell Park then 10 mins walk. Holloway Rd, then 5 min Bus 43, 271 to Manor Gardens stop.* Home-made teas. **Adm £4, chd free. Sun 6 July (2-6); Sun 7 Sept (1-5). Visitors also welcome by appt June to Sept. Children welcome under supervision.**

Created by the garden designer owner, strong geometry compliments the contemporary architecture of the house extension, softened by billowing Prairie-style planting in the sunny area and shade tolerant shrubs and perennials in the woodland. There is openness and seclusion, light and shade, with the generous planting and vegetable plot discreetly framed by simple hard landscaping.

41 MILL HILL ROAD, W3

London W3 8JE. Marcia Hurst, 020 8992 2632, marcia.hurst@sudbury-house.co.uk. *Acton, W London. Piccadilly Line to Acton Town, turn R, Mill Hill Rd 3rd on R off Gunnersbury Ln.* Wine and soft drinks (July), home-made cakes (Aug). **Adm £3, chd free. Evening Opening £4.50, chd free, wine, Sun 6 July (5-8); Fri 8 Aug (2-6). Visitors also welcome by appt May to Oct. No min, 20 max visitors.**

120ft x 40ft garden. A surprisingly large and sunny garden, with lavender and hornbeam hedges, herbaceous planting and climbers, incl unusual plants as the owner is a compulsive plantaholic. Lots of space to sit and enjoy the garden. Plants growing in the garden are for sale. Featured in Daily Mail.

2 MILLFIELD PLACE, N6

London N6 6JP. c/o Peter Lloyd, 020 8348 6487, daisydogone@aol.com. *Off Highgate West Hill, E side of Hampstead Heath. Buses: C2, C11 or 214 to Parliament Hill Fields.* Home-made teas. **Adm £4, chd free. Sun 4 May (2-6). Evening Opening £5, chd free, wine, Wed 18 June (5.30-9). Also open Southwood Lodge Sun 4 May. Visitors also welcome by appt Apr to Sept.**

1½-acre spring and summer garden with camellias, rhododendrons, many flowering shrubs and unusual plants. Spring bulbs, herbaceous borders, spacious lawns, small pond and extensive views over Hampstead Heath. Wheelchair access with separate entrance, assistance available, please ask at gate.

66 MUSWELL AVENUE, N10

London N10 2EL. Kay Thomson & Nick Wood-Glover, 07872 952959, kaythomson@valox.demon.co.uk. *1st L into Muswell Ave from Alexandra Park Rd. Tube: Bounds Green or E Finchley then bus 102 or 299, alight Colney Hatch stop.* Soft drinks available. **Evening Openings £4.50, chd free, wine, Tue 1, Tue 8 July (6-8.30). Visitors also welcome by appt June to Sept.**

Celtic coastal echoes in suburbia. Tiny courtyard opens into Mediterranean terrace with oleander, jasmine and grape vine. Lawn area with borders planted according to astrological signs guided by Culpepper, leads through pergola to pond with flourishing wildlife, pebble beach, boat, patio and drystone wall's unexpected delights. Four contrasting atmospheres and environments. Mallard ducks visit. Fish feeding - 6.30 p.m. Featured in Daily Mail's 'Visit this . . .' column, Ham & High 'Making the signs of the Zodiac through plantings'.

27 NASSINGTON ROAD, NW3
Hampstead, London NW3 2TX. Lucy Scott-Moncrieff. *From Hampstead Heath rail stn & bus stops at South End Green, go up South Hill Park, then Parliament Hill, R into Nassington Rd.* Home-made teas. **Adm £4, chd free. Sun 18 May (2-6).**
Double-width town garden planted for colour and to support wildlife. Spectacular ancient wisteria, and herbs, fruit and vegetables in with the flowers. The main feature is a large eco-pond, designed for swimming, with colourful planting in and out of the water.

◆ NATURAL HISTORY MUSEUM WILDLIFE GARDEN, SW7
Cromwell Road, London SW7 5BD. Natural History Museum, 020 7942 5011, www.nhm.ac.uk/wildlife-garden. *Natural History Museum. Tube: South Kensington, 5 mins walk.* **Adm by donation. For NGS: Sat 5 Apr (12-5). For other opening times and information, please phone or see garden website.**
Set in the Museum grounds, the Wildlife Garden has provided a lush and tranquil habitat in the heart of London since 1995. It reveals a varied range of British lowland habitats, incl deciduous woodland, heathland, meadow and ponds. With over 2000 plant and animal species, it beautifully demonstrates the potential for wildlife conservation in the inner city. Spring wildlife displays, workshops, activities and talks. Observation beetree. Wild flower plant sale. Nature Live talks 12.30pm and 14.30pm. Awarded Brighter Kensington and Chelsea Scheme Wildlife Garden Award.

9 Dulwich Village

17A NAVARINO ROAD, E8
London E8 1AD. Ben Nell & Darren Henderson, 07734 773990, darren.henderson@hotmail.co.uk. *Buses 30, 38, 242 or 277 alight Graham Rd. Short walk from Hackney Central or London Fields stns on Overground line.* **Adm £3, chd free. Sat 19 Apr, Sun 15 June, Sun 13 July (2-5). Visitors also welcome by appt Apr to Aug.**
Established Italian and Japanese water garden reborn under new ownership. Features a square pond with Corinthian fountain, topiary yew border, lilies and Mediterranean trees. Leading to Japanese garden with pond, bridge and stream cutting the Soleirolia soleirolii landscape, with acer, cypress, ferns and bamboo, overlooked by a beautiful tea house.

15 NORCOTT ROAD, N16
Stoke Newington, London N16 7BJ. Amanda & John Welch. *Buses: 67, 73, 76, 106, 149, 243, 393, 476. Clapton & Rectory Rd mainline stns. One way system: by car approach from Brooke Rd which crosses Norcott Rd, garden in S half of Norcott Rd.* Home-made teas. **Adm £3, chd free. Plant Sale, Sun 27 Apr (2-5); Sun 8 June (2-6).**
Two very different openings: 1. A brilliant value plant sale in April featuring herbaceous clumps and over-wintered seedlings to enable your purchases to get established for 2014 flowering. 2. A summer opening for tea in our abundantly flowering cottage-style walled garden with herbaceous borders, pond, fruit trees (and a few plants for sale). Or come to both days with our reduced rate £5.00 ticket covering plant sale and open day.

5 NORTHAMPTON PARK, N1
Islington, London N1 2PP. Andrew Bernhardt & Anne Brogan. *5 mins walk from Canonbury stn, 10 mins from Highbury & Islington Tube (Victoria Line) Bus: 30, 277, 341, 476.* **Evening Opening £4, chd free, wine, Wed 1 Jan (4-7).**
S-facing walled garden, 161 yrs old, saved from neglect and developed over the last 21 yrs. The use of arches with box and yew hedging creates contrasting areas of interest which are evolving from cool North European blues, whites and greys to 'hot' splashes of Mediterranean influence.

94 OAKWOOD ROAD, NW11
Hampstead Garden Suburb, London NW11 6RN. Michael Franklin, 020 8458 5846, mikefrank@onetel.com. *1m N of Golders Green. Tube: Golders Green then H2 bus stops on request at junction of Northway & Oakwood Rd. Parking free in local rds*. Light refreshments. **Adm £3.50, chd free. Sun 18 May (2-6). Visitors also welcome by appt May to July. Please phone or email details.**
A romantic cottage garden in a beautiful woodland setting. Herbaceous beds with many unusual plants. A mature garden, still developing new areas of planting.

Children particularly welcome - a treasure hunt with prizes . . . !

OLDEN GARDEN COMMUNITY PROJECT, N5
Opp 22 Whistler Street, Islington, London N5 1NH. London Borough of Islington, 020 7226 0222. *Opposite Drayton Park Train Station.* Home-made teas. **Adm £4, chd free. Sun 15 June (2-5).**
Olden Garden Community Project is a 2-acre oasis of beauty and retreat from the busy streets surrounding it. A top terrace of beautiful herbaceous borders, lawn and patio and a stunning Rambling Rector rose. On the lower slopes there is an orchard, a meadow, vegetable beds and a greenhouse. In springtime, there is blossom and golden daffodils. Islington in Bloom - Overall Winner Community Garden with Gold and Silver Awards. Wheelchair access to all areas of top terrace. Disabled WC.

ORMELEY LODGE
Ham Gate Avenue, Richmond TW10 5HB. Lady Annabel Goldsmith. *From Richmond Pk exit at Ham Gate into Ham Gate Ave, 1st house on R. From Richmond A307, after 1½ m, past New Inn on R at T-lights turn L into Ham Gate Ave.* **Adm £4, chd free. Sun 22 June (3-6).**
Large walled garden in delightful rural setting on Ham Common. Wide herbaceous borders and box hedges. Walk through to orchard with wild flowers. Vegetable garden, knot garden, aviary. Trellised tennis court with roses and climbers.

◆ OSTERLEY PARK AND HOUSE
Jersey Road, Isleworth TW7 4RB. National Trust, 020 8232 5050, www.nationaltrust.org.uk. *4m N of Richmond. Sat Nav postcode TW7 4RD.* **Adm £4.50, chd £2.30. For NGS: Sun 1 June (11-4.30). For other opening times and information, please phone or see garden website.**
C18 garden created by the Child family, owners of Osterley Park House, in late 1700s. Currently being restored to its former glory following much research incl the discovery of documents in America showing lists of plants purchased for the garden in 1788. Highlights incl a Robert Adam designed Garden House, the Great Meadow and Mrs Child's Flower Garden. Osterley Park House also available to visit. Joint House and Gardens ticket Adults £10.25. Child £5.15. Featured in Gardens Illustrated. Garden paths level, compacted gravel. Some uneven and muddy paths, slopes, some cobbles. Outdoor wheelchair available and PMV's. No advance booking.

ALLOTMENTS

PADDOCK ALLOTMENTS & LEISURE GARDENS, SW20
51 Heath Drive, Raynes Park SW20 9BE. Paddock Horticultural Society. *Bus:57, 131, 200 to Raynes Pk station then 10 min walk or bus 163. 152 to Bushley Rd 7 min walk; 413 5 min walk from Cannon Hill Lane. Street parking*. Home-made teas. **Adm £3, chd free. Sat 12 July (12-5).**
Whilst walking round our 5½ acre site with over 150 plots, we would like you to help us judge our scarecrow competition. Our tenants are from diverse cultural communities growing a wide variety of flowers, fruit and vegetables, some are purely organic and well worth a visit. Winners of London in Bloom Best Allotment for 3yrs running. Plants, jams and surplus produce for sale. Display of arts and crafts by members of the Paddock Hobby Club. Paved and grass paths, mainly level.

3 THE PARK, N6
off Southwood Lane, London N6 4EU. Mr & Mrs G Schrager, 020 8348 3314, buntyschrager@gmail.com. *3 mins from Highgate tube, up Southwood Lane. The Park is 1st on R. Buses: 43, 134, 143, 263*. Home-made teas. **Adm £3.50, chd free. Sun 1 June (2.30-5.30). Visitors also welcome by appt Mar to Oct.**
Established large garden with informal planting for colour, scent and bees. Pond with fish, frogs and tadpoles. Tree peonies, Crinodendron hookerianum and a new Heptacodium. Plants and home-made jam for sale. Children particularly welcome - a treasure hunt with prizes!

11 PARK AVENUE NORTH, N8
Crouch End, London N8 7RU. Mr Steven Buckley & Ms Liz Roberts. *Tube: Finsbury Park & Turnpike Lane, nearest bus stop W3*. Home-made teas. **Adm £3.50, chd free. Sun 29 June (11-6).**
An exotic 250ft T-shaped garden, threaded through an old orchard and rose garden. Dramatic, mainly spiky, foliage dominates, with the focus on palms, agaves, dasylirions, aeoniums, bananas, tree ferns, nolinas, cycads, bamboos, yuccas, cacti and many species of succulents. Flowering aloes are a highlight. Rocks and terracotta pots lend a Mediterranean accent.

18 PARK CRESCENT, N3
Finchley, London N3 2NJ. Rosie Daniels. *Tube: Finchley Central. Buses: 82 to Essex Park, also 125, 460, 626, 683*. Home-made teas. **Adm £3, chd free. Sun 22 June, Sun 27 July (2-6).**
Constantly evolving, charming small garden designed and densely planted by owner. Roses and clematis with interesting plants through the summer. New small pond, tub water feature and bird haven. Stepped terrace with lots of pots. Glass installation and sculptures by owner.

Hidden seating with view through garden. Children's 'treasure' hunt. Secluded, peaceful, restorative.

4 PARK VILLAGE EAST, NW1
Regents Park, London NW1 7PX. Eveline Carn, 020 7388 1113, eveline@carnfamily.co.uk. *Tube: Camden Town or Mornington Crescent 7 mins. Bus: C2 or 274 3 mins. Opp The York & Albany, just off junction of Parkway/Prince Albert Rd.* Home-made teas. **Adm £4, chd free. Sun 29 June (2-5.30). Also open 70 Gloucester Crescent and The Holme. Visitors also welcome by appt May to Aug.**
A garden of various textures and shades of green where the formality of box and yew hedging provides symmetry and structure for looser more naturalistic planting. Three terraces lead down from a Regency house to what used to be the Regents Canal. An unexpectedly large yet skilfully landscaped town garden, punctuated with architectural plants, sculpture, ponds, and mature trees. Many steps.

174 PECKHAM RYE, SE22
London SE22 9QA. Mr & Mrs Ian Bland. *Stn: Peckham Rye. Buses: 12, 37, 63, 197, 363. Overlooks Peckham Rye Common from Dulwich side.* Home-made teas. **Adm £3.50, chd free (share to St Christopher's Hospice). Sun 8 June (2.30-5.30). Also open 4 Cornflower Terrace, 35 Camberwell Grove, Choumert Square, Dulwich Village Two Gardens and 9 Dulwich Village.**
Visitors call our garden an oasis of calm in Peckham. Every year the garden changes and matures. It is densely planted with a wide variety of contrasting foliage. Unusual plants are combined with old favourites. It remains easy-care and child-friendly. Garden originally designed by Jude Sharpe. Our ever-popular plant sale and famed cakes will be available again. Easy access via side alley into a flat garden.

GROUP OPENING

PENGE GARDENS, SE20
London SE20 7QG. *Nr junction A213 & A234. Short walk from Kent House (5mins) mainline stn. Buses: 176, 227, 356 & 358. Tram: Beckenham Rd.* Home-made teas. **Combined adm £6, chd free. Sun 25 May (2-5).**

43 CLEVEDON ROAD
Elizabeth Parker

26 KENILWORTH ROAD D
Mhairi & Simon Clutson
Visitors also welcome by appt Apr to Aug. Refreshments available for groups 10+.
020 8402 3978
mhairi@grozone.co.uk
www.grozone.co.uk

Two contrasting gardens: one is a small, minimalist, modern garden with clever juxtaposition of sandstone landscaping and plants, and the other is a cottage garden. 43 Clevedon Rd is 50ft x 22ft, with unusual trees and shrubs incl snake-bark maple, sorbus cashmiriana and itea ilicifolia. Abundant rambler roses, incl Félicité Perpétue, colourful mixed borders and pots on terrace. 26 Kenilworth Rd is a garden designers' completely re-designed inspirational contemporary garden providing maximum impact in a small space. An inventive layout extends the living space with seating and large trough planters. The planting is bold and textural featuring a diverse selection of drought-tolerant Mediterranean plants providing yr round interest with seasonal colour.

PETERSHAM HOUSE
Petersham Road, Petersham, Richmond TW10 7AA. Francesco & Gael Boglione, www.petershamnurseries.com. *Stn: Richmond, then 65 bus to Dysart PH. Entry to garden off Petersham Rd, through nursery. Parking very limited on Church Lane.* **Adm £3.50, chd free. Sun 27 Apr, Sun 20 July (11-4).**
Broad lawn with large topiary, generously planted double borders. Productive vegetable garden with chickens. Adjoins Nursery with extensive plant sales, shop and cafe.

NEW **18 PETTITS BOULEVARD**
Rise Park, Romford RM1 4PL. Mr & Mrs Nutley. *From M25 take A12 towards London, at Pettits Lane junction turn R then R again into Pettits Boulevard.* Home-made teas. **Adm £3, chd free. Sat 14, Sun 15 June, Sat 26, Sun 27 July (1-6).**
Small garden on 3 levels with trees, shrubs and perennials, many in pots. There is an ornamental pond, woodland themed area and interesting agricultural implements and garden ornaments. There are seating areas situated throughout the garden. Limited wheelchair access.

4 PIERMONT GREEN, SE22
East Dulwich, London SE22 0LP. Janine Wookey. *Triangle of green facing Peckham Rye at the Honor Oak end. Stns: Peckham Rye & Honor Oak. Buses: 63 (passes the door) & 12. No parking on Green but free parking on side sts nearby.* Home-made teas. **Adm £3.50, chd free. Sun 13 July (2-5.30). Also open 7 Canonbie Rd.**
A small formal front garden faces the triangular Green with box parterres and an olive, framed by swagged 'Zephirine Drouhin' rose. In the 120ft back garden, a terrace leads through a gravel garden with gaura and dierama. The vista opens up onto a circular lawn edged with deep borders. A vegetable garden and a shady yellow-themed 'edible' garden complete the picture.

1 The Crest, Berrylands Gardens Group

© Nicola Stocken Tomkins

GROUP OPENING

PRINCES AVENUE GARDENS, N10

Muswell Hill, London N10 3LS. *Buses: 43 & 134 from Highgate tube; also W7, 102, 144, 234, 299. Princes Ave opp M&S in Muswell Hill Broadway, or John Baird PH in Fortis Green*. Home-made teas. **Combined adm £3.50, chd free. Sun 18 May (2-6).**

15 PRINCES AVENUE
Eliot & Emma Glover

28 PRINCES AVENUE
Ian & Viv Roberts

In a beautiful Edwardian avenue in the heart of Muswell Hill Conservation Area, two very different gardens reflect the diverse life-styles of their owners. The large S-facing family garden at No. 15 has been designed for entertaining and yr-round interest. White and blue themed beds with alliums and a wide variety of perennials and shrubs frame an exceptional lawn. A Wendy house and hidden wooden castle provide delight for children of all ages. The charming annexe garden at No.17, where tea can be enjoyed, has a beautiful Hosta display. No. 28 is a well-established traditional garden reflecting the charm typical of the era. Mature trees, shrubs, mixed borders and woodland garden creating an oasis of calm just off the bustling Broadway. 'Both of these gardens feel loved, lived in and welcoming which is doubtless why visitors like to spend a long time in them. Both have generous planting of alliums and are rich in trees with plenty of colour and varied foliage.' Ham & High.

GROUP OPENING

RAILWAY COTTAGES, N22

Dorsett Road, Alexandra Palace N22 7SL. *Tube: Wood Green, 10 mins walk. Overground: Alexandra Palace, 3 mins. Buses W3, 184. 3 mins. Free parking in local streets on Sundays*. Home-made teas at 2 Dorset Rd. **Combined adm £4, chd free. Sun 13 July (2-5.30).**

2 DORSET ROAD
Jane Stevens

4 DORSET ROAD
Mark Longworth

14 DORSET ROAD
Cathy Brogan

22 DORSET ROAD
Mike & Noreen Ainger

NEW **24A DORSET ROAD**
Eddie & Jane Wessman

A row of historical railway cottages, tucked away from the bustle of Wood Green near Alexandra Palace, takes the visitor back in time. No. 4 Is a pretty secluded woodland garden, (accessed through the rear of No. 2), sets off sculptor owner's figurative and abstract work among acers, sambucus nigra, species shrubs and old fruit trees. Within the pretty surroundings sits the owner's working studio. Three front gardens at Nos. 14, 22 and 24a, one nurtured by the grandson of the original railway worker occupant, show a variety of planting, incl aromatic shrubs, herbs, jasmine, flax, fig, fuchsia and vines. A modern raised bed vegetable garden is a new addition this year. The tranquil country-style garden at No. 2 Dorset Rd flanks 3 sides of the house. Hawthorn topiary (by the original owner) and clipped box hedges contrast with climbing roses, clematis, honeysuckle, abutilon and cottage plants. Trees incl mulberry, quince, fig, apple and a mature willow creating an opportunity for an interesting shady corner. There is an emphasis on scented flowers that attract bees and butterflies and the traditional medicinal plants found in cottage gardens.

◆ ROOTS AND SHOOTS, SE11

Walnut Tree Walk, Kennington, London SE11 6DN. Trustees of Roots and Shoots, www.rootsandshoots.org.uk. *Tube: Lambeth North. Buses: 3, 59, 159, 360. Just S of Waterloo Stn, off Kennington Rd, 5 mins from Imperial War Museum. No car parking on site*. Cream teas. **Adm £2, chd free. For NGS: Fri 20 June (2-7). For other opening times and information, please phone or see garden website.**

1/2 -acre wildlife garden run by innovative charity providing training and garden advice. Summer meadow, observation beehives, 2 large ponds, hot borders, Mediterranean mound, old roses and echiums. Learning centre with photovoltaic roof, solar heating, rainwater catchment, three planted roofs, one brown roof. Wildlife garden study centre exhibition with photo, video and other wildlife interpretation materials.

ALLOTMENTS

THE ROSE GARDEN AT GOLF COURSE ALLOTMENTS, N11
Winton Avenue, London N11 2AR. GCAA/Mr George Dunnion, www.gcaa.pwp.blueyonder.co.uk. *Tube: Bounds Green, 1km Buses: 102,184 299 to Sunshine Garden Centre Durnsford Rd*. Home-made teas. **Adm £3.50, chd free. Sun 29 June (1-6).**
Large allotment plot displaying over 120 different roses comprising much of the history of the rose; there are Gallicas, Damasks, Albas, Portlands etc., as well as around 40 Austin roses and many others. The roses are interplanted with a wide range of perennials as well as vegetables. Colourful chards and red cabbages grasses, clematis and rare exotic plants. Owners will share their extensive knowledge with visitors. Award of Merit 'Gardening Against the Odds' and featured on Gardeners World.

131 ROSEBERY ROAD, N10
Muswell Hill, London N10 2LD. Kirsty Monaghan. *Tube: Highgate, then bus 43 or 134 to Muswell Hill Broadway. Bus W7 from Finsbury Park Tube. Walk down Dukes Ave or bus 102, 299 alight Rosebery Rd*. Home-made teas. **Adm £3, chd free. Sun 6 July (2-6).**
Garden designer's family garden based on circles and fluid curves. Circular layout and attention to fine detail reflects Kirsty's past career in jewellery design. The sinuous path, laid in sandstone sets, divides two lawns. Planting designed to provide interesting foliage, textures and colour combinations incl roses, clematis, hardy geraniums and honeysuckles, with tall perennials and grasses for height and movement. Three seating areas. Featured in Real Homes and 25 Beautiful Homes.

ROYAL COLLEGE OF PHYSICIANS MEDICINAL GARDEN, NW1
11 St Andrews Place, London NW1 4LE. Royal College of Physicians of London, www.rcplondon.ac.uk/museum-and-garden/garden. *Outer Circle, opp SE corner of Regents Park. Tubes: Great Portland St & Regent's Park. Garden is one block N of station exits, on Outer Circle opp SE corner of Regent's Park*. Light refreshments. **Adm £4, chd free. Mon 23 June, Thur 10 July (10.30-4).**
1100 different plants used in conventional and herbal medicines around the world during the past 3000 yrs; plants named after physicians and plants with medical implications. The plants are labelled, and arranged by continent except for the plants from the College's Pharmacopoeia of 1618. Guided tours all day, explaining the uses of the plants, their histories and stories about them. Books about the plants in the medicinal garden will be for sale. Featured in Evening Standard and on BBC London Evening news. Wheelchair ramps at steps.

Simple, unfussy with a contemporary feel, calm, quiet and peaceful . . .

5 RUSSELL ROAD, N13
Bowes Park, London N13 4RS. Angela Kreeger. *Close to N Circular Rd & Green Lanes. Tube: Bounds Green, 10 mins walk. Mainline: Bowes Park, 3 mins walk. Numerous bus routes. Off Whittington Rd*. Home-made teas. **Adm £3, chd free. Sun 8 June, Sun 7 Sept (2-6). Also open 23 Imperial Rd Sun 7 Sept.**
A 'poem for the eyes'. First time June opening with burgeoning growth - full of vigour. Billowing, overflowing, balanced by flat lawn. Airy, dreamy planting in small woodland, a pebble garden marks the border. Not manicured. Simple, unfussy with a contemporary feel, calm, quiet and peaceful. Autumn is rusty, loose and soft. Golden in sunlight. Small bespoke greenhouse reminiscent of Dungeness and Hastings. Front garden vegetable bed.

90 ST GEORGE'S AVENUE, N7
Tufnell Park, London N7 0AH. Ms J Chamberlain & Mr R Hamilton. *Tube: Tufnell Park, or bus 4 to Tufnell Park Rd, alight Dalmeny Rd*. **Adm £3.50, chd free. Sun 1 June (2-6).**
An 80 foot garden divided into 2 distinct sections by a clematis-covered pergola adjoining a bed of evergreen shrubs and a beautiful acer griseum. Climbers on the fences, mixed planting in the borders, and a side patio filled with pots containing hostas, camellias, fatsia and hydrangeas which thrive in damp shade. Sunny front garden with Mediterranean-type planting.

7 ST GEORGE'S ROAD
St Margarets, Twickenham TW1 1QS. Richard & Jenny Raworth, 020 8892 3713, jraworth@gmail.com, www.raworthgarden.com. *1½ m SW of Richmond. Off A316 between Twickenham Bridge & St Margarets r'about*. **Evening Opening £5.50, chd free, wine, Sat 7 June (6-8). Visitors also welcome by appt May to July. Groups 10+.**
Exuberant displays of Old English roses and vigorous climbers with unusual herbaceous perennials. Massed scented crambe cordifolia. Pond with bridge converted into child-safe lush bog garden. Large N-facing luxuriant conservatory with rare plants and climbers. Pelargoniums a speciality. Sunken garden and knot garden. Pergola covered with climbing roses and clematis.

30 ST JAMES'S ROAD
Hampton Hill TW12 1DQ. Jean Burman. *Between A312 (Uxbridge Rd) & A313 (Park Rd). Bus: 285 from Kingston stops at end of rd (15 mins walk). Stn: Fulwell (20 mins walk)*. **Evening Opening £3.50, chd free, wine, Thur 11 Sept (7-10).**
Lovely SE-facing garden (35ft x 90ft) with tasteful features throughout, subdivided into 5 rooms of interest. Decking with seating leads to ponds, surrounded by grasses and shrubs and an African-themed thatched exterior 'sitting room'. Fairy lights and candles make this perfect for a magical evening's visit.

87 ST JOHNS ROAD, E17
London E17 4JH. Andrew Bliss, blisshand@yahoo.co.uk. *15 mins walk from W'stow tube/overground or 212/275 bus. Ring bell at petrol station. 10 mins walk from Wood St overground. Very close to N Circular.* Home-made teas. **Adm £3, chd free. Sat 16, Sat 23 Aug (1-5). Visitors also welcome by appt July to Sept.**
A typical terrace garden measuring 15ft x 25ft (plus the side bit!) with concrete screed on slabs, has been transformed into an oasis of raised borders, decking, slate and bamboo walling, water features, canopies and sculpture. A calming purple, blue and pink planting ensures utter relaxation. The garden owner is an artist who creates beautiful and eye-catching mirror mosaics on roof slates and other objets trouvés, for use in garden or home.

NEW **16 ST MARGARETS ROAD, E12**
London E12 5DP. Linda & Brian Linden. *Nearest tube Wanstead or mainline Manor Park. Bus 101. Alight at Empress Avenue.* **Adm £3.50, chd free. Sun 31 Aug (1-5).**
Stylish modern suburban garden 100 ft x 25 ft. Well established trees inc. Indian Bean, Robinia, Olive, white Lilac and Bananas. Formal lawn, box hedging, dazzling beds of dahlias, cannas and other exotics. Secret second garden at the end to discover. Emphasis on lots of colour and low maintenance.

ST MICHAEL'S CONVENT
56 Ham Common, Ham, Richmond TW10 7JH. Community of the Sisters of the Church. *2m S of Richmond. On 65 bus route. Alight at Ham Gate Avenue.* **Adm £3, chd free. Sun 15 June (2-5).**
4-acre organic garden comprises walled vegetable garden, orchards, vine house, ancient mulberry tree, extensive borders, meditation and Bible gardens. Some gravel paths.

57 ST QUINTIN AVENUE, W10
London W10 6NZ. Mr H Groffman, 020 8969 8292. *1m from Ladbroke Grove or White City tube. Buses: 7, 70, 220 all to North Pole Rd. Parking in street.* Home-made teas. **Adm £3, chd free. Sun 6, Sun 27 July (2-6). Also open 29 Addison Ave Sun 27 July. Visitors also welcome by appt June to July. Parking restrictions do not apply on Sundays.**
30ft x 40ft walled garden; wide selection of plant material incl evergreen and deciduous shrubs for foliage effects. Patio area mainly furnished with bedding material, colour themed. Focal points throughout. Refurbished with new plantings and special features. Received many awards incl three First Prizes in London garden competitions.

5 ST REGIS CLOSE, N10
Alexandra Park Road, London N10 2DE. Ms S Bennett & Mr E Hyde, 020 8883 8540, suebearlh@yahoo.co.uk. *Muswell Hill. Tube: Bounds Green then 102 or 299 bus, or E.Finchley take 102. Alight St Andrews Church. 134 or 43 bus stop at end of Alexandra Pk Rd, follow arrows.* Home-made teas. **Adm £3.50, chd free. Sun 4 May, Sun 22 June, Sun 27 July (2-6.30). Visitors also welcome by appt Feb to Dec. Can provide light lunches/wine for large groups.**
A cornucopia of sensual delights! Artists' garden renowned for unique architectural features and delicious cakes. Baroque temple, pagodas, oriental raku-tiled mirrored wall conceals plant nursery. American Gothic shed overlooks newly built 'LIBERACE TERRACE'. Maureen Lipman's favourite garden, combining colour, humour and trompe l'oeil with wildlife-friendly ponds, waterfalls, weeping willow and lawns. Imaginative container planting and abundant borders, creating an inspirational and re-energising experience. Open studio with ceramics and prints. Featured in 'Garden Answers'. Photos by Marianne Majerus. Wheelchair access to all parts of garden unless waterlogged.

22 SCUTARI ROAD, SE22
East Dulwich, London SE22 0NN. Sue Hillwood-Harris & David Hardy. *S side of Peckham Rye Park. B238 Peckham Rye/Forest Hill Rd, turn into Colyton Rd (opp Herne Tavern). 3rd rd on R. Bus: 63. Stn: East Dulwich.* Home-made teas. **Adm £3, chd free. Sun 18 May, Sun 22 June (2-6). Also open Stone Hill House Sun 18 May and Lyndhurst Square Group Sun 22 June.**
Sue's ongoing, possibly never ending, labour of total love is now in its 10th year. This ever-evolving garden has a cottagey area, water, trees, ferns and a multitude of shrubs. A centrepiece is the palatial chicken house in which reside a quartet of pampered feathers. Steps and narrow paths may make access difficult for less mobile visitors. Featured in many books and magazines and on BBC's Open Gardens show.

2 SHARDCROFT AVENUE, SE24
Herne Hill, London SE24 0DT. Catriona Andrews. *Short walk from Herne Hill rail station & bus stops. Buses: 3, 68, 196, 201, 468 to Herne Hill. Parking in local streets.* Home-made teas. **Adm £3, chd free. Sun 15 June (2-6). Also open Grove Park Camberwell Group.**
A designer's garden with loose, naturalistic planting. Geometric terracing accommodates a natural slope, framing vistas from the house. Drought tolerant beds with cascading perennials and grasses, scented courtyard, formal wildlife pond, woodland glade with fire pit and green roofed shed provide wildlife habitats and a feast for the senses. Planted ecologically to benefit wildlife, pond, nesting boxes and log piles, green roofed shed, seating circle with fire pit.

28 SIBELLA ROAD, SW4
London SW4 6HX. Lorraine Johnson Rosner, www.gardenhousedesigns.com. *Tube: Clapham North less than 10 mins. Buses: 77, 87, 452. From Clapham High Rd, take Gauden Rd. then 2nd R into Bromfelde Rd, Sibella Rd is on L.* Home-made teas. **Adm £3.50, chd free.**

Sun 25 May (3-6).
An elegant, garden designer's garden with a great sense of style and space. The front garden is a parterre. The back garden incl a formal garden with lily pool, a potager with raised beds and a woodland area with an oak summerhouse.

A long London patch maximised; a descent that frays into a wild blossom wood . . .

SOUTH LONDON BOTANICAL INSTITUTE, SE24
323 Norwood Road, London SE24 9AQ. South London Botanical Institute, www.slbi.org.uk. *Mainline stn: Tulse Hill. Buses: 68, 196, 322 & 468 stop at junction of Norwood & Romola Rds.* **Adm £3, chd free (share to South London Botanical Institute). Sun 22 June (2-5). Also open Lyndhurst Square Group and 22 Scutari Road.**
London's smallest botanical garden, densely planted with 500 labelled species grown in a formal layout of themed borders. Wild flowers flourish alongside medicinal herbs. Carnivorous, scented, native and woodland plants are featured, growing among rare trees and shrubs. The pond is home to frogs, newts, dragonflies. The fascinating SLBI building is also open. Unusual plants for sale.

41 SOUTHBROOK ROAD, SE12
Lee, London SE12 8LJ. Barbara & Marek Polanski, 020 8333 2176, polanski101@yahoo.co.uk. *Situated at Southbrook Rd, off S Circular, off Burnt Ash Rd. Train: Lee & Hither Green, both 10 mins walk. Bus: P273.* Home-made teas. **Adm £3.50, chd free. Sun 15 June (2-5.30). Also open 2 Shardcroft Avenue and Grove Park Camberwell Group. Visitors also welcome by appt June to Aug (2-5:30).**
Developed over 10yrs, this large garden has a formal layout, with wide mixed herbaceous borders full of colour and interest, surrounded by mature trees, framing sunny lawns, a central box parterre and an Indian pergola. Ancient pear trees festooned in June with clouds of white 'Kiftsgate' and 'Rambling Rector' roses. Discover fishes and damselflies in 2 lily ponds. Many places to sit and relax. Enjoy home-made tea and cake in a small classical garden building. Featured in Garden News. Side access just wide enough for wheelchairs.

SOUTHWOOD LODGE, N6
33 Kingsley Place, Highgate, London N6 5EA. Mr & Mrs C Whittington, 020 8348 2785, suewhittington@hotmail.co.uk. *Tube: Highgate then 6 min walk up Southwood Ln. 4 min walk from Highgate Village along Southwood Ln. Buses: 143, 210, 214, 271.* Home-made teas. **Adm £4, chd free. Sun 4 May, Sun 15 June (2-5.30). Also open 2 Millfield Place Sun 4 May. Visitors also welcome by appt Apr to July. Refreshments by arrangement.**
Unusual garden hidden behind C18 house (not open), laid out last century on steeply sloping site, now densely planted. Ponds, waterfall, frogs and newts. Lots of different topiary shapes formed from self-sown yew trees. Beautiful working greenhouse, also good for tea on rainy days! Many unusual plants grown and propagated for sale - rare pelargoniums a speciality at June opening. Toffee hunt for children.

GROUP OPENING

SPEER ROAD GARDENS
Thames Ditton KT7 0PJ. *2m SW of Kingston. Thames Ditton stn 5mins walk.* Home-made teas. **Combined adm £5, chd free (share to Born Too Soon Kingston Hospital). Sun 25 May (12-5).**

53 SPEER ROAD
Mrs Jayne Thomas

UNDERWOOD
Diana Brown & Dave Matten

2 contrasting gardens within 4 mins walking distance of each other. 37 Speer Rd is a garden designer's family garden, transformed to provide areas of interest with large mixed shrub and herbaceous borders, planted to give a long season of interest incl a late season display of colour. Ornamental trees and silver birches create a calm woodland setting with a wild meadow. Many plants from designers gardens at Hampton Court. Underwood is an 1920s landscaped garden, maintained by present owners to the original design with emphasis on imaginative and carefully clipped topiary. The boundary is edged by 7 small fish pools, which also mark an ancient public right of way for villagers to drive their sheep to pastures beyond. The garden is an evocative reminder of the '20s. Croquet on the lawn at Underwood.

GROUP OPENING

SPITALFIELDS GARDENS GROUP, E1
London E1 6QH. *10 mins walk from Aldgate E tube station & 5 mins walk from Liverpool St stn.* **Combined adm £12, chd free. Sat 7 June (10-4).**

NEW **20 FOURNIER STREET**
Ms Charlie de Wet

NEW **7 FOURNIER STREET**
John Nicolson

NEW **31 FOURNIER STREET**
Rodney Archer

34 HANBURY STREET
Mr Philip Vracas

21 PRINCELET STREET
Marianne & Nicholas Morse

21 WILKES STREET
Rupert Wheeler

A group of gardens within the Spitalfields conservation area. Often described as hidden treasures behind some of London's finest houses. 2014 will be the second time gardens in the area have opened as a group and this year there are 3 gardens in Fournier Street opening for the first time.

NEW 160A STAPLETON HALL ROAD

Stroud Green, London N4 4QJ. Peter Beardsley. *Nr to Parkland Walk; http://parkland-walk.org.uk/ Local Buses: W3, W5. Nearest trains: Crouch Hill, Harringay Rail*. Home-made teas. **Adm £3.50, chd free. Sun 8 June (12-6).**
Designer's hillside garden. A long London patch maximised; a descent that frays into a wild blossom wood. South-facing. Mature trees and hedges compartmentalise a sequence of loosely planted perennial gardens. A meander of woodland tracks and narrow steps connect a series of sitting glades. Richly planted and floral. Vegetable patch. Greenhouse. Vintage watering can collection. Cake!

STOKES HOUSE

Ham Street, Ham, Richmond TW10 7HR. Peter & Rachel Lipscomb, 020 8940 2403, rlipscomb@virginmedia.com. *2m S of Richmond off A307. 1/4 m from A307. Trains & tube to Richmond and train to Kingston which link with 65 bus to Ham Common*. Home-made teas. **Adm £3.50, chd free. Sun 15 June (2-5). Visitors also welcome by appt May to Sept.**
Originally an orchard, this 1/2 -acre walled country garden is abundant with roses, clematis and perennials. There are mature trees incl ancient mulberries and wisteria. The yew hedging, pergola and box hedges allow for different planting schemes throughout the year. Compost area. Supervised children are welcome to play on the slide and swing. Georgian house, herbaceous borders, brick garden, wild garden, large compost area and interesting trees. Many plants for sale at June opening. Double doors from street with 2 wide steps that will allow wheelchair access.

STONEY HILL HOUSE, SE26

Rock Hill, London SE26 6SW. Cinzia & Adam Greaves. *Off Sydenham Hill. Train: Sydenham, Gipsy Hill or Sydenham Hill stns. Buses: Crystal Palace or 363 along Sydenham Hill, house at end of cul-de-sac on L*. Home-made cakes, delicious! **Adm £3.50, chd free. Sun 18 May (2-6). Also open 49 Alleyn Park and 22 Scutari Road.**
Garden and woodland of approx 1-acre providing a secluded green oasis in the city. Paths meander through mature rhododendron, oak, yew and holly trees, offset by pieces of contemporary sculpture. The garden is set on a slope and a number of viewpoints set at different heights provide varied perspectives of the garden. The planting in the top part of the garden is fluid and informal. Shallow, wide steps at entrance to garden with grass slope alongside. Wheelchair access possible if these can be negotiated.

Espalier apple trees reach into a planting space that generates an exquisite effect . . .

58 SUMMERLEE AVENUE, N2

London N2 9QH. Edwina & Nigel Roberts. *Tube to E Finchley, cross main rd, Summerlee Ave located off Southern Rd. Walking distance from Muswell Hill. Entry via alley at back of house*. Home-made teas. **Combined adm £4.50, chd free. Sun 25 May (2-6). Combined with 64 Summerlee Avenue.**
Beautiful acer, densely planted borders with mixture of shrubs and herbaceous perennials and spring and summer bulbs. Fences clothed with climbing roses, wisteria, clematis and honeysuckle. Woodland planting under acer. Small wildlife pond and planting is chosen to attract birds and insects and for fragrance. Several seating areas arranged to allow different views of garden. New gravel garden.

64 SUMMERLEE AVENUE, N2

London N2 9QH. Ms Ana Sanchez Martin. *Tube to East Finchley, cross main rd, Summerlee Ave is located off Southern Rd. Walking distance from Muswell Hill*. **Combined adm £4.50, chd free. Sun 25 May (2-6). Combined with 58 Summerlee Avenue.**
Maximalist contemporary garden; lush, bold planting, counter pointed by graphic elements. An oxidised moongate creates a dramatic invitation into the exotic garden. The afternoon sun makes the planting sing. Strong sustainable ethos, only UK materials are used; oxidised steel from Essex, sweet chestnut from Herefordshire and handmade bricks from Yorkshire.

D

93 TANFIELD AVENUE, NW2

Dudden Hill, London NW2 7SB. Mr James Duncan Mattoon, 020 8830 7410. *Dudden Hill - Neasden. Nearest station: Neasden- Jubilee line then 10 mins walk; or various bus routes to Neasden Parade or Tanfield Av*. Home-made teas. **Adm £3.50, chd free. Sun 17 Aug (2-6). Visitors also welcome by appt June to Sept. Max group 20.**
Professional plantsman's petite hillside paradise! Arid/tropical deck with panoramic views of Wembley and Harrow, descends through Mediterranean screes and warm sunny slopes, to sub-tropical oasis packed with many rare and exotic plants EG Hedychium, Plumbago, Punica, Tetrapanax. To rear, jungle shade terrace and secret summer house offer cool respite on sunny days. Stunning views of Wembley Stadium, Kingsbury and Harrow-on-the-Hill. Previous garden was Tropical Kensal Rise (Doyle Gardens) featured on BBC2 Open Gardens and Sunday Telegraph. Also featured in Ham & High Express.

NEW 81 TANTALLON ROAD, SW12

Balham, London SW12 8DQ. Mr Jonathan McKee. *5 mins from Balham or Wandsworth Common stations. No parking restrictions*. Home-made teas. **Adm £3.50, chd free. Sun 29 June (11.30-5).**
Very small, but stunning garden, in a Victorian terrace, making the most of available space - a blaze of colour throughout with structural and annual planting that peaks in early summer. Espalier apple trees reach into a planting space that generates an exquisite effect. Gardeners will notice that maturing plans will provide more interest in years to come as the planting scheme evolves around them.

58A TEIGNMOUTH ROAD, NW2
Cricklewood, London NW2 4DX. Drs Elayne & Jim Coakes, 020 8208 0082, elayne@coakes.co.uk. *Cricklewood. Tube: Willesden Green or Kilburn 10 mins walk. Buses: 16, 32, 189, 226, 260, 266, 316, 332, 460. Teignmouth Rd just off Walm Ln.* Home-made teas. **Adm £3.50, chd free. Sun 13 July (3-7). Also open 121 Anson Road and 27 Menelik Road, combined adm (3 gardens) £7, chd free. Visitors also welcome by appt May to Sept. Good advanced notice required, max 15 people.**
Award winning front garden and back garden with eclectic planting schemes incl colour co-ordinated beds, pergola with wisteria, climbing roses and 40+ clematis, 2 ponds, water features, acers, hardy, and unusual plants. Rainwater harvesting with integral watering system, native plants and organic treatment means a home for frogs, newts and bees. Water harvesting system. Featured in Mr Partner, Japanese Lifestyle Magazine. Some areas accessible only by stepping stones. Deep pond.

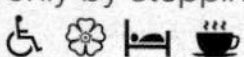

GROUP OPENING

TEWKESBURY LODGE GARDEN GROUP, SE23
Forest Hill, London SE23 3DE. *Off S Circular (A205) behind Horniman Museum & Gardens. Station: Forest Hill, 10 mins walk. Buses: 176, 185, 312, P4.* Home-made teas at 53 Ringmore Rise, Sun 1 June. **Combined adm £7, chd free (share to St Christopher's Hospice and Marsha Phoenix Trust). Tickets at 27 Horniman Drive. Evening Opening £7, chd free, wine, Sat 31 May (5-8); Sun 1 June (2-6).**

THE COACH HOUSE
Pat Rae

27 HORNIMAN DRIVE
Rose Agnew
Visitors and groups also welcome by appt Apr to Oct. 020 8699 7710 roseandgraham@talktalk.net

28 HORNIMAN DRIVE
Frankie Locke

53 RINGMORE RISE
Valerie Ward

These four very different hillside gardens are within a short walk of each other with spectacular views over London and the North Downs. Discover a sculptor's creative courtyard 'container' garden crammed with unusual plants and the artist's sculptures and ceramics (for sale). A small SE-facing garden has borders with rich colours within formal outlines to complement a modern extension plus mini meadow and a tranquil vegetable garden with seating, greenhouse and compost area. The front garden of another, inspired by Beth Chatto's dry garden, has stunning borders in soft mauves, yellows and white, interspersed with drifts of red and purple poppies. A hilltop country garden is in two sections, with deep informal flower borders under mature trees, raised vegetable beds, a fruit cage, greenhouse, chickens, and wildlife areas to encourage interest and diversity. Story Hunt for children. Great views. Plants for sale at 27 Horniman Drive.

7 The Grove

TREETOPS
Sandy Lane, Northwood HA6 3ES. Mrs Carole Kitchner. *Opp Northwood HQ. Tube: Northwood, 10 mins walk. Bus 8 stops at bottom of lane. Parking in Lane.* Light refreshments and homemade teas. **Adm £3.50, chd free. Sun 13 July (2-6).**
Nestling in quiet lane in Northwood conservation area, sloping garden with long terrace and large pots. Rose-covered pergola, water feature, small lawn, wide variety unusual shrubs incl magnolia grandiflora, paulownias, trochodendron. Peaking in high summer, heleniums, agapanthus, lobelias, eryngiums, crocosmias present a vibrant vision - well worth a visit!

TRINITY HOSPICE, SW4
30 Clapham Common North Side, London SW4 0RN. Trinity Hospice, www.trinityhospice.org.uk. *Tube: Clapham Common. Buses: 35, 37, 345,137 stop outside.* Light refreshments. **Adm £2.50, chd free. Sat 5, Sun 6 Apr, Sat 2, Sun 3 Aug (10-3).**
Trinity's beautiful, award winning gardens play an important therapeutic role in the life and function of Trinity Hospice. Over the years, many thousands of people have enjoyed our gardens and today they continue to be enjoyed by patients, families and visitors alike. Set over nearly two acres, they offer space for quiet contemplation, family fun and make a great backdrop for events. Ramps and pathways.

35 Turret Grove

© Jacqui Hurst

22 TRINITY ROAD, N2

East Finchley N2 8JJ. Janet Maitland. *Tube: East Finchley 12 mins walk. Bus: 263 to library, turn L into Church Lane, R into Trinity Rd. Car: turn into Trinity Rd from Long Lane.* **Adm £3, chd free. Sun 15 June (2-5). Also open 79 Church Lane.**

Densely planted courtyard of vivid contrasts. Cottage garden plants mingle happily with elegant ferns and grasses. A majestic black bamboo towers over pots of dainty annuals. Neatly clipped box accentuates sprawling climbers. Giant trachycarpus palm falls over a feathery tamarix. Sturdy fig tree guards a small pond.

TRUMPETERS HOUSE & SARAH'S GARDEN

Richmond TW9 1PD. Baron & Baroness Van Dedem. *Richmond riverside. 5 mins walk from Richmond Station via Richmond Green in Trumpeter's Yard. Parking on Richmond Green & Old Deer Park car park only.* Home-made teas. **Adm £5, chd free. Sun 15 June (2-5).**

The 2-acre garden is on the original site of Richmond Palace. Long lawns stretch from the house to banks of the River Thames. There are clipped yews, a box parterre and many unusual shrubs and trees, a rose garden and oval pond with carp. The ancient Tudor walls are covered with roses and climbers. Discover Sarah's secret garden behind the high walls. Wheelchair access on grass and gravel.

35 TURRET GROVE, SW4

Clapham Old Town, London SW4 0ES. Wayne Amiel, www.turretgrove.com. *Off Rectory Grove. 10 mins walk from Clapham Common Tube & Wandsworth Rd Mainline. Buses: 87, 137.* Home-made teas. **Adm £3.50, chd free. Sun 20 July (10-5).**

This garden shows what can be achieved in a small space (8m x 25m). The owners, who make no secret of disregarding the rule book, describe this visual feast of intoxicating colours as 'Clapham meets Jamaica'. This is gardening at its most exuberant, where bananas, bamboos, gingers, tree ferns and fire-bright plants flourish beside the traditional. Featured in Amateur Gardening and in Village.

7 UPPER PHILLIMORE GARDENS, W8

Kensington, London W8 7HF. Mr & Mrs B Ritchie. *From Kensington High St turn into Phillimore Gdns or Campden Hill Rd; entrance at rear in Duchess of Bedford Walk.* Light refreshments. **Adm £3, chd free. Sun 27 Apr (2-6).**

Well planned mature garden on different levels creating areas of varied character and mood. Pergola with Italian fountain and fishpond, lawn with border plants leading to the sunken garden with rockery. Also groundcover, mature trees (making a secluded haven in central London), flowering shrubs and a fine display of spring bulbs.

NEW 91 VICAR'S MOOR LANE, N21

London N21 1BL. Mr David & Dr Malkanthie Anthonisz. *Tube: Southgate then W9 to Winchmore Hill Green then short walk. Train: Winchmore Hill then short walk via Wades Hill.* Home-made teas. **Adm £3.50, chd free. Sun 25 May (2-6).**

Established characterful garden. Paths wind through species acers, clematis, climbers shrubs, perennials planted for colour and form. Waterfall and stream flows under raised pergola viewing platform, to carp pond. Exotic elements, and art abound in this much loved evolving paradise. Summerhouse,terraces, sunken garden provide tranquil, comfortable places to sit and contemplate. Home bred koi carp.

208 WALM LANE, THE GARDEN FLAT, NW2

London NW2 3BP. Miranda & Chris Mason, www.thegardennw2.co.uk. *Tube: Kilburn. Garden at junction of Exeter Rd & Walm Lane. Buses: 16, 32, 189, 226, 245, 260, 266, 316 to Cricklewood Broadway, then consult A-Z.* Home-made teas. **Adm £3.50, chd free. Sun 29 June (2-6).**

Tranquil oasis of green. Meandering lawn with island beds, curved and deeply planted borders of perennials, scented roses and flowering shrubs. An ornamental fishpond with fountain. Shaded mini woodland area of tall trees underplanted with rhododendrons, ferns, hostas and lily of the valley with winding path from oriental-inspired summerhouse to secluded circular seating area. Live music, plant sale and raffle prizes.

WALWORTH GARDEN FARM, SE17
Braganza Street/Manor Place, Kennington, London SE17 3BN. Trustees of Walworth Garden Farm, www.walworthgardenfarm.org.uk. *Kennington. Tube: Kennington, 500yds down Braganza St, corner of Manor Place. From Walworth Rd down Manor Place to the corner with Braganza St.* **Adm £2, chd free. Sat 7, Sun 8 June (10-4.30). Also open The Garden Museum.**
Walworth Garden Farm is an oasis in Southwark. From a derelict site this charity has created a productive garden full of organically grown fruit and vegetables surrounded by colourful flowerbeds. It is a working garden with greenhouses, a large newly constructed apiary, bee hives, ponds (a haven for wildlife) and a vital part of the local community providing training and development in horticulture. Majority of garden accessible by wheelchair users.

NEW **12 WARNER ROAD, N8**
London N8 7HD. Linnette Ralph. *Nr Alexandra Palace, between Crouch End & Muswell Hill. Turning off Priory Rd. Tube to Finsbury Park then take W3 bus to Hornsey Fire Station. Buses W7 and 144.* **Adm £3.50, chd free. Sun 15 June (2-5).**
Long, narrow garden divided into two distinct areas - a formal flower garden and a functional kitchen garden. Mixed planting including white foxgloves, irises and alliums surround a circular lawn. A curved path leads through to the newly planted kitchen garden. Raised vegetable beds, potting shed and seating area are separated by gravel paths.

WARREN HOUSE
Warren Road, Kingston Hill, Kingston-upon-Thames KT2 7HY. Dr Philip Brown, www.warrenhouse.com. *16m from M25, J10. From the A3 Robin Hood junction take A308 for 1m. Turn L at Zebra crossing into Warren Rd.* Teas and light refreshments. **Adm £3.50, chd free. Sun 11 May, Sun 12 Oct (2-5). Also open The Watergardens.**
A 4 acre garden with Grade II listed features and yr round interest. Italianate terrace, grotto, sunken garden and wild flower meadow. Rose garden and many spring flowers. Terrace area for dining and teas. Most of the site is accessible by wheelchair. Some pathways are loose gravel or grass. All main areas have paving and disabled parking is available.

This is a hard-working garden with well-equipped shed including a beer fridge . . . !

THE WATERGARDENS
Warren Road, Kingston-upon-Thames KT2 7LF. The Residents' Association. *1m E of Kingston. From Kingston take A308 (Kingston Hill) towards London; after approx ½ m turn R into Warren Rd.* **Adm £3.50, chd free. Sun 11 May, Sun 12 Oct (2-4.30). Also open Warren House.**
Japanese landscaped garden originally part of Coombe Wood Nursery, planted by the Veitch family in the 1860s. Approx 9 acres with ponds, streams and waterfalls. Many rare trees which, in spring and autumn, provide stunning colour. For the tree-lover this is a must-see garden. Gardens attractive to wildlife.

WEST LODGE PARK
Cockfosters Road, Hadley Wood EN4 0PY. Beales Hotels, 020 8216 3904, headoffice@bealeshotels.co.uk. *2m S of Potters Bar. On A111. J24 from M25 signed Cockfosters.* **Adm £4, chd free. Sun 18 May (2-5); Sun 26 Oct (1-4). Visitors also welcome by appt May to Oct.**
Open for the NGS for over 25yrs, the 35-acre Beale Arboretum consists of over 800 varieties of trees and shrubs, incl National Collection of Hornbeam cultivars (Carpinus betulus) and 2 planned collections (Taxodium and Catalpa). Network of paths through good selection of conifers, oaks, maples and mountain ash - all specimens labelled. Beehives and 2 ponds. Stunning collection within the M25.
NCH

WHITE COTTAGE
Crockenhill Road, Kevington, Orpington BR5 4ER. John Fuller & Alida Burdett, 01689 875134, alidaburdett@aol.com. *3m NE of Orpington. Crockenhill Rd is B258. Garden at junction with Waldens Rd.* Home-made teas. **Adm £4, chd free. Sun 8 June (1-5). Visitors also welcome by appt May to Sept.**
Traditional box, clipped hedging and reclaimed materials give structure to this informal garden surrounding a Victorian gardener's cottage. Colour themed beds contain grasses, perennials, shrubs and fruit trees. There is a small but productive vegetable garden, a pond, rare chickens and bees. Wildlife promotion is a priority. There are plenty of places to sit and enjoy the garden. Produce for sale.

5 WILDWOOD RISE, NW11
London NW11 6TA. Judy & David Green. *1m N of Golders Green. Tube: Golders Green then buses 210, 268 along North End Rd to Hampstead Way. 10 mins walk along Hampstead Way & Wildwood Rd.* Home-made teas. **Adm £5, chd free. Sun 13 July (2-6).**
Stunningly beautiful garden on the edge of Hampstead Heath. Architectural planting with some interesting clipped trees, especially the 'cloud' bay tree. Good selection of unusual and decorative shrubs and perennials throughout the yr. Elegantly planted box parterre.

NEW **74 WILLIFIELD WAY, NW11**
London NW11 6YJ. David Weinberg, 0208 201 9052, davidwayne@hotmail.co.uk. *From Golders Green Tube, H2 bus or 82,102,460 to Temple Fortune. Walk up Hampstead Way, turn L at The Orchard, walk through to Willifield Way.* **Adm £3.50, chd free. Sun 15 June (2-6). Also open 91 Willifield Way. Visitors also welcome by appt June to Aug. Phone for appointment.**
A very peaceful English country garden packed with herbacious borders and perfumed rose beds with wonderful containers to the patio area. A large variety of herbacious plants together with highly perfumed roses. Wheelchair access to patio area only.

86 WILLIFIELD WAY, NW11
Hampstead Garden Suburb, London NW11 6YJ. Diane Berger, 020 8455 0455, dianeberger@hotmail.co.uk. *1m N of Golders Green. Tube: Golders Green, then H2 bus to Willifield Way. Buses 82, 102, 460 to Temple Fortune, walk along Hampstead Way, turn L at The Orchard*. Home-made teas. **Adm £3.50, chd free. Sun 20 July (1-6). Visitors also welcome by appt June to Sept.**
Beautiful, constantly evolving cottage garden with year round interest set behind listed Arts and Crafts cottage. Wildlife pond, gazebo, pergola, private decked area, spectacular colour-themed herbaceous borders all encased by host of mature trees, shrubs and perennials. A real plantswoman's delight. Visit by HRH Prince Edward, Earl of Wessex, covered in Ham and High. and local papers. Winner of Suburb in Bloom.

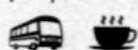

91 WILLIFIELD WAY, NW11
Hampstead Garden Suburb, London NW11 6YH. Mrs Karen Grant. *1m N of Golders Green. Tube: Golders Green, then H2 bus to Willifield Way. Or buses 82, 102, 460 to Temple Fortune, walk along Hampstead Way, turn L at The Orchard*. Home-made teas. **Adm £3, chd free. Sun 15 June (2-6). Also open 74 Willifield Way.**
Pass the topiary-framed windows, and enter through a door in the hedge to this enchanting secret garden behind a 1909 Arts and Crafts cottage. A white dovecote hovers over box-edged beds infilled with cottage garden favourites. The scent of blush roses, pale honeysuckle and white jasmine hangs on the still air. All is private and dreamy, enclosed by high hedges and guarded by an ancient oak. Home-made teas served on the lawn.

61 WOLSEY ROAD
East Molesey KT8 9EW. Jan & Ken Heath. *Rail: From Hampton Court stn ½ m towards E Molesey, into Wolsey Rd*. Home-made teas. **Adm £3, chd free. Sun 15 June (2-6).**
Romantic, secluded and peaceful garden of two halves designed and maintained by the owners. Part is shaded by two large copper beech trees with woodland planting and shade-loving plants. The second reached through a beech arch has cottage garden planting, pond and wooden obelisks covered with roses and sweet peas. Beautiful octagonal gazebo overlooks pond. Plenty of seating in both shade and sun. Most of garden wheelchair accessible.

NEW **21 WOMERSLEY ROAD, N8**
Womersley Road, London N8 9AE. Dr Karen Moloney, www.gardenandalus.wordpress.com. *Take W3 bus from Finsbury Park, alight at Mount View Rd or W7 from Finsbury Park, alight at Crouch Hill. Entrance on Elm Grove*. Home-made teas incl gluten free, vegetarian cakes and biscuits. **Adm £3.50, chd free. Sun 20 July (1-5).**
A modern urban garden with colour and texture provided mostly by spectacular foliage: large daturas, bright coleus, deep-viened heuchera, variegated pelargonia. Mature trees incl Ginkgo, Dicksonia Antartica, Trachycarpus fortunei. This is a hard-working garden with well-equipped shed (incl beer fridge), pretty potager. Delicious teas, vegan cakes. Planting scheme provided. The owner is a writer. Her latest book (Gardens that Mend Marriages) describes the creation of this London garden and contrasts it with the building of a new Persian garden in Andalusia, southern Spain, along with others visited across the world.

7 WOODBINES AVENUE
Kingston-upon-Thames KT1 2AZ. Mr Tony Sharples & Mr Paul Cuthbert. *Kingston-upon-Thames. Accessed by rd from Portsmouth Rd or by foot from Penrhyn Rd. By train: Surbiton Stn, then bus 71, 281, K2 or K3 from outside Waitrose. From Kingston Stn, go to Eden St bus stn then bus 281 or 71, exit at Kingston University*. Home-made teas. **Adm £3.50, chd free. Sun 24 Aug (1-6).**
We have created a winding path through our 70ft garden with trees, evergreen structure, perennial flowers and grasses which will take you through different 'zones'. We have used deep borders to create depth, variety, texture and interest around the garden. This will be our 2nd year and we promise some new plants and a 'garden party' feel. Wide herbaceous borders, an ancient grapevine, a box hedge topriary garden, and a hot summer terrace providing a contrast.

21 WROXHAM GARDENS, N11
London N11 2AY. Mrs L Coleman. *Buses: 102, 184, 299 from Bounds Green stn, alight Albert Rd. Walk up Wroxham Gardens, beside Sunshine Garden Centre*. Home-made teas. **Adm £3, chd free. Sun 15 June (2-7).**
Artist's garden delights with lush planting and winding paths revealing sculpture and pottery amidst fragrant herbaceous borders filled with scented flowers and rambling roses. Wildlife is nurtured, with areas of natural planting, a pond, active beehive and insect hotel, while fruit trees benefit all the residents of this lovely organic garden.

ZEN GARDEN, W3
55 Carbery Avenue, Acton, London W3 9AB. Three Wheels Buddhist Centre, www.threewheels.co.uk. *Tube: Acton Town 5 mins walk, 200yds off A406*. Home-made teas. **Adm £3, chd free. Sat 7, Sun 8 June, Sat 5, Sun 6 July (2-5.30).**
Pure Japanese Zen garden (so no flowers) with 12 large and small rocks of various colours and textures set in islands of moss and surrounded by a sea of grey granite gravel raked in a stylised wave pattern. Garden surrounded by trees and bushes outside a cob wall. Oak-framed wattle and daub shelter with Norfolk reed thatched roof. Japanese tea ceremony demonstration and talks by designer/creator of the garden. Buddha Room open to visitors.

19 Hillfield Park

© Jacqui Hurst

London County Volunteers

County Organiser

Penny Snell, Moleshill House, The Fairmile, Cobham, Surrey KT11 1BG, 01932 864532, pennysnellflowers@btinternet.com

County Treasurer

Richard Raworth, 7 St George's Road, St Margarets, Twickenham TW1 1QS, 07831 476088, raworth.r@blueyonder.co.uk

Booklet Distributor

Joey Clover, 13 Fullerton Road, London SW18 1BU, 020 8870 8740, joeyclover@dsl.pipex.com

Assistant County Organisers

Clapham & surrounding area Sue Phipps, 20 Clapham Mansions, Nightingale Lane SW4 9AQ, 020 8675 1272, sue@suephipps.com

Dulwich & Surrounding area Clive Pankhurst, 24 Grove Road, Camberwell, London SE5 5LH, 07941 536934, alternative.ramblings@gmail.com

NW London Susan Bennett & Earl Hyde, 5 St Regis Close, Alexandra Park Road, Muswell Hill, London N10 2DE, 020 8883 8540, suebearlh@yahoo.co.uk

Caroline Broome, 79 Church Lane, London N2 0TH, 020 8444 2329, carosgarden@virginmedia.com

SW London Joey Clover as above

Islington Nell Darby Brown, 26 Canonbury Place, London N1 2NY, 020 7226 6880, pendarbybrown@blueyonder.co.uk

Gill Evansky, 25 Canonbury Place, London N1 2NY, 020 7359 2484

E London Teresa & Stuart Farnham, 17 Greenstone Mews, London E11 2RS, 020 8530 6729, farnhamz@yahoo.co.uk

Outer W London Julia Hickman, Little Lodge, Watts Road, Thames Ditton KT7 0BX, 020 8339 0931, julia.hickman@virgin.net

Hampstead Ruth Levy, 5 Frognal Gardens, London NW3 6UY, 020 7435 4124, ruthlevy@tiscali.co.uk

Hackney Philip Lightowlers, 8 Almack Road, London E5 0RL, 07910 850276, plighto@gmail.com

Outer NW London James Duncan Mattoon, 93 Tanfield Avenue, Neasden, London NW2 7SB, 020 8830 7410, jamesmattoon@msn.com

Outer SW London Mhairi Clutson, 26 Kenilworth Road, Penge, London SE20 7QG, 020 8402 3978, mhairi@grozone.co.uk

W London, Barnes & Chiswick Jenny Raworth, 7 St George's Road, St Margarets, Twickenham TW1 1QS, 020 8892 3713, jraworth@googlemail.com

Highgate, St John's Wood & Holland Park Sue Whittington, Southwood Lodge, 33 Kingsley Place, London N6 5EA, 020 8348 2785, suewhittington@hotmail.co.uk

SE London Janine Wookey, 4 Piermont Green, London SE22 0LP, 020 8693 1015, j.wookey@btinternet.com

NORFOLK

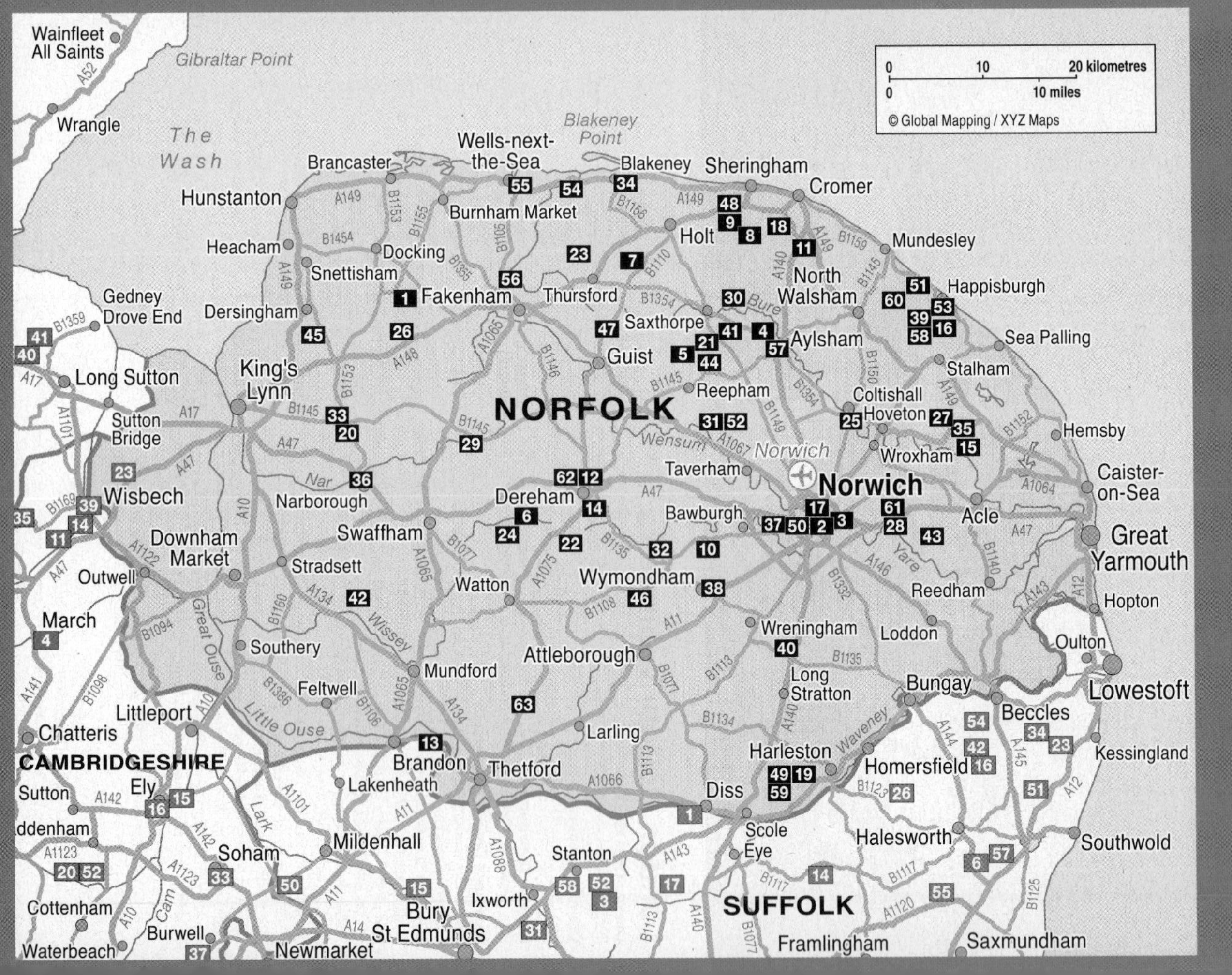
0 10 20 kilometres
0 10 miles
© Global Mapping / XYZ Maps
NORFOLK
SUFFOLK
CAMBRIDGESHIRE
Norwich
Great Yarmouth
Lowestoft
King's Lynn
Caister-on-Sea
Hemsby
Sea Palling
Happisburgh
Mundesley
Cromer
Sheringham
Blakeney
Blakeney Point
Wells-next-the-Sea
Burnham Market
Brancaster
Hunstanton
Heacham
Dersingham
Snettisham
Docking
Fakenham
Thursford
Holt
North Walsham
Aylsham
Saxthorpe
Guist
Reepham
Coltishall
Hoveton
Wroxham
Stalham
Acle
Reedham
Loddon
Hopton
Oulton
Kessingland
Southwold
Beccles
Bungay
Homersfield
Halesworth
Saxmundham
Framlingham
Harleston
Long Stratton
Wreningham
Taverham
Bawburgh
Wymondham
Dereham
Swaffham
Watton
Attleborough
Larling
Diss
Scole
Eye
Thetford
Mundford
Brandon
Lakenheath
Mildenhall
Ixworth
Stanton
Bury St Edmunds
Newmarket
Narborough
Stradsett
Southery
Feltwell
Downham Market
Outwell
Wisbech
Sutton Bridge
Long Sutton
Gedney Drove End
Wrangle
Wainfleet All Saints
March
Chatteris
Littleport
Ely
Soham
Burwell
Sutton
Cottenham
Waterbeach
The Wash
Gibraltar Point
Bure
Wensum
Yare
Waveney
Wissey
Nar
Little Ouse
Great Ouse
Lark
Cam

Opening Dates

All entries subject to change. For latest information check www.ngs.org.uk

February

Sunday 9
35 The Mowle

Saturday 22
25 Horstead House

Sunday 23
1 Bagthorpe Hall

Thursday 27
9 Chestnut Farm

March

Sunday 2
9 Chestnut Farm

Sunday 30
23 Hindringham Hall
30 Mannington Hall

Oval garden with herbaceous borders, woodland garden, shrub roses in the orchard and bamboo glade . . .

April

Sunday 6
13 Desert World Gardens
20 Gayton Hall

Saturday 12
16 East Ruston Old Vicarage

Sunday 13
6 Bradenham Hall

Sunday 20
64 Wretham Lodge

Monday 21
9 Chestnut Farm
64 Wretham Lodge

Thursday 24
9 Chestnut Farm

Sunday 27
43 Plovers Hill
62 16 Witton Lane

May

Sunday 4
28 Lake House
43 Plovers Hill

Monday 5
9 Chestnut Farm
28 Lake House
43 Plovers Hill
61 Witton Hall

Thursday 8
9 Chestnut Farm

Sunday 11
24 Holme Hale Hall

Sunday 18
27 How Hill Farm
29 Lexham Hall

Thursday 22
48 Sheringham Park

Sunday 25
55 Warborough House

Saturday 31
34 NEW The Merchants House

June

Sunday 1
41 Oulton Hall

Thursday 5
48 Sheringham Park

Festival Weekend

Saturday 7
49 NEW Shorelands Wildlife Gardens

Sunday 8
39 The Old Rectory, Ridlington
59 West View
63 Wood Hill

Wednesday 11
8 Chaucer Barn

Sunday 15
11 Daisy Cottage
15 The Dutch House
22 High House Gardens
33 Manor Farmhouse, Gayton
42 Oxburgh Hall

Monday 16
18 Felbrigg Hall

Wednesday 18
22 High House Gardens

Saturday 21
38 167 Norwich Road

Sunday 22
21 The Grange, Heydon
37 North Lodge
38 167 Norwich Road
50 Strangers Hall Garden
64 Wretham Lodge

Wednesday 25
36 Narborough Hall

Friday 27
30 Mannington Hall (Evening)

Sunday 29
3 Bishop's House
7 NEW Brinton Grange
31 Manor Farm House, Swannington
37 North Lodge
52 Swannington Manor
56 Wells-Next-The-Sea Gardens

July

Saturday 5
2 The Bear Shop
54 NEW Walcott House

Sunday 6
2 The Bear Shop
5 NEW Blickling Lodge
13 Desert World Gardens
17 68 Elm Grove Lane
26 Houghton Hall Walled Garden
35 The Mowle

Saturday 12
32 Manor Farm, Coston

Sunday 13
6 Bradenham Hall

Saturday 19
4 Blickling Estate

Sunday 20
57 West Barsham Hall
58 West Lodge

Sunday 27
12 Dale Farm
17 68 Elm Grove Lane
44 Salle Park

August

Sunday 3
10 Church Farm
14 Dunbheagan
24 Holme Hale Hall

Sunday 10
43 Plovers Hill
47 Severals Grange

Sunday 17
11 Daisy Cottage
42 Oxburgh Hall

Saturday 23
51 NEW Suil Na Mara
60 NEW Whartons Rose Fields

Sunday 24
51 NEW Suil Na Mara
60 NEW Whartons Rose Fields

Monday 25
51 NEW Suil Na Mara

September

Sunday 7
6 Bradenham Hall

You are always welcome at an NGS garden!

Sunday 14
22 High House Gardens

Monday 15
18 Felbrigg Hall

Wednesday 17
22 High House Gardens

Sunday 21
40 NEW The Old Rectory, Tasburgh

October

Saturday 11
4 Blickling Estate
16 East Ruston Old Vicarage

Gardens open to the public

4 Blickling Estate
16 East Ruston Old Vicarage
18 Felbrigg Hall
23 Hindringham Hall
26 Houghton Hall Walled Garden
30 Mannington Hall
36 Narborough Hall
42 Oxburgh Hall
45 Sandringham Gardens
47 Severals Grange
48 Sheringham Park
50 Strangers Hall Garden

By appointment only

19 Furze House
46 Sea Mere

Also open by appointment

6 Bradenham Hall
9 Chestnut Farm
12 Dale Farm
13 Desert World Gardens
14 Dunbheagan
15 The Dutch House
20 Gayton Hall
24 Holme Hale Hall
28 Lake House
35 The Mowle
38 167 Norwich Road
43 Plovers Hill
51 Suil Na Mara
57 West Barsham Hall
58 West Lodge

The Gardens

1 BAGTHORPE HALL

Bagthorpe, nr Bircham PE31 6QY. Mr & Mrs D Morton, 01485 578528, dgmorton@hotmail.com. *3½ m N of East Rudham, off A148. At King's Lynn take A148 to Fakenham. At East Rudham (approx 12m) turn L opp The Crown, 3½ m into hamlet of Bagthorpe. Farm buildings on L, wood on R, white gates set back from road, at top of drive.* Home-made teas. **Adm £3.50, chd free. Sun 23 Feb (11-4).**
Snowdrops carpeting woodland walk, walled garden and main garden. The garden will take wheelchairs, but not the woodland walk.

2 THE BEAR SHOP

Elm Hill, Norwich NR3 1HN. Robert Stone. *Norwich City Centre. From St Andrews, L to Princes St, then L to Elm Hill. Garden at side of shop through large wooden gate and along alleyway.* Teas. **Adm £3, chd free. Sat 5, Sun 6 July (11-5).**
Considered to be based on a design by Gertrude Jekyll, a small terraced garden behind a C15 house in the historic Cathedral Quarter of Norwich. Enjoy the tranquillity of the riverside.

3 BISHOP'S HOUSE

Bishopgate, Norwich NR3 1SB. The Bishop of Norwich, www.dioceseofnorwich.org/about/bishops/norwich/bishops-gardens/. *City centre. Located in the city centre near the Law Courts & Adam & Eve PH.* Home-made teas. **Adm £3, chd free. Sun 29 June (1-5).**
4-acre walled garden dating back to C12. Extensive lawns with specimen trees. Borders with many rare and unusual shrubs. Spectacular herbaceous borders flanked by yew hedges. Rose beds, meadow labyrinth, kitchen garden, woodland walk and long border with hostas and bamboo walk. Popular plant sales. Featured in local press and national publications. Gravel paths, slopes.

4 ◆ BLICKLING ESTATE

Aylsham, Norwich NR11 6NF. National Trust, 01263 738030, www.nationaltrust.org.uk/blickling. *14m N of Norwich just off the A140. 1½ m NW of Aylsham on N side of B1354.* Light refreshments. **Adm £8.95, chd £4.95. For NGS: Sats 19 July; 11 Oct (10.30-5.30). For other opening times and information, please phone or see garden website.**
Four centuries of good husbandry have made this 55 acre garden one of the greatest in England. Norah Lindsay, the society gardener, created the garden you see today, which incl an C18 Orangery, Temple, secret garden, beautiful double borders and parterre, lake and ancient yew hedges. New rose garden is taking shape. Gravel paths, electric vehicles to borrow. Sorry, no dogs. Garden open every day of the year except Christmas. Wheelchairs and powered mobility vehicles available to borrow. WC, gravel paths.

5 NEW BLICKLING LODGE

Blickling, Norwich, Norwich NR11 6SP. Henrietta Lindsell. *½ m N of Aylsham. On the Old Cromer Rd towards Ingworth house on the RH-side.* Home-made teas. **Adm £4, chd free. Sun 6 July (2-5).**
Georgian house (not open) set in 17 acres of parkland including cricket pitch, mixed border, walled kitchen garden, yew garden, river and woodland walk. Some variation of levels.

Wooded walk also includes orchard, walled vegetable garden and wild flower meadow . . .

6 BRADENHAM HALL

Bradenham, Thetford IP25 7QP. Chris & Panda Allhusen, 01362 687279, www.bradenhamhall.co.uk. *6m E of Swaffham. 5m W of East Dereham off A47. Turn S signed Wendling & Longham. 1m turn S signed Bradenham, 2m.* Home-made teas. **Adm £5, chd free. Suns 13 Apr; 13 July; 7 Sept (2-5). Groups also welcome by appt.**
A garden for all seasons. Flower gardens, formally designed and richly planted, rose gardens, paved garden, unusual climbers, herbaceous and shrub borders, traditional kitchen gardens with 2 glasshouses. Arboretum of over 800 different trees, all labelled. Massed daffodils in spring. A delight and an education.

7 NEW BRINTON GRANGE

Stody Road, Brinton, Melton Constable NR24 2QH. Richard & Lesley Ellis. *Brinton, between Melton Constable & Holt. From Norwich take A1067 turn R at Guist on B1110. From Holt take B1110 to Guist. From Fakenham take B1354 towards Briston turn L on B1110.* Home-made teas. **Adm £5, chd free.** **Sun 29 June (11-4).**

Mixed garden created over past 12 years with formal and informal areas, specimen trees, parterre, and wooded walk also includes orchard, walled vegetable garden and wild flower meadow. Wheelchair access is limited but it is possible to reach most of the garden. Access to walled garden and meadow is more difficult as gravel.

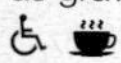

8 CHAUCER BARN

Holt Road, Gresham NR11 8RL. James Mermagen, www.chaucerbarn.com. *3m S of Sheringham. Turn off A149 nr junction of A149 & A1082 signed Gresham/East Beckham. Turn L at T junction. 1st building in Gresham, gravel drive on L.* Home-made teas. **Adm £3.50, chd free.** **Wed 11 June (2-6).**

5-acre garden created by owner over 20 years in ruins of farmyard. Uphill drive flanked by topiary leads to award winning barn conversion. Knot/herb garden leads to lawn flanked by walled herbaceous borders and pergola leading through contemporary topiary garden to stunning views over rolling hills to woodland. Woodland path leads downhill to wild flower meadow and young arboretum.

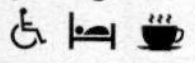

9 CHESTNUT FARM

Church Road, West Beckham NR25 6NX. Mr & Mrs John McNeil Wilson, 01263 822241, john@mcneil-wilson.freeserve.co.uk. *2½ m S of Sheringham. On A148 at Sheringham Park entrance. take the rd signed BY WAY TO WEST BECKHAM, about ¾ m to the village sign, & you have arrived.* Light refreshments. **Adm £4.50, chd free.** **Thur 27 Feb; Sun 2 Mar (11-4); Mons, Thurs 21, 24 Apr; 5, 8 May (11-5). Visitors also welcome by appt Feb to Sept, refreshments by arrangement.**

A 3 acre garden for all seasons, created over many years by enthusiastic plant lovers. Lawns, formal areas, herbaceous borders, vegetables and fruit. Woodland garden, specimen trees and shrubs. In the spring there are over 60 varieties of snowdrops with crocus, hellebores and daphnes planted in natural surroundings. There is always something new to see. Plant sales and visiting nurseries at all openings. Refreshments at all events. Wheelchair access weather permitting.

10 CHURCH FARM

Wymondham Road, Wramplingham, Wymondham NR18 0RU. Mr Peter Howard. *7m W of Norwich, 3m N of Wymondham. Leave Norwich on B1108 Watton Rd. Wramplingham is signed to L just before Barford. From Wymondham follow signposts for Wramplingham off Tuttles Lane.* Light refreshments. **Adm £4, chd free.** **Sun 3 Aug (11-5).**

An half acre garden of two eras. One a vista of calm formality packed with colourful herbaceous borders, some edged with lavender punctuated with a perfumed rose pergola. The other a beautiful cottage garden full of hot and pastel shades with a koi pond. The gardens have an overall relaxing feel. Large gravel areas access gardens.

11 DAISY COTTAGE

Chapel Road, Roughton, Norwich NR11 8AF. Miss Geraldine Maelzer & Miss Anne Callow. *3½ m S of Cromer. A140 from Norwich, in Roughton Village take B1436, signed Felbrigg Hall NT. Daisy Cottage is 150yds on L.* Light refreshments. **Adm £4, chd free.** **Suns 15 June; 17 Aug (11-5).**

2 acre garden not to be missed, with areas dedicated for wildlife, incl stream, pond, and more formally a Japanese style garden. Among its features are mixed borders, vegetable garden and apiary, chickens and ducks. The garden has an individual charm whatever the season. Produce and plants for sale. Bees and bugs in the garden demo. Featured on Radio Norfolk Garden Party. Limited wheelchair access to pathed areas only.

12 DALE FARM

Sandy Lane, Dereham NR19 2EA. Graham & Sally Watts, 01362 690065, grahamwatts@dsl.pipex.com. *16m W of Norwich. 12m E of Swaffham. From A47 take B1146 signed to Fakenham, turn R at T-junction, ¼ m turn L into Sandy Lane (before pelican crossing).* Home-made teas. **Adm £4, chd free.** **Sun 27 July (11-5). Visitors also welcome by appt June to Aug, groups of 10+.**

2 acre plant lover's garden with spring fed lake. Over 700 plant varieties featured in exuberantly planted borders and waterside gardens. Kitchen garden, orchard, naturalistic planting areas, gravel garden and sculptures. Gravel drive and some grass paths. Wide range of plants for sale incl rare hydrangeas. Rutland Wind Ensemble playing. Finalist and bronze medal winner in Britain's Gardener's Garden Competition.

Manor Farm, Coston

13 DESERT WORLD GARDENS
Thetford Road (B1107), Santon Downham IP27 0TU. Mr & Mrs Barry Gayton, 01842 765861. *4m N of Thetford. On B1107 Brandon 2m.* Light refreshments. **Adm £3.50, chd free.** **Suns 6 Apr; 6 July (10-5). Visitors also welcome by appt, 9-5.**
1¼ acres plantsman's garden, specialising in tropical and arid plants. Hardy succulents - sempervivums & plectranthus. Bamboos, herbaceous, ferns, spring/summer bulbs, primula theatre, over 70 varieties of magnolias. View from roof garden. New area of primula auriculas. National Gardeners Question Time. Radio Cambridge gardener. Glasshouses cacti/succulents 12500, viewing by appt. Large primula area including theatre Large collection of hardy Ferns.

14 DUNBHEAGAN
Dereham Road, Westfield NR19 1QF. Jean & John Walton, 01362 696163, jandjwalton@btinternet.com. *2m S of Dereham. From Dereham take A1075 towards Shipdham. L into Westfield Rd at Vauxhall Gge. At Xrds ahead into lane, becomes Dereham Rd. Parking at Anema's Farm.* Home-made teas. **Adm £4, chd free.** **Sun 3 Aug (12.30-5). Visitors also welcome by appt June, July & September only.**
1.4 acre plantsman's garden. Relax and enjoy walking among the borders and beds full of colour well into late Summer with plants of all descriptions. Extensive collection of rare and unusual plants plus the more recognisable. We try to provide the 'wow' factor. Reepham Ensemble playing 2-4pm. Featured in Garden News and Daily Telegraph. Gravel driveway.

15 THE DUTCH HOUSE
Ludham NR29 5NS. Mrs Peter Seymour, 01692 678225, janes.seymour@gmail.com. *5m W of Wroxham. B1062 Wroxham to Ludham 7m. Turn R by Ludham village church into Staithe Rd. Garden ¼ m from village.* Home-made teas. **Adm £4, chd free.** **Sun 15 June (2-5). Visitors also welcome by appt June to July.**
Romantic 2½ acre garden originally designed and planted by painter Edward Seago. Informal borders lead to wild areas of old fashioned roses and shrubs. Steep bridge and uneven paths through Marsh and Wood lead one to Womack water (limited access). Wheelchair access limited to main part of garden.

Stunning plant combinations, wild flower meadows, old-fashioned cornfield . . .

16 ◆ EAST RUSTON OLD VICARAGE
East Ruston, Norwich NR12 9HN. Alan Gray & Graham Robeson, 01692 650432, www.eastrustonoldvicaragegardens.co.uk. *3m N of Stalham. Turn off A149 onto B1159 signed Bacton, Happisburgh. After 2m turn R 200yds N of East Ruston Church (ignore sign to East Ruston).* Tea. **Adm £8, chd free.** **For NGS: Sats 12 Apr; 11 Oct (1-5.30). For other opening times and information, please phone or see garden website.**
20-acre exotic coastal garden incl traditional borders, exotic garden, desert wash, sunk garden, topiary, water features, walled and Mediterranean gardens. Many rare and unusual plants, stunning plant combinations, wild flower meadows, old-fashioned cornfield, vegetable and cutting gardens.

17 68 ELM GROVE LANE
Norwich NR3 3LF. Selwyn Taylor. *1¾ m N of Norwich city centre. Proceed from Norwich city centre to Magdalen St, to Magdalen Rd, bear L to St. Clements Hill turn L into Elmgrove Lane. No.68 is at bottom on R.* Home-made teas. **Adm £3, chd free.** **Suns 6, 27 July (11-4).**
This extended living/working space is the owner's endeavour to redefine a suburban garden and to provide inspiration when viewed from his studio window. Aesthetic values, initially took precedent over gardening know-how, but over 30yrs a more balanced approach has resulted in an eclectic array of informal planting, rich in colour and form and full of surprises.

18 ◆ FELBRIGG HALL
Felbrigg NR11 8PR. National Trust, 01263 837444, www.nationaltrust.org.uk/felbrigg. *2½ m SW of Cromer. S of A148; main entrance from B1436.* **Adm £5, chd £2.10.** **For NGS: Mons 16 June; 15 Sept (11-5). For other opening times and information, please phone or see garden website.**
Extensive pleasure gardens comprising of Walled Garden The walled garden is one of the finest in the area with potager vegetable beds, fruit trees and community allotments, and West Garden with working dovecote, fruit trees, vegetable beds, herb borders, Mediterranean beds, glasshouses, orangery and orchard. Botanical interest. 1 electric and 2 manual wheelchairs available.

19 FURZE HOUSE
Harleston Road, Rushall, Diss IP21 4RT. Philip & Christine Greenacre, 01379 852375 or 07967 966698, philip@furzehouse.com, www.furzehouse.com. *2m W of Harleston. From A140 Scole r'about to Dickleburgh Village, turn R at church, after 3m garden on L.* **Adm £3.50, chd free.** **Visitors welcome by appt May to Sept.**
A 5yr old 2-acre plantaholics' country garden with many unusual perennials, trees, shrubs and some seldom seen varieties. Informal island beds intensely planted create a long season of colour throughout. Interesting stone and wood feature in the borders, rockery, scree and wildlife pond. Some sheltered tender and rare specimens.

20 GAYTON HALL
Gayton PE32 1PL. The Earl & Countess of Romney, 015536 36259, ciciromney@tiscali.co.uk. *6m E of King's Lynn. On B1145; R on B1153. R down Back St 1st entrance on L.* Home-made teas. **Adm £4, chd free.** **Sun 6 Apr (12-5). Visitors also welcome by appt Feb to Oct.**
20-acre water garden, with over 2 miles of paths. Lawns, woodland,

lakes, streams and bridges. Many unusual trees and shrubs. Spring bulbs and autumn colour. Traditional and waterside borders. Primulas, astilbes, hostas, lysichitums, gunneras and magnificent rambling roses through trees and yews in June. Gravel and grass paths.

21 THE GRANGE, HEYDON

Heydon, Norwich NR11 6RH. Mrs T Bulwer-Long. *13m N of Norwich. 7m from Holt off B1149 signed Heydon 2m, on entering village, 1st drive on R, signed The Grange.* Teas. **Adm £4, chd free.** **Sun 22 June (12-5.30).**

Heydon Grange is a predominantly C17 Dutch style Gabled Farmhouse in mellow rose brick. The Garden has been extenively rejuvinated over the last 7 years and is semi enclosed by ancient brick walls and yew hedges with various topiary that was planted cica 1920. There are a mixture of herbaceous borders and a wide selection of shrub and climbing roses. Music, flower and plants stalls, sculpture.

22 HIGH HOUSE GARDENS

Blackmoor Row, Shipdham, Thetford IP25 7PU. Mr & Mrs F Nickerson. *6m SW of Dereham. Take the airfield or Cranworth Rd off A1075 in Shipdham. Blackmoor Row is signed.* Home-made teas. **Adm £4, chd free.** **Suns, Weds 15, 18 June; 14, 17 Sept (2-5).**

Plantsman's garden with colour-themed herbaceous borders with extensive range of perennials. Box-edged rose and shrub borders. Woodland garden, pond and bog area. Newly planted orchard and vegetable garden. Wildlife area. Glasshouses. Gravel paths.

23 ◆ HINDRINGHAM HALL

Blacksmiths Lane, Hindringham NR21 0QA. Mr & Mrs Charles Tucker, 01328 878226, www.hindringhamhall.org. *7m from Holt/Fakenham/Wells. Turn off A148 between Holt and Fakenham at Crawfish PH. Drive into Hindringham (2m). Turn L into Blacksmiths Lane.* Home-made teas at the hall. **Adm £6, chd free.** **For NGS: Sun 30 Mar (10-4). For other opening times and information, please phone or see garden website.**

Tudor Manor House surrounded with complete C13 moat. Victorian nut walk, formal beds and wild garden. Surrounding the moat are thousands of narcissi (32 varieties), a working walled vegetable garden and stream garden ablaze with hellebore and primula in the spring. Carving of female legs with head buried in ground. Open Sun April 6 to Oct 5 2-5, Weds May 14 to Sept 3 10-2. Coaches by appt - see website for details. Featured in Uniquely magazine.

24 HOLME HALE HALL

Holme Hale, Thetford IP25 7ED. Mr & Mrs Simon Broke, 01760 440328, simon.broke@hotmail.co.uk. *6m E of Swaffham, 8m W of Dereham, 5m N of Watton. 2m S of Necton off A47 main rd.* Light refreshments. **Adm £5, chd free.** **Suns 11 May; 3 Aug (12-4). Visitors also welcome by appt May to Sept, coach parties very welcome.**

Noted for its spring display of tulips and aliums, historic wisteria plus mid and late summer flowering. Walled kitchen garden and front garden designed and planted in 2000 by Chelsea winner Arne Maynard. The garden incorporates herbaceous borders, trained fruit, vegetables and traditional greenhouse. We are creating a terrace and nuttery and restoring the Victorian Ice House. Articles in local press and Homes and Gardens. Wheelchair access available to the Front Garden, Kitchen Garden and tearoom.

25 HORSTEAD HOUSE

Mill Road, Horstead, Norwich NR12 7AU. Mr & Mrs Matthew Fleming. *6m NE of Norwich on North Walsham rd, B1150. Down Mill Rd opposite the Recruiting Sargeant PH.* Tea. **Adm £4, chd free.** **Sat 22 Feb (11-4).**

Millions of beautiful snowdrops carpet the woodland setting with winter flowering shrubs. A stunning feature are the dogwoods growing on a small island in R Bure, which flows through the garden. Small walled garden. Wheel chair access to main snowdrop area.

26 ◆ HOUGHTON HALL WALLED GARDEN

New Houghton, King's Lynn PE31 6UE. The Cholmondeley Gardens Trust, 01485 528569, www.houghtonhall.com. *11m W of Fakenham. 13m E of King's Lynn. Signed from A148.* **Adm £9, chd £3 (5-16).** **For NGS Sun 6 July (10.45-5.30). For opening times and information, please phone or see garden website.**

Superbly laid-out award-winning 5-acre walled garden divided by clipped yew hedges into 'garden rooms', incl large mixed kitchen garden. Magnificently colourful 120m double herbaceous border. Rose parterre with over 120 varieties. Fountains, incl 'Waterflame' by Jeppe Hein, glasshouse, statues, rustic temple and croquet lawn. Gravel and grass paths. Electric buggies available for use in the walled garden.

27 HOW HILL FARM

Ludham NR29 5PG. Mr P D S Boardman. *2m W of Ludham. On A1062; then follow signs to How Hill. Farm garden S of How Hill.* Home-made teas. **Adm £4, chd free.** **Sun 18 May (1-5).**

Broadland garden. 2 very different gardens around the house. 3rd garden started 1968 on green field site with 3 acre broad dug 1978 with views of Turf Fen Mill, R Ant and Reedham Marshes. Approx 12 acres incl Broad, 4 ponds, site of old Broad with 100yr old Tussock sedges 5ft tall, approx 1 acre of indigenous ferns under oak and alder. Paths through rare conifers, rhododendrons, azaleas, ornamental trees, shrubs and herbaceous plants. Collection of holly species and varieties. Various very old stone carvings used for seats, excellent vistas.

Dunbheagan

28 LAKE HOUSE

Postwick Lane, Brundall NR13 5LU. Mrs Janet Muter, 01603 712933, janetmuter28@talktalk.net. *5m E of Norwich. On A47; take Brundall turn at r'about. Turn R into Postwick Lane at T-junction.* Home-made teas. **Adm £6, chd free. Sun 4, Mon 5 May (11-5). Combined with Plovers Hill. Visitors also welcome by appt, refreshments by arrangement.**

In the centre of Brundall Gardens, a series of ponds descends through a wooded valley to the shore of a lake. Steep paths wind through a variety of shrubs and flowers in season, which attract many kinds of rare birds, dragonflies and mammals. This is an historic water garden. Spectacular woodland in spring and autumn. . Collection of geraniums and shrubs. Limited wheelcahir access only to viewing platform.

29 LEXHAM HALL

nr Litcham PE32 2QJ. Mr & Mrs Neil Foster, www.lexhamestate.co.uk. *2m W of Litcham. 6m N of Swaffham off B1145.* Home-made teas. **Adm £5, chd free. Sun 18 May (11-5).**

Fine C17/C18 Hall (not open). Parkland with lake and river walks. Formal garden with terraces, yew hedges, roses and mixed borders. Traditional kitchen garden with crinkle crankle wall. A garden of all year round interest, acid loving shrubs are the highlight in May. Rhododendrons, azaleas, camellias and magnolias dominate the 3 acre woodland garden. Fine trees. Bulbs with emerging perennials and shrubs in the many walled garden borders.

30 ◆ MANNINGTON HALL

nr Saxthorpe/Corpusty NR11 7BB. The Lord & Lady Walpole, 01263 584175, www.manningtongardens.co.uk. *18m NW of Norwich. 2m N of Saxthorpe via B1149 towards Holt. At Saxthorpe/Corpusty follow sign posts to Mannington.* Light refreshments. **Adm £6, chd free. For NGS: Sun 30 Mar (12-5). Evening Opening light refreshments, Fri 27 June (6-9). For other opening times and information, please phone or see garden website.**

20 acres feature shrubs, lake, trees and roses. Heritage rose and period gardens. Borders. Sensory garden. Extensive countryside walks and trails. Moated manor house and Saxon church with C19 follies. Wild flowers and birds. Gravel paths, one steep slope.

31 MANOR FARM HOUSE, SWANNINGTON

Swannington NR9 5NR. Mr & Mrs John Powles. *7m NW of Norwich. From Swannington Manor Drive or via Romantic Garden Nursery.* **Adm £5, chd free. Sun 29 June (11-5). Also open with Swannington Manor.**

Small garden including knot garden with central fountain, rose garden enclosed by hornbeam hedging, and terrace with large pots of lavender and agapanthus. Access to the Romantic Garden Nursery, which ajoins the garden.

32 MANOR FARM, COSTON

Coston Lane, Coston, nr Barnham Broom NR9 4DT. Mr & Mrs J O Hambro. *10m W of Norwich. Off B1108 Watton Rd. Take B1135 to Dereham at Kimberley. After approx 300 yds sharp L bend, go straight over down Coston Lane.* Home-made teas. **Adm £4, chd free. Sat 12 July (11-5).**

Approx 3 acre country garden, several small garden rooms with both formal and informal planting. Walled kitchen garden, white, grass and late summer gardens, roses, herbaceous and shrub borders. Wild flower areas with new Pictorial Meadows border for 2014. Many interesting plants. Dogs and picnics most welcome. Plant sale. Some gravel paths and steps.

33 MANOR FARMHOUSE, GAYTON

Back Street, Gayton, King's Lynn PE32 1QR. Alistair & Christa Beales. *6m E of King's Lynn. Signed from B1145 and B1153.* Home-made teas. **Adm £4, chd free. Sun 15 June (12-5.30).**

Colourful, heavily planted cottage garden created 2001 on circa half acre plot ruined by major building work to house. Small gravel garden added 2002, courtyard garden and conservatory 2006. Land purchase in 2013 increased garden size by around 40% and work continues to integrate and plant up the new plot. Garden changes constantly as owner progresses from non-gardener to garden fanatic. Gravel paths, ramps provided on steps.

34 NEW THE MERCHANTS HOUSE

Blakeney, Holt NR25 7NT. Mr & Mrs David Marris. *Centre of Blakeney Village. Garden located N of A149 (New Road) up Little Lane in Blakeney*. Tea. **Adm £4, chd free. Sat 31 May (12-5).**

2 acres of walled secret garden with terrace woodland walk, parterre, shrub borders, orchard, kitchen garden, herbaceous border and ice house. Most of the garden is suitable for wheelchairs.

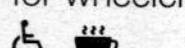

35 THE MOWLE

Staithe Road, Ludham NR29 5NP. Mrs N N Green, 01692 678213, ann@mowlegreen.fsnet.co.uk. *5m E of Wroxham. A1062 Wroxham to Ludham 7m. Turn R by Ludham village church into Staithe Rd. Garden 1/4 m from village*. Home-made teas. **Adm £4.50, chd free. Sun 9 Feb (11-2); Sun 6 July (1.30-5.30). Visitors also welcome by appt Apr to Dec.**

Approx 2 1/2 acres running down to marshes. The garden incl several varieties of catalpa. Japanese garden and enlarged wildlife pond with bog garden. A special border for gunnera as in Aug 2008 we were given full National Collection status. Boardwalk into wild area. Featured in Norfolk Magazine. 85% of the garden is acessable to wheelchairs.

36 ◆ NARBOROUGH HALL

Narborough PE32 1TE. Dr Joanne Merrison, 01760 338827, www.narboroughhallgardens.com. *2m W of Swaffham off A47. Narborough located off A47 between Swaffham & King's Lynn*. Light refreshments. **Adm £4.50, chd free. For NGS: Wed 25 June (11-5). For other opening times and information, please phone or see garden website.**

Gently evolving, romantic English garden. Herbs, wild flowers and fruit are planted through sumptuous herbaceous borders. Lake, river and woodland walks, ancient parkland, willow sculpture. Subtle and unusual colour schemes, lots of planting for wildlife, particularly in the gravel paths and the' wild at heart' garden. House open for history tours by appointment. Some gravel paths.

37 NORTH LODGE

51 Bowthorpe Road, Norwich NR2 3TN. Bruce Bentley & Peter Wilson. *1 1/2 m W of Norwich City Centre. Turn into Bowthorpe Rd off Dereham Rd, garden 150 metres on L. By bus,5,19,20,21,22,23,24 from city*. Home-made teas. **Adm £3, chd free. Sun 22, Sun 29 June (11-5).**

Town garden of almost 1/5 acre on difficult triangular plot surrounding Victorian Gothic Cemetery Lodge (not open). Strong structure and attention to internal vista with Gothic conservatory, formal ponds and water features, pergola, classical-style summerhouse and 80ft deep well! Predominantly herbaceous planting. Self guided walk around associated historic parkland cemetery also available. House extension nominated for architectural award. Slide show of house and garden history. Featured in Sunday Times, and on Radio Norfolk.

38 167 NORWICH ROAD

Wymondham NR18 0SJ. Rachel & Richard Dylong, 07884 120685, richarddylong@hotmail.co.uk. *3/4 m N of Wymondham centre. 3/4 m N of Wymondham centre. A11 to Wymondham. Take exit, straight to Waitrose and turn L at r'about. Garden on R after 1/4 m*. Home-made teas. **Adm £3, chd free. Sat 21, Sun 22 June (10-5). Visitors also welcome by appt Apr to Aug.**

In our 1/4 -acre town garden, created from a blank canvas 10 years ago, meandering pathways round a circular lawn to a secluded tropical haven, on to a sunken pergola, greenhouse with cactus collection and fruit and vegetable plot. We love to recycle and experiment. Featured in Amateur Gardening.

39 THE OLD RECTORY, RIDLINGTON

Ridlington, nr North Walsham NR28 9NZ. Peter & Fiona Black, 01692 650247, ridlingtonoldrectory@gmail.com, www.oldrectorynorthnorfolk.co.uk. *4m E of North Walsham 4m N of Stalham. Take B1159 Stalham to Bacton Rd, turn L at By Way to Foxhill sign continue to Xrds turn R past farm continue for 1/2 m house on R*. Home-made teas. **Combined adm £5, chd free with West View. Sun 8 June (12-5).**

A tranquil 2 acre garden around a former rectory. Established trees and some topiary. Mixed borders of shrubs, perennials, roses and bulbs, raised vegetable beds. A peaceful spot for a cup of tea! Children's treasure hunt. BBQ 12-2. Gravel drive and some paths might be difficult if wet.

Green garden with a magnificent cedar, extensive topiary and yew hedges, Italian garden for colour . . .

40 NEW THE OLD RECTORY, TASBURGH

Church Hill, Tasburgh, Norwich NR15 1NB. John Mixer & Nigel Handley. *9m S of Norwich. From the A140 at Tasburgh turn into Church Road. At the end of the village turn into Church Hill. The entrance is next to the church*. Teas. **Adm £4, chd free. Sun 21 Sept (11-5).**

A creative restoration of an early C19 rectory garden carried out over the last 30 years. The site is part of the iron age hill fort overlooking the valley. Basically a green garden with a magnificent cedar, extensive topiary and yew hedges with an enclosed Italian garden for colour. Wheelchair access the entrance drive is gravelled and there are steep slopes and steps.

41 OULTON HALL

Oulton, Aylsham NR11 6NU. Bolton Agnew. *4m W of Aylsham. From Aylsham take B1354. After 4m Turn L for Oulton Chapel, Hall 1/2 m on R. From B1149 (Norwich/Holt rd) take B1354, next R, Hall 1/2 m on R*. Home-made teas. **Adm £5, chd free. Sun 1 June (1-5).**

C18 manor house (not open) and clocktower set in 6-acre garden with lake and woodland walks. Chelsea designer's own garden - herbaceous, Italian, bog, water, wild, verdant, sunken and parterre gardens all flowing from one tempting vista to another. Developed over 16yrs with emphasis on structure, height and texture, with a lot of recent replanting in the contemporary manner.

42 ◆ OXBURGH HALL

Oxborough PE33 9PS. National Trust, 01366 328926, www.nationaltrust.org.uk. *7m SW of Swaffham. At Oxborough on Stoke Ferry rd.* Light refreshments. **Adm £4.70, chd £2.35, family £11.75. For NGS: Suns 15 June; 17 Aug (11-4). For other opening times and information, please phone or see garden website.**

Hall and moat surrounded by lawns, fine trees and herbaceous border; charming parterre garden of French design dating back to 1845. Orchard and vegetable garden. Woodland walks. A garden steward is on duty on open days to lead 4 free tours throughout the day. A map is available on arrival showing suitable paths for wheelchair access, footpaths which take you round the outside of the Hall.

43 PLOVERS HILL

Buckenham Road, Strumpshaw NR13 4NL. Jan Saunt, 01603 714587, jan@saunt.vispa.com. *9m E of Norwich. Off A47 at Brundall continuing through to Strumpshaw village. Turn R 300yds past PO, then R at T-junction. Plovers Hill is 1st on R up the hill.* Home-made teas. **Adm £4, chd free. Suns 27 Apr; 4, Mon 5 May; Sun 10 Aug (11-5). Combined with 16 Witton Lane adm £5, 27 April & with Lake House adm £6, 4, 5 May. Visitors also welcome by appt May to Sept.**

1-acre garden of contrasts, small C18 house (not open) with RIBA award winning orangery. Formal lawn hedged with yew and lesser species, huge mulberry, gingko, liquidambar and Japanese bitter orange, herbaceous borders with a range of varied plants and spring bulbs. Kitchen garden with orchard and soft fruits. Garden sculptures. Water feature. Cast aluminium silver birches. Wheelchair access to main part of garden, some gentle steps to teas.

44 SALLE PARK

Salle, Reepham NR10 4SF. Sir John White, www.salleestategardens.com. *1m N of Reepham. Off B1145, between Cawston & Reepham.* Home-made teas in The Orangery. **Adm £4, chd free. Sun 27 July (12-5).**

Fully productive Victorian kitchen garden with original vine houses, double herbaceous borders, ice house, and Norfolk Heritage Fruit orchard. Formal Georgian pleasure gardens with yew topiary, rose gardens and lawns. Some bark chip paths.

45 ◆ SANDRINGHAM GARDENS

Sandringham PE35 6EN. Her Majesty The Queen, 01485 545408, www.sandringhamestate.co.uk. *6m NW of King's Lynn. By gracious permission, the House, Museum & Gardens at Sandringham will be open.* Light refreshments at visitor centre resturant and tea room. **Adm £9, chd £4.50. For opening times and information, please phone or see garden website.**

60 acres of formal gardens, woodland and lakes, with rare plants and trees. Donations are given from the Estate to various charities. Open 1 Apr to 2 Nov. Closed 18 April, 26 July to 1 Aug. Gravel paths (not deep), long distances - please tel or visit website for our Accessibility Guide.

46 NEW SEA MERE

Seamere Road, Hingham, Norwich NR9 4LP. Judy Watson, 01953 850217, judywatson@seamere.com, www.seamere.com. *Off the B1108, 1m E of Hingham. From Norwich B1108, 2m after Kimberley railway crossing, turn L into Seamere Rd. Sea Mere drive is 2nd on L.* Home-made teas In the Sea Mere Study Centre, adjacent to the house. **Adm £6, chd free. Visitors welcome by appt Apr to Sept groups of 10+.**

The gardens border a 20 acre circular mere with spectacular views over terraced lawns, gunnera and new wetland garden, providing a purple hazed link with the native reeds beyond. Mature trees, shrubs and perennials frame the view. The 5 acre garden incl an ornamental potager, formal oval garden with herbaceous borders, woodland garden, shrub roses in the orchard and bamboo glade. The higher levels, near the house are wheelchair accessible. WC suitable for disabled use.

47 ◆ SEVERALS GRANGE

Holt Road, Wood Norton NR20 5BL. Jane Lister, 01362 684206, www.hoecroft.co.uk. *8m S of Holt, 6m E of Fakenham. 2m N of Guist on LH-side of B1110. Guist is situated 5m SE of Fakenham on A1067 Norwich rd.* Home-made teas. **Adm £3, chd free. For NGS: Sun 10 Aug (1-5). For other opening times and information, please phone or see garden website.**

The gardens surrounding Severals Grange and the adjoining nursery Hoecroft Plants are a perfect example of how colour, shape and form can be created by the use of foliage plants, from large shrubs to small alpines. Movement and lightness is achieved by interspersing these plants with a wide range of ornamental grasses, which are at their best in late summer. Extensive range of ornamental grasses and shrubs in various garden settings. Groups by appt July - Sept.

48 ◆ SHERINGHAM PARK

Wood Farm Visitors Centre, Upper Sheringham NR26 8TL. National Trust, 01263 820550, www.nationaltrust.org.uk/sheringham. *2m SW of Sheringham. Access for cars off A148 Cromer to Holt Rd, 5m W of Cromer, 6m E of Holt, signs in Sheringham town.* Light refreshments. **Adm by donation. For NGS: Thurs 22 May; 5 June (9-5). For other opening times and information, please phone or see garden website.**

80 acres of species rhododendron, azalea and magnolia. Also numerous specimen trees incl handkerchief tree. Viewing towers, waymarked walks, sea and parkland views. No adm charge to Sheringham Park, car park charge payable, £4.90 for non NT members. Special walkway and WCs for disabled. 1½ m route is assessable for wheelchairs, mobility scooters available to hire.

49 NEW SHORELANDS WILDLIFE GARDENS

Langmere Road, Langmere, Diss IP21 4QA. Ben & Sarah Potterton, www.shorelands.org.uk. *1½ m from A140, follow Brown Tourist signs from Dickleburgh Village.* Light refreshments. **Adm £4, chd £3. Sat 7 June (10-5).**

Shorelands offers something for visitors of all ages, borders overflowing with unusual perennials, gravel beds with grasses and bulbs, shrubberies containing rare and unusual trees and a new edible garden situated next to our collection of rare breed poultry. The garden is predominantly known for its free roaming animals that incl flocks of cranes on the lawns and marmoset monkeys in the trees. Largest crane (Birds) breeder in the country, birds can bee seen on all lawns. Free Range Monkeys! 4 groups of Marmosets and Tamarins free in the garden. Also open the Iris and Peony Festival, with Floral Art, Floral Displays and Specialist Nurseries. Garden owner is a BBC Radio Norfolk Gardener. Featured in the local press almost weekly throughout the Spring and Summer due to its animal collection. Visitors with wheelchairs can be dropped directly at the entrance ramp to the main gardens, all paths in the main garden are on grass.

50 ◆ STRANGERS HALL GARDEN

Charing Cross, Norwich NR2 4AL. Norfolk Museums & Archaeology Service, 01603 667229, www.museums.norfolk.gov.uk. *City Centre. At the city end of St Benedicts Street, just past Hog in Armour PH. Nearest parking - St Andrews car park. 3mins walk from market place.* Teas. **Adm £3, chd free (to garden only). For NGS: Sun 22 June (11-4). For other opening times and information, please phone or see garden website.**

¼ acre hidden behind Strangers' Hall, home of the wealthy merchants and mayors of C16 & C17 provides an unexpected peaceful oasis in a busy city. This urban garden offers glimpses of history with small herb beds, abutting the Eastern window of a C14 church, knot garden and borders with historic roses. Herbs used for culinary, medicinal and dyeing purposes. The garden is maintained by a small group of enthusiastic volunteers. Share to Friends of Norwich Museums. (Museum not open NGS day). Crafts activities, refreshments, garden games.

51 NEW SUIL NA MARA

North Walsham Road, Bacton, Norwich NR12 0LG. Bill Kerr & Bev Cole, 01692 652386, billkerr1@btinternet.com. *19m N of Norwich on the North Norfolk coast. Take the B1152 from North Walsham to Bacton. When you reach the Coastguard Station in Pollard St, 3rd bungalow on L.* Light refreshments. **Adm £3.50, chd free. Sat 23, Sun 24, Mon 25 Aug (11-5). Visitors also welcome by appt June to Sept.**

This ¼ acre exotic garden incorporates more than 130 plant varieties in an unusual mix of lush semi tropical planting meets Norfolk Coast meets Industrial and rural decay. Set in a series of garden rooms the striking architectural plants mixed with beachcombed wood, rusty metal and unusual water features all provides plenty to look at and enjoy. Often described as a 'Tardis' of a garden! Small photographic and Art Studio also on site with photos and artwork featuring the beautiful North Norfolk Coast. Featured in the Eastern Daily Press, North Norfolk News, Dereham Times and The Lowestoft Journal - August 2013.

52 SWANNINGTON MANOR

Norwich NR9 5NR. David Prior. *7m NW of Norwich. Almost ½ way between A1067 (to Fakenham) & B1149 (to Holt). In village look for black wrought iron gates opp post box in church wall.* Home-made teas. **Adm £4, chd free. Sun 29 June (11-5). Also open with Manor Farm House.**

The C17 manor house (not open) creates a stunning backdrop to this romantic garden which is framed by extensive 300yr old hedges, thought to be unique in this country. Mixed shrub and herbaceous borders, water garden, sunken rose and knot gardens, specimen trees and sloping lawns combine to make this garden both delightful and unusual.

> Lush semi tropical planting meets Norfolk Coast meets Industrial and rural decay . . .

54 NEW WALCOTT HOUSE

Walcott Green, Walcott, Norwich NR12 0NU. Mr Nick Collier. *3m N of Stalham. Off the Stalham to Walcott rd (B1159).* Light refreshments. **Adm £3.50, chd free. Sat 5 July (1.30-5.30).**

A garden in the making with emphasis on formal structure around the house and a traditional set of Norfolk farm buildings. These provide a series of connecting gardens which, through a south facing garden wall, lead to further gardens of clipped box, pleached hornbeam, fruit trees and roses. All set within recently planted woodland providing avenues and vistas. Small single steps to negotiate when moving between gardens in the yards.

55 WARBOROUGH HOUSE

2 Wells Road, Stiffkey NR23 1QH. Mr & Mrs J Morgan. *13m N of Fakenham, 4m E of Wells-Next-The-Sea on A149 in the centre of village. Please DO NOT park in the main rd as this causes congestion. Parking is signed at garden entrance. Coasthopper bus stop outside garden.* Home-made teas. **Adm £4, chd free. Sun 25 May (12-5).**

7 acre garden on a steep chalk slope, surrounding C19 house (not open) with views across the Stiffkey valley and to the coast. Woodland walks, formal terraces, shrub borders, lawns and walled garden create a garden of contrasts. Garden slopes steeply in parts. Paths are gravel, bark chip or grass. Disabled parking allows access to garden nearest the house and teas.

GROUP OPENING

56 WELLS-NEXT-THE-SEA GARDENS

Wells-Next-The-Sea NR23 1DP. *10m N of Fakenham. B1105 from Fakenham. Also off A149 Kings Lynn to Cromer Rd. Wells is served by Norfolk Green Coast Hopper bus (Cromer - Kings Lynn) or NG. Car Park at Stearman's Yard behind the Captain's Table PH, The Buttlands or Market Lane [close to gardens on Burnt St]. Advisable to tour gardens on foot.* Home-made teas Bishop Ingle House, Clubbs Lane. **Combined adm £5, chd free.** **Sun 29 June (11-5).**

NEW BISHOP INGLE HOUSE
Clubbs Lane. Gilly & Peter Cook

NORFOLK HOUSE
Burnt St. Katrina & Alan Jackson.
Next to Poacher Cottage

OSTRICH HOUSE
Burnt St. Mr Stuart Rangeley-Wilson & Ms Janey Burland.
Opp Norfolk House & Poacher Cottage

POACHER COTTAGE
Burnt St. Roger & Barbara Oliver.
Next door to Norfolk House. Coasthopper + X29 buses pass the house

Wells-next-the-Sea is a small friendly coastal town on the glorious North Norfolk Coast: popular with families, walkers and bird watchers. The harbour has shops, cafes, fish and chips, while a mile along The Run lies Wells Beach, served by a narrow gauge railway. Of the four in the group two are smaller town gardens and two are somewhat larger: all demonstrate a variety of design and planting approaches incorporating herbaceous borders, "cottage", shrub and fruit, with the two larger gardens providing different "rooms". The route around the four gardens takes in the Parish Church of St Nicholas, the High Street with its beautiful once-shop windows and the tree lined Georgian green square, The Buttlands. Wheelchair access at most gardens.

57 WEST BARSHAM HALL

Fakenham NR21 9NP. Mr & Mrs Jeremy Soames, 01328 863519, susannasoames@gmail.com. *3m N of Fakenham. From Fakenham take A148 to Cromer then L on B1105 to Wells. After ½ m L again to Wells. After 1½ m R The Barshams & West Barsham.* Home-made teas. **Adm £4.50, chd free. Sun 20 July (11-5). Visitors also welcome by appt Apr to Sept, groups welcome.**
Large garden with lake, approx 10 acres. Mature yew hedging and sunken garden originally laid out by Gertrude Jeykll. Swimming pool garden, shrub borders, kitchen garden with herbaceous borders, fruit cage and cutting garden. New bog garden. Separate old fashioned cottage garden also open. Some slopes and gavel paths.

58 WEST LODGE

Aylsham NR11 6HB. Mr & Mrs Jonathan Hirst, jonathan.hirst@btinternet.com. *¼ m NW of Aylsham. Off B1354 Blickling Rd out of Aylsham, turn R down Rawlinsons Lane, garden on L.* Home-made teas. **Adm £5, chd free. Sun 20 July (12-5). Visitors also welcome by appt, please email.**
9-acre garden with lawns, splendid mature trees, rose garden, well-stocked herbaceous borders, ornamental pond, magnificent 2½ acre C19 walled kitchen garden (maintained as such). Georgian house (not open) and outbuildings incl a well-stocked tool shed (open) and greenhouses. Most of the garden is easliy accessible to wheelchair users. Some recently repaired gravel areas a bit more difficult.

59 WEST VIEW

Youngmans Lane, East Ruston, nr Stalham NR12 9JN. Chris & Bev Hewitt. *3m N of Stalham. Take B1159 Stalham to Bacton Rd turn L after East Ruston Church, continue ¾ m turn L by Butchers Arms PH.* Home-made teas The Old Rectory Ridlington. **Combined adm £5, chd free with The Old Rectory, Ridlington. Sun 8 June (12-5).**
1 acre plantsmans garden incl borders with trees and shrubs underplanted with carpets of hellebores and bulbs, pergolas with roses and clematis, greenhouse with many interesting plants, a summer border with mixed perennials, vegetable parterre, tropical border, orchard and pond. Gravel Paths.

60 NEW WHARTONS ROSE FIELDS

c/o Langmere Road, Langmere, Diss IP21 4QA. Mr & Mrs R Wharton. *Visitors are directed to Blacksmiths Cottage Nursery, can collect a map and then drive to the fields situated on Bunn's Lane, IP20 9PE.* Light refreshments at Blacksmiths Cottage Nursery, Langmere Road, IP214QA. **Adm £3, chd free. Sat 23, Sun 24 Aug (10-3).**
Whartons Roses are the UK largest rose grower, producing 1.4 million plants in the fields of South Norfolk. The sight and smell of over 300 varieties in full flower is amazing! A rose grower will be onsite to talk about varieties and how they are grown. Visitors should arrive at Blacksmiths Cottage Nursery, collect a map and then drive a further 10mins to the fields off Bunn's Lane. Family nursery businesses founded in 1947. Largest grower in the UK.

A garden in the making . . .

61 WITTON HALL

nr North Walsham NR28 9UF. Sally Owles. *3½ m from North Walsham. From North Walsham take Happisburgh Rd or Byway to Edingthorpe Road off North Walsham bypass.* Light refreshments. **Adm £3, chd free. Mon 5 May (11-4.30).**
A natural woodland garden. Walk past the handkerchief tree and wander through carpets of English bluebells, rhododendrons and azaleas. Walk from the garden down the field to the church. Stunning views over farmland to the sea. Wheelchair access difficult if wet.

62 16 WITTON LANE

Little Plumstead NR13 5DL. Sally Ward & Richard Hobbs. *5m E of Norwich. Take A47 to Yarmouth, 1st exit after Postwick, turn L. to Witton Green and Gt Plumstead, then 1st R into Witton Lane for 1½ m. Garden on L.* Light refreshments. **Adm £3, chd free.** **Sun 27 Apr (11-4). Combined with Plovers Hill adm £5.**

An 'Aladdin's Cave' for the alpine and woodland plant enthusiast. Tiny garden with wide range of rare and unusual plants will be of great interest with its species tulips, daffodils, Scillas, dog's tooth violets, other bulbous plants and many Trilliums and wood anemones. A garden for the plant specialist. National Collection of Muscari. Featured in The Garden, Amateur Gardening etc.

NCH

63 WOOD HILL

Hill Farm, Gressenhall, East Dereham NR19 2NR. Mr & Mrs John Bullard. *1m W of East Dereham. ½ m W of Dereham off A47 N on Draytonhall Lane, B1146, R at T junction, 1st L Rushmeadow Rd, 1m over small bridge, entrance on R.* Home-made teas. **Adm £4, chd free.** **Sun 8 June (12-5.30).**

3 acres, the garden is set in mature parkland, incls water features, statues/stones, lily pond, varied rose gardens, yew hedging, vegetable garden, lawns with floodlighting for mature hardwood trees. One of East Anglia's oldest Tulip trees, beautiful oaks and copper Beech.

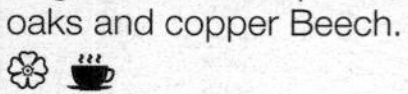

Wretham Lodge

© Val Corbett

64 WRETHAM LODGE

East Wretham IP24 1RL. Mr Gordon Alexander. *6m NE of Thetford. A11 E from Thetford, L up A1075, L by village sign, R at Xrds then bear L.* Teas in Church. **Adm £4, chd free.** **Sun 20, Mon 21 Apr; Sun 22 June (11-5).**

In spring masses of species tulips, hellebores, fritillaries, daffodils and narcissi; bluebell walk. In June hundreds of old roses. Walled garden, with fruit and interesting vegetable plots. Mixed borders and fine old trees. Double herbaceous borders. Wild flower meadows. Featured in House and Garden.

Norfolk County Volunteers

County Organiser

Fiona Black, The Old Rectory, Ridlington, North Walsham NR28 9NZ, 01692 650247, blacks7@email.com

County Treasurer

Neil Foster, Lexham Hall, King's Lynn PE32 2QJ, 01328 701288, neilfoster@lexhamestate.co.uk

Publicity

Graham Watts, Dale Farm, Sandy Lane, Dereham NR19 2EA, 01362 690065, grahamwatts@dsl.pipex.com

Booklet Coordinator

Sue Guest, The Old Rectory, Stone Lane, Brandon Parva, Norwich NR9 4DL, 01362 858317, guest63@btinternet.com

Assistant County Organisers

Panda Allhusen, Bradenham Hall, Bradenham, Thetford IP25 7QP, 01362 687243/687279, panda@bradenhamhall.co.uk
Jenny Dyer, Orchard Barn,4 Lacey's Farm, Long Lane, Colby,NR11 7EF, 01263 761811, jandrdyer@btinternet.com
Stephanie Powell, Creake House, Wells Road, North Creake, Fakenham NR21 9LG, 01328 730113, stephaniepowell@creake.com
Jan Saunt, Plovers Hill, Buckenham Road, Strumpshaw NR13 4NL, 01603 714587, jan@saunt.vispa.com
Julia Stafford Allen, Tudor Lodgings, Castle Acre, Kings Lynn PE32 2AN, 01760 755334, jstaffordallen@btinternet.com

NORTH EAST

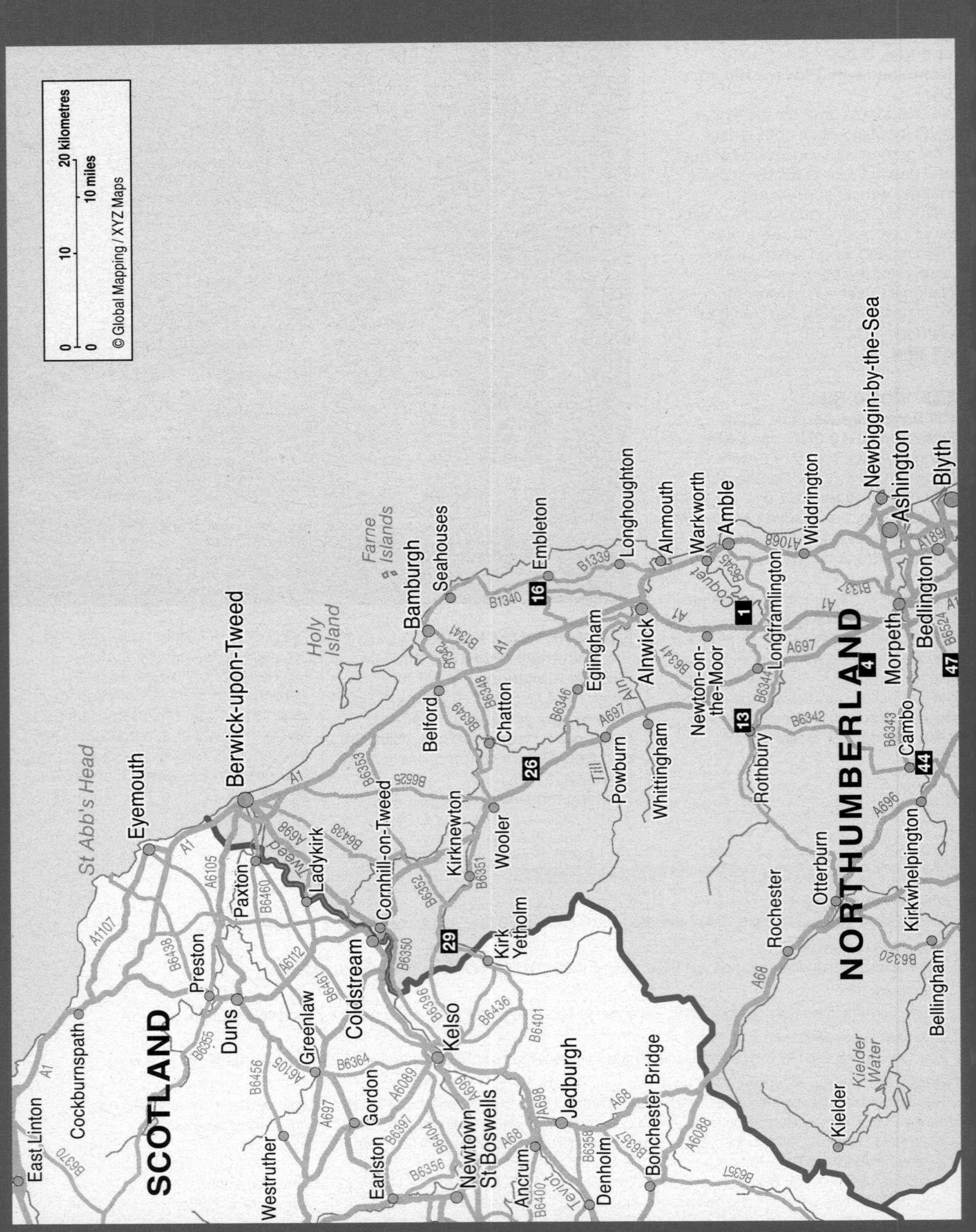

0
10
20 kilometres
0
10 miles
© Global Mapping / XYZ Maps
SCOTLAND
NORTHUMBERLAND
St Abb's Head
Holy Island
Farne Islands
Kielder Water
Eyemouth
Berwick-upon-Tweed
Bamburgh
Seahouses
Embleton
Longhoughton
Alnmouth
Warkworth
Amble
Widdrington
Newbiggin-by-the-Sea
Ashington
Blyth
Bedlington
Morpeth
Longframlington
Alnwick
Eglingham
Newton-on-the-Moor
Belford
Chatton
Powburn
Whittingham
Rothbury
Cambo
Kirkwhelpington
Otterburn
Rochester
Bellingham
Kielder
Wooler
Kirknewton
Cornhill-on-Tweed
Ladykirk
Paxton
Kirk Yetholm
Coldstream
Kelso
Preston
Duns
Greenlaw
Cockburnspath
East Linton
Gordon
Westruther
Earlston
Newtown St Boswells
Jedburgh
Bonchester Bridge
Ancrum
Denholm
Tweed
Till
Aln
Coquet
Teviot
1
4
13
16
26
29
44
47
A1
A68
A697
A698
A699
A6088
A6089
A6105
A6112
A1068
A696
A1107
B6342
B6343
B6344
B6346
B6348
B6349
B6350
B6351
B6352
B6353
B6358
B6364
B6396
B6397
B6400
B6401
B6404
B6436
B6437
B6438
B6456
B6460
B6461
B6525
B6320
B6355
B6356
B6357
B6370
B1339
B1340
B1341

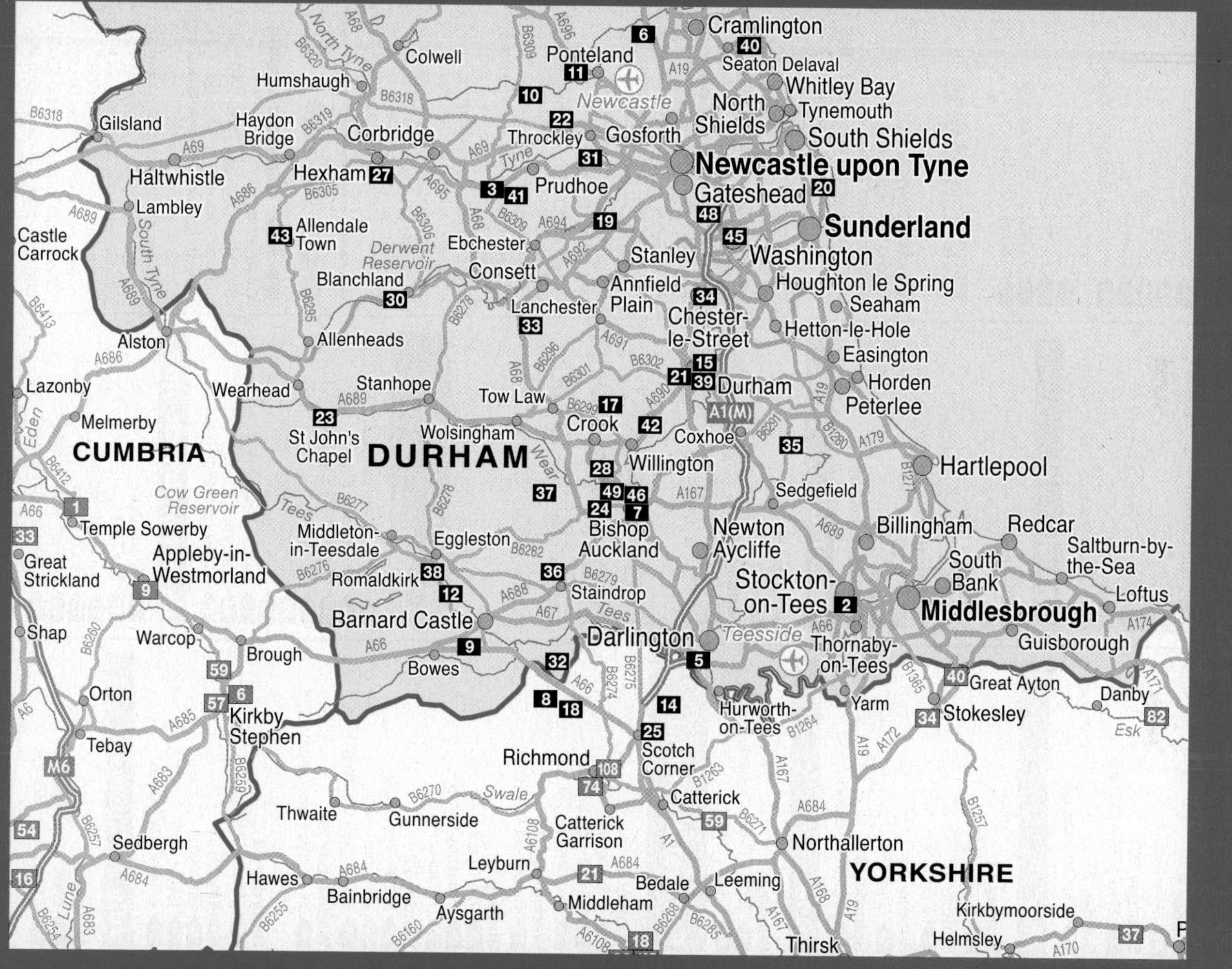
CUMBRIA
DURHAM
YORKSHIRE
Cramlington
Seaton Delaval
Whitley Bay
North Shields
Tynemouth
South Shields
Newcastle upon Tyne
Gateshead
Sunderland
Washington
Houghton le Spring
Seaham
Hetton-le-Hole
Easington
Horden
Peterlee
Durham
Chester-le-Street
Hartlepool
Redcar
Saltburn-by-the-Sea
Loftus
South Bank
Middlesbrough
Guisborough
Billingham
Stockton-on-Tees
Thornaby-on-Tees
Teesside
Yarm
Great Ayton
Stokesley
Danby
Esk
Sedgefield
Newton Aycliffe
Darlington
Hurworth-on-Tees
Scotch Corner
Richmond
Catterick
Catterick Garrison
Northallerton
Thirsk
Leeming
Bedale
Middleham
Leyburn
Aysgarth
Bainbridge
Hawes
Gunnerside
Thwaite
Swale
Kirkbymoorside
Helmsley
Ponteland
Newcastle
Gosforth
Throckley
Prudhoe
Colwell
Humshaugh
Haydon Bridge
Corbridge
Hexham
Gilsland
Haltwhistle
Lambley
Castle Carrock
South Tyne
North Tyne
Tyne
Allendale Town
Derwent Reservoir
Ebchester
Consett
Blanchland
Stanley
Annfield Plain
Lanchester
Allenheads
Alston
Wearhead
Stanhope
Tow Law
Crook
Coxhoe
Willington
Wolsingham
St John's Chapel
Wear
Bishop Auckland
Eggleston
Middleton-in-Teesdale
Romaldkirk
Staindrop
Tees
Barnard Castle
Bowes
Cow Green Reservoir
Lazonby
Melmerby
Eden
Temple Sowerby
Great Strickland
Appleby-in-Westmorland
Shap
Warcop
Brough
Orton
Kirkby Stephen
Tebay
Sedbergh
Lune

Opening Dates

All entries subject to change. For latest information check www.ngs.org.uk

April

Sunday 6
46 West House

Saturday 26
4 Bide-a-Wee Cottage

Sunday 27
32 The Old Vicarage,

May

Sunday 11
44 Wallington

Sunday 18
6 Blagdon

Sunday 25
14 Croft Hall

Saturday 31
40 Seaton Delaval Hall

June

Sunday 1
2 NEW Barnard Avenue Gardens
26 Lilburn Tower

Festival Weekend

Sunday 8
18 The Forge
33 Oliver Ford Garden
45 Washington Old Hall

Wednesday 11
15 Crook Hall & Gardens

Sunday 15
3 The Beacon
8 Broaches Farm
43 Thornley House

Sunday 22
25 NEW Hinkleside
29 Mindrum
38 Romaldkirk Gardens

Wednesday 25
8 Broaches Farm (Afternoon & Evening)

Saturday 28
16 Fallodon Hall

Sunday 29
9 Browside
20 Glebe Farm
27 Loughbrow House

July

Sunday 6
7 NEW Briarhurst
10 Cheeseburn Grange
23 High Hill Top
30 Newbiggin House
39 St Margaret's Allotments

Saturday 12
13 Cragside

Sunday 13
5 Blackwell Gardens
12 Cotherstone Village Gardens
18 The Forge
44 Wallington
47 Whalton Manor Gardens

Sunday 27
11 NEW Coldcotes Moor Farm

August

Saturday 2
4 Bide-a-Wee Cottage

Sunday 3
24 NEW Hillside Cottages

Sunday 10
31 No. 2 Ferndene

Sunday 31
37 Ravensford Farm

September

Saturday 6
19 Gibside

Sunday 21
22 Halls of Heddon

Wisteria covered pergola, wild flower area, willow tunnel and arbour . . .

Gardens open to the public

4 Bide-a-Wee Cottage
13 Cragside
15 Crook Hall & Gardens
19 Gibside
22 Halls of Heddon
36 Raby Castle
40 Seaton Delaval Hall
44 Wallington
45 Washington Old Hall

By appointment only

1 Acton House
17 The Fold
21 14 Grays Terrace
28 10 Low Row
34 25 Park Road South
35 Polemonium Plantery
41 Skara Brae
42 4 Stockley Grove
48 Woodlands
49 Woodside House

Also open by appointment

3 The Beacon
8 Broaches Farm
18 The Forge
23 High Hill Top
24 2 Hillside Cottage, Hillside Cottages
27 Loughbrow House
31 No. 2 Ferndene
39 St Margaret's Allotments
43 Thornley House

The Gardens

1 ACTON HOUSE

Felton, Morpeth NE65 9NU. Mr Alan & Mrs Eileen Ferguson, Contact Head Gardener 0777 986 0217. *N of Morpeth. On old A1 N of Felton. Take turning to Acton, follow rd for ½ m until fork. Take R fork & follow signs.* **Adm £4, chd free. Visitors welcome by appt July to Aug, for groups of 10+.**

This stunning walled garden has structure, colour and variety of planting, with abundant herbaceous perennials and different grasses. Planted in the spring of 2011, it has sections devoted to fruit and vegetables, David Austin rose borders, standard trees and climbers spreading over the brick walls. There are additional mixed borders, a ha-ha, and developing woodland planting, in total extending over 5 acres. Herbaceous perennial plantings include species and varieties favoured by butterflies and bees (info available).

♿

GROUP OPENING

2 NEW BARNARD AVENUE GARDENS

Stockton-On-Tees TS19 7AB. *Off Gainford Rd, off Oxbridge Rd on W side of Stockton. From A66 heading E or W from or towards Middlesbrough take slip rd marked Hartburn & Stockton West. Turn L into Greens Lane & follow yellow signs. Parking in Gainford Road please.* Home-made teas No. 27 (Briarcroft). **Combined adm £3.50, chd free. Sun 1 June (1.30-5.30).**

NEW **10 BARNARD AVENUE**
Jennifer Hodgson

NEW **22 BARNARD AVENUE**
Laura & Peter Davison

BRIARCROFT D
27 Barnard Avenue. Mr Glenn Sunman

Enjoy a visit to three, small urban gardens. No. 10 is a mature secluded garden with several seating areas. Recently landscaped, it is divided into 'rooms' and backed by mature trees. There are two small ponds, a water feature, a Judas tree which is magnificent when in flower in spring and, apart from hanging baskets, no annuals. No. 22 is a quiet and relaxing suburban garden divided into three areas: a secluded sunny seating area, a larger lawned area with mixed borders and a shady section under a mature ash tree. No 27 has a wisteria covered pergola, wild flower area, willow tunnel and arbour, aerial hedge, kitchen garden and herbaceous borders. gravel paths in some areas.

3 THE BEACON
10 Crabtree Road, Stocksfield NE43 7NX. Derek & Patricia Hodgson, 01661 842518, patandderek@btinternet.com. *12m W of Newcastle upon Tyne. From A69 follow signs into village. Station & cricket ground on L. Turn R into Cadehill Rd then 1st R into Crabtree Rd (cul de sac) Park on Cadehill.* Cream teas. **Adm £4, chd free. Sun 15 June (2-6). Visitors also welcome by appt May to Aug, for groups of 10+.**
This garden illustrates how to make a cottage garden with loads of interest at different levels. Planted with acers, apple and lilac trees. Water runs gently through it and there are tranquil places to sit.

4 ◆ BIDE-A-WEE COTTAGE
Stanton, Morpeth NE65 8PR. Mr M Robson, 01670 772238, www.bideawee.co.uk. *7m NNW of Morpeth. Turn L off A192 out of Morpeth at Fairmoor. Signed Netherwitton, Stanton is 6m along this rd.* **Adm £3, chd free. For NGS: Sats 26 Apr, 2 Aug (1.30-5). For other opening times and information, please phone or see garden website.**

Ravensford Farm

Unique secret garden created over the last 35 yrs out of a small sandstone quarry, it features natural rock and water. Unusual perennials are woven within a matrix of ferns, trees and shrubs. The garden contains the National Collection of Centaurea, and many other plants seldom seen. Featured in The English Garden. Partial wheel chair access.

NCH

GROUP OPENING

5 BLACKWELL GARDENS
45 & 46 Blackwell, Darlington DL3 8QT. *SW of Darlington next to the R Tees. 1/2 way along Blackwell, which links Bridge Rd (on A66 just past Blackwell Bridge) & Carmel Rd.* Cream teas. **Combined adm £4, chd free. Sun 13 July (2-5).**

45 BLACKWELL
Cath & Peter Proud

46 BLACKWELL
Christopher & Yvonne Auton

Two contrasting town gardens. No. 46 is a plantsman's garden - compact but with a collection of unusual plants and trees, a pond and a summerhouse. No. 45 rises from the R Tees up to a garden with many mature trees, a wildlife meadow, pond, a herb and Mediterranean garden, shady borders, lawns and a colourful herbaceous border. Some neighbouring gardens may open. Featured in Northern Echo....'the gardens, seen together, provide you with two sides of the spectrum: an ordinary garden filled with passion and understated grandeur and a stately garden stripped back to its roots'.

6 BLAGDON
Seaton Burn NE13 6DE. Viscount Ridley, www.blagdonestate.co.uk. *5m S of Morpeth on A1. 8m N of Newcastle on A1, N on B1318, L at r'about (Holiday Inn) & follow signs to Blagdon. Entrance to parking area signed.* Home-made teas. **Adm £4, chd free. Sun 18 May (1-4.30).**
Unique 27 acre garden encompassing formal garden with Lutyens designed 'canal', Lutyens structures and walled kitchen garden. Valley with stream and various follies, quarry garden and woodland walks. Large numbers of ornamental trees and shrubs planted over many generations. National Collections of Acer, Alnus and Sorbus. Trailer rides around the estate (small additional charge) and stalls selling local produce. Limited wheelchair access.

NCH

7 NEW BRIARHURST
Byron Avenue, Bishop Auckland DL14 6AP. Gillian Wales. *Follow signs to Bishop Auckland hospital. Approaching from the S turn L into Cleveland Ave, 2nd L into Byron Ave.* Light refreshments. **Adm £3, chd free. Sun 6 July (11-4).**
An established Edwardian town house garden unexpectedly to be found in the centre of Bishop Auckland. Mixed herbaceous planting surrounds mature apple and pear trees, greenhouse, small pond area and summerhouse. Images can be found on A Garden for Pablo blog.

8 BROACHES FARM
Dalton, Richmond DL11 7HW. Mr & Mrs Hutchinson, 01833 621369, jude1@farmersweekly.net. *7m W of Scotch Corner. From Scotch Corner on A66 W, 7m turn L at A66 motel. After ½ m turn L to Dalton. Farm on L after 1m.* Home-made teas. **Adm £3, chd free. Sun 15 June (1-5); Afternoon and Evening opening Wed 25 June (2-5) and (6-8). Visitors also welcome by appt May to Aug.**
In 1996 this wonderful garden was a field. It now includes 2 ponds, one with koi, stream, bog garden and wooded area. Mixed colourful borders are full of herbaceous perennials. Informal and naturalistic, this is a rural idyll. Lots of wildlife incl kingfishers, dippers, wagtails, frogs and toads.

9 BROWSIDE
Boldron, Barnard Castle DL12 9RQ. Mr & Mrs R D Kearton. *3m S of Barnard Castle. A66 W of Greta Bridge, turn R to Boldron, then proceed ½ m. Entrance opp junction. From Barnard Castle take A67 to Bowes, after 2m turn L to Boldron.* Home-made teas. **Adm £2.50, chd free. Sun 29 June (1-5.30).**
1¼ acres with unusual water features and large collection of conifers, topiary and acers, with a wide range of plants and imaginative stone objects. Wonderful tranquil seating areas. Off/road wheelchair access to most of garden. Over grass and slight raised lawn areas to bottom of garden.

10 CHEESEBURN GRANGE
Stamfordham NE18 0PT. Mr & Mrs S Riddell. *8m W of Newcastle upon Tyne. From A1 take B6324 through Westerhope towards Stamfordham. Cheeseburn Grange - 4m beyond Western Way Garage on R. From Stamfordham village follow signs to Newcastle, after approx.1m take 1st L signed Newcastle. 1st entrance L. Disabled parking on hard standing, nr house.* Light refreshments and home-made teas. **Adm £4, chd free. Sun 6 July (11-4).**
Peaceful oasis just 8m from Newcastle, this garden of approx 8 acres surrounds the beautiful Dobson designed house (not open) and St Francis Xavier church (open). Extensive lawns, mature trees, parkland views, roses, mixed borders and parterre. Vegetable area, fruit trees and Victorian walled garden. Woodland walk with many varieties of birds. Featured in Hexham Courant, Morpeth Herald and The Journal.

11 NEW COLDCOTES MOOR FARM
Ponteland, Newcastle Upon Tyne NE20 0DF. Ron & Louise Bowey. *Off A696 N of Ponteland. From S, leave Ponteland on A696 towards Jedburgh, after 1m take L turn marked 'Milbourne 2m'. After 400yds turn L into drive.* Home-made teas. **Adm £4, chd free. Sun 27 July (1-5).**
The garden, landscaped grounds and woods cover around 15 acres. The wooded approach opens out to lawned areas surrounded by new ornamental and woodland shrubs and trees. A courtyard garden leads to an ornamental walled garden, beyond which is an orchard, vegetable garden and rose arbour. To the south the garden looks out over a lake and field walks, with woodland walk to the west. Small children's play area. Children's treasure hunt. Featured in the Newcastle Journal and Hexham Courant. Most areas can be accessed though sometimes by circuitous routes or an occasional step. WC access involves three steps.

GROUP OPENING

12 COTHERSTONE VILLAGE GARDENS
Cotherstone, Barnard Castle DL12 9QW. *4m NW of Barnard Castle. On B6277 Middleton-in-Teesdale to Barnard Castle road. Gardens are spread throughout the village.* Home-made teas Village Hall. **Combined adm £4, chd free. Sun 13 July (10.30-4.30).**
A warm welcome awaits you in one of the best 20 villages in the country. Very picturesque at the confluence of the Rivers Tees and Balder. A variety of country gardens and allotments will be open: small, medium, large, Edwardian, wooded and naturalist, with some weaving in local and natural history. Cotherstone and the surrounding area is a beautiful place for walking.There are 2 pubs and a shop in the village where refreshments can also be obtained. Owing to the variety of gardens and allotments some may not be accessible for wheelchair users.

13 ◆ CRAGSIDE
Rothbury NE65 7PX. National Trust, 01669 620333, www.nationaltrust.org.uk. *13m SW of Alnwick. (B6341); 15m NW of Morpeth (A697).* **Adm £10.20, chd £5.20. For NGS: Sat 12 July (10-7). For other opening times and information, please phone or see garden website.**
The Formal Garden is in the 'High Victorian' style created by the 1st Lord and Lady Armstrong. Including orchard house, carpet bedding, ferneries and Italian terrace. New double herbaceous border for 2013. The largest sandstone Rock Garden in Europe with its tumbling cascades. Extensive grounds of over 1000 acres famous for Rhododendrons in June, large lakes and magnificent conifer landscape. The House, mainly the design of Norman Shaw, with its very fine arts and crafts interiors is worth a separate visit. Limited access to the Formal Garden.

14 CROFT HALL

Croft-on-Tees DL2 2TB. Mr & Mrs Trevor Chaytor Norris. *3m S of Darlington. On A167 to Northallerton, 6m from Scotch Corner. Croft Hall is 1st house on R as you enter village from Scotch Corner.* Home-made teas. **Adm £4, chd free.**
Sun 25 May (2-5).
A lovely lavender walk leads to a Queen Anne-fronted house (not open) surrounded by a 5-acre garden, comprising a stunning herbaceous border, large fruit and vegetable plot, two ponds and wonderful topiary arched wall. Pretty rose garden and mature box Italianate parterre are beautifully set in this garden offering peaceful, tranquil views of open countryside. Some gravel paths.

15 ◆ CROOK HALL & GARDENS

Sidegate, Durham City DH1 5SZ. Maggie Bell, 0191 384 8028, www.crookhallgardens.co.uk. *Centre of Durham City. Crook Hall is short walk from Durham's Market Place. Follow the tourist info signs. Parking available at entrance.* Light refreshments. **Adm £6.50, chd £5. For NGS: Wed 11 June (11-5). For other opening times and information, please phone or see garden website.**
Described in Country Life as having 'history, romance and beauty'. Intriguing medieval manor house surrounded by 4 acres of fine gardens. Visitors can enjoy magnificent cathedral views from the 2 walled gardens. Other garden 'rooms' incl the silver and white garden, and an orchard, moat, pool, maze and Sleeping Giant give added interest! Featured on Radio 4 with John McCarthy, and Clare Balding, on Radio 4 Gardeners Question Time and in Independent and the ' I ' as number 9 in the top ten places to visit in Britain.

16 FALLODON HALL

Alnwick NE66 3HF. Mr & Mrs Mark Bridgeman. *5m N of Alnwick 2m off A1. Turn R on B6347 signed Christon Bank & Seahouses, & turn into Fallodon gates after exactly 2m, at the Xrds. Follow drive for 1m.* Home-made teas in stable yard. **Adm £4, chd free. Sat 28 June (2-5).**
Extensive, well established garden, including a 30m border, finishing beside a hot greenhouse and bog garden. The late C17 walls of the kitchen garden surround cutting and vegetable borders and the fruit greenhouse. The sunken garden from 1898 has been replanted by Natasha McEwen. Woodlands, pond and arboretum extend over 10 acres to explore. Renowned home-made teas in stable yard, and plant sale, predominantly of Fallodon plants. Featured in Morpeth Herald. Limited wheelchair access.

Pergola leading to secret garden, with scented plants and a selection of unusual containers . . .

17 THE FOLD

High Wooley, Stanley Crook DL15 9AP. Mr & Mrs G Young, 01388 768412, gfamyoung@madasafish.com. *3m N of Crook. Directions given when visit is booked.* Home-made teas. **Adm £3.50, chd free. Visitors welcome by appt May to Sept, groups of 10+.**
Large, cottage-style garden, approx ½ acre at 700ft and with splendid views over countryside. Winner of Alan Siggens Memorial Award 2011: Beautiful Durham. Herbaceous borders and island beds. Ponds and numerous mature trees. Small roof garden, wide range of plants, many grown from seed and cuttings. Emphasis on colour, harmony and texture. Featured in Northern Echo.

18 THE FORGE

Ravensworth, Richmond DL11 7EU. Mr & Mrs Peter & Enid Wilson, 01325 718242. *7m N of Richmond. Travel 5½ m W on the A66 from Scotch Corner. Turn L to Ravensworth and follow NGS signs.* Cream teas. **Adm £2.50, chd free. Suns 8 June; 13 July (1-6). Visitors also welcome by appt June to Oct.**
The Blacksmith's Secret Garden - the garden is hidden from view behind The Forge House, Cottage and the working Blacksmith's Forge. It has small wildlife ponds with two natural stone features. There is a variety of trees, shrubs and mixed borders leading to a hay meadow. New features are being developed for 2014. Wheelchair access across gravel path.

19 ◆ GIBSIDE

Rowlands Gill NE16 6BG. National Trust, 01207 541820, www.nationaltrust.org.uk/gibside. *6m SW of Gateshead. Follow brown signs from the A1 & take the A694 towards Rowlands Gill.* Light refreshments in Potting Shed Cafe. **Adm £7, chd £4.50. For NGS: Sat 6 Sept (10-6). For other opening times and information, please phone or see garden website.**
C18 landscape park designed by Stephen Switzer for one of the richest men in Georgian England, George Bowes, and his celebrated daughter Mary Eleanor. Inner pleasure grounds with tree-lined avenue and productive walled garden, plus miles of woodland and riverside walks in the Derwent Valley. Ongoing restoration of the gardens and woodland, one of the National Trust's most ambitious such projects. Behind the scenes guided talks by the head gardener; see the walled garden come back to life as we restore it. If you have special access needs, please call us in advance of your visit.

20 GLEBE FARM

Moor Lane, Whitburn, Sunderland SR6 7JP. John & Kathryn Moor. *2m N of Sunderland. At W end of Whitburn Village. Will be signed from A1018 between Sunderland & Cleadon, & from A183 coast rd.* Home-made teas. **Adm £3.50, chd free. Sun 29 June (2-4.30).**
This lovely garden is on the edge of the picturesque village of Whitburn. Its ¾ acre has a range of colours, moods and styles - lawned and gravelled areas surrounded by herbaceous borders with David Austin roses, a wide variety of shrubs and herbaceous perennials. Ornamental trees, herb garden and small woodland. Views of the sea, and the North York Moors (on a good day).

No. 2 Ferndene

21 14 GRAYS TERRACE

Redhills, Durham DH1 4AU. Mr Paul Beard, 0191 5972849, pauljofraeard@yahoo.co.uk. *Just off A167 on W side of Durham. ½ m S of A167 / A691 r'about, turn L into Redhills Lane. When road turns R with no entry sign, Grays Terrace is ahead. No.14 is at the very end.* **Adm by donation. Visitors welcome by appt Apr to Aug.**

A steeply sloping garden of about ⅔ acre with a superb view over Durham Cathedral, Castle and surroundings. Very informal garden; no bedding and a significant wild area. Planting is mixed with interest throughout the yr. Many unusual and rare plants. Particularly knowledgeable owner who is happy to escort groups round the garden.

22 ◆ HALLS OF HEDDON

West Heddon Nursery, Heddon-on-the-Wall, Newcastle Upon Tyne NE15 0JS. Mr David Hall, 01661 852445, www.hallsofheddon.co.uk. *Approx 5m W of Newcastle upon Tyne. Approx 1m NW of Heddon on the Wall signed off B6318 (Military Rd) at the bridge crossing the A69.* Light refreshments. **Adm % of sales to NGS. For NGS: Sun 21 Sept (10.30-4). For other opening times and information, please phone or see garden website.**

Halls is a world renowned family owned nursery, full of plants set against the backdrop of an orginal heated wall garden. September sees a spectacular display of colour and foliage in its dahlia and chrysanthemum trial fields. Row upon row of brilliant hues of plants arranged to show type, colour and height. It lifts the spirits as winter approaches and makes a dahlia/chrysanthemum lover of every gardener. Introductory talks with a question and answer session will be provided throughout the day by David Hall.

23 HIGH HILL TOP

St John's Chapel DL13 1RJ. Mr & Mrs I Hedley, 01388 537952. *7m W of Stanhope. On A689. Turn L into Harthope Rd after Co-op shop in St John's Chapel. Up hill for ½ m past the Animal Hotel. Garden next house on L.* Home-made teas. **Adm £3.50, chd free. Sun 6 July (10-4). Visitors also welcome by appt June to Aug.**

See what can be achieved in an exposed garden at 1200ft. Mixed planting includes a wonderful collection of sorbus, hostas, ferns, eucalyptus and candelabra primulas. The magnificent backdrop of the North Pennines offers stunning views from a garden full of thoughtfully placed pathways, interesting bridges and still and flowing water with associated planting. Featured in Northern Echo and Weardale Gazette.

GROUP OPENING

24 NEW HILLSIDE COTTAGES

Low Etherley, Bishop Auckland DL14 0EZ. *Off the B6282 in Low Etherley, Near Bishop Auckland. To reach the gardens walk down the track opp number 63 Low Etherley. Parking will be available at Green Croft Farm on S side of the rd.* Light refreshments. **Combined adm £4, chd free. Sun 3 Aug (1.30-5).**

NEW 1 HILLSIDE COTTAGES
Eric & Delia Ayes

2 HILLSIDE COTTAGE
Mrs M Smith
Visitors also welcome by appt Feb to Nov.
01388 832727
mary@maryruth.plus.com

The gardens of these two C19 cottages offer contrasting styles. At Number 1, grass paths lead you through a layout of trees and shrubs including many interesting specimens. Number 2 is based on island beds and has a cottage garden feel with a variety of perennials among the trees and shrubs and also incl a wild area, vegetables and fruit. Both gardens have ponds and water features.

25 NEW HINKLESIDE

Middleton Tyas, Richmond DL10 6RB. Baz & Doreen Porritt. *2m E of the A1M at Scotch Corner. From the A1 at Scotch Corner follow signs for Middleton Tyas. Through village follow signs for Croft for 2m & NGS yellow signs.* Home-made teas. **Adm £4, chd free. Sun 22 June (2-5).**

'Brass on the Grass' - a 'two for one' treat! Enjoy an afternoon in this garden and be entertained by a local brass band. This is a garden for both wildlife and plants set in 5 acres of gently sloping grassland overlooking the Cleveland Hills and incl a small woodland area, pond for wildlife and various flowerbeds. Uneven grassland may make it difficult for some wheelchairs.

26 LILBURN TOWER

Alnwick NE66 4PQ. Mr & Mrs D Davidson. *3m S of Wooler. On A697.* Home-made teas. **Adm £4, chd free. Sun 1 June (2-6).**

10 acres of magnificent walled and formal gardens set above river; rose parterre, topiary, scented garden, Victorian conservatory, wild flower meadow. Extensive fruit and vegetable garden, large glasshouse with vines. 30 acres of woodland with walks. Giant lilies, meconopsis around pond garden. Rhododendrons and azaleas. Also ruins of Pele Tower, and C12 church. Limited wheelchair access.

27 LOUGHBROW HOUSE

Hexham NE46 1RS. Mrs K A Clark, 01434 603351, patriciaclark351@btinternet.com. *1m S of Hexham. 1m S of Hexham on B6306. Dipton Mill Rd. Road signed Blanchland, ¼ m take R fork; then ¼ m at fork, lodge gates & driveway at intersection.* Home-made teas. **Adm £3, chd free. Sun 29 June (2-5). Mrs Clark welcomes visitors by appt Mar to Oct.**

Country house garden with sweeping, colour themed herbaceous borders set around large lawns. Unique Lutyens inspired rill with grass topped bridges. Part walled kitchen garden and paved courtyard. Bog garden with pond. Developing new border. Wild flower meadow with specimen trees. Woodland quarry garden with rhododendrons, azaleas, hostas and rare trees. Home made jams and chutneys. Featured in Hexham Courant and The Northumbrian.

'Brass on the Grass' - a 'two for one' treat! Enjoy an afternoon in this garden and be entertained by a local brass band . . .

28 10 LOW ROW

North Bitchburn, Crook DL15 8AJ. Mrs Ann Pickering, 01388 766345, keightleyann@yahoo.co.uk. *3m NW of Bishop Auckland. From Bishop Auckland take A689 (N) to Howden-le-Wear. R up Bank before petrol stn, 1st Right in village at 30mph sign. Park in the village.* **Adm £2. Visitors welcome by appt Jan to Dec except Tuesdays, for individuals and groups max 20.**

Quirky, original and truly organic garden: 90% grown from seeds and cuttings. Created without commercially bought plants or expense. Environmentally friendly. A haven for wildlife: frogs have colonised a bath! Sloping garden with a myriad of paths and extensive views over the Wear valley. Beautiful yr-round from snowdrops to autumn leaves. Open all yr except Tuesdays. Book by phone or e-mail.

29 MINDRUM

Mindrum, nr Cornhill on Tweed & Yetholm TD12 4QN. Mrs V Fairfax, www.mindrumgarden.co.uk. *6m SW of Coldstream, 9m NW of Wooler. Off B6352, 4m N of Yetholm. 5m from Cornhill on Tweed.* Cream teas. **Adm £4, chd free. Sun 22 June (2-6).**

3 acres of romantic planting with old fashioned roses, lilies, herbs, sweet peas, scented shrubs, and intimate garden areas hedged by yew. Glasshouses with vines, jasmine. Large hillside rock garden with water leading to a pond, delightful stream, woodland and wonderful views across Bowmont valley with further river walks. Plants galore. Large plant sale, mostly home grown. Featured in The English Garden, Country Living and The Northumbrian. Limited wheelchair access due to landscape. Blue badge parking close to house. Wheelchair accessible WC available.

30 NEWBIGGIN HOUSE

Blanchland DH8 9UD. Mrs A Scott-Harden. *12m S of Hexham. From Blanchland village take Stanhope Rd. ½ m along narrow rd follow yellow signs up tarmac drive into car park.* Cream teas. **Adm £4, chd free. Sun 6 July (2-5).**

5-acre landscaped garden at 1000ft, started in 1996 and maturing beautifully. Old-fashioned herbaceous border, peonies, shrubs, roses, bog and wild garden incl wild rose walk. Magnificent collection of unusual trees and shrubs. Limited wheelchair access.

31 NO. 2 FERNDENE

2 Holburn Lane Court, Holburn Lane, Ryton NE40 3PN. Maureen Kesteven, 01914 135937, maureen@patrickkesteven.plus.com. *In Ryton Old Village, 8m W of Gateshead. Off B6317, on Holburn Lane in Old Ryton Village. Park in Co-op carpark on High St, cross rd & walk through Ferndene Park.* Home-made teas. **Adm £4, chd free. Sun 10 Aug (1-4.30). Visitors also welcome by appt Apr to May groups of 10+.**

A garden, approx. ¾ acre, developed over the last 4 years, surrounded by mature trees. Informal areas of herbaceous perennials, more formal Box bordered area, vegetable patch, sedum roof, wildlife pond, bog and fern gardens. Early interest - hellebores, snowdrops, daffodils, bluebells and tulips, as well as later summer flowering perennials. 1½ acre mixed broadleaf wood being restored. Pizzas cooked in wood fired oven.

32 THE OLD VICARAGE,
Hutton Magna, nr Richmond, N Yorkshire DL11 7HJ. Mr & Mrs D M Raw. *8m SE of Barnard Castle. 6m W of Scotch Corner on A66. Turn R, signed Hutton Magna. Continue to, and through, village. Garden 200yds past village on L, on corner of T-junction.* Home-made teas. **Adm £3, chd free. Sun 27 Apr (2-5).**
S-facing garden, elevation 450ft. Plantings, since 1978, now maturing within original design contemporary to 1887 house (not open). Cut and topiary hedging, old orchard, rose and herbaceous borders featuring hellebores in profusion, with tulips and primulas. Large and interesting plant sale.

33 OLIVER FORD GARDEN
Longedge Lane, Rowley, Consett DH8 9HG. Bob & Bev Tridgett, www.gardensanctuaries.co.uk. *5m NW of Lanchester. Signed from A68 in Rowley. From Lanchester take rd towards Sately. Garden will be signed as you pass Woodlea Manor.* Light refreshments. **Adm £3, chd free. Sun 8 June (1-5).**
Spectacular 1½ -acre woodland garden developed and planteed by 2007 BBC gardener of the year. Mini arboretum specialising in bark that includes rare acers, stewartia, betula and prunus. Stream, wildlife pond and bog garden. Semi-shaded Japanese maple and dwarf rhododendron garden. 80 sq metre rock garden. Large insect nectar garden. Orchard and 1½ -acre upland meadow. Annual wild flower area.

34 25 PARK ROAD SOUTH
Chester le Street DH3 3LS. Mrs A Middleton, 0191 388 3225. *4m N of Durham. Located at S end of A167 Chester-le-St bypass rd. Precise directions provided when booking visit.* Tea. **Adm £2.50, chd free. Visitors welcome by appt May to July.**
Plantswoman's garden with all-yr round interest, colour, texture and foliage. Unusual perennials, grasses, shrubs and container planting. Cool courtyard garden using foliage only. Small front gravel garden. Lots of unusual plants for sale! Featured in North East Life.

35 NEW POLEMONIUM PLANTERY
28 Sunnyside Terrace, Trimdon Grange TS29 6HF. Dianne & David Nichol-Brown, 01429 881529. *10m SE of Durham. Signed Trimdon Grange, off A181. S end of Trimdon Grange village behind infants school. Turn L at St Aidan's Church, then R at tel box.* **Adm £2, chd free. Visitors welcome by appt.**
National Collection of polemoniums and related genera among a wide variety of other plants in a very small cottage garden. Pergola leading to secret garden, with scented plants and a selection of unusual containers. Children's treasure hunt. A key feature of a visit to this garden will be the extensive knowledge of the garden owner.

NCH

36 ◆ RABY CASTLE
Staindrop, Darlington DL2 3AH. Lord Barnard, 01833 660202, www.rabycastle.com. *12m NW of Darlington, 1m N of Staindrop. On A688, 8m NE of Barnard Castle.* **For opening times and information, please phone or see garden website.**

45 Blackwell, Blackwell Gardens

C18 walled gardens set within the grounds of Raby Castle. Designers such as Thomas White and James Paine have worked to establish the gardens, which now extend to 5 acres, displaying herbaceous borders, old yew hedges, formal rose gardens and informal heather and conifer gardens. Assistance will be needed for wheelchairs.

37 RAVENSFORD FARM

Hamsterley DL13 3NH. Jonathan & Caroline Peacock. *7m W of Bishop Auckland. From A68 at Witton-le-Wear turn off W to Hamsterley. Go through village & turn L just before tennis courts at far end.* Home-made teas. **Adm £4, chd free. Sun 31 Aug (2-5).**

This popular garden is open again after two years of closure, during which several changes have been made. 30 years ago the garden was non-existent. It is now well-established and the simple guiding principal has been to grow ever-better plants. In this wind-swept frost pocket they all have to be extremely hardy - and they are! Live music in the background. Some gravel, so assistance will be needed for wheelchairs.

GROUP OPENING

38 ROMALDKIRK GARDENS

Teesdale DL12 9DZ. *6m NW of Barnard Castle. On B6277, 2m S of Eggleston.* Home-made teas in The Reading Room, opp the Rose and Crown Hotel. **Combined adm £4, chd free. Sun 22 June (2-5.30).**

A group of 8 gardens of great variety. Most gardens are clustered around the village greens. Some are a short walk/drive to the edge of the village. Romaldkirk is an interesting, old fashioned village with a water pump, stocks and attractive church of St Romald. Some gardens are typical cottage gardens with herbaceous borders, another larger garden incls a pond and grotto, one has lawns, a rockery and interesting shrubs. Another garden which is well established has an attractive design of lawns, pond, herbaceous borders, trees and shrubs. Wheelchair access to some gardens.

ALLOTMENTS

39 ST MARGARET'S ALLOTMENTS

Margery Lane, Durham DH1 4QG, 0191 386 1049, carolereeves21@btinternet.com. *From A1 take A690 to City Centre/ Crook. Straight ahead at T-lights after passing 4 r'abouts.* Home made teas in hall adjacent to allotments. **Combined adm £3, chd free. Sun 6 July (2-5). Visitors also welcome by appt June to Sept.**

5 acres of 82 allotments against the spectacular backdrop of Durham Cathedral. This site has been cultivated since the Middle Ages, and was saved from development 20yrs ago, allowing a number of enthusiastic gardeners to develop plots which display a great variety of fruit, vegetables and flowers. Display about successful campaign to save the allotments from development. Live music on the community plot. Guided Tours. Art in the Allotments.

40 ◆ SEATON DELAVAL HALL

The Avenue, Seaton Sluice, nr Whitley Bay NE26 4QR. National Trust, www.nationaltrust.org.uk/seatondelaval-hall. *2m N of Whitley Bay. N of Newcastle, between Seaton Delaval & Seaton Sluice, A190 linking to A193 coastal rd & A19. 5m from A1. Follow brown signs.* Light refreshments. **For NGS: Sat 31 May (11-4.30). For other opening times and information, please phone or see garden website.**

Formal gardens designed by James Russell in 1950 with topiary parterre, pond and fountain, rose garden and striking sculptures, Greatly improved in recent years, with colourful borders and new bee garden, to complement the magnificent C18 baroque hall, designed by Sir John Vanbrugh, said to be the finest house in North East England. (Normal entry charge applies to area beyond NGS plant stalls). Super Plant Sale.

41 SKARA BRAE

20 Tynedale Gardens, Stocksfield NE43 7EZ. Ann Mates, 01661 843175. *14m W of Newcastle upon Tyne. 9m E of Hexham. A1/A69 then B6309 to Stocksfield. From W, past station & cricket ground. At Quaker meeting house turn into New Ridley Rd. 2nd R is Tynedale Gardens.* Tea. **Adm £3, chd free. Visitors welcome by appt June to Aug, minibuses acceptable.**

A charming, developing cottage-style garden, with established shrubs and herbaceous planting in wide borders, that is continuously being improved, on SW-facing site 150ft x 40ft. Added interest of statuary and water features, including small stream at bottom of the garden, and seating areas to sit and relax. Featured in Tynedale Life.

42 4 STOCKLEY GROVE

Brancepeth DH7 8DU. Mr & Mrs Bainbridge, 07944 523551, fabb63@waitrose.com. *5m W of Durham City. Situated on the A690 between Durham & Crook. From Durham direction turn L at the end of village & from Crook turn 1st R on entering.* Home-made teas. **Adm £4, chd free. Visitors welcome by appt May to Sept.**

A stunning ½ -acre garden with inspirational planting to provide yr-round colour and interest. Landscaped with hidden grassy paths with many unusual trees, shrubs and plants incl wildlife pond, rockery area and water features. Winner of the best large garden category and best in show in the Beautiful Durham Awards.

43 THORNLEY HOUSE

Thornley Gate, Allendale, Northum NE47 9NH. Ms Eileen Finn, 01434 683255, enquiries@thornleyhouse.co.uk, www.thornleyhouse.co.uk. *1m W of Allendale. Take rd down hill from Allendale inn for 1m to 5 road junction. Thornley House is just opp.* Tea. **Adm £4, chd free (share to Brooke Charity for Working Animals). Sun 15 June (2-5). Visitors also welcome by appt.**

1-acre country garden with perennials, wild flowers, shrubs, conifers, stream and pond. Vegetables and fruit, rose avenue and peaceful woodland reached across field. A feline theme is evident throughout this child-friendly garden. Seek and find quiz is available for family fun. Maine Coon cats and ornamental animals enhance this garden. Tombola. Live classical piano music.

44 ◆ WALLINGTON

Cambo NE61 4AR. National Trust, 01670 774389, www.nationaltrust.org.uk/wallington. *12m W of Morpeth 20m NW Newcastle. From N B6343; from S via A696 from Newcastle, 6m W of Belsay, B6342 to Cambo.* **Adm £11, chd £5.50. For NGS: Suns 11 May; 13 July (10-5). For other opening times and information, please phone or see garden website.**

Walled, terraced garden with fine herbaceous and mixed borders; Edwardian conservatory; 100 acres woodland and lakes. House dates from 1688 but altered, interior greatly changed c1740; exceptional rococo plasterwork by Francini brothers. Peat free plant sales. Head Gardener's Question Time 12-4 both days 11 May & 13 July. Wheelchair access limited to top terrace in Walled Garden but elsewhere possible with care and support.

45 ◆ WASHINGTON OLD HALL

The Avenue, Washington Village NE38 7LE. National Trust, 01914 166879, www.nationaltrust.org.uk. *7m SE of Newcastle upon Tyne. From A19 onto A1231 From A1 exit junction 64 onto A195 In both cases stay on road until you pick up brown signs to Washington Old Hall.* Home-made teas Friends tearoom in the garden (run by volunteers). **Adm to garden by donation. Normal price applies to enter Hall. For NGS: Sun 8 June (11.30-4.30). For other opening times and information, please phone or see garden website.**

The picturesque stone manor house and its gardens provide a tranquil oasis in an historic setting. It contains a formal Jacobean garden with box hedging borders around evergreens and perennials, vegetable garden, wild flower nut orchard with bee hives. Places to sit out and enjoy a picnic or afternoon tea. Refreshments supplied by Friends of Washington Old Hall. NGS Bargain Garden Plant Sale 11.30-4.30. Garden lift which wheelchair users full access to the whole area.

> Quirky, with tropical themed planting and Caribbean inspired bar. A fun garden . . .

46 WEST HOUSE

5 Etherley Lane, Bishop Auckland DL14 7QR. Dr & Mrs R McManners. *Park in Bondgate car park, Bishop Auckland. 250 metre walk to house; route clearly signed.* Home-made teas. **Adm £3.50, chd free. Sun 6 Apr (2-5).**

A domestic, semi-rustic town garden surrounding 3 sides of this mid C19 town house (not open). Probably originally laid out in 1856, there is now a more recent terraced garden on the site of the original orchard. To the rear of the house is a small, walled 'Dutch Yard Garden', complete with fountain which may well have been enjoyed by Sir Edward Elgar during his many visits to West House. Featured in Amateur Gardening. Wheelchair access to viewing point.

47 ◆ WHALTON MANOR GARDENS

Whalton NE61 3UT. Mr & Mrs T R P S Norton, norton@whaltonmanor.fsnet.co.uk, www.whaltonmanor.co.uk. *5m W of Morpeth. On the B6524, the house is at E end of the village & will be signed.* Home-made teas. **Adm £4, chd free. For NGS: Sun 13 July (2-5.30). For other opening times and information, please phone or see garden website.**

The historic Whalton Manor, altered by Sir Edwin Lutyens in 1908, is surrounded by 3 acres of magnificent walled gardens, designed by Lutyens with the help of Gertrude Jekyll. The gardens have been developed by the Norton family since the 1920s and incl extensive herbaceous borders, 30yd peony border, rose garden, listed summerhouses, pergolas and walls, festooned with rambling roses and clematis. Open by appt. See website. Partial wheelchair access, some stone steps.

48 NEW WOODLANDS

Peareth Hall Road, Gateshead NE9 7NT. Liz Reid, 7719875750, lizreid52@ntlworld.com. *3½ m N Washington Galleries. 4m S Gateshead town centre. OnB1288 turn opp Guide Post PH (NE9 7RR) onto Peareth Hall Rd. Continue for ½ m passing 2 bus stops on L. Third drive on L past Highbury Ave.* Home-made teas. **Adm £3, chd free. Visitors welcome by appt June to Sept, groups of 10+.**

Mature gardens on a site of approx 0.7acres - quirky, with tropical themed planting and Caribbean inspired bar. A fun garden with lots of deep mid-late summer colour, interesting plants, informal beds and borders, pond area and decks.

49 WOODSIDE HOUSE

Witton Park, Bishop Auckland DL14 0DU. Charles & Jean Crompton, 01388 609973, j.crompton@talktalk.net. *2m N of Bishop Auckland. from Bishop Auckland take A68 to Witton Park. In village DO NOT follow sat nav. Go down track next to St Pauls Church.* Home-made teas. **Adm £4, chd free. Visitors welcome by appt Apr to Sept.**

Stunning 3-acre, mature, undulating garden full of interesting trees, shrubs and plants. Superbly landscaped with island beds, flowing herbaceous borders, an old walled garden, rhododendron beds, fernery, 3 ponds and vegetable garden. Delightful garden full of interesting and unusual features, much to fire the imagination. Winner of Bishop Auckland in bloom. Featured in The Telegraph. Limited wheelchair access.

Loughbrow House

© Susie White

North East County Volunteers

County Organisers

County Durham Jean Morley, The Willows, Lumley Lane, Kirkby Fleetham, Northallerton DL7 0SH, 01609 748066, morley@the-willows.wanadoo.co.uk

Northumberland and Tyne and Wear Maureen Kesteven, No. 2 Ferndene, Holburn Lane Court, Ryton NE40 3PN, 0191 4135937, maureen@patrickkesteven.plus.com

County Treasurers

County Durham Gill Naisby, 44 Whitebridge Drive, Darlington DL1 3TY, 01325 381324, gillnaisby@tiscali.co.uk

Northumberland and Tyne and Wear David Oakley, 01434 618994, david@susie-white.co.uk

Publicity

County Durham Kay Duggan, Braeside, Barningham, Richmond, North Yorkshire DL11 7DW, 01833 621455, kay@kayduggan.fsnet.co.uk

Northumberland and Tyne and Wear Susie White, 07941 077595, susie@susie-white.co.uk

Assistant County Organisers

County Durham Alison Morgan, 12 Dickens Wynd, Durham DH1 3QR, 0191 384 3842, morganalisonm@gmail.com

County Durham Mary Smith, 2 Hillside Cottage, Low Etherley, Bishop Auckland DL14 0EZ, 01388 832727, mary@maryruth.plus.com

County Durham Sue Walker, 49 Elton Parade, Darlington, DL3 8PJ, 01325 481881, walker.sdl@gmail.com

Northumberland and Tyne and Wear Patricia Fleming, Wooperton Hall, Alnwick NE66 4XS 01668 217009

Northumberland and Tyne and Wear Natasha McEwen, natashamcewengd@aol.co.uk, 07917 754155

Northumberland and Tyne and Wear Liz Reid, Woodlands, Peareth Hall Road, Gateshead NE9 7NT, 07719 875750, lizreid52@ntworld.com

NORTHAMPTONSHIRE

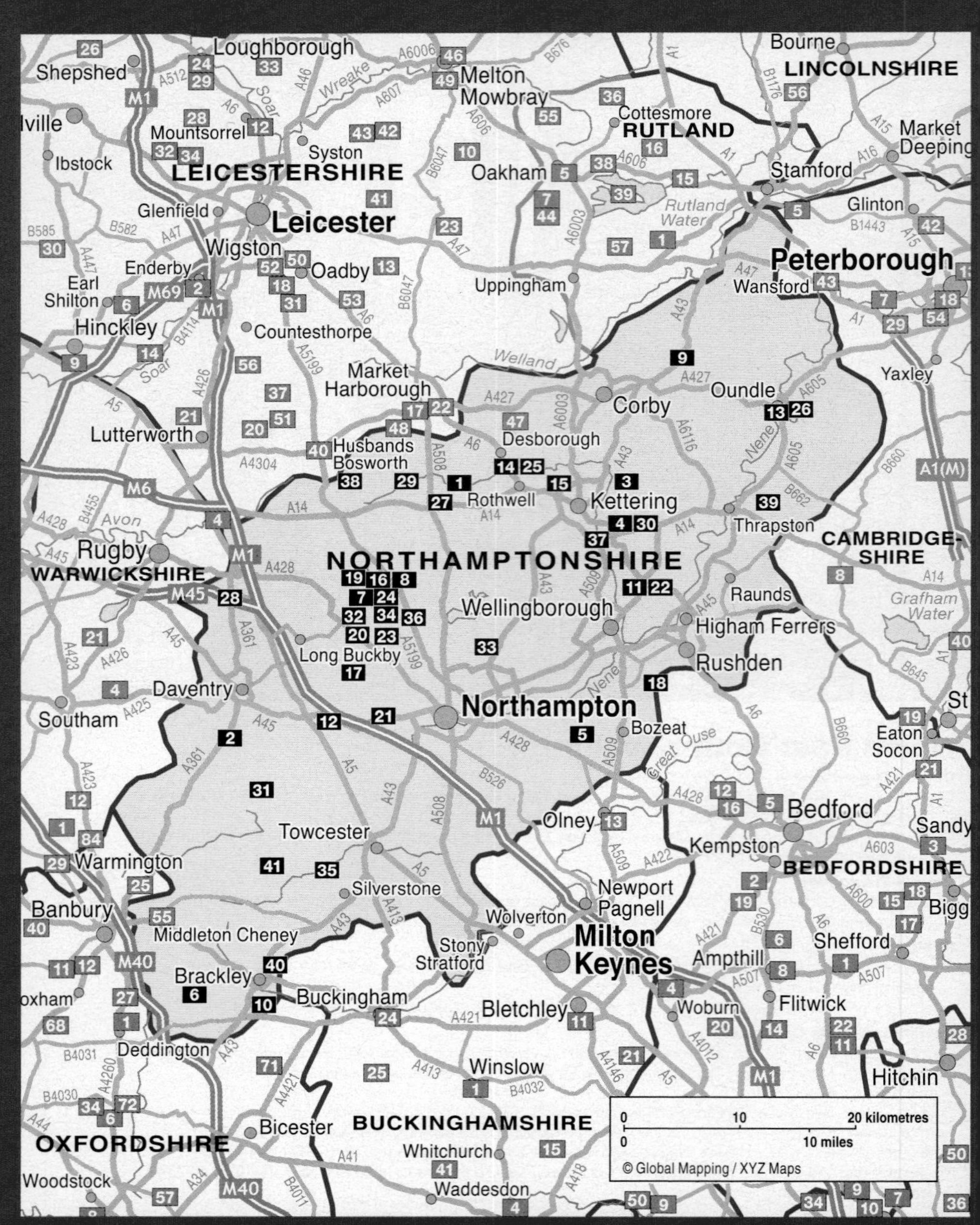

Opening Dates

All entries subject to change.
For latest information check
www.ngs.org.uk

February

Sunday 16
3 Boughton House

Sunday 23
3 Boughton House
26 Jericho

March

Sunday 2
18 Greywalls
34 Rosemount

Sunday 9
22 67-69 High Street

April

Sunday 13
4 Briarwood
8 Cottesbrooke Hall Gardens
12 Flore Gardens

Saturday 19
29 The Maltings

Sunday 20
29 The Maltings

Monday 21
29 The Maltings

Thursday 24
38 Sulby Gardens

Saturday 26
19 Guilsborough Gardens

Sunday 27
19 Guilsborough Gardens

May

Saturday 3
10 Evenley Wood Garden

Sunday 4
10 Evenley Wood Garden
17 Great Brington Gardens

Tuesday 6
7 Coton Manor Garden

Sunday 11
36 Spratton Gardens

Wednesday 14
27 Kelmarsh Hall

Sunday 18
2 Badby and Newnham Gardens
6 Charlton Gardens
9 Deene Park
26 Jericho
39 Titchmarsh House

Saturday 24
29 The Maltings

Sunday 25
29 The Maltings

Monday 26
29 The Maltings

June

Sunday 1
11 Finedon Gardens
31 Preston Capes Gardens

Thursday 5
22 67-69 High Street (Evening)

Festival Weekend

Saturday 7
20 Haddonstone Show Gardens

Sunday 8
13 Foxtail Lilly
20 Haddonstone Show Gardens
21 Harpole Gardens
28 Kilsby Gardens

Thursday 12
22 67-69 High Street (Evening)
25 Hostellarie (Evening)

Saturday 14
39 Titchmarsh House

Sunday 15
30 NEW 34 Poplars Farm Road

Thursday 19
22 67-69 High Street (Evening)
38 Sulby Gardens

Saturday 21
12 Flore Gardens

Sunday 22
12 Flore Gardens
33 Rosearie-de-la-Nymph
35 NEW Slapton Gardens

Thursday 26
22 67-69 High Street (Evening)

Sunday 29
1 Arthingworth Open Gardens
11 Finedon Gardens
33 Rosearie-de-la-Nymph
41 Weedon Lois & Weston Gardens

July

Sunday 6
5 Castle Ashby Gardens
40 Turweston Gardens

Friday 11
25 Hostellarie (Evening)

Sunday 13
32 Ravensthorpe Gardens

Saturday 19
29 The Maltings

Sunday 20
29 The Maltings

Sunday 27
14 Froggery Cottage

August

Sunday 3
37 NEW 67 Stratfield Way

Thursday 7
37 NEW 67 Stratfield Way (Evening)

Sunday 10
24 Hollowell Gardens

Sunday 17
23 Holdenby House Gardens

Thursday 21
38 Sulby Gardens

Saturday 30
20 Haddonstone Show Gardens

Sunday 31
20 Haddonstone Show Gardens

October

Thursday 9
38 Sulby Gardens

Sunday 26
3 Boughton House

November

Thursday 13
38 Sulby Gardens

3-acre organic garden around a picturesque C17 thatched cottage . . .

February 2015

Sunday 22
26 Jericho

Gardens open to the public

3 Boughton House
5 Castle Ashby Gardens
7 Coton Manor Garden
8 Cottesbrooke Hall Gardens
9 Deene Park
10 Evenley Wood Garden
20 Haddonstone Show Gardens
23 Holdenby House Gardens
27 Kelmarsh Hall

By appointment only

- 15 Glendon Hall
- 16 Gower House

Also open by appointment

- 1 Bosworth House, Arthingworth Open Gardens
- 4 Briarwood
- 12 The Old Bakery, Flore Gardens
- 13 Foxtail Lilly
- 18 Greywalls
- 19 Dripwell House, Guilsborough Gardens
- 21 The Close, Harpole Gardens
- 21 19 Manor Close, Harpole Gardens
- 22 67-69 High Street
- 24 Ivy Cottage, Hollowell Gardens
- 26 Jericho
- 28 Pytchley House, Kilsby Gardens
- 29 The Maltings
- 30 34 Poplars Farm Road
- 32 Mill House, Ravensthorpe Gardens
- 32 Ravensthorpe Nursery, Ravensthorpe Gardens
- 34 Rosemount
- 39 Titchmarsh House

The Gardens

GROUP OPENING

1 ARTHINGWORTH OPEN GARDENS

Arthingworth, nr Market Harborough LE16 8LA. *6m S of Market Harborough. From Market Harborough via A508 after 4m take L to Arthingworth. From Northampton, A508 turn R just after Kelmarsh.* Home-made teas at Bosworth House & village hall. **Combined adm £5, chd free. Sun 29 June (2-6).**

BOSWORTH HOUSE
Mr & Mrs C E Irving-Swift.
From the phone box, when in Oxendon Rd, take the little lane with no name, second to the R
Visitors also welcome by appt Feb to July for groups 10+. 01858 525202

CHURCH FARM
Mr & Mrs Charles Blake

NEW **5 CHURCH FARM WAY**
Mr & Mrs Leigh & Carol Brewin

NEW **CHURCH VIEW**
Oxendon Rd. Mr Greg Ellis

NEW **THE HAWTHORNS**
Kelmarsh Rd. A Knott.
Entry through Bulls Head PH car park

10 OXENDON ROAD
Mr & Mrs J Audley

SCHOOL HOUSE
Mr & Mrs R Tinkler

1 SUNNYBANK
Miss Jane Perry

Arthingworth welcomes you with 8 gardens to visit, from 'the good life' to 'to the manor born' or nearly. Come and enjoy the diversity, we aim to give visitors an afternoon of 'discovery'. Our gardens have been chosen because they are all different in spirit, and tended by young and weathered gardeners. We have gardens with; stunning views, traditional with herbaceous borders and vegetables, walled, artisan, and even a secret one. The village is looking forward to welcoming you. Wheelchair access not available at all gardens.

GROUP OPENING

2 BADBY AND NEWNHAM GARDENS

Daventry NN11 3AR. *3m S of Daventry. E-side of A361. Maps provided for visitors.* Home-made teas at Badby and Newnham Churches. **Combined adm £4, chd free. Sun 18 May (2-6).**

HILLTOP
Newnham. David & Mercy Messenger

THE LILACS
Badby. Matthew & Ruth Moser

SHAKESPEARES COTTAGE
Badby. Sarah & Jocelyn Hartland-Swann

SOUTHVIEW COTTAGE
Badby. Alan & Karen Brown

TRIFIDIA
Badby. Colin & Shirley Cripps

5 gardens within 2 beautiful villages with attractive old houses of golden-coloured Horton stone set around their village greens. In Badby there are 4 gardens of differing styles. A wisteria-clad thatched cottage with modern sculptures, a terraced garden with vegetables, an orchard and a newly developed garden with views over the village. The 4th garden with pond, conservatory, glasshouses and vegetables has unusual plants that aims for yr-round interest. In Newnham, there is a 3-acre organic garden around a picturesque C17 thatched cottage with large cottage garden style borders and pruned shrubs and hedges. Spring bulbs and planted pots and tubs give continuity. A garden to wander through. NB both villages are hilly.

3 ◆ BOUGHTON HOUSE

Geddington, Kettering NN14 1BJ. Duke of Buccleuch & Queensberry, KBE, 01536 515731, www.boughtonhouse.org.uk. *3m NE of Kettering. From A14, 2m along A43 Kettering to Stamford, turn R in to Geddington, house entrance 1½ m on R.* Light refreshments in the C18 Stableblock. **Adm £5, chd £2. For NGS: Sun 16, Sun 23 Feb, Sun 26 Oct (11-3). For other opening times and information, please phone or see garden website.**

The Northamptonshire home of the Duke and Duchess of Buccleuch. The garden opening incl opportunities to see the historic walled kitchen garden and herbaceous border incl the newly created sensory and wildlife gardens. The wilderness woodland will open for visitors to view the spring flowers or the autumn colours. As a special treat the garden originally created by Sir David Scott (cousin of the Duke of Buccleuch) will also be open.

4 BRIARWOOD
4 Poplars Farm Road, Barton Seagrave, Kettering NN15 5AF. Elaine Christian & William Portch, 01536 522169, www.elainechristian-gardendesign.co.uk. *1½ m SE of Kettering Town Centre. J10 off A14 turn onto Barton Rd (A6) towards Wicksteed Park. R into Warkton Lane, after 200 metres R into Poplars Farm Rd.* Home-made teas. **Adm £3, chd free. Sun 13 Apr (10.30-4). Visitors also welcome by appt.**
A garden in 2 parts with quirky original sculptures and many faces. Firstly a S-facing lawn and colourful borders with spring bulbs, blossom trees, summer colour, hedging, palms, climbers, lily pond, and sunny terrace. Secondly, a secret garden with summerhouse, small orchard, raised bed potager and water feature. Crafts for sale and children's quiz.

5 ◆ CASTLE ASHBY GARDENS
Northampton NN7 1LQ. Earl Compton, 01604 695200, www.castleashbygardens.co.uk. *6m E of Northampton. 1½ m N of A428, turn off between Denton & Yardley Hastings. Follow brown tourist signs.* **Adm £5, chd £4.50 (under 10 free). For NGS: Sun 6 July (10-5.30). For other opening times and information, please phone or see garden website.**
25-acres within a 10,000-acre estate of both formal and informal gardens, incl Italian gardens with orangery and arboretum with lakes, all dating back to the 1860s. Rare breed farmyard, tea-rooms and gift shop. Gravel paths within estate.

GROUP OPENING

6 CHARLTON GARDENS
Banbury OX17 3DR. *7m SE of Banbury, 5m W of Brackley. From B4100 turn off N at Aynho, or from A422 turn off S at Farthinghoe. Parking at village hall.* Tea at Walnut House. **Combined adm £5, chd free. Sun 18 May (2-5.30).**

8 CARTWRIGHT ROAD
Miss Valerie Trinder

CHARLTON LODGE
Mr & Mrs Andrew Woods

Rose Cottage, Great Brington Gardens

THE CROFT
Mr & Mrs R D Whitrow

HOME FARM HOUSE
Mrs N Grove-White

WALNUT HOUSE
Sir Paul & Lady Hayter

Pretty stone village with a selection of gardens large and small, incl a cottage garden with colourful planting, interesting corners and lovely views; a walled garden with roses and clematis; a large garden behind C17 farmhouse with colour-themed borders, separate small gardens and a hot gravel garden created in 2011; a large terraced garden with a 140ft-long herbaceous border and raised-bed vegetable patch, overlooking a lake; and a mainly dry gravel garden with good perennials, grasses and bamboos.

7 ◆ COTON MANOR GARDEN
Nr Guilsborough, Northampton NN6 8RQ. Mr & Mrs Ian Pasley-Tyler, 01604 740219, www.cotonmanor.co.uk. *10m N of Northampton, 11m SE of Rugby. From A428 & A5199 follow tourist signs.* Light refreshments at at Stableyard Cafe. **Adm £7, chd £2.50. For NGS: Tue 6 May (12-5.30). For other opening times and information, please phone or see garden website.**
10-acre garden set in peaceful countryside with old yew and holly hedges and extensive herbaceous borders containing many unusual plants. Other areas incl rose, water, herb and woodland gardens, our famous bluebell wood, and wild flower meadow. Adjacent specialist nursery with over 1000 plant varieties propagated from the garden. Some narrow paths inaccessible and the site is on a slope, so not all areas are accessbile to wheelchair users.

8 ◆ COTTESBROOKE HALL GARDENS
Cottesbrooke NN6 8PF. Mr & Mrs A R Macdonald-Buchanan, 01604 505808, www.cottesbrooke.co.uk. *10m N of Northampton. Signed from J1 on A14. Off A5199 at Creaton, A508 at Brixworth.* Home-made teas. **Adm £5.50, chd £3. For NGS: Sun 13 Apr (2-5.30). For other opening times and information, please phone or see garden website.**
Award winning gardens by Geoffrey Jellicoe, Dame Sylvia Crowe, James Alexander Sinclair and more recently Arne Maynard. Formal gardens and terraces surround Queen Anne house with extensive vistas onto the lake and C18 parkland containing many mature trees. Wild and woodland gardens, which are exceptional in spring, a short distance from the formal areas. Most of garden accessible. Paths are grass, stone and gravel. Access map identifies best route.

9 ◆ DEENE PARK

Nr Corby, Deene NN17 3EW. Mr Edmund Brudenell, 01780 450278, www.deenepark.com. *6m N of Corby. Off A43 between Stamford & Corby.* Light refreshments in the 'Old Kitchen' tea room. **Adm £6, chd £3. For NGS: Sun 18 May (2-5). For other opening times and information, please phone or see garden website.**

Interesting garden set in beautiful parkland. Large parterre with topiary designed by David Hicks echoing the C16 decoration on the porch stonework, long mixed borders, old-fashioned roses, Tudor courtyard and white garden. Lake and waterside walks with rare mature trees in natural garden. Wheelchair access available to main features of garden.

10 ◆ EVENLEY WOOD GARDEN

Evenley, Brackley NN13 5SH. Timothy Whiteley, 07776 307849, www.evenleywoodgarden.co.uk. *3/4 m S of Brackley. Turn off at Evenley r'about on A43 & continue through village towards Mixbury before taking 1st turn L.* **Adm £5, chd £1. For NGS: Sat 3, Sun 4 May (11-5). For other opening times and information, please phone or see garden website.**

This 60-acre woodland is a plantsman's garden with a huge variety of plants all of which are labelled. Mainly trees, shrubs, bulbs and lilies. Many magnolias, azaleas, rhododendrons and camellias. All paths are grass.

GROUP OPENING

11 FINEDON GARDENS

Finedon NN9 5JN. *2m NE of Wellingborough. 6m SE Kettering. All gardens individually signed from A6/A510 junction.* Cream teas at 67-69 High Street. **Combined adm £3.50, chd free. Sun 1, Sun 29 June (2-6).**

NEW CHURCH HOUSE
Chris & Polly Smith

29 EASTFIELD CRESCENT
Terry & Linda Goodman

67-69 HIGH STREET
Mary & Stuart Hendry

11 THRAPSTON ROAD
John & Gillian Ellson

All 4 gardens are very different with everything from vegetables to flowers on show. 67-69 High Street is an ever evolving 1/3 -acre garden of a C17 cottage (not open) with mixed borders, many obelisks and containers. Planting for varied interest spring to autumn. 29 Eastfield Crescent is a garden in 4 sections which incl lawn with mixed borders and pond leading to paved area with containers, water feature and arbour seat. Fruit and vegetable garden with 2 greenhouses. Shady end section with borders and summer house. Front garden with varied hanging baskets and containers.
11 Thrapston Road is a 1/5 -acre cottage garden with lawns and mixed borders, gravel and paved seating areas with planters and water features. Pergola, rose arches, summer house and tree house. Mixed vegetable plot, and soft fruit and apple trees. Church House is a 1-acre mature garden with trees, shrubs and lawns. Currently undergoing renovation. Large selection of home-raised plants for sale at some locations - all proceeds to the NGS. Generally good access for wheelchairs but with some gravel paths and grassed areas.

A secret walled garden crammed with fruit, flowers and vegetables . . .

GROUP OPENING

12 FLORE GARDENS

Flore NN7 4LQ. *7m W of Northampton. 2m W of J16 M1. 5m E of Daventry on A45. Garden map provided at official free car park, signed from A45. Coaches welcome, please phone 01327 341225 for parking advice. Tickets giving admission to all gardens can be purchased in any of the open gardens.* Home-made teas in the chapel school room (Apr), chapel school room and church, with lunches in chapel tea-room (June). **Combined adm £5, chd free (June only, share to All Saints Church and United Reform Church). Sun 13 Apr (2-6); Sat 21, Sun 22 June (11-6).**

NEW ADAMS COTTAGE
8-10 Kings Lane. Susie Morris.
Open June dates only

BLISS LANE NURSERY
34 Bliss Lane. Geof & Chris Littlewood

24 BLISS LANE
John & Sally Miller

THE CROFT
John & Dorothy Boast

THE GARDEN HOUSE
Edward & Penny Aubrey-Fletcher.
Open June dates only. A shared entrance drive with the Charterhouse Retreat

3 MEADOW FARM CLOSE
Eric & Jackie Ingram.
Open April date only

4 MEADOW FARM CLOSE
Bob & Lynne Richards.
Open April date only. Located off Bliss Lane

THE OLD BAKERY
John Amos & Karl Jones.
From the A45 turn R immed on corner of White Hart PH. The Old Bakery is 300m on the RH-side of Sutton St
Visitors also welcome by appt Apr to Aug for groups of 20-50. 01327 349080 yeolbakery@aol.com www.johnnieamos.co.uk

NEW ROCK SPRINGS
Sutton Street. Tom Higginson & David Foster

RUSSELL HOUSE
Peter Pickering & Stephen George

Flore gardens have been open for many yrs as part of the Flore Flower Festival and the partnership with the NGS started in 1992. Flore is an attractive village with views over the upper Nene valley. There is a C12 church and Victorian chapel which are also open in June with floral displays. We have a varied mix of gardens, developed by friendly and enthusiastic owners including 2 new gardens for 2014. Our gardens provide interest throughout the year. There is a varied selection of garden structures, incl greenhouses, gazebos and summerhouses with seating providing opportunities to rest while enjoying the gardens. In spring there are early flowering perennials, interesting trees, shrubs, and bulbs in pots and border drifts. There is planting for all situations from shade to full sun. The June gardens incl formal and informal designs with lots of roses, clematis and many varieties of trees, shrubs, perennials, herbs, fruit and vegetables. June gardens open in association with Flore Flower Festival. Wheelchair access possible in most gardens, some assistance may be required.

---

13 FOXTAIL LILLY

41 South Road, Oundle PE8 4BP. Tracey Mathieson, 01832 274593, www.foxtail-lilly.co.uk. *1m town centre. From A605 at Barnwell Xrds take Barnwell Rd, 1st R to South Rd.* Home-made teas. **Adm £3.50, chd free. Sun 8 June (11-5.30). Visitors also welcome by appt May to July.**
A cottage garden where perennials and grasses are grouped creatively together amongst gravel paths, complementing one another to create a natural look. Some unusual plants and quirky oddities create a different and colourful informal garden. Lots of flowers for cutting, shop in barn. New meadow pasture turned into new cutting garden.

14 FROGGERY COTTAGE

85 Breakleys Road, Desborough NN14 2PT. Mr John Lee. *6m N of Kettering. 5m S of Market Harborough. Signed off A6 & A14.*
Adm £2.50, chd free. Sun 27 July (11.30-5).
1-acre plantsman's garden full of rare and unusual plants. NCCPG Collection of 435 varieties of penstemons incl dwarfs and species. Artefacts on display incl old ploughs and garden implements. Workshops throughout the day.

15 GLENDON HALL

Kettering NN14 1QE. Rosie Bose, 01536 711732, rosiebose@googlemail.com. *1½ m E of Rothwell. A6003 to Corby (J7 on A14) W of Kettering, turn L onto Glendon Rd signed Rothwell, Desborough, Rushton. Entrance 1½ m on L past turn for Rushton.* **Adm £3, chd free. Visitors welcome by appt Apr to Sept for groups of 25 max.**
Mature specimen trees, topiary, box hedges, herbaceous borders stocked with many unusual plants, large walled kitchen gardens with restored glass house. Some gravel & slopes, but possible to get round via longer route.

16 GOWER HOUSE

Guilsborough, Northampton NN6 8PY. Ann Moss, 01604 740755, cattimoss@aol.com. *Off High St by Ward Arms PH, through PH car park.* **Adm £5, chd free. Visitors welcome by appt Apr to July for combined visit with Dripwell House.**
Although Gower House garden is small it is closely planted with specimen trees, shrubs, perennials, orchids, thyme lawn, wild flowers and alpines, some rare or unusual, with foliage colour being important. Several seating areas designed for elderly relatives incorporating recycled materials. Soft fruit and vegetable garden, shared with Dripwell, is an important part of our gardening. Very steep site unsuitable for those with mobility difficulties.

GROUP OPENING

17 GREAT BRINGTON GARDENS

nr Northampton NN7 4JJ. *7m NW of Northampton. Off A428 Rugby Rd. From Northampton, 1st L turn past main gates of Althorp. Free parking. Programmes & maps available at car park.* Teas at parish church, morning coffee & lunches in the reading room. **Combined adm £4.50, chd free. Sun 4 May (11-5).**

7 BEDFORD COTTAGES
Whilton Road. Mrs Felicity Bellamy

FOLLY HOUSE
Sarah & Joe Sacarello

66 MAIN STREET
Mr & Mrs A Clayton

THE OLD RECTORY
Mr & Mrs R Thomas

ROSE COTTAGE
David Green & Elaine MacKenzie

THE STABLES
Mrs A George

NEW **SUNDERLAND HOUSE**
Mrs Margaret Rubython.
We are next door to The Stables in Hamilton Lane

Great Brington, recently named 'Best Small Village in Northamptonshire - 2013/2014', is renowned for its warm welcome with dozens of parish volunteers helping on the day; manning the free car park and plant stall, serving lunches and teas, stewarding and providing information about the village and its gardens. A particularly picturesque, predominately stone and thatch village, Great Brington is well worth a visit in its own right. The C12 church, rated as one of Simon Jenkins' 1000 Best, has connections with the Spencers of Althorp and George Washington. Our open gardens provide immense variety from a small cottage garden with a summerhouse to a 3-acre formal garden complete with an extensive vegetable patch and orchard. Many of the gardens continue to evolve each year, several have unique water features, and most are planned and maintained by their owners. Local history exhibition. Local press and radio/television coverage.

---

18 GREYWALLS

Farndish NN29 7HJ. Mrs P M Anderson, 01933 353495, patricia@greywalls.tradaweb.net. *2½ m SE of Wellingborough. A609 from Wellingborough, B570 to Irchester, turn to Farndish by cenotaph. House adjacent to church.* Light refreshments. **Adm £3, chd free. Sun 2 Mar (12-4). Visitors also welcome by appt, coaches welcome.**
2-acre mature garden surrounding old vicarage (not open). Over 100 varieties of snowdrops, drifts of hardy cyclamen and hellebores. Alpine house and raised alpine beds. Water features and natural ponds with views over open countryside. Rare breed hens.

Walnut House, Charlton Gardens

20 ◆ HADDONSTONE SHOW GARDENS

The Forge House, Church Lane, East Haddon, Northampton NN6 8DB. Haddonstone Ltd, 01604 770711, www.haddonstone.com. *7m NW of Northampton. Brown tourism signs from A428. Located in centre of village near church, opp school.* **Adm £2.50, chd free. For NGS: Sat 7, Sun 8 June, Sat 30, Sun 31 Aug (11-5). For other opening times and information, please phone or see garden website.**

See Haddonstone's classic garden ornaments in the beautiful setting of the walled Manor gardens including planters, fountains, statues, bird baths, sundials, balustrades and follies. Garden is on different levels with roses, clematis, climbers, herbaceous borders, ornamental flowers, topiary, specimen shrubs and trees. New wild flower meadow, contemporary garden and statue walk. Featured in The Daily Telegraph. Wheelchair access to all areas of main garden.

GROUP OPENING

19 GUILSBOROUGH GARDENS

Guilsborough NN6 8PT. *10m NW of Northampton. 10m E of Rugby. Between A5199 & A428. J1 off A14. Car parking in field on Hollowell Rd out of Guilsborough. Information point on The Green (maps provided).* Home-made teas in the village hall. **Combined adm £5, chd free. Sat 26, Sun 27 Apr (2-6).**

DRIPWELL HOUSE
Mr J W Langfield & Dr C Moss
Visitors also welcome by appt Apr to July for combined visit with Gower House.
01604 740140
cattimoss@aol.com

FOUR ACRES
Mark & Gay Webster

THE GATE HOUSE
Mike & Sarah Edwards

GUILSBOROUGH HOUSE
Mr & Mrs John McCall

NORTOFT GRANGE
Lady Lowther

OAK DENE
Mr & Mrs R A Darker

THE OLD HOUSE
Richard & Libby Seaton Evans

THE OLD VICARAGE
John & Christine Benbow

Eight varied village gardens in an attractive rural setting. Two small cottage-style gardens, one belonging to a keen flower arranger, the other a secret walled garden crammed with fruit, flowers and vegetables. The remaining gardens are larger, ranging from a magical woodland garden on a very steep site to formal gardens with sweeping lawns, mature trees and beautiful views. There is plenty of room to sit and relax. Walled kitchen gardens and a potager are an important part of our gardening. Plants for sale will incl both the rare and unusual from our plantsmen's gardens, a true highlight here. Dripwell House, open for the NGS since 1986, was originally an individual garden as was Nortoft Grange. There is thus a lot to see and visitors find that they need the whole afternoon. Wheelchair access at Four Acres, Guilsborough House, Oak Dene, The Old House & The Old Vicarage only. Dogs not permitted at all gardens.

GROUP OPENING

21 HARPOLE GARDENS

Harpole NN7 4BX. *4m W Northampton. On A45 towards Weedon. Turn R at The Turnpike Hotel into Harpole. Village maps given to all visitors.* Home-made teas at The Close. **Combined adm £4.50, chd free. Sun 8 June (1-6).**

BRYTTEN-COLLIER HOUSE
James & Lucy Strickland

THE CLOSE
Michael Orton-Jones.
Approx 400-yds from A4500 and Beefeater Premier Inn, High St. There is a long high stone wall with big trees behind
Visitors also welcome by appt.
01604 830332
michael@orton-jones.com

19 MANOR CLOSE
Caroline & Andy Kemshed
Visitors also welcome by appt in June.
01604 830512
carolinekemshed@live.co.uk

NEW **THE MANOR HOUSE**
Mrs Katy Smith

MILLERS
Mrs M Still

THE OLD DAIRY
David & Di Ballard

Attractive Northamptonshire village well known for its annual scarecrow festival (2nd weekend Sept). Enjoy a lovely farmhouse garden with an acre of lawn, mixed borders, mature trees, views overlooking the farm and strawberry field. Visit a partly walled S-facing garden with wonderful herbaceous borders, many climbing roses and clematis and a beautiful tree house. See a sheltered cottage garden with clematis, roses and luxuriant planting. View a smaller garden (40 x 10yd) belonging to a more recently constructed house. This is a flower arranger's garden of interesting design with water features and mixed borders. Come and see a former walled vegtable garden enhanced into a family garden in the last 6-yrs. Take tea in an old fashioned country garden with large lawn, herbaceous borders and mature trees. An interesting and varied afternoon is guaranteed with a warm welcome to all. Wheelchair access at Brytten-Collier House, The Close and The Old Dairy only.

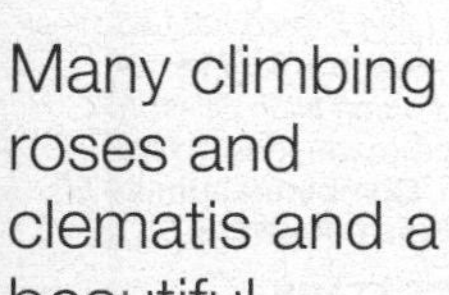
Many climbing roses and clematis and a beautiful tree house . . .

22 67-69 HIGH STREET

Finedon NN9 5JN. Mary & Stuart Hendry, 01933 680414, sh_archt@hotmail.com. *6m SE Kettering. Garden signed from A6/A510 junction.* **Adm £3.50, chd free; incl soup and a roll (March), wine and nibbles (June). Sun 9 Mar (11-3); Evening Openings on Thurs 5, 12, 19, 26 June (5-8.30). Visitors also welcome by appt Feb to Sept for evening visits with wine and nibbles.**

Constantly evolving, 1/3 -acre rear garden of C17 cottage (not open). Mixed borders, many obelisks and containers, kitchen garden and herb bed, and rope border. Spring garden with snowdrops, bluebells and hellebores, summer and autumn borders all giving varied interest from Feb through to Oct. Plant surgery by local expert (June openings only), bring along your plants or questions. Home raised plants for sale. Most areas accessible via hard paved paths, with some gravel paths and grass.

23 ◆ HOLDENBY HOUSE GARDENS

Northampton NN6 8DJ. Mr & Mrs James Lowther, 01604 770074, www.holdenby.com. *6m NW of Northampton. From A5199 or A428 between East Haddon & Spratton. Follow brown tourist signs.* Cream teas served in the tea-room. **Adm £5, chd £3.50. For NGS: Sun 17 Aug (1-5). For other opening times and information, please phone or see garden website.**

The 20-acre, Grade I listed garden set in stately lawns and hedges, has several special features. Away from the formal gardens lie the terraces of the Elizabethan rose garden - one of the best preserved examples of their kind. There is also a delightful walled kitchen garden with the original Victorian greenhouse. The estate incl gravel paths.

GROUP OPENING

24 HOLLOWELL GARDENS

Hollowell NN6 8RR. *8m N of Northampton. 1/2 m off A5199, turn off at Creaton. Roads are narrow and twisting, so please use car park, which is clearly signed.* Light refreshments at village hall.
Combined adm £4, chd free. Sun 10 Aug (11-5).

HILLVIEW
Jan & Crawford Craig

IVY COTTAGE
Rev John & Mrs Wendy Evans
Visitors also welcome by appt May to Sept, tea or coffee arranged by request in advance.
revjohnwenevans@yahoo.co.uk

ROSEMOUNT
Mr & Mrs J Leatherland
(See separate entry)

Three contrasting gardens with plenty of interest. Rosemount is a plantsman's garden, developed over 50yrs. The owners propagate their favourite plants, many of which are for sale. Ivy Cottage is a haven for wildlife with relaxed planting, a stream, orchard and vegetable area. Hillview is a traditional country garden on three levels, dating from the 1930s, with colourful, informal planting. No wheelchair access at Hillview, limited access at remaining two gardens. Steep hills.

25 HOSTELLARIE

78 Breakleys Road, Desborough NN14 2PT. Stella & Stan Freeman. *6m N of Kettering. 5m S of Market Harborough. From church and war memorial turn R into Dunkirk Avenue, then 3rd R. From cemetery L into Dunkirk Avenue then 4th L.* **Evening Openings £4, chd free, incl wine on Thur 12 June, Fri 11 July (5.30-8.30).**

Down a quiet town road you will find our over 180ft long town garden. Divided into rooms of different character, courtyard garden with a sculptural clematis providing shade, colour themed flower beds, ponds and water features, cottage gardens and gravel borders, all linked by lawns and grass paths. Collection of over 40 hostas.

26 JERICHO

42 Market Place, Oundle PE8 4AJ. Stephen & Pepita Aris, 01832 275416, stephenaris@btinternet.com. *East Jericho. From Oundle Market Place, find Hambleton Bakery, go through red door & down yard to garden.* Light refreshments. **Adm £3, chd free. Sun 23 Feb, Sun 18 May (12-4); Sun 22 Feb 2015 (12-5). Visitors and groups also welcome by appt Feb to July (best between mid-May and late July).**

Inspired by Vita Sackville-West 50-yrs-ago, the 100m, S-facing, walled garden is divided into a series of 'secret' spaces. House (not open) is clothed in wisteria, clematis and roses. A plant-led garden with massive hornbeam hedge, clipped box and lavender. Over 50 labelled species roses, plus a 'hot' border. Snowdrops, crocus and hellebore in early spring. Full-page feature in Peterborough Evening Telegraph.

27 ◆ KELMARSH HALL
Main Road, Kelmarsh, Northampton NN6 9LY. The Kelmarsh Trust, 01604 686543, www.kelmarsh.com. *Northamptonshire. From A14, exit at J2 & head N towards Market Harborough. Kelmarsh is at Xrds. From A508 the hall is 5m S of Market Harborough and 11m N of Northampton.* Light refreshments in the tea-room. **Adm £5.50, chd £3.50. For NGS: Wed 14 May (11-5). For other opening times and information, please phone or see garden website.**
Kelmarsh Hall is an C18 country house, set in gardens inspired by society decorator Nancy Lancaster and surrounded by woodland and an estate of rolling Northamptonshire countryside. Hidden gems in the gardens incl a double border, sunken garden, a 30m long border, rose garden and at the heart of it all, a historic walled kitchen garden. Highlights incl snake's head fritillaries, tulips, alliums, peonies, roses, cottage garden perennials and sweet peas. Visit late summer for dahlias and the long border. Disabled parking is available close to the Visitor Centre entrance. Blue badges must be displayed. Please advise staff on arrival.

GROUP OPENING

28 KILSBY GARDENS
Kilsby Village CV23 8XP. *5m SE of Rugby. 6m N of Daventry on A361. The road through village is the B4038.* Home-made teas at Kilsby Village Hall. **Combined adm £4, chd free. Sun 8 June (1-5).**

NEW GRAFTON HOUSE
4 Rugby Road. Mr & Mrs Andy & Sally Tomkins

NEW 3 MIDDLE STREET
Mr & Mrs Don & Linda Attwell.
Once in the village, Middle St is the 2nd turning along Rugby Rd

PYTCHLEY HOUSE
Mr & Mrs T F Clay
Visitors also welcome by appt May to July for groups of 10-20 with 4 wks notice please. 01788 822373 the.clays@tiscali.co.uk

RAINBOW'S END
7 Middle Street. Mr & Mrs J Madigan

Kilsby is a stone and brick village with historic interest, home of St Faith's Church dating from the C12. The village was the site of one of the first skirmishes of the Civil War in 1642 and also gave its name to Stephenson's nearby lengthy rail tunnel built in the 1830s. This year 4 attractive gardens will be open, all within easy walking distance within the village. Do please come and see us. Wheelchair access at Grafton House via ramp.

A profusion of anthemis, helenium, hostas, agapanthus and silver birch. . . .

29 THE MALTINGS
10 The Green, Clipston, Market Harborough LE16 9RS. Mrs Hamish Connell & Mr William Connell, 01858 525336, j.connell118@btinternet.com. *4m S of Market Harborough, 9m W of Kettering, 10m N Northampton. From A14 take J2, A508 N. After 2m turn L for Clipston.* Cream teas. **Adm £3, chd free. Sat 19 Apr (2-6); Sun 20, Mon 21 Apr (11-6); Sat 24 May (2-6); Sun 25, Mon 26 May (11-6); Sat 19 July (2-6); Sun 20 July (11-6). Visitors also welcome by appt for groups of 10+. Light refreshments available.**
3/4-acre sloping plantsman's garden designed for yr-round interest by the present owner. Many unusual plants, shrubs, old and new trees. Over 60 different clematis, wild garden walk, spring bulb area, over 30 different species roses, 2 ponds connected by a stream, and bog garden. Fruit, vegetables and greenhouse. Home made cake stall. Swing and slide for children. Partial wheelchair access. Gravelled drive, some narrow paths, and some steps.

30 NEW 34 POPLARS FARM ROAD
Barton Seagrave, Kettering NN15 5AG. Rev. Dr & Mrs J Smith, 01536 513786. *1½ m SE of Kettering. J10 off A14 onto Barton Rd (A6) towards Wicksteed Park & Kettering. Turn R onto Warkton Lane, then R into Poplars Farm Rd.* **Adm £3, chd free. Sun 15 June (2-5). Visitors also welcome by appt May to July.**
A 1-acre garden divided by archways, numerous mixed borders and beds created from a large lawn 15-yrs-ago. A parterre planted with shrubs, herbs, hostas and perennials leads to an arch of roses and apple trees. There is a profusion of anthemis, helenium, hostas, agapanthus and silver birch. A long hazel arch leads to a small meadow planted with specimen trees overlooking open countryside. The garden contains some gravel pathways.

GROUP OPENING

31 PRESTON CAPES GARDENS
Little Preston, Daventry NN11 3TF. *6m SW of Daventry. 13m NE of Banbury. 3m N of Canons Ashby. Parking for Little Preston at Old West Farm - follow signs. For Preston Capes parking off High St - follow signs.* Home-made teas at Old West Farm. **Combined adm £4.50, chd free. Sun 1 June (12-5).**

CITY COTTAGE
Mrs Gavin Cowen.
Off High St, Church Way. Garden behind letter box

LADYCROFT
Mervyn & Sophia Maddison

NORTH FARM
Mr & Mrs Tim Coleridge.
¾ m E of Preston Capes

THE OLD RECTORY
Luke & Victoria Bridgeman

OLD WEST FARM
Mr & Mrs Gerard Hoare.
¾ m E of Preston Capes on road to Maidford

VILLAGE FARM
High St. Trevor & Julia Clarke

A varied selection of gardens in a beautiful unspoilt south Northamptonshire ironstone village mostly with wonderful views. Gardens range from contemporary through to classical country style to large extensive with woodland walk and ponds. Features incl local sandstone houses and cottages, Norman Church and wonderful views. Limited wheelchair access in some parts of the gardens.

GROUP OPENING

32 RAVENSTHORPE GARDENS

Ravensthorpe NN6 8ES. *7m NW of Northampton. Signed from A428. Mill House immed on R as you turn off A428 down Long Lane. 1m from village.* Home-made teas at village hall. **Combined adm £5, chd free. Sun 13 July (1.30-5.30).**

NEW 72 GUILSBOROUGH ROAD
Mr & Mrs Liz & John Peachey

MILL HOUSE
Ken & Gill Pawson
Visitors also welcome by appt. 01604 770103 gill@gpplanning.co.uk

RAVENSTHORPE NURSERY
Mr & Mrs Richard Wiseman
Visitors also welcome by appt, tea or coffee and biscuits for groups by prior arrangement. 01604 770548 ravensthorpenursery@hotmail.com

NEW 2 THE ORCHARDS
Chris & Tricia Freeman.
A small close off Guilsbrough Rd

Attractive village in Northamptonshire uplands near to Ravensthorpe reservoir and Top Ardles Wood Woodland Trust which have bird watching and picnic opportunities. Four established and developing gardens set in beautiful countryside displaying a wide range of plants, many of which are available from the Nursery, offering inspirational planting, quiet contemplation, beautiful views, water features, gardens encouraging wildlife, fruit and vegetable gardens including one owned by a Heritage Seed Library Guardian. Partial wheelchair access to 72 Guilsborough Road and 2 The Orchards.

Briarwood

33 ROSEARIE-DE-LA-NYMPH

Northampton NN3 7UE. Peter Hughes, Mary Morris, Irene Kay & Jeremy Stanton. *N of Northampton town. Take to Holcot Rd from the one-way system in the village centre.* Refreshments available in the village. **Adm £4, chd free. Sun 22, Sun 29 June (10-5).**

We have been developing this garden for about 10-yrs and now have over 1000 roses, incl English, French and Italian varieties. Many unusual water features and specimen trees. Roses, scramblers and ramblers, climb into trees, over arbours and arches. We have tried to time our open days to cover the peak flowering period.

♿

34 ROSEMOUNT

18 Church Hill, Hollowell NN6 8RR. Mr & Mrs J Leatherland, 01604 740354. *10m NW of Northampton, 5m S J1 A14. Between A5199 and A428. Parking at village hall.* Light refreshments at village hall. **Adm £3.50, chd free. Sun 2 Mar (11-3). Visitors also welcome by appt in Mar, Apr and Aug only.**

The Leatherlands have been developing this ½ -acre garden for over 50yrs. Both are keen and knowledgeable plantspeople, who love collecting and propagating their favourite plants, many of which are for sale. March opening features their collection of over 200 different snowdrops, hellebores and unusual spring bulbs. In August the garden is full of colour and interest with unusual shrubs, herbaceous and clemati. Limited wheelchair access.

Spratton Grange Farm, Spratton Gardens

GROUP OPENING

35 NEW SLAPTON GARDENS
Slapton, Towcester NN12 8PE. *A hamlet 4m W of Towcester ¼ m N of the Towcester to Wappenham Rd.* Home-made teas at Slapton Lodge. **Combined adm £4.50, chd free. Sun 22 June (2-5.30).**

NEW BOXES FARM
James & Mary Miller

BRADDEN COTTAGE
Mrs Philippa Heumann

NEW 1 CHAPEL LANE
Kathryn McLaughlin

NEW CORNER HOUSE
Mr & Mrs S Bell

NEW FELLYARD
Mr & Mrs R Owen

NEW OLD ROYAL OAK
Mr & Mrs A Young.
Old Royal Oak is the 1st house on the L as you enter the village from the Abthorpe/Wappenham Rd

NEW SLAPTON HOUSE
Mr & Mrs B Leadsom.
On the corner of the main street and Mill Lane

NEW SUNNYSIDE
Chapel Lane. Miss Jackie Balfe

Slapton is a very pretty Northamptonshire hamlet with only 30 houses of which 8 are opening their gardens. The gardens vary from classic formal to small cottage gardens including one completely redesigned on a steep clay-based slope. There is the lovely C12 St Botolph's Chuch with rare medieval wall paintings. Partial wheelchair access. Narrow and gravel paths.

GROUP OPENING

36 SPRATTON GARDENS
Spratton NN6 8HL. *6½ m NNW of Northampton. From A5199 turn W at Holdenby Rd for Spratton Grange Farm. Others turn E at Brixworth Rd. Car park in village with close access to 1st garden.* Light refreshments at St Andrew's Church. **Combined adm £5, chd free. Sun 11 May (11-5).**

DALE HOUSE
Fiona & Chris Cox
01604 846458
fionacox19@aol.com

THE GRANARY
Stephanie Bamford & Mark Wilkinson

11 HIGH STREET
Philip & Frances Roseblade

MULBERRY COTTAGE
6 Yew Tree Lane. Michael & Morley Heaton

NEW NORTHBANK HOUSE
Manor Road. Helen Millichamp

SPRATTON GRANGE FARM
Dennis & Christine Yardy

THE STABLES
Pam & Tony Woods

WALTHAM COTTAGE
Norma & Allan Simons

The old part of this picturesque village has many late C17 stone built houses and turn of the C19/20 brick-built ones. These line the route between the seven inner village gardens, which are of a very varied nature. One is more formal with courtyard, walled garden and orchard, another a natural stream and pond, one has a 300-yr-old Holm (evergreen) oak. Three gardens are cottage-style, with one well-stocked with tulips. Many interesting shrubs with good use of foliage colour. Three gardens show how much can be made of a small area. Several gardens have fine views over rolling agricultural countryside. The garden outside of the village centre was created from a farm and at 2-acres is the largest. Natural pond, bog garden and beautiful courtyard where once cows stood. One of the gardens will be hosting a massive plant sale. Attractive village with C12 Grade I Norman church which is a very fine example and its many interior features can be admired whilst enjoying some light refreshments. No wheelchair access to Northbank House.

37 NEW 67 STRATFIELD WAY
Kettering NN15 6GS. Mrs Paula Mantle. *5 mins off A14 (J9) Kettering. At 1st mini-r'about turn R, at next r'about turn L, then turn R to Stratfield Way. Take 1st R & 67 is on the L. A disabled parking space is at the rear of the property in front of the garage. A disabled parking sign is displayed.* **Adm £3, chd free. Sun 3 Aug (2-5); Evening Opening on Thur 7 Aug (6.30-8.30).**
After an accident in 2010 that left me injured, my garden became my soul mate. This is a pretty garden with structure and softness, work has been done at a recovering pace with bursts of energy and colour alongside gentler combinations of delicate willowy flowers. From a 3 metre fatsia to dainty alpines, climbing hydrangea, wisteria, bold dahlias, geraniums, crocosmia, fuscia, alliums, hosta, and maples.

Treat yourself to a plant from the plant stall

38 SULBY GARDENS
Sulby, Northampton NN6 6EZ. Mrs Alison Lowe. *16m NW of Northampton, 2m NE of Welford off A5199. Past Wharf House Hotel take 1st R, signed Sulby. After R & L bends, turn R at sign for Sulby Hall Farm. Turn R at junction, garden is 1st L. Parking limited, no vans or buses please.* Home-made teas. **Adm £4, chd free. Thurs 24 Apr, 19 June, 21 Aug (2-5.30); Thur 9 Oct (2-5); Thur 13 Nov (1-4).**
Unusual property covering 12-acres comprising working Victorian kitchen garden, orchard, and C19 Ice House, plus nature reserve incl woodland, ponds, stream and wild flower meadows. NB: Children welcome but under strict supervision because of deep water. Oct Opening: Apple Day showing examples of apple varieties and a little bit about them. Nov Opening: for late autumn colour and tree shapes.

39 TITCHMARSH HOUSE
Chapel Street, Titchmarsh NN14 3DA. Sir Ewan & Lady Harper, 01832 732439, jennifer.harper3@virginmedia.com. *2m N of Thrapston. 6m S of Oundle. Exit A14 at junction signed A605, Titchmarsh signed as turning to E.* Tea at community shop (May) and at village fete (June). **Adm £3, chd free. Sun 18 May (2-6); Sat 14 June (12-4.30). Visitors also welcome by appt Apr to June, refreshments by arrangement.**
4½ -acres extended and laid out since 1972. Cherries, magnolias, herbaceous, irises, shrub roses, range of unusual shrubs, walled borders and ornamental vegetable garden. Most of the garden can be visited without using steps.

GROUP OPENING

40 TURWESTON GARDENS
Brackley NN13 5JY. *2m E of Brackley. A43 from M40 J10. On Brackley bypass turn R on A422 towards Buckingham, ½ m turn L signed Turweston.* Cream teas at Versions Farm and drinks at Oatleys Hall. **Combined adm £4, chd free. Sun 6 July (2-5.30).**

OATLEYS HALL
Caroline & Ralph Grayson

TURWESTON HOUSE
Mr & Mrs C Allen

TURWESTON MILL
Mr Harry Leventis

VERSIONS FARM
Mrs E T Smyth-Osbourne

Charming unspoilt stone built village in a conservation area. 4 quite large beautiful gardens. The Mill with bridges over the millstream and a spectacular waterfall, wildlife pond and newly designed kitchen garden. A 3-acre plantsman's garden with old stonewalls, terraces, pond and small water garden. 5-acre garden with woodland and pond. Formal terrace designed by James Alexander-Sinclair in 2008. 5-acre garden with lake, woodland walk with magnificent trees. Walled garden with flowers and vegetables.

GROUP OPENING

41 WEEDON LOIS & WESTON GARDENS
Weedon Lois, Towcester NN12 8PJ. Sir John & Lady Greenaway. *7m W of Towcester. 7m N of Brackley. Old Barn & Hillside are on High St, Weedon Lois. Home Close, Kettle End is just off High St & Ridgeway Cottage is on Weston High St.* Cream teas at Weston Community Centre. **Combined adm £4.50, chd free. Sun 29 June (2-5.30).**

HILLSIDE
Mrs Karen Wilcox

HOME CLOSE
Clyde Burbidge

LOIS WEEDON HOUSE
Sir John & Lady Greenaway

OLD BARN
Mr & Mrs John Gregory

RIDGEWAY COTTAGE
Jonathan & Elizabeth Carpenter

Two adjacent villages in South Northants with a handsome medieval church in Weedon Lois. The extension churchyard contains the graves of the poets Dame Edith Sitwell and her brother Sir Sacheveral Sitwell who lived in Weston Hall. There are four gardens in Weedon Lois comprising a large garden with terracing, large borders and outstanding views, a plantsman's garden, an award winning garden and a garden with lovely stone terracing. In Weston there is a charming cottage garden and teas being provided in the community centre.

Northamptonshire County Volunteers

County Organisers
David Abbott, Wroxton Lodge, 1 Church Hill, Finedon, Wellingborough NN9 5NR, 01933 680363, d_j_abbott@btinternet.com
Gay Webster, Four Acres, The Green, Guilsborough NN6 8PT, 01604 740203, gay.webster6@gmail.com

County Treasurer & Publicity
Michael Heaton, Mulberry Cottage, 6 Yew Tree Lane, Spratton NN6 8HL, 01604 846032, ngs@mimomul.co.uk

Assistant County Organisers
Philippa Heumann, Bradden Cottage, Slapton, Towcester, NN12 8PE, 01327 860142, pmheumann@gmail.com
Geoff Sage, West Cottage, West End, West Haddon NN6 7AY, 01788 510334, geoffsage@aol.com

NOTTINGHAMSHIRE

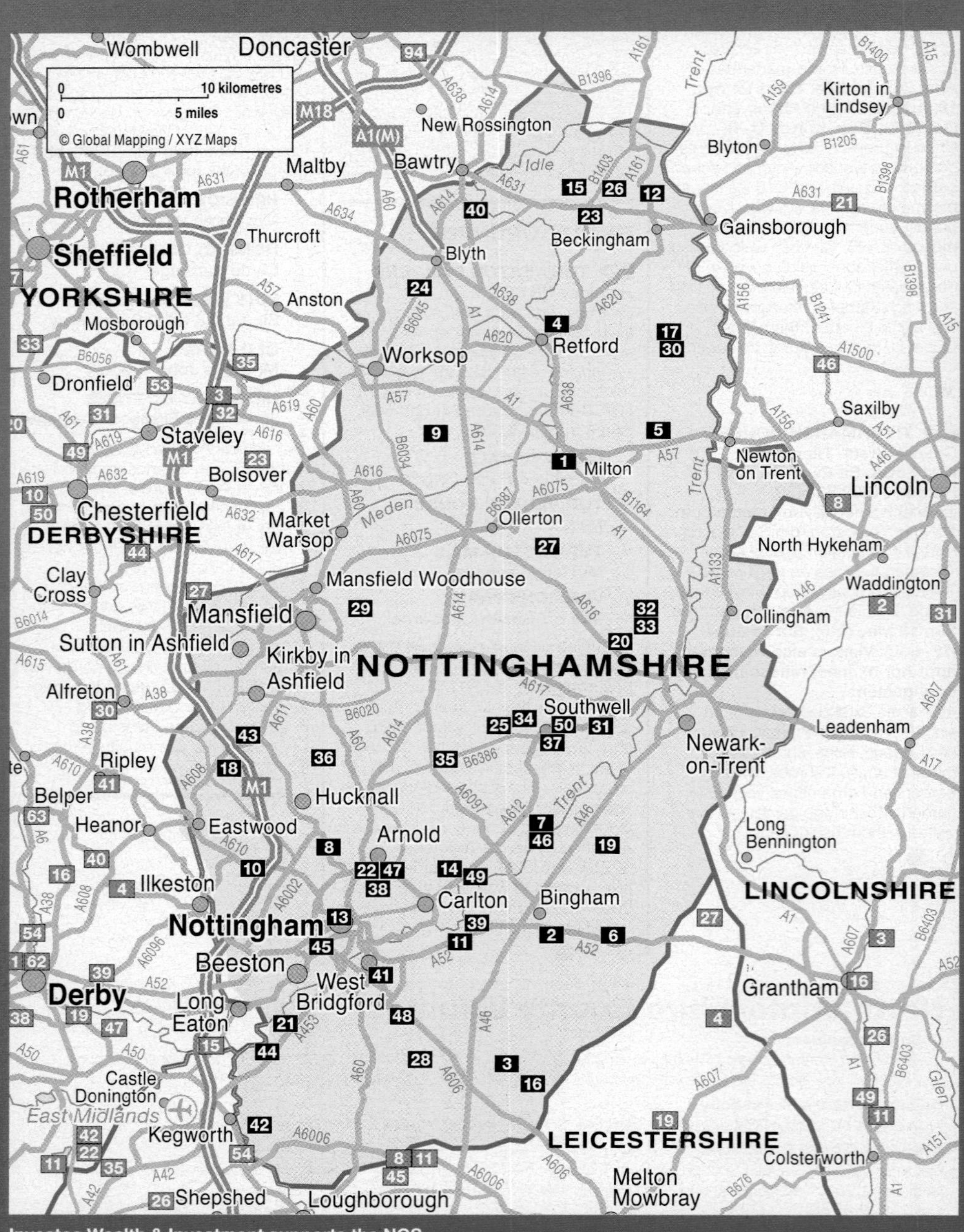

Opening Dates

All entries subject to change. For latest information check **www.ngs.org.uk**

February

Sunday 16
1 The Beeches

Wednesday 19
1 The Beeches

March

Sunday 23
15 Ellicar Gardens

Sunday 30
1 The Beeches

The lawn is awash with crocus, fritillarias, anemones, narcissi and cyclamen . . .

April

Sunday 13
5 NEW Broadlea
7 Capability Barn

Sunday 20
18 Felley Priory

Sunday 27
1 The Beeches
43 Sycamores House

May

Monday 5
10 7 Collygate

Sunday 11
12 Cross Lodge
49 Woodpeckers

Sunday 18
14 Dumbleside
33 Norwell Nurseries
46 West Farm and Church House Gardens

Sunday 25
25 Holbeck Lodge
34 The Old Vicarage
36 Papplewick Hall

Monday 26
26 Holmes Villa
39 Riseholme, 125 Shelford Road

June

Sunday 1
19 NEW Flintham House
46 West Farm and Church House Gardens

Festival Weekend

Saturday 7
25 Holbeck Lodge
31 NEW Manor Farm

Sunday 8
7 Capability Barn
8 The Chimes
13 Darby House
19 NEW Flintham House
23 Gringley Gardens
30 Lodge Mount

Saturday 14
31 NEW Manor Farm

Sunday 15
28 Home Farm House, 17 Main Street
35 Oxton Village Gardens

Wednesday 18
50 The Workhouse

Saturday 21
25 Holbeck Lodge
34 The Old Vicarage

Sunday 22
2 Bingham Gardens
3 Bishops Cottage
4 Bolham Manor
10 7 Collygate
40 NEW Scrooby Gardens

Sunday 29
22 The Glade
32 Norwell Gardens
43 Sycamores House
47 6 Weston Close
48 NEW White House

July

Wednesday 2
32 Norwell Gardens (Evening)

Wednesday 9
38 48 Penarth Gardens (Evening)

Saturday 12
9 Clumber Park Walled Kitchen Garden

Sunday 13
20 NEW Floral Media
47 6 Weston Close

Sunday 20
11 Cornerstones
37 Park Farm
38 48 Penarth Gardens
44 Thrumpton Hall

Wednesday 23
39 Riseholme, 125 Shelford Road (Evening)

Sunday 27
17 The Elms
34 The Old Vicarage
41 The Small Exotic Garden

August

Sunday 3
8 The Chimes
29 29 Lime Grove
41 The Small Exotic Garden

Sunday 10
6 5 Burton Lane
11 Cornerstones
21 The Forge

Sunday 17
27 NEW The Holocaust Centre
45 University of Nottingham Gardens

Sunday 24
27 NEW The Holocaust Centre
34 The Old Vicarage

September

Sunday 7
30 Lodge Mount
42 Sutton Bonington Arboretum and Gardens

Sunday 21
15 Ellicar Gardens

October

Sunday 12
33 Norwell Nurseries

Gardens open to the public

9 Clumber Park Walled Kitchen Garden
18 Felley Priory
24 Hodsock Priory Gardens
33 Norwell Nurseries
50 The Workhouse

By appointment only

16 Elm House

Also open by appointment

1 The Beeches
3 Bishops Cottage
4 Bolham Manor
6 5 Burton Lane
7 Capability Barn
10 7 Collygate
11 Cornerstones
13 Darby House
14 Dumbleside
15 Ellicar Gardens
17 The Elms
22 The Glade
25 Holbeck Lodge

It greets you with an impact of unexpected colour . . .

The Gardens

1 THE BEECHES

The Avenue, Milton, Tuxford, Newark NG22 0PW. Margaret & Jim Swindin, 01777 870828, james91.swindin@mypostoffice.co.uk. *1m S A1 Markham Moor. Exit A1 at Markham Moor, take Walesby sign into village (1m). From Main St, L up The Avenue.* **Adm £3, chd free. Sun 16, Wed 19 Feb (11-4); Sun 30 Mar, Sun 27 Apr (2-5.30). Visitors also welcome by appt Feb to May.**
1-acre garden full of colour and interest to plant enthusiasts looking for unusual and rare plants. Spring gives some 250 named snowdrops together with hellebores and early daffodils. The lawn is awash with crocus, fritillarias, anemones, narcissi and cyclamen. Large vegetable garden on raised beds. Lovely views over open countryside. Newcastle Mausoleum (adjacent) open. Featured in Newark Advertiser, Nottingham Post and Daily Telegraph. Some gravel paths, steps and slopes.

GROUP OPENING

2 BINGHAM GARDENS

Fisher Lane, Bingham, nr Nottingham NG13 8BQ. *8m E of Nottingham. Short walk between these two very different gardens.* Home-made teas 22 Long Acre East. **Combined adm £3.50, chd free. Sun 22 June (2-5).**

8A FISHER LANE
Michael & Sylvia Bennett

22 LONG ACRE EAST
Sue Hull & Stewart Haggart

The gardens consist of a small, varied terraced town garden and developing formal contemporary designed garden. Something for everyone.

3 BISHOPS COTTAGE

89 Main Street, Kinoulton, Nottingham NG12 3EL. Ann Hammond, s.ahammond@btinternet.com. *8m SE of West Bridgford. Kinoulton is off A46 just N of intersection with A606. Into village, pass school & village hall. Garden on R after bend on Main St.* Home-made teas. **Adm £3, chd free. Sun 22 June (1-5). Visitors also welcome by appt June to July.**
This is a large, mature cottage garden with mixed herbaceous borders, old fruit trees, two ponds - one formal with fish, one natural. Old varieties of roses with the emphasis on scent and colour co-ordination. Vegetable patch to the rear of the property. Open views across the countryside. Gravel drive.

4 BOLHAM MANOR

Bolham Way, Bolham, Retford DN22 9JG. Pam & Butch Barnsdale, 01777 703528, pamandbutch@bolham-manor.com, www.bolham-manor.com. *1m from Retford. A620 Gainsborough Rd from Retford, turn L onto Tiln Lane, signed 'A620 avoiding low bridge'. At sharp R bend take rd ahead to Tiln then L Bolham Way.* Home-made teas. **Adm £3.50, chd free. Sun 22 June (1-5). Visitors also welcome by appt May to July for groups 15+.**
Enjoy this much loved 3-acre garden with its stream of meadow flowers, mature trees, herbaceous borders, and meandering terraced planting down to the ponds and cave. Stroll across the croquet lawn, down mown paths into the old orchard where Paul's Himalyan Musk and other ramblers are there to greet you. Wheelchair access limited to parts of garden.

5 NEW BROADLEA

North Green, East Drayton, Retford DN22 0LF. David & Jean Stone. *From A1 take A57 towards Lincoln, East Drayton is signed off A57. North Green runs N from church. Garden last gate on R.* Home-made teas. **Adm £3, chd free. Sun 13 Apr (2-5).**
Our aim in this 1 acre garden is to have interest throughout the yr and attract wildlife. There is plenty to see, woodland walk, many perennials, shrubs and spring bulbs. Large pond is a haven for wildlife and a kitchen garden together with wild bank and dyke add attraction to the formal vistas. Parts of garden accessible to wheelchair users.

6 5 BURTON LANE

Whatton in the Vale NG13 9EQ. Ms Faulconbridge, 01949 850942, jpfaulconbridge@hotmail.co.uk. *3m E of Bingham. Follow signs to Whatton from A52 between Bingham & Elton. Garden nr Church in old part of village. Follow yellow NGS signs.* **Adm £3, chd free. Sun 10 Aug (2-6). Visitors also welcome by appt May to Sept.**
Medium-sized, organic, wildlife-friendly garden. Attractive fruit and vegetable areas at front and side. Back has romantic atmosphere with scented plants and seating. Large beds have stepping stone paths with great variety of plants, incl rarities, climbers, wild flowers and herbs. Also features gravel garden, pond, shade planting and trained fruit. Historic church, attractive village with walks.

7 CAPABILITY BARN

Gonalston Lane, Hoveringham NG14 7JH. Malcolm & Wendy Fisher, 0115 966 4322, wendy.fisher111@btinternet.com, www.capabilitybarn.co.uk. *8m NE of Nottingham. A612 from Nottingham through Lowdham. Take 1st R into Gonalston Lane. 1m on L.* Home-made teas. **Adm £3.50, chd free. Sun 13 Apr, Sun 8 June (1.30-4.30). Visitors also welcome by appt Apr to June, adm £5.00 incl refreshments.**

Spring is a riot of colourful bulbs: 80 varieties of daffodils alongside hyacinths tulips and fritillarias. Early Summer rich plantings of herbaceous perennials; delphiniums, hostas and roses take centre stage. All this within a framework of mature trees, lawns and views over open countryside. Orchard, new vegetable and fruit gardens and a maturing wild flower meadow complete the scene. Extensive collection of foliage and flowering begonias.

8 THE CHIMES

37 Glenorchy Crescent, Heronridge NG5 9LG. Stan & Ellen Maddock. *4m N of Nottingham. A611 towards Hucknall onto Bulwell Common. Turn R at Tesco Top Valley up to island. Turn L 100 yds. 1st L then 2nd L onto Glenorchy Crescent to bottom.* **Adm £3, chd free. Sun 8 June, Sun 3 Aug (12-5).**

We would like to invite you to visit our small but well stocked garden. Full of roses, peonies, lilies and much more. We have a small pond and plenty of pots and baskets.

9 ◆ CLUMBER PARK WALLED KITCHEN GARDEN

Clumber Park, Worksop S80 3AZ. National Trust, 01909 476592, www.nationaltrust.org.uk. *4m S of Worksop. From main car park or main entrance follow directions to the Walled Kitchen Garden.* **Adm £3, chd free. For NGS: Sat 12 July (10-5). For other opening times and information, please phone or see garden website.**

Beautiful 4 acre walled kitchen garden, growing unusual and old varieties of vegetables and fruits. Herbs and flower beds, incl the magnificent 400ft double herbaceous borders. 450ft glasshouse with grapevines. Museum of gardening tools. Soft fruit garden, rose garden, collections of regional apples and culinary rhubarbs. Featured on ITV 'Daybreak' programme. Gravel paths and slopes.

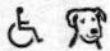

10 7 COLLYGATE

Swingate, Kimberley NG16 2PJ. Doreen Fahey, 01159 192690, dfahey456@hotmail.com. *6m W of Nottingham. From M1 J26 take A610 towards Nottingham. L at next island (B600 to Kimberley) L at Sainsbury's mini island. L at top. Park here. Garden 500yds on R.* Home-made teas. **Adm £3, chd free. Mon 5 May, Sun 22 June (1-5). Visitors also welcome by appt May to Aug coaches welcome, refreshments by arrangement.**

Sycamores House

Delightful garden created by serious plant enthusiast and tucked away at the end of a short narrow lane in Swingate. It greets you with an impact of unexpected colour and delights you with the variety and sensitivity of the planting. A peaceful backwater in an urban setting. Greenhouse and vegetable plot in cottage garden. Wheelchair access but some gravel paths.

11 CORNERSTONES

15 Lamcote Gardens, Radcliffe-on-Trent, Nottingham NG12 2BS. Judith & Jeff Coombes, 01158 458055, judith.coombes@gmail.com, www.cornerstonesgarden.co.uk. *4m E of Nottingham. From A52 take Radcliffe exit at RSPCA junction, then 2nd L just before hairpin bend.* Home-made teas. **Adm £3, chd free. Sun 20 July, Sun 10 Aug (1.30-5.30). Visitors also welcome by appt July to Aug for groups 10+.**

Plant lovers' garden, approaching 1/2 acre. Flowing colour-themed and specie borders, with rare, exotic and unusual plants, provide a wealth of colour and interest, whilst the unique fruit and vegetable garden generates an abundance of produce. Bananas, palms, fernery, fish pond, bog garden, lovely new summerhouse area and greenhouse. Enjoy tea and delicious home-made cake in a beautiful setting. Wheelchair access but some bark paths and unfenced ponds.

12 CROSS LODGE

Beckingham Road, Walkeringham DN10 4HZ. John & Betty Roberts. *A620 from Retford, A631 from Bawtry/Gainsborough, A161 to Walkeringham. Garden on A161. Parking at Village Hall approx 150 metres N of garden. For SatNav use DN10 4JF.* Home-made teas in Walkeringham Village Hall. **Adm £2.50, chd free. Sun 11 May (1-5).**

Ever changing 1 1/4 -acre garden with successive displays of spring and summer flowers. Rhododendron walk in which there are over 50 varieties is at its best in May. Shrubs and perennial borders, rockeries, roses, conifers, old orchard and small woodland with large pond. Wheelchair access to all main features, except pond-side paths.

13 DARBY HOUSE

10 The Grove, Southey Street, Nottingham NG7 4BS. Jed Brignal, 07960 065042, jedbrignal@yahoo.co.uk, www.jedbrignal.co.uk. *3/4 m NE of city centre take A610, turn R into Bentinck Rd, turn R at lights into Southey St.* Light refreshments. **Adm £3, chd free. Sun 8 June (2-5). Visitors also welcome by appt Mar to Sept.**

Unusual city garden designed and developed by artist owner. A tranquil oasis in unlikely location. Victorian walled garden with ponds, gazebos and fairy-tale shady area surrounded by mature trees. Wide variety of rare and unusual perennials incl hardy geraniums. Also home to charming construction formed from stained glass. House (1849) and gardens provide temporary home and sanctuary for actors, writers, dancers and other creative visitors. Rare plant nursery and bespoke art and craft stalls. Featured on local and national TV and in many magazine articles. Limited wheelchair access to terrace.

14 DUMBLESIDE

17 Bridle Road, Burton Joyce NG14 5FT. Mr P Bates, 0115 931 3725. *5m NE of Nottingham. Very narrow lane to walk up 100 yds - please park on Lambley Lane & walk if possible. Drop off if necessary for those with difficulty.* Home-made teas at nearby United Reformed Church. **Adm £3.50, chd free. Sun 18 May (2-6). Visitors also welcome by appt Mar to Oct, refreshments on request.**

2-acre garden of varied habitat. Raised gravel beds for small sun lovers. Natural springs planted with primulas, fritillaries; the stream runs beside woodland paths, bordered by shade loving tree ferns, arisaemas and trilliums. 50yd mixed border. Stepping stones to meadow/orchard, with bulbs and extensive wild flowers in grass. Steep slopes towards stream.

15 ELLICAR GARDENS

Ellicar House, Carr Road, Gringley-on-the-Hill DN10 4SN. Will & Sarah Murch, 01777 817218, sarah@ellicargardens.co.uk, www.ellicargardens.co.uk. *Gringley-on-the-Hill. Turn L onto Leys Lane (after school) & follow rd approx 1½ m. Ellicar Gardens is on L opp cream house.* Home-made teas. **Adm £4, chd free. Sun 23 Mar (1-4); Sun 21 Sept (1-5). Combined with Gringley Gardens, combined adm £5, chd free, Sun 8 June. Visitors also welcome by appt Mar to Oct.**

This young, vibrant family garden is a wildlife hotspot. Sweeping borders, specimen trees, gravel garden, old rose garden, wildflower meadows, orchard, winter garden, and a bog garden. Children love exploring school garden, willow maze and tree house. New bird garden with crab apple avenue leads to 'Hannah's Wood'. Garden visitors are greeted by our rare breed pet pig, ponies, geese and goats. Natural swimming pool; school garden; wildlife rich garden. Featured on BBC2 Great British Garden Revival series. Some uneven surfaces, grass and gravel paths.

16 ELM HOUSE

Main Street, Hickling, Melton Mowbray LE14 3AJ. David & Deborah Chambers, 01664 822928, davidgeorgechambers@gmail.com. *12m E of Nottingham. 7m W of Melton Mowbray. From Nottingham take A606 E. After crossing A46 turn L at Bridgegate Lane signed Hickling. In village turn R at T-junction. Elm House is last on R.* Light refreshments. **Adm £3, chd free. Visitors welcome by appt Apr to July for groups 10+.**

Large, interesting garden of over an acre with many different areas. Lovely in spring with more than 25 varieties of magnolia and many spring bulbs. Herbaceous in June/July. Other features incl a railway garden, seaside garden, small walled garden, and pond with fish. Newly-formed stumpery. Level garden with some gravel paths.

17 THE ELMS

Main Street, North Leverton DN22 0AR. Tim & Tracy Ward, 01427 881164, tracy@wardt2.fsnet.co.uk. *5m E of Retford, 6m SW of Gainsborough. From Retford take rd to Leverton for 5m, into North Leverton with Habblesthorpe.* Home-made teas. **Adm £2.50, chd free. Sun 27 July (2-5). Visitors also welcome by appt July to Sept.**

This garden is very different, creating an extension to the living space. Inspiration comes from tropical countries, giving a Mediterranean feel. Palms, bamboos and bananas, along with other exotics, create drama and yet make a statement true to many gardens, that of peace and calm. North Leverton Windmill will be open for visitors. The garden is fully viewable however wheelchair access onto decked and tiled areas is restricted.

18 ◆ FELLEY PRIORY

Underwood NG16 5FJ. Ms Michelle Upchurch for the Brudenell Family, 01773 810230, www.felleypriory.co.uk. *8m SW of Mansfield. Off A608 ½ m W M1 J27.* **Adm £4, chd free. For NGS: Sun 20 Apr (10-4). For other opening times and information, please phone or see garden website.**

Garden for all seasons with yew hedges and topiary, snowdrops, hellebores, herbaceous borders and rose garden. There are pergolas, a white garden, small arboretum and borders filled with unusual trees, shrubs, plants and bulbs. The grass-edged pond is planted with primulas, bamboo, iris, roses and eucomis. Bluebell woodland walk. Orchard with extremely rare daffodils. Light refreshments.

19 NEW FLINTHAM HOUSE

Main Street, Flintham, Newark NG23 5LA. Mr & Mrs Digby Burley. *5m S of Newark on A46. Flintham E junction off A46 past cricket club down Inholmes Rd to Main St. PLEASE park carefully in village.* Home-made teas available undercover if weather bad. **Adm £3.50, chd free. Sun 1, Sun 8 June (2-5).**

Our family home for 50+yrs. Come, enjoy peace within a walled garden of formal area, apple orchard, herb garden and seated arbour for quiet moments. Views across the Vale of Belvoir - unusual rockery built from volcanic rock brought to England by a former resident - a merchant seaman. Flintham has many listed buildings within the largest conservation area in Rushcliffe. Flintham Museum will be open - nationally accredited, award-winning museum offering a glimpse of rural life through the eyes of a village shop-keeper. Some gravel in yard area.

20 NEW FLORAL MEDIA

Norwell Road, Caunton, Newark NG23 6AQ. Mr & Mrs Steve Routledge. *Take Norwell Rd from Caunton. Approx 1/2 m from Caunton on L.* Refreshments in purpose-built garden room. **Adm £3, chd free.** **Sun 13 July (10-4).**

A beautifully well-maintained cottage garden. Beds overflowing with a variety of roses, shrubs and flowers. A gravel garden and wildlife pond, vegetable, herb and fruit garden. Full wheelchair access incl disabled WC.

21 THE FORGE

Barton in Fabis, Nottingham NG11 0AE. Angela Plowright & Paul Kaczmarczuk, paul.kaczmarczuk@gmail.com. *6m SW of Nottingham. A453 from Clifton 1st R Barton 1 1/2 m from Crusader PH r'about 1st house on R down hill by red 'phone box. From M1 J24 3 1/2 m, 2nd sign to Barton on L.* Cream teas. **Adm £3, chd free.** **Sun 10 Aug (2-5.30).**

Step back in time in this romantic cottage garden divided into several intimate 'rooms', each overflowing with perennials and herbs chosen to attract butterflies and bees. Original buildings incl old farmyard with wildflowers, pond and agricultural bygones. Home-made cakes and undercover seating. Barton in Fabis won Gold Medal in Britain in Bloom finals and was joint winner in the Small Village category. Featured in 'House Beautiful' as Britain's Greenest Garden and East Midlands in Bloom Judges' Award for 'Exquisite and Magical Cottage Garden'.

22 THE GLADE

2a Woodthorpe Avenue, Woodthorpe, Nottingham NG5 4FD. Tony Hoffman, 07836 207196, a.hoffman@insideoutgroup.co.uk. *3m N of Nottingham. A60 Mansfield Rd from Nottingham. After Sherwood shops turn R at T-lights by Woodthorpe Park into Woodthorpe Drive. 2nd L into Woodthorpe Avenue.* Home-made teas at 6 Weston Close. **Sun 29 June (1-5).** **Combined with 6 Weston Close, combined adm £4, chd free. Visitors also welcome by appt June to Sept.**

Exquisite medium-sized garden developed over 8 yrs on the site of a former Great Western Railway track with very free draining soil which allows Mediterranean plants to thrive. Feature plants incl tree ferns, 30 ft high bamboos, fan palms, acers and other shrubs rarely seen. The railway arch, enclosed in trellis work, provides shade for a variety of ferns and hostas.

GROUP OPENING

23 GRINGLEY GARDENS

Gringley-on-the-Hill, Doncaster DN10 4QT. *5m E of Bawtry. Gringley is midway between Bawtry & Gainsborough on A631. Follow yellow NGS signs off by-pass into village.* Home-made teas at Ellicar Gardens. **Combined adm £5, chd free.** **Sun 8 June (1-5).**

ELLICAR GARDENS
Will & Sarah Murch
(See separate entry)

HONEYSUCKLE COTTAGE
Miss J Towler

THE SUMMER HOUSE
Helena Bishop
01777 817248,
jbt@waitrose.com

Three diverse gardens in different settings: The Summer House, a charming English garden, lovingly planted with outstanding views framed by overflowing borders. A romantic rose garden, wildflower meadow, and winter border are maturing and the water garden with stream makes a stunning focal point. Honeysuckle Cottage, a traditional terraced cottage garden with interesting hard landscaping. Mixed borders, small vegetable garden with raised beds, some soft fruit (raspberries, gooseberries and blackcurrants) and a very old Bramley Apple tree. Some new developments following the addition of a garden room in 2011/12. Ellicar Gardens, young, vibrant and naturalistic, this 5 acre family garden is a wildlife hotspot. Enjoy our gravel garden, old roses, wildflower meadows, orchard, winter garden, and beautiful natural swimming pool. Children love exploring the school garden, willow maze and tree house. New bird garden, wood and poolside garden. Say hello to our friendly rare breed pets, goats, geese, ponies, pig. Ellicar Gardens featured on BBC 2 Great British Garden Revival. Regret no wheelchair access at Honeysuckle Cottage.

Step back in time in this romantic cottage garden divided into several intimate 'rooms' . . .

24 ◆ HODSOCK PRIORY GARDENS

Blyth, Worksop S81 0TY. Sir Andrew & Lady Buchanan, 01909 591204, www.snowdrops.co.uk. *4m N of Worksop off B6045. Blyth-Worksop rd approx 2m from A1M. Well signed locally.* **For opening times and information, please phone or see garden website.**

Enjoy exploring our estate and nearby attractions. Visitors to the snowdrops can enjoy a leisurely walk through the gardens and woods. See our website for special offers, opening times and full details of our snowdrop events, talk and tours. Some paths difficult for wheelchairs when wet.

The Forge

25 HOLBECK LODGE
Manor Fields, Halam, Newark NG22 8DU. Paul & Jane Oakley, 01636 813896, pauloakley07@btinternet.com. *1½ m W of Southwell. From B6386 in Halam village 350yds past church, R into Manor Fields. Parking on Radley Rd.* **Adm £3.50, chd free. Sun 25 May, Sat 7, Sat 21 June (1-5). Combined with The Old Vicarage, Halam Sun 25 May and Sat 21 June, combined adm £4, chd free. Visitors also welcome by appt June to July.**
Starting with a blank canvas in 2001 when Holbeck Lodge was built, this ½ -acre garden was designed and planted to flow from semi-formal to more natural planting bordering open countryside. A vegetable garden with raised beds is contained by a rose trellis, leading through herbaceous beds, hostas, roses, betula, sorbus and several spectacular Cornus Kousa. Bordering beck. Chilli plants for sale by 'Chilli Bob', passionate about chilli plants/varieties (7 June only). Some sloping areas which may not be suitable for wheelchairs.

26 HOLMES VILLA
Holmes Lane, Walkeringham, nr Gainsborough DN10 4JP. Peter & Sheila Clark, 01427 890233, clarkshaulage@aol.com. *4m NW of Gainsborough. A620 from Retford or A631 from Bawtry/Gainsborough and A161 to Walkeringham then towards Misterton. Follow yellow NGS signs for 1m.* Home-made teas in local church. **Adm £2, chd free. Mon 26 May (1-5). Visitors also welcome by appt Apr to July, please email for bookings.**
1¾ -acre plantsman's interesting and inspirational garden; surprises around every corner with places to sit and ponder, gazebos, arbours, ponds, hosta garden. Unusual perennials and shrubs for flower arranging. Lots of ideas to copy. Old tools, wildlife pond and scarecrows A flower arranger's artistic garden. Specialist plant sale. Driftwood stall bric-a-brac. Featured in various local publications.

27 NEW THE HOLOCAUST CENTRE
Laxton, Newark NG22 0PA. Janet Mills, www.holocaustcentre.net. *Take A614 from Nottingham. At Ollerton r'about take 4th exit A6075 signed Tuxford. On leaving Boughton turn sharp R signed Laxton.* Light refreshments. **Adm £3, chd free. Sun 17, Sun 24 Aug (10.30-4).**
Since 1995, over 1000 highly scented Margaret Merrill roses have been planted in this poignant memorial garden. Each individual plaque reminds us that those murdered during the Holocaust were people with names and families not just statistics. Explore also the delightful Koi pond and see other sculptures and memorials. Visitors are welcome to view museum exhibitions (seperate charge). Disabled parking and WC facilities.

28 HOME FARM HOUSE, 17 MAIN STREET

Keyworth, Nottingham NG12 5AA. Graham & Pippa Tinsley, 0115 9377122, Graham_Tinsley@yahoo.co.uk. *7m S of Nottingham. Follow signs for Keyworth from A60 or A606 & head for church. Garden about 50 yds down Main St. Car parks at village hall or on Bunny Lane.* Home-made teas. **Adm £3, chd free. Sun 15 June (1-5). Visitors also welcome by appt June to Aug.**

Large, atmospheric garden hidden behind old farmhouse in the village centre. Beech walk, orchard, ponds, turf mound, pergolas, new summer house, winter garden and old garden with herbaceous borders. High yew hedges hide a secret rose garden. Many trees incl cedars, oaks and chestnuts. A place to be explored. Wheelchair access via gravel yard.

29 29 LIME GROVE

Forest Town, Mansfield NG19 0HR. Laurence & Margaret Brown. *2m E of Mansfield. On B6030 through Forest Town on Clipstone Rd W. Lime Grove R immed before Shell garage. Narrrow entry. Park in field adjacent no 20 on R.* Home-made teas. **Adm £3, chd free. Sun 3 Aug (1-5).**

Beautifully laid out plant lovers' garden of 1.3 acres. Large neat front garden with topiary and many varieties of colourful perennials for yr round colour. Rear garden is a gardener's joy with lawn, irregular colourful herbaceous borders, beds and koi pond. All varieties of planting with specimen trees leading through to nursery and vegetable beds. Wild flower meadow planted in 2013.

30 LODGE MOUNT

Town Street, South Leverton, Retford DN22 0BT. Mr A Wootton-Jones, 01427 884949, a.wj@live.co.uk. *4m E of Retford. Opp Bradley's Garage on Town Street.* Home-made teas. **Adm £3, chd free. Sun 8 June, Sun 7 Sept (10-5). Visitors also welcome by appt Aug to Oct.**

Following organic principles, an orchard and large vegetable and fruit plots are complemented by an area of unusual perennial edibles, and helpful plants, with a view to self-sufficiency. Originally a field, much of the 1/2 -acre garden, although planned on paper for years, was landscaped within a few months during 2012 in order to fulfill an ambition following Helen Wootton-Jones' terminal cancer diagnosis. Helen's aunt also had cancer and the garden was specifically designed to opening for the NGS to raise money for cancer charities.

31 NEW MANOR FARM

Main Street, Upton, Nr Southwell NG23 5ST. Ron & Stefanie Coles. *PLEASE use car park at The British Horological Institute approx 250 metres from garden.* Light refreshments available under cover barn if wet. **Adm £3.50, chd free. Sat 7, Sat 14 June (1-5).**

A series of garden rooms created from scratch within an old farmyard with the C18 Grade II listed farmhouse and barns in its midst. Walk through a secret door to the orchard past the vegetable patch down to a large wild life pond where foxes, the occasional deer and bees from the apiary drink. Old fashioned cottage garden plants make up the colourful borders.

GROUP OPENING

32 NORWELL GARDENS

Nr Newark NG23 6JX, www.norwellnurseries.co.uk. *6m N of Newark. 1/2 way between Newark & Southwell. Off A1 at Cromwell turning, take Norwell Rd at bus shelter. Or off A616 take Caunton turn.* Home-made teas in village hall (29th June) & Norwell Nurseries (2nd July). **Combined adm £4, chd free. Sun 29 June (1-5). Evening Opening £4, chd free, Home-made teas, Wed 2 July (6.30-9).**

ARTISAN'S COTTAGE
Mr & Mrs B Shaw

THE BAKEHOUSE
Peter & Linda Jones

NEW HOPBINE FARMHOUSE, OSSINGTON
Mr & Mrs Geldart

NORWELL ALLOTMENT PARISH GARDENS
Norwell Parish Council

◆ NORWELL NURSERIES
Andrew & Helen Ward
(See separate entry)

THE OLD FORGE
Adam & Hilary Ward

THE OLD MILL HOUSE, NORWELL
Mr & Mrs M Burgess

SOUTHVIEW COTTAGE
Margaret & Les Corbett

Range of different, very appealing gardens all making superb use of the beautiful backdrop of a quintessentially English village and countryside. They incl an outstanding plantsman's garden with over 2,500 different plants radiating from a 'Monet' pond. 32 allotments of different sizes are tended by gardeners from all generations growing fruit, vegetables and a wealth of cut flowers. Also walled, scented gardens, water features, sun and shade gardens, pools of perennial colour, gardens where innovative features abound with lush and colourful plantings incl roses and grasses. The development of a family garden will allow visitors to follow its progress over the next few yrs. Exhibition vegetables and flowers amongst hardyish exotics and borders built to entice insects. A modern house with angular lines is echoed by a bold, evolving contemporary garden which manages to blend effortlessly into the rolling countryside. The beautiful medieval church and its peaceful churchyard with grass labyrinth will be open. A special display and flower arrangements reflecting the theme of both the effects of WWI in Norwell and soldiers on the roll of honour board in the church will be on show. Featured in Newark Advertiser and Amateur Gardener.

Range of different, very appealing gardens all making superb use of the beautiful backdrop of a quintessentially English village . . .

33 ◆ NORWELL NURSERIES
Woodhouse Road, Norwell NG23 6JX. Andrew & Helen Ward, 01636 636337, wardha@aol.com, www.norwellnurseries.co.uk. *6m N of Newark half way between Newark & Southwell. Off A1 at Cromwell turning, take rd to Norwell at bus stop. Or from A616 take Caunton turn.* Home-made teas. **Adm £2.50, chd free. For NGS: Sun 18 May, Sun 12 Oct (2-5). For other opening times and information, please phone or see garden website.**
Jewel box of over 2,500 different, beautiful and unusual plants sumptuously set out in a 3/4 -acre plantsman's garden incl shady garden with orchids, woodland gems, cottage garden borders, alpine and scree areas. Pond with opulently planted margins. Extensive herbaceous borders and effervescent colour-themed beds. New borders every yr. Nationally renowned nursery with over 1,000 different rare plants for sale also open. Autumn opening features UK's largest collection of hardy chrysanthemums. Featured in the highly prestigious 'Best Gardens to visit 2014'. Grass paths, no wheelchair access to woodland paths.

There are hidden nooks and crannies . . .

34 THE OLD VICARAGE
Halam Hill, Halam NG22 8AX. Mrs Beverley Perks, 01636 812181, perks.family@talk21.com. *1m W of Southwell. NG22 8AX - Please park diagonally into beech hedge on verge with speed interactive sign OR in the village - a busy road so NO parking on roadside.* Home-made teas in the conservatory if wet! **Adm £3.50, chd free. Sun 25 May, Sat 21 June, Sun 27 July, Sun 24 Aug (1-5). Combined with Holbeck Lodge Sun 25 May and Sat 21 June, combined adm £4, chd free. Visitors also welcome by appt May to Oct for groups 10+.**
This beautifully planted, organic, relaxing garden on south facing hillside, offers history, wonder and design. Bounteous borders of unusual herbaceous plants, clematis, roses, shrubs and trees. There are hidden nooks and crannies, varied wildlife ponds, swimming pool planting, orchard, productive kitchen garden, new wildflower meadow with glorious views - soak up the peace and quiet, slightly disturbed by our friendly chickens. Beautiful C12 Church open only short walk into the village or across field through attractive churchyard - rare C14 stained glass window. Featured in Nottingham Post and on Radio Nottingham Interview. Slopes but cheerful help available.

GROUP OPENING

35 OXTON VILLAGE GARDENS
Forest Road, Oxton NG25 0SZ. Oxton Village Gardens. *5m W of Southwell. From B6386 turn into village (Blind Lane). Turn R before PH for Roman Way & Wesley Grange. Turn R after PH for Lilac & Crows Nest Cottages.* Home-made teas at Crows Nest Cottage. **Combined adm £5, chd free. Sun 15 June (12-6).**

CROWS NEST COTTAGE
Joan Arnold & Tom Heinersdorff
Visitors also welcome by appt Apr to Sept for groups 10+. 01159 653789 trebleclef.arnold@btinternet.com

NEW LILAC COTTAGE
Matthew Bramble & Anita Garfield

ROMAN WAY
Corby & Lewie Lewington

WESLEY GRANGE
Judith & Phil Meats

Enjoy 4 very different gardens in this lovely, rural village. In Blind Lane, Roman Way, a bijoux garden, has a sunny rockery, manicured lawn, water feature and shady corners. Along Chapel Lane, Wesley Grange's gravelled courtyard garden is set around a converted barn with a sunny Mediterranean feel. Up Forest Road, Lilac Cottage boasts spectacular delphiniums and perennial borders while Crow's Nest Cottage is a larger, bird-friendly garden with ponds, running water, scented beds and lovely clematis. Crows Nest Cottage featured as Garden of the Week in Garden News. Wheelchair access in some of the gardens will require help.

36 PAPPLEWICK HALL
Blidworth Waye, Papplewick NG15 8FE. J R Godwin-Austen Esq, www.papplewickhall.co.uk. *7m N of Nottingham. N end of Papplewick village on B683, off A60. Parking at Hall.* **Adm £3.50, chd free (share to St James' Church). Sun 25 May (2-5).**
This historic, mature, 8-acre garden, mostly shaded woodland, abounds with rhododendrons, hostas, ferns, and spring bulbs. Suitable for wheelchair users but section of paths are gravel.

37 PARK FARM
Crink Lane, Southwell NG25 0TJ. Dr & Mrs Ian Johnston, 01636 812195, v.johnston100@gmail.com. *1m SE of Southwell. A612 from Southwell towards Newark, take rd to Fiskerton & 200yds up hill turn R into Crink Lane. Park Farm is on 2nd bend.* Cream teas. **Adm £3.50, chd free. Sun 20 July (2-5). Visitors also welcome by appt May to Sept. Guided tour 50p per person. Regret, no refreshments offered for by appointment visits but please bring your own to enjoy in the garden.**
3-acre garden with extensive borders comprising a large range of plants, shrubs and trees, many unusual. Woodland garden, oak arches with roses, long flower borders, large wild flower meadow, pond and ha-ha complement the garden with spectacular views across fields to The Minster. New large alpine rock/gravel garden.

38 48 PENARTH GARDENS
Sherwood Vale, Nottingham NG5 4EG. Josie & Geoff Goodlud, 01159 609067. *Approx 2 1/2 m N of Nottingham. Take B684 (Woodborough Rd) from Nottingham. Turn L after Autopark Garage into Woodthorpe Rd & L again into Penarth Rise, then L into Penarth Gdns.* Home-made teas. **Adm £3, chd free. Evening Opening £4, chd free, wine and light refreshments, Wed 9 July (6-9); Sun 20 July (1-5). Visitors and groups also welcome by appt July to Aug.**
One of Nottingham city's hidden

gems is to be found in the unlikely setting of the old Nottingham Brickwork Quarry. The landscape has been transformed with pathways, steps and a summer house. Clever planting with trees, fences, bamboos, palms and specimen shrubs, lead to flowing herbaceous borders which provide colour and interest with many unusual plants.

39 RISEHOLME, 125 SHELFORD ROAD

Radcliffe on Trent NG12 1AZ. John & Elaine Walker, 0115 9119867. *4m E of Nottingham. From A52 follow signs to Radcliffe. In village centre take turning for Shelford (by Co-op). Approx ¾ m on L.* Home-made teas. **Adm £3, chd free. Mon 26 May (1.30-5.30). Evening Opening £4, chd free, wine, Wed 23 July (6-9). Visitors also welcome by appt May to Sept for groups 10+.**

Just under ½ acre, intensely planted with many varieties of perennials, grasses, bulbs and shrubs to provide colour and interest all year. Colour themed beds, jungle area with tropical style planting, tender perennials in pots. Unique garden mirrors and other objects complement planting. Always something new to see.

GROUP OPENING

40 NEW SCROOBY GARDENS

Scrooby, Doncaster DN10 6BS. *1m S of Bawtry on Retford Rd. Turn L at Pilgrim Fathers PH. Parking by village hall in centre of village. From village hall, proceed along low rd, around 90 degree bend, Holmefield croft is on L.* Home-made teas in the village hall. **Combined adm £3, chd free. Sun 22 June (1-5).**

NEW 2 HOLMEFIELD CROFT
Mr & Mrs P Walton

NEW OLD VICARAGE
Mark & Sheila Firth

Two small contrasting gardens and a community Pinfold. The new garden is vibrant with clipped box parterre, topiary, attractive moongate and pleached hornbeams. The vicarage overlooks the spire of the historic church which is associated with the Pilgrim Father William Brewster. An old Mulberry tree forms the centre of the garden, which contains herbs, hostas, shrubs and an old rambling rose that covers a wall of the house. There is an interesting square of box hedges. The Pinfold is planted with roses and herbaceous plants. There will be an exhibition of paintings by the Doncaster Art Club in the church which will be decorated with flowers. Plant sales.

200 year-old cedars overlooking ponds, waterfalls and croquet lawn . . .

41 THE SMALL EXOTIC GARDEN

26 Selby Road, West Bridgford, Nottingham NG2 7BL. Tim & Jenny Martin, 01159 813657, jennyandtim@tiscali.co.uk. *2m SE of Nottingham, off A52 Ring Rd. Selby Rd is sandwiched between (& runs parallel to) Melton Rd (A606) & Musters Rd. It can be accessed from either rd via Devonshire Rd or Boundary Rd.* **Adm £2.50, chd free. Sun 27 July, Sun 3 Aug (11-4). Visitors also welcome by appt only between Sun 27 July and Sun 3 Aug (incl evenings).**

Small green oasis planted for foliage effect. Ornamental vegetable patch, patio with bamboo bed and exotic potted plants. 3 steps down to lower garden with bark paths encircling desert style beds and 'mini jungle' beyond with wildlife pond and secluded 'jungle' hut. New 'tropical island-style' beach hut and patio water feature.

42 SUTTON BONINGTON ARBORETUM AND GARDENS

University Campus, College Road, Sutton Bonington LE12 5RD. University of Nottingham, www.nottingham.ac.uk. *2m SE of Kegworth. Yellow NGS signs visible at junction of Melton Rd & College Rd.* Light refreshments in campus cafe. **Adm £3, chd free. Sun 7 Sept (2-5).**

Sutton Bonington Arboretum is a little-known resource that began life during the 'Plant a Tree in '73' campaign. The Arboretum has an interesting collection of over 300 evergreen and deciduous trees. Notable specimens incl big cone pine, Corsican pine, cedar, eucalyptus, American chestnut, maple and Persian ironwood. The campus gardens are extensive and feature a lake and a historic lime avenue. Picnic area, cafe, guided tour.

43 SYCAMORES HOUSE

Salmon Lane, Annesley Woodhouse, Nottingham NG17 9HB. Lynne & Barrie Jackson, 01623 750466, landbjackson@googlemail.com. *From M1 J27 follow Mansfield signs to 'Badger Box' T-lights. Turn L. The gate is on L just past the 'No footway for 600 yds' sign.* Home-made teas. **Adm £3, chd free. Sun 27 Apr, Sun 29 June (1-5).**

A young garden of about 1½ acres on a gentle southerly slope. A grassy field in 2005, it now comprises traditional herbaceous borders along with wilder areas and a large, productive, organic vegetable garden and orchard. There is still much to develop and the garden will continue to evolve over the coming years as plants, trees and hedges mature. New spring bed and enlarged shade area for 2014. Children's trail for under 5s. Garden suitable for wheelchair users. Couple of short steep slopes. Gravel paths near house, grass further down. Ramp available for entrance steps.

44 THRUMPTON HALL

Thrumpton NG11 0AX. Miranda Seymour, 01159 830333, www.thrumptonhall.com. *7m S of Nottingham. M1 J24 take A453 towards Nottingham. Turn L to Thrumpton village & continue to Thrumpton Hall.* **Adm £3, chd free. Sun 20 July (2-5).**

2 acres incl lawns, rare trees, lakeside walks, flower borders, rose-garden and box-bordered sunken herb garden, all enclosed by C18 ha-ha and encircling a Jacobean house. Garden is surrounded by C18 landscaped park and is bordered by a river. Rare opportunity to visit Thrumpton Hall (separate ticket). Jacobean mansion, unique carved staircase, Great Saloon, State Bedroom, Priest's Hole.

45 UNIVERSITY OF NOTTINGHAM GARDENS

University Park, Nottingham NG7 2RD. University of Nottingham, www.nottingham.ac.uk. *SW of centre of Nottingham. The Millennium garden (where tickets are on sale) will be signed from N & W entrances of Nottingham University & within internal rd network.* Light refreshments. **Adm £3, chd free. Sun 17 Aug (1.30-5).**
University Park has many beautiful gardens incl the award-winning Millennium Garden with its dazzling flower garden, timed fountains and turf maze, the huge Lenton Firs rock garden, the dry garden and Jekyll garden. During summer, the walled garden will be alive with exotic plantings. In total, 300 acres of landscape and gardens. Picnic area, cafe, walking tours, accessible minibus to feature gardens within campus. Some gravel paths and steep slopes. Minibus provided to reach all main areas.

GROUP OPENING

46 WEST FARM AND CHURCH HOUSE GARDENS

Gonalston Lane, Hoveringham NG14 7JH. *Centre of Hoveringham village. 6m NE of Nottingham. Signed from A612 Nottingham to Southwell rd, on Southwell side of Lowdham.* Light refreshments. **Combined adm £4, chd free. Sun 18 May, Sun 1 June (1-5).**

CHURCH HOUSE
Alex & Sue Allan
Visitors also welcome by appt Apr to June (with West House).
07976 966795
suziewoo109@hotmail.com

WEST FARM HOUSE
Dr R S & Mrs C D Torr
Visitors also welcome by appt Apr to June.
01159 664771
richard-torr1@tiscali.co.uk

2 contrasting gardens in the centre of Hoveringham village near St Michael's Church. West Farm House is a large cottage-style garden and Church House is a small, but perfectly formed, walled garden. Both gardens host a wide range of features and plants, with specialist collections in each. Cacti and succulent collection at West Farm House. Auricula theatre and Japanese area at Church House. Gravel at both gardens and narrow, uneven access at Church House, very difficult for wheelchairs.

47 6 WESTON CLOSE

Woodthorpe NG5 4FS. Diane & Steve Harrington, 01159 857506, mrsdiharrington@gmail.com. *3m N of Nottingham. A60 Mansfield Rd. Turn R at T-lights into Woodthorpe Drive. 2nd L Grange Road. R into The Crescent. R into Weston Close. Park in The Crescent.* Home-made teas. **Adm £3, chd free. Sun 29 June, Sun 13 July (1-5). Combined with The Glade Sun 29 June, combined adm £4, chd free. Visitors also welcome by appt June to Aug for groups 6+.**
Set on a substantial slope with 3 separate areas, dense planting creates a full, varied yet relaxed display including many scented roses, clematis and a collection of dozens of mature hostas in the impressive colourful rear garden. Large plant sale packed with good value home propagated plants. Occasional craft stalls. Featured in Garden News.

48 NEW WHITE HOUSE

39 Melton Road, Tollerton, Nottingham NG12 4EL. Joan Dean, 01159 375031, joandean4el@btinternet.com. *5m S of Nottingham. From A52 Wheatcroft island, take A606 towards Melton Mowbray. Garden is approx 1½ m on L. Parking in front of Post Office (45 Melton Rd).* Light refreshments. **Adm £3, chd free. Sun 29 June (1-5). Visitors also welcome by appt May to Sept, adm incl tea/coffee.**
The garden has many features and points of interest that incl a stumpery, a hint of the Orient, a wildlife pond and a large patio area. Many species of herbaceous plants, mature trees and bushes provide much to investigate.

49 WOODPECKERS

35 Lambley Lane, Burton Joyce, Nottingham NG14 5BG. Lynn & Mark Carr, 01159 313237, info@woodpeckersdining.co.uk. *6m N of Nottingham. In Burton Joyce, turn off A612 (Nottingham to Southwell rd) into Lambley Lane, turn L onto private drive to access gardens. Ample parking.* Home-made teas. **Adm £3.50, chd free. Sun 11 May (12-5). Visitors also welcome by appt Feb to Oct.**
4 acres of mature woodland and formal gardens with spectacular views over the Trent Valley. Over 500 rhododendrons and azaleas. Newly established Rose gardens. Balustraded terrace for teas or pimms. Glade with 200 yr-old cedars overlooking ponds, waterfalls and croquet lawn. Bog garden and sunken area below ha-ha, created in 2009 and planted to tempt the eye onwards towards ancient well. Gravel and grass paths, steep slopes.

50 ◆ THE WORKHOUSE

Upton Road, Southwell NG25 0PT. National Trust, 01636 817260, www.nationaltrust.org.uk. *1m E of Southwell on A612. Signed from centre of Southwell.* **Adm £8.50, chd £4.25. For NGS: Wed 18 June (12-4). For other opening times and information, please phone or see garden website.**
Originally started in 1825 to provide food and labour for the pauper inmates, the north side was cultivated to provide potatoes, and the south was used to grow vegetables and a pasture for two cows. Volunteers have recreated the vegetable garden using traditional techniques and heritage varieties of produce. Featured in NT publications, local press and Nottingham Magazine. Compact stone paths between beds allow for close inspection of growing areas.

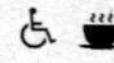

Ellicar Gardens

Nottinghamshire County Volunteers

County Organiser

Georgina Denison, Ossington House, Newark NG23 6LD, 07710 344118, campden27@aol.com

County Treasurer

Rowan & Janet McFerran, Juxta Mill, Main Street, Norwell NG23 6JN 01636 636921 rowancf@btinternet.com, janetmcferran@btinternet.com

Publicity

Ronnie Ogier, Smithy Cottage, 18 Main Street, Calverton NG14 6GQ, 01159 116786, ronnie.ogier@ntlworld.com

Booklet Coordinator

Dave Darwent, 12 Ansell Road, Ecclesall, Sheffield S11 7PE, 01142 665881, dave@poptasticdave.co.uk

Assistant County Organisers

Joan Arnold, Crows Nest Cottage, Forest Road, Oxton NG25 0SZ, 01159 653789, trebleclef.arnold@btinternet.com

Ian Cooke, 14 Park Close, Mapperley NG3 5FB, 01159 524755, iankcooke@ntlworld.com

Judy Geldart, Hopbine Farm House, Hopbine Farm, Main Street, Ossington, Newark NG23 6LJ, 01636 823832, petergeldart@btinternet.com

Beverley Perks, The Old Vicarage, Halam Hill, Halam, Nr Southwell NG22 8AX, 01636 812181, perks.family@talk21.com

Mary Thomas, Piecemeal, 123 Main Street, Sutton Bonington, Loughborough LE12 5PE, 01509 672056, admet123@btinternet.com

OXFORDSHIRE

Opening Dates

All entries subject to change. For latest information check www.ngs.org.uk

February

Sunday 23
19 14 Chawley Lane

March

Sunday 2
49 Lime Close

Sunday 30
57 Monks Head
74 Trinity College

April

Sunday 6
4 Ashbrook House
14 Buckland Lakes
78 Wadham College

Sunday 13
21 Church Farm Field
50 Magdalen College

Sunday 20
79 Waterperry Gardens

Monday 21
44 Kencot Gardens

Wednesday 23
2 NEW Allsorts

Sunday 27
37 Hollyhocks
42 Horton cum Studley Gardens
57 Monks Head

May

Every Wednesday
86 **Woolstone Mill House**

Sunday 4
12 Broughton Grange
59 NEW Old Boars Hill Gardens

Monday 5
69 Sparsholt Manor

Sunday 11
16 Charlbury Gardens
46 Kingston Bagpuize House

Saturday 17
68 South Newington House

Sunday 18
7 36 Bertie Road
19 14 Chawley Lane
34 The Grove
37 Hollyhocks
47 Lady Margaret Hall
57 Monks Head
68 South Newington House

Wednesday 21
36 Hearns House

Friday 23
36 Hearns House

Sunday 25
6 Barton Abbey
65 Salford Gardens
84 Wildwood
85 Wolfson College

Monday 26
53 NEW Meadow Cottage
84 Wildwood

Eco-friendly garden with borrowed view over the Lye Valley Nature Reserve . . .

June

Every Wednesday
86 **Woolstone Mill House**

Sunday 1
21 Church Farm Field
49 Lime Close
72 Steeple Aston Gardens
75 Troy & Gould's Grove Farmhouse
80 Wayside

Festival Weekend

Saturday 7
29 Foxcombe Hall

Sunday 8
24 NEW 103 Dene Road
25 Eaves Cottage
43 Iffley Gardens
45 NEW Kennett Road Gardens
83 Whitehill Farm

Tuesday 10
33 Greys Court

Saturday 14
58 32 New Yatt Road

Sunday 15
9 Blewbury Gardens
12 Broughton Grange
48 Langford Gardens
58 32 New Yatt Road

Thursday 19
77 Upper Chalford Farm

Friday 20
5 Asthall Manor (Evening)

Saturday 21
38 Holywell Manor
62 50 Plantation Road
64 St Hugh's College

Sunday 22
26 Egrove Park
38 Holywell Manor
55 Middleton Cheney Gardens
61 The Old Vicarage, Bledington
62 50 Plantation Road
77 Upper Chalford Farm
81 Westwell Manor
82 Wheatley Gardens

Tuesday 24
32 Greenfield Farm (Evening)

Saturday 28
8 Blenheim Palace
51 The Manor
56 Mill Barn

Sunday 29
1 Adderbury Gardens
10 Brize Norton Gardens
23 Corpus Christi College
41 Home Farm House
51 The Manor
56 Mill Barn
66 Sibford Gower Gardens
67 Somerville College Gardens

July

Every Wednesday
86 **Woolstone Mill House**

Wednesday 2
36 Hearns House

Friday 4
36 Hearns House

Sunday 6
13 Broughton Poggs & Filkins Gardens

Sunday 13
17 Chastleton Glebe
28 NEW The Filberts
31 Green and Gorgeous, The Cutting Garden
35 Headington Gardens
59 NEW Old Boars Hill Gardens
77 Upper Chalford Farm
78 Wadham College

Sunday 20
15 Chalkhouse Green Farm

Sunday 27
11 Broughton Castle
12 Broughton Grange
54 Merton College Oxford Fellows' Garden
58 32 New Yatt Road
73 Thame Gardens
74 Trinity College

August

Every Wednesday
86 **Woolstone Mill House**

Sunday 17
63 Radcot House

You are always welcome at an NGS garden!

September

Every Wednesday
86 **Woolstone Mill House**

Sunday 7
4 Ashbrook House
18 Chastleton House and Garden
46 Kingston Bagpuize House

Tuesday 16
76 University of Oxford Botanic Garden

Wednesday 17
2 NEW Allsorts

Sunday 21
79 Waterperry Gardens

October

Sunday 5
21 Church Farm Field
63 Radcot House

February 2015

Sunday 22
19 14 Chawley Lane

Gardens open to the public

8 Blenheim Palace
11 Broughton Castle
18 Chastleton House and Garden
33 Greys Court
46 Kingston Bagpuize House
76 University of Oxford Botanic Garden
79 Waterperry Gardens

By appointment only

3 Appleton Dene
20 Chivel Farm
22 Clock House
27 Fairfield
30 NEW The Grange
39 Home Close
40 Home Farm
52 Manor House
60 The Old Vicarage
70 64 Spring Road
71 Springhill House

Also open by appointment

2 NEW Allsorts
4 Ashbrook House
15 Chalkhouse Green Farm
21 Church Farm Field
31 Green and Gorgeous, The Cutting Garden
32 Greenfield Farm
35 40 Osler Road, Headington Gardens
36 Hearns House
37 Hollyhocks
42 Upper Green, Horton cum Studley Gardens
45 10 Kennett Road, Kennett Road Gardens
49 Lime Close
57 Monks Head
59 Uplands, Old Boars Hill Gardens
61 The Old Vicarage, Bledington
65 Old Rectory, Salford Gardens
65 Willow Tree Cottage, Salford Gardens
68 South Newington House
72 Primrose Gardens, Steeple Aston Gardens
77 Upper Chalford Farm
80 Wayside
82 Breach House Garden, Wheatley Gardens
82 The Manor House, Wheatley Gardens
82 The Studio, Wheatley Gardens
82 Wheatley Gardens
83 Whitehill Farm

The Gardens

GROUP OPENING

1 ADDERBURY GARDENS

Adderbury OX17 3LS. *3m S of Banbury. Adderbury is on A4260. At The Green turn into village.* Home-made teas at Church House (Library), High St. **Combined adm £5, chd free (share to Katharine House Hospice). Sun 29 June (2-6).**

CANALIA
Mr Jeffrey Moore

CROSSHILL HOUSE
Mr & Mrs Gurth Hoyer Millar
www.oxoniangardener.co.uk

THE OLD VICARAGE
Christine & Peter Job

PLACKETTS
High Street. Dr D White.
Enter village After 300yds garden on L. From Bloxham garden straight ahead as you pass Tithe Barn in village

SORBROOK MANOR
Cross Hill Road. Mr & Mrs Robin Thistlethwayte

Attractive Ironstone village, with gardens ranging from quite small to very large. **Crosshill House** 4-acre classic Victorian walled garden and grounds with ha-ha. **The Old Vicarage** Walled front garden, large rear garden stretching from ha ha to small lake and flood meadows. Unusual plants and trees. Japanese maple plantation. **Placketts** 1/5 -acre walled garden with sheltered gravel courtyard, main garden exposed, with views. Plethora of colourful plants throughout the yr with late summer colour. **Canalia** notable for remarkable collection of Mints. **Sorbrook Manor** 3-acres of lawns, ornamental trees and shrubs gently sloping down to Sor Brook. Wheelchair access at Crosshill House, restricted access at Placketts. Dogs allowed at Crosshill House and The Old Vicarage.

A garden noted for its wealth of wildlife including a variety of birds and butterflies . . .

2 NEW ALLSORTS

Cleycourt Road, Shrivenham, Swindon SN6 8BN. Mr & Mrs Jane-anne & Andrew Morrison, 07521 448422. *5m from Swindon. Just off B4000 or A420 Swindon/Oxford Rds.* Light refreshments. **Adm £3, chd 0-12 free. Wed 23 Apr, Wed 17 Sept (10.30-4.30). Visitors also welcome by appt Apr to Sept for groups of 8 max.**
This is a garden that gives colour throughout the year with some shrubs and climbers, herbaceous plants and alpines. It is not large but offers a variety of planting areas with some unusual plants and a bank of wild flowers; and through the year there are spring and summer bulbs. Amongst this we do encourage some cottage garden annuals. Featured in Oxfordshire & Wiltshires 'Whats on'. Assistance dogs only. No WC on-site.

3 APPLETON DENE

Yarnells Hill, Botley, Oxford OX2 9BG. Mr & Mrs A Dawson, 07701 000977, annrobe@aol.com. *3m W of Oxford. Take W road out of Oxford, through Botley Rd, pass under A34, turn L in to Westminster Way, Yarnells Hill 2nd on R, park at top hill. Walk 200 metres.* Home-made teas. **Adm £3.50, chd free. Visitors welcome by appt May to Sept, phone in advance.**
Beautiful secluded new garden set in

a hidden valley bordered by woods and a field. The 1/4 -acre garden on a steeply sloping site surrounds a mature tulip tree. There is a skillfully incorporated level lawn area overlooked by deep borders incl a wide variety of plants for long seasonal interest. There will also be some outdoor floral displays. Featured in Garden News Magazine.

4 ASHBROOK HOUSE

Blewbury OX11 9QA. Mr & Mrs S A Barrett, 01235 850810, janembarrett@me.com. *4m SE of Didcot. Turn off A417 in Blewbury into Westbrook St. 1st house on R. Follow yellow signs for parking in Boham's Rd.* **Adm £4, chd free. Sun 6 Apr, Sun 7 Sept (2-5.30). Visitors also welcome by appt Mar to Sept, light refreshments by arrangement.**
The garden where Kenneth Grahame read Wind in the Willows to local children and where he took inspiration for his description of the oak doors to Badger's House. Come and see - you may catch a glimpse of Toad and friends in this 3 1/2 -acre chalk and water garden in a beautiful spring-line village. In spring the banks are a mass of daffodils and in late summer the borders are full of unusual plants. Plant Sale (April only).

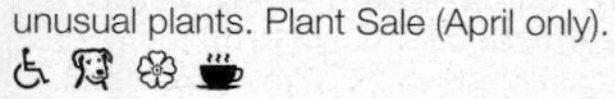

5 ASTHALL MANOR

Asthall, nr Burford OX18 4HW. Rosanna Pearson, www.asthallmanor.com. *3m E of Burford. Going from Witney to Burford on A40, turn R at r'about. Coming from Chipping Norton, come through Shipton-under-Wychwood and Swinbrook.* **Evening Opening £7.50, chd free, wine, Fri 20 June (6.30-9.30).**
6-acres of garden surround this C17 manor house (not open), once home to the Mitford family and overlooking the Windrush Valley. The gardens, designed by I & J Bannerman in 1998, offer 'a beguiling mix of traditional and contemporary'. Exuberant scented borders, sloping box parterres, wild flowers, gypsy waggon, turf sculpture and hidden lake are all part of the mix. The UK's leading exhibition of sculpture in stone 'on form 2014' will be open. Featured in The English Garden 'Visitors can enjoy the romance of those rose-covered limestone walls as well as cutting-edge outdoor sculpture, and revel in the warmth

40 Osler Road, Headington Gardens

and sense of fun of this exceptional family garden'. Partial wheelchair access.

6 BARTON ABBEY

Steeple Barton OX25 4QS. Mr & Mrs P Fleming. *8m E of Chipping Norton. On B4030, 1/2 m from junction of A4260 and B4030.* **Adm £5, chd free. Sun 25 May (2-5).**
15-acre garden with views from house (not open) across sweeping lawns and picturesque lake. Walled garden with colourful herbaceous borders, separated by established yew hedges and espalier fruit, contrasts with more informal woodland garden paths with vistas of specimen trees and meadows. Working glasshouses and fine display of fruit and vegetables.

7 36 BERTIE ROAD

Cumnor, Oxford OX2 9PS. Esther & Neil Whiting. *3 1/2 m W of Oxford. Take W road out of Oxford, through Botley and continue up hill. At car showrooms turn R. Park in Bertie/Norreys Rd.* Home-made teas at 14 Chawley Lane. **Combined Adm £4, chd free with 14 Chawley Lane. Sun 18 May (2-5).**
Professionally designed developing garden planted in 2008 in pleasant suburban setting. Structured layout, relaxed planting, incl hemerocallis and ornamental grasses. Small area of gravel path.

8 ◆ BLENHEIM PALACE

Woodstock OX20 1PX. His Grace the Duke of Marlborough, www.blenheimpalace.com. *8m N of Oxford. Bus: S3 Oxford-Chipping Norton, alight Woodstock.* **Adm £4, chd £2. For NGS: Sat 28 June (10-6). For other opening times and information, please see garden website.**
Blenheim Gardens, originally laid out by Henry Wise, incl the formal Water Terraces and Italian Garden by Achille Duchêne, Rose Garden, Arboretum, and Cascade. The Secret Garden, opened in 2004, offers a stunning garden paradise in all seasons. Blenheim Lake, created by Capability Brown and spanned by Vanburgh's Grand Bridge, is the focal point of over 2,000-acres of landscaped parkland. The Pleasure Gardens complex incl the Herb and Lavender Garden and Butterfly House. Other activities incl the Marlborough Maze, adventure play area, giant chess and draughts. Some gravel paths, terrain can be uneven in places. Dogs allowed in park only.

The Secret Garden offers a stunning garden paradise in all seasons . . .

GROUP OPENING

9 BLEWBURY GARDENS

Blewbury OX11 9QB. *4m SE of Didcot. On A417. Follow yellow signs for car parks.* Home-made teas at The Manor, all proceeds to the NGS. **Combined adm £5, chd free.** **Sun 15 June (2-6).**

BLEWBURY MANOR
Mr & Mrs M R Blythe

BROOKS END
Jean & David Richards

GREEN BUSHES
Phil Rogers, phil.rgs@gmail.com

HALL BARN
Malcolm & Deirdre Cochrane

THE OLD MILL
Dermot & Helen Mathias

STOCKS
Norma & Richard Bird

As celebrated by Rachel de Thame in Gardener's World. Six gardens in charming downland village. **Blewbury Manor** a manor house with moat set in a garden of about 10-acres. Features incl a parterre; flower garden, herbaceous and mixed borders; pergola; vegetable and herb garden; stream planting and woodland area; lake and sunken gravel gardens. Large traditional courtyard with late season flowering borders. **Brooks End** 1960's bungalow, newly designed garden with colour themed beds, damp border, hidden garden, small orchard, new shady border area added, greenhouse and vegetable garden. **Green Bushes** created by plant lover Rhon (dec'd 2007) around C16 cottage. Colour themed borders, ponds and poolside planting, alpine troughs, ferns, pleached limes and roses. **Hall Barn** extends over 4-acres with traditional herbaceous borders, kitchen garden and a croquet lawn. C16 dovecote, thatched cob wall and clear chalk streams. **The Old Mill** 3-acre garden bounded by streams with unusual trees, mill pond, herbaceous and mixed borders, newly designed and planted shrub border. Further acre with small orchard in wild flower field, cutting garden and vegetable plot. **Stocks** an early cruck-constructed thatched cottage, surrounded by densely planted lime tolerant herbaceous perennials offering tiers of colour yr-round. Plant stall in the car park.

GROUP OPENING

10 BRIZE NORTON GARDENS

Brize Norton OX18 3LY. *3m SW of Witney. Brize Norton Village, S of A40, between Witney and Burford. Parking at various locations in village. Coaches welcome with plenty of parking nearby.* Home-made teas at Elderbank Hall. **Combined adm £4, chd free.** **Sun 29 June (1-6).**

BARNSTABLE HOUSE
Mr & Mrs P Butcher

CHURCH FARM HOUSE
Philip & Mary Holmes

CLUMBER
Mr & Mrs S Hawkins

16 DAUBIGNY MEAD
Bob & Margaret Watts

2 ELM GROVE
Brian De'Ath & Joy Lee

GRANGE FARM
Mark & Lucy Artus

MIJESHE
Mr & Mrs M Harper

PAINSWICK HOUSE
Mr & Mrs T Gush

ROSEDALE
Mr & Mrs S Finlayson

95 STATION ROAD
Mr & Mrs P A Timms

STONE COTTAGE
Mr & Mrs K Humphris

Pretty village on the edge of the Cotswold's offering a number of gardens open for your enjoyment. You can see a wide variety of planting incl ornamental trees, herbaceous borders, ornamental grasses and traditional fruit and vegetable gardens. Features incl a Mediterranean style patio, courtyard garden, water features, C14 dovecote plus many gardens where you can just sit and relax. Some gardens have limited wheelchair access, some have gravel paths.

11 ◆ BROUGHTON CASTLE

nr Banbury OX15 5EB. Lord Saye & Sele, 01295 276070, www.broughtoncastle.com. *2½m SW of Banbury. On Shipston-on-Stour road (B4035).* Cream teas. **Adm £5, chd free. For NGS: Sun 27 July (2-4.30). For other opening times and information, please phone or see garden website.**
1-acre; shrubs, herbaceous borders, walled garden, roses, climbers seen against background of C14-C16 castle surrounded by moat in open parkland. House also open with extra charge.

12 BROUGHTON GRANGE

Wykham Lane, Broughton OX15 5DS, www.broughtongrange.com. *¼ m out of village. From Banbury take B4035 to Broughton. Turn L at Saye & Sele Arms PH up Wykham Lane (one way). Follow road out of village for ¼ m. Entrance on R.* **Adm £6, chd free. Sun 4 May, Sun 15 June, Sun 27 July (10-5).**
An impressive 25-acres of gardens and light woodland in an attractive Oxfordshire setting. The centrepiece is a large terraced walled garden created by Tom Stuart-Smith in 2001. Vision has been used to blend the gardens into the countryside. Good early displays of bulbs followed by outstanding herbaceous planting in summer. Formal and informal areas combine to make this a special site incl newly laid arboretum with many ongoing projects.

D

GROUP OPENING

13 BROUGHTON POGGS & FILKINS GARDENS

nr Lechlade GL7 3JH, www.filkins.org.uk. *3m N of Lechlade. 5m S of Burford. Just off A361 between Burford and Lechlade on the B4477. Map of the gardens available.* Home-made teas in Filkins Village Hall. **Combined adm £5, chd free. Sun 6 July (2-6).**

BROUGHTON HALL
Karen & Ian Jobling

BROUGHTON POGGS MILL
Charlie & Avril Payne

FIELD COTTAGE
Peter & Sheila Gray

FILKINS HALL
Filkins Hall Residents

NEW **MILLER'S COTTAGE**
Mr Luke Bailey

PIGEON COTTAGE
Lynne Savege

PIP COTTAGE
G B Woodin

ST PETER'S HOUSE
John Cambridge

THE TALLOT
Mr & Mrs Don Stowell

TAYLOR COTTAGE
Mr & Mrs Ian & Ronnie Bailey

WILLOW COTTAGE
Sue Logan

11 gardens in these beautiful and vibrant Cotswold stone twin villages. Scale and character vary from the grand landscape setting of Filkins Hall and the equally extensive but more intimate Broughton Hall, to the small but action-packed Pigeon Cottage and The Tallot. Broughton Poggs Mill has a rushing mill stream with an exciting bridge, Pip Cottage combines topiary, box hedges and a fine rural view. In these and the other equally exciting gardens horticultural interest abounds. Plant stall by professional local nursery, Swinford Museum of Cotswolds tools and artefacts and Cotswold Woollen Weavers. Many gardens have gravel driveways but most suitable for wheelchair access. Most gardens welcome dogs on leads.

14 BUCKLAND LAKES

nr Faringdon SN7 8QW.
The Wellesley Family. *3m NE of Faringdon. Signed to Buckland off A420, lane between 2 churches. Minibus shuttle available between car park and tea rooms.* Home-made teas at Memorial Hall. **Adm £4, chd free (share to RWMT (community bus)). Sun 6 Apr (2-5).**
Descend down wooded path to two large secluded lakes with views over undulating historic parkland, designed by Georgian landscape architect Richard Woods. Picturesque mid-C18 rustic icehouse, cascade with iron footbridge, thatched boathouse and round house, and renovated exedra. Many fine mature trees, drifts of spring bulbs and daffodils amongst shrubs. Norman church adjoins. Cotswold village. Children must be supervised due to large expanse of open water which is unfenced.

15 CHALKHOUSE GREEN FARM

nr Kidmore End RG4 9AL. Mr & Mrs J Hall, 01189 723631, chgs@btinternet.com, www.chgs.info. *2m N of Reading, 5m SW of Henley-on-Thames. Situated between A4074 and B481. From Kidmore End take Chalkhouse Green Rd. Follow yellow signs.* Home-made teas. **Adm £3.50, chd free. Sun 20 July (2-6). Visitors also welcome by appt.**
1-acre garden and open traditional farmstead. Herbaceous borders, herb garden, shrubs, old-fashioned roses, trees incl medlar, quince and mulberries, walled ornamental kitchen garden. New cherry orchard. Rare breed farm animals incl an ancient breed of British White cattle, Suffolk Punch and Percheron horses, donkeys, Berkshire pigs, piglets, chickens, ducks and turkeys. Plant and jam stall, donkey rides, swimming in covered pool, trailer rides, farm trail, horse logging demonstration, bee display. Limited wheelchair access.

GROUP OPENING

16 CHARLBURY GARDENS

Charlbury OX7 3PP. *6m SE of Chipping Norton. Large Cotswold village on B4022 Witney-Enstone Rd.* Home-made teas at St Mary's Church, Charlbury. **Combined adm £4, chd free. Sun 11 May (2-6).**

GOTHIC HOUSE
Mr & Mrs Andrew Lawson.
In the centre of Charlbury, between church & The Bell Hotel

THE PRIORY GARDEN
Dr D El Kabir & Colleagues

2 varied gardens in the centre of this large Cotswold village, in the context of traditional stone houses. Gothic House. 1/3 -acre walled garden designed with sculpture and colour in mind. New area of planted squares replaces lawn. False perspective, pleached lime walk, trellis, terracotta containers. The Priory Garden has 1-acre of formal terraced topiary gardens with Italianate features. Foliage colour schemes, shrubs, parterres with fragrant plants, old roses, water features, sculpture and inscriptions aim to produce a poetic, wistful atmosphere. Arboretum of over 3-acres borders the R Evenlode and incl wildlife garden and pond.

Secluded lakes with views over parkland . . .

17 CHASTLETON GLEBE

Moreton-in-Marsh GL56 0SZ.
Prue Leith. *Chastleton. 3m SE of Moreton-in-Marsh off A44 / 4m NW of Chipping Norton.* **Adm £5, chd free. Sun 13 July (2-6).**
5-acres, old trees, terraces (one all red); small lake, island; Chinese-style bridge, pagoda; views; rose tunnel. Vegetable and flower parterres. Gravel paths and grass areas dependent on weather.

18 ◆ CHASTLETON HOUSE AND GARDEN

Chaselton, Moreton-in-Marsh GL56 0SU. National Trust, 01608 674981, www.nationaltrust.org.uk. *Follow brown signs for Chastleton House from A44 between Morton in Marsh and Chipping Norton.* Teas in Chastleton Brewhouse. **Adm £3.50, chd £1.80. For NGS: Sun 7 Sept (12.30-5). For other opening times and information, please phone or see garden website.**
Chastleton is a historic garden that represents the decline of one family from 1607-1991. Made up of various rooms, it still shows how certain areas were accessed depending on your status in the Jacobean household. The garden has a variety of topiaries, shrubs, fruit, vegetables, trees and herbaceous planting with an ancient feel. It has 2 croquet lawns and is home of croquet. Garden tours, meet garden volunteers and the gardener. Plant/produce stall, honey from the garden for sale, meet the bee keeper, garden fruit advice. Gravel, some slopes and steps.

Appleton Dene

19 14 CHAWLEY LANE

Cumnor, Oxford OX2 9PX. Alice & Paul Munsey. *3m W of Oxford. From W Oxford, at top of Cumnor Hill, turn R opp Ridgeway garage into Chawley Lane. Garden 50 metres on R. Parking in Norreys and Bertie Rd.* Home-made teas. **Adm £4, chd free. Sun 23 Feb (1.30-4); Sun 18 May (2-5); Sun 22 Feb 2015 (1.30-4). Combined with 36 Bertie Road on Sun 18 May only.**

Plantsman's 1/2 -acre garden with wide and interesting range of plants, many unusual. Owner has a particular interest in alpines and woodland plants. Lovely views over valley and Wytham Woods. Area of developing 'meadow'. Well laid out vegetable garden. Extensive range of snowdrops. One slight slope. Small step to WC.

20 CHIVEL FARM

Heythrop OX7 5TR. Mr & Mrs J D Sword, 01608 683227, rosalind.sword@btinternet.com. *4m E of Chipping Norton. Off A361 or A44.* Light refreshments. **Adm £4, chd free. Visitors welcome by appt Mar to Oct, adm fee is dependent on group size.**

Beautifully designed country garden, with extensive views, designed for continuous interest. Colour-schemed borders with many unusual trees, shrubs and herbaceous plants. Small formal white garden. Conservatory. Garden continuously evolving.

21 CHURCH FARM FIELD

Church Lane, Epwell, Banbury OX15 6LD. Mrs D V D Castle, 01295 788473. *7 1/2 m W of Banbury on N side of Epwell Village.* **Adm £2, chd free. Sun 13 Apr, Sun 1 June, Sun 5 Oct (2-6). Visitors also welcome by appt Apr to Sept.**

Woods; arboretum with wild flowers (planting started 1992); over 90 different trees and shrubs in 4 1/2 -acres. Paths cut through trees for access to various parts.

22 CLOCK HOUSE

Coleshill SN6 7PT. Denny Wickham & Peter Fox, 01793 762476, denny.andrews@virgin.net. *3 1/2 m SW of Faringdon. On B4019.* **Adm £3, chd free. Visitors welcome by appt Apr to Oct, refreshments by arrangement.**

Rambling garden on hilltop overlooking NT parkland and Vale of the White Horse. On the site of Coleshill House, burnt down in 1952, the floor plan has been laid out as a garden with lavender and box 'walls' and gravel 'rooms' full of self-sown butterfly-attracting flowers. Exuberant, not too tidy, garden with unusual plants; walled garden; vegetables.

23 CORPUS CHRISTI COLLEGE

Merton Street, Oxford OX1 4JF. Domestic Bursar, www.ccc.ox.ac.uk. *Entrance from Merton St.* **Adm £2, chd free. Sun 29 June (2-6).**

David Leake, the College gardener since 1979, eschewing chemicals and sprays, has created a marvellous 'wild' garden by blending a huge range of wild and cultivated flowers into a vivid, yet harmonious, landscape. In amongst beautiful buildings and with wonderful views of Christ Church meadows from the mound beside the ancient city wall, the Corpus garden is a real treasure. The garden incl one slope.

24 NEW 103 DENE ROAD

Headington, Oxford OX3 7EQ. Mr & Mrs Steve & Mary Woolliams. *S Headington nr Nuffield. Dene Rd accessed from 'The Slade' from the N or from 'Hollow Way' from the S. Both access roads are B4495. Garden on sharp bend.* Home-made teas. **Adm £3, chd free. Sun 8 June (2-5.30). Combined Adm £4, chd free with** Kennett Road Gardens.

A surprising eco-friendly garden with borrowed view over the Lye Valley Nature Reserve. Lawns, a wild flower meadow, pond and large kitchen garden are incl in a suburban (60' x 120') sloping garden. Fruit trees, soft fruit and mixed borders of shrubs, hardy perennials, grasses and bulbs, designed for seasonal colour. This garden has been noted for its wealth of wildlife incl a variety of birds and butterflies, incl the rare Brown Hairstreak butterfly.

25 EAVES COTTAGE

Williamscot, Banbury OX17 1AD. Ken & Sandra Atack. *3m NE of Banbury. From J11 M40 take A361 to Daventry. After 3m L into Williamscot. Eaves Cottage on L at end of village.* Home-made teas. **Adm £4, chd free (share to Pancreatic Cancer UK). Sun 8 June (2-5).**

Cottage garden set in 1-acre of C17 house with SE facing slope. Planted for yr-round interest with many different shrubs, trees and herbaceous borders. Pond, stream and bog area with natural planting. Large vegetable and fruit area.

26 EGROVE PARK

Oxford Said Business School, Egrove Park, Oxford OX1 5NY. Mr Nick Bishop. *2m from Oxford city centre. Egrove Park is situated just off A34 Hinskey Hill interchange. Follow signs for Kennington Village.* Light refreshments. **Adm £3, chd free. Sun 22 June (2-5).**

Egrove Park grounds are a 37-acre site consisting of vast lawns, wild flower meadows, mixed woodlands and ponds, there are many fine specimen trees around the grounds. The crowning glory of our tree collection is the Silver Pendant Lime. It reaches 32 metre in height and 4.45 metres in girth and is in the top ten recorded limes in the country, second in girth to a tree in Wiggington. This tree can be found standing in front of Egrove House. There is plenty of opportunity to lose yourself in these grounds as we have many wooded areas, we also have two wild flower meadows which have a diverse range of wild flowers incl two species of orchid.

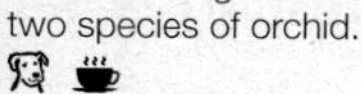

27 FAIRFIELD

Cross Hill Road, Adderbury, Banbury OX17 3EQ. Mr Mike & Mrs Val Adams, 01295 810109. *From A4260 follow road via Adderbury. House 900yds on L.* Light refreshments. **Adm £3, chd free. Visitors welcome by appt June to Aug, with Placketts (High Street, Adderbury) by arrangement.**

This exquisite, tiny, paved garden is a tapestry of beautiful plants and a patchwork of colour, interwoven with a selection of unusual and interesting clematis and climbers. Notable for late summer colour.

28 NEW THE FILBERTS

High Street, North Moreton, nr Didcot OX11 9AT. Mr & Mrs Prescott, 07544 512501, enquiries@bestinhorticulture.co.uk. *From Didcot turn R off A4130 to Wallingford after 1½ m at Xrds, R into High St, parking on recreation ground off Bear Lane.* Home-made teas in the village hall. **Adm £3, chd free. Sun 13 July (2-5).**

1-acre garden used for teaching RHS courses so demonstrating many different styles: formal colour-themed garden with lily and fish ponds; island beds for old roses, architectural foliage, grasses; large informal pond; colourful mixed borders; secluded 'Japanese' area; over 100 varieties of clematis; formal parterre with roses and herbs; vegetable garden; sweet peas grown over fruit cage; orchard. There is ramped access to the garden but some paths are narrow and many are of gravel.

A prairie with many grasses inspired by the Dutch style . . .

29 FOXCOMBE HALL

Boars Hill, Oxford OX1 5HR. The Open University in the South. *3m S of Oxford. From Oxford Ring Rd S follow signs for Wootton and Boars Hill. At Berkeley Rd turn R. At 1st bend to L look for car park on L.* Light refreshments. **Adm £3, chd free. Sat 7 June (1-5).**

Come and explore 15-acres of beautiful garden at Foxcombe Hall, home to The Open University in the South and formerly owned by Lord Randall Berkeley. The grounds are mostly natural woodland and incl an artificial lake, Italian garden with terrace and rockery, rhododendrons and magnolias. The grounds are not usually open to the public. Indoor display of cacti and succulents with presentations at 2pm and 4pm by Dr Colin Walker, President of The British Cactus and Succulent Society. Tours of the building will also be available on the day. Limited wheelchair access. Some paths very slippery when wet.

30 NEW THE GRANGE

Berrick Road, Chalgrove, Oxford OX44 7RQ. Mrs Vicky Farren, 01865 400883, vickyfarren@mac.com. *12m E of Oxford and 4m from Watlington off B480.* **Adm £4, chd free. Visitors welcome by appt May to Sept.**

10-acre plot with an evolving garden incl herbaceous borders and a prairie with many grasses inspired by the Dutch style. Lake with bridges and an island, a brook running through the garden, wild flower meadow, a further pond, arboretum, old orchard and vegetable garden. There is deep water and bridges may be slippery when wet. Grass paths.

31 GREEN AND GORGEOUS, THE CUTTING GARDEN

Little Stoke, Wallingford OX10 6AX. Rachel Siegfried, 07977 445041, www.greenandgorgeousflowers.co.uk. *3m S of Wallingford. Off B4009 between N and S Stoke; follow single track road down to farm.* Home-made teas. **Adm £3.50, chd free. Sun 13 July (12-5). Visitors also welcome by appt June to Aug.**

6-acre working flower farm next to R Thames. Organically grown cut flowers (many unusual varieties) in large plots and polytunnels, planted with combination of annuals, bulbs, perennials, roses and shrubs, plus some herbs, vegetables and fruit to feed the workers! Flowers selected for scent, novelty, nostalgia and naturalistic style. Floristry demonstrations. Short grass paths, large concrete areas.

32 GREENFIELD FARM

Christmas Common, nr Watlington OX49 5HG. Andrew & Jane Ingram, 01491 612434, abingram@hotmail.co.uk. *4m from J5 of M40, 7m from Henley. J5 M40; A40 towards Oxford for ½ m; turn L signed Christmas Common. ¾ m past Fox & Hounds PH. Turn L at Tree Barn sign.* **Evening Opening £4, chd free, Tue 24 June (6-8). Visitors also welcome by appt June to Sept.**

10-acre wild flower meadow, surrounded by woodland, established 16-yrs-ago under the Countryside Stewardship Scheme. Traditional Chiltern chalkland meadow in beautiful peaceful setting with 100 species of perennial wild flowers, grasses and 5 species of orchids. ½m walk from parking area to meadow. Opportunity to return via typical Chiltern beechwood. A guided tour at 6.00pm. The tour will last approx 2hrs and is 1½ m long.

33 ◆ GREYS COURT
Rotherfield Greys, Henley-on-Thames RG9 4PG. National Trust, 01491 628529, www.nationaltrust.org.uk/greys-court. *2m W of Henley-on-Thames. From Nettlebed mini-r'about on A4130 take B481 and property is signed to the L after approx 3m.* **Adm £4, chd £2. For NGS: Tue 10 June (10-5). For other opening times and information, please phone or see garden website.**
The tranquil gardens cover 9-acres and surround a Tudor house with many alterations, as well as a Donkey Wheel and Tower. They incl lawns, a maze and small arboretum. The highlights are the series of enchanting walled gardens, a colourful patchwork of interest set amid medieval walls. Meet the gardeners and volunteers who look after the gardens. Limited wheelchair access. Loose gravel paths, slopes and some cobbles in garden.

34 THE GROVE
North Street, Middle Barton, Chipping Norton OX7 7BZ. Ivor & Barbara Hill. *7m E Chipping Norton. On B4030, 2m from junction A4260 and B4030, opp Carpenters Arms PH. Parking in street.* Home-made teas. **Adm £3, chd free. Sun 18 May (1.30-5).**
Mature informal plantsman's garden. 1/3 -acre planted for all year interest around C19 Cotswold Stone cottage (not open). Numerous borders with wide variety of unusual shrubs, trees and hardy plants; several species weigela syringa viburnum and philadelphus. Pond area, well-stocked greenhouse. Plant list available. Home-made preserves for sale. Wheelchair access to most of garden.

GROUP OPENING

35 HEADINGTON GARDENS
Old Headington OX3 9BT. *2m E from centre of Oxford. After T-lights, centre of Headington, towards Oxford, 2nd turn on R into Osler Rd. Gardens at end of road in Old Headington.* Home-made teas in Crinkle Crankle Cafe at Ruskin College. **Combined adm £4, chd free (share to Ruskin College). Sun 13 July (2.30-5.30).**

THE COACH HOUSE
The Croft. Mr & Mrs David Rowe.
Open July date

40 OSLER ROAD
Nicholas & Pam Coote.
Open July date
Visitors also welcome by appt Apr to Sept.
07804 932748
pamjcoote@gmail.com

NEW RUSKIN COLLEGE
Crinkle Crankle Wall and Walled Garden, Dunstan Road, Ruskin College.
Open July date
01865 759649
enquiries@ruskin.ac.uk
http://www.headington.org.uk/crinklecrankle/history/index.html

35 ST ANDREWS ROAD
Mrs Alison Soskice.
Open July date

37 ST ANDREWS ROAD
Judith & David Marquand.
Open July date. No. 37 shares a driveway with No. 35

WHITE LODGE
Osler Road. Denis & Catharine Macksmith & Roger & Frances Little.
Open July date

Situated high above Oxford, Headington is centred round an old village that is remarkable for its mature trees, high stone walls, narrow lanes and Norman church. The 6 gardens provide a rare glimpse behind the walls. The Coach House combines a formal setting with hedges, lawn and flowers and a sunny courtyard on 2 levels. 40 Osler Road is a well-established garden with an Italian theme brimming with exotic planting. White Lodge provides a large park-like setting for a Regency property, and 35 & 37 St Andrews Road are 2 delightful smaller gardens, one including vegetables and one planted for all-year interest. New this year is the newly-restored walled vegetable garden in the grounds of Ruskin College, which incorporates a Grade II listed Crinkle Crankle Wall designed to maximise the sunshine available to trained fruit trees. Some gravel paths in one garden.

36 HEARNS HOUSE
Gallowstree Common RG4 9DE. John & Joan Pumfrey, 01189 722848, joanpumfrey@lineone.net. *5m N of Reading, 5m W of Henley. From A4074 turn E at Cane End.* Home-made teas. **Adm £4, chd free. Wed 21, Fri 23 May, Wed 2, Fri 4 July (11-5). Visitors also welcome by appt May to Sept with introductory talk by owner.**
2-acre garden provides yr-round interest with pergolas, crinkle-crankle walls, sculpture, ponds. Inspirational variety of indigenous and exotic planting. Some self-sown plants are allowed to flourish where they enhance the original design. The nursery is full of wonderful plants propagated from the garden. National Collections of brunnera and omphalodes.

NCH

Inspirational variety of indigenous and exotic planting . . .

37 HOLLYHOCKS
North Street, Islip, nr Kidlington OX5 2SQ. Avril Hughes, 01865 377104, ahollyhocks@btinternet.com. *3m NE of Kidlington. From A34 - exit Bletchingdon/Islip. B4027 direction Islip, turn L into North St.* Home-made teas. **Adm £3, chd free. Sun 27 Apr, Sun 18 May (2-5.30). Combined Adm £5, chd free with Monkshead. Visitors also welcome by appt Feb to Aug.**
Plantswoman's small garden brimming with yr-round interest. Divided into areas with bulbs, herbaceous borders, roses, clematis, shade and woodland planting with a particular interest in ferns. There are several alpine troughs as well as lots of pots around the house.

38 HOLYWELL MANOR
Manor Road, Oxford OX1 3UH. Balliol College Graduate Centre. *1m E of Carfax. Close to town centre. Corner of Manor Rd and St Cross Rd off Longwall St.* **Adm £2.50, chd free. Sat 21, Sun 22 June (1-5).**
A serene college garden imaginatively laid out 80-yrs-ago. Within the 1-acre

is an avenue of mature ginkgo trees as well as many fine unusual shrubs and trees and thought-provoking sculptures. Recent planting embraces an informal approach with emphasis on plants that attract bees and other pollinating insects together with a wild flower meadow. Uneven pavements and gravel paths. Wheelchair access at rear of property.

39 HOME CLOSE

Southend, Garsington OX44 9DH. Ms M Waud & Dr P Giangrande, 01865 361394. *3m SE of Oxford. Southend. N of B480. Opp Garsington Manor.* **Adm £4, chd free. Visitors welcome by appt Apr to Sept, refreshments by arrangement.**

2-acre garden with listed house (not open) and listed granary. Unusual trees and shrubs planted for yr-round effect. Terraces, walls and hedges divide the garden and the planting reflects a Mediterranean interest. Vegetable garden and orchard. 1-acre mixed tree plantation with fine views.

40 HOME FARM

Balscote OX15 6JP. Mr Godfrey Royle, 01295 738194. *5m W of Banbury. ½ m off A422.* Light refreshments. **Adm by donation. Visitors welcome by appt Apr to Dec, advanced notice required so help can be arranged.**

Formerly a plant lover's peaceful garden, but now redesigned as low maintenance with flowering shrubs, mature trees and poetry! A unique Balscote-sur-Mer theme adds a touch of humour, with lovely views of surrounding countryside from various viewpoints in the garden. Two undulating lawns give a feeling of spaciousness and contrast beautifully with slate and gravel, continuing the beach theme. An art event, 'Poetry in the Garden', by artist Zizi Lagadec is planned for 2014.

41 HOME FARM HOUSE

Pusey, Faringdon SN7 8QB. Mr & Mrs Hugh Buchanan. *Take B4508 marked to Pusey from Oxford - Swindon A420. After 1m turn L into no through road beside 3 Georgian cottages. Garden ½ m further on R.* **Adm £4, chd free. Sun 29 June (2-6).**

A newly formed garden in a particularly peaceful, rural setting, which has been created over the last 10yrs. Features incl a walled garden, courtyard garden, seasonal shrubs, peonies, irises and rose garden. Partial wheelchair access. Steep slope to rose garden and some gravel paths.

GROUP OPENING

42 HORTON CUM STUDLEY GARDENS

Brill Road, Horton Cum Studley OX33 1BU. *6m NE of Oxford. From Headington/Green Rd r'about on Oxford ring road, take Bayswater Rd. After 1m, turn R and immed L at staggered X-rds. Continue to village.* Tea at Yew Tree Cottage. **Combined adm £4, chd free. Sun 27 Apr (2-5).**

HILL TOP COTTAGE
Mrs Sarah Rogers.
Enter village. R up Horton Hill. Hill Top Cottage ½ -way up. 2 disabled spaces, other parking at bottom of hill

NEW HORSESHOE COTTAGE
Jilly & Alan Heather

UPPER GREEN
Susan & Peter Burge.
Enter village, turn R up Horton Hill. At T-junction turn L into Brill Rd. Upper Green 250 yds on R - 2 gates before pillar box. Roadside parking
Visitors also welcome by appt Feb to Oct for groups of up to 20.
01865 351310
sue.burge@ndm.ox.ac.uk

YEW TREE COTTAGE
Richard & Rachel Hawes.
Enter village, L into Church Lane. Past church to end of lane ignore Ragnall's Lane. Parking at house

Explore four contrasting gardens in this Otmoor village with almshouses (1636) and church designed by William Butterfield (1867). New this year, Horseshoe Cottage, a ½ -acre garden with traditional cottage planting in front. The back garden is hard landscaped, split into different rooms separated by mature shrubs and trees, incl a 'Japanese' area, vegetable garden, brick paved seating area and lawns. Upper Green: ½ -acre garden with views to Chilterns and incl gravel garden, mixed borders, small potager, bog area and small pond (great crested newts in residence). Old apple trees. The garden is carpet of colour with a wide range of perennials, bulbs and shrubs. Hilltop Cottage: large cottage garden with productive vegetable plot and soft fruit, beds incl herbaceous, shrubbery and prairie-look. Informal plantings of shrubs, bulbs, perennials and grasses. Small trees e.g. acer griseum. Many spring bulbs, primulas, anemones, less usual hellebores and dogwoods. Yew Tree Cottage: 1-acre garden developed since 2001. Mixed and shrub beds, spring bulbs, clematis grown up homemade trellis, and other features made from reclaimed materials. Two ponds and formal vegetable garden. Splendid views of Otmoor.

Ashbrook House

GROUP OPENING

43 IFFLEY GARDENS

Iffley, Oxford OX4 4EJ. *2m S of Oxford. Within Oxford's ring road, off A4158 Iffley road from Magdalen Bridge to Littlemore r'about to Iffley Village. Map provided at each garden.* Home-made teas in village hall. **Combined adm £5, chd free.** **Sun 8 June (2-6).**

15 ABBERBURY ROAD
Allen & Boglarka Hill

86 CHURCH WAY
Helen Beinart & Alex Coren

122 CHURCH WAY
Sir John & Lady Elliott

6 FITZHERBERT CLOSE
Tom & Eunice Martin

THE MALT HOUSE
Helen Potts

THE THATCHED COTTAGE
Martin & Helen Foreman

Secluded old village with renowned Norman church, featured on cover of Pevsner's Oxon Guide. Visit 6 gardens ranging in variety and style from an English cottage garden with Californian plants to a small professionally designed Japanese style garden, with maples and miniature pines. Varied planting throughout the gardens incl herbaceous borders and shade loving plants, roses, fine specimen trees and plants in terracing. Features incl water features, formal gardens, small lake and riverbank. Plant Sale at The Malt House.

GROUP OPENING

44 KENCOT GARDENS

Kencot, nr Lechlade GL7 3QT. *5m NE of Lechlade. E of A361 between Burford and Lechlade. Village maps available.* Home-made teas in village hall. **Combined adm £4, chd free.** **Mon 21 Apr (2-6).**

THE ALLOTMENTS
Amelia Carter Trust

DE ROUGEMONT
David & Susan Portergill

HILLVIEW HOUSE
John & Andrea Moss

IVY NOOK
Gill & Wally Cox

KENCOT HOUSE
Tim & Kate Gardner

THE MALT HOUSE
Hilary & Chris Bradshaw

MANOR FARM
Jane & Jonathan Fyson

PINNOCKS
Joy & John Coxeter

WELL HOUSE
Gill & Ian Morrison

The Allotments with the emphasis on organic vegetables, flowers and soft fruit. **De Rougemont** ½ -acre of bulbs and flowers, soft fruit cage, apples and pears, grape vines in greenhouse and 1920s well. **Hillview House** 2-acre garden with lime tree drive, established trees, shrubs, borders and abundant spring flowers incl daffodils and aconites, a lovely family garden. **Ivy Nook** inherited from plantsmen parents is a yr-long mass of flowers, shrubs and borders, rockery and small pond with waterfall under magnolia and old apple. **Kencot House** 2-acres with gingko tree, shrubs and 50 varieties of clematis: a wonderful backdrop to abundant spring bulbs. Interest provided by clockhouse, summerhouse and carved C13 archway. The new owners are keen to retain the haven of tranquillity for wildlife and charming garden ambience. **The Malt House** was transformed from gravel parterres to a more open, relaxed format of lawn, roses and herbaceous borders. Water features in corners with fruit trees and productive grape vine framing the late mediaeval stone buildings. **Manor Farm** Grade II C17 house (not open) with 2-acre garden that incl bulbs, wood anemones, fritillaria in mature orchard with varieties of old English apples, quince, medlar and mulberry. Pleached limewalk, clipped 130-yr-old yew balls, allium box, walled kitchen garden, greenhouse with ancient Black Hamburg vine, geese, chickens and 2 alpacas in paddock, stream along boundary. **Pinnocks** 2 gardens divided by the house. Mixed shrub and herbaceous borders, spring bulbs and flowers, no space left unplanted incl roadside with daffodils. Wow factor old magnolia. **Well House** ⅓ -acre garden with mature trees and hedges, miniature woodland glade, wildlife pond with waterfall and small bog area. Island beds and mixed borders all yr, enclosed patio with dry-stone walling, rockeries and bulb containers. Plant sale at Manor Farm. Norman church with Easter flowers. The Allotments featured in Sunday Times. Wheelchair access to all gardens except The Allotments.

Traditional laundress garden that leads you on an adventure of discovery . . .

GROUP OPENING

45 NEW KENNETT ROAD GARDENS

Kennett Road, Headington OX3 7BJ. *2m E of Oxford in central Headington. S of London Rd between New High St with the shark to the W and Windmill Rd to E. Residents' parking only.* Home-made teas at 103 Dene Road. **Combined adm £4, chd free.** **Sun 8 June (2-5.30). Combined with 103 Dene Road.**

10 KENNETT ROAD
Linda & David Clover
Visitors also welcome by appt.
01865 765881
linda.clover@ndcn.ox.ac.uk

NEW 29 KENNETT ROAD
Joyce & Brendan McCullagh

39 KENNETT ROAD
Stephanie Jenkins
www.headington.org.uk/private/garden

Three very different town gardens incl an award winning 'Oxford in Bloom' best kept rear garden. Number 10 is a densely packed oasis of mixed shrub and herbaceous planting with fernery and a small wildlife pond. Number 39 is traditional laundress garden that leads you on an adventure of discovery through mature shrubs, perennials and much more, brought to life by decorative hens that will keep the children amused. Number 29, a double-width town garden has areas of sun, shade and lawns densely planted with a wide selection of unusual shrubs, trees and herbaceous plants, small vegetable plot and pond features.

Church Cottage, Middleton Cheney Gardens

46 ◆ KINGSTON BAGPUIZE HOUSE
Kingston Bagpuize, nr Abingdon OX13 5AX. Mrs Francis Grant, 01865 820259, www.kingstonbagpuizehouse.com. *5m W of Abingdon. In Kingston Bagpuize just off A415, 1/4 m S of A415/A420 and accessed from Rectory Lane*. Home-made teas. **Adm £5, chd free. For NGS: Sun 11 May, Sun 7 Sept (2-5). For other opening times and information, please phone or see garden website.**
Notable collection of unusual trees, incl magnolias, shrubs, perennials, snowdrops and other bulbs, providing yr-round interest and colour. Large mixed borders, interesting summer flowering trees and shrubs. Restoration of copses and new planting in garden and parkland continues. House open - extra charge of £2.50. Featured in House & Garden (Conde Nast). Guide Dogs only beyond carpark. Gravel and grass paths. Disabled WC.

47 LADY MARGARET HALL
Norham Gardens, Oxford OX2 6QA. Principal & Fellows of Lady Margaret Hall. *1m N of Carfax. From Banbury Rd, R at T-lights into Norham Gardens*. Cream teas. **Adm £3, chd free. Sun 18 May (2-5.30).**
Beautiful college garden, full of interesting plants, wonderful buildings and riverside walk. One of the best college gardens, great trees, plenty of seats, the perfect retreat, grasses a speciality, 10-acres to wander at your leisure.

GROUP OPENING

48 LANGFORD GARDENS
nr Lechlade GL7 3LF. *6m S of Burford A361 towards Lechlade. 1 1/2 m E of Filkins. Large free car park in village. Maps of gardens available*. Teas at Pember House and village hall. **Combined adm £5, chd free. Sun 15 June (2-7).**

ANSELLS FARM
Mr & Mrs R Kirby

BAKERY COTTAGE
Mr & Mrs R Robinson

THE BARN
Mr & Mrs D E Range

BAY TREE COTTAGE
Mr & Mrs R Parsons

BRIDGEWATER HOUSE
Mr & Mrs T R Redston

2 CHURCH LANE
Chris Donlan & Mandy Wood

3 CHURCH LANE
Miss C Davies

5 CHURCH LANE
Derek & Pat Potter

CORKSCREW COTTAGE
Fiona Gilbert & Garry Maguire

COTSWOLD BUNGALOW
John & Hilary Dudley

COTSWOLD COTTAGE
Mr & Mrs Tom Marshall

26 THE ELMS
Mr R Stacey

THE GRANGE
Mr & Mrs J Johnston

KEMPS YARD
Mr & Mrs R Kemp

LANE HATCH
Mrs Susan Nevill-Gliddon

LIME TREE COTTAGE
Diane & Michael Schultz

LOCKEY HOUSE
Ms Sophie Hanson

LOWER FARM HOUSE
Mr & Mrs Templeman

THE OLD BAKERY
Mr & Mrs G Edwards

THE OLD SCHOOL
David Freeman

THE OLD VICARAGE
Mr & Mrs C Smith

SPRINGFIELD
Mr & Mrs M Harris

STONECROFT
Christine Apperley

WELLBANK
Dr Hilary Pomeroy

WELLBANK HOUSE
Mr & Mrs Robert Hill

Ancient Cotswold stone village with Grade I listed church incorporating Saxon carvings and well known Langford Rood. Flower festival held in St Matthew's Church as well as bell ringing demonstrations. Music at Pember House. Langford has a population of approx 300 people living in a variety of small and large houses with origins dating back to C15 and C16. Evidence has been found of various occupations required to meet people's needs over the yrs. Total of 25 varied gardens from small cottage to large formal ones will be open. A sense of calm and tranquility can be found wherever you go. Well known for growing roses. The Cotswold stone walls are a riot of colour. Every garden is a must see! So, come and make a day of it. Some gardens have gravel paths so wheelchair access may be varied.

49 LIME CLOSE
35 Henleys Lane, Drayton, Abingdon OX14 4HU. M C de Laubarede, mail@mclgardendesign.com. *2m S of Abingdon. Henleys Lane is off main road through Drayton*. Cream teas. **Adm £4, chd free (share to CLIC Sargent Care for Children). Sun 2 Mar (2-5); Sun 1 June (2-5.30). Visitors also welcome by appt Feb to June for groups of 10+.**
3-acre mature plantsman's garden with rare trees, shrubs, perennials and bulbs. Mixed borders, raised beds, pergola, unusual topiary and shade borders. Herb garden designed by Rosemary Verey. Listed C16 house (not open). Cottage garden designed by MCL Garden Design, focusing on colour combinations and an iris garden with over 100 varieties of tall bearded irises. Many winter bulbs, hellebores and shrubs. Plants for sale from Phoenix Plants Nursery.

50 MAGDALEN COLLEGE

Oxford OX1 4AU. Magdalen College, www.magd.ox.ac.uk. *Entrance in High St.* **Adm £5, chd £4. Sun 13 Apr (1-6).**
60-acres incl deer park, college lawns, numerous trees 150-200yrs old; notable herbaceous and shrub plantings. Magdalen meadow, where purple and white snake's-head fritillaries can be found, is surrounded by Addison's Walk, a tree-lined circuit by the R Cherwell developed since the late C18. Ancient herd of 60 deer. Some uneven ground. Not all areas are accessible for wheelchairs.

51 THE MANOR

Mill Lane, Chalgrove, Oxford OX44 7SL. Paul & Rachel Jacques. *Chalgrove is 12m E of Oxford and 4m from Watlington off B480. The Manor is W of Chalgrove, 300yds S of Lamb PH. Parking in field behind The Manor.* Home-made teas. **Combined Adm £5, chd free with Mill Barn. Sat 28, Sun 29 June (2-6).**
The Manor garden has a lake and wildlife areas. Mixed shrub and herbaceous beds surround the C15, Grade I listed Manor house. The kitchen garden incl hotbeds and companion planting. Parking on mown grass; gravel paths, some shallow steps.

52 MANOR HOUSE

Manor Farm Road, Dorchester-on-Thames OX10 7HZ. Mr & Mrs S H Broadbent, 01865 340101, mab2@o2.co.uk. *8m SSE of Oxford. Off A4074. Disabled parking at house.* **Adm £3, chd free. Visitors welcome by appt.**
2-acre garden in beautiful setting around Georgian house (not open) and Medieval abbey. Spacious lawn leading to riverside copse of towering poplars from which there are fine views of Dorchester Abbey. Terrace with rose and vine covered pergola around lily pond. Colourful herbaceous borders, small orchard and vegetable garden. Gravel paths.

53 NEW MEADOW COTTAGE

Christmas Common, Watlington OX49 5HR. Mrs Zelda Kent-Lemon. *1m from Watlington. Coming from Oxford: M40 to J6. Turn R and go to Watlington. Turn L up Hill Rd to top. Turn L, then R. Down gravel track.* Home-made teas. **Adm £3.50, chd free. Mon 26 May (11-5).**
1¾ -acre garden adjoining ancient bluebell woods created by the owner from 1995 onwards, with many areas to explore. A professionally-designed vegetable garden, large composting areas, wild flower garden and pond, old and new fruit trees, many shrubs, much varied hedging and large areas of lawn. Shrubs, indigenous trees, copious hedges, C17 barn. Tennis court and swimming pool. During the month of May, bluebell woodland. Not all areas suitable for wheelchairs as gravel driveway and lawns.

54 MERTON COLLEGE OXFORD FELLOWS' GARDEN

Merton Street, Oxford OX1 4JD. Merton College. *Merton St runs parallel to High St.* **Adm £4.50, chd free. For NGS: Sun 27 July (2-5).**
Ancient mulberry, said to have associations with James I. Specimen trees, long mixed border, recently-established herbaceous bed. View of Christ Church meadow.

GROUP OPENING

55 MIDDLETON CHENEY GARDENS

Middleton Cheney OX17 2ST. *3m E of Banbury. From M40 J11 follow A422, signed Middleton Cheney. Map available at all gardens.* Home-made teas at Peartree House. **Combined adm £5, chd free. Sun 22 June (1-6).**

CHURCH COTTAGE
David & Sue Thompson

19 GLOVERS LANE
Michael Donohoe & Jane Rixon

21 GLOVERS LANE
Mr & Mrs Richard Walmsley

20 HORTON ROAD
Steve & Vicky Paxton

38 MIDWAY
Margaret & David Finch

PEARTREE HOUSE
Roger & Barbara Charlesworth

Church Cottage's narrow garden invites exploration of its cottage garden style planting, with feature summerhouse and statuary. 19 Glovers Lane has a strong modern design with flowing curves that create an elegant, serene feeling echoed in a cool, restrained water feature. Planted for foliage and texture as well as colour. 21 Glovers Lane has a bold modern design incorporating formal elements of oak pergola, water feature and pleached trees contrasting with colourful beds and borders. 20 Horton Road is exuberant with lush, dense planting. A summerhouse entices you across a Japanese-style bridge over a classic carp pond. At 38 Midway mature small front and back gardens planted in great profusion create a powerful sensation of a private, intimate haven incl pond and waterfall. Peartree House is a mature garden with an air of mystery and romance, full of hidden corners and surprises, with the ever-changing sight and sound of water.

Grade II listed Crinkle Crankle Wall designed to maximise the sunshine available to trained fruit trees . . .

56 MILL BARN

25 Mill Lane, Chalgrove OX44 7SL. Pat Hougham. *12m E of Oxford. Chalgrove is 4m from Watlington off B480. Mill Barn is in Mill Lane on the W of Chalgrove, 300yds S of Lamb PH. Parking in field behind the Manor.* Home-made teas at The Manor (opposite). **Combined Adm £5, chd free with The Manor, Chalgrove. Sat 28, Sun 29 June (2-6).**
Mill Barn has an informal cottage garden with a variety of flowers, shrubs and fruit trees incl medlar, mulberry and quince in sunny and shaded beds. Wheelchair-friendly brick paths with rose arches and a pergola leading to a vegetable plot surrounded by cordon of fruit trees all set in a mill stream landscape.

Recycle – bring a bag for your plant purchases

57 MONKS HEAD
Weston Road, Bletchingdon OX5 3DH. Sue Bedwell, 01869 350155. *Approx 4m N of Kidlington. From A34 take B4027 to Bletchingdon, turn R at Xrds into Weston Rd.* Home-made teas. **Adm £3, chd free. Sun 30 Mar (2-5); Sun 27 Apr, Sun 18 May (2.30-5.30). Combined Adm £5, chd free with Hollyhocks Apr & May dates only. Visitors also welcome by appt Feb to Oct.**
Plantaholics' garden for all year interest. Bulb frame and alpine area, greenhouse.

A cottage garden full of scents, roses and other floral treats . . .

58 32 NEW YATT ROAD
Witney OX28 1NZ. Montserrat & Nigel Holmes. *1/2 m NE of Witney town centre. Turn off A4095 towards Wood Green. Follow New Yatt Rd in NE direction. Garden is close to District Council offices (Elmfield).* **Adm £3, chd free. Sat 14, Sun 15 June, Sun 27 July (2-6).**
An exuberant, plantswoman's suburban oasis, brimming with traditional and unusual plants in a small, but long, rear garden to an Edwardian house. Features a 70 metre mixed herbaceous border with over 60 old fashioned roses. Also contains island beds, small shrubbery, vegetable patch plus a patio crammed with exotic and tender container plants. Short but flat shingle driveway to access garden.

GROUP OPENING

59 NEW OLD BOARS HILL GARDENS
Jarn Way, Boars Hill, Oxford OX1 5JF. Charles & Lyn Sanders. *3m S of Oxford. From S ring road towards A34 at r'about follow signs to Wootton and Boars Hill. Up Hinksey Hill take R fork. 1m R into Berkley Rd to Old Boars Hill.* Home-made teas at Uplands and Tall Trees. **Combined adm £4 (May), £5 (July), chd free. Sun 4 May (2-5.30); Sun 13 July (2-6).**

NEW HEDDERLY HOUSE
Old Boars Hill. Mrs Julia Bennett.
May opening only. Close to Jarn Mound

NEW TALL TREES
Jarn Way. Suzanne & David Clark.
At junction up Hinksey Hill turn R. After 1m turn R into Berkley Rd and next L into Jarn Way

UPLANDS
Charles & Lyn Sanders
Visitors also welcome by appt Apr to Oct.
01865 739486
sandersc4@hotmail.com

NEW WHITSUN MEADOWS
Berkeley Road. Jane & Nigel Jones.
July opening only

NEW YEW COTTAGE
Old Boars Hill. John Hewitt.
July opening only. House on L, descending Old Boars Hill, opp Orchard Lane

Five delightful gardens in a semi-rural conservation area with views over Oxford. Each garden has a different setting: A thatched cottage nestled into it's new redesigned plot as well as the treat of seeing the owner's vintage cars; An extensive preambulating garden incl mature trees, many herbaceous borders and other delights and surprises, (summer opening only). A southerly-facing garden full of colour and an extensive range of plants for all seasons and a cottage garden full of scents, roses and other floral treats. A terraced hillside garden with wooded walks and ponds with extensive views over the Vale of the White Horse, (spring opening only).

60 THE OLD VICARAGE
Aston Rowant, Watlington OX49 5ST. Julian & Rona Knight, 01844 351315, jknight652@aol.com. *Between Chinnor and Watlington, off B4009. From M40 J6, take B4009 towards Chinnor and Princes Risborough. After 1m L signed Aston Rowant Village only.* Home-made teas. **Adm £4, chd free. Visitors welcome by appt June to Oct for groups of 10-30.**
Romantic, 1 3/4 -acre vicarage garden lovingly rejuvenated and enjoyed by the present family. Centered around a croquet lawn surrounded by beds brimming with shrubs and herbaceous plants, hot bed and roses. Lushly planted pond leading through a pergola overflowing with roses and clematis to a tranquil green garden. Small vegetable and cutting garden.

61 THE OLD VICARAGE, BLEDINGTON
Main Road, Bledington, Chipping Norton OX7 6UX. Sue & Tony Windsor, 01608 658525, tony.windsor@tiscali.co.uk. *6m SW of Chipping Norton. 4m SE of Stow-on-the-Wold. On the main st, B4450, through Bledington. NOT next to church.* Home-made teas. **Adm £4, chd free. Sun 22 June (2-6). Visitors also welcome by appt May to July, refreshments by prior arrangement.**
1 1/2 -acre garden around a late Georgian (1843) vicarage (not open). Borders and beds filled with hardy perennials, shrubs and trees. Informal rose garden with 350 David Austin roses. Small pond and vegetable patch. Paddock with trees, shrubs and herbaceous border. Planted for yr-round interest. Gravel driveway, gentle sloped garden can be hard work.

62 50 PLANTATION ROAD
Oxford OX2 6JE. Philippa Scoones. *Central Oxford. N on Woodstock Rd take 2nd L. Coming into Oxford on Woodstock Rd turn R after Leckford Rd. No disabled parking nr house.* **Adm £3.50, chd free. Sat 21, Sun 22 June (2-6).**
Surprisingly spacious small city garden. North facing front garden, side alley filled with shade-loving climbers, lawn with mature and unusual plants including Mount Etna Broom, conservatory, terraced area and secluded water garden with rill, woodland plants and alpines.

63 RADCOT HOUSE
Radcot OX18 2SX. Robin & Jeanne Stainer, www.radcothouse.com. *1 1/4 m S of Clanfield. On A4095 between Witney and Faringdon, 300yds N of Radcot bridge.* Cream teas. **Adm £5, chd free. Sun 17 Aug, Sun 5 Oct (2-6).**
Approx 2 1/2 -acres of dramatic yet harmonious planting in light and

10 Kennett Road, Kennett Road Gardens

shade, formal pond, fruit and vegetable cages. Convenient seating at key points enables relaxed observation and reflection. Extensive use of grasses and unusual perennials and interesting sculptural surprises. Spectacular autumn display.

64 ST HUGH'S COLLEGE

St Margaret's Road, Oxford OX2 6LE. St Hugh's College. *1m N of city centre. Corner of St Margaret's Rd and Banbury Rd. Enter via porters lodge gate.* Cream teas. **Adm £4, chd free. Sat 21 June (1-5).**

Fine trees, shrub borders and herbaceous plantings in a 14-acre site with plenty of interest throughout the year in a relaxed and informal setting. A peaceful oasis between 2 busy roads.

GROUP OPENING

65 SALFORD GARDENS

Salford OX7 5YN. *2m W of Chipping Norton. Off A44 Oxford-Worcester Rd.* Home-made teas in Salford Village Hall. **Combined adm £4, chd free. Sun 25 May (2-6).**

GREYSANDS HOUSE
DJ & LJ Stevens

OLD RECTORY
Mr & Mrs N M Chambers.
Visitors also welcome by appt.
01608 643969

WILLOW TREE COTTAGE
Mr & Mrs J Shapley
Visitors also welcome by appt May to July.
01608 642478
john.shapley@virgin.net

Willow Tree Cottage Small walled twin gardens with shrub and herbaceous borders, many clematis; one garden created from old farmyard with large alpine garden. Small grass beds. Plantsman's garden with many interesting plants. **Greysands House** Completely re-landscaped. Only 7-yrs-old. Walls, pond, raised beds, fantastic views, interesting corners. **The Old Rectory** A large garden, surrounding Old Rectory (not open). Herbaceous borders, orchard and vegetable garden. Greysands - limited wheelchair access as there are steep steps.

GROUP OPENING

66 SIBFORD GOWER GARDENS

Sibford Gower OX15 5RX. *7m W of Banbury. Nr the Warwickshire border, S of B4035, in centre of village nr Wykham Arms PH.* Home-made teas at The Manor House. **Combined adm £5, chd free. Sun 29 June (2-6).**

BUTTSLADE HOUSE
Mrs Diana Thompson
01295 788818
diana@buttsladehouse.co.uk

CARTER'S YARD
Sue & Malcolm Bannister

GOWERS CLOSE
Judith Hitching & John Marshall
01295 780348
j.hitching@virgin.net

GREEN ACRES
Paul & Margaret Hobson

THE MANOR HOUSE
Michael Donovan & Alison Jenkins

Charming small village off the beaten track, with thatched stone cottages. Five gardens open, all different, all very interesting. The cottage gardens complement the ancient houses they surround. Masses of roses, wisteria and clematis clamber over walls and pergolas. Box parterres, clipped yew hedges, herb gardens, bosky borders in pinks and purples plus productive kitchen gardens. Some new and innovative planting with unusual plants, plus a woodland walk with mown paths, rare trees and wild flowers.

67 SOMERVILLE COLLEGE GARDENS

Woodstock Road, Oxford OX2 6HD. Somerville College. *½ m E of Carfax Tower. Enter from Woodstock Rd, S of Radcliffe Infirmary.* **Adm £2.50, chd free (share to Friends of Oxford Botanic Garden). Sun 29 June (1-6).**

Approx 2-acres, robust college garden planted for yr-round interest. Formal bedding, colour-themed and extensive vibrant old-fashioned mixed herbaceous borders.

68 SOUTH NEWINGTON HOUSE

Barford Road, South Newington OX15 4JW. Mr & Mrs David Swan, 01295 721866, claire_ainley@hotmail.com. *6m SW of Banbury. South Newington is between Banbury and Chipping Norton. Take Barford Rd off A361, 1st L after 100yds in between oak bollards. For Sat Nav use OX15 4JL.* Home-made teas. **Adm £4.50, chd free. Sat 17, Sun 18 May (1-5). Visitors also welcome by appt Feb to Sept.**

Meandering tree lined drive leads to 2-acre garden full of unusual plants, shrubs and trees. Richly planted herbaceous borders designed for yr-round colour. Organic garden with established beds and rotation planting scheme. Orchard full of fruit trees with pond encouraging wildlife. A family garden beautifully designed to blend seamlessly into the local environment. Some gravel paths but generally full access for wheelchair users.

69 SPARSHOLT MANOR

nr Wantage OX12 9PT. Sir Adrian & Lady Judith Swire. *3½ m W of Wantage. Off B4507 Ashbury Rd.* **Adm £3, chd free. Mon 5 May (2-6).**

Lakes and wildfowl; ancient boxwood, wilderness and summer borders. Wheelchair access in most of the garden.

70 64 SPRING ROAD

Abingdon OX14 1AN. Mrs Janet Boulton, j.boulton89@btinternet.com, www.janetboulton.co.uk. *S Abingdon from A34 take L turn after police station into Spring Rd. Minute's drive to number 64 on L.* Home-made teas. **Adm £5, chd free. Visitors welcome by appt June to Oct for limited numbers only.**

An artists garden (4.5 x 30.5 m) behind a Victorian terrace house, narrow with steps. Predominantly green it contains numerous sculptures with inscriptions relating to art, history and the human spirit. Featured in Homes & Gardens (2014).

71 SPRINGHILL HOUSE

Main Street, Hethe OX27 8ES. Mrs Penny Jacoby, 01869 277971, peezweezel@gmail.com. *4m N of Bicester. L off A4421 N from Bicester. Follow signs to Hethe.* **Adm £5, chd free. Visitors welcome by appt May to Aug.**

A secret 1¾ -acre garden cascading down a slope to a delightfully planted extensive pond. The walled garden area is heavily planted with many varieties of plants. There are over 200 roses, a Mediterranean garden incl many tender and exotic plants, vegetable garden and small arboretum. True plantswoman's garden. No wheelchair access to Mediterranean garden.

GROUP OPENING

72 STEEPLE ASTON GARDENS

Steeple Aston OX25 4SP. *14m N of Oxford, 9m S of Banbury. ½ m E of A4260.* Home-made teas in village hall. **Combined adm £5, chd free. Sun 1 June (1-6).**

ACACIA COTTAGE
Jane & David Stewart

NEW **COMBE PYNE**
Water Lane. Mr Chris Cooper

KRALINGEN
Mr & Mrs Roderick Nicholson

THE LONGBYRE
Mr Vaughan Billings

PRIMROSE GARDENS
Richard & Daphne Preston
Visitors also welcome by appt.
01869 340512
richard.preston5@btopenworld.com

TOUCHWOOD
Gary Norris

Steeple Aston, often considered the most easterly of the Cotswold villages, is a beautiful stone built village with gardens that provide a huge range of interest. A stream meanders down the hill as the landscape changes from sand to clay. The 6 open gardens incl: small floriferous cottage gardens, large landscaped gardens, natural woodland areas, ponds and bog gardens, themed borders. No wheelchair access at Primrose Gardens or Touchwood.

A family garden beautifully designed to blend seamlessly into the local environment . . .

GROUP OPENING

73 THAME GARDENS

Thame OX9 3LA. *From M40 J7/8 follow signs to Thame mid-way between Oxford and Aylesbury on A418.* Home-made teas. **Combined adm £5, chd free. Sun 27 July (2-5.30).**

19 CHINNOR ROAD
Dr Wendie Norris

10 HAMILTON ROAD
Lesley Winward & Wendy Reid

NEW **33 LUDSDEN GROVE**
Sandra & Graham Matthews.
High St, L to East St, L into Wellington St, 2nd R into Ludsden Grove

7 NEWBARN CLOSE
Mary & Brian Dover

12 PARK TERRACE
Maggie & Colin Sear

NEW **4/6 PARLIAMENT ROAD**
Lea Park. Shirley Denny.
Off bypass S, R into Cromwell Rd, R into Chalgrove Rd, R into Parliament Rd

THE STABLES
Bell Lane. Pam & Roger Smith

Seven gardens set in the historic market town of Thame, incl a secluded garden planted with herbaceous beds and small vegetable plot; a well-stocked garden designed to contrast with a modern bungalow, with borders brimming with perennials and climbers; walled garden with raised beds containing fruit trees and in-filled with climbers and perennials; a small, quiet retreat planted with foliage for summer colour with easy care perennials and a cottage-style garden filled with pots, pools and perennials including some unusual varieties of old favourites. Two new gardens join this year, one is a colourful corner plot packed with every imaginable plant and the second is a small, secluded Japanese themed garden with tropical plants and sculptures.

74 TRINITY COLLEGE
Oxford OX1 3BH. Paul Lawrence, Head Gardener, www.trinity.ox.ac.uk. *Central Oxford. Entrance in Broad St.* Home-made teas. **Adm £2.50, chd free. Sun 30 Mar, Sun 27 July (2-5).**
Historic main College Gardens with specimen trees incl aged forked catalpa, spring bulbs, fine long herbaceous border and handsome garden quad originally designed by Wren. President's Garden surrounded by high old stone walls, mixed borders of herbaceous, shrubs and statuary. Fellows' Garden: small walled terrace, herbaceous borders; water feature formed by Jacobean stone heraldic beasts. Award-winning lavender garden and walk-through rose arbour.

75 TROY & GOULD'S GROVE FARMHOUSE
Ewelme, Wallingford OX10 6PY. David & Tania Ruck-Keene & Mrs Anstey Wild. *3m NE of Wallingford. From r'about on A4074/A4130 take exit signed Ewelme, RAF Benson (Clacks Lane). Approx 1½ m turn R at T-junction towards Henley.* Home-made teas. **Adm £3.50, chd free. Sun 1 June (2-5).**
An early C19 Grade II farmhouse, formally home of Jerome K Jerome, in a setting of fields and paddocks is surrounded by 1½ -acres of garden, which is a mixture of mature formal and natural design and planting. Extensive lawns end in a ha-ha and across the fields are stunning views of Oxfordshire. A gazebo and summerhouse, where Jerome and HG Wells are known to have worked, are delightful. The adjoining cottage garden at Gould's Grove Farmhouse has interesting shrubs and Jacob sheep.

Mature garden with an air of mystery and romance with the ever-changing sight and sound of water . . .

76 ◆ UNIVERSITY OF OXFORD BOTANIC GARDEN
Rose Lane, Oxford OX1 4AZ. University of Oxford, 01865 286690, www.botanic-garden.ox.ac.uk. *1m E of Oxford city centre. Bottom of High St in central Oxford, on banks of the R Cherwell by Magdalen Bridge and opp Magdalen College Tower.* **Adm £4.50, chd free. For NGS: Tue 16 Sept (9-5). For other opening times and information, please phone or see garden website.**
The Botanic Garden contains more species of plants per acre than anywhere else on earth. These plants are grown in 7 glasshouses, water and rock gardens, large herbaceous border, walled garden and every available space. In total there are around 5,000 different plants to see. National Collection of Euphorbia. Glasshouses Systematic beds Euphorbia collection Herbaceous border Merton borders Tolkien's pine tree. Gravel paths.

NCH

77 UPPER CHALFORD FARM
between Sydenham & Postcombe, Chinnor OX39 4NH. Mr & Mrs Paul Rooksby, 01844 351320. *4½ m SE of Thame. M40 exit J6. A40 to Postcombe turn R to Chalford (L if on A40 from Oxford). After 1m L at 1st telegraph pole (between Sydenham & Postcombe).* Cream teas. **Adm £4, chd free. Thur 19 June (3.30-7); Sun 22 June, Sun 13 July (2-5.30). Visitors also welcome by appt for groups of up to 45.**
Jacobean farmhouse garden, old roses, shrubs and perennials. Unusual trees and an ancient black pine. Hidden gardens with different plantings and peaceful places to sit. Spring-fed pond and stream with damp planted banks leading to reclaimed woodland with treehouse. Newly established bog garden and landscaping. Short gravel drive from car park. A closer drop-off point is possible.

78 WADHAM COLLEGE
Parks Road, Oxford OX1 3PN. The Warden & Fellows. *Central Oxford.* **Adm £2, chd free. Sun 6 Apr, Sun 13 July (2-5).**
5-acres, best known for trees, spring bulbs and mixed borders. In Fellows' main garden, fine ginkgo and *Magnolia acuminata*; bamboo plantation; in Back Quadrangle very large *Tilia tomentosa* 'Petiolaris'; in Mallam Court white scented garden est 1994; in Warden's garden an ancient tulip tree; in Fellows' private garden, Civil War embankment with period fruit tree cultivars, recently established shrubbery with unusual trees and ground cover amongst older plantings.

79 ◆ WATERPERRY GARDENS
Waterperry, nr Wheatley OX33 1JZ. School of Economic Science, 01844 337264, www.waterperrygardens.co.uk. *9m E of Oxford. For Sat-navs please use OX33 1LG.* Light refreshments. **Adm £6.50, chd free. For NGS: Sun 20 Apr (10-5); Sun 21 Sept (10-5.30). For other opening times and information, please phone or see garden website.**
Waterperry Gardens are an inspiration. 8-acres of landscaped gardens incl rose and formal knot garden, water lily canal, riverside walk and one of the country's finest purely herbaceous borders. There's also a plant centre, garden shop, teashop, art gallery, museum and Saxon church. National Collection of Kabschia and Silver Saxifrages. Fritillaries looking fantastic for April opening. Michaelmas weekend coincides with Sept NGS open day. Riverside Walk may be inaccessible to wheelchair users if very wet.

NCH

80 WAYSIDE

82 Banbury Road, Kidlington OX5 2BX. Margaret & Alistair Urquhart, 01865 460180, alistairurquhart@ntlworld.com. *5m N of Oxford. On R of A4260 travelling N through Kidlington.* Home-made teas. **Adm £3, chd free. Sun 1 June (2-6). Visitors also welcome by appt May to June.**

¼ -acre garden shaded by mature trees. Mixed border with some rare and unusual plants and shrubs. A climber clothed pergola leads past a dry gravel garden to the woodland garden with an extensive collection of hardy ferns. Conservatory, and large fern house with a collection of unusual species of tree ferns and tender exotics. Limited access for wheelchairs.

81 WESTWELL MANOR

Westwell, nr Burford OX18 4JT. Mr Thomas Gibson. *2m SW of Burford. From A40 Burford-Cheltenham, turn L ½ m after Burford r'about signed Westwell. After 1½ m at T-junction, turn R and Manor is 2nd house on L.* Home-made teas in the village. **Adm £5, chd free (share to St Marys Church, Westwell). Sun 22 June (2.30-6).**

6-acres surrounding old Cotswold manor house (not open), knot garden, potager, shrub roses, herbaceous borders, topiary, earth works, moonlight garden, rills and water garden, auricula ladder.

GROUP OPENING

82 WHEATLEY GARDENS

High Street, Wheatley OX33 1XX, 01865 875022, echess@hotmail.co.uk. *5m E of Oxford. Leave A40 at Wheatley, turn into High St. Gardens at W-end of High St, S-side.* Cream teas at The Manor House. **Combined adm £4.50, chd free. Sun 22 June (2-6). Visitors also welcome by appt.**

BREACH HOUSE GARDEN
Liz Parry
Visitors also welcome by appt. 01865 876278

THE MANOR HOUSE
Mrs Edward Hess
Visitors also welcome by appt. 01865 875022 ehess@hotmail.co.uk

THE STUDIO
S & A Buckingham.
At the rear of the Wheatley Manor Garden
Visitors also welcome by appt. ann.buckingham@alexlive.com

Three adjoining gardens in the historic coaching village of Wheatley. Breach House Garden has an established main area with extensive shrubs and perennials, also a more contemporary reflective space with a wild pond. The Manor House is a 1½ -acre garden surrounding an Elizabethan manor house (not open). Formal box walk, herb garden, cottage garden with rose arches and a shrubbery with old roses. A romantic oasis in this busy village. The Studio is a cottage-style walled garden developed from what was once a farm yard. Herbaceous borders, climbing roses and clematis, shrubs, vegetable plot and fruit trees. All in all a lovely little collection of gardens set in the busy village of Wheatley. Various musical events. Wheelchair accessible with assistance, although there are gravel paths, 2 shallow steps and grass.

83 WHITEHILL FARM

Widford nr Burford OX18 4DT. Mr & Mrs Paul Youngson, 01993 823218, a.youngson@virgin.net, www.whitehillfarmnursery.co.uk. *1m E of Burford. From A40 take turn signed Widford. Follow signs to Whitehill Farm Nursery.* Home-made teas. **Adm £3.50, chd free. Sun 8 June (2-6). Visitors also welcome by appt May to Aug, teas for groups of 10+ only.**

2-acres of hillside gardens and woodland with spectacular views overlooking Burford and Windrush valley. Informal plantsman's garden being continuously developed in various areas. Herbaceous and shrub borders, ponds and bog area, old-fashioned roses, ground cover, ornamental grasses, bamboos and hardy geraniums.

84 WILDWOOD

Farnborough OX17 1EL. Mr & Mrs M Hart. *5m N of Banbury, 8m S of Southam. On A423 at Oxon/Warwicks border. Next to Farnborough Garden Centre.* Home-made teas. **Adm £3.50, chd free. Sun 25, Mon 26 May (1-5).**

Delightful ½ -acre garden in the country set amongst mature trees and shrubs providing a haven for wildlife. Garden is stocked with many unusual plants and shrubs and also contains interesting rustic garden features, many of which are made by the owner. Cut flower garden. Rare plants for sale.

85 WOLFSON COLLEGE

Oxford OX2 6UD. President & Fellows of Wolfson College, www.wolfson.ox.ac.uk. *¾ m N of Oxford city centre. Turn R off Banbury Rd to end of Linton Rd.* Home-made teas. **Adm £3, chd free. Sun 25 May (2-6).**

A splendid modern garden of 9-acres by R Cherwell developed in recent yrs with comprehensive plant collection tolerant of alkaline soils, grown in interesting and varied habitats around a framework of fine mature trees.

86 WOOLSTONE MILL HOUSE

Woolstone, nr Faringdon SN7 7QL. Mr & Mrs Anthony Spink, 01367 820219, pennyspink@gmail.com. *7m W of Wantage. 7m S of Faringdon. Woolstone is a small village off B4507 below Uffington White Horse Hill.* Home-made teas. **Adm £5, chd free. Every Wed 7 May to 24 Sept (2-5).**

2-acre garden in pretty hidden village. Stream runs through garden. Large mixed herbaceous and shrub circular border bounded by yew hedges. Small gravel, cutting, kitchen and bog gardens. Topiary. Medlars and old-fashioned roses. Tree house with spectacular views to Uffington White Horse and White Horse Hill. C18 mill house and barn (not open). Partial wheelchair access.

St Hugh's Cottage

Oxfordshire County Volunteers

County Organisers

Marina Hamilton-Baillie, Rectory House, Church Green, Stanford in the Vale, SN7 8HU, 01367 710486, marina_hamilton_baillie@hotmail.com

David White, Placketts, High Street, Adderbury, Banbury OX17 3LS, 01295 812679, david.white@doctors.org.uk

Treasurer

David White, Placketts, High Street, Adderbury, Banbury OX17 3LS, 01295 812679, david.white@doctors.org.uk

Publicity & North West Oxon

Priscilla Frost, 27 Ditchley Road, Charlbury, Chipping Norton OX7 3QS, 01608 810578, info@oxconf.co.uk

Booklet Coordinator

Catherine Pinney, Pond House, Pyrton, Watlington OX49 5AP, 01491 612638

Assistant County Organisers

Lynn Baldwin, 9 Toy Lane, Chipping Norton OX7 5FH, 01608 642754, elynnbaldwin@gmail.com

Graham & Rosemarie Lenton, The Old School, 25A Standlake Road, Ducklington, Witney OX29 7UR, 01993 899033, grahamlenton@btopenworld.com

John & Joan Pumfrey, Hearns House, Gallows Tree Common, Reading RG4 9DE, 01189 722848, joanpumfrey@lineone.net

Charles & Lyn Sanders, Uplands, Old Boars Hill, Oxford OX1 5JF, 01865 739486, sandersc4@hotmail.com

SHROPSHIRE

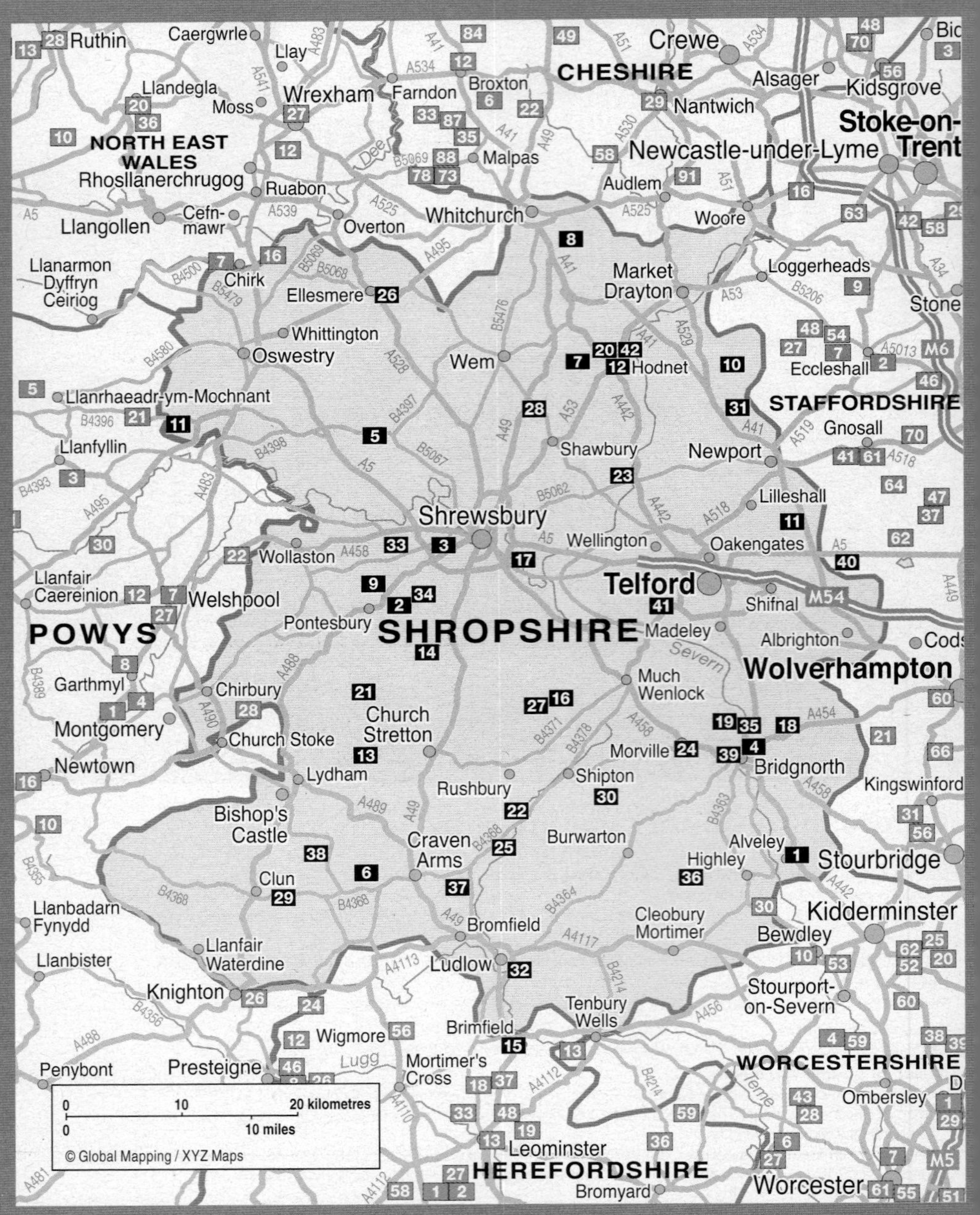
Ruthin
Caergwrle
Llay
Crewe
CHESHIRE
Alsager
Kidsgrove
Stoke-on-Trent
Llandegla
Moss
Wrexham
Farndon
Broxton
Nantwich
NORTH EAST WALES
Rhosllanerchrugog
Ruabon
Malpas
Newcastle-under-Lyme
Audlem
Llangollen
Cefn-mawr
Overton
Whitchurch
Woore
Dee
Llanarmon Dyffryn Ceiriog
Chirk
Ellesmere
Market Drayton
Loggerheads
Stone
Whittington
Oswestry
Wem
Hodnet
Eccleshall
STAFFORDSHIRE
Llanrhaeadr-ym-Mochnant
Gnosall
Llanfyllin
Shawbury
Newport
Lilleshall
Shrewsbury
Wellington
Oakengates
Wollaston
Telford
Llanfair Caereinion
Welshpool
Shifnal
Pontesbury
SHROPSHIRE
Madeley
Albrighton
Cods
POWYS
Severn
Wolverhampton
Garthmyl
Chirbury
Much Wenlock
Montgomery
Church Stretton
Church Stoke
Morville
Bridgnorth
Newtown
Lydham
Shipton
Rushbury
Kingswinford
Bishop's Castle
Craven Arms
Burwarton
Alveley
Highley
Stourbridge
Clun
Llanbadarn Fynydd
Bromfield
Cleobury Mortimer
Kidderminster
Bewdley
Llanfair Waterdine
Llanbister
Ludlow
Knighton
Tenbury Wells
Stourport-on-Severn
Wigmore
Brimfield
Lugg
Mortimer's Cross
WORCESTERSHIRE
Penybont
Presteigne
Teme
Ombersley
Leominster
HEREFORDSHIRE
Worcester
Bromyard
0 10 20 kilometres
0 10 miles
© Global Mapping / XYZ Maps

Opening Dates

All entries subject to change. For latest information check www.ngs.org.uk

February

Date to be announced see NGS website
23 Moortown

April

Sunday 20
39 8 Westgate Villas (Evening)

Monday 21
39 8 Westgate Villas

Tuesday 22
29 Radnor Cottage

Sunday 27
19 Lyndale House

Tuesday 29
5 Brownhill House

May

Sunday 4
14 Holly Grove
17 Longner Hall
22 Millichope Park

Friday 16
42 Wollerton Old Hall

Sunday 18
1 Ancoireán
7 The Citadel
26 Oteley

Sunday 25
38 Walcot Hall

Monday 26
27 Preen Manor
38 Walcot Hall

Tuesday 27
5 Brownhill House

Wednesday 28
10 Goldstone Hall Gardens

June

8 The Croft (Every Tuesday)

Sunday 1
10 Goldstone Hall Gardens
21 Marehay Farm
35 Stanley Hall
37 NEW Tower House

Wednesday 4
9 Edge Villa

Festival Weekend

Sunday 8
24 Morville Hall Gardens
33 Shoothill House

Saturday 14
30 Ruthall Manor

Sunday 15
12 Hodnet Hall Gardens
30 Ruthall Manor
39 8 Westgate Villas
41 Windy Ridge

Monday 16
30 Ruthall Manor

Saturday 21
32 Secret Garden
36 Stottesdon & Chorley Village Gardens

Sunday 22
6 NEW Caudibrook House
19 Lyndale House
36 Stottesdon & Chorley Village Gardens

Tuesday 24
5 Brownhill House

Sunday 29
15 Holmcroft

July

8 The Croft (Every Tuesday)

Wednesday 2
40 Weston Park

Sunday 6
3 Bowbrook Allotment Community
4 NEW 48 Bramble Ridge
13 Holly Cottage

Tuesday 8
25 Mynd Hardy Plants

Sunday 13
20 Marchamley House Garden
31 NEW Sambrook Manor
41 Windy Ridge

Wednesday 16
10 Goldstone Hall Gardens

Sunday 20
1 Ancoireán
10 Goldstone Hall Gardens
25 Mynd Hardy Plants

Sunday 27
16 Jessamine Cottage

August

8 The Croft (Every Tuesday)

Sunday 3
2 NEW Avocet

Wednesday 6
10 Goldstone Hall Gardens

Sunday 10
10 Goldstone Hall Gardens
41 Windy Ridge

Sunday 17
9 Edge Villa
31 NEW Sambrook Manor

Sunday 31
16 Jessamine Cottage

September

Sunday 7
41 Windy Ridge

Sunday 14
33 Shoothill House

October

Sunday 5
27 Preen Manor

Sunday 12
22 Millichope Park

Gardens open to the public

16 Jessamine Cottage
40 Weston Park
42 Wollerton Old Hall

By appointment only

11 Heath Garden
18 Lower Hall
28 Preston Hall
34 Sibberscote Manor

Also open by appointment

1 Ancoireán
3 Bowbrook Allotment Community
5 Brownhill House
9 Edge Villa
10 Goldstone Hall Gardens
13 Holly Cottage
14 Holly Grove
21 Marehay Farm
26 Oteley
27 Preen Manor
29 Radnor Cottage
31 NEW Sambrook Manor
32 Secret Garden
33 Shoothill House
38 Walcot Hall
41 Windy Ridge

The Gardens

1 ANCOIREÁN

24 Romsley View, Alveley WV15 6PJ. Judy & Peter Creed, 01746 780504, pdjc@me.com. *6m S Bridgnorth off A442 Bridgnorth to Kidderminster rd. North from Kidderminster turn L just after Royal Oak PH. S from Bridgnorth turn R after Squirrel PH. Take 3rd turning on R & follow NGS signs.* Home-made teas. **Adm £3.50, chd free.** Suns 18 May; 20 July (1-5). **Visitors also welcome by appt May to July 20+.**

Natural garden layout on several levels, developed over 30yrs, with a large variety of herbaceous plants and shrubs, water features, wooded area with bog garden containing numerous varieties of ferns and hostas, and colouful Alpine scree. Features incl chickens in wooded area, stumpery, ornamental grass border and Spring Bulb collection. New for 2014 Clematis collection, acer and azalea beds. Selection of plants and bird and insect boxes for sale. Close to Severn Valley Railway and Country Park and Dudmaston Hall NT. Featured in Shropshire Star and Bridgnorth Journal.

2 NEW AVOCET

3 Main Road, Plealey, Shrewsbury SY5 0UZ. Malc & Jude Mollart. *6m SW of Shrewsbury. From A5 take A488 signed Bishops Castle, approx ½ m past Lea Cross Tavern turn L signed Plealey. In ¾ m turn L, garden on R.* Tea. **Adm £3, chd free.** Sun 3 Aug (11-5).

Cottage style garden with modern twists owned by plantaholics. Designed around a series of garden compartments. Features incl wildlife pool, mixed borders, trained fruit trees, chickens and sculpture. Quiz sheet for children. Countryside views and walks from garden.

ALLOTMENTS

3 BOWBROOK ALLOTMENT COMMUNITY

Mytton Oak Road, Shrewsbury SY3 5BT, malcandjude@btinternet.com, www.bowbrookallotments.co.uk. *½ m from Royal Shrewsbury Hospital. From A5 Shrewsbury bypass take B4386 following signs for hospital. Allotments situated ½ m along B4386. (Mytton Oak Rd) on R.* Tea. **Combined adm £3.50, chd free.** Sun 6 July (2-6). **Visitors also welcome by appt June to Aug, groups of 10+.**

Recipient of RHS National Certificate of Distinction, this 5 acre site, recently extended to 93 plots, has featured in a variety of magazines and on local radio stations and displays wide ranging cultivation methods. Members cultivate organically with nature in mind using companion planting and attracting natural predators. Green spaces flourish throughout and include Gardens of the 4 Seasons, orchards, and many wildlife features including wild flower meadows. The gardens provide a peaceful haven for members and visitors. Children are encouraged to be part of the community and have their own special places such as a story telling willow dome, willow tunnel, sensory garden and turf spiral with textured totem pole. New for this year are a Contemplation Garden, a Prairie Garden and a large wildlife pond is under development. Visitors can participate in voting for Favourite Plot and follow the interest trail. Children are particularly welcome and can enjoy their own quizzes. Displays by Shropshire Hardy Plant Society, Shropshire Wildlife Trust and Shropshire Master Composters.. Wheelchair access, flat wide grass paths allow access to the main features of the site and to the interest trail.

4 NEW 48 BRAMBLE RIDGE

Bridgnorth WV16 4SQ. Chris, Heather & Lucy. *From Bridgnorth N on B4373 signed Broseley. 1st on R Stanley Lane, 1st R Bramble Ridge. From Broseley S on B4373, nr Bridgnorth turn L into Stanley Lane, 1st R Bramble Ridge.* Tea. **Adm £4, chd free.** Sun 6 July (1-5.30).

Steep garden with many steps, part wild, part cultivated, terraced in places and overlooking the Severn valley with views to High Rock and Queens Parlour. Described by some as fascinating and full of interest; the garden incl shrubs, perennials, small vegetable plot, herbs, wildlife pond and summerhouse. Other cottage style gardens also open in Bramble Ridge.

BROOK FARM

See Worcestershire

5 BROWNHILL HOUSE

Ruyton XI Towns, Shrewsbury SY4 1LR. Roger & Yoland Brown, 01939 261121, brownhill@eleventowns.co.uk, www.eleventowns.co.uk. *10m NW of Shrewsbury on B4397. On the B4397 in the village of Ruyton XI Towns.* Home-made teas. **Adm £3.50, chd free.** Tues 29 Apr; 27 May; 24 June (1.30-5.30). **Visitors also welcome by appt Apr to July, individuals or groups.**

'Has to be seen to be believed'. A unique hillside garden (over 700 steps) bordering R Perry. Wide variety of styles and plants from formal terraces to woodland paths, plus large kitchen garden. Kit cars on show. Featured in GGG and Shropshire Life.

Overlooking the Severn valley with views to High Rock and Queens Parlour . . .

6 NEW CAUDIBROOK HOUSE

Hopesay, Craven Arms SY7 8HD. Chris & Carol Clarke. *4m Craven Arms, 7m Bishops Castle, 11m Ludlow. From A49 take B4368 to Aston on Clun, R over bridge signed Hopesay & Edgeton. After 1m enter Hopesay, 1st R signed Round oak. Park as directed.* Home-made teas. **Adm £3.50, chd free.** Sun 22 June (2-5).

This 20yrs old, ¾ acre garden has gravel paths leading through to a stream and views of fields and Hopesay Hill. Set out in mixed borders of ornamental and fruit trees, shrubs and hardy perennials. An alpine garden, large vegetable plot and fruit cage. Roses and peonies predominate in June with a thyme lawn giving a purple hue.

The Citadel

© Julia Stanley

7 THE CITADEL

Weston-under-Redcastle SY4 5JY. Mr Beverley & Mrs Sylvia Griffiths, www.thecitadelweston.co.uk. *12m N of Shrewsbury on A49. At Xrds turn for Hawkstone Park, through village of Weston-under-Redcastle, 1/4 m on R beyond village.* Home-made teas. **Adm £3.50, chd free.** **Sun 18 May (2-5).**

Imposing castellated house (not open) stands in 4 acres. Mature garden, with fine trees, rhododendrons, azaleas, acers and camellias. Herbaceous borders; walled potager and Victorian thatched summerhouse provide added interest. Paths meander around and over sandstone outcrop at centre.

8 THE CROFT

Ash Magna, Whitchurch SY13 4DR. Peter & Shiela Martinson. *2m S of Whitchurch. From Whitchurch bypass take A525 Newcastle (A530 Nantwich). 'Ash' signposted at r'about. Village centre 2 miles. Follow signs to garden.* Home-made teas. **Adm £3, chd free.** **Every Tue 6 May to 26 Aug (1-5).**

Just how much food can be produced on about an acre, whilst still indulging a love of colour and the natural world? A wonderful place for children to run, play and discover, shared with contented animals, flowers, fruit and vegetables with a 'green man' hiding in the woodland. Sheep, pigs and chickens. Pond dipping.

9 EDGE VILLA

Edge, nr Yockleton SY5 9PY. Mr & Mrs W F Neil, 01743 821651, bill@billfneil.fsnet.co.uk. *6m SW of Shrewsbury. From A5 take either A488 signed to Bishops Castle or B4386 to Montgomery for approx 6m then follow NGS signs.* Home-made teas. **Adm £3, (Wed), £4 (Sun) chd free.** **Wed 4 June (9.30-1); Sun 17 Aug (2-5). Visitors also welcome by appt May to Aug, adm £4, group 20+.**

Two acres nestling in South Shropshire hills. Self-sufficient vegetable plot. Chickens in orchard, foxes permitting. Large herbaceous borders. Dewpond surrounded by purple elder, irises, candelabra primulas and dieramas. Large selection of fragrant roses. Comprehensive plant stall. Teas in sheltered courtyard. Wed 4 June is a morning opening with plant sale. Some gravel paths.

10 GOLDSTONE HALL GARDENS

Goldstone, Market Drayton TF9 2NA. Miss Victoria Cushing, 01630 661202, enquiries@goldstonehall.com, www.goldstonehall.com. *5m N of Newport on A41. Follow brown signs from Hinstock. From Shrewsbury A53, R for A41 Hinstock & follow brown signs.* Home-made teas. **Adm £3.50, chd free.** **Weds, Suns 28 May; 1 June; 16, 20 July; 6, 10 Aug (2-5). Visitors also welcome by appt June to Sept, groups of 10+.**

Mature setting of Goldstone Hall: large well ordered kitchen garden with raised beds and herbal walkway cover over a third of an acre; double tiered herbaceous border; award winning oak framed pavilion perfect for afternoon tea; Edibles garden showcasing unusual food crops from the Himalayas and Andes; restructured Fern border and redesigned and newly planted front driveway all in 5 acres. Majority of garden can be accessed on gravel and lawns.

11 HEATH GARDEN

Heath Hill, Sheriffhales, Shifnal TF11 8RR. Gordon Malt, 01952 691341, 1malt@supanet.com. *1m N of Sherriffhales on B4379.* Home-made teas. **Adm £3, chd free.** Visitors welcome by appt **Apr to Oct.**

A developing garden with a wide range of interesting plants (some less usual) incl climbing and wall plants, silver foliage, seasonal pots and containers, salvias, ornamental grasses, bulbous plants and productive vegetable plot and fruit area. Demonstrations available for groups. Some gravel paths.

Marie Curie
Cancer Care
NGS donations
have helped fund
342 Marie Curie
Nurses

12 HODNET HALL GARDENS

Hodnet, nr Market Drayton TF9 3NN. Mr & The Hon Mrs Heber-Percy, www.hodnethallgardens.org. *5½ m SW of Market Drayton. 12m NE Shrewsbury. At junction of A53 & A442.* Light refreshments. **Adm £6, chd £3.** Sun 15 June (12-5).

60-acre landscaped garden with series of lakes and pools; magnificent forest trees, great variety of flowers, shrubs providing colour throughout season. Unique collection of big-game trophies in C17 tearooms. Kitchen garden. For details please see website.

13 HOLLY COTTAGE

Prolley Moor, Wentnor SY9 5EH. Julian French & Heather Williams, 01588 650610, heatherannw56@yahoo.co.uk. *7m NE of Bishop's Castle. From A489 take rd signed Wentnor. In Wentnor pass The Crown on R. Take next R signed Prolley Moor, then 1st L, signed Adstone.* Light refreshments. **Adm £3, chd free.** Sun 6 July (2-6). **Visitors also welcome by appt May to Aug.**

Organic garden of 2½ acres set in beautiful countryside under the Long Mynd. Areas incl 1 acre of 10yr old native woodland, wild flower meadow with willow circle and allotment area. Nearer the house the flower garden is stocked with herbaceous plants, trees and shrubs with pond, trellis and improved layout in old orchard. Display by local gardening club. Gravel and grass paths.

14 HOLLY GROVE

Church Pulverbatch SY5 8DD. Peter & Angela Unsworth, 01743 718221, angela.unsworth@btinternet.com. *6m S of Shrewsbury. Midway between Stapleton & Church Pulverbatch. From A49 follow signs to Stapleton & Pulverbatch.* Home-made teas. **Adm £4, chd free.** Sun 4 May (2-5). **Visitors also welcome by appt May to July for 10+. Also in winter for snowdrops.**

3-acre garden set in S Shropshire countryside. Yew and beech hedges enclosing 'rooms', box parterres, pleached limes, vegetable garden, rose and herbaceous borders containing many rare plants. Arboretum, lake and wild flower meadows. Opportunity to see rare White Park cattle and Soay sheep. Wheelchair access to most areas.

15 HOLMCROFT

Wyson Lane, Brimfield, nr Ludlow SY8 4NW. Mr & Mrs Michael Dowding, www.anenglishcottageonline.com. *4m S of Ludlow & 6m N of Leominster. From Ludlow or Leominster leave the A49 at the Salway Arms PH, turn into lane signed Wyson only. From Tenbury Wells cross the A49 into Wyson Lane.* Home-made teas. **Adm £4, chd free.** Sun 29 June (2-5.30).

C17 thatched cottage set in terraced gardens of ¾ acre. Sunken, gravel and terraced garden with its roses. Woodland walk to fern bank. Orchard with rose poles and kitchen garden with views of Mortimer Forest and Clee Hill. A willow tunnel takes you to the long borders and then through the moon gate. Only the woodland walk is inaccessible for wheelchairs.

HUNTERS END

See Worcestershire

16 ◆ JESSAMINE COTTAGE

Kenley, Shrewsbury SY5 6NS. Lee & Pamela Wheeler, 01694 771279, www.stmem.com/jessamine-cottage. *6m W of Much Wenlock. Signed from B4371 Much Wenlock to Church Stretton Rd and from A458 Shrewsbury to Much Wenlock Rd at Harley.* Home-made teas. **Adm £4, chd £1.** For NGS: Suns 27 July; 31 Aug (2-6). **For other opening times and information, please phone or see garden website.**

'A slice of heaven' and 'inspirational': typical comments from visitors to this 3-acre garden which incl mature wildlife pond, mixed island beds, lime avenue, large kitchen garden; parterre; stream and woodland. All-season colour is provided by a rose garden and ornamental trees, large range of attractive perennials and shrubs. Groups by appointment. Featured in Shropshire Magazine. Wheelchair access to most areas.

17 LONGNER HALL

Atcham, Shrewsbury SY4 4TG. Mr & Mrs R L Burton. *4m SE of Shrewsbury. From M54 follow A5 to Shrewsbury, then B4380 to Atcham. From Atcham take Uffington rd, entrance ¼ m on L.* Home-made teas. **Adm £4, chd free.** Sun 4 May (2-5).

A long drive approach through parkland designed by Humphry Repton. Walks lined with golden yew through extensive lawns, with views over Severn Valley. Borders containing roses, herbaceous and shrubs, also ancient yew wood. Enclosed walled garden containing mixed planting, garden buildings, tower and game larder. Short woodland walk around old moat pond. 1-acre walled garden currently being restored now open to visitors. Woodland walk not suitable for wheelchairs.

18 LOWER HALL

Worfield WV15 5LH. Mr & Mrs C F Dumbell, 01746 716419, claireevitts666@btinternet.com. *3½ m E of Bridgnorth. ½ m N of A454 in village centre.* Light refreshments. **Adm £5, chd free.** Visitors welcome by appt **May to June, minimum group 20+.**

4 acres on R Worfe. Garden

developed by present owners. Courtyard with fountain, walled garden with old-fashioned roses, clematis and mixed borders. Water garden with pool, primula island and rock garden. Woodland garden with rare trees incl magnolias, paper bark and Japanese maples.

19 LYNDALE HOUSE
Astley Abbots, Bridgnorth WV16 4SW. Bob & Mary Saunders. *2m out of Bridnorth off B4373. From High Town Bridgnorth take B4373 Broseley Rd for 1½ m, then take lane signed Astley Abbotts & Colemore Green.* Tea. **Adm £3.50, chd free.** **Suns 27 Apr; 22 June (1-5).**
Large 1½ acre garden which has evolved over 20yrs. Terrace with roses, alliums and iris surrounded by box hedging. Specimen trees planted in large lawn. Hundreds of tulips for spring colour. Clematis and allium walk to pool and waterfall. Vegetable garden and working greenhouses. Densely planted borders. Pool with waterfall and 'pebble beach'. Courtyard garden with slate and topiary garden. Please ask owner about wheelchair friendly access.

20 MARCHAMLEY HOUSE GARDEN
Marchamley, nr Hodnet SY4 5LE. Mr & Mrs A Davies. *6m SW of Market Drayton. At Hodnet on A53 between Market Drayton & Shrewsbury take rd opp the Bear Hotel to Marchamley & follow NGS signs for parking.* Home-made teas. **Adm £3, chd free.** **Sun 13 July (12.30-5).**
2-acre garden set in the Shropshire countryside with stunning views. Lily pond and herb garden with shrub and herbaceous perennial borders, fruit trees and vegetable garden. Sloping lawn leads down to a large pond with mature trees, with a meadow walk beyond. Exhibition and sale of pictures by Botanical Artist Mary Morton.

21 MAREHAY FARM
Gatten, Ratlinghope SY5 0SJ. Stuart & Carol Buxton, 01588 650289, candsbuxton@gmail.com. *6½ m W of Church Stretton, 9m NNE of Bishops Castle. 1½ m from 'The Bridges' Xrds & the intersection of the Longden, Pulverbatch & Bishops Castle rd and the minor rd from Church Stretton to the Stiperstones.* Home-made teas. **Adm £3, chd free.** **Sun 1 June (11-6). Visitors also welcome by appt May to Aug, refreshments with prior notice of numbers.**
In 1982 a building society surveyor reported 'there is no garden and at this height (1100ft), elevation and aspect there never will be!' Since 1990, on heavy boulder clay a 1½ acre woodland/water garden evolved, with primulas, hostas, iris, damp/shade tolerant perennials. Rhododendrons, azaleas, various conifers, trees, roses and shrubs complementing the location. In an area of outstanding beauty AONB. Splendid isolation. A 'primularium' is being established as part of a woodland walk. Featured in WI Life and Shropshire Star. Some gravel, assistance may be required for wheelchairs.

Medieval stew pond, shrub borders and large lawns, all offering glorious views across the Mor Valley . . .

22 MILLICHOPE PARK
Munslow, Craven Arms, Munslow SY7 9HA. Mr & Mrs Frank Bury. *8m NE of Craven Arms. From Ludlow (11m) turn L off B4368, just ½ m outside village of Munslow.* Home-made teas in village clubroom. **Adm £5, chd free.** **Sun 4 May (2-6); Sun 12 Oct (2-5).**
Historic landscape gardens covering 14 acres with lakes, cascades dating from C18, woodland walks and wildflowers. Bluebells in May. Autumn colour in October. Rare opportunity to see the Bouts Viola. UK's largest collection of hardy, perennial, scented violas. Many varieties for sale during the May opening. Limited wheelchair access, incl WC.

23 MOORTOWN
nr Wellington TF6 6JE. Mr David Bromley, 01952 770205. *8m N of Telford. 5m N of Wellington. Take B5062 signed Moortown 1m between High Ercall & Crudgington.* **Adm £4, chd free.** **Opening for Snowdrops in late February 2014. See website for opening times as they depend on the weather!**
Approx 1-acre plantsman's garden. Here may be found the old-fashioned, the unusual and even the oddities of plant life, in mixed borders of 'controlled' confusion.

GROUP OPENING

24 MORVILLE HALL GARDENS
Bridgnorth WV16 5NB. *3m W of Bridgnorth. On A458 at junction with B4368.* Home-made teas in Morville Church. **Combined adm £5, chd free (share to Morville Church).** **Sun 8 June (2-5).**

THE COTTAGE
Mrs J Bolton

THE DOWER HOUSE
Dr Katherine Swift

1 THE GATE HOUSE
Mr & Mrs Rowe

2 THE GATE HOUSE
Mrs G Medland

MORVILLE HALL
Dr & Mrs J C Douglas & The National Trust

An interesting group of gardens that surround a beautiful Grade I listed mansion (not open). The Cottage has a walled cottage garden which is currently being re-developed. The Dower House is a horticultural history lesson about Morville Hall which incl a turf maze, cloister garden, Elizabethan knot garden, C18 canal garden, Edwardian kitchen garden and more. It is the setting of Katherine Swift's bestselling book 'The Morville Hours', and the sequel 'The Morville Year'. 1 & 2 The Gate House are cottage-style gardens with colourful borders, formal areas, lawns and wooded glades. The 4-acre Morville Hall (NT) garden has a parterre, medieval stew pond, shrub borders and large lawns, all offering glorious views across the Mor Valley. Mostly all level but areas of gravel in some gardens.

The Dower House, Morville Hall Gardens

25 MYND HARDY PLANTS

Delbury Hall Estate, Mill Lane, Diddlebury, Craven Arms SY7 9DH. Mr Mark Zenick, www.myndhardyplants.co.uk. *8m W of Craven Arms. 1m off B4368, Craven Arms to Bridgnorth, through village of Diddlebury, turn R at Mynd Hardy Plants sign.* Home-made teas. **Adm £3, chd free. Tue 8, Sun 20 July (1-5).**

Commercial nursery within old walled garden, offering and selling more than 800 varieties of herbaceous perennials. Speciality is hemerocallis with more than 150 day lily varieties, American hybrids, field grown. More than 80% of day lily varieties cannot be seen elsewhere in the UK. Gravel and grass paths.

26 OTELEY

Ellesmere SY12 0PB. Mr & Mrs R K Mainwaring, 01691 622514. *1m SE of Ellesmere. Entrance out of Ellesmere past Mere, opp Convent nr to A528/495 junction.* Home-made teas. **Adm £3, chd free. Sun 18 May (1-5). Visitors also welcome by appt May to July, for groups 10+.**

10 acres running down to Mere, incl walled kitchen garden; architectural features; many interesting trees, rhododendrons and azaleas, incl wild woodland walk, views across Mere to Ellesmere Church. Wheelchair access if dry.

27 PREEN MANOR

Church Preen SY6 7LQ. Mrs Ann Trevor-Jones, 01694 771207. *6m W of Much Wenlock. Signed from B4371.* Home-made teas. **Adm £5, chd free. Mon 26 May (2-6); Sun 5 Oct (2-5). Visitors also welcome by appt May to July, for groups of 10+.**

6-acre garden on site of Cluniac monastery and Norman Shaw mansion. Kitchen, chess, water and wild gardens. Fine trees in park; woodland walks. Developed for over 30yrs with changes always in progress. Thanksgiving 4.30pm in church adjacent to garden (Oct).

28 PRESTON HALL

Preston Hall, Preston Brockhurst, Shrewsbury SY4 5QA. C C & L Corbet, 01939 220312, corbetleil@btinternet.com. *8m N of Shrewsbury on A49. Coaches must enter gates from the South.* Tea & coffee in the house kitchen. **Adm £5, chd free. Visitors welcome by appt Apr to Sept. Corbet Bed Embroideries talk.**

A large informal garden with interesting trees (planted about 1995). Large oval herbaceous border. Formal garden in front of 1700 stone house (not open) and large sunken courtyard at the back. Walled garden with a newly restored 1911 Cricket Pavilion (open), meadow walk with small pond and ducks. Grass paths, courtyard has steps.

29 RADNOR COTTAGE

Clun SY7 0JA. Pam & David Pittwood, 01588 640451. *7m W of Craven Arms. 1m E of Clun on B4368.* Home-made teas. **Adm £3, chd free (share to Hope House Children's Hospice). Tue 22 Apr (2-6). Visitors also welcome by appt Apr to Sept.**

2 acres on S-facing slope, overlooking Clun Valley. Wide variety of garden habitats all densely planted. Incl sunny terracing with paving and dry-stone walling; alpine troughs; cottage garden borders; damp shade for white flowers and gold foliage; pond, stream and bog garden; orchard; rough grass with naturalised bulbs and wild flowers.

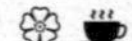

30 RUTHALL MANOR

Ditton Priors, Bridgnorth WV16 6TN. Mr & Mrs G T Clarke. *7m SW of Bridgnorth. Ruthall Rd signed nr garage in Ditton Priors*. Home-made teas. **Adm £3.50, chd free. Sat 14, Sun 15, Mon 16 June (12-6).**

1-acre garden with ha-ha and old horse pond planted with candelabra primulas, iris and bog plants. Rare specimen trees. Designed for easy maintenance with lots of ground cover and unusual plants. Gravel art garden and other areas for low maintenance incl stumpery. New features being added year by year. Jigsaws for sale.

31 NEW SAMBROOK MANOR

Sambrook, Newport TF10 8AL. Mrs E Mitchell, 01952 550256, sambrookmanor@btconnect.com. *Between Newport & Ternhill. 1m off A41 in the village of Sambrook*. Light refreshments. **Adm £4, chd free. Suns 13 July; 17 Aug (12.30-6). Visitors also welcome by appt June to Sept, for groups 10+.**

The garden surrounds the early C18 manor house (not open) and contains a wide selection of herbaceous plants and roses. Features incl a waterfall down to a pond and various acers. A new development leading to the river along the edge of the garden is filled with a variety of shrubs and trees.

32 SECRET GARDEN

21 Steventon Terrace, Steventon New Road, Ludlow SY8 1JZ. Mr & Mrs Wood, 01584 876037, carolynwood2152@yahoo.co.uk. *Park & Ride if needed, stops outside garden*. Light refreshments. **Adm £3, chd free. Sat 21 June (12-6). Visitors also welcome by appt, throughout the year.**

½ -acre of very secret S-facing garden, divided into different sections, roses, herbaceous borders, lawn and summer house. Developed over 30yrs by present owners. Terraced vegetable garden and greenhouses. ¼ -acre project incl poly tunnel, vegetable plot, chickens, completed in 2011. Mediterranean style terrace garden. 2nd award in Ludlow in Bloom and 1st in 2013. Photographs in the Shropshire Star and Shropshire Life.

33 SHOOTHILL HOUSE

Ford, Shrewsbury SY5 9NR. Colin & Jane Lloyd, 01743 850795, jane@lloydmasters.com. *5m W of Shrewsbury. From A458 turn L towards Shoothill (signed)*. Home-made teas. **Adm £4, chd free. Sun 8 June, Sun 14 Sept (2-6). Visitors also welcome by appt June to Sept, min group 10+.**

6-acre garden, incl small wood with swamp garden, wild flower meadows, tree house and several lawned areas surrounded by mixed borders. Large well maintained Victorian greenhouse in renovated walled kitchen garden. New areas of garden created in 2012. Mature wildlife pond surrounded by species trees and shrubs with extensive views over Welsh hills.

Rural setting designed with the panoramic views of the Corvedale very much in mind . . .

34 SIBBERSCOTE MANOR

Lea Cross, Shrewsbury SY5 8JF. Lady Kingsland, 01743 860985. *5m S of Shrewsbury. Take A488 S off Shrewsbury bypass, 4m take L turn in Lea Cross to Arscott*. Light refreshments. **Adm £5, chd free. Visitors welcome by appt June to July, min 20.**

Garden created to complement C16 timbered farmhouse (not open). Lovely views over 4-acre lake and S Shropshire hills. Artistically planted with roses, herbaceous and shrub borders, interesting topiary and showing a collection of sculpture. Teas in renovated farm buildings. Partial access on gravel and grass.

35 STANLEY HALL

Bridgnorth WV16 4SP. Mr & Mrs M J Thompson. *½ m N of Bridgnorth. Leave Bridgnorth by N gate; B4373; turn R at Stanley Lane. Pass Golf Course Club House on L & turn L at Lodge*. Home-made teas. **Adm £4, chd free. Sun 1 June (2-6).**

Drive ½ m with rhododendrons, azaleas, fine trees and chain of pools. Restored ice-house. Woodland walks with steps, slopes and pools. Also open **The Granary** (Mr & Mrs Jack Major) Charming small trellis garden. Profusion of flowers in hanging baskets and herbaceous borders. And **Dower House** Mr & Mrs Colin Wells.

GROUP OPENING

36 STOTTESDON & CHORLEY VILLAGE GARDENS

Stottesdon, Kidderminster DY14 8TZ. Stottesdon Garden Committee. *Between Bridgnorth & Cleobury Mortimer. Stottesdon is signed from B4364 between Bridgnorth & Ludlow and B4363 between Bridgnorth & Cleobury Mortimer. The B4194 from Bewdley joins the B4363 4m from village. Look for yellow signs. Please leave the PH car parks for their customers and park as directed*. Light refreshments are available in addtition to traditional teas at Stottesdon Church and Chorley Village Hall. **Combined adm £5, chd free. Sat 21, Sun 22 June (11-6).**

Joint winners of Shropshire Village Gardens of the Year 2012. Stottesdon and Chorley, located in unspoilt Shropshire countryside separated by 3m but share the same parish council. The 12 gardens are spread over the area with the main cluster in Stottesdon for those with less time to visit all of them. The Schoolgarden is open with activities for young children but no creche facilities. It was designed by the pupils and is tended by the school gardening club. A detailed itinerary for those with mobility issues will be available at the ticket centres.There will be a Planted Pot competition which will be judged by the visiting public. (Last year there was a Maori theme) but this year is the Chinese year of the Horse which is also a tribute to the name of Stottesdon. Activities suitable for primary school children. Large plants stall with planted pot competition. Coaches by prior arrangement. Featured in various local papers and magazine's in the county and on local radio. Most gardens have wheelchair access. Suitable gardens will be listed.

37 NEW TOWER HOUSE
Bache, Craven Arms SY7 9LN. Lady Spicer. *7m NW of Ludlow. B4365 Ludlow to Much Wenlock. Turn L after 3m (Bache, Burley), garden at top of hill after 1½ m. B4368 Craven Arms to Bridgnorth. Turn R at Xrds after 1½ m immed fork L, garden after ¾ m* Home-made teas. **Adm £4, chd free. Sun 1 June (2-5).**
2-acres in a rural setting designed with the panoramic views of the Corvedale very much in mind. The garden has been created slowly over 40yrs, with formal and informal flowers, vegetable plot and woodland areas. Rough paths.

38 WALCOT HALL
Lydbury North SY7 8AZ. Mr & Mrs C R W Parish, 01588 680570, maria@walcothall.com, www.walcothall.com. *4m SE of Bishop's Castle. B4385 Craven Arms to Bishop's Castle, turn L by Powis Arms, in Lydbury North.* Home-made teas. **Adm £3.50, chd free. Sun 25, Mon 26 May (1.30-5.30). Visitors also welcome by appt Mar to Oct, for groups of 15+.**
Arboretum planted by Lord Clive of India's son, Edward. Cascades of rhododendrons, azaleas amongst specimen trees and pools. Fine views of Sir William Chambers' Clock Towers, with lake and hills beyond. Walled kitchen garden; dovecote; meat safe; ice house and mile-long lakes. Outstanding ballroom where excellent teas are served. Russian wooden church, grotto and fountain now complete and working; tin chapel. Beautiful borders and rare shrubs. Lakeside replanted, and water garden at western end re-established. The garden adjacent to the ballroom is accessible via a sloping bank, as is the walled garden and arboretum.

39 8 WESTGATE VILLAS
Salop Street, Bridgnorth WV16 4QX. Bill & Marilyn Hammerton. *From A458 Bridgnorth bypass, take rd into Bridgnorth at Ludlow Rd r'about signed town centre. At T-junction (pay & display parking at B/N council offices here) turn R, garden 100yds on L just past entrance to Victoria Rd.* Tea. **Adm £3.50, chd free. Evening Opening £5, chd free, wine, Sun 20 Apr (7-9.30); Mon 21 Apr; Sun 15 June (2-5.30).**
Town garden having formal Victorian front garden with box hedging and water feature to complement house. Back garden has a shade border, lawn, small knot garden and orchard, together with a strong oriental influence incl Japanese style teahouse and zen garden and path in Chinese style. Music and garden lighting at evening opening.

40 ◆ WESTON PARK
Weston-under-Lizard, Shifnal TF11 8LE. The Weston Park Foundation, 01952 852100, www.weston-park.com. *6m E of Telford. Situated on A5 at Weston-under-Lizard. 8m off J12 M6 & 3m off J3 M54.* Tea. **Adm £5.50, chd £3.50. For NGS: Wed 2 July (10.30-6). For other opening times and information, please phone or see garden website.**
Capability Brown landscaped gardens and parkland. Formal gardens restored to original C19 design, rose garden and long border together with colourful adjacent Broderie garden. Orchard in the walled garden. Lady Joan, sister of the 6th Earl of Bradford, died in a horse riding accident aged just 19. This 1030's water cascade garden created in her memory, has been restored by Head Gardener Martin Gee and his team and can be found in Temple Wood. Disabled route map available on request.

41 WINDY RIDGE
Church Lane, Little Wenlock, Telford TF6 5BB. George & Fiona Chancellor, 01952 507675, fionachancellor@btinternet.com. *2m S of Wellington. Follow signs for Little Wenlock from N (J7, M54) or E (off A5223 at Horsehay). Parking signed. Do not rely on Sat Nav.* Home-made teas. **Adm £5, chd free. Suns 15 June; 13 July; 10 Aug; 7 Sept (12-5). Visitors also welcome by appt May to Sept, suitable for coaches.**
'Stunning' and 'inspirational' are how visitors frequently describe this multi-award-winning ⅔ -acre village garden. The strong design and exuberant colour-themed planting (over 1000 species, mostly labelled) offer a picture around every corner. The grass and perennial gravel garden has created a lot of interest and versions are now appearing in gardens all over the country!. Featured in The English Garden. Some gravel paths but help available.

42 ◆ WOLLERTON OLD HALL
Wollerton, Market Drayton TF9 3NA. Lesley & John Jenkins, www.wollertonoldhallgarden.com. *4m SW of Market Drayton. On A53 between Hodnet & A53-A41 junction. Follow brown signs.* Light refreshments. **Adm £6, chd £1. For NGS: Fri 16 May (12-5). For other opening times and information, please see garden website.**
4-acre garden created around C16 house (not open). Formal structure creates variety of gardens each with own colour theme and character. Planting is mainly of perennials, the large range of which results in significant collections of salvias, clematis, crocosmias and roses. Ongoing lectures by Gardening Celebrities including Chris Beardshaw, Jules Hudson and Sir Roy Strong. Chris Beardshaw's article in The English Garden. BBC2 in Chelsea week. Partial wheelchair access.

8 Westgate Villas

Shropshire County Volunteers

County Organiser

Chris Neil, Edge Villa, Edge, Yockleton, Shrewsbury SY5 9PY, 01743 821651, bill@billfneil.fsnet.co.uk ,

County Treasurer

Melinda Laws, 50 Sheinton Street, Much Wenlock TF13 6HU, 01952 727237, melinda@mlaws.freeserve.co.uk

Publicity

Allison Walter, Holly Cottage, Great Argoed, Mellington, nr Church Stoke SY15 6TH, 01588 620055, allison.walter2@btinternet.com

Leaflet Coordinator

Fiona Chancellor, Windy Ridge, Little Wenlock, Telford TF6 5BB, 01952 507675, fionachancellor@btinternet.com

Assistant County Organisers

Bill Neil, Edge Villa, Edge, Yockleton, Shrewsbury SY5 9PY, 01743 821651, bill@billfneil.fsnet.co.uk

Penny Tryhorn, The Granary, Folley Road, Ackleton WV6 7JL, 01746 783931, pennypottingshed@hotmail.co.uk

SOMERSET, BRISTOL AREA & SOUTH GLOUCESTERSHIRE incl Bath

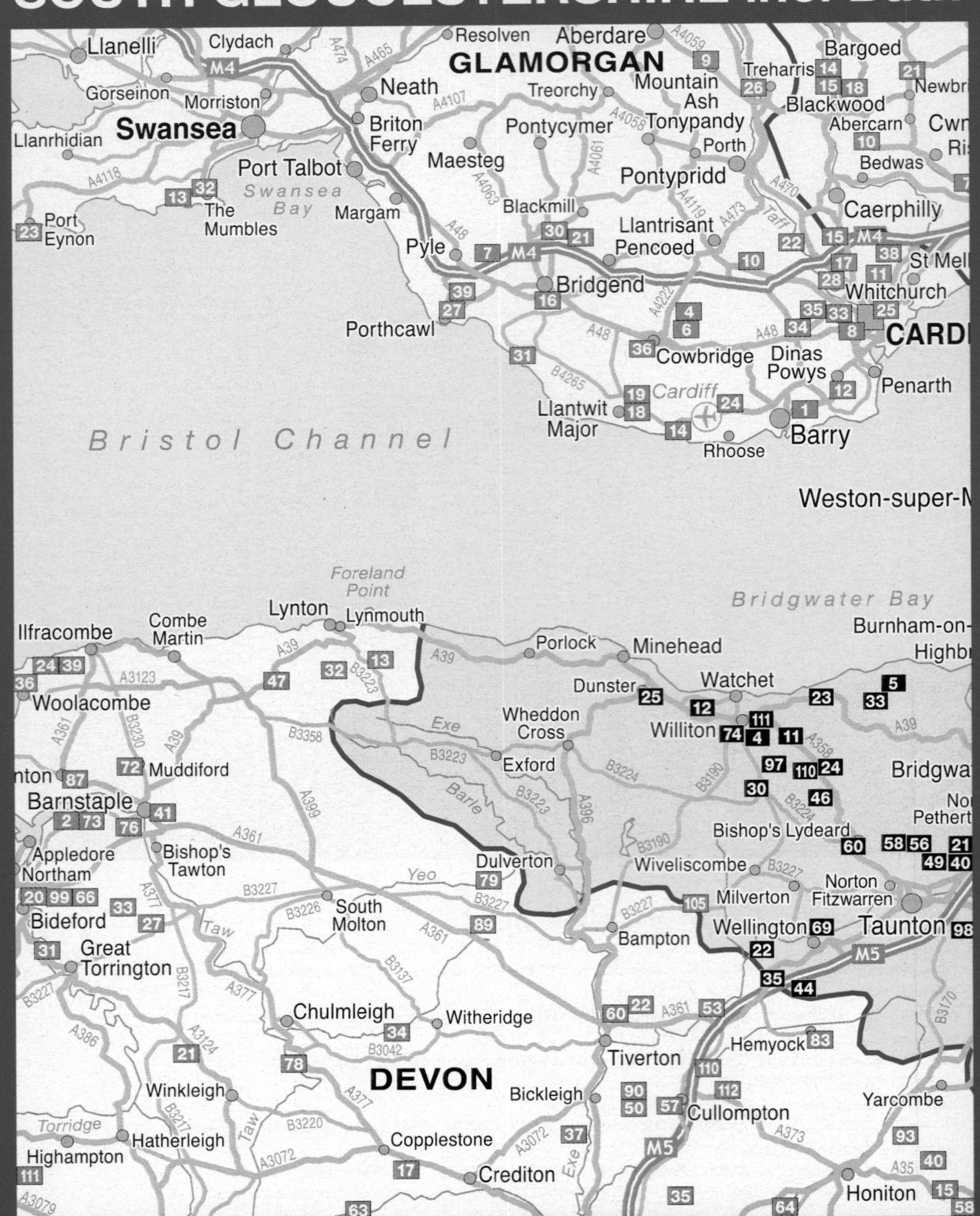

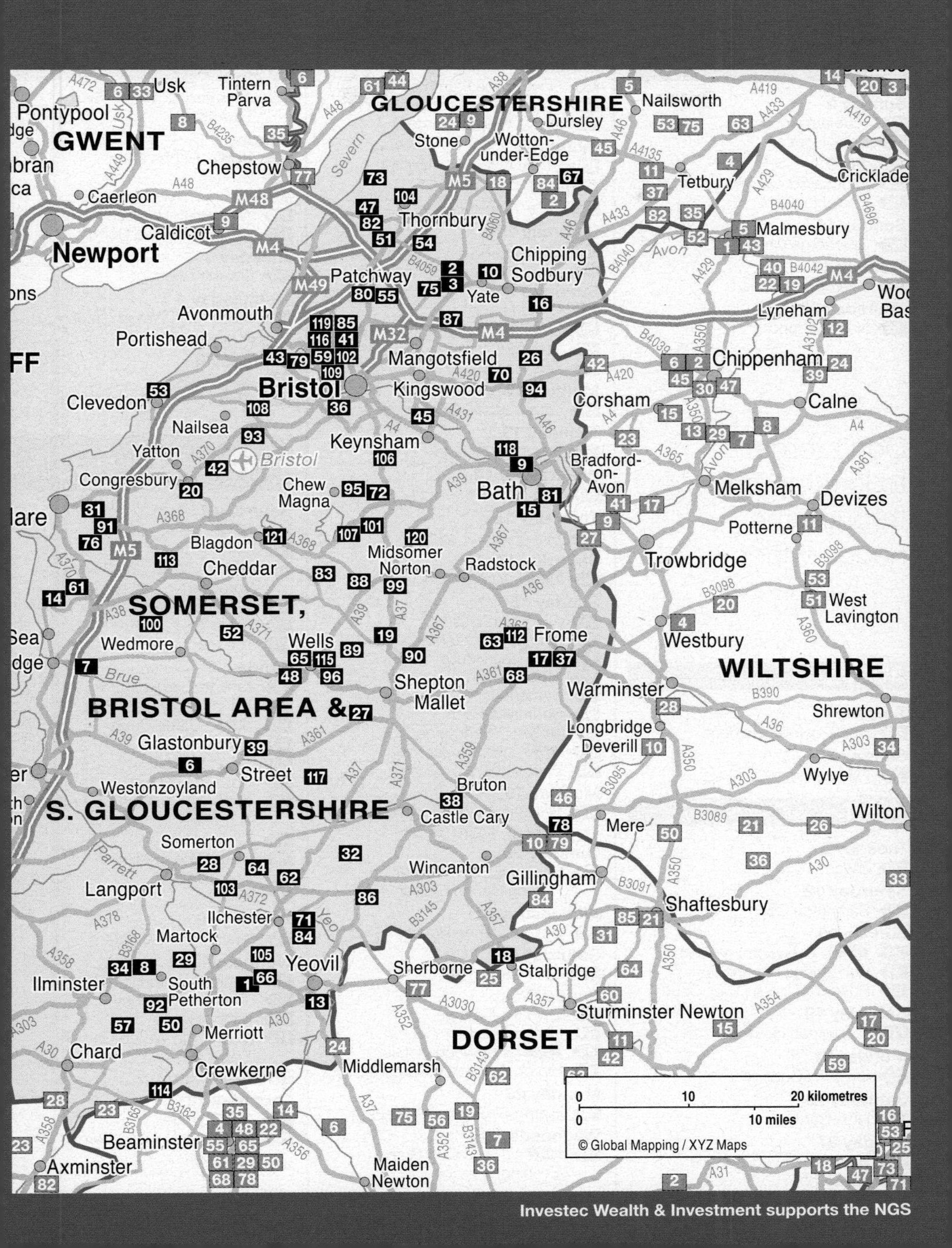
GWENT
GLOUCESTERSHIRE
SOMERSET,
BRISTOL AREA &
S. GLOUCESTERSHIRE
WILTSHIRE
DORSET
Usk
Tintern Parva
Pontypool
Chepstow
Caerleon
Caldicot
Newport
Stone
Dursley
Wotton-under-Edge
Nailsworth
Tetbury
Cricklade
Thornbury
Malmesbury
Chipping Sodbury
Patchway
Yate
Avonmouth
Portishead
Lyneham
Mangotsfield
Kingswood
Chippenham
Bristol
Clevedon
Corsham
Calne
Nailsea
Keynsham
Yatton
Bradford-on-Avon
Congresbury
Chew Magna
Bath
Melksham
Devizes
Blagdon
Midsomer Norton
Radstock
Potterne
Cheddar
Trowbridge
Wedmore
Wells
West Lavington
Frome
Westbury
Shepton Mallet
Warminster
Glastonbury
Street
Longbridge Deverill
Shrewton
Westonzoyland
Bruton
Wylye
Castle Cary
Mere
Wilton
Somerton
Wincanton
Gillingham
Langport
Shaftesbury
Ilchester
Martock
Yeovil
Sherborne
Stalbridge
Ilminster
South Petherton
Sturminster Newton
Merriott
Chard
Crewkerne
Middlemarsh
Beaminster
Axminster
Maiden Newton
Severn
Avon
Brue
Parrett
Yeo
0 10 20 kilometres
0 10 miles
© Global Mapping / XYZ Maps

Opening Dates

All entries subject to change. For latest information check www.ngs.org.uk

February

Sunday 2
45 Hanham Court
82 Rock House

Sunday 9
29 East Lambrook Manor Gardens
82 Rock House

Sunday 16
88 Sherborne Garden

Monday 17
88 Sherborne Garden

Thursday 20
67 Newark Park

Don't forget to look up and through the hedge windows . . .

March

Tuesday 4
49 Hestercombe Gardens

Sunday 30
33 Fairfield

April

Tuesday 8
30 Elworthy Cottage

Saturday 12
8 Barrington Court

Sunday 13
24 NEW Crowcombe Court
44 Hangeridge Farmhouse
83 Rose Cottage & Coley Court

Saturday 19
117 Westbrook House

Monday 21
30 Elworthy Cottage

Saturday 26
57 Little Garth

Sunday 27
46 NEW Hartwood House
113 Watcombe
121 The Yeo Valley Organic Garden at Holt Farm

Tuesday 29
9 Bath Priory Hotel

May

Sunday 4
44 Hangeridge Farmhouse
81 Prior Park Landscape Garden
100 Stone Allerton Gardens

Monday 5
100 Stone Allerton Gardens

Friday 9
58 Little Yarford Farmhouse

Saturday 10
57 Little Garth
58 Little Yarford Farmhouse

Sunday 11
23 Court House
58 Little Yarford Farmhouse
64 Midney Gardens
96 Stoberry Garden

Monday 12
58 Little Yarford Farmhouse

Tuesday 13
30 Elworthy Cottage

Wednesday 14
90 Somerfoss

Thursday 15
99 Ston Easton Park

Saturday 17
111 NEW Wall House

Sunday 18
4 Aller Farmhouse
29 East Lambrook Manor Gardens
59 Lucombe House
65 Milton Lodge
90 Somerfoss
93 Southfield Farm
102 NEW 1 Sunnyside
111 NEW Wall House
113 Watcombe

Monday 19
86 Self Realization Meditation Healing Centre Garden

Tuesday 20
86 Self Realization Meditation Healing Centre Garden

Wednesday 21
42 Goblin Combe House

Saturday 24
57 Little Garth

Sunday 25
30 Elworthy Cottage
44 Hangeridge Farmhouse
46 NEW Hartwood House
50 Hinton St George Gardens

Monday 26
50 Hinton St George Gardens

Wednesday 28
112 NEW The Walled Garden (Evening)

Thursday 29
112 NEW The Walled Garden (Evening)

Saturday 31
7 NEW Babbs Farm
32 Esotera

June

53 **Jasmine Cottage (Every Thursday)**

Sunday 1
7 NEW Babbs Farm
32 Esotera
74 Orchard Wyndham
116 West Bristol Gardens
120 NEW Woodlea Bottom

Tuesday 3
30 Elworthy Cottage

Wednesday 4
112 NEW The Walled Garden (Evening)

Thursday 5
5 Ash Cottage
112 NEW The Walled Garden (Evening)

Festival Weekend

Saturday 7
40 NEW Glebe Court
57 Little Garth
73 NEW Oldbury on Severn Gardens
76 3 Palmer's Way
110 Vellacott
119 18 Woodgrove Road

Sunday 8
6 Ashcott Gardens
20 Congresbury Gardens
40 NEW Glebe Court
45 Hanham Court
65 Milton Lodge
66 Montacute House
73 NEW Oldbury on Severn Gardens
76 3 Palmer's Way
80 Pretoria Road Allotments
105 Tintinhull
110 Vellacott

Tuesday 10
49 Hestercombe Gardens

Wednesday 11
42 Goblin Combe House
62 Lytes Cary Manor
106 Tranby House
112 NEW The Walled Garden (Evening)
113 Watcombe

Thursday 12
5 Ash Cottage
112 NEW The Walled Garden (Evening)

You are always welcome at an NGS garden!

Saturday 14
32 Esotera
70 The Old Rectory, Doynton
119 18 Woodgrove Road

Sunday 15
19 Church Farm House
21 Coombe Gardens at Thurloxton
24 NEW Crowcombe Court
32 Esotera
101 Stowey Gardens
120 NEW Woodlea Bottom

Wednesday 18
19 Church Farm House
42 Goblin Combe House

Thursday 19
94 Special Plants

Friday 20
41 Glenwood Garden (Evening)

Saturday 21
56 Kingston St Mary Hidden Treasures
57 Little Garth
61 Lympsham Manor
91 52 South Lawn
118 Weston Village Gardens

Sunday 22
56 Kingston St Mary Hidden Treasures
60 NEW Lydeard House
61 Lympsham Manor
68 Nunney Gardens
69 Nynehead Court
79 Penny Brohn Cancer Care
91 52 South Lawn
95 Stanton Court Nursing Home
97 Stogumber Gardens
118 Weston Village Gardens

Wednesday 25
17 9 Catherston Close
42 Goblin Combe House
72 NEW 2 Old Tarnwell (**Pre-booking essential**)

Thursday 26
46 NEW Hartwood House (Afternoon/Evening)

Saturday 28
76 3 Palmer's Way
91 52 South Lawn

Sunday 29
11 NEW Bicknoller Gardens
35 Fernhill
37 Frome Gardens
45 Hanham Court
76 3 Palmer's Way
85 St Peter's Hospice
91 52 South Lawn

July

53 **Jasmine Cottage (Every Thursday)**

Wednesday 2
17 9 Catherston Close

Aller Farmhouse

Saturday 5
29 East Lambrook Manor Gardens
39 NEW Glastonbury Secret Gardens
57 Little Garth
63 NEW Mells Park

Sunday 6
25 Dunster Castle Gardens
39 NEW Glastonbury Secret Gardens
63 NEW Mells Park
75 Organic Blooms
85 St Peter's Hospice

Wednesday 9
17 9 Catherston Close
72 NEW 2 Old Tarnwell (**Pre-booking essential**)

Thursday 10
84 Rugg Farm (Evening)
106 Tranby House

Friday 11
41 Glenwood Garden (Evening)

Saturday 12
15 Brewery House
51 Holly Trees
107 Truffles

Sunday 13
14 Brent Knoll Gardens
23 Court House
27 East Burford House
38 Gants Mill & Garden
51 Holly Trees
54 NEW Jekka's Herbetum
65 Milton Lodge
69 Nynehead Court
84 Rugg Farm
107 Truffles
109 University of Bristol Botanic Garden
114 Wayford Manor

Monday 14
27 East Burford House

Thursday 17
94 Special Plants

Friday 18
41 Glenwood Garden (Evening)

Saturday 19
8 Barrington Court
57 Little Garth

Sunday 20
19 Church Farm House
36 1 Frobisher Road
44 Hangeridge Farmhouse
47 Haywood House
52 Honeyhurst Farm
89 Sole Retreat
103 Sutton Hosey Manor
108 Tyntesfield

Wednesday 23
19 Church Farm House
72 NEW 2 Old Tarnwell (**Pre-booking essential**)
99 Ston Easton Park

Saturday 26
13 1 Braggchurch (Evening)

Sunday 27
13 1 Braggchurch (Evening)
16 Camers
22 Cothay Manor & Gardens
35 Fernhill
46 NEW Hartwood House

August

53 **Jasmine Cottage (Every Thursday)**

Saturday 2
57 Little Garth

Sunday 3
12 Binham Grange Gardens
24 NEW Crowcombe Court
54 NEW Jekka's Herbetum
88 Sherborne Garden

Saturday 9
117 Westbrook House

Sunday 10
19 Church Farm House
106 Tranby House

Monday 11
92 South Meade

Tuesday 12
92 South Meade

Wednesday 13
19 Church Farm House
92 South Meade

Thursday 14
92 South Meade

Friday 15
92 South Meade

Saturday 16
57 Little Garth
92 South Meade

Sunday 17
36 1 Frobisher Road
44 Hangeridge Farmhouse

Thursday 21
94 Special Plants

Sunday 24
7 NEW Babbs Farm
30 Elworthy Cottage
35 Fernhill
89 Sole Retreat

Monday 25
7 NEW Babbs Farm

Saturday 30
57 Little Garth

Sunday 31
44 Hangeridge Farmhouse

September

Wednesday 3
99 Ston Easton Park

Friday 5
26 Dyrham Park

Saturday 6
26 Dyrham Park

Sunday 7
106 Tranby House

Monday 8
44 Hangeridge Farmhouse

Tuesday 9
9 Bath Priory Hotel

Saturday 13
57 Little Garth
78 Pen Mill Farm

Sunday 14
10 Beechwell House
78 Pen Mill Farm

Thursday 18
94 Special Plants

Friday 19
64 Midney Gardens

Sunday 21
104 Thornbury Park Estate/The Sheiling School

October

Thursday 16
94 Special Plants

Subtropical garden with exotic planting . . .

February 2015

Sunday 1
82 Rock House

Sunday 8
29 East Lambrook Manor Gardens
82 Rock House

Sunday 15
88 Sherborne Garden

Monday 16
88 Sherborne Garden

Gardens open to the public

8 Barrington Court
12 Binham Grange Gardens
22 Cothay Manor & Gardens
23 Court House
25 Dunster Castle Gardens
26 Dyrham Park
29 East Lambrook Manor Gardens
30 Elworthy Cottage
45 Hanham Court
49 Hestercombe Gardens
54 Jekka's Herbetum
62 Lytes Cary Manor
64 Midney Gardens
65 Milton Lodge
66 Montacute House
67 Newark Park
81 Prior Park Landscape Garden
88 Sherborne Garden
94 Special Plants
99 Ston Easton Park
105 Tintinhull
108 Tyntesfield
109 University of Bristol Botanic Garden
112 The Walled Garden
121 The Yeo Valley Organic Garden at Holt Farm

By appointment only

1 Abbey Farm
2 Algars Manor
3 Algars Mill
18 Cherry Bolberry Farm
28 East End Farm
31 14 Eskdale Close
34 Farndon Thatch
43 16 Gordano Gardens
48 Henley Mill
55 Jen's Gardyn
71 The Old Rectory, Limington
87 Serridge House
98 Stoke St Mary Gardens
115 Wellfield Barn

Also open by appointment

4 Aller Farmhouse
7 Babbs Farm
14 Copse Hall, Brent Knoll Gardens
15 Brewery House
16 Camers
19 Church Farm House
27 East Burford House
35 Fernhill
44 Hangeridge Farmhouse
46 Hartwood House
50 Hooper's Holding, Hinton St George Gardens
52 Honeyhurst Farm
53 Jasmine Cottage
56 Kingston St Mary Hidden Treasures
57 Little Garth
58 Little Yarford Farmhouse
69 Nynehead Court
72 2 Old Tarnwell
76 3 Palmer's Way
78 Pen Mill Farm
82 Rock House
83 Rose Cottage, Rose Cottage & Coley Court
84 Rugg Farm
86 Self Realization Meditation Healing Centre Garden
89 Sole Retreat
90 Somerfoss
91 52 South Lawn
97 Knoll Cottage, Stogumber Gardens
100 Badgers Acre, Stone Allerton Gardens
103 Sutton Hosey Manor
107 Truffles
110 Vellacott
113 Watcombe
116 4 Haytor Park, West Bristol Gardens
116 West Bristol Gardens

Visit a garden in your own time – look for by appointment gardens

The Gardens

1 ABBEY FARM

Montacute TA15 6UA. Alisdair & Elizabeth McFarlane, 01935 823572, ct.fm@btopenworld.com. *4m from Yeovil. Follow A3088, take slip rd to Montacute, turn L at T-junction into village. Turn R between Church & King's Arms (no through rd).* **Adm £5, chd free. Visitors welcome by appt June, July only.**

2½ acres of mainly walled gardens on sloping site provide the setting for Cluniac Medieval Priory gatehouse. Interesting plants incl roses, shrubs, grasses, clematis. Herbaceous borders, white garden, gravel garden. Small arboretum. Pond for wildlife - frogs, newts, dragonflies. Fine mulberry, walnut and monkey puzzle trees. Seats for resting. Gravel area & one steep slope.

2 ALGARS MANOR

Station Road, Iron Acton BS37 9TB. Mrs B Naish, 01454 228372, bhnaish@gmail.com. *9m N of Bristol. 3m W of Yate/Chipping Sodbury. Turn S off Iron Acton bypass B4059, past village green, 200yds, then over level Xing (Station Rd).* **Adm £4, chd free. Combined with Algars Mill. Groups of 10+ welcome by appt Mar to July.**

2 acres of woodland garden beside R Frome, mill stream, native plants mixed with collections of 60 magnolias and 70 camellias, eucalyptus and other unusual trees and shrubs. Mar/Apr camellias, magnolias; Apr/May/June rhododendrons, azaleas. Limited wheelchair access, gravel paths, some steep slopes.

3 ALGARS MILL

Station Road, Iron Acton BS37 9TD. Mr & Mrs John Wright, 01454 228373, marilyn@algarsmill.plus.com. *9m N of Bristol. 3m W of Yate/Chipping Sodbury. (For directions see Algars Manor).* **Adm £4, chd free. Combined with Algars Manor. Groups of 10+ welcome by appt Mar to July.**

2-acre woodland garden bisected by R Frome; spring bulbs, shrubs; very early spring feature (Feb-Mar) of wild Newent daffodils. 300-400yr-old mill house (not open) through which millrace still runs.

4 ALLER FARMHOUSE

Williton, nr Taunton TA4 4LY. Mr & Mrs Richard Chandler, 01984 633702. *7m E of Minehead, 1m S of Williton. From A358 Taunton turn L into Sampford Brett. Follow signs to Capton. Follow lane downhill to Aller Farm. Car park in field beyond house.* **Adm £4, chd free. Sun 18 May (2-5.30). Visitors also welcome by appt Apr to Oct.**

2-3 acres. Hot, dry, sunny, S-facing, surrounded by pink stone walls and sub-divided into 5 separate compartments by same. Cliff Garden is old 3-sided quarry. Old magnolias, figs, Judas, etc; newer acacias; many unusual and/or tender plants incl eremurus, beschorneria, dendromecon, echiums in variety and buddleia colvilei. Partial wheelchair access.

5 ASH COTTAGE

Shurton, Stogursey, Bridgwater TA5 1QF. Barbara & Peter Oates. *8m W of Bridgwater. From A39 nr Holford, follow signs to Stogursey then to Shurton. From A39 at Cannington follow signs to Hinkley Point then Shurton.* Cream teas. **Adm £3.50, chd free. Thur 5, Thur 12 June (2-5.30).**

Tranquil cottage garden in rural area, approx ⅔ acre, wrapping around 3 sides of early C16 cottage (not open). Colour-themed borders and flowerbeds incl island bed, with raised 40ft border reached by steps from either end. Admire our amazing south-facing wall! Natural stream with planted banks runs through garden. Children must be supervised at all times. Some gravel paths and shallow steps.

GROUP OPENING

6 ASHCOTT GARDENS

Bridgwater TA7 9QB. *3m W of Street on A39. Turn opp The Retreat into Middle St. At T-junction turn R to car park at village hall.* Home-made teas in Village Hall. **Combined adm £6, chd free. Sun 8 June (2-5.30).**

CHERRY ORCHARD
17 Chapel Hill. Geoff & Sue Wilton

HOLLY TREE COTTAGE
Chapel Hill. Robin & Denise Wale

LITTLE KIMBLE
Fulpitts Lane. Simon & Elaine Hayne

MANOR HOUSE
11 Middle Street. Peter & Daphne Willis

MILLGREEN
3 Station Road. Ruth & Gus Wans

THE NORMANS
22 Middle Street. Mary & David Adkins

Ashcott village is a pleasant and friendly village situated in the Polden Hills with magnificent views. This group opening for the NGS comprises 6 interesting and varied gardens ranging in size from the small colourful garden to 1 acre reclaimed from a field, now nicely mature. Bog areas with hardy and tender exotics, several ponds and 2 waterfalls. 4 vegetable gardens, fruits. Details of each garden can be found on NGS website www.ngs.org.uk. Wheelchair access to 4 gardens, gravel entrance at The Normans. Limited access to vegetable area at Manor House. Gravel entrance at Mill Green.

Watcombe

7 NEW BABBS FARM
Westhill Lane, Bason Bridge, Highbridge TA9 4RF. Sue and Richard O'Brien, 01278 793244. *2.5 km E of Highbridge, 2.5 km SSE of M5 exit 22. Turn into Westhill Lane off B3141 (Church Rd), 100yds S of where it joins B3139 (Wells-Highbridge rd).* Home-made teas. **Adm £3.50, chd free. Sat 31 May; Sun 1 June; Sun 24, Mon 25 Aug (2-5). Visitors also welcome by appt May to Sept.**
3/4 acre plantsman's garden in Somerset Levels, gradually created out of fields surrounding old farmhouse over last 20 yrs and still being developed. Trees, shrubs and herbaceous perennials planted with an eye for form and shape, in big flowing borders. Various ponds (formal and informal) box garden, patio area and conservatory.

8 ◆ BARRINGTON COURT
Barrington, Ilminster TA19 0NQ. National Trust, 01460 241938, www.nationaltrust.org.uk. *5m NE of Ilminster. In Barrington village on B3168. Follow brown NT signs.* Light refreshments at Beagles Cafe and Strode Restaurant. **Adm £10.50, chd £5.20. For NGS: Sat 12 Apr, Sat 19 July (10-5). For other opening times and information, please phone or see garden website.**
Well known garden constructed in 1920 by Col Arthur Lyle from derelict farmland (the C19 cattle stalls still exist). Gertrude Jekyll suggested planting schemes for the layout. Paved paths with walled rose and iris, white and lily gardens, large kitchen garden. The Kitchen Garden has been in continuous production for over 90 years. Some paths a little uneven.

9 BATH PRIORY HOTEL
Weston Road, Bath BA1 2XT. Jane Moore, Head Gardener, 01225 331922, www.thebathpriory.co.uk. *Close to centre of Bath. From Bath centre take Upper Bristol Rd, turn R at end of Victoria Park & L into Weston Rd.* Home-made teas. **Adm £3, chd free. Tue 29 Apr, Tue 9 Sept (2-5.30).**
Discover 3 acres of mature walled gardens. Quintessentially English, the garden has billowing borders, croquet lawn, wild flower meadow and ancient specimen trees. Spring is bright with tulips and flowering cherries; autumn alive with colour. Perennials and tender plants provide summer highlights while the kitchen garden supplies herbs, fruit and vegetables to the restaurant. Gravel paths and some steps Please note No Parking. Drop off and parking for disabled only. Meter parking available in Victoria Park.

NCH

10 BEECHWELL HOUSE
51 Goose Green, Yate BS37 5BL. Tim Wilmot, www.beechwell.com. *10m NE of Bristol. From Yate centre, go N onto Church Ln. After 1/2 m turn L onto Greenways Rd then R onto Church Ln. After 300yds take R-fork, garden 100yds on L.* Home-made teas. **Adm £3, chd free. Sun 14 Sept (1-5).**
Enclosed, level, subtropical garden created over last 23 yrs and filled with exotic planting, incl palms (over 6 varieties), tree ferns, yuccas, agaves and succulent bed, rare shrubs, bamboos, bananas, aroids and other architectural planting. Wildlife pond and koi pond. C16 40ft deep well. Rare plant raffle every hour. Some narrow pathways.

GROUP OPENING

11 NEW BICKNOLLER GARDENS
Bicknoller, Taunton TA4 4EG. *13.5m NW of Taunton. A358 from Taunton.* Light refreshments at Bicknoller Village Hall. **Combined adm £5, chd free. Sun 29 June (2-5.30).**

NEW HOVE TO
Trendle Lane. Marie & Peter Robinson

NEW LADY FURLONG
6 Trendle Lane. Mr & Mrs Julian Anderson

NEW MELBREAK
44 Church Lane. Chris and Judy Yates

Hove To: A small garden with mature trees, herbaceous borders, a small rockery, some climbing roses and English roses, a number of lilies and a water feature. Lady Furlong: A young, developing, pollinator friendly garden with magnificent views and artist's studio. Melbreak: owners formerly opened The Scented Garden, Littlebredy, Dorset. 1/4 -acre plantsman's garden, artistically

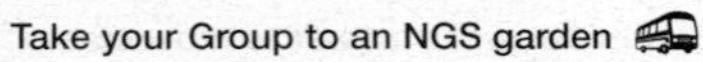

arranged for colour, shape and form, containing many interesting and unusual perennials. Densely planted beds and borders highlighted with collections of old shrub and climbing roses, lavenders and other scented plants. Bicknoller is a much sought after village in the Quantock Hills, Britain's first AONB. With its own Inn/PH and Shop and it is ideal for walkers who relish areas of outstanding natural beauty and tranquility combined with magnificent views. Access available for all gardens, except Lady Furlong where only motorised wheelchairs can be used. At Melbreak there are some gravel paths.

12 ◆ BINHAM GRANGE GARDENS
Old Cleeve, Minehead TA24 6HX. Stewart & Marie Thomas, 01984 640056, mariethomas@btconnect.com. *4m E of Dunster. Take A39 for Minehead, R at Xrds after Washford to Blue Anchor, past Old Cleeve, garden on L.* Home-made teas. **Adm £3.50, chd free. For NGS: Sun 3 Aug (1-5.30). For other opening times and information, please phone or email.**
Established garden set in 300 acres of farmed Somerset countryside with extensive views. Parterre garden to the front of house, Italian-style garden, pergola, island beds, cutting and vegetable garden. Splendid Irises in the spring. Plants for the senses working with the seasons. Interesting and unusual plants. View the dairy herd coming for milking from the Garden Terrace. Views of West Somerset steam train passing the farm.

13 1 BRAGGCHURCH
93 Hendford Hill, Yeovil BA20 2RE. Veronica Sartin. *Walking distance of Yeovil centre. Approaching Yeovil on A30 from Quicksilver Mail PH r'about, 1st driveway on R down Hendford Hill. Roadside parking at Southwoods (next R down hill). Car park at bottom of Henford Hill.* **Evening Openings £3.50, chd free, Light refreshments, Sat 26, Sun 27 July (5-9).**
Old garden of undulating lawns and mature trees evolving, since May 2002, to semi-wild, nature-friendly, woodland garden with a few surprises within the new planting - refurbished tree house, dancing figures, Anderson shelter, pond, willow weaving, retreat with poetry, medlar tree enclosure, rhododendron hideaway and courtyard curios/mosaics.

GROUP OPENING

14 BRENT KNOLL GARDENS
nr Highbridge TA9 4DF. Susan Boss & Tony Hill. *2m N of Highbridge. Off A38 & M5 J22 From M5 take A 38 N (Cheddar etc) first L into Brent Knoll.* Cream teas at Copse Hall. **Combined adm £7, chd free. Sun 13 July (11-6).**

BURROWS GREEN
Brent Street. Yvonne Radford.
on L from A38 see signs

COPSE HALL
Mrs S Boss & Mr A J Hill.
From A38 follow signs to Woodlands Hotel then L into car park
Visitors also welcome by appt Feb to Oct.
01278 760301
susan.boss@gmail.com

LABURNUM COTTAGE
Middle Street. Catherine Weber.
Follow signs through village - 1st L after turning to Burnham

The distinctive hill of Brent Knoll, an iron age hill fort, is well worth climbing 449ft for the 360° view of hills incl Glastonbury Tor and levels. Lovely C13 church renowned for its bench ends. Copse Hall: S-facing Edwardian house (not open) on lower slopes of Knoll. Front garden newly designed with curving slopes and paths. Ha-ha, wild area and kitchen garden remain. Views to Quantock and Polden Hills. Kitchen garden enclosed by crinkle crankle wall, has heritage vegetables, wall fruit, kiwifruit and feijoas amongst the usual fruit and vegetables. New front garden is now pretty well established and colourful. Burrows Green is a tiny garden packed with plants, many unusual. Laburnum Cottage is a fascinating garden well known for its many hemerocallis (about 150). Wide sweeping borders and winding paths. Open in conjunction with Plant Heritage specialist plant sale. Wheelchair access in all gardens, some restricted.

15 BREWERY HOUSE
Southstoke, Bath BA2 7DL. John and Ursula Brooke, 01225 833153, jbsouthstoke@gmail.com. *2½ m S of Bath. A367 Radstock Rd from Bath. At top of dual carriageway turn L onto B3110. Straight on at double r'about. Next R into Southstoke.* Home-made teas. **Adm £3.50, chd free. Sat 12 July (1.30-5). Visitors also welcome by appt.**
Established garden on 2 levels with fine views to the S. Herbaceous perennials, grasses, bamboos, euphorbias, hydrangeas, clematis. All organic. Upper garden surrounded by 10ft stone wall. Trees incl walnut, davidia, medlar, apple, mulberry etc. Large pool/water garden. A number of unusual plants. Wheelchair access restricted to lower part of garden.

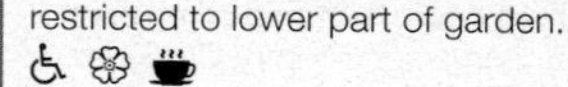

Refurbished tree house, dancing figures . . .

16 CAMERS
Old Sodbury BS37 6RG. Mr & Mrs A G Denman, 01454 322430, dorothydenman@camers.org, www.camers.org. *2m E of Chipping Sodbury. Entrance in Chapel Lane off A432 at Dog Inn.* Home-made teas. **Adm £5, chd free. Sun 27 July (2-5). Groups of 20+ also welcome by appt Feb to Sept.**
Elizabethan farmhouse (not open) set in 4 acres of constantly developing garden and woodland with spectacular views over Severn Vale. Garden full of surprises, formal and informal areas planted with very wide range of species to provide yr-round interest. Parterre, topiary, Japanese garden, bog and prairie areas, waterfalls, white and hot gardens, woodland walks. Some steep slopes.

17 9 CATHERSTON CLOSE

Frome. BA11 4HR. Dave & Prue Moon. *15m S of Bath. Town centre W towards Shepton Mallet (A361). R at Sainsbury's r'about, follow lane for 1/2 m. L into Critchill Rd. Over Xrds, 1st L Catherston Close.* **Adm £3, chd free. Weds 25 June; 2, 9 July (12-5). Also open with The Bastion Garden 29 June (Frome Gardens).**

A town garden which has grown over the years to 1/3 acre! Colour-themed shrub and herbaceous borders, pond, patios, pergolas and wild meadow areas lead to wonderful far reaching views. Productive vegetable and fruit garden with greenhouse. Exhibition of garden photography, from near and far, by the garden owner is displayed in the summerhouse. Featured in regional press, Somerset Country Gardener and on BBC Radio Somerset and Radio Bristol. 8 times gold winner in Frome-in-Bloom. Several shallow steps, gravel paths.

18 CHERRY BOLBERRY FARM

Furge Lane, Henstridge BA8 0RN. Mrs Jenny Raymond, 01963 362177, cherrybolberryfarm@tiscali.co.uk. *6m E of Sherborne. In centre of Henstridge, R at small Xrds signed Furge Lane. Continue straight up lane, over 2 cattle grids, garden at top of lane on R.* Home-made teas. **Adm £4, chd free. Visitors welcome by appt June.**

38 yr-old award-winning, owner-designed and maintained 1-acre garden planted for yr-round interest with wildlife in mind. Colour-themed island beds, shrub and herbaceous borders, unusual perennials and shrubs, old roses and specimen trees. Vegetable and flower cutting garden, greenhouses, nature ponds. Wonderful extensive views. Garden surrounded by our dairy farm which has been in the family for nearly 100 years. You will see Jersey cows, sheep, horses and hens!

19 CHURCH FARM HOUSE

Turners Court Lane, Binegar, Radstock BA3 4UA. Susan & Tony Griffin, 01749 841628, smgriffin@beanacrebarn.co.uk, www.beanacrebarn.co.uk. *4m NE of Wells. From Wells B3139 NE for 4.5m, turn R sign Binegar, yellow NGS sign at Xrds. From A37 in Gurney Slade signed Binegar, Xrds turn R Turners Ct Lane.* **Adm £3.50, chd free. Suns, Weds 15, 18 June; 20, 23 July; 10, 13 Aug (11-4.30). Visitors also welcome by appt June to Aug incl.**

Wrapped around an old farmhouse are two walled gardens planted in contemporary cottage style, roses and clematis on walls and unusual perennials in deep borders give interest all seasons. South garden has progressive colourist design and the ever-expanding insect-friendly planting in the gravel of the old farmyard creates an interesting display of form and colour often with self-seeded surprises! Featured in regional press/radio. Gravel forecourt, 2 shallow steps.

GROUP OPENING

20 CONGRESBURY GARDENS

Congresbury, Bristol BS49 5DN. *Approx halfway between Bristol and Weston-super-Mare. 12m S of Bristol on A370. At T-lights in Congresbury look for signs.* Light refreshments/teas at Middlecombe Nursery and Yeo Meads. **Combined adm £5, chd free. Sun 8 June (10.30-4.30).**

FERNBANK
High Street. Julia Thyer.
From T-lights on A370 at Ship & Castle, turn into High St (B3133). Garden 100yds on R, park in side streets or car park N of river
http://juliathyer.blogspot.co.uk

MARTY'S GARDEN
Woodhill Nursery, Woodhill. Mr John Dunster.
Woodhill is a lane off B3133 Congresbury-Yatton rd. Garden is at Woodhill Nursery 3/4 m from turn on R, 3rd hole in the hedge

MIDDLECOMBE NURSERY
Wrington Rd. Nigel J North.
On edge of Congresbury, on Bristol side, turn to Wrington along the Wrington Rd off A370 Weston to Bristol rd. Garden 250yds on L
www.middlecombenursery.co.uk

29 STONEWELL LANE
Mike & Janet Sweeting.
Stonewell Lane is after PO and shops in High St, continue to bottom, 29 is bungalow with 2 odd chimney pots in front of you

YEO MEADS
High Street. Debbie Fortune & Mark Hayward.
150yds along High St from Ship & Castle PH on L. Park in Ship and Castle public car park

Village group of 5 strikingly contrasting gardens. Yeo Meads - large garden with many trees amongst which is a 350 year old Cedar of Lebanon which fell in 2007 but survives as a feature, together with Victorian pond and thatched octagonal summerhouse. Middlecombe Nursery - 3-acre nursery site in country setting with series of different gardens, owned by Nigel North, a regular contributor to BBC Radio Bristol. Marty's Garden - 1-acre garden with borders of herbaceous plants and alstroemeria plus rare clematis bred at Cannington College. 29 Stonewell Lane - garden to encourage wildlife with a cottage garden feel with borders, mature trees, a pond and herbaceous perennials. Fernbank - romantic haven for wildlife. Follow paths to surprises, explore the potager and picturesque greenhouse, potter in the potting shed, discover the lily ponds with trickling water, be inspired by banks of potted plants and a furnished Wendy house.

Village group of 5 strikingly contrasting gardens . . .

GROUP OPENING

21 COOMBE GARDENS AT THURLOXTON

Nr Taunton TA2 8RE. *6m S of Bridgwater, 4m N of Taunton. Signed off A38 between Taunton and Bridgwater.* Cream teas at Coombe Quarry. **Combined adm £5, chd free. Sun 15 June (2-6).**

COOMBE QUARRY
Coombe, West Monkton. Miss Patricia Davies-Gilbert

COOMBE WATER
Coombe, West Monkton. Mr & Mrs M K Paul

NEW DINGLEBROOK
Coombe Bottom, West Monkton. Paul Wills and Penny Sharp

NEW LONGFIELD
Coombe, West Monkton. Mrs Pauline Foster

Delightful medium-sized gardens in hamlet between Weston Monkton & Thurloxton. Coombe Quarry: cottage garden with quarry walk. Roses, shrubs, vegetables, fruit and animals. Partial wheelchair access, quarry walk inaccessable. Coombe Water: cottage garden in secluded valley, stream and pond. Wide variety of trees, plants and roses. Longfield being totally re-vamped has stream and dry bank with variety of planting. Dinglebrook: divided garden with much colour next to Coombe Water. Thurloxton Church worth a visit with the two Jubilee windows Victoria and ER. Wheelchair access in 3 gardens.

22 ◆ COTHAY MANOR & GARDENS

Greenham, nr Wellington TA21 0JR. Mr & Mrs Alastair Robb, 01823 672283, www.cothaymanor.co.uk. *5m SW of Wellington. 7m off M5 via A38, Signed Greenham, follow Brown Signs for Cothay Manor & Gardens. See website for more detailed directions.* Cream teas. **Adm £7.50, chd £3.75. For NGS: Sun 27 July (2-5). For other opening times and information, please phone or see garden website.**

Few gardens are as evocatively romantic as Cothay. Laid out in 1920s and replanted in 1990s within the original framework, Cothay encompasses a rare blend of old and new. Plantsman's paradise set in 12 acres of magical gardens. Antiques; garden shop; tea room. Sorry no dogs or picnicing in gardens. Sunday house tours 11:45 and 2:15. £6.75, advance booking recommended. Partial wheelchair access, gravel paths.

23 ◆ COURT HOUSE

East Quantoxhead TA5 1EJ. East Quantoxhead Estate (Hugh Luttrell Esq), 01278 741271, hugh_luttrell@yahoo.co.uk. *12m W of Bridgwater. Off A39; house at end of village past duck pond. Enter by Frog Lane (Bridgwater/Kilve side from A39). Car park 50p in aid of church.* Home-made teas In Village Hall. **Adm £4, chd free. For NGS: Sun 11 May, Sun 13 July (1-5). For other opening times and information, please phone or email.**

Lovely 5 acre garden; trees, shrubs, many rare and tender; herbaceous and 3 acre woodland garden with spring interest and late summer borders. Traditional kitchen garden (all chemical free). Views to sea and Quantocks. Groups welcome by appointment, proceeds not to NGS. Gravel and stone paths, some mown grass paths.

24 NEW CROWCOMBE COURT

Crowcombe, Taunton TA4 4AD. Mr & Mrs David Kenyon. *W of Taunton. On A358.* Home-made teas in Great Hall of house. **Adm by donation. Suns 13 Apr; 15 June; 3 Aug (2-6).**

Magnificent Grade 1 listed house which has benefitted from extensive refurbishment. The 10 acres of gardens, previously sadly neglected, are now being rejuvenated under new ownership. Woodland garden, lake, walled garden, all undergoing a rescue mission! Tours at 2.15, 3.15 and 4.15. Featured in The Field magazine and Taunton Life. Mostly wheelchair access.

25 ◆ DUNSTER CASTLE GARDENS

Dunster TA24 6SL. National Trust, 01643 821314, www.nationaltrust.org.uk. *3m SE of Minehead. NT car park approached direct from A39 Minehead to Bridgwater rd, nr to A396 turning. Car park charge to non-NT members.* Light refreshments at Camellia House. **Adm £5.80, chd free. For NGS: Sun 6 July (10-5). For other opening times and information, please phone or see garden website.**

Hillside woodland garden surrounding fortified mansion, previously home to the Luttrell family for 600yrs. Terraced areas, interlinked by old carriage drives and paths, feature tender plants. Fine views over polo lawns and landscape with C18 features. Winter interest border. Dream garden with dahlia displays in main season. Play elements within the River gardens.

26 ◆ DYRHAM PARK

Bath SN14 8ER. National Trust, 01179 371330, www.nationaltrust.org.uk/dyrham-park. *8m N of Bath, 12m E of Bristol. On Bath to Stroud rd (A46), 2m S of Tomarton interchange with M4, exit 18. Sat nav use SN14 8HY.* **Adm £5, chd £2.60. For NGS: Fri 5, Sat 6 Sept (10-5). For other opening times and information, please phone or see garden website.**

C17 mansion with formal gardens on W side, lawns, herbaceous borders, fine yew hedges, ponds and cascade. Nichols orchard with perry pear trees. Continuing project to refresh new areas. On E side of house is C17 orangery traditionally used for citrus plants. Garden tours, including a look at the historic pear orchard, at various times during both days. Please see NT website for times. Special tours for NGS opening, ask at Visitor Reception on the day. Steep slopes in park, cobbles in courtyard. Disabled WC.

27 EAST BURFORD HOUSE

Summer Hill Lane, West Compton, Pilton, Shepton Mallet BA4 4PA. Christopher & Lindsay Bond, 01749 890352, bondchristopher@btconnect.com. *3m W of Shepton Mallet. Xrds at bottom of hill in Pilton on A361 go uphill between PH and former shop for 1/2 m into bottom of valley, black gates on L beyond turn to farm.* Home-made teas. **Adm £4, chd free. Sun 13, Mon 14 July (11-5). Visitors also welcome by appt July.**

Garden full of surprises. 3 acres surround fine country house (not open) set in isolated Mendip valley. Formal walled and wild gardens, different areas incl herbaceous, bog, woodland, gravel, wisteria, pergola, desert and raised strawberry beds, lake with shell beach, rills, pagoda, pavilion, sculptures and children's playground. Hillside woodland walk, bring own picnic, wear stout shoes, dogs welcome. Nursery stand, craft shop. Featured on BBC Radio Somerset/Radio Bristol and in Folio Magazine/regional press. Wheelchair access limited to formal garden.

28 EAST END FARM

Pitney, Langport TA10 9AL. Mrs A M Wray, 01458 250598. *2m E of Langport. Please telephone for directions.* **Adm £3, chd free. Visitors welcome by appt June.**

Approx 1/3 acre. Timeless small garden of many old-fashioned roses in beautiful herbaceous borders set amongst ancient listed farm buildings. Mostly wheelchair access.

29 ◆ EAST LAMBROOK MANOR GARDENS

East Lambrook TA13 5HH. Mike & Gail Werkmeister, 01460 240328, www.eastlambrook.com. *2m N of South Petherton. Follow brown tourist signs from A303 South Petherton r'about or B3165 Xrd with lights N of Martock.* **Adm £5.75, chd free. For NGS: Sun 9 Feb, Sun 18 May, Sat 5 July, Sun 8 Feb 2015 (10-5). For other information, please phone or see garden website.**

The quintessential English cottage garden created by C20 gardening legend Margery Fish. Plantsman's paradise with old-fashioned and contemporary plants grown in a relaxed and informal manner to create an extraordinary garden of great beauty and charm. With noted collections of snowdrops, hellebores and geraniums and the excellent specialist Margery Fish Plant Nursery. Snowdrops Feb. Art exhibitions: Moish Sokal July. Also open Feb/May to July Tues to Sun and BH Mons; Mar/Apr/Aug to Oct Tue to Sat and BH Mons; (10-5). Featured in The English Garden, Garden News, Country Gardener and on BBC Gardeners' World and local radio. Partial wheelchair access only due to narrow paths and steps.

Home-made teas in Great Hall . . .

30 ◆ ELWORTHY COTTAGE

Elworthy, Taunton TA4 3PX. Mike & Jenny Spiller, 01984 656427, mike@elworthy-cottage.co.uk, www.elworthy-cottage.co.uk. *12m NW of Taunton. On B3188 between Wiveliscombe and Watchet.* **Adm £3, chd free. For NGS: Tue 8, Mon 21 Apr, Tue 13, Sun 25 May, Tue 3 June, Sun 24 Aug (11-5). For other information, please phone or see garden website.**

1-acre plantsman's garden in tranquil setting. Island beds, scented plants, clematis, unusual perennials and ornamental trees and shrubs to provide yr-round interest. In spring, pulmonarias, hellebores and more than 200 varieties of snowdrops. Planted to encourage birds, bees and butterflies, lots of birdsong. Wild flower areas, decorative vegetable garden, living willow screen. Stone ex privy and pigsty feature. Adjoining nursery. Also open Thurs Apr - Aug incl (10-5). All fees for visits by appt incl groups and coach parties to be donated to NGS.

31 14 ESKDALE CLOSE

Weston-super-Mare BS22 8QG. Janet & Adrian Smith, 01934 414543, nanandpops14@hotmail.co.uk. *1 1/2 m E of WsM town centre. From M5 J21, take B3440 to town centre, L at Corondale Rd, R into Garsdale Rd.Take footpath next to number 37.* Home-made teas. **Adm £2.50, chd free. Visitors welcome by appt Apr to Aug groups of no more than 25.**

Unexpected size for town garden, containing over 250 different plants. Interesting and naturally planted in cottage style. Four areas: pond with seating, packed borders with climbing roses, Mediterranean garden and conifer rockery. A wisteria archway leads to a productive area of fruit trees, herb garden, and vegetable plot. No wheelchair access to vegetable patch.

32 ESOTERA

Foddington, nr Babcary TA11 7EL. Andrew & Shirley Harvey. *6m E of Somerton, 6m SW of Castle Cary. Signs to garden off A37 Ilchester to Shepton Mallet and B3153 Somerton to Castle Cary. (Old) A303 from Sparkford.* Home-made teas. **Adm £4, chd free. Sat 31 May, Sun 1, Sat 14, Sun 15 June (11-5).**

2-acre established informal country garden housing 3 wildlife ponds. Large prairie border. Contemporary new potting shed with shrubs and herbaceous planting. Mature trees, boxed topiary, courtyard and meadow walk leading to shepherd hut. New Olympic hen house. Children must be supervised at all times. Featured in Country Living Magazine.

33 FAIRFIELD

Stogursey, Bridgwater TA5 1PU. Lady Acland Hood Gass. *7m E of Williton. 11 miles W of Bridgwater From A39 Bridgwater to Minehead rd turn N. garden 1 1/2 m W of Sturgursey on Stringston rd. No coaches.* Tea. **Adm £3.50, chd free. Sun 30 Mar (2-5).**

Woodland garden with bulbs, shrubs and fine trees; paved maze. Views of Quantocks and sea.

34 FARNDON THATCH

Puckington, Ilminster TA19 9JA. Bob & Jane St John Wright, 01460 259845, info@bandbinsomerset.com, www.bandbinsomerset.com. *3m N of Ilminster. From Ilminster take B3168 to Langport. Through Puckington village, last house on L. No Parking at house, arrangements by appointment.* **Adm £3.50, chd**

free. Visitors welcome by appt 26 May to 24 July only.
With panoramic views to die for, this 1-acre plantaholic's garden comes complete with C16 thatched cottage. Banks and borders brimming with shrubs and perennials. Planted for yr-round interest. Terrace and courtyard with pots; sculptures, vegetable garden, fine trees and lawns and areas of natural tranquility. An undulating garden following the contours of the land. Some wheelchair access.

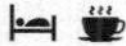

35 FERNHILL

Whiteball, nr Wellington TA21 0LU. Peter & Audrey Bowler, 01823 672423, muldoni@hotmail.co.uk, www.sampfordarundel.org.uk/fernhill/. *3m W of Wellington. At top of Whiteball hill on A38 on L going W just before dual carriageway, parking on site.* **Adm £3, chd free. Suns 29 June; 27 July; 24 Aug (2-5). Groups of 10+ also welcome by appt July and Aug.**
In approx 2 acres, a delightful garden to stir your senses, with a myriad of unusual plants and features. Intriguing almost hidden paths, leading through English roses, and banks of hydrangeas. Scenic views stretching up to the Blackdowns and its famous monument. Truly a Hide and Seek garden ... for all ages. Well stocked herbaceous borders, octagonal pergola and water garden with slightly wild boggy area. Wheelchair access to terrace and other parts of garden from drive.

36 1 FROBISHER ROAD

Ashton Gate, Bristol BS3 2AU. Karen Thomas. *2m SW of city centre. Bristol City FC on R, next R Duckmoor Rd, 5th turning L before bollards.* Home-made teas. **Adm £3, chd free. Sun 20 July, Sun 17 Aug (2-5).**
Cheek by jowl planting, arches, obelisks, hanging baskets, containers, 2 metal deer sculptures, hidden paths, seating areas, metal Victorian scroll gazebo, 3.4m high, 3 water features: one solar powered, one with tree in pond, water flowing from its leaves and stone lady in smaller pond with water flowing from jug. Daffodil design metal gates to house leading to compact city garden.

Jen's Gardyn

GROUP OPENING

37 FROME GARDENS

Frome BA11 4HR. *15m S of Bath. The Bastion Garden is in the town centre on Cork St. 9 Catherston Close signed from Sainsbury r'about, W side of town, towards Shepton Mallet A361.* Home-made teas at The Bastion Garden. **Combined adm £4, chd free. Sun 29 June (12-5).**

THE BASTION GARDEN
Mrs Karen Harvey-Lloyd.
Access to garden via Zion Path, next to Catherine House Care Home opp Cork St car park

9 CATHERSTON CLOSE
Dave & Prue Moon
(See separate entry)

2 varied gardens. The Bastion Garden: C18 extensively restored but still a work in progress. Features reveted banks, raised platforms, yew hedges and unusual shaped pond. The emphasis is on shape and form not extensive floral planting. Colourful 50-metre curved border of David Austin roses with low box hedging. 9 Catherston Close: A town garden which has grown over the years to 1/3 acre! Colour-themed shrub and herbaceous borders, pond, patios, pergolas and wild meadow areas leads to wonderful far reaching views. Productive vegetable and fruit garden with greenhouse. Exhibition of garden photography, from near and far, by garden owner is displayed in summerhouse. Featured in regional press, and on BBC Radio Somerset and Radio Bristol. Some gravel, slopes and small steps.

38 GANTS MILL & GARDEN

Gants Mill Lane, Bruton BA10 0DB. Elaine & Greg Beedle, www.gantsmill.co.uk. *1/2 m SW of Bruton. From Bruton centre take Yeovil rd, A359, under railway bridge, 100yds uphill, fork R down Gants Mill Lane. Parking for wheelchair users.* Home-made teas. **Adm £6, chd free. Sun 13 July (2-5).**
3/4 -acre garden. Clematis, rose arches and pergolas; streams, ponds, waterfalls. Riverside walk to top weir; delphiniums, day lilies, 100+ dahlia varieties; also vegetable, soft fruit and cutting flower garden. The garden is overlooked by the historic watermill, open on NGS day. Firm wide paths round the garden. Narrow entrance to mill not accessible to wheelchairs. WC.

GROUP OPENING

39 NEW GLASTONBURY SECRET GARDENS

BA6 9JJ. *100yds from Glastonbury Mkt Cross in Northload St (Pedestrian Area). From A39 turn off at Beckery r'about into Sedgemoor Way, take 2nd R (400yds) into Northload West C/P. Garden entrance clearly visible from C/P.* Home-made teas. **Combined adm £4, chd free. Sat 5, Sun 6 July (2-4).**

NEW JACOB'S LOFT
7/9 Northload Street. William Knight
01458 835144
info@glastonburyholidayhomes.com
www.glastonburyholidayhomes.com

NEW ST.MARGARET'S CHAPEL GARDEN
Magdalene Street. Ms Sandra Booth.
The garden is behind 38 Magdalene Sreet
http://stmargaretschapel.org.uk/

Jacob's Loft: Inner town courtyard garden, an example of what can be achieved in an urban environment. St Margaret's Chapel garden (Best Community Entry - Gold - in Mendip in Bloom) is accessed down a rather small alleyway, but in turning the corner everyone, without exception, gasps at the calm splendour of the garden, the peace of the C11 St Margaret's Chapel and the ancient Almshouses. Whether you are a pilgrim or a garden lover or both, we welcome you to these havens of peace, beauty, and tranquillity. While in bohemian Glastonbury visit our curious/quirky range of shops, our famous Abbey and if you feel energetic climb Glastonbury Tor. Both gardens have been winners of the Mendip District Council community garden award and the Glastonbury 'In Bloom' competition.

40 NEW GLEBE COURT

West Monkton, Taunton TA2 8QT. Mr and Mrs Anthony Pugh-Thomas. *2m NE of Taunton. Follow signs to West Monkton from A38. In village take driveway (entrance marked by two large 5 mph signs) leading to Church.* Home-made teas in neighbouring church. **Adm £4, chd free. Sat 7, Sun 8 June (2-5.30).**

Walled garden with greenhouses, orchard,vegetable plots, fruit tree cages and flower beds; herbaceous and shrub borders; copse and paddocks with some unusual trees; series of ponds. 11 acres in all surrounding Georgian Rectory (not open to the public). Partial wheelchair access: some uneven steps. Access to walled garden up slope and through gate with couple of low steps.

41 GLENWOOD GARDEN

6 Glenwood Rd, Henleaze BS10 5HQ. Pat & Graham Thomas. *3½ m N of Bristol city centre/2 miles S J16 M5. A4018 Westbury Rd across Durdham Down then B4056 Henleaze Rd. From J16 take A38 S to B4056 Southmead/Henleaze Rd. Mini r'about 2nd exit Lake Rd then 1st R.* **Evening Openings £4, chd free, wine, Fri 20 June, Fri 11, Fri 18 July (6-8).**

Front: SW-facing, variety of warm climate plants. Main garden: NE-facing, woodland outlook, dominated by large Sequoia tree. Water feature surrounded by acers, azaleas, rock garden. Sitting area in lower garden surrounded by (new) pseudo Japanese garden, adjacent to streamside with rhododendrons, ferns and hostas. Herbaceous beds and lawned area. Patio with many baskets and pots.

42 GOBLIN COMBE HOUSE

Plunder Street, Cleeve, Bristol BS49 4PQ. Mrs H R Burn. *10m S of Bristol. A370, turn L onto Cleeve Hill Rd before Lord Nelson Inn; 300m L onto Plunder St, 1st drive on R. Parking just beyond Plunder St turning.* Home-made teas. **Adm £3.50, chd free. Weds 21 May; 11, 18, 25 June (11-5).**

2-acre terraced garden with interesting collection of trees, shrubs and many different plants in borders, surrounded by orchards, fields and woodlands. Home to the rare plant Purple Gromwell found on woodland edges with alkaline soils. The garden contains uneven and steep paths which are very slippery in the rain. Highly recommended by Trevor Fry from Radio Bristol. Wide range of plants on sale.

43 16 GORDANO GARDENS

Easton in Gordano BS20 0PD. Mr & Mrs Milsom, 01275 373463. *5m W of Bristol. M5 J19 Gordano Services, exit Bristol. 1st L to Easton-in-Gordano, past King's Arms PH. Park in church hall car park by football field (BS20 0PR).* **Adm £3, chd free. Visitors welcome by appt July to Aug.**

Cottage-style garden 80ft long with many pretty and unusual features incl decked area, natural pond with waterfall, grasses and herbaceous plants.

44 HANGERIDGE FARMHOUSE

Wrangway, Wellington TA21 9QG. Mrs J M Chave, 01823 662339, hangeridge@hotmail.co.uk. *2m S of Wellington. 1m off A38 bypass signed Wrangway. 1st L towards Wellington Monument, over mway bridge 1st R.* Home-made teas. **Adm £3, chd free. Suns 13 Apr; 4, 25 May; 20 July; 17, 31 Aug; Mon 8 Sept (2-5). Visitors also welcome by appt May to Aug.**

Informal, relaxing, mature family garden set under Blackdown Hills. Seats to enjoy views across Somerset landscape. Atmospheric mix of herbaceous borders and this lovely and still-evolving garden contains wonderful flowering shrubs, heathers, mature trees, rambling climbers and seasonal bulbs. Content and design belie its 1-acre size. Garden not to be missed.

45 ◆ HANHAM COURT

Ferry Rd, Hanham Abbots, S Gloucestershire BS15 3NT. Hanham Court Gardens, 07800 536628, www.hanhamcourtgardens.co.uk. *5m E of Bristol centre. Old Bristol Rd A431 from Bath, through Willsbridge (past Queen's Head), L at mini r'about, down Court Farm Rd for 1m.*

Drive entrance on L at bend. **Adm £5, chd free. For NGS: Sun 2 Feb (12-4); Sun 8, Sun 29 June (12-5). For other opening times and information, please phone or see garden website.**
Hanham Court Gardens develop this rich mix of bold formality, water, woodland, orchard, meadow and kitchen garden with emphasis on scent, structure and romance, set amid a remarkable cluster of manorial buildings between Bath and Bristol. Also open Sats 7 Feb (Snowdrops); 7, 28 June. Partial wheelchair access via slopes.

46 NEW HARTWOOD HOUSE

Crowcombe Heathfield, Taunton TA4 4BS. Cdr and Mrs David Freemantle, 01984 667202, hartwoodhouse@hotmail.com, hartwoodhousebandb.co.uk. *approx 10m from Taunton, 5m from Williton. Clearly signed from A358. Situated in quiet tree-lined lane known locally as the Avenue.* Cream teas. **Adm £3, chd free. Sun 27 Apr, Sun 25 May (2-5.30). Evening Opening £3, chd free, light refreshments, Thur 26 June (4-7.30); Sun 27 July (2-5.30). Visitors also welcome by appt Apr to Sept, adm by donation.**
2-acre garden surrounded by magnificent oak and beech trees. Wide range of specimen trees and flowering shrubs provide colour and scent all yr. The formal garden has a circular theme and colour-coded borders. Extensive vegetable and fruit garden laid out in potager style, further on grassy paths lead into an ancient cider apple orchard being replanted with native trees. Garden is generally flat, firm underfoot with wide gateways. Teas and toilet facilities are easily accessed by wheelchair users.

47 HAYWOOD HOUSE

Littleton-upon-Severn, Bristol BS35 1NT. Andrew & Kath Bealing. *3½ m SW of Thorbury. Located between Elberton & Littleton on Severn, R from Elberton just after Bristol Water.* **Adm £3, chd free. Sun 20 July (1-6).**
Approx 1½ acres with panoramic views over the Severn Estuary. Lawns, mixed borders, Koi pond, small arboretum, rockeries. Gravel paths.

48 HENLEY MILL

Henley Lane, Wookey BA5 1AW. Peter & Sally Gregson, 01749 676966, millcottageplants@gmail.com, www.millcottageplants.co.uk. *2m W of Wells. Off A371 towards Cheddar. Turn L into Henley Lane, driveway 50yds on L through white pillars to end of drive.* **Adm £4.50. Visitors welcome by appt Apr to Sept teas/home-made cake by arrangement.**
2½ acres beside R Axe. Scented garden with roses, hydrangea borders, shady folly garden and late summer borders with grasses and perennials. New zig-zag boardwalk at river level. Ornamental kitchen garden. Rare Japanese hydrangeas. The garden is on one level, but the paths can get a bit muddy after heavy rain.

> Formal garden has a circular theme and colour-coded borders . . .

49 ◆ HESTERCOMBE GARDENS

Cheddon Fitzpaine TA2 8LG. Hestercombe Gardens Trust, 01823 413923, www.hestercombe.com. *4m N of Taunton. Follow the brown tourist signs rather than sat nav.* Cream teas in Courtyard café and in seasonal Mill Tea Garden. **Adm £9.70, chd £3.70. For NGS: Tues 4 Mar; 10 June (10-5). For other opening times and information, please phone or see garden website.**
Georgian landscape garden designed by Coplestone Warre Bampfylde, Victorian terrace/shrubbery and stunning Edwardian Lutyens/Jekyll formal gardens together make up 50 acres of woodland walks, temples, terraces, pergolas, lakes and cascades. Restored watermill and barn, Lesser Horseshoe bats and kids trail. Featured in The Garden, Telegraph Gardening, Garden History Society, Somerset Life, Somerset County Gazette. Gravel paths, steep slopes, steps. All abilities route marked.

GROUP OPENING

50 HINTON ST GEORGE GARDENS

High Street, nr Crewkerne TA17 8SE. *3m N of Crewkerne. N of A30 Crewkerne-Chard; S of A303 Ilminster Town Rd, at r'about signed Lopen & Merriott, then R to Hinton St George.* Home-made teas at Hooper's Holding. **Combined adm £4, chd free. Sun 25, Mon 26 May (2-5.30).**

END HOUSE
West Street. Helen Newman

HOOPER'S HOLDING
Ken & Lyn Spencer-Mills
Visitors also welcome by appt May to Aug.
01460 76389
kenlyn@devonrex.demon.co.uk

THE OLIVE GARDEN
Lopen Road. Pat Read

3 cottage gardens varying in size and style in beautiful hamstone village. C15 church. Country seat of the Earls of Poullett for 600yrs until 1973. Hooper's Holding: ½ -acre garden in colour compartments. Rare plants, many exotics, garden mosaics and sculptures. End House has sweeping lawns, gravel gardens and interesting trees and shrubs including colourful azaleas (approx ½ acre). The Olive Garden is a loving restoration of a site which had been neglected for decades, maturing well. Good wheelchair access at End House. Help available over gravel drive at Hooper's Holding. The Olive Garden is sloping but largely viewable from rd.

51 HOLLY TREES

Alveston Road, Old Down, Bristol BS32 4PH. Vicki & Tracy Watkeys. *2m S of Thornbury. Off A38 N of Almondsbury down Fern Hill, into Tockington, 1st R after Swan PH, 1st L up Old Down Hill then 1st R, garden approx 300yds on L.* **Adm £3, chd free. Sat 12, Sun 13 July (2-5).**
Large garden, approx 1 acre cultivated, partitioned with yew hedges into separate rooms. Landscaping started 1999, still ongoing! Sunken patio, herbaceous borders, small orchard, vegetable garden and more. Limited wheelchair access. Narrow paths and some steep steps.

Westbrook House

© Heather Edwards

52 HONEYHURST FARM
Honeyhurst Lane, Rodney Stoke, Cheddar BS27 3UJ. Don & Kathy Longhurst, 01749 870322, donlonghurst@btinternet.com. *4m E of Cheddar. From A371 between Wells and Cheddar, turn into Rodney Stoke signed Wedmore. Pass church on L and continue for almost 1m.* Home-made teas. **Adm £3, chd free. Sun 20 July (2-5). Groups of 10 to 40 also welcome by appt Apr to Sept.**
2/3 -acre part walled rural garden with babbling brook and 4-acre cider orchard, with views. Specimen hollies, copper beech, paulownia, yew and poplar. Pergolas, arbour and numerous seats. Mixed informal shrub and perennial beds with many unusual plants. Pots planted with shrubs, hardy and half-hardy perennials. Level, grass and some shingle.

53 JASMINE COTTAGE
26 Channel Road, Clevedon BS21 7BY. Margaret & Michael Redgrave, 01275 871850, margaret@bologrew.net, http://jasminecottage.bologrew.net. *12m W of Bristol. M5 J20 from Clevedon seafront travel N (0.8m), via Wellington Terrace, follow winding rd to St Mary's Church, R into Channel Rd, approx 100yds on L.* **Adm £3, chd free. Every Thur 5 June to 28 Aug (12.30-4.30). Visitors also welcome by appt June to Aug.**
Cottage garden with a difference. 1/3 acre with intriguing re-designed layout. New beds and borders are abundant with unusual plant varieties incl rhodochiton, dicentra macrocapnos and salvias, which are home grown and usually for sale. Early June delights with scented wisterias, old-fashioned sweet peas and roses. Salvias and tender perennials augment the feast of colour July onwards. RHS Partner Garden.

54 NEW ◆ JEKKA'S HERBETUM
Shellards Lane, Alveston, Bristol BS35 3SY. Mrs Jekka McVicar, 01454 418878, www.jekkasherbfarm.com. *7m N of M5 J16, or 6m S from J14 of M5. 1m off A38 signed Itchington. From M5 J16, A38 to Alveston, past church turn R at junction signed Itchington. M5 J14 on A38 turn L after T-lights to Itchington.* Home-made teas. **Adm £5, chd free. For NGS: Sun 13 July, Sun 3 Aug (10-4). For other opening times and information, please phone or see garden website.**
Jekka's Herboretum displays the largest collection of culinary herbs in the UK. It is a wonderful resource for plant identification for the gardener and a gastronomic experience for chefs & cooks. Featured on BBC2 Great British Garden Rival and BBC2 Mary Berry Cooks. Wheelchair access possible however terrain is rough from car park to Herbetum.

55 JEN'S GARDYN
4 Wroxham Drive, Little Stoke BS34 6EJ. Jennifer & Gary Ellington, 01454 610317, jensgardyn@hotmail.com, www.jensgardyn.com. *5m N of Bristol city centre. From Cribbs Causeway r'about go S on A38. Over next r'about, L into Stoke Lane, 4th L into Braydon Ave, 1st L into Wroxham Dr.* Light refreshments. **Adm £3, chd free. Visitors welcome by appt Aug.**
Inconceivably just 15' x 31'... astonishingly vibrant, intimate, exotic jungle! Collections of palms, bamboos, grasses, cycads, hostas, fuchsias, clematis and fernery. Organically grown, aromatic, culinary, medicinal and magical herbs! Wildlife stream, goldfish pools, fragrant living arbour. Beautiful sculptures, mystical shell grotto - an inspirational oasis of tropical eye-candy galore! Free herb tasting and talks. Featured on BBC Gardeners World and in local Press/radio. Not suitable for wheelchairs due to uneven, narrow gravel paths.

GROUP OPENING

56 KINGSTON ST MARY HIDDEN TREASURES

Kingston St. Mary, Taunton TA2 8HR, 01823 451513. *3.5m N of Taunton. Take Kingston Road North out of Taunton,signed in centre of village.* Home-made teas Kingston St Mary Village Hall. **Combined adm £4, chd free. Sat 21, Sun 22 June (2.30-5.30). Visitors also welcome by appt May to Aug to four of the gardens in the group - Boweys & Rose Cottage, Myrtle Cottage, The Old Parsonage and Winpenny Cottage. Combined adm: £4.**

BOWEYS AND ROSE COTTAGE
Church Lane. Mr N Palfrey, Mrs G Campbell, Mrs J M Palfrey & Miss D Palfrey.
Close to church in village. No parking at house, please use church car park. Disabled parking at Boweys
www.country-matters.co.uk

NEW BROOKSIDE
Nailsbourne. John Hayes.
Signed off Kingston St Mary Rd 1½ m N of Taunton

MYRTLE COTTAGE
Church Lane. Gaye Fox

NEW THE OLD PARSONAGE
Richard & Bella Flood

NEW THREEWAYS
Jenny Butcher.
From Kingston Village Hall turn R, straight on at The Swan. At T-Junction park on R. Garden on R

WINPENNY COTTAGE
Winpenny Lane. Mrs Carla Griffith

Magical gardening in a small space: plants, design, art, conservation and much more. Boweys and Rose Cottage: Two interconnecting mature cottage gardens, fascinating stonework, water and topiary with imaginative planting. Brookside: A garden in the countryside with meandering stream and wide views framed by trees and shrubs. Myrtle Cottage: High-walled garden belonging to artist/designer. Rose-filled patio leads by secret gate into the garden with its wild flower meadow, gazebo, herbaceous beds, stream and jungle, seating to savour its varying moods. Artist's work on show in studio. Myrtle Cottage featured in Somerset Life. The Old Parsonage: Charming southerly aspect with steep slope, mature trees and running water. Threeways: A mature plantsman's garden with rare plants attractively displayed. Winpenny Cottage: organic gardening on a pocket handkerchief with abundance of exotic plants from around the world, pond, mini jungle and collection of succulents.

57 LITTLE GARTH

Dowlish Wake, Ilminster TA19 0NX. Roger & Marion Pollard, 01460 52594. *2m S of Ilminster. R off Ilminster to Crewkerne rd at Kingstone Cross, then L, follow Dowlish Wake sign. L at white cottage before reaching church. Turn R, follow signs.* Teas and light refreshments at Perry's Cider Mill. **Adm £3, chd free. Sats 26 Apr; 10, 24 May; 7, 21 June; 5, 19 July; 2, 16, 30 Aug; 13 Sept (10.30-5.30). Visitors also welcome by appt Apr to Sept.**

½ -acre plantsman's garden for all seasons with many interesting and unusual perennials. Although essentially cottage style, emphasis is placed on the artistic arrangement of plants, using foliage, grasses and colour themes. Refreshments, plants for sale and public toilets at nearby Cider Mill, proceeds to Cider Mill. Park in front of nearby church. Mostly wheelchair access.

58 LITTLE YARFORD FARMHOUSE

Kingston St Mary, Taunton TA2 8AN. Brian Bradley, 01823 451350, yarford@ic24.net. *3½ m N of Taunton. From Taunton on Kingston St Mary rd. At 30mph sign turn L at Parsonage Lane. Continue 1¼ m W, to Yarford sign. Continue 400yds. Turn R up concrete rd.* Light refreshments. **Adm £4, chd free. Fri 9 May (11-5); Sat 10, Sun 11 May (2-6); Mon 12 May (11-5). Visitors also welcome by appt Mar to Oct, guided tours of trees.**

This unusual garden embraces a C17 house (not open) overgrown with a tapestry of climbing plants. The 3 ponds exhibit a wide range of aquatic gems. Of special interest is the collection of over 300 trees of rare and unusual cultivars, both broad leaf and conifer, all differing in form and colour including weeping and fastigiate. The 5 acres are a delight to both artist and plantsman. 'An inspirational, magical experience'. Featured in Somerset Art Weeks Brochure as part of the Abundance Garden Trail. Mostly wheelchair access.

Magical gardening in a small space . . .

59 LUCOMBE HOUSE

12 Druid Stoke Ave, Stoke Bishop, Bristol BS9 1DD. Malcolm Ravenscroft. *4m NW of Bristol centre. On L at top of Druid Hill. Garden on R 200m from junction.* Home-made teas. **Adm £3, chd free. Sun 18 May (2-5). Also open 1 Sunnyside.**

Woodland area with over 30 mature trees planted in last 4 yrs underplanted with bluebells and white foxgloves. Area redesigned for 2014 following removal of large conifer. Separate semi-formal area and untouched wild area under 220yr-old Lucombe oak. Landscape gardener will be on site and happy to answer questions. Rough paths in woodland area, 2 steps to patio.

60 NEW LYDEARD HOUSE

West Street, Bishops Lydeard, Taunton TA4 3AU. Mrs Colin Wilkins. *5m NW of Taunton. A358 Taunton to Minehead, do not take 1st 3 R turnings to Bishops Lydeard but 4th signed to Cedar Falls. Follow signs to Lydeard House.* Home-made teas. **Adm £4, chd free. Sun 22 June (2-5.30).**

4-acre garden with C18 origins and many later additions. Sweeping lawns, lake overhung with willows, canal running parallel to Victorian rose-covered pergola, along with box parterre, chinoiserie-style garden, recent Temple Folly and walled vegetable garden plus wonderful mature trees. Plants for sale from local nursery. Children must be supervised because of very deep water. Featured in Country Gardener. Deep gravel paths and steps but most features accessible by lawn.

61 LYMPSHAM MANOR

Lympsham, Weston-super-Mare BS24 0DT. James & Lisa Counsell. *5m S of Weston-super-Mare and 5m N of Burnham on Sea. Junction 22 M5.* Home-made teas. **Adm £4, chd free. Sat 21, Sun 22 June (2-5).**
Early C19 gothic pinnacled, castellated Rectory Manor House with 2 octagonal towers set in 10 acres of formal and semi-formal garden surrounded by paddocks and farmland. The garden's main features are its carefully preserved, fully working Victorian kitchen garden and greenhouse, an arboretum of trees from all parts of the world, large stocked fish pond and a beautiful old rose garden.

62 ◆ LYTES CARY MANOR

Nr Kingsdon TA11 7HU. National Trust, 01458 224471, www.nationaltrust.org.uk/lytes-cary-manor. *3m SE of Somerton. Signed from Podimore r'about at junction of A303, A37, take A372.* **Adm £9, chd £4.50. For NGS: Wed 11 June (10.30-5). For other opening times and information, please phone or see garden website.**
Arts and Crafts style garden with many contrasts, topiary and mixed borders. Home of medieval herbalist Henry Lyte. Estate walks: Garden and Behind the Scenes tour at 2pm. Uneven paths.

63 NEW MELLS PARK

Mells, Frome BA11 3QB. The Hon Michael and Mrs Samuel. *4m W of Frome. Frome, take A362 (Egford Hill), after 1½ m R sign Vobster (Knaptons Hill) Mells Park 2½ m at bottom of hill on L through high metal gates.* Light refreshments. **Adm £5, chd free. Sat 5, Sun 6 July (10-4.30).**
The Grade 1 listed parkland & lakes date back to C18. Vast parkland, early C20 gardens by Lutyens & Jekyll, under restoration, around Grade II listed country house (not open). Walled vegetable garden, meadow of flowers, thyme walk, lavender and rose hedges, redwood trees, colour-themed planting, box parterre, Edwardian greenhouses. Walk to Temple Garden. Extensive views and walks. Wheelchair access in parts, uneven paths, gravel.

Meadow of flowers, thyme walk, lavender and rose hedges . . .

64 ◆ MIDNEY GARDENS

Mill Lane, Midney, Somerton TA11 7HR. David Chase and Alison Hoghton, 01458 274250, www.midneygardens.co.uk. *1m SE of Somerton. 100yds off B3151. From Podimore r'about on A303 take A372. After 1m R on B3151 towards Street. After 2m L on bend into Mill Lane.* Home-made teas. **Adm £3.50, chd free. For NGS: Sun 11 May, Fri 19 Sept (11-5). For other opening times and information, please phone or see garden website.**
New 1-acre plantsman's garden, where unusual planting combinations, interesting use of colour, subtle themes and a natural flowing style create a garden full of variety and inspiring ideas. Incl seaside garden, Clarice Cliff inspired garden, white garden, vegetables and borders. Nursery offers herbaceous perennials, alpines, herbs and grasses.

65 ◆ MILTON LODGE

Old Bristol Road, Wells BA5 3AQ. Simon Tudway Quilter, 01749 672168, www.miltonlodgegardens.co.uk. *½ m N of Wells. From A39 Bristol-Wells, turn N up Old Bristol Rd; car park first gate on L signed.* **Adm £5, chd free. For NGS: Sun 18 May, Sun 8 June, Sun 13 July (2-5). For other opening times and information, please phone or see garden website.**
Mature Grade II, terraced garden conceived c1900. Sloping ground transformed into architectural terraces with profusion of plants, capitalising on views of Wells Cathedral and Vale of Avalon. 1960, garden lovingly restored to former glory, orchard replaced with raised collection of ornamental trees. Cross Old Bristol Rd to 7-acre woodland garden, the Combe, natural peaceful contrast to formal garden at Milton Lodge. First opened for NGS 1962.
Also open Tues, Weds, Suns, BHs, Easter - 31 Oct (2-5). Featured in regional press, on Radio Somerset, Radio Bristol and Glastonbury fm.

66 ◆ MONTACUTE HOUSE

Montacute TA15 6XP. National Trust, 01935 823289, grahame.meaden@nationaltrust.org.uk, www.nationaltrust.org.uk/montacute-house. *4m W of Yeovil. NT signs off A3088 & A303.* **Adm £12.40, chd £6.20. For NGS: Sun 8 June (10-4.30). For other opening times and information, please phone or see garden website.**
Magnificent Elizabethan house with contemporary garden layout. Fine stonework provides setting for informally planted mixed borders and old roses; range of garden features illustrates its long history. 80% wheelchair access.

67 ◆ NEWARK PARK

Ozleworth GL12 7PZ. National Trust, 01453 842644, www.nationaltrust.org.uk/newarkpark. *2m NE of Wotton-under-Edge. Signposted Newark Park/Ozleworth from A4135 Tetbury - Dursley rd and from Wotton-under-Edge. SAT NAV not suitable. Disabled drop off/parking at house.* Light refreshments, tea, coffee, cake. **Adm £7.90, chd £3.90. For NGS: Thur 20 Feb (11-4.30). For other opening times and information, please phone or see garden website.**
Wild woodland garden with a great display of snowdrops and some lovely aconites. The house and garden have wonderful views to the South. Limited wheelchair access, steep slopes.

GROUP OPENING

68 NUNNEY GARDENS

Horn Street, Nunney, Nr Frome BA11 4NP. *3m S of Frome. Nunney Catch, A361 between Frome and Shepton Mallet, follow signs to Nunney (1 m). In market sq, follow car park signs then NGS arrows.* Home-made teas at Sunny Bank.
Combined adm £5, chd free. Sun 22 June (11-4).

THE MILLER'S HOUSE
17 Horn Street. Caroline Toll

SUNNY BANK
High Street. Mr & Mrs S Thomas

Picturesque village clustered around C15 church, duck pond fed by Nunney Brook, ruined medieval castle with moat and market sq. 2 contrasting gardens. Miller's House: garden of person who considers herself to be an untidy planter! A mostly perennial garden with terraced borders, rockeries, large mill pond and wild section between the leat and Nunney Brook. Many areas to sit and enjoy views of garden. Be sure to look at terraced vegetable patch as well as a few small modern sculptures around garden. Caution with children and on steps and path around mill pond. Sunny Bank has been transformed from a former vegetable plot into an intriguing ½-acre garden, providing variety and interest in its numerous sections. Two subtropical houses containing cacti and succulents, as featured in Amateur Gardening Magazine, are interspersed with fossils and unusual natural objects. In contrast to this are damp shaded areas containing hostas, ferns and woodland plants leading to raised carp pond and herbaceous borders.

69 NYNEHEAD COURT
Nynehead, Wellington TA21 0BN. Nynehead Care Ltd, 01823 662481/07834 773441, nyneheadcare@aol.com. *2m S of Wellington. M5 J26 B3187 towards Wellington. R on r'about marked Nynehead & Poole, follow lane for 1 m, take Milverton turning at fork.* Tea in Orangery. **Adm £3.50, chd free. Sun 22 June, Sun 13 July (2-5). Visitors also welcome by appt, large groups must book 1 month in advance.**
Nynehead Court Gardens are on English Heritage's list of gardens of historic interest. Once the ancestral home of the Sanford family. Gardens laid out during the Victorian period, points of interest - pinetum, ice house, parterre and extended walks within parkland of old estate. Garden tours by head gardener, Justin Cole, start 2pm prompt (tour lasts 1 hr approx). Gravel paths, slight slopes, cobbled yard (ice house).

Tuckers Farmhouse, Stoke St Mary Gardens

70 THE OLD RECTORY, DOYNTON
18 Toghill Lane, Doynton, Bristol BS30 5SY. Edwina & Clive Humby. *At heart of village of Doynton, between Bath and Bristol. Follow Toghill Lane up from The Holy Trinity Church about 500 metres, around cricket field to car park field. Signs to garden.* Home-made teas. **Adm £4, chd free. Sat 14 June (11-3).**
Doynton's Grade II-listed Georgian Rectory's walled garden and extended 15-acre estate. Renovated over 12 years, it sits within AONB. Garden has diversity of modern and traditional elements, fused to create atmospheric series of garden rooms. It is both a landscaped and large kitchen garden, featuring a canal, vegetable plots, fruit cages and tree house. Partial wheelchair access, some narrow gates and uneven surfaces.

71 THE OLD RECTORY, LIMINGTON
Church St, Limington, nr Yeovil BA22 8EQ. John Langdon & Paul Vintner, 01935 840127, jdlpv@aol.com. *2m E of Ilchester. From A303 exit on A37 to Yeovil/Ilchester. At 1st r'about L to Ilchester/Limington. 2nd R to Limington. Continue 1½ m.* Light refreshments. **Adm £3.50, chd free. Visitors welcome by appt Mar to June prebook by email or telephone.**
Romantic walled gardens of 1½ acres. Formal parterres, herbaceous borders. Many unusual shrubs and trees incl 200 yr-old lucombe oak, liriodendron, paulownia, laburnocytisus, leycesteria and poncirus. Extensive planting of bulbs incl galanthus, anemone blanda, winter aconites, tulips and alliums. Gravel drive, one gentle slope only.

72 NEW 2 OLD TARNWELL
Stanton Drew, Bristol BS39 4EA. Mrs Mary Payne, 01275 333146. *6m S of Bristol. Between B3130 & A368 just W of Pensford. Detailed directions will be given when appt is made.* Tea. **Adm £5. Due to limited space, pre-booking essential: Weds 25 June; 9, 23 July (10-4). Groups of 8-10 also welcome by appt June/July.**
A quart of good plants poured into a quarter-pint sized plot. Front garden planted in contemporary 'steppe' style in shades of yellow and orange. Back garden more traditional in style with cool shades. Small greenhouse. Interesting design details offer plenty of ideas for small gardeners! Regret not suitable for children. Featured on BBC Radio Bristol. Not suitable for wheelchairs.

GROUP OPENING

73 NEW OLDBURY ON SEVERN GARDENS

Oldbury-On-Severn, Bristol BS35 1QA. *3 miles W of Thornbury. A38 N from Bristol to Thornbury. Signed Oldbury on Severn. Turn L into village. Follow yellow signs.* Home-made teas at The Pound. **Combined adm £5, chd free. Sat 7, Sun 8 June (1-5).**

NEW CHRISTMAS COTTAGE
Church Road. Angela Conibere & Doug Mills

NEW IVYDENE
Church Road. Colin and Sue Keedwell

NEW ORCHARD CROFT
Camp Road, Oldbury-On-Severn, Bristol. Carole and Gerald Dyke

NEW THE POUND
Church Road, Oldbury-On-Severn, Bristol. Paul and Janet Astle

Four village gardens varying in size and structure. A mix of traditional country vegetable gardening, interesting planting and planning. The Pound is a large garden incorporating many interesting features designed for children. A dry garden area, an interesting selection of trees and many climbing roses. Shrub and flower borders and an attractive pergola area. Ivydene is a large traditional country garden with an excellent mix of flowers, fruit trees and productive vegetable garden. The owner is a dedicated sweet pea grower. Plants for sale. Christmas Cottage has a mix of flower beds, shrubbery and lawn. Formal fishpond and some artefacts. Orchard Croft has a very pretty garden surrounding the house. Flower and shrub borders and vegetable garden. Ivydene not suitable for wheelchairs (steps into main access).

74 ORCHARD WYNDHAM

nr Williton TA4 4HH. The Wyndham Trustees. *7m SE of Minehead, 16m from Taunton. Out of Williton take A39 towards Minehead then signed L and up long drive to house. Exit past Bakelite Museum.* Teas in Bakelite Museum. **Adm £3, chd free. Sun 1 June (2-5).**

Garden of historic house (not open on NGS days) in parkland setting: woods, interesting old trees, borders, rose walk, 2 small lakes, wild garden.

75 ORGANIC BLOOMS

Latteridge Road (Latteridge Hill), Latteridge, Bristol BS37 9TS. Jo & Chris Wright, www.organicblooms.co.uk. *5m W of Yate. On B4059, approx 150m from Latteridge Green. Entrance is at end of green steel corrugated fence that runs along site boundary.* Light refreshments. **Adm £3, chd free. Sun 6 July (1.30-4.30).**

Working cut flower nursery run as social enterprise. We specialise in growing traditional cut flower crops from sweet williams and anemone to zinnias, dahlias and sweetpeas. Flowers grown using organic principles. We offer supported work experience and training to people with learning difficulties and mental health support needs. Hand-tied bouquet demonstration. Tour and talk on organic cut flower production and the social enterprise. Paths are woodchip, so wheelchair access may be more difficult in very wet conditions.

76 3 PALMER'S WAY

Hutton, Weston-super-Mare BS24 9QT. Mary & Peter Beckett, 01934 815110, macbeckett@tiscali.co.uk. *3m S of Weston-super-Mare. From A370 follow signs to Hutton. L at PO, 1st L St Mary's Rd, car park 2nd R. Garden 3 mins walk, signed. Limited disabled parking at garden.* Home-made teas. **Adm £3, chd free. Sat 7, Sun 8, Sat 28, Sun 29 June (11.30-5.30). Also open 52 South Lawn, Locking 28/29 June. Visitors also welcome by appt June to July for groups less than 20.**

Average suburban plot featuring 11 fruit trees among unusual perennials, herbs, grasses, hardy geraniums, bananas and other tropical plants, wildlife ponds and box knot garden. Not much space for your daily constitutional but room to stroll or sit and admire the informal tapestry of this densely-packed plantsman's garden. Tea among the bougainvilleas, and lots of plants for sale. Home-made preserves using locally-grown produce for sale. Some steps. Wheelchair access more limited if wet.

78 PEN MILL FARM

Pen Selwood, Wincanton BA9 8NF. Mr & Mrs Peter FitzGerald, 01747 840895, fitzgeraldatpen@aol.com, www.penmillcottage.co.uk. *1m from Stourhead, off A303 between Mere and Wincanton. Leave A303 on A3091 (Bruton exit). Turn off old A303 to Penselwood. 2nd L fork up narrow unsigned lane. R at grass triangle to Zeals down steep hill.* Ploughman's lunches available on Sunday and delicious home made cakes and scones both days. **Adm £3.50, chd free. Sat 13 Sept (2-5); Sun 14 Sept (12-5). Also open Chiffchaffs, Chaffeymoor, Bourton, Gillingham SP8 5BY (2 fields away). Groups of 10+ very welcome by appt May to Oct.**

Romantic garden with acid-loving mature trees and shrubs in secluded valley on Dorset, Somerset and Wiltshire border where tributary of R Stour cascades into the lake. Late summer herbaceous borders with abundant colour and over 40 salvias. Enjoy the peace and quiet of this lovely setting. Penselwood plant stall, many unusual salvia and penstemon plants. Featured in Garden Answers, The County Gardener and The Dorset Gardens Trust Journal. Mostly wheelchair access.

1 Braggchurch

79 PENNY BROHN CANCER CARE
Chapel Pill Lane, Pill, North Somerset BS20 0HH. Penny Brohn Cancer Care, www.pennybrohncancercare.org. *4m W of Bristol. Off A369. Clifton Suspension Bridge to M5 (J19 Gordano Services). Follow signs to Penny Brohn Cancer Care and to Pill and Ham Green.* **Adm £4, chd £1. Sun 22 June (11-5).**
3.5-acre tranquil garden surrounds a Georgian mansion with many mature trees, wild flower meadow, flower garden, cedar summerhouse, fine views from historic gazebo overlooking R Avon, courtyard gardens with water features. Garden is maintained by volunteers and plays an active role in the Charity's Living Well with Cancer approach. Plants, teas & music. Gift shop. Tours of centre to find out more about the work of Penny Brohn Cancer Care. Some gravel and grass paths.

ALLOTMENTS

80 PRETORIA ROAD ALLOTMENTS
Patchway, Bristol BS34 5PX. Pretoria Road Allotments, jennylloyd1949@gmail.com, www.growpretoria.org. *6m N of Bristol city centre. From Cribbs Causeway A4018 follow signs for Patchway onto start of Highwood Rd. Take first L onto Coniston Rd. R into Windermere Rd, L for Pretoria Rd. Entrance between house nos 84 & 86.* Home-made teas. **Adm £3.50, chd free. Sun 8 June (11-3).**
Large allotment site on flat ground. Grass paths between plots. Vegetables, soft fruits (incl grapes and hops), trees, herbs and flowers. Shop selling garden sundries, jams, pickles and handmade cards. Many plot-holders will be available to answer questions. Plants and produce for sale. Disabled access WC. Partial wheelchair access, grass pathways between plots.

81 ◆ PRIOR PARK LANDSCAPE GARDEN
Ralph Allen Drive, Bath BA2 5AH. National Trust, 01225 833422, www.nationaltrust.org.uk. *1m S of Bath. Visitors are advised to use public transport as there is no parking at Prior Park or nearby, except for disabled visitors.* Light refreshments by the lakes. **Adm £6.30, chd £3.30. For NGS: Sun 4 May (10-5.30). For other opening times and information, please phone or see garden website.**
Beautiful and intimate C18 landscape garden created by Bath entrepreneur Ralph Allen (1693-1764) with advice from the poet Alexander Pope and Capability Brown. Sweeping valley with magnificent views of city. Palladian bridge and lakes. Wilderness restoration, completed in 2007, involved reinstating the serpentine lake, cascade and cabinet to their former glory. Drifts of wild garlic carpeting the woodlands. Limited wheelchair access (the wilderness and view point are accessible, steep slopes, gravel paths and steps in rest of garden).

Four new village gardens . . .

82 ROCK HOUSE
Elberton BS35 4AQ. Mr & Mrs John Gunnery, 01454 413225. *10m N of Bristol. 3½ m SW Thornbury. From Old Severn Bridge on M48 take B4461 to Alveston. In Elberton, take 1st turning L to Littleton-on-Severn and turn immed R.* **Adm £3, chd free (share to St Johns Church, Elberton). Suns 2, 9 Feb 2014; 1, 8 Feb 2015 (11-4). Visitors also welcome by appt Jan to Sept.**
1-acre walled garden undergoing improvement. Pond and old yew tree, mixed borders, cottage garden plants and developing woodland with many snowdrops. Limited wheelchair access.

GROUP OPENING

83 ROSE COTTAGE & COLEY COURT
Coley BS40 6AN and E Harptree BS40 6BY, 01761 221627, bandjcruse@gmail.com. *5m N of Wells, 15m S of Bristol. Please see individual gardens for directions.* Home-made teas at Rose Cottage. **Combined adm £4.50, chd free. Sun 13 Apr (2-5). Visitors also welcome by appt Apr to July Rose Cottage.**

COLEY COURT
Coley, East Harptree, Bristol. Mrs M J Hill.
A39 at Chewton Mendip take B3114 for 2m, turn R signed Coley & Hinton Blewitt. B3114 East Harptree to Chewton Mendip for 1m turn L signed Coley

ROSE COTTAGE
East Harptree, Bristol. Bev & Jenny Cruse.
From B3114 turn into High St in East Harptree. L at Clock Tower and immed R into Middle St, up hill for 1m. From B3134 take East Harptree turning opp Castle of Comfort, continue 1½ m. Car parking in field opp cottage
Visitors also welcome by appt Apr to July.
01761 221627
bandjcruse@gmail.com

2 contrasting gardens. Coley Court: 1 acre garden surrounds an early Jacobean house (not open). The garden, surrounded by stone walls, consists of spring bulbs; vegetable area, as well as an acre of old mixed orchard. Rose Cottage: 1-acre hillside cottage garden with panoramic views over Chew Valley. Garden, carpeted with primroses, spring bulbs and hellebores and in summer with roses and hardy geraniums. It is bordered by stream and established mixed hedges. Plenty of seating areas to enjoy the views and teas, as well as the music of Congresbury Brass Band. Wildlife area and pond in corner of car park field. Featured in regional press, Radio Somerset, Bristol and Glastonbury fm.

84 RUGG FARM
Church Street, Limington, nr Yeovil BA22 8EQ. Morene Griggs, Peter Thomas & Christine Sullivan, 01935 840503, griggsandthomas@btinternet.com. *2m E of Ilchester. From A303 exit on A37 to Yeovil/ Ilchester. At 1st r'about L to Ilchester/Limington, 2nd R to Limington, continue 1½ m.* Cream teas. **Adm £4, chd free. Evening Opening £4, chd free, light refreshments, Thur 10 July (5-8);**

159 Westbury Lane, West Bristol Gardens

Sun 13 July (11-5). Visitors also welcome by appt July to Sept, we particularly enjoy welcoming groups of 8+.
2-acre garden created since 2007 around former farmhouse and farm buildings. Diverse areas of interest. Ornamental, kitchen and cottage gardens, lawn and borders, courtyard container planting, orchard, wildlife meadows and pond, developing shrubberies, woodland plantings and walk (unsuitable for wheelchairs). Exuberant annuals and perennials throughout. Compost Champion in residence. Metalwork designs by Andy Stevenson Garden Sculptures. Featured in Somerset County Gardener. Some gravel paths.

85 ST PETER'S HOSPICE

Charlton Road, Brentry, Bristol BS10 6NL. St Peter's Hospice. *4m N of Bristol. From Durdham Downs follow A4018 N towards M5, follow signs for St Peter's Hospice onto Charlton Rd. Enter carpark on L.* Home-made teas Cafe at St Peter's Hospice. **Adm £3.50, chd free. Sun 29 June, Sun 6 July (11-3.30).**
Spacious, tranquil garden for patients and visitors. Historically a remnant of nearby Repton House grounds. Distant view across Severn Estuary. Large lawns with mature and maturing trees, wild flower area and moon daisy bank. Pergola with climbers, herbaceous borders, formal bedding display, tubs and baskets. Plenty of seating for resting and picnics. Teas, cakes and ice creams available. Most of garden is accessible by wheelchair.

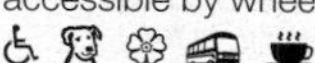

86 SELF REALIZATION MEDITATION HEALING CENTRE GARDEN

Laurel Lane, Queen Camel BA22 7NU. SRMHC Charitable Trust, 01935 850266, info@selfrealizationcentres.org, www.selfrealizationcentres.org. *6m NE of Yeovil. 1m S of A303 from Sparkford r'about on A359. Follow rd, 1st R past the Mildmay Arms.* Home-made teas. **Adm £3, chd free. Mon 19, Tue 20 May (2-5). Visitors also welcome by appt May to Oct.**
Peaceful 3-acre garden with varied vistas, trees and lawns, surrounding spiritual retreat and training centre. Stunning herbaceous borders and fragrant old roses around C17 farmhouse (not open). Wildlife pond, newly planted maze, herb beds and meditation room garden. Oriental garden and koi pond by arrangement only. Gravel drive and some uneven flagstone paths. Steps avoidable with detour.

87 SERRIDGE HOUSE

Henfield Road, Coalpit Heath BS36 2UY. Mrs J Manning, 01454 773188. *9m N of Bristol. On A432 at Coalpit Heath T-lights (opp church), turn into Henfield Rd. R at PH, 1/2 m small Xrds, garden on corner with Ruffet Rd, park on Henfield Rd.* Home-made teas. **Adm £4, chd free. Groups of 10 - 40 welcome by appt July to Aug.**
2 1/2 -acre garden with mature trees, heather and conifer beds, island beds mostly of perennials, woodland area with pond. Colourful courtyard with old farm implements. Lake views and lakeside walks. Unique tree carvings. Mostly flat lawn and path. Wheelchair access to lake difficult.

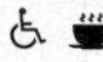

88 ◆ SHERBORNE GARDEN

Litton, Radstock, Somerset BA3 4PP. Mr & Mrs John Southwell, 01761 241220. *15m S of Bristol. 15m W of Bath, 7m N of Wells. On B3114 Chewton Mendip to Harptree rd, 1/2 m past The Kings Arms.* **Adm £4, chd free. For NGS: Sun 16, Mon 17 Feb; Sun 3 Aug 2014 (11-4); Sun 15, Mon 16 Feb 2015 (11-4). For other opening times and information, please phone or see garden website.**

4 1/2 -acre gently sloping garden with small pinetum, holly wood and many unusual trees and shrubs. Cottage garden leading to privy. 3 ponds linked by wadi and rills with stone and wooden bridges. Snowdrops and hellibores. Hosta walk leading to pear and nut wood. Rondel and gravel gardens with grasses and phormiums. Collections of day lilies, rambling and rose species. Good labelling. Plenty of seats. Featured on Radio Bristol for presentation of Prunus incisa variegata after 30 years of garden opening for NGS.

Garden reflects owners' creative interests and innovative ideas . . .

89 SOLE RETREAT

Haydon Drove, Haydon, West Horrington, Wells BA5 3EH. Jane Clisby, 01749 672648/07790 602906, janeclisby@aol.com, www.soleretreat.co.uk. *3m NE of Wells. From Wells take B3139 towards the Horringtons. Keep on main road. after 3m L for Sole Retreat Reflexology, signed, garden 50yds on L.* Home-made teas. **Adm £3.50, chd free. Sun 20 July, Sun 24 Aug (11-5). Visitors also welcome by appt June to Aug.**

It is a challenge to garden at almost 1000ft on the Mendip Hills Area of Outstanding Natural Beauty. Peaceful garden full of old garden favourites set in 1/3 acre. Cottage garden style within dry stone walls and raw face bedrock. 9 differing areas incl sun terrace, herbaceous borders, water feature and pool, therapy and contemplation gardens, fernery and vegetable plot. Best Overall Garden in the Parish Garden in Bloom. Featured in regional press, on Radio Somerset and Bristol and Glastonbury fm. Some gravel.

90 SOMERFOSS

Bath Road, Oakhill, Radstock BA3 5AG. Ewan & Rosemary Curphey, 01749 840542, ECurphey@aol.com. *3m N of Shepton Mallet. From Oakhill School 1/4 m N on A367. Parking in lay-by on R.* Home-made teas. **Adm £4, chd free. Wed 14, Sun 18 May (2-6). Individuals and groups welcome daytime or evening by appt Apr/May.**

An unusual and surprising garden awaits you at Somerfoss. The S-facing valley provides several different plant areas and beds full of unusual shrubs and perennials. Particular features are a natural rock area, a damp area with a stand of wild orchids flowering in June. There is a large raised deck, a great place to view the garden and enjoy a cup of tea or coffee with homemade cake. Featured in regional press. Steep slopes, steps and uneven ground.

91 52 SOUTH LAWN

Locking, Weston-Super-Mare BS24 8AD. Bill & Shirley Marlow, 01934 822077, sparra52@hotmail.co.uk. *2 m E of Weston-super-Mare. From A370, WsM, over 2nd r'about, R into Locking Village just before garage onto Elm Tree Rd, then 2nd R into South Lawn, last bungalow on R.* Home-made teas. **Adm £3, chd free. Sat 21, Sun 22, Sat 28, Sun 29 June (11-5). Also open 3 Palmers Way on 28/29 June. Visitors also welcome by appt June to Aug.**

Garden reflects owners' creative interests and innovative ideas, not only in the evergreen and fragrant planting; the variety of textures, topiary, colours and themes stimulate the imagination. Stroll around winding pathways into attractive seating areas in which to relax and enjoy the unusual features. Gaudi-style mosaic features. Original sculptures and folly with stained glass features amongst evergreen and fragrant planting. Indoor and outdoor seating areas to relax and enjoy an interesting, colourful garden. Scrumptious cakes and teas in our own Mad Hatter's Tea Shop.

92 SOUTH MEADE

Meade Lane, Seavington St Mary TA19 0QL. Charo & Robin Ritchie. *3m E of Ilminster. Via B3168 to Seavington St Michael, near PH turn down Water Street to Seavington Millenneum Hall, Shop and Café and see parking signs and map.* Light refreshments, teas and light lunches at village café. **Adm £3, chd free. Mon 11, Tue 12, Wed 13, Thur 14, Fri 15, Sat 16 Aug (1-5.30).**

Beautiful country views all around. Mix of herbaceous, shrubs, roses and over 100 clematis are dotted around the garden. Absorb nature sitting in the Mediterranean patio and special Japanese pond areas. The searching for garden perfection is what fills my heart with joy. Exhibition of watercolour floral art.

93 SOUTHFIELD FARM

Farleigh Road, Backwell, Bristol BS48 3PE. Pamela & Alan Lewis. *6m S of Bristol. On A370, 500yds after George Inn towards WsM. Farm directly off main rd on R with parking. Large car park.* Home-made teas. **Adm £4, chd free. Sun 18 May (2-5).**

2-acre owner-designed garden of rooms with lovely views. Mixed shrub and herbaceous borders, perennials,bulbs and blossom. Roses, climbers, pergolas and seating. Formal ponds. Orchard, vegetable garden, summerhouse, terracing and courtyards. Pathway to 1-acre woodland garden and to large wildlife pond with paths, seating and bird hide. Tearooms in old stable courtyard. Wheelchair access to most areas. Some gravel. Small courtyard and terrace only accessible by steps.

94 ◆ SPECIAL PLANTS

Greenways Lane, Nr Cold Ashton SN14 8LA. Derry Watkins, 01225 891686, www.specialplants.net. *6m N of Bath. From Bath on A46, turn L into Greenways Lane just before r'about with A420.* Home-made teas in house. **Adm £4.50, chd free. For NGS: Thurs 19 June; 17 July; 21 Aug; 18 Sept; 16 Oct (11-5). For**

other opening times and information, please phone or see garden website.
Architect-designed ¾ -acre hillside garden with stunning views. Started autumn 1996. Exotic plants. Gravel gardens for borderline hardy plants. Black and white (purple and silver) garden. Vegetable garden and orchard. Hot border. Lemon and lime bank. Annual, biennial and tender plants for late summer colour. Spring-fed ponds. Bog garden. Woodland walk. Allium alley. Free list of plants in garden. New wavy bridge linking field and woods. Featured in Gardens Illustrated and The Garden magazines.

95 STANTON COURT NURSING HOME
Stanton Drew BS39 4ER. Pam Townsend, stantoncourtnh.net. *5m S of Bristol. From Bristol on A37, R onto B3130 signed Chew Magna. 1.4m, L at old thatched toll house into Stanton Drew, 1st property on L.* Light refreshments. **Adm £2.50, chd free. Sun 22 June (1-4).**
2 acres of tranquil gardens around gracious Georgian House (grade II listed). Mature trees, extensive herbaceous borders with many interesting plants and spring bulbs. Large vegetable garden, fruit trees and soft fruit bushes. Gardener Judith Chubb Whittle keeps this lovely garden interesting in all seasons. Set in beautiful countryside. Delicious light lunches and teas available on NGS open days. Stanton Drew's ancient Stone Circle can be seen from the end of the garden - it is just a short walk from Stanton Court.

96 STOBERRY GARDEN
Stoberry Park, Wells BA5 3LD. Frances & Tim Young, 01749 672906, stay@stoberry-park.co.uk, www.stoberry-park.co.uk. *½ m N of Wells. From Bristol - Wells on A39, L into College Rd and immed L through Stoberry Park, signed.* **Adm £5, chd free. Sun 11 May (2-5.30).**
With breathtaking views over Wells and the Vale of Avalon, this 6-acre family garden planted sympathetically within its landscape provides a stunning combination of vistas accented with wildlife ponds, water features, sculpture, 1½ -acre walled garden, sunken garden, gazebo, potager, lime walk. Colour and interest in every season; spring bulbs, irises, roses, acer glade, salvias. Featured in regional press, Mendip Times; Somerset Life; Bath Life; Wells Life monthly magazines. Gravel paths, steep slopes.

Crafts and art and prairie-style meadow . . .

GROUP OPENING

97 STOGUMBER GARDENS
Station Road, Stogumber TA4 3TQ. *11m NW of Taunton. 3m W of A358. Signed to Stogumber, W of Crowcombe. Maps given to all visitors.* Home-made teas in Village Hall. **Combined adm £5, chd free. Sun 22 June (2-6).**

BRAGLANDS BARN
TA4 3TP. Simon & Sue Youell www.braglandsbarn.com

BROOK HOUSE
TA4 3SZ. Jan & Jonathon Secker-Walker

CRIDLANDS STEEP
TA4 3TL. Audrey Leitch

HIGHER KINGSWOOD
TA4 3TN. Fran & Tom Vesey

KNOLL COTTAGE
Elaine & John Leech
Visitors also welcome by appt Apr to Oct.
01984 656689
john@knoll-cottage.co.uk
www.knoll-cottage.co.uk

POUND HOUSE
TA4 3SZ. Barry & Jenny Hibbert

6 delightful and very varied gardens in picturesque village at edge of Quantocks. 2 surprisingly large gardens in village centre, a semi-wild garden, and 3 very large gardens on outskirts of village, with many rare and unusual plants. Conditions range from waterlogged clay to well-drained sand. Features include a walled garden, ponds, bog gardens, rockery, vegetable and fruit gardens, a collection of over 80 different roses, even a cider-apple orchard. Fine views of surrounding countryside. Dogs on leads allowed in 5 gardens. Wheelchair access to main features of all gardens.

GROUP OPENING

98 STOKE ST MARY GARDENS
Taunton TA3 5BY, 01823 442556, stepcroc@btinternet.com, www.rebeccapow.com. *2½ m SE of Taunton. From M5 J25, take A358 S towards Ilminster. 1st R after 1½ m. 1st R in Henlade, then 1st L signed Stoke St Mary. Car parking at village hall.* Home-made teas at either garden. **Combined adm £5, chd free. Groups of 10+ welcome by appt Apr to Sept.**

FYRSE COTTAGE
Miss S Crockett

TUCKERS FARMHOUSE
Rebecca Pow & Charles Clark.
Two doors down from PH
www.rebeccapow.com

Village nestles below beautiful backdrop of Stoke Hill. C13 church (with stained glass windows by the renowned Patrick Reyntiens), popular Half Moon Inn. Fyrse Cottage: designed by owner landscape architect, Stephanie Crockett, secluded cottage garden with oriental flavour. ½ acre of lush planting with pond, pergola, lots of sculptures and Chinese pots. Birch avenue leading to ½ -acre wildlife area. Gravel and flower gardens. Oil paintings and cards for sale. Tuckers Farmhouse: gardening journalist Rebecca Pow's family garden in lovely rural location. Formal/cottage-style extending to natural with wildlife. Jekyll-style border and 'busy persons' gravel/grass border. Topiary, exotic planting in courtyard, pear tree avenue. Fruit garden, raised bed vegetable garden, a very small smallholding. Emphasis on wildlife gardening with mown paths through wild grasses and trees. Personal tours by Stephanie and Rebecca! Tuckers Farmhouse featured in Somerset Life, in West Country Magazine and on BBC Somerset. Wheelchair access to Tuckers Farmhouse.

99 ◆ STON EASTON PARK

Ston Easton BA3 4DF. Ston Easton Ltd, 01761 241631, www.stoneaston.co.uk. *On A37 between Bath & Wells. Entrance to Park from main rd A37 in centre of village, opp bus shelter.* Light refreshments In hotel or gardeners' cottage depending on climate of the day. **Adm £4, chd free. For NGS: Thur 15 May, Wed 23 July, Wed 3 Sept (10.30-4). For other opening times and information, please phone or see garden website.**

A hidden treasure in the heart of the Mendips. Walk through the glorious parkland of the historic 30 acres of Repton landscape, alongside the quietly cascading R Norr, to the productive walled Victorian kitchen garden. Visit the octagonal rose garden, stunning herbaceous border, numerous colourful flowerbeds, fruit cage and orchard. The parkland at Ston Easton Park is now the only remaining Humphry Repton landscape in Somerset. His Red Book, a facsimile demonstrating his plans in Before and After stages, illustrated in wonderful watercolours, can be found in the hotel reception. Featured in Wells Life, regional press, Radio Somerset, Bristol and Glastonbury fm. Gravel paths, steep slopes, shallow steps.

GROUP OPENING

100 STONE ALLERTON GARDENS

Stone Allerton BS26 2NW. *2m from A38, signed from Lower Weare.* Home-made teas at Greenfield House. **Combined adm £6, chd free. Sun 4, Mon 5 May (2-5.30).**

BADGERS ACRE
Lucy Hetherington & Jim Mathers
Visitors also welcome by appt Apr to June please request refreshments when booking, adm £4.
01934 713159
lucyhetherington@btinternet.com

GREENFIELD HOUSE
Mr & Mrs Bull

OLD CHAPEL HOUSE
Pat & George Hacker

Three distinctly different beautiful gardens on the edge of the Somerset levels. Badgers Acre: 1-acre garden. Colour themed mixed borders. Secret walk, pond and colourful rockery. Semi-circular tulip and allium bed surrounded by box. Vegetable potager with pergola draped in rambling roses and clematis. Greenfield House: 4 main gardens all manageable size. Grass and shrub border, colour garden, cottage garden. Large range of shrubs, perennial plants, bulbs, many unusual. How to make a garden using garden centre bargains. Various ponds for fish and wildlife. Chicken area. Old Chapel House: House dates back to early 1800's. Approx 1-acre delightful garden. To the front is a newly constructed pergola with wisteria and climbing roses. Enter through an avenue of Prunus pissardii Nigra trees to lawns, shrubs, ornamental trees, vegetable patch and orchard. Three large island beds including new grass bed. Featured in Mendip Times May.

GROUP OPENING

101 STOWEY GARDENS

Bishop Sutton, Bristol BS39 5TL. *10m W of Bath. Stowey Village A368 between Bishop Sutton and Chelwood. From Chelwood r'about take Weston-s-Mare rd A368. At Stowey Xrds turn R for carpark.* Home-made teas Stowey Mead. **Combined adm £6, chd free. Sun 15 June (2-6).**

DORMERS
Stowey Bottom.
Mr & Mrs G Nicol

1 STOWEY CROSS COTTAGE
Stowey Bottom.
Deborah & Kim Heath

2 STOWEY CROSS COTTAGE
Stowey Crossroads.
Viv & Roger Hodge

STOWEY MEAD
Stowey. Mr Victor Pritchard

4 gardens opening for 2nd yr for NGS provide a varied and interesting afternoon's viewing. From some large, informal and interesting planting to designer-planned and loved smaller gardens there is something of interest for everyone. All within 10 minutes walk of parking area, natural progression from one to another. Delicious home-made teas for sale at Stowey Mead. Featured in Cheddar Valley Gazette.

102 NEW 1 SUNNYSIDE

Stoke Bishop, Bristol BS9 1BQ. Mrs Magda Goss. *1 Sunnyside, Stoke Bishop. Approach via Stoke Hill or Druid Hill,near shops. Parking on Druid Hill, gate with sloping gravel drive.* Home-made teas at Lucombe House. **Adm £2.50, chd free. Sun 18 May (2-5). Also open Lucombe House.**

C17 Cottage in heart of Stoke Bishop with part walled, cottage-style front garden. Garden sculptures dominated by large magnolia, perennials, roses and spring bulbs. Courtyard garden with open studio at rear.

Secret primrose path and shell garden . . .

103 SUTTON HOSEY MANOR

Long Sutton TA10 9NA. Roger Bramble, 0207 3906700, rbramble@bdbltd.co.uk. *2m E of Langport, on A372. Gates N of A372 at E end of Long Sutton.* Home-made teas. **Adm £4, chd £2. Sun 20 July (2.30-6.30). Visitors also welcome by appt Aug to Sept.**

3 acres, of which 2 walled. Lily canal through pleached limes leading to amelanchier walk past duck pond; rose and juniper walk from Italian terrace; Judas tree avenue; Ptelea walk. Ornamental potager. Drive-side shrubbery. Music by players of Sinfonia of Westminster.

104 THORNBURY PARK ESTATE/THE SHEILING SCHOOL

The Sheiling School, Park Road, Thornbury BS35 1HP. Camphill Communities Thornbury. *12m N of Bristol, off A38. Follow signs to Park Rd from Gloucester Rd, until first R after Castle School. Or from Castle St, into Park Rd, then 2nd L after church.* Home-made teas. **Adm £4, chd free. Sun 21 Sept (11-4.30).**

Estate comprises 15 acres of mature parkland with many magnificent trees, together with 20 acres of biodynamic/organic farmland, hay meadow, orchard, walled garden with secluded artist's garden behind it.

Ponds, stream and some woodland areas. A rarely seen part of Thornbury's conservation area. Sensory garden with bog garden, pond, flow form, and sculptures, flower meadow, grass labyrinth, cut flower garden, new plant dye area, and new herb area. Crafts and art from our school community. Continuing development of prairie-style meadow with emphasis on late summer and autumn flowers. Featured in The Daily Telegraph - 'Portrait of the Garden as a Place of Art and Therapy'. Wheelchair access to some areas difficult but most of parkland estate accessible.

105 ◆ TINTINHULL
nr Yeovil BA22 8PZ. National Trust, 01935 823289, www.nationaltrust.org.uk/tintinhull-garden. *5m NW of Yeovil. Tintinhull village. Signs on A303, W of Ilchester.* **Adm £7.50, chd £3.75. For NGS: Sun 8 June (11-4.30). For other opening times and information, please phone or see garden website.**
C17 and C18 house (part open). Famous 2-acre garden in compartments, developed 1900 to present day, influenced by Hidcote; many good and uncommon plants. with care, uneven paths.

106 TRANBY HOUSE
Norton Lane, Whitchurch, Bristol BS14 0BT. Jan Barkworth. *5m S of Bristol. 1/2 m S of Whitchurch. Leave Bristol on A37 Wells Rd, through Whitchurch village, 1st turning on R signed Norton Malreward.* **Adm £3.50, chd free. Wed 11 June, Thur 10 July (1-4); Sun 10 Aug, Sun 7 Sept (2-5).**
1 1/4 -acre well-established informal garden, designed and planted to encourage wildlife. Wide variety of trees, shrubs and cottage garden plants; ponds and wild flower meadow. Garden still evolving to provide colour and interest from spring to autumn. Plants for sale in aid of The Wildlife Trust.

107 TRUFFLES
Church Lane, Bishop Sutton, Bristol BS39 5UP. Sally Monkhouse, 01275 333665, sallymonkhouse961@btinternet.com. *10m W of Bath. On A368 Bath to Weston-super-Mare rd. Take rd opp PO/stores uphill towards Hinton Blewett. 1st R into Church Lane.* Home-made teas. **Adm £4, chd free. Sat 12, Sun 13 July (2-6). Groups of 6+ welcome by appt July.**
2 acres, a different and surprising, relaxing garden with views. Formal and wildlife planting linked with meandering paths, lots of seating. Hidden valley, small stream, wildlife pond, flower meadows. Unique 1/4 -acre kitchen garden with several 21ft long x 4ft wide large waist high raised beds; rose garden; new beds. Featured on BBC1 Britain's Great Wildlife Revival and in Mendip Times. Grass and gravel paths, part of garden accessible to wheelchair users.

108 ◆ TYNTESFIELD
Wraxall BS48 1NX. National Trust, 01275 461900, www.nationaltrust.org.uk/tyntesfield. *7m SW of Bristol. Nr Nailsea, entrance off B3128. Follow brown signs.* **Adm £9.45, chd £4.75. For NGS: Sun 20 July (10-6). For other opening times and information, please phone or see garden website.**
Remarkably intact Victorian garden with formal bedding display, rose garden, and a productive walled kitchen garden which offers produce for sale to the public, and supplies the Cow Barn Kitchen on site. The grounds also include an arboretum, wildflower meadows and an orangery. Talks and demonstrations throughout the day. Steep slopes, steps and gravel paths throughout garden. Courtesy bus from Visitor Centre to Kitchen Garden.

109 ◆ UNIVERSITY OF BRISTOL BOTANIC GARDEN
Stoke Park Road, Stoke Bishop, Bristol BS9 1JG. University of Bristol, 0117 3314906, www.bristol.ac.uk/BotanicGarden. *1/4 m W of Durdham Downs. Located in Stoke Bishop next to Durdham Downs 1m from city centre. After crossing the Downs to Stoke Hill, Stoke Park Rd is first on R.* Light refreshments. **Adm £4.50, chd free. For NGS: Sun 13 July (10-5). For other opening times and information, please phone or see garden website.**
Exciting contemporary botanic garden with organic flowing network of paths which lead visitors through collections of Mediterranean flora, rare native, useful plants (incl. European and Chinese herbs) and those that illustrate plant evolution. Large floral displays illustrating pollination/flowering plant evolution. Glasshouses, home to Giant Amazon Waterlily, tropical fruit and medicine plants, orchids, cacti and unique sacred lotus collection. Special tours of garden throughout day; plants for sale; refreshments. Wheelchair available to borrow from Welcome Lodge. Wheelchair friendly route through garden available upon request, also accessible WC.

110 VELLACOTT
Lawford, Crowcombe TA4 4AL. Kevin & Pat Chittenden, 01984 618249, kevinchit@hotmail.co.uk. *9m NW of Taunton. Off A358, signed Lawford. For directions please phone.* Home-made teas. **Adm £3, chd free. Sat 7, Sun 8 June (1-5). Visitors also welcome by appt May to Sept, max 30.**
1-acre informal garden on S-facing slope with lovely views of the Quantock and Brendon Hills. Profusely stocked with wide selection of herbaceous plants, shrubs and trees. Other features include ponds, ruin and potager. Plenty of places to sit and enjoy the surroundings. Not suitable for wheelchairs.

VENN CROSS RAILWAY GARDENS
See Devon

Esotera

111 NEW WALL HOUSE

41 Tower Hill, Williton, Taunton TA4 4JR. Carole & Philip Stoate. *On outskirts of Williton on A358 Taunton rd. 750m from Williton centre, or 200m after entering village from Taunton.* **Adm £3.50, chd free. Sat 17, Sun 18 May (2-6).**

Formal walled garden, ½ acre, with allée of apple trees and clipped hedges. Rockery, large pond, small organic vegetable potager and herb garden. Lawns with curving flower and island beds, pergolas with clematis and roses. Interesting spring trees and shrubs. Panoramic terrace known as The Admirals Walk. Secret primrose path and shell garden for young children. Mostly wheelchair access.

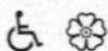

112 NEW ◆ THE WALLED GARDEN

Selwood Street, Mells, Frome BA11 3PN. Ms Jo Illsley, 01373 812579, jo@thewalledgardenatmells.co.uk, www.thewalledgardenatmells.co.uk. *4m W of Frome. Follow signs to Mells village. Garden is located between the village shop and the Talbot Inn PH.* Light refreshments. Pizzas are available from our wood fired pizza oven, please order when booking visit. You are welcome to bring a bottle for a sml corkage charge. **For NGS: By appointment - Evening Openings £4, chd free, light refreshments, Wed 28, Thur 29 May, Wed 4, Thur 5, Wed 11, Thur 12 June (6-9), groups welcome. For other opening times and information, please phone or see garden website.**

A warm welcome awaits you at the C17 Walled Garden. A garden dedicated to English grown cut flowers, gorgeous traditional hardy garden plants and a café with seating under the shade of apple trees. Just the place for you to enjoy seeing environmentally sustainable seasonal flowers growing. The Walled Garden offers visitors an opportunity to relax, and recharge in beautiful surroundings. Featured in Somerset Life and Country Living magazines. Wheelchair access to café area possible with assistance. Surface is gravelled throughout garden, steps to WC.

113 WATCOMBE

92 Church Road, Winscombe BS25 1BP. Peter & Ann Owen, 01934 842666, peter.o@which.net. *12 m SW of Bristol, 3m N of Axbridge. 100 yds after signs on A38 turn L (from S), R (from N) into Winscombe Hill. After 1m reach The Square. Pink house on L after further 150yds.* **Adm £3.50, chd free. Sun 27 Apr, Sun 18 May, Wed 11 June (2-5.30). Visitors also welcome by appt Apr to July.**

¾ -acre mature Edwardian garden with colour-themed, informally planted herbaceous borders. Topiary, box hedging, lime walk, pleached hornbeams, cordon fruit trees, vegetable plot, 2 small formal ponds, many unusual trees and shrubs. Approx. 80 Clematis varieties. Strong framework separating several different areas of the garden, pergola with varied wisteria, lime walk, unusual topiary, growing collection of clematis! See video clips on www.threesixtyvr.co.uk/tours/Watcombe_2/Watcombe.html. Some steps but most areas accessible by wheelchair with minimal assistance.

114 WAYFORD MANOR

Wayford, Crewkerne TA18 8QG. Wayford Manor. *3m SW of Crewkerne. Turning N off B3165 at Clapton; or S off A30 Chard to Crewkerne rd.* **Adm £5, chd £2.50. Sun 13 July (2-5).**

The mainly Elizabethan manor (not open) mentioned in C17 for its 'fair and pleasant' garden was redesigned by Harold Peto in 1902. Formal terraces with yew hedges and topiary have fine views over W Dorset. Steps down between spring-fed ponds past mature and new plantings of magnolia, rhododendron, maples, cornus and, in season, spring bulbs, cyclamen, giant echium. Primula candelabra, arum lily, gunnera around lower ponds.

115 WELLFIELD BARN

Walcombe Lane, Wells BA5 3AG. David & Virginia Nasmyth, 01749 675129, david.nasmyth@talktalk.net. *½ m N of Wells. From A39 Bristol to Wells rd turn R at 30 mph sign into Walcombe Lane. Entrance at 1st cottage on R, parking signed.* Home-made teas. **Adm £4, chd free. Visitors welcome by appt June to July, max 29 seat coach on site.**

1½ -acre gardens, made by owners over the past 17yrs from concrete farmyard. Ha-ha, wonderful views, pond, lawn, mixed borders, formal sunken garden, grass walks and interesting young and semi-mature trees. Structured design integrates house and garden with landscape. New areas under development. Special interest plants are the hardy geranium family. Featured in regional press and on Radio Somerset and Bristol and Glastonbury fm. Moderate slopes in places, some gravel paths.

GROUP OPENING

116 WEST BRISTOL GARDENS

BS9 2PY/. BS9 2LR, 07779 203626, p.l.prior@gmail.com. *3m NW of Bristol city centre. Please see* *individual gardens for directions*. Home-made teas at 159 Westbury Lane. **Combined adm £5, chd free. Sun 1 June (2-6). Visitors also welcome by appt May to Sept groups 10 to 25.**

4 HAYTOR PARK
Bristol. Mr & Mrs C J Prior.
From A4162 Inner Ring Rd take turning into Coombe Bridge Ave, Haytor Park is 1st on L. Please no Parking in Haytor Park
Groups of 10 to 30 also welcome by appt May to Aug. 07779 203626 p.l.prior@gmail.com

159 WESTBURY LANE
Coombe Dingle. Maureen Dickens.
L A4162/Sylvan Way, B4054/Shirehampton Rd, R to Westbury Lane. 1st house on R
Visitors also welcome by appt May to Sept groups 10 to 25. 01179 043008 159jmd@googlemail.com

Pair of interesting and contrasting gardens. 4 Haytor Park: Unremarkable suburban semi hides peaceful haven for wildlife, unusual plants, pots, ponds and flower-laden arches. Much to discover down winding paths, arty objects, places to sit, dragons, nooks and crannies and tantalising glimpses of the green-roofed studio and maybe beyond? So stop, dream a while and forget the city here!159 Westbury Lane: Lovely quiet garden, barely overlooked on edge of City. Planted to owners' design from scratch in cottage garden style. Full of interesting and many unusual plants bought from specialist nurseries. Primarily an early summer garden but being developed to show flowers all yr. Quirky touch with garden artifacts in many places. Many interesting visiting birds. A garden full of interesting plants full of colour and leaf structure with lots of hidden artefacts to find.

117 WESTBROOK HOUSE
West Bradley BA6 8LS. Keith Anderson and David Mendel, 01458 850604, mail@westbrook-bed-breakfast.co.uk. *4m E of Glastonbury. From A361 at W Pennard follow signs to W Bradley (2m).* **Adm £3.50, chd free (share to West Bradley Church). Sat 19 Apr, Sat 9 Aug (11-5). Groups of 10+ also welcome by appt May to Aug.**
4 acres comprising 3 distinct gardens with formal layout around house which leads to meadow and orchard with spring bulbs, species roses and lilacs. Planting and layout began 2004.

GROUP OPENING

118 WESTON VILLAGE GARDENS
Weston, Bath BA1 3NS. *2m NW of Bath. Follow signs for Royal United Hospital. 45a Combe & Mulberry 50mtrs from RUH. Parking at RUH & adjacent rds - NOT Church Rd.* Home-made teas at Glenfield. **Combined adm £6, chd free. Sat 21, Sun 22 June (1-5).**

94 BROADMOOR LANE
Liz & Peter Winney.
From RUH to Crown Rd, then High St to r'about, 2nd exit, 1st L into Broadmoor Lane approx 20 mins walk

9 CHURCH ROAD
Jane & Bernard Rymer.
Close to All Saints Church. No parking in Church Rd
Groups of 10+ also welcome by appt May to Sept. 01225 427377 bernardrymer@gmail.com

45A COMBE PARK
Stephen Brook.
Follow signs for the RUH. Garden can be found by main entrance to hospital on opp side of rd
Groups of 10+ also welcome by appt June to Sept. 01225 428288 ingleside_sb@btinternet.com

GLENFIELD
Mrs Sue Haskins.
500m from War Memorial - go up Crown Hill past Old Crown PH on R and almost to end of Weston Park

MULBERRY
39 Combe Park. Paul & Catherine Bright.
Opp entrance RUH

5 gardens tucked away in a village community. 94 Broadmoor Lane: large SW facing sloping garden with beautiful views up to Kelston Round Hill. Herbaceous borders, roses, clematis and wisteria. Terracing and raised vegetable garden, soft fruit, rockery with alpines. 9 Church Road: 1/3 acre. Colour-themed shrubs, herbaceous plants, ferns and annuals. Summerhouse. Numerous sitting areas. Rear walled garden with rose garden pond and waterfall. 45a Combe Park (Winner Bath in Bloom 2012): walled garden creatively landscaped on 3 levels. Raised borders of colour-themed perennials, grasses, phormiums and acers. Tree fernery, pond, secluded seating areas. Glenfield: 1 acre. Formal design with series of rooms with scented and colour-themed plants. Herb garden, woodland walk, pastel sunken garden, kitchen garden, exuberant rose pergola. Mulberry: enclosed town garden in Victorian style, combining formality with informal planting. Period style greenhouse and summerhouse, ornamental lily pond, rose arches, scented climbers. Mature mulberry tree. Plant sales for Weston Village Gardening Club. Dogs allowed at 45a Combe Park and 9 Church Rd. Wheelchair access to 9 Church Rd, Mulberry and (partial) 94 Broadmoor Lane.

Dragons, nooks and crannies and tantalising glimpses . . .

119 18 WOODGROVE ROAD
Henbury, BRISTOL BS10 7RE. Peter & Ruth Whitby. *4m N of Bristol. M5 J17, follow B4018, R at 3rd r'about signed Blaise Castle. R opp Blaise Castle car park - rd next to Avon riding centre.* Home-made teas. **Adm £3, chd free. Sat 7, Sat 14 June (2-6).**
Medium-sized garden divided into 3 sections. Traditional flower garden with Bonsai display and small wildlife pond. Cottage garden with greenhouse and plant sale area. Small orchard with dwarf fruit trees and small vegetable garden. Peter's art studio open for sale of watercolour and oil paintings, 10% to NGS. Gravel path from patio, or grass access for wheelchairs.

Truffles

120 NEW **WOODLEA BOTTOM**
Greyfield Road, High Littleton, Bristol BS39 6YA. Adrian and Jane Neech. *Follow A39 to High Littleton. Turn into Greyfield Rd, opp Dando's Stores. Garden 400 yds on L. Parking on Greyfield Rd.* **Adm £3, chd free. Sun 1, Sun 15 June (10.30-4.30).**
A garden of rooms, each with a different theme. A balance of naturalised planting and herbaceous borders alongside productive greenhouses and fruit and vegetable areas. Interesting specimen trees and roses, don't forget to look up and through the hedge windows! Summerhouse and attractive garden pots. No dogs please. Unsuitable for wheelchairs.

121 ◆ **THE YEO VALLEY ORGANIC GARDEN AT HOLT FARM**
Bath Road, Blagdon BS40 7SQ. Mr & Mrs Tim Mead, 01761 461650, www.theyeovalleyorganicgarden.co.uk. *12m S of Bristol. Off the A368. Entrance is approx 1/2 m outside Blagdon towards Bath, on L, then follow the garden signs past the dairy.* Light refreshments. **Adm £5, chd free. For NGS: Sun 27 Apr (11-5). For other opening times and information, please phone or see garden website.**
The only organic ornamental garden as certified by the Soil Association, 6.5 acres of contemporary planting, quirky sculptures, bulbs in their thousands, purple palace, glorious meadows and posh veggie patch. Great views, green ideas, light lunches and teas available. Garden lectures, events, workshops and exhibitions held throughout the year. Featured in West Country Life, Western Daily Press,The English Garden.

Bristol Area County Volunteers

County Organiser
Su Mills, 3 Over Court Mews, Over Lane, Almondsbury BS32 4DG, 01454 615438, susanlmills@gmail.com

County Treasurer
Ken Payne, 2 Old Tarnwell, Stanton Drew, Bristol BS39 4EA, 01275 333146, kg.payne@yahoo.co.uk

Booklet Co-ordinator/County Booklet Advertising
Jean Damey, 2 Hawburn Close, Brislington, Bristol BS4 2PB, 0117 9775587, jeandamey@gmail.com

Assistant County Organisers
Angela Conibere, Christmas Cottage, Church Rd, Oldbury-on-Severn BS35 1QA, 01454 413828, aeconibere@hotmail.com
Graham Guest, The Caves, Downside Road, Backwell BS48 3DH, 01275 472393, gandsguest@btinternet.com
Christine Healey, The Walled Garden, The Street, Olveston, BS35 4DR, 01454 612795, christine.healey@uwclub.net
Margaret Jones, Weir Cottage, Weir Lane, Marshfield, Chippenham SN14 8NB, 01225 891229, ian@weircott.plus.com
Jeanette Parker, The School Yard, 2 High St, Wickwar GL12 8NE, 01454 299699, jeanette_parker@hotmail.co.uk
Jane Perkins, Woodland Cottage, Oldbury-on-Severn BS35 1PL, 01454 414570, janekperkins@gmail.com

Somerset County Volunteers

County Organiser
Lucy Hetherington, Badgers Acre, Stone Allerton, Axbridge BS26 2NW, 01934 713159, lucyhetherington@btinternet.com

County Treasurer
David Bull, Greenfield House, Stone Allerton, Nr Axbridge BS26 2NH, 01934 712609, d.bull08@btinternet.com

Publicity
Roger Peacock, Barum, 50 Edward Road, Clevedon BS21 7DT, 01275 341584, barum@blueyonder.co.uk

Presentations
Dave & Pru Moon, 9 Catherston Close, Frome BA11 4HR, 01373 473381, davidmoon202@btinternet.com

Group Tour Coordinator
Dilly Bradley, Little Yarford Farmhouse, Kingston St Mary, Taunton TA2 8AN, 01823 451350, yarford@ic24.net

Booklet Distribution
Chris & Dianne McKinley, Grove Rise, Downhall Drive, Wembdon, Bridgwater TA6 7RT, 01278 421675, chrismckinley80@hotmail.com

Photographer
John Wyatt, 85 Devonshire Road, Weston-super-Mare BS23 4NU, 07775 866224, jhg.wyatt@btopenworld.com

Beneficiaries
Sarah Wilcox, Epworth, Kingston St. Mary, Taunton TA2 8HZ, 01823 451402, wilcoxsarah@hotmail.co.uk

Assistant County Organisers
Brian & Dilly Bradley, Little Yarford Farmhouse, Kingston St Mary, Taunton TA2 8AN, 01823 451350, yarford@ic24.net
Patricia Davies-Gilbert, Coombe Quarry, West Monkton, Taunton TA2 8RE, 01823 412187, pdaviesgilbert@btinternet.com
Alison Highnam, Candleford, Fernhill, East Stour, Nr Gillingham SP8 5ND, 01747 838133, allies1@btinternet.com
Laura Howard, The Old Manse, Fivehead, Taunton TA3 6QH, 01460 282911, laurafivehead@btinternet.com
Rosemary Lee, 6 Buttle Close, Shepton Beauchamp TA19 0LU, 01460 249594, rosemarylee@supanet.com
Judith Stanford, Bowden Hill Cottage, Chilcompton, Radstock BA3 4EN, 01761 233045, judithstanford.ngs@hotmail.co.uk

STAFFORDSHIRE

Birmingham & West Midlands

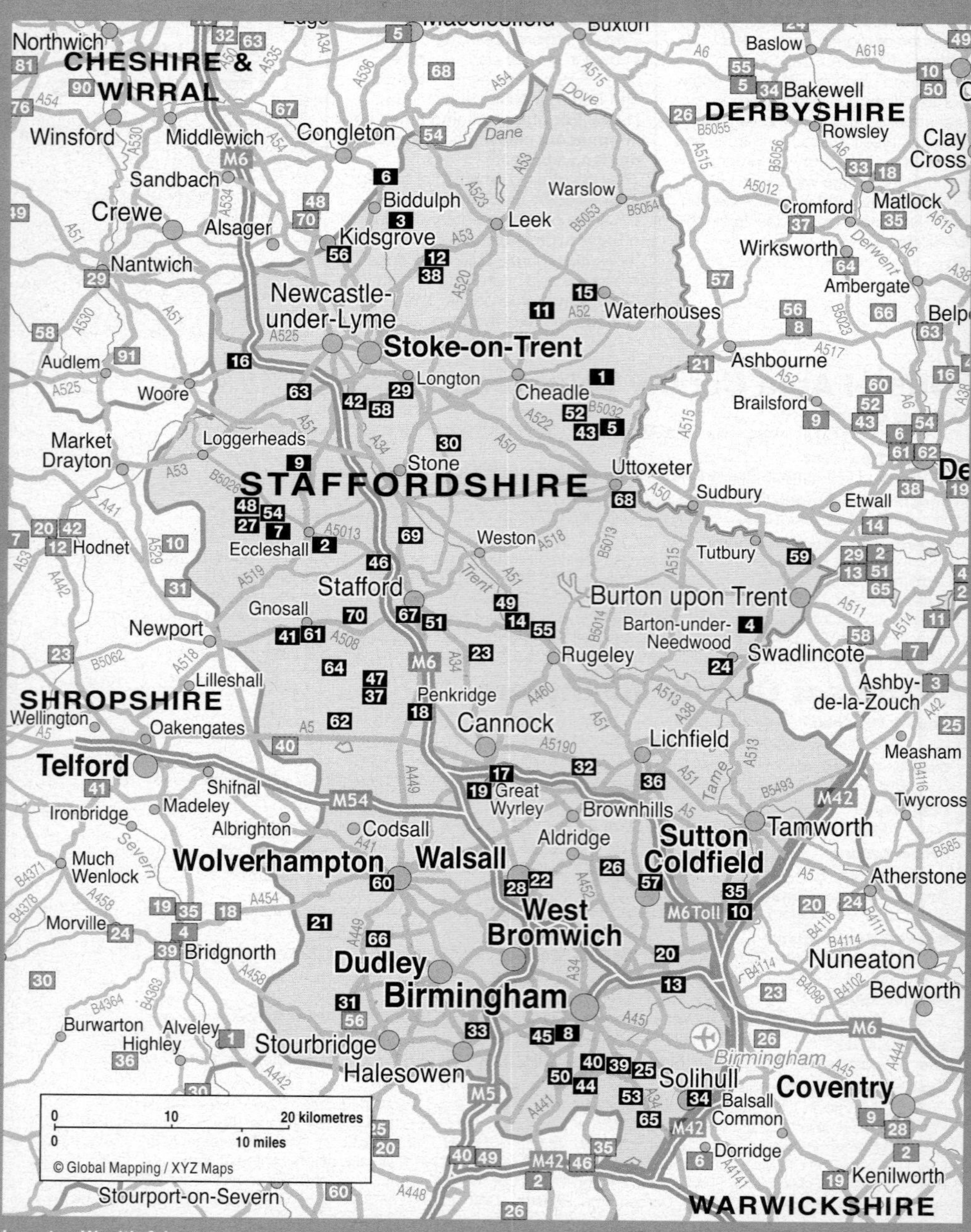

Opening Dates

All entries subject to change. For latest information check www.ngs.org.uk

March

Sunday 23
51 NEW St John's Gardens

April

Sunday 6
36 Millennium Garden

Sunday 20
52 Stonehill Quarry Garden

Sunday 27
45 Pereira Road Gardens

Trees and colourful foliage separate tranquil seating areas . . .

May

Sunday 4
25 Hall Green Gardens
70 Yew Tree Cottage

Wednesday 7
8 Birmingham Botanical Gardens

Friday 16
51 NEW St John's Gardens (Evening)

Saturday 17
50 NEW Selly Manor Museum Garden
59 NEW 41 Twentylands

Sunday 18
5 The Beeches
19 Dorset House
49 The Secret Garden
50 NEW Selly Manor Museum Garden
55 Tanglewood Cottage

Wednesday 21
29 High Trees

Sunday 25
3 NEW Badger Hill
13 Castle Bromwich Hall Gardens Trust
26 Hamilton House
42 The Old Dairy House
70 Yew Tree Cottage

Monday 26
10 Bridge House
22 Four Seasons
42 The Old Dairy House

Thursday 29
70 Yew Tree Cottage

June

Sunday 1
23 The Garth
46 The Pintles

Wednesday 4
29 High Trees

Friday 6
14 Coley Cottage
49 The Secret Garden

Festival Weekend

Saturday 7
6 Biddulph Grange Garden

Sunday 8
2 Ashcroft and Claremont
34 NEW 89 Marsh Lane
36 Millennium Garden
57 91 Tower Road
60 19 Waterdale

Thursday 12
70 Yew Tree Cottage

Friday 13
1 Alton Towers Gardens

Sunday 15
16 Courtwood House
39 NEW Moseley Corner, The Art of Gardens
47 NEW Priory Farm
63 Wilkins Pleck

Sunday 22
14 Coley Cottage
35 Middleton Hall
40 Moseley Gardens South
49 The Secret Garden
51 NEW St John's Gardens

Thursday 26
70 Yew Tree Cottage

Sunday 29
5 The Beeches
12 Brooklyn
23 The Garth
24 Grafton Cottage
37 Mitton Manor
41 The Mount, Coton, Gnosall
45 Pereira Road Gardens
61 West View
67 NEW Woodland Grange Gardens

July

Wednesday 2
58 The Trentham Estate (Evening)

Saturday 5
69 Yarlet House

Sunday 6
7 Birch Trees
33 13 Lansdowne Road
46 The Pintles
62 The Wickets

Wednesday 9
58 The Trentham Estate (Evening)
62 The Wickets

Thursday 10
70 Yew Tree Cottage

Saturday 12
11 37 Brookfields Road
68 Woodleighton Grove Gardens

Sunday 13
11 37 Brookfields Road
15 Colour Mill
18 4 Dene Close
68 Woodleighton Grove Gardens

Sunday 20
19 Dorset House
24 Grafton Cottage
25 Hall Green Gardens
38 Moorfield
56 NEW Tilewright Close
60 19 Waterdale
64 Willow Cottage
70 Yew Tree Cottage

Wednesday 23
64 Willow Cottage

Saturday 26
55 Tanglewood Cottage

Sunday 27
3 NEW Badger Hill
5 The Beeches
20 198 Eachelhurst Road
43 NEW The Old Vicarage
63 Wilkins Pleck

August

Friday 1
65 Wits End

Sunday 3
9 The Bowers
24 Grafton Cottage
28 Hidden Gem
65 Wits End

Sunday 10
24 Grafton Cottage
32 Kosynook
54 Sugnall Walled Garden

Wednesday 13
14 Coley Cottage
49 The Secret Garden

Saturday 16
50 NEW Selly Manor Museum Garden

Sunday 17
50 NEW Selly Manor Museum Garden
59 NEW 41 Twentylands
64 Willow Cottage

Wednesday 20
64 Willow Cottage

Thursday 21
15 Colour Mill

Sunday 24
7 Birch Trees
30 NEW Idlerocks Farm
62 The Wickets
65 Wits End

Monday 25
7 Birch Trees
10 Bridge House

Sunday 31
5 The Beeches

Shrubs and foliage plants, rather than flowers are used to create a naturalistic setting attractive to wildlife. . .

September

Friday 5
55 Tanglewood Cottage (Evening)

Thursday 18
4 Bankcroft Farm

Thursday 25
4 Bankcroft Farm

Sunday 28
48 Rowley House Farm
54 Sugnall Walled Garden

October

Sunday 19
31 John's Garden
52 Stonehill Quarry Garden

Sunday 26
52 Stonehill Quarry Garden

Gardens open to the public

1 Alton Towers Gardens
6 Biddulph Grange Garden
8 Birmingham Botanical Gardens
13 Castle Bromwich Hall Gardens Trust
35 Middleton Hall
50 Selly Manor Museum Garden
54 Sugnall Walled Garden
58 The Trentham Estate

By appointment only

17 12 Darges Lane
21 The Elms
27 Heath House
44 Paul's Oasis of Calm
53 172 Stonor Road
66 The Wombourne Wodehouse

Also open by appointment

5 The Beeches
7 Birch Trees
9 The Bowers
10 Bridge House
11 37 Brookfields Road
14 Coley Cottage
15 Colour Mill
18 4 Dene Close
19 Dorset House
23 The Garth
24 Grafton Cottage
25 16 Burnaston Road, Hall Green Gardens
25 37 Burnaston Road, Hall Green Gardens
25 120 Russell Road, Hall Green Gardens
28 Hidden Gem
30 Idlerocks Farm
33 13 Lansdowne Road
37 Mitton Manor
38 Moorfield
41 The Mount, Coton, Gnosall
48 Rowley House Farm
49 The Secret Garden
51 St John's Gardens
55 Tanglewood Cottage
60 19 Waterdale
62 The Wickets
65 Wits End
68 Woodleighton Grove Gardens
70 Yew Tree Cottage

The Gardens

1 ◆ ALTON TOWERS GARDENS

Alton, Stoke on Trent ST10 4DB. Alton Towers Resort, 01538 703344, www.altontowers.com. *6m N of Uttoxeter. From A50, follow 'brown signs' for Alton Towers. At the theme park follow signs for Alton Towers Hotel. Enter garden through the Alton Towers Hotel*. Tea. **Adm £4, chd free. For NGS: Fri 13 June (3.30-6).** For other opening times and information, please phone or see garden website.

Alton Tower's magnificent early C19 gardens, designed by the flamboyant 15th Earl of Shrewsbury, feature pools, pagoda fountain, statues, mature trees, shrubs, rhododendrons and azaleas set in a steep sided valley with steep walks and viewing terraces. Access via the 1m long 'woodland walk' from the Alton Towers Hotel. Refreshments in hotel. One of the first gardens in Staffordshire to 'Open' for the NGS in 1932. Unfortunately the historic nature of the gardens makes them unsuitable for wheelchair users or those with limited mobility.

GROUP OPENING

2 ASHCROFT AND CLAREMONT

Eccleshall ST21 6JP. *7m W of Stafford. J14 M6. At Eccleshall end of A5013 the garden is 100 metres before junction with A518. On street parking nearby*. Home-made teas at Ashcroft. **Combined adm £4, chd free. Sun 8 June (2-5).**

ASHCROFT
1 Stafford Road. Peter & Gillian Bertram

CLAREMONT
26 Claremont Road. Maria Edwards

Two gardens as different as Monet's soft pastel colours are to Vincent's bright sunflowers. Ashcroft is a 1-acre wildlife-friendly garden, pond and covered courtyard. Rooms flow seamlessly around the Edwardian house. Herb bed, treillage, greenhouse with raised beds. Find the topiary peacock that struts in the gravel bed. In the woodland area Gollum lurks in the steps of the ruin. Claremont is a small town garden its design based on feng shui principles. Manicured lawns, herbaceous borders, shrubs, perennials and annuals. Constantly evolving with colour and new features, maintaining interest throughout the year. Come and be inspired!. Tickets, home-made teas & plants available at Ashcroft. Featured in Gardens News - Ashcroft and Amateur Gardening - Claremont. Wheelchair access at Ashcroft only.

3 NEW BADGER HILL

Rock End, Biddulph Moor, Stoke-on-Trent ST8 7NP. Mr & Mrs Shirley & Michael Bligh-Smith, 01782 519203. *1½ m SE of Biddulph. Off A527 Stoke to Congleton Rd. At Knypersley T-lights turn onto Park Lane signed Biddulph Moor. Rock End & driveway to garden is approx 1m. Parking at Booth's Garage.* Home-made teas. **Adm £4, chd free. Suns 25 May; 27 July (12-5).**
This 1 acre terraced garden, in a unique country setting, approached along a drive with a steep bank on one side where native trees, shrubs and plants grow among rocky outcrops. In the main garden, gravel paths link herbaceous borders, island beds, rockeries and several water features incl a wildlife pool. Trees and colourful foliage separate tranquil seating areas. The garden has been planted for all year round interest..

4 BANKCROFT FARM

Tatenhill, Burton-on-Trent DE13 9SA. Mrs Penelope Adkins. *2m SW of Burton-on-Trent. Take Tatenhill Rd off A38 Burton-Branston flyover. 1m, 1st house on L approaching village. Parking on farm.* **Adm £3, chd free. Thurs 18, 25 Sept (2-5).**
Lose yourself for an afternoon in our 1½ -acre organic country garden. Arbour, gazebo and many other seating areas to view ponds and herbaceous borders, backed with shrubs and trees with emphasis on structure, foliage and colour. Productive fruit and vegetable gardens, wildlife areas and adjoining 12-acre native woodland walk. Picnics welcome. Many gravel paths.

5 THE BEECHES

Mill Street, Rocester ST14 5JX. Ken & Joy Sutton, 01889 590631, suttonjoy2@gmail.com. *5m N of Uttoxeter. On B5030 turn R into village by JCB factory. At Red Lion PH & mini r'about take rd for Marston Montgomery. Garden 250 yds on R. Car park at JCB academy.* Home-made teas. **Adm £3, chd free. Suns 18 May; 29 June; 27 July; 31 Aug (1.30-5). Visitors also welcome by appt May to Aug, min adm £60 if less than 20 people.**
Stroll along the driveway containing island beds planted with mixed shrubs and perennials, and enter a stunning plant lover's garden of approx ⅔ acre, enjoying views of surrounding countryside. Box garden, mixed shrubs incl rhododendrons and azaleas, vibrant colour-themed herbaceous borders, roses, clematis and climbing plants, fruit trees, pools and late flowering perennials also raised vegetable and soft fruit garden, yr-round garden. Featured in local press. Partial wheelchair access.

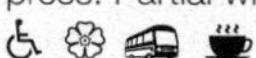

The Bowers

© Linda Greening

6 ◆ BIDDULPH GRANGE GARDEN

Grange Road, Biddulph ST8 7SD. National Trust, 01782 517999, www.nationaltrust.org.uk. *3½ m SE of Congleton. 7m N of Stoke-on-Trent off A527, Congleton to Biddulph rd.* Light refreshments. **Adm £7.50, chd £3.77. For NGS: Sat 7 June (11-5.30). For other opening times and information, please phone or see garden website.**
Amazing Victorian garden created by Darwin contemporary and correspondent James Bateman as an extension of his beliefs, scientific interests and collection of plants. Visit the Italian terrace, Chinese inspired garden, dahlia walk and the oldest surviving golden larch in Britain brought from China by the great plant hunter Robert Fortune.

7 BIRCH TREES

Copmere End, Eccleshall ST21 6HH. Susan & John Weston, 01785 850448, johnweston123@btinternet.com. *1½ m W of Eccleshall. On B5026, turn at junction signed Copmere End. After ½ m straight across Xrds by Star Inn.* Home-made teas. **Adm £3, chd free. Suns 6 July; 24, Mon 25 Aug (1.30-5.30). Also open The Pintles, 6 July. Visitors also welcome by appt June to Aug, groups of 10 - 30, adm £5 incl tea and biscuits.**
Surprising ½ acre SW-facing sun trap which takes advantage of the 'borrowed landscape' of the surrounding countryside. Take time to explore the pathways between the island beds which contain many unusual herbaceous plants, grasses and shrubs; also vegetable patch, stump bed, alpine house and water features. Featured in Garden News.

8 ◆ BIRMINGHAM BOTANICAL GARDENS

Westbourne Road, Edgbaston B15 3TR. Birmingham Botanical & Horticultural Society, 01214 541860, www.birminghambotanicalgardens.org.uk. *1½ m SW of the centre of Birmingham. From J6 M6 take A38(M) to city centre. Follow underpasses signed Birmingham West to A456. At Fiveways island turn L onto B4217 (Calthorpe Rd) signed Botanical Gardens*. Light refreshments. **Adm £7. For NGS: Wed 7 May (9-5). For other opening times and information, please phone or see garden website.**

Extensive botanical garden set in a green urban environment with a comprehensive collection of plants from throughout the world growing in the glasshouses and outside. Four stunning glasshouses take you from tropical rainforest to arid desert. Fifteen acres of beautiful landscaped gardens. Roses, alpines, perennials, rare trees and shrubs. Playground, Children's Discovery Garden, Gallery.

9 THE BOWERS

Church Lane, Standon, nr Eccleshall ST21 6RW. Maurice & Sheila Thacker, 01782 791244, metbowers@gmail.com. *5m N of Eccleshall. Take A519 & at Cotes Heath turn L signed Standon. After 1m turn R at Xrds by church, into Church Lane ½ m on L*. Home-made teas. **Adm £3, chd free. Sun 3 Aug (1-5). Visitors also welcome by appt July to Aug, adm £5 incl light refreshments.**

Come and share our tranquil ⅓ acre cottage style garden. Meander around the grass paths which enclose colour -themed borders containing over 200 clematis and many hardy geraniums and hostas. You will see height, blossom and flowers in abundance. Our garden is always evolving with new features each year. Small water feature, obelisks, arches and trellising. Many unusual and rare clematis.

10 BRIDGE HOUSE

Dog Lane, Bodymoor Heath B76 9JF. Mr & Mrs J Cerone, 01827 873205, janecerone@btinternet.com. *5m S of Tamworth. From A446 at Belfry Island take A4091 after 1m turn R onto Bodymoor Heath Lane & continue 1m into village, parking in field opp garden*. Home-made teas. **Adm £3.50, chd free. Mons 26 May; 25 Aug (2-5). Visitors also welcome by appt May to Sept, for groups 5-30.**

1-acre garden surrounding converted public house. Divided into smaller areas with a mix of shrub borders, azalea and fuchsia, herbaceous and bedding, orchard, kitchen garden and wild flower meadow. Pergola walk, wisteria, formal fish pool, pond, bog garden and lawns. Kingsbury Water Park and RSPB Middleton Lakes Reserve located within a mile.

11 37 BROOKFIELDS ROAD

Ipstones ST10 2LY. Pat & Pam Murray, 01538 266224, patpam37@hotmail.com. *7m SE of Leek. From N on A 523 turn onto B 5053 S-wards at Bottomhouse. From S on A52 turn N onto B5053 at Froghall. Follow signs from centre of village*. Home-made teas. **Adm £3, chd free. Sat 12, Sun 13 July (1.30-5.30). Also open Colour Mill, 13 July. Visitors also welcome by appt May to July.**

A magical, organic garden full of hidden delights. Enjoy views over Churnet Valley, an established white garden, herbaceous borders, large vegetable patch, log arch and wildlife pond. Further exploration reveals a path snaking down to a wild flower bank, peaceful woodland and a stream spanned by a wooden bridge.The 1-acre garden, incl dry stone walls, hedges and stone buildings, has been crafted over 15yrs to harmonise with the surrounding area. Children love it too!.

12 BROOKLYN

Gratton Lane, Endon, Stoke-on-Trent ST9 9AA. Janet & Steve Howell. *4m W of Leek. 6m from Stoke-on-Trent on A53 turn at Black Horse PH into centre of village, R into Gratton Lane 1st house on R. Parking signed in village*. Home-made teas. **Adm £3, chd free. Sun 29 June (12-5).**

A plant lovers country cottage garden in the heart of the old village of Endon. Small pretty front garden, borders overflowing with geraniums, astrantia, alliums and roses. Rear garden features shady area with hostas and ferns, small waterfall and pond. Steps to lawn surrounded by well-stocked borders, summerhouse, seating areas with village and rural views. Enjoy tea and cake in the potting shed.

13 ◆ CASTLE BROMWICH HALL GARDENS TRUST

Chester Road, Castle Bromwich, Birmingham B36 9BT. Castle Bromwich Hall & Gardens Trust, 0121 749 4100, www.cbhgt.org.uk. *4m E of Birmingham. 1m J5 M6 (exit N only)*. Light refreshments. **Adm £4.50, chd £1. For NGS: Sun 25 May (12.30-4.30). For other opening times and information, please phone or see garden website.**

A delightful 10-acre English formal walled garden. Comprising orchards, formal period planting schemes and a unique kitchen garden of the C17 and early C18. An all-season garden.

Plants from the gardens will be on sale at No.7 for you to take home . . .

14 COLEY COTTAGE

Coley Lane, Little Haywood ST18 0UU. Yvonne Branson, 01889 882715, yvonnebranson0uu@btinternet.com. *5m SE of Stafford. A51 from Rugeley or Weston signed Little Haywood. ½ m from Seven Springs. A513 Coley Lane from Red Lion PH past Back Lane, 100yds on L opp red post box*. Home-made teas on the premises. **Adm £2.50, chd free. Fri 6, Sun 22 June; Wed 13 Aug (11-4.30). Also open The Secret Garden. Visitors also welcome by appt June to Aug, pre bookings for 10+.**

A plant lover's cottage garden, full of subtle colours and perfume, every inch packed with plants. Clematis and old roses covering arches, many hostas and agapanthus, a wildlife pool, all designed to attract birds and butterflies. This garden is now 7yrs old, trees, roses and herbaceous planting has become well established. Visited and interviewed by radio Stoke.

15 COLOUR MILL
Winkhill, Leek, Staffs ST13 7PR. Bob & Jackie Pakes, 01538 308680, robert.pakes@virgin.net, www.colourmill.webplus.net. *7m E of Leek. Follow A523 from either Leek or Ashbourne*. Home-made teas. **Adm £3, chd free.** Sun 13 July; Thur 21 Aug (1.30-5). **Also open 37 Brookfields Road, 13 July. Visitors also welcome by appt June to Sept.**
3/4 -acre S-facing garden, created in the shadow of a former iron foundry, set beside the delightful R Hamps frequented by kingfisher and dipper. Informal planting in a variety of rooms surrounded by beautiful 7ft beech hedges. Large organic vegetable patch complete with greenhouse. Maturing trees provide shade for the interesting seating areas.

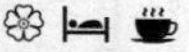

16 COURTWOOD HOUSE
3 Court Walk, Betley CW3 9DP. Mike Reeves. *6m S of Crewe. On the A531 toward Keele & Newcastle under Lyme or from J16 off the M6 pickup A531 off the A500 on the Nantwich rd, into village by Betley Court*. Light refreshments. **Adm £3.50, chd free.**
Sun 15 June (12.30-5).
Small L-shaped, walled garden, which is designed as a walk-through sculpture. Mainly shrubs with structures and water features, hidden spaces and seating areas, with strong shapes and effects utilising a wide range of materials, incl. a synthetic lawn. Small art gallery with acrylic paintings by owner for sale.

17 12 DARGES LANE
Great Wyrley WS6 6LE. Mrs A Hackett, 01922 415064, annofdarges@orange.net. *2m SE of Cannock. From A5 take A34 towards Walsall. Darges Lane is 1st turning on R (over brow of hill). House on R on corner of Cherrington Drive*. Tea. **Adm £3, chd free.** Visitors welcome by appt **Apr to Sept.**
1/4 -acre well-stocked enthusiastic plantsman's garden on two levels. Foliage plants are a special feature, together with shrubaceous borders containing rare and unusual plants, divided into areas that link with each other. The use of an extensive collection of clematis gives height in small spaces. Objects of art are eased into every corner, and the owner's own artwork is available to view. Constant updating gives fresh interest to both owner and visitors.

18 4 DENE CLOSE
Penkridge ST19 5HL. David & Anne Smith, 01785 712580. *6m S of Stafford. On A449 from Stafford. At far end of Penkridge turn L into Boscomoor Lane, 2nd L into Filance Lane, 3rd R Dene Close. Please park with consideration in Filance Lane. Disabled only in Dene Close*. Home-made teas. **Adm £3, chd free.** Sun 13 July (11-5). **Visitors also welcome by appt June to Aug, coaches permitted.**
A medium-sized garden of many surprises. Vibrant colour-themed herbaceous areas. Many different grasses and bamboos creating texture and interest in the garden. Attractive display of many unusual hostas shown for great effect 'theatre style'. Shady area for ferns etc. Water feature. Summerhouse and quiet seating areas within the garden. Featured in local press.

19 DORSET HOUSE
68 Station Street, Cheslyn Hay WS6 7EE. Mary & David Blundell, 01922 419437, david.blundell@talktalk.net. *2m SE of Cannock J11 M6 A462 towards Willenhall. L at island. At next island R into 1-way system (Low St), at T junction L into Station St. A5 Bridgetown L to island, L Coppice St. R into Station St*. Home-made teas. **Adm £3, chd free.** Suns 18 May; 20 July (11-5). **Visitors also welcome by appt May to July, groups of 10+.**
Step back in time with a visit to this inspirational 1/2 -acre garden which incorporates country cottage planting at its very best. Unusual rhododendrons, acers, shrubs and perennials planted in mixed borders. Clematis-covered arches and hidden corners with water features including stream and wildlife pool all come together to create a haven of peace and tranquillity. Featured in local papers.

20 198 EACHELHURST ROAD
Walmley, Sutton Coldfield B76 1EW. Jacqui & Jamie Whitmore. *5mins N of Birmingham. M6 J6, A38 Tyburn Rd to Lichfield, continue to T-lights at Lidl and continue on Tyburn Rd, at island take 2nd exit to destination rd*. Home-made teas. **Adm £3, chd free.**
Sun 27 July (12.30-4.30).
A long garden approx 210ft x 30ft divided by arches and pathways. Plenty to explore incl wildlife pond, cottage garden and hanging baskets leading to formal garden with box-lined pathways, well, stocked borders, willow gazebo and chicken house then through to raised decking area, overlooking Pype Hayes golf course, with summer house and bar and Mediterranean plants.

21 THE ELMS
Post Office Road, Seisdon, Wolverhampton WV5 7HA. Mr Alec Smith & Ms Susan Wilkinson, 01902 893482, kissjewellery@gmail.com. *6m W of Wolverhampton. From Wolverhampton A454,L at Shipley (Fox PH) take Fox Rd to Seisdon, L at Seven Stars. L into Post Office Rd, Elms 500yd on R*. **Adm £3.50, chd free.** Visitors welcome by appt **Mar to Aug, groups of 10 - 30, guided tour by owner.**
4-acre garden surrounding large country house. Walled tropical style garden around swimming pool. Large mixed herbaceous borders with all-yr interest. Over 125 roses around garden pergolas and hidden areas. Kitchen garden with box hedging. Many unusual plants most named. New and ancient trees. Victorian bandstand from Ilfracombe pier. Fully restored by present owner. Some slopes.

56 St Agnes Road, Moseley Corner, The Art of Gardens

22 FOUR SEASONS
26 Buchanan Road, Walsall WS4 2EN. Marie & Tony Newton, www.fourseasonsgarden.co.uk. *Adjacent to Walsall Arboretum. From Ring Rd A4148 near Walsall town centre. At large junction take A461 to Lichfield. At 1st island 3rd exit Buchanan Ave, fork R into Buchanan Rd*. Tea. **Adm £3.50, chd free. Mon 26 May (10-5).**
Stunning tapestry of colour in all seasons. Suburban, S-facing 1/3 acre, gently sloping to arboretum. 180 acers, 350 azaleas, bulbs, hellebores, camellias, perennials, begonias, bright conifers, topiary and shrubs. Interesting barks and berries. Many 'rooms'. Themes incl contrast of red, blue and yellow. Jungle, oriental pagoda, bridges, water features and stone ornaments. Some steps. WC. Featured in Garden Answers, Garden News and many international publications.

23 THE GARTH
2 Broc Hill Way, Milford, Stafford ST17 0UB. Mr & Mrs David Wright, 01785 661182, anitawright1@yahoo.co.uk, www.anitawright.co.uk. *4 1/2 m SE of Stafford. A513 Stafford to Rugeley rd; at Barley Mow turn R (S) to Brocton; L after 1/2 m*. Cream teas. **Adm £3, chd free. Suns 1, 29 June (2-6). Visitors also welcome by appt.**
1/2 -acre garden of many levels on Cannock Chase AONB. Acid soil loving plants. Series of small gardens, water features, raised beds. Rare trees, island beds of unusual shrubs and perennials, many varieties of hosta and ferns. Varied and colourful foliage. Ancient sandstone caves. Featured on BBC Radio Stoke and Express & Star.

24 GRAFTON COTTAGE
Barton-under-Needwood DE13 8AL. Margaret & Peter Hargreaves, 01283 713639, marpeter1@btinternet.com. *6m N of Lichfield. Leave A38 for Catholme S of Barton, follow sign to Barton Green, L at Royal Oak, 1/4 m*. Home-made teas. **Adm £3, chd free (share to Alzheimer's Research Trust). Suns 29 June; 20 July; 3, 10 Aug (11.30-5). Visitors also welcome by appt June to Aug, min adm £60 per group.**
This is where the bees and owners work overtime producing a traditional cottage garden, admired over the years. A visitor commented it's like indulging in a memorable meal which lingers on the palate'. Coloured themed borders with unusual herbaceous plants and perfume from old fashioned roses, sweet peas, violas, dianthus, phlox and lilies. Particular interests are viticella clematis, delphiniums, cottage garden annuals and use of foliage plants. Stream and small vegetable plot. Featured in Gardens Illustrated, local press and on ITV Love your Garden.

GROUP OPENING

25 HALL GREEN GARDENS
Burnaston Road, Birmingham B28 8DH. *Off A34, 3m city centre, 6m from M42 J4. All gardens near A34 Hall Green. From City Centre, turn L into Shaftmoor Lane for Russell Road, from M42 J4 follow signs to B'ham to Robin Hood Island*. Home-made teas at 16 Burnaston Rd and 120 Russell Road. **Combined adm £4, chd free. Suns 4 May; 20 July (2-5.30).**

NEW **42 BODEN ROAD**
Mrs Helen Lycett.
Take A34 to Hall Green, take 4th turning, Shirley Rd, 5th L into Boden Rd

16 BURNASTON ROAD
Howard Hemmings & Sandra Hateley
Visitors also welcome by appt May to Aug.
0121 624 1488
howard.hemmings@blueyonder.co.uk

37 BURNASTON ROAD
Mrs Carolyn Wynne-Jones
Visitors also welcome by appt May to July.
0121 608 2397

120 RUSSELL ROAD
Mr David Worthington
Visitors also welcome by appt Apr to Sept.
0121 624 7906
hildave@hotmail.com

19 STAPLEHURST ROAD
Mrs Sheena Terrace. *Located off A34 Stratford Rd Hall Green, between junctions of Fox Hollies Rd/Highfield Rd and School Rd/Colebank Rd B28 9AR*

A group of 5 suburban gardens, each unique in style. A S-facing lawned and border garden with interesting features incl a log display, conifers, water feature and various artefacts. 'Find IT' quiz for children. A tranquil garden with curving borders containing different perennials, shade areas, soft fruit and vegetables and a surprise around the corner. Plantsman's garden featuring formal raised pool and hosta collection with unusual perennials and container planting. A shady garden with mature trees, pond, cottage style borders and vegetable area and new for this year a large restful garden with mature trees, 2 lawns and cottage style borders. Limited wheelchair access to 19 Staplehurst Rd and 37 Burnaston Rd. Steps to garden at 19 Staplehurst Rd and 16 Burnaston Rd not accessible.

26 HAMILTON HOUSE
Roman Grange, Roman Road, Little Aston Park, Sutton Coldfield B74 3GA. Philip & Diana Berry, www.hamiltonhousegarden.co.uk. *3m N of Sutton Coldfield. Follow A454 (Walsal Rd) & enter Roman Rd, Little Aston Pk. Roman Grange is 1st L after church but enter rd via pedestrian gate.* Home-made teas. **Adm £3.50, chd free.**
Sun 25 May (2-5).
½ -acre N-facing English woodland garden in tranquil setting, making the most of challenging shade, providing haven for birds and other wildlife. Large pond with stone bridge, pergolas, water features, box garden with a variety of roses and herbs. Interesting collection of rhododendrons, hostas, ferns and old English roses. An NGS day to remember, so join us for afternoon tea, home-made cakes to die for and a few hours of English garden heaven. Sip a glass of chilled Pimm's punch at leisure whilst listening to music and admire - (or not) the art of our garden. Featured in The Journal and Sutton Coldfield Observer.

27 HEATH HOUSE
Offley Brook, nr Eccleshall ST21 6HA. Dr D W Eyre-Walker, 01785 280318, neyrewalker@btinternet.com. *3m W of Eccleshall. From Eccleshall take B5026 towards Woore. At Sugnall turn L, after 1½ m turn R immed by stone garden wall. After 1m straight across Xrds.* **Adm £5, chd free.**
Visitors welcome by appt Apr to Aug, refreshments for small numbers. Use Satnav, mobile phones do not work locally.
1½ -acre country garden of C18 miller's house in lovely valley setting, overlooking mill pool. Plantsman's garden containing many rare and unusual plants in borders, bog garden, woodland, alpine house, raised bed and shrubberies and incl slowly expanding collection of hardy terrestrial orchids.

28 HIDDEN GEM
15 St Johns Road, Pleck, Walsall WS2 9TJ. Maureen & Sid Allen, 07825 804670, hsallen@virginmedia.com. *2m W of Walsall. Off J10 M6. Head for Walsall on A454 Wolverhampton Rd. Turn R into Pleck Rd A4148 then 4th R into St Johns Rd.* Tea. **Adm £3, chd free.**
Sun 3 Aug (1-4). Visitors also welcome by appt June to Aug, groups of 10+.
Situated between two busy motorway junctions. Come and visit our 'Hidden Gem.' What a surprise! A long narrow pretty garden, lovely foliage in June, pretty perennials, shrubs, trees, lush tropical plants from July onwards. Japanese area with stream. Shady walk with ferns,into pretty gravel garden lots of wildlife. Very relaxing atmosphere. WHAT A GEM!. Featured in Garden inspirations and on QVC.

29 HIGH TREES
18 Drubbery Lane, nr Longton Park ST3 4BA. Peter & Pat Teggin. *5m S of Stoke-on-Trent. Off A5035, midway between Trentham Gardens & Longton. Opp Longton Park.* Cream teas. **Adm £3, chd free.**
Weds 21 May; 4 June (1-4).
Garden designer and plantswoman's pretty, perfumed hidden garden. Colourful herbaceous plants juxtapose to create a rich woven tapestry of spires, flats and fluffs interwoven with structure planting and focal points. An ideas garden continuing to inspire, evoking orderly diversity. All within two minutes walk of a Victorian park.

30 NEW IDLEROCKS FARM
Hilderstone Road, Spot Acre, nr Stone ST15 8RP. Barbara Dixon, 01889 505450. *3m E of Stone. From Stone take the A520 to Meir Heath, turn R onto B5066 towards Hilderstone, farm 1½ m on R. ½ m drive with parking in the field by the house.* Home-made teas. **Adm £3, chd free. Sun 24 Aug (1.30-5). Visitors also welcome by appt July to Aug, also February for Snowdrops.**
Medium sized garden set in farmland and woodland, 800ft above sea level. Long herbaceous border, wildlife pond, views across the Trent Valley to the Wrekin and Clee Hills.

The tranquillity of this elegant garden is enhanced by a Victorian style fish pond with fountain and waterfall . . .

31 JOHN'S GARDEN
Ashwood Lower Lane, Ashwood, nr Kingswinford DY6 0AE. John Massey, www.ashwoodnurseries.com. *5m S of Wolverhampton. S of Wolverhampton, 1m past Wall Heath on A449 turn R to Ashwood along Doctor's Lane. At T-junction turn L. Park at Ashwood Nurseries.* Light refreshments at Ashwood Nurseries. **Adm £5, chd free.**
Sun 19 Oct (10-4).
A plantsman's garden bordered by the Staffordshire and Worcestershire canal containing a huge plant collection. Autumn brings fruits, berries and foliage colour as well as many late summer flowers. Tearooms at Ashwood Nurseries. Disabled access difficult if very wet.

32 KOSYNOOK

25 Cannock Road, Burntwood WS7 0BL. Mr & Mrs Brian & Judith Littler. *5m W of Lichfield. Midway between Cannock & Lichfield on A5190, 200yds from Swan Island. Parking at shopping centre.* Home-made teas. **Adm £3, chd free.** **Sun 10 Aug (1-5).**

1/3 acre of lovingly maintained S-facing flat garden, stocked with a large variety of shrubs and plants that give an all-yr- round impressive viewing. Several water features a dovecote pond and ornaments are to be seen along with a variety of hanging baskets and tubs containing a beautiful array of colour. Mature trees. Ample seating is available. Three times winner of Burntwood in Bloom for best rear garden. A garden not to be missed.

33 13 LANSDOWNE ROAD

Hurst Green, Halesowen B62 9QT. Mr Peter Bridgens & Mr Michael King, 0121 421 7796, peterwbridgens@hotmail.co.uk. *7m W of Birmingham. A458 Hagley Rd out of Birmingham, towards Stourbridge., From M5 J2 take 1st exit A4123 towards Birmingham.* Home-made teas. **Adm £3.50, chd free.** **Sun 6 July (12.30-5.30).** **Visitors also welcome by appt May to Sept.**

A plantsman's suburban garden designed to ensure maximum use of space. The garden features rare and unusual plants, incl Mecanopsis, Buddleia agathosma, Stewartia, Halesia, Schizandra. Water features and bog area. The mixed borders are planted giving a long season of interest. Attention paid to plant association and colour themes. The garden presents a softly planted look with a tropical twist. No Wheelchair access.

34 NEW 89 MARSH LANE

Solihull B91 2PE. Mrs Gail Wyldes. *1/2 m from Solihull town centre. A41 from M42 J5. Turn sharp L at first T-lights. Garden on R. Parking 400 metres further along Marsh Lane at Solihull Cricket Club by mini r'about.* Home-made teas. **Adm £3.50, chd free.** **Sun 8 June (2-5).**

Suburban Oasis. Trees, shrubs and herbaceous planting for all year interest with emphasis on leaf shape and structure. Wildlife pond, bog garden, water features, summer house, gravel gardens, shady places and sunny seating areas. Patio with pergola and raised beds. Hostas and ferns abound. The garden is continually evolving with new plants and features. Small step from patio to the main back garden and paths may be a little narrow.

35 ◆ MIDDLETON HALL

Tamworth B78 2AE. Middleton Hall Trust, 01827 283095, www.middleton-hall.org.uk. *4m S of Tamworth, 2m N J9 M42. On A4091 between The Belfry & Drayton Manor.* Light refreshments. **Adm £4, chd £1.** **For NGS: Sun 22 June (1-5).** **For other opening times and information, please phone or see garden website.**

Two walled gardens set in 40 acres of grounds surrounding Grade 2 Middleton Hall, the C17 home of naturalists Sir Francis Willoughby and John Ray. Large colour-themed herbaceous borders radiating from a central pond, restored gazebo, pergola planted with roses, clematis and wisteria. Courtyard garden with raised beds. Musical entertainment in the Hall.

36 MILLENNIUM GARDEN

London Road, Lichfield WS14 9RB. Carol Cooper. *1m S of Lichfield. Off A38 along A5206 towards Lichfield 1/4 m past A38 island towards Lichfield. Park in field on L. Yellow signs on field gate.* Home-made teas. **Adm £3.50, chd free.** **Suns 6 Apr; 8 June (1-5).**

2-acre garden with mixed spring bulbs in the woodland garden and a host of golden daffodils fade slowly into the summer borders in this English country garden. Designed with a naturalistic edge and with the environment in mind. A relaxed approach creates a garden of quite sanctuary with the millennium bridge sitting comfortably, and its surroundings of lush planting and mature trees. Well stocked summer borders give shots of colour to lift the spirit and the air fills with the scent of wisterias and climbing roses. A stress free environment awaits you at the Millennium Garden.

37 MITTON MANOR

Mitton, Penkridge, Stafford ST19 5QW. Mrs E A Gooch, 07970 457457, eag@eguk.co.uk. *2m W of Penkridge. Property is on Whiston Rd. Parking in field before house.* Cream teas. **Adm £5, chd free.** **Sun 29 June (11.30-4.30).** **Visitors also welcome by appt May to July, groups of 10 - 30, no parking for coaches.**

This 7-acre country garden was started in 2001 and has been developed from an overgrown wilderness. The garden surrounds a Victorian manor (not open) and contains rooms of different styles, formal box/topiary, prairie planting and natural woodland bordered by a stream. Stunning vistas, water features and sculpture. Live music. Many levels, narrow and gravel paths.

38 MOORFIELD

Post Lane, Endon, Stoke-on-Trent ST9 9DU. Ian & June Sellers, 01782 504096. *4m W of Leek. 6m from Stoke-on-Trent A53. Turn into Station Rd over railway line, canal bridge with lights, 1st on L opp Endon Cricket Club.* Home-made teas. **Adm £3, chd free.** **Sun 20 July (1.30-5).** **Visitors also welcome by appt June to Aug.**

Flower arranger's delight situated in 1/3 acre. This colourful garden has a variety of different styles ranging from herbaceous borders to areas with a Mediterranean feel. The garden incl many structural features such as unusual wooden tree stumps to a spacious summerhouse. Wide variety of unusual plants. Featured in Leek Post and Times, on Radio Stoke.

GROUP OPENING

39 NEW MOSELEY CORNER, THE ART OF GARDENS

Birmingham B13 9PN. *3m S of city centre. From Moseley take St Mary's Row which becomes Wake Green Rd. After $^1/_2$ m turn R into St Agnes Rd and L at the church, park here for all gardens.* Home-made teas 56 St Agnes Road. **Combined adm £3.50, chd free.** **Sun 15 June (1-3.30).**

56 ST AGNES ROAD
Michael & Alison Cullen

NEW 269 YARDLEY WOOD ROAD
Miss Marion Stoddart

NEW 271 YARDLEY WOOD ROAD
Mrs Gillian Hattley

These three gardens are all situated near the corner of Yardley Wood Rd and St Agnes Rd in Moseley. All three demonstrate unique design, each expressing the garden owners' creative vision and endeavour. 56 is immaculately maintained with curving borders around a formal lawn with delicate acers and contemporary sculpture. The tranquillity of this elegant garden is enhanced by a Victorian style fish pond with fountain and waterfall. 271 has a looser style and informality with patio and rockery, colourful herbaceous borders and mature trees with fruit section and vegetable garden. 269 has 3 rooms with a terrace and pergola adorned with hops, clematis, roses, jasmine and solanum leading up steps to a lawn with gazebo, many shrubs and herbaceous borders. The hidden top garden is tranquil with stream, pond and architectural planting.

GROUP OPENING

40 MOSELEY GARDENS SOUTH

Moseley/Kings Heath, Birmingham B13 9TF. *3m city centre. Halfway between Kings Heath & Moseley village, Birmingham. Our gardens can be found between the A435 (Alcester Rd) and B4217 (Wake Green Rd) in S Birmingham.* Home-made teas at 51 Valentine Road. **Combined adm £4, chd free.** **Sun 22 June (2-6).**

39 ASHFIELD AVENUE
Kings Heath. Judy Cottrell

7 ASHFIELD ROAD
Hilary Bartlett

16 PROSPECT ROAD
Andy Horn

19 PROSPECT ROAD
Tony White

65 SCHOOL ROAD
Wendy Weston

51 VALENTINE ROAD
Kings Heath. Clare Goulder

34 WOODFIELD ROAD
Rosemary Chatfield

Come and explore our 7 beautiful and varied urban plots, from small city gardens to a $^1/_2$ acre of spreading lawns with mature trees. Moseley has many fine Edwardian and Victorian villas hiding wonderful secret gardens. Some of our front gardens are worth seeing too! The street containers and hanging baskets of award-winning Moseley in Bloom enhance the area. We have wildlife and koi ponds, other water features, fruit and vegetable cultivation, outdoor artworks, chickens and ducks and as many different design ideas as gardeners. These incl wildlife, child-friendly, and easy maintenance gardens. Amongst our special features on Open Day are a quiz or treasure trail for children, live classical music and live jazz! Meet our gardeners, and enjoy tea and home-made cakes in a quintessentially English setting. Well-stocked, mature borders, scree garden, a variety of seating areas, excellent plants and preserves for sale, and teas with home-made cakes. Featured in B13 magazine. Partial wheelchair access.

41 THE MOUNT, COTON, GNOSALL

Stafford ST20 0EQ. Andrew & Celia Payne, 01785 822253, ac.payne@waitrose.com. *8m W of Stafford. From Stafford take A518 W towards Newport/Telford. Go through Gnosall, over canal.Garden on edge of Gnosall village on LH-side of A518.* Home-made teas. **Adm £3, chd free.** **Sun 29 June (2-5.30). Also open West View. Visitors also welcome by appt June to July.**

Richly planted wildlife friendly garden with large collection of unusual plants set in $^3/_4$ acre. Divided into areas, incl a wild flower meadow, cottage garden and vegetable plot, highlights consist of over 100 different hosta varieties, many colourful hardy geraniums, bamboos and a huge Kiftsgate rose. The plant stall will have over 40+ varieties of hosta for sale plus other interesting plants.

42 THE OLD DAIRY HOUSE

Trentham Park, Stoke-on-Trent ST4 8AE. Philip & Michelle Moore. *S edge of Stoke-on-Trent. Next to Trentham Gardens. Off Whitmore Lane. Please follow NGS signs or signs for Trentham Park Golf Club. Parking in church car park.* Light refreshments. **Adm £3, chd free.** **Sun 25, Mon 26 May (12.30-4.30).**

Grade 2 listed house (not open) designed by Sir Charles Barry forms backdrop to this 2-acre garden in parkland setting. Shaded area for rhododendrons, azaleas plus expanding hosta and fern collection. Mature trees, 'cottage garden' and long borders. Narrow brick paths in vegetable plot. Large courtyard area for teas. Some gravel paths but lawns are an option.

An excellent opportunity to explore an evolving garden . . .

43 NEW THE OLD VICARAGE

Hollington Road, Croxden, Uttoxeter ST14 5JQ. Ms Kerry Alvey. *5m N of Uttoxeter. From A50 at Uttoxeter take B5030 to Rocester. At JCB Headquarters turn L to Hollington. Garden is approx. $2^3/_4$ m on R.* Home-made teas. **Adm £3, chd free.** **Sun 27 July (2-5).**

The first opening of approx 1.7 acres of country garden set in beautiful Staffordshire countryside. The current owners who took over 4 years ago are restoring the gardens which incl orchard, fruit trees, vegetable plot, borders, lawns, arbour and a newly created brook walk. An excellent opportunity to explore an evolving garden. Most of the garden accessible to wheelchair. Some of it via lawned areas.

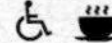

From tiny back plots to country estates

44 PAUL'S OASIS OF CALM

18 Kings Close, Kings Heath, Birmingham B14 6TP. Mr Paul Doogan, 0121 444 6943, gardengreen18@hotmail.co.uk. *4m from city centre. 5m from the M42 J4. Take A345 to Kings Heath High St then B4122 Vicarage Rd. Turn L onto Kings Rd then R to Kings Close.* Home-made teas. **Adm £2.50, chd free. Visitors welcome by appt May to Aug.**

Garden cultivated from nothing into a little oasis. Measuring 18ftx70ft. It's small but packed with interesting and unusual plants, water features and 7 seating areas. It's my piece of heaven.

Wildlife in abundance, stables, wonderful wood and walks, dells and orchard. A truly unique country hideaway. Step back in time . . .

GROUP OPENING

45 PEREIRA ROAD GARDENS

Harborne, Birmingham B17 9JN. *1/2 m N of Harborne High Street. Between Gillhurst Rd & Margaret Grove, 1/4 m from Hagley Rd or 1/2 m from Harborne High St.* Tea at 12 Pereira Road (June). **Combined adm £3.50, chd free. Suns 27 Apr; 29 June (2-5).**

14 PEREIRA ROAD
Mike Foster

50 PEREIRA ROAD
Peg Peil

55 PEREIRA ROAD
Emma Davies & Martin Commander.
Not open 27 April

Group of 3 different urban gardens. No.14 is a well established suburban garden with mixed herbaceous and shrub borders. Wildlife-friendly with 2 ponds and wild flower area. Ongoing alterations provide new area of interest each year. No. 50 is a plantaholic's paradise with over 1000 varieties, many rare, incl fruits, vegetables, herbs, grasses and large bed of plants with African connections. Over 100 varieties on sale - see how they grow. No. 55 is a sloping garden, incl gravelled beds with mixed planting, grasses and a small pond. All gardens have steps. Please note that No 55 is open June only.

46 THE PINTLES

18 Newport Road, Great Bridgeford, Stafford ST18 9PR. Peter & Leslie Longstaff, *J14 M6 take A5013 towards Eccleshall. In Great Bridgeford turn L onto B5405. Car park on L after 1/2 m in front of Village Hall.* Home-made teas. **Adm £3, chd free. Suns 1 June; 6 July (1-5). Also open on 6 July with Birch Trees.**

Traditional semi-detached house in a semi-rural location. Medium-sized garden designed to be wildlife friendly, including vegetable plot, pool, weather station, 2 greenhouses and collection of 200 cacti and succulents. Plenty of seating and a surprise at the end. Featured in Amateur Gardening. Steep ramp and steps into main garden.

47 NEW PRIORY FARM

Mitton Road, Bradley, Stafford ST18 9ED. Debbie Farmer. *3 1/2 m W Penkridge. At Texaco island on A449 in Penkridge take Bungham Lane. Cont for 2 1/2 m past Swan & Whiston Hall to Mitton. Turn R to Bradley, cont 1m to Priory Farm on L.* Home-made teas. **Adm £4, chd free. Sun 15 June (11-4).**

A hidden gem. Delightful 120yr old cottage with own lake set in mature gardens and grounds. Wildlife in abundance, stables, wonderful wood and walks, dells and orchard. A truly unique country hideaway. Step back in time.

48 ROWLEY HOUSE FARM

Croxton, Stafford ST21 6PJ. Tony & Beryl Roe, 01630 620248. *4m W of Eccleshall. Between Eccleshall & Loggerheads on B5026. At Wetwood Xrds turn for Fairoak. Take 1st L turn & continue for 3/4 m.* **Adm £3.50, chd free. Sun 28 Sept (2-5). Visitors also welcome by appt June to July.**

Quiet country garden, part reclaimed from farm rick-yard. Shrub roses in orchard, soft fruits, vegetables and water feature incl. Extensive views towards the Wrekin and Welsh hills from adjacent land at 570ft, with plantings of 95 varieties of 7 species of ilex, various corylus and specimen trees. Small water feature. Gravel paths.

49 THE SECRET GARDEN

3 Banktop Cottages, Little Haywood ST18 0UL. Derek Higgott & David Aston, 01889 883473, poshanddeks@yahoo.co.uk. *5m SE of Stafford. A51 from Rugeley or Weston signed Little Haywood A513 Stafford Coley Lane, Back Lane R into Coley Grove. Entrance 50 metres on L.* Home-made teas. **Adm £3, chd free. Sun 18 May; Fri 6, Sun 22 June; Wed 13 Aug (11-4). Also open Tanglewood Cottage 18 May. Coley Cottage 6, 22 June, 13 Aug. Visitors also welcome by appt June to Aug.**

Wander past the other cottage gardens and through the evergreen arch and there before you a fantasy for the eyes and soul. Stunning garden approx 1/2 acre, created over the last 26yrs. Strong colour theme of trees and shrubs, underplanted with perennials, 1000 bulbs and laced with clematis; other features include water, laburnum and rose tunnel and unique buildings. Is this the jewel in the crown? Raised gazebo with wonderful views over untouched meadows and Cannock Chase. HPS Plant Fair in village hall on Sun 18 May. Featured in Gardeners World. Some slopes.

50 NEW ◆ SELLY MANOR MUSEUM GARDEN

Maple Road, Bournville, Birmingham B30 2AE. Miss Gillian Ellis, 0121 667 1090, www.sellymanormuseum.org.uk. *4 m S from Birmingham city centre. Off A4040, 100m from the Sycamore Rd & Linden Rd junction.* Light refreshments. **Adm £3.50, chd free. For NGS: Sats, Suns 17,18 May; 16, 17 Aug (11-4). For other opening times and information, please phone or see garden website.**

Approximately 2/3 acre of garden surround two timber framed museum buildings in the heart of Bournville

Brooklyn

garden village. The cottage style garden features herbaceous borders, espaliered and fan trained fruit trees, a laurel and lavender parterre, woodland plant area, fern border, herb and vegetable garden, box topiary, lawns, wild flower area, native hedge and fig trees. The garden is fully accessible for wheelchairs. Access to the museum buildings is limited to the ground floor.

GROUP OPENING

51 NEW ST JOHN'S GARDENS

St Johns Road, Stafford ST17 9AS. Fiona Howarth, 01785 258923, fiona_horwath@yahoo.co.uk. ½ m *S of Stafford town centre. Just a few mins from J13 M6 off A449 just after Rising Brook. Through entrance to private park. Please park considerately*. Home-made teas at no.29. **Combined adm £4, chd free.** Sun 23 Mar (2-5). Evening Opening £5, chd free, wine, Fri 16 May (6.30-9); Sun 22 June (2-5). **Visitors also welcome by appt Mar to Sept.**

23 ST JOHNS ROAD
Colin & Fiona Horwath

NEW 29 ST JOHN'S ROAD
Mrs Carol Shanahan

Two near neighbours who share a passion for all things horticultural - we are lucky that our respective gardens enjoy a southerly aspect which we use to its full advantage. However, you will also find plenty of ideas for dry shade and challenging areas. You are most welcome to sit and relax with home-made tea and cake whilst being inspired by the well-stocked beds that surround you. No.23 is a Victorian house (not open) and as you pass through the black and white gate you enter a part-walled plant lover's haven. There are bulbs and shady woodlanders in spring and a plethora of herbaceous plants and climbers. At no.29, against a backdrop of mature Hornbeams there are 2 acres of informal garden made up of many complementary areas. View the wooded 'dingly dell', colourful terraces, abundant kitchen garden, bronze armillary, water features, circular lawns plus the roses and clematis that scramble through the trees. Don't miss the working area of the garden for the most upmarket compost bins - all made from decking. As both gardens are keen hardy planters and sow far too many seeds there is always something good for sale.

52 STONEHILL QUARRY GARDEN

Great Gate, Croxden, nr Uttoxeter ST10 4HF. Mrs Caroline Raymont. *6m NW of Uttoxeter. From A50 at Uttoxeter take B5030 to JCB Rocester, turn L to Hollington. Take 3rd R Croxden Abbey. At Great Gate turn L at T junction to Stonehill.* **Adm £3.** Suns 20 Apr; 19, 26 Oct (2-5). 6 acre plantsman's landscape garden set in a historical quarry with bamboo jungle, rock garden, mixed borders and small wildlife pond. Particular features in season are spring bulbs underneath trees and autumn colour. ¼ m steep drive to house. C12 Cistercian Abbey ruins (adm free) ½ kilometre away.Churnet Valley walks and Alton Towers 10mins away. Included in 'Historical Gardens of England:- Staffordshire' by Timothy Mowle and Dianne Barre. Disabled parking only at house. Wheelchair access to main terrace and main lawn only. Garden unsuitable for children.

53 172 STONOR ROAD
Hall Green, Birmingham B28 0QJ. Mrs O Walters, 0121 745 2894, gwenowalt@yahoo.co.uk. *1m NW of Shirley. A34 Stratford Rd, at Robin Hood Island, take Baldwins Lane & Stonor Rd is 2nd L.* Home-made teas. **Adm £3, chd free. Visitors welcome by appt Apr to Sept, groups 1 - 10.**
Dedicated plantswoman's back garden 19 metres x 10 metres with wide variety of plants from alpine gravel bed at top to choice woodlanders at the bottom. Trilliums, fritillaries, podophyllum ferns etc. Acers, clematis and other climbers. Small conservatory with half-hardy shrubs and perennials. Medium-sized front garden with interesting, shrubs, perennials and bulbs. Wheelchair access to front garden only.

54 ◆ SUGNALL WALLED GARDEN
Sugnall, Stafford ST21 6NF. Dr & Mrs David Jacques, 01785 850820, www.sugnall.co.uk. *2½ m NW of Eccleshall. Just off B5026 Eccleshall to Loggerheads Rd. Turn at the Sugnall Xrds & use the Sugnall Business Centre car park.* Home-made teas. **Adm £3, chd free. For NGS: Suns 10 Aug; 28 Sept (11-4.30). For other opening times and information, please phone or see garden website.**
Historic walled kitchen garden of 1737, renovated for today. Work in progress, e.g. glass houses still to be repaired, but most of the 2 acres is under cultivation with 200 apple and pear dwarf pyramids, 50 fan-trained wall fruit and a wide variety of produce within the quarters. Flower borders around events area. Apple tasting on 28 September. Accessable WC.

55 TANGLEWOOD COTTAGE
Crossheads, Colwich, Stafford ST18 0UG. Dennis & Helen Wood, 01889 882857, shuvitdog@hotmail.com, Tanglewood cottage, Facebook. *5m SE of Stafford. A51 Rugeley/Weston R into Colwich. Church on L school on R, under bridge right into Crossheads Lane follow railway approx ¼ m (it does lead somewhere). Parking signed.* Light refreshments in conservatory. Wine and BBQ (evening opening) in new courtyard. **Adm £3, chd free. Sun 18 May, Sat 26 July (12-4). Evening Opening £4, chd free, light refreshments, Fri 5 Sept (7-10). Also open The Secret Garden18 May. Visitors also welcome by appt May to Sept, catering requirements on request, groups 15+.**
A country cottage garden. Mixed borders, koi carp pool, tranquil seated areas, courtyard, vegetables and fruit, chickens and aviary. An array of wonderful perennials. A garden of peace and tranquillity, recently described as a spiritual garden. Year on year people spend many hours relaxing with us. Art & jewellery display & sales. Wine evening HPS Plant Fair in village hall Sun 18 May. Lots of gravel paths, people with walking sticks seem to manage quite well.

56 NEW TILEWRIGHT CLOSE
7 Tilewright Close, Kidsgrove ST7 4TR. Karon Hackney-Bourne. *Travelling N, leave A500 at exit signed Kidsgrove A50. At Xrds in Kidsgrove turn R into Mount Rd, 3rd L into Whiteridge Rd, 2nd R into Tilewright Close.* Home-made teas. **Adm £2.50, chd free. Sun 20 July (12-4.30).**
An unexpected, highly maintained suburban garden, containing over 20 clematis, alongside honeysuckle and climbing roses. With garden rooms, each designed with a specific purpose in mind. This is a family garden on different levels, on a dificult landscape and includes three seating areas, a fire pit, various trees, formal lawn and deep herbaceous borders. An interesting plot which will inspire you. Silver Gilt award for Residential Garden from Newcastle in Bloom.

57 91 TOWER ROAD
Four Oaks, Sutton Coldfield B75 5EQ. Heather & Gary Hawkins. *3m N Sutton Coldfield. From A5127 at Mere Green island, turn onto Mere Green Rd, L at St James Church, L again onto Tower Road.* Cream teas. **Adm £3, chd free. Sun 8 June (1.30-5.30).**
163ft S-facing garden with sweeping borders and island beds planted with an eclectic mix of shrubs and perennials. A well stocked fishpond, imposing cast iron water feature and a hiding griffin enhance your journey around the garden. A vast array of home made cakes to tempt you during your visit. The ideal setting for sunbathing, children's hide and seek and lively garden parties. Amazing selection of home-made cream teas to eat in the garden or take away. More than just an Open Garden, we like to think of it as a garden party!. Featured in Sutton Coldfield Observer and Garden News magazine.

Chinese garden with chess pavilion and bonsai, water features, small pond with lilys and wood carving, greenhouses . . .

58 ◆ THE TRENTHAM ESTATE
Stone Road, Stoke-on-Trent ST4 8JG. Michael Walker, 01782 646646, www.trentham.co.uk. *M6 J15. Well signed on roundabout, A34 with A5035.* **For NGS: Evening Openings £5, chd £5, light refreshments, Weds 2, 9 July (6-9). For other opening times and information, please phone or see garden website.**
One of the largest garden regeneration projects in Britain, using award winning designers Tom Stuart-Smith and Piet Oudolf, who have introduced vast contemporary plantings, using over 300,000 choice perennials and bulbs. Collection of show gardens and new 7 acre garden by Piet Oudolf. NGS Special Evening Opening. Trenthams' Head of Garden and Estate, Michael Walker, will provide a complimentary tour of the garden starting at 6.30pm on both evening openings.

D

59 NEW 41 TWENTYLANDS
Rolleston-on-Dove, Burton-on-Trent DE13 9AJ. Maureen & Joe Martin. *3m E of Tutbury. At r'about on Tutbury by-pass A511 take Rolleston Lane. Continue through Rolleston-on-Dove, past Scout HQ. Twentylands on R.* Home-made teas. **Adm £3, chd free. Sat 17 May, Sun 17 Aug (12-5).**
Small back garden. Every corner used and packed with plants. Herbaceous borders with fruit trees and shrubs. Herb corner, fernery, bog

Look out for the NGS yellow arrows ...

garden with many candelabra primulas and other bog plants. Chinese garden with chess pavilion and bonsai, water features, small pond with lilys and wood carving, greenhouses, Water harvesting and composting systems. Many plants raised from seed. Tutbury Castle and Blue Cross Horse Sanctuary near by.

60 19 WATERDALE

Compton, Wolverhampton WV3 9DY. Anne & Brian Bailey, 01902 424867, m.bailey1234@btinternet.com, www.facebook.com/pages/Garden-of-Surprises/165745816926408. *1½ m W of Wolverhampton city centre. From Wolverhampton Ring Rd take A454 towards Bridgnorth for 1m. Waterdale is on the L off A454 Compton Rd West.* Home-made teas. **Adm £3, chd free.** Suns 8 June; 20 July (1.30-5.30). **Visitors also welcome by appt May to Aug for groups of 10-35, adm £5.**

Secluded town garden which gradually unfolds from the sunny terrace and upper garden, through shady fernery to gothic folly and on to Japanese garden, complete with teahouse, hidden by towering bamboo. The return journey leads to a summerhouse and shell grotto. Densely planted, in spite of dry conditions, incl many unusual perennials and shrubs. Featured in the Wolverhampton Magazine.

61 WEST VIEW

Cross Street, Gnosall ST20 0BX. Bev & John Smith. *8m W of Stafford on A518. From Stafford take the A518 W towards Newport/Telford. Park on Methodist Chapel car park. Take 1st L The Rank 1st R Cross St West View 2nd house on L.* Home-made teas. **Adm £3, chd free.** Sun 29 June (1-5). **Also open The Mount.**

Take a journey through our gem of a garden and be prepared to be surprised. Travel via the pot filled decking and down through the archway, or descend the steps under the scented pergola by the stream and through the arbour. Either way, you enter a hidden oasis of calm and colour where flowers and foliage blend in perfect harmony. Enjoy!.

WESTACRES

See Worcestershire.

62 THE WICKETS

47 Long Street, Wheaton Aston ST19 9NF. Tony & Kate Bennett, 01785 840233, ajtonyb@talktalk.net. *8m W of Cannock, 10m N of Wolverhampton, 10m E of Telford. M6 J12 W towards Telford on A5; 3m R signed Stretton; 150yds L signed Wheaton Aston; 2+m L; over canal garden on R or at Bradford Arms on A5 follow signs.* Tea. **Adm £3, chd free.** Sun 6, Wed 9 July; Sun 24 Aug (1.30-5). **Visitors also welcome by appt June to Aug.**

This quirky garden is full of humour and surprises. The interlocking themed areas have new and original ideas for gardens of all sizes. Features incl a fernery, grasses bed, herbaceous islands, dry stream, many pots, tubs and baskets and a cricket match! It will stimulate your imagination as you sit and enjoy our acclaimed tea and cake. Featured in Wolverhampton Magazine and Express and Star. 2 steps in garden.

63 WILKINS PLECK

off Three Mile Lane, Whitmore, nr Newcastle-under-Lyme ST5 5HN. Sheila & Chris Bissell, www.wilkinspleckgarden.com. *5m SW from Newcastle-under-Lyme. Take A53 SW from Newcastle-under-Lyme. At Whitmore turn R at Mainwaring Arms PH. Signed R at Cudmore Fisheries.* Home-made teas. **Adm £5, chd free.** Suns 15 June; 27 July (1-5).

5½ acres of paradise in North Staffordshire in the true Arts and Crafts Tradition. A series of enclosed gardens, parterres and yew hedges. Pleached lime avenue. Herbaceous borders which move from cool colours to hot. Pyramidal roofed summerhouse. Beyond lies a lake spanned by two Monet-style bridges, and young arboretum. See website for more information. Please No Dogs in the car park in the field at landowner's request. Featured in Period Living Magazine and Mail on Sunday.

64 WILLOW COTTAGE

High Street, Church Eaton ST20 0AG. Sue & Jeremy Bach. *7½ m SW of Stafford. A518. At Haughton tn L for Church Eaton. At T-junction, turn R down High St to Royal Oak PH car park. Walk back to Cottage.* Tea. **Adm £3, chd free.** Suns, Weds 20, 23 July; 17, 20 Aug (1-5).

Behind the country cottage frontage is an oasis of flower and colour. The gentle sound of water welcomes you to walk amongst the herbaceous beds, water features, ponds and vegetable plot. Sit in some of the quiet corners of this garden and enjoy the passing wildlife. Featured in Nova magazine.

This quirky garden is full of humour and surprises . . .

65 WITS END

59 Tanworth Lane, Shirley B90 4DQ. Sue Mansell, 0121 744 4337, wits-end@hotmail.co.uk. *2m SW of Solihull. Take B4102 from Solihull for 2m. R at island onto A34. After next island (Sainsbury's) Tanworth Lane 1st L off A34.* Home-made teas. **Adm £2.50, chd free.** Fri 1 Aug (11-3); Suns 3, 24 Aug (2-5). **Visitors also welcome by appt July to Aug, groups 10+.**

Interesting all-yr-round plantaholic's cottage-style garden. Perennials and shrubs, many unusual in various shaped beds (some colour co-ordinated) plus spectacular late summer border. Various containers displaying an array of sempervivum and jovibarba. New water features, scree and design changes planned for late summer.

66 THE WOMBOURNE WODEHOUSE

Wolverhampton WV5 9BW. Mr & Mrs J Phillips, 01902 892202. *4m S of Wolverhampton. Just off A449 on A463 to Sedgley.* **Adm £5, chd free.** Visitors welcome by appt **Apr to July, small or large groups welcome preferably weekdays.**

18-acre garden laid out in 1750. Rhododendrons, azaleas, woodland walk and 180 different varieties of tall bearded irises in walled kitchen garden (mid May to early June), 66yd herbaceous border, also 2 small borders and water garden (June and July). Partial wheelchair access.

GROUP OPENING

67 NEW WOODLAND GRANGE GARDENS

Rowley Hall Drive, Stafford ST17 9FF. *1m SW of Stafford town centre. Off A518, Newport Rd. Turn into Rowley Ave, signed Rowley Hall Hospital. Continue through the white gates of Rowley Park following the lane straight on. Keep going despite the lane narrowing and park in hospital car park (signed). There is no access from A449 Wolverhampton Rd despite what your Satnav may say!.* Light refreshments Strawberries & cream/ice cream. **Combined adm £4, chd free.** Sun 29 June (1-5).

NEW 7 ROWLEY HALL DRIVE
Mr Paul Brett

NEW 10 ROWLEY HALL DRIVE
Mr & Mrs Wootton

NEW 12 ROWLEY HALL DRIVE
Jane & Chris Whitney-Cooper

A trio of smaller-scale suburban 'real-life' gardens to spark the imagination. Three suburban gardens established over the past 20 years on a site that was once part of the grounds of Rowley Hall. They are planted in contrasting styles, but all draw on features of the parkland that still surrounds these modern houses. No. 10 is a villa-style garden, open and spacious, with formal lawns surrounded by professionally laid-out borders for year-round colour and interest. No.12 is a country/cottage style garden, combining productive vegetable areas as well as attractive borders and mixed planting. The owners use organic principles and have completed their country-style 'Good Life' with a brood of hens. No.7 is an edge of woodland style garden with a feel of peace, calm and tranquillity. It uses focal points and perspective principles to enhance this effect. Shrubs and foliage plants, rather than flowers are used to create a naturalistic setting attractive to wildlife. Ice-creams together with strawberries and cream will be available at No.10, tea and cakes at No.12 and plants from the gardens will be on sale at No.7 for you to take home to your own 'earthly paradise'. Parking at Rowley Hall, short walk down drive to Rowley Hall Drive. Gardens will be signed. Tickets available at 10 Rowley Hall Drive.

GROUP OPENING

68 WOODLEIGHTON GROVE GARDENS

Woodleighton Grove, Uttoxeter ST14 8BX, 01889 563930, cityofgold@lineone.net. *SE of Uttoxeter. From Uttoxeter take B5017 (Marchington). Go over Town Bridge, 1st exit at r'about, then 3rd exit at r'about into Highwood Rd, After ¼ m turn R.* Home-made teas. **Combined adm £3.50, chd free.** Sat 12 July (11-5); Sun 13 July (1-5). **Visitors also welcome by appt June to July min 12. Adm £6 per head incl home-made teas.**

APOLLONIA
Helen & David Loughton

KARIBU
Graham & Judy White

These two adjacent gardens demonstrate varied and fascinating approaches to design, layout and planting, and are said to have inspired and given many people ideas for their own gardens. Apollonia is a Plantaholics Garden, strong structure on several levels. summerhouse, greenhouse, fruit arch under development, natural stream, some steep steps. Unusual and interesting planting including bamboos, bananas, hostas and agaves. A place to relax and enjoy. Karibu is a distinctive and intriguing garden with a number of absorbing features. Informally planted on two levels, with a natural stream, summerhouse, greenhouse, folly, gazebo and stumpery. Archways, bridges, steps and a boardwalk lead to a selection of tranquil resting places. The garden discreetly houses many fascinating artefacts, plus a collection of antique horticultural and agricultural hand tools. The greenhouse contains nearly 400 cacti and succulents, A quiz and garden search are available. Wheelchair access limited to top gardens and greenhouses.

69 YARLET HOUSE

Yarlet, Stafford ST18 9SU. Mr & Mrs Nikolas Tarling. *2m S of Stone. Take A34 from Stone towards Stafford, turn L into Yarlet School and L again into car park.* Home-made teas. **Adm £4, chd free (share to Staffordshire Wildlife Trust).** Sat 5 July (10-2).

4 acre garden with extensive lawns, walks, lengthy herbaceous borders and traditional Victorian box hedge. Water gardens with fountain and rare lilies. Sweeping views across Trent Valley to Sandon. Victorian School Chapel. 9 hole putting course. Boules pitch. Yarlet School Art Display. Gravel paths.

70 YEW TREE COTTAGE

Podmores Corner, Long Lane, nr White Cross, Haughton, Stafford ST18 9JR. Clive & Ruth Plant, 01785 282516, pottyplantz@aol.com. *4m W of Stafford. Take A518 W Haughton, turn R Station Rd (signed Ranton) 1m, then turn R at Xrds ¼ m on R.* Home-made teas. **Adm £3, chd free.** Suns 4, 25 May (2-5); Thurs 29 May; 12, 26 June; 10 July (11-5); Sun 20 July (2-5). **Visitors also welcome by appt Apr to July.**

Hardy Planter's garden brimming with unusual plants. All-yr-round interest incl meconopsis, trillium, arisaema and dierama. ½ -acre incl pond, gravel garden, herbaceous borders, vegetable garden and plant sales area. Covered courtyard with oak-timbered vinery to take tea in if the weather is unkind, and seats in the garden for lingering on sunny days.

Coley Cottage

© Julia Stanley

Staffordshire County Volunteers

County Organisers

Susan & John Weston, Birch Trees, Copmere End, Eccleshall, Stafford ST21 6HH, 01785 850448, johnweston123@btinternet.com

County Treasurer

John Weston, Birch Trees, Copmere End, Eccleshall, Stafford ST21 6HH, 01785 850448, johnweston123@btinternet.com

Publicity and Booklet Coordinators

Graham & Judy White, Karibu, 9 Woodleighton Grove, Uttoxeter ST14 8BX, 01889 563930, cityofgold@lineone.net

Assistant County Organisers

Jane Cerone, Bridge House, Dog Lane, Bodymoor Heath, Sutton Coldfield B76 9JF, 01827 873205, janecerone@btinternet.com
Sheila Thacker, The Bowers, Bowers, Standon, Stafford ST21 6RW, 01782 791244, metbowers@gmail.com

SUFFOLK

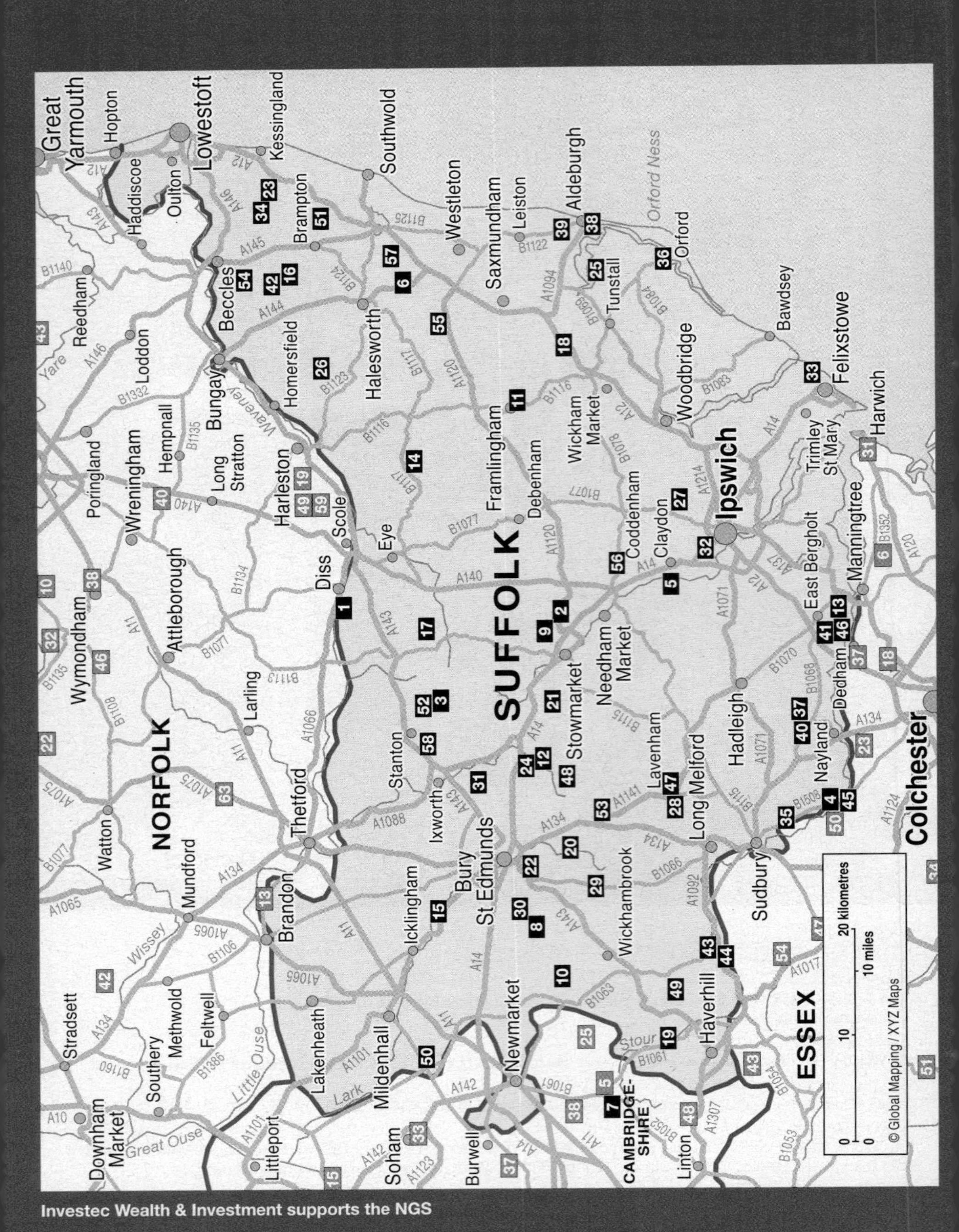

SUFFOLK
NORFOLK
ESSEX
CAMBRIDGESHIRE
Great Yarmouth
Hopton
Lowestoft
Kessingland
Southwold
Haddiscoe
Oulton
Brampton
Westleton
Saxmundham
Leiston
Aldeburgh
Orford Ness
Orford
Reedham
Beccles
Halesworth
Tunstall
Bawdsey
Felixstowe
Loddon
Bungay
Homersfield
Woodbridge
Wickham Market
Framlingham
Harwich
Trimley St Mary
Ipswich
Poringland
Hempnall
Wreningham
Long Stratton
Harleston
Scole
Eye
Debenham
Coddenham
Claydon
Manningtree
East Bergholt
Wymondham
Attleborough
Diss
Needham Market
Stowmarket
Dedham
Larling
Stanton
Hadleigh
Nayland
Colchester
Watton
Thetford
Ixworth
Lavenham
Long Melford
Mundford
Brandon
Bury St Edmunds
Wickhambrook
Sudbury
Icklingham
Haverhill
Stradsett
Methwold
Feltwell
Lakenheath
Mildenhall
Newmarket
Southery
Downham Market
Littleport
Soham
Burwell
Linton
Great Ouse
Little Ouse
Lark
Stour
Waveney
Wissey
Yare
20 kilometres
10 miles
© Global Mapping / XYZ Maps

Opening Dates

All entries subject to change. For latest information check www.ngs.org.uk

February

Sunday 16
5 Blakenham Woodland Garden

Sunday 23
16 Gable House

March

Every day except Mondays
57 **Wootens**

Saturday 29
26 The Laburnums

April

Every day except Mondays
57 **Wootens**

Sunday 6
19 Great Thurlow Hall
52 NEW Walsham-le-Willows by The Street
56 Woodwards

Sunday 13
3 The Beeches

Sunday 20
46 Rosemary

Sunday 27
13 East Bergholt Place - The Place for Plants

River walk newly restored and trout lake with extensive display of daffodils and blossom . . .

May

Every day except Mondays
57 **Wootens**

Monday 5
4 Bevills

Saturday 10
27 Larks' Hill

Sunday 11
5 Blakenham Woodland Garden
13 East Bergholt Place - The Place for Plants
50 Street Farm

Sunday 18
33 Old Felixstowe Gardens
38 Priors Hill, Aldeburgh
40 The Priory
45 Rosedale

Sunday 25
29 NEW Mill Hill House
56 Woodwards

Monday 26
47 NEW 22 Shilling Street

June

Every day except Mondays
57 **Wootens**

Sunday 1
9 Columbine Hall
16 Gable House

Festival Weekend

Saturday 7
7 Brinkley Gardens
58 Wyken Hall

Sunday 8
7 Brinkley Gardens
20 NEW The Green Cottage
28 Lavenham Hall
41 Ravenscroft
58 Wyken Hall

Tuesday 10
56 Woodwards

Saturday 14
27 Larks' Hill
35 NEW Old Rectory House

Sunday 15
32 428 Norwich Road
36 Orford Gardens

Sunday 22
19 Great Thurlow Hall
24 Hessett House
25 NEW Iken Gardens
48 Smallwood Green Gardens
51 Uggeshall Hall

Saturday 28
12 NEW Drinkstone Park
34 NEW The Old Rectory

Sunday 29
2 Bays Farm
11 28 Double Street
12 NEW Drinkstone Park
18 NEW Glemham Hall
22 NEW Hardwick Manor
34 NEW The Old Rectory
37 Polstead Mill
39 Priors Oak
55 Wood Farm

July

Every day except Mondays
57 **Wootens**

Tuesday 1
56 Woodwards

Sunday 6
6 Bramfield Hall
30 Moat House
42 Redisham Hall
52 NEW Walsham-le-Willows by The Street

Saturday 12
27 Larks' Hill
54 White House Farm

Sunday 13
14 Frythe Barn
31 NEW Mulberry House
44 Riverside House
45 Rosedale
49 Southleigh

Sunday 20
1 Batteleys Cottage
12 NEW Drinkstone Park
56 Woodwards

Sunday 27
43 NEW Richmond House

August

Every day except Mondays
57 **Wootens**

Saturday 2
53 NEW Water End Cottage

Sunday 3
15 Fullers Mill Garden
45 Rosedale
53 NEW Water End Cottage

Tuesday 5
56 Woodwards

Saturday 9
17 Gislingham Gardens

Sunday 10
8 Cobbs Hall
17 Gislingham Gardens
27 Larks' Hill

Sunday 17
21 Green Farmhouse

Sunday 24
56 Woodwards

September

Every day except Mondays
57 **Wootens**

Sunday 21
23 Henstead Exotic Garden

October

Every day except Mondays
57 **Wootens**

Sunday 12
13 East Bergholt Place - The Place for Plants

February 2015

Sunday 15
16 Gable House

You are always welcome at an NGS garden!

Gardens open to the public

- **5** Blakenham Woodland Garden
- **13** East Bergholt Place - The Place for Plants
- **15** Fullers Mill Garden
- **18** Glemham Hall
- **57** Woottens
- **58** Wyken Hall

By appointment only

- **10** Dip-on-the-Hill

Also open by Appointment

- **1** Batteleys Cottage
- **2** Bays Farm
- **8** Cobbs Hall
- **9** Columbine Hall
- **12** NEW Drinkstone Park
- **14** Frythe Barn
- **16** Gable House
- **21** Green Farmhouse
- **25** Church Farm, Iken Gardens
- **27** Larks' Hill
- **30** Moat House
- **32** 428 Norwich Road
- **33** 41 Westmorland Road, Old Felixstowe Gardens
- **37** Polstead Mill
- **38** Heron House, Priors Hill, Aldeburgh
- **39** Priors Oak
- **43** Richmond House
- **45** Rosedale
- **47** 22 Shilling Street
- **48** Smallwood Farmhouse, Smallwood Green Gardens
- **53** Water End Cottage
- **54** White House Farm
- **56** Woodwards

The Gardens

1 BATTELEYS COTTAGE

The Ling, Wortham, Diss IP22 1ST. Mr & Mrs Andy & Linda Simpson, 07949 204820, lindaruth11@googlemail.com. *3m W of Diss. Turn signed from A143 Diss/Bury Rd at Wortham. By church turn R at T junction. At top of hill turn L. Go down hill & round sharp L corner.* Home-made teas. **Adm £4, chd free. Sun 20 July (1-5.30). Visitors also welcome by appt Apr to Sept, refreshments for groups by arrangement.**

Renovated over last 4yrs and still developing. 1 acre garden with plantings of a wide range of perennials and grasses. Mature and more recently planted trees and shrubs. Ponds and stream, potager garden, fruit and vegetable garden, orchard and meadow area. Varied local habitat and mixed planting in the garden makes this a haven for birds. View over open countryside. Featured in Garden News - Garden of the Week. Wheelchair access to most parts of the garden, gravel, grass and bark paths.

2 BAYS FARM

Forward Green, Earl Stonham, Stowmarket IP14 5HU. Richard & Stephanie Challinor, 01449 711286, stephanie@baysfarmsuffolk.co.uk, www.baysfarmsuffolk.co.uk. *3½ m E of Stowmarket. J50 A14, take A1120 direction Stowupland. Proceed through Stowupland on A1120 for 1m, at sharp L bend turn R signed Broad Green. 1st house on R.* Home-made teas. **Adm £3.50, chd free. Sun 29 June (2-6.30). Visitors also welcome by appt Apr to Sept.**

2-acre plantsman's garden extensively renovated and beautifully designed. Formal gardens comprising shady borders, scented and sun-loving beds with woodland and butterfly planting. Large kitchen gardens, greenhouse, orchard and wild flower area. Herb garden as pictured in Homes and Gardens. From 2013 the rear terraces continue to develop with new planting. Home-made teas, savouries and wine. Formal gardens designed by Chelsea Gold Medal winner, Xa Tollemache of Helmingham Hall. Gravel paths.

3 THE BEECHES

Grove Road, Walsham-le-Willows IP31 3AD. Dr A J Russell. *11m E of Bury St Edmunds. A143 to Diss. Turn R to Walsham-le-Willows. 1st Xrds in village turn R. Church on L. After 100yds turn L. Beeches on L.* Tea. **Adm £3.50, chd free (share to St Marys Church, Walsham-le-Willows). Sun 13 Apr (2-5).**

150yr-old, 3-acre garden, which incl specimen trees, pond, stream, potager, memorial garden, lawns and a variety of beds. Stream area landscaped. Mediterranean bed and camellia bed. Gravel paths.

4 BEVILLS

Sudbury Road, Bures CO8 5JW. Mr & Mrs G T C Probert. *4m S of Sudbury. Just N of Bures on the Sudbury rd B1508.* Home-made teas. **Adm £4, chd free. Mon 5 May (2-6).**

A beautiful house (not open) overlooking the Stour Valley with parkland trees, hills and woodland. The gardens are formal and Italianate in style with hedges and lawns flanked by Irish yews and mature specimen trees. Terraces, borders, ponds, vistas and woodland walks. Spring bulbs and bluebell wood. Gravel paths.

5 ◆ BLAKENHAM WOODLAND GARDEN

Little Blakenham, Ipswich IP8 4LZ. Lord & Lady Blakenham, www.blakenhamwoodlandgarden.org.uk. *4m NW of Ipswich. Follow signs at Little Blakenham, 1m off B1113.* Home-made teas. **Adm £3, chd £1.50. For NGS: Suns 16 Feb; 11 May (10-5). For other opening times and information, please see garden website.**

Beautiful 6-acre woodland garden with variety of rare trees and shrubs. Chinese rocks and a landscape sculpture. Especially lovely in spring with daffodils, camellias, magnolias and bluebells followed by roses in early summer. Special snowdrop opening February 16. Partial wheelchair access.

6 BRAMFIELD HALL

Bramfield, Halesworth IP19 9HX. Mr Simon Robey. *3m S of Halesworth on A144. From Halesworth drive through Bramfield & once out of village entrance on R.*

From A12 entrance is past rd to Sibton Green. Home-made teas. **Adm £4, chd free. Sun 6 July (2-5).**
Garden consists of formal and informal areas. Within the garden there are yew topiarys, a parterre rose garden, herbaceous borders, ponds, vegetable garden and greenhouses; and has been extensively renovated in the last 10yrs by current owner. The garden is reached from a drive through parkland containing some fine trees. This garden was one of the first to open when the NGS was formed in 1927. Gravel paths and some slopes.

GROUP OPENING

7 BRINKLEY GARDENS

Newmarket CB8 0SB. *6m S of Newmarket. Enter village and follow yellow signs*. Home-made teas. **Combined adm £4, chd free. Sat 7, Sun 8 June (1.30-5.30).**

THE GROVE
High Street. Dr & Mrs Alexander Gimson.
At Carlton end of the High St, opp open field

THE OLD RECTORY
Hall Lane. Mrs Julie Coley.
Hall Lane is a turning off Brinkley High St

Two lovely gardens, one of one acre and one of two acres in the attractive village of Brinkley. The Grove 1-acre garden surrounding C19 house (not open), with mature yew trees and beech hedges. Walled garden area has established shrubs and wisteria, with new beds and planting created over the last 8yrs. This incls a dry bed with irises, terrace beds with tulips and a mixed herbaceous border along the curved wall.
The Old Rectory two acre garden started in 1973. Interesting trees planted to supplement beech, yew and chestnut already there. Mixed Herbaceous borders. Traditional potager with box hedges planted in 1993. Small woodland area still being developed.

8 COBBS HALL

Great Saxham IP29 5JN. Dick & Sue Soper, 01284 850678, soperdoc@gmail.com. *4½m W of Bury St Edmunds. A 14 exit to Westley. R at Westley Xrds. L fork at Lt.Saxham towards Chevington. 1.4m to sign on R. Mustard coloured house 300yds on L*. Home-made teas. **Adm £4, chd free (share to St Andrews Church, Gt Saxham). Sun 10 Aug (2-5.30). Visitors also welcome by appt June to Sept.**
2 acres of lawns and borders, ornamental trees, large fish/lily pond. Parterre, folly, walled kitchen garden, fernery/stumpery, grass tennis court and pretty courtyard. Featured in The Telegraph. Generally flat with a few gentle slopes and some gravel paths.

Green Farmhouse

9 COLUMBINE HALL

Gipping Road, Stowupland, Stowmarket IP14 4AT. Hew Stevenson & Leslie Geddes-Brown, 01449 612219, dovebooks@aol.com, www.columbinehall.co.uk. *1½m NE of Stowmarket. Turn N off A1120 opp Total garage across village green, then R at T-junction into Gipping Rd. Garden on L just beyond derestriction sign*. Home-made teas. **Adm £4, chd free. Sun 1 June (2-6). Visitors also welcome by appt Mar to Dec, refreshments by arrangement.**
George Carter's formal garden and herb garden surround moated medieval manor (not open). Outside the moat, vistas, stream, ponds and bog garden, Mediterranean garden, colour-themed vegetable garden, cutting garden, orchards and parkland. Gardens developed since 1994 with constant work-in-progress, incl transformed farm buildings and eyecatchers. Featured in Suffolk Magazine, English Garden, Gardens Illustrated and Daily Telegraph.

10 DIP-ON-THE-HILL

Ousden, Newmarket CB8 8TW. Dr & Mrs. Geoffrey Ingham, 01638 500329, gki1000@cam.ac.uk. *5m E of Newmarket; 7m W of Bury St Edmunds. From Newmarket: 1m from junction of B1063 & B1085. From Bury St Edmunds follow signs for Hargrave. Parking at village hall*. Home-made teas. **Adm £3.50, chd free. Visitors welcome by appt July to Sept.**
Approx one acre in a dip on a S-facing hill based on a wide range of architectural/sculptural evergreen trees, shrubs and groundcover: pines; grove of Phillyrea latifolia; 'cloud pruned' hedges; palms; large bamboo; ferns; range of kniphofia and croscosmia. Visitors may wish to make an appointment when visiting gardens nearby.

11 28 DOUBLE STREET
Framlingham, Woodbridge IP13 9BN. Mr & Mrs David Clark. *250yrds from Market Hill (main square) Framlingham opp Church. Leave square from top L into Church St. Double St is 100yds on R. Car parking in main square & near to Framlingham Castle.* Home-made teas. **Adm £2.50, chd free. Sun 29 June (12-5).**
A recently developed town garden featuring roses together with a wide range of perennials and shrubs. Conservatory, greenhouse, gazebo, summerhouse and terrace full of containers all add interest to the garden. Good views of Framlingham's roofscape. Fine shingle access drive with two ramps.

12 NEW DRINKSTONE PARK
Drinkstone, Bury St. Edmunds IP30 9ST. Ms Christine Harbutt, 01359 272513, chris@drinkstonepark.co.uk, www.drinkstonepark.co.uk. *6m from Bury St Edmunds. E on A14 J46 turn R & head for Drinkstone. W on A14 J46 take R next junction turn L and immed R to Drinkstone.* Home-made teas. **Adm £3.50, chd free. Sat 28, Sun 29 June; Sun 20 July (12-5). Visitors also welcome by appt June to Oct.**
Three acre garden with wildlife pond formal Koi pond, herbaceous borders, orchard, woodland and wildlife area, large productive vegetable plot with poly tunnel and greenhouses. Some gravel paths.

13 ◆ EAST BERGHOLT PLACE - THE PLACE FOR PLANTS
East Bergholt CO7 6UP. Mr & Mrs Rupert Eley, 01206 299224, www.placeforplants.co.uk. *2m E of A12, 7m S of Ipswich. On B1070 towards Manningtree, 2m E of A12. Situated on the edge of East Bergholt.* Home-made teas. **Adm £6, chd free. For NGS: Suns 27 Apr; 11 May (2-5); 12 Oct (1-4.30). For other opening times and information, please phone or see garden website.**
20-acre garden originally laid out at the turn of the last century by the present owner's great grandfather. Full of many fine trees and shrubs, many seldom seen in East Anglia. A fine collection of camellias, magnolias and rhododendrons, topiary, and the National Collection of deciduous Euonymus. Featured on Gardeners World with Rachel de Thame. In dry conditions there is wheelchair access to the main and central top part of the garden. It is essential to ring prior to check conditions.
NCH

Qni
The Queen's Nursing Institute
With NGS support, we make a real difference to patient care

14 FRYTHE BARN
Wilby Road, Stradbroke, Eye IP21 5JP. Don & Carol Darling, 1379388098, caroldon01@gmail.com. *11m SE of Diss, 10m N of Framlingham. From Framlingham B1118 to Stradbroke. Through Wilby past Neaves Lane on R 2nd driveway on R From Diss B1118 to Stradbroke, R church, immed L.* Home-made teas. **Adm £4, chd free. Sun 13 July (1-5). Visitors also welcome by appt Apr to Oct, coaches welcome.**
A maze of concrete and brick buildings transformed in 6 yrs into a delightfully relaxing 2 acre garden.Take a stroll via a willow tunnel, spinney with bee hives and bog garden through the orchard to a leafy arbour, surrounded by flowing grasses.View from here the large pond and stream to the left, sensitively planted borders to the right and Italian style patio in front of the renovated barn. Wild life area, large grass beds, pond, mixed borders, roses. No wheelchair access to spinney/wild flower meadow.

15 ◆ FULLERS MILL GARDEN
West Stow IP28 6HD. Perennial - The Gardeners Royal Benevolent Society, 01284 728888, www.fullersmillgarden.org.uk. *6m NW of Bury St Edmunds. Turn off A1101 Bury to Mildenhall Rd, signed West Stow Country Park, go past Country Park continue for 1/4 m, garden entrance on R. Sign at entrance.* Home-made teas. **Adm £4, chd free. For NGS: Sun 3 Aug (2-5). For other opening times and information, please phone or see garden website.**
An enchanting 7 acre garden on the banks of R Lark. A beautiful site of light, dappled woodland with a plantsman's paradise of rare and unusual shrubs, perennials and marginals planted with great natural charm. Euphorbias and lilies are a particular feature. A garden with interest in every season. In late Sept colchicums in flower incl outstanding white variety. Also yellow crocus-like Sternbergia should be in bloom. Partial wheelchair access around garden.

16 GABLE HOUSE
Halesworth Road, Redisham,, Beccles NR34 8NE. John & Brenda Foster. *5m S of Beccles. A144 S from Bungay, L at St Lawrence School, 2m to Gable House. Or A12 Blythburgh, A145 to Beccles, Brampton Xrds L to Station Rd. 3m on is Garden.* Soup lunches for snowdrop opening and teas. **Adm £3.50, chd free (share to St Peter's Church, Redisham). Sun 23 Feb (11-4); Sun 1 June (11-5); Sun 15 Feb 2015. Visitors also welcome by appt, Feb, May and June, groups max 50.**
1-acre plantsman's garden of all-year interest. Vast collection of snowdrops, cyclamen, hellebores etc for the February opening. The June open day brings colour and variety from shrub roses, perennials and interesting trees and shrubs. Greenhouses contain rare bulbs and tender plants. Vast collection of snowdrops for the February Open Day Many unusual trees and shrubs.

GROUP OPENING

17 GISLINGHAM GARDENS
Mill Street, Eye IP23 8JT. *4m W of Eye. Gislingham 2 1/2 m W of A140. 9m N of Stowmarket, 8m S of Diss. Disabled parking at Ivy Chimneys. No parking on Dunton Drive.* Home-made teas at Aughton House. **Combined adm £3.50, chd free. Sat 9, Sun 10 Aug (11-4.30).**

AUGHTON HOUSE
Anthony & Dee Ambler

IVY CHIMNEYS
Iris & Alan Stanley

2 varied gardens in a picturesque village with a number of Suffolk timbered houses. Ivy Chimneys is planted for yr round interest with ornamental trees, some topiary, exotic borders and fishpond set in an area of Japanese style. Wisteria draped pergola supports a productive vine. Also a separate ornamental vegetable garden. Aughton House lies alongside Ivy Chimneys and has ½ acre garden. Still maturing it has vivid late summer colour, a cottage garden, formal garden, gravel garden with drought resistant planting and many interesting features. Wheelchair access to the terrace at Ivy Chimneys.

18 NEW ◆ GLEMHAM HALL

Little Glemham IP13 0BT. Philip & Raewyn Hope-Cobbold, www.glemhamhall.co.uk. *3m NE of Wickham Market. Entrance (brown tourist sign) from A12.* Home-made teas. **Adm £4, chd free. For NGS: Sun 29 June (11-5). For other opening times and information, please see garden website.**
Parkland of 300 acres with ancient oak trees and beautiful C18 walled garden. Recently refurbished Edwardian style Rose Garden surrounded by mixed herbaceous borders undergoing restoration. Established and beautiful herbaceous garden including new Sculpture by John Moore and Anthony Gormley. Apple orchard with very old varieties, espaliered pear trees, yew walk and shrubbery. Partial wheelchair access.

19 GREAT THURLOW HALL

Haverhill CB9 7LF. Mr & Mrs George Vestey. *12m S of Bury St Edmunds, 4m N of Haverhill. Great Thurlow village on B1061 from Newmarket; 3½ m N of junction with A143 Haverhill/Bury St Edmunds rd.* Home-made teas. **Adm £4, chd free. Suns 6 Apr; 22 June (2-5).**
River walk newly restored and trout lake with extensive display of daffodils and blossom. Spacious lawns, shrubberies and roses. Walled kitchen garden.

20 NEW THE GREEN COTTAGE

The Green, Hawstead, Bury St. Edmunds IP29 5NN. Mr Glyn Hammond. *Bury St. Edmunds S on A134. After 1m turn R, bear L after ½ m. Then 2m to Hawstead Green, L to Bell's Lane: Green Cottage set back on N of green.* Home-made teas. **Adm £4, chd free. Sun 8 June (2-6).**
Created on a field in the early 1980s, the 3 acre garden now extends into an adjacent woodland gull, allowing the making of a water /dell garden. Numerous beautiful, varied, well stocked borders and fine trees.

21 GREEN FARMHOUSE

The Green, Shelland, Stowmarket IP14 3JE. Miss Rosemary Roe, 01449 736591. *4m NW of Stowmarket, 10m SE of Bury St Edmunds. A14 W-bound. A1308- signed Wetherden, L in Harleston, follow NGS signs. A14 E-bound take Wetherden/Haughley Park turn, then R signed Buxhall. Follow NGS signs.* Ploughman's lunch, home-made teas. **Adm £3.50, chd free. Sun 17 Aug (11-5). Visitors also welcome by appt June to Sept, adm £5 to incl refreshments.**
2 acre garden surrounding thatched cottage (not open), overlooking a private green. Established shrub/herbaceous borders with lawns and vistas, natural pond, courtyard garden and small feature gardens. A wide variety of plants. Also a developing wild flower meadow with trees and wonderful views of the Suffolk countryside. Limited wheelchair access.

22 NEW HARDWICK MANOR

off Sharp Road, Bury St. Edmunds IP33 2RD. Mrs Jenny Woodhead. *Pass West Suffolk Hospital on L, turn L into Hardwick Lane & take 1st L into Sharp Rd.* Home-made teas. **Adm £3.50, chd free. Sun 29 June (2-5).**
Classic garden containing a mixture of shrubs and herbaceous plants. A lovely pergola runs though the centre bisecting the garden which is covered in wisteria, honeysuckle and a number of other climbing plants. It is surrounded by parkland and grazing sheep and although close to Bury, it is a million miles away. There is a lovely arboretum to walk around and a good place to exercise any visiting dog.

23 HENSTEAD EXOTIC GARDEN

Church Road, Henstead, Beccles, Suffolk NR34 7LD. Andrew Brogan, www.hensteadexoticgarden.co.uk. *Equal distance between Beccles, Southwold & Lowestoft approx 5m. 1m from A12 turning after Wrentham (signed Henstead) very close to B1127.* Home-made teas. **Adm £3.50, chd free. Sun 21 Sept (11-4).**
2-acre exotic garden featuring 100 large palms, 20+ bananas and 200 bamboo plants. 2 streams, 20ft tiered walkway leading to Thai style wooden covered pavilion. Mediterranean and jungle plants around 3 large ponds with fish. Suffolk's most exotic garden. Newly extended this year. Newly installed composting toilet straight out of Lord of the Rings/Harry Potter! It is 15ft tall with framed glass windows.

Surrounded by parkland and grazing sheep and although close to Bury, it is a million miles away. . .

24 HESSETT HOUSE

Drinkstone Road, Beyton, Bury St Edmunds IP30 9AH. Mr & Mrs Richard Holt. *5m E of Bury St Edmunds. 1m up Drinkstone Rd, from Beyton on R.* Home-made teas. **Adm £3.50, chd free. Sun 22 June (2-6).**
Large country garden with S-facing lawns, looking over the ha ha to parkland planted with native mature trees and a young copse. The rose garden is set in 16 formal beds of mature old fashioned roses backed by a pergola of roses and clematis. Shrub beds border the lawns. Swimming pool and tennis court gardens with hedges of yew and viburnum and beech hedge of impressive size. A gate leads through to young arboretum and beds of hydrangea. No steps. Flat garden.

Drinkstone Park

GROUP OPENING

25 NEW IKEN GARDENS
Tunstall Road, Woodbridge IP12 2ER. *3m from Tunstall & Snape. From A12 take A1094 towards Aldeburgh. At Snape Church turn R to Snape. Past Snape Maltings turn L signed Orford. At next Xrds turn L signed Iken. After 1m Church Farm & Decoy Cottage on R.* Home-made teas at Church Farm. **Combined adm £3.50, chd free.**
Sun 22 June (12-5).

CHURCH FARM
Mrs Caroline Erskine
Visitors also welcome by appt May to Oct.
01728 687485
cerskine30@timicomail.com

NEW DECOY COTTAGE
Sir Thomas Hughes-Hallett

Two adjoining gardens in a charming Suffolk village. Decoy Cottage is a twenty acre country garden with woods orchard, lake and highland cattle on show. Church Farm is a two acre area surrounded by mature alders and pines. Many young specimen trees and shrubs planted over the last six years. Mixed planting of perennials, grasses and smaller shrubs. Wheelchair access is fine for garden but not for woods etc. No access for wheelchairs through Church Farm garden.

26 THE LABURNUMS
St. James South Elmham, Halesworth IP19 0HN. Mrs Jane Bastow, 01986 782413, jane.bastow@btinternet.com. *6m W of Halesworth, 7m E of Harleston & 6m S of Bungay. Parking at nearby village hall. For disabled parking please phone to arrange.* Light refreshments. **Adm £3.50, chd free.**
Sat 29 Mar (11-5).
1-acre garden is 20+ years old and is packed with annuals, perennials, flowering shrubs and trees and areas dedicated to wild flowers. The spring garden is awash with colour-snowdrops, aconites, hellebores, daffodils and much more. There are three ponds, a sunken garden and two glasshouses. There will be a plant stall and as the open day is the day before Mothering Sunday presents could be an option. Gravel drive. Limited access to front garden. Steps to sunken garden. Concrete path in back garden.

27 LARKS' HILL
Clopton Road, Tuddenham St Martin IP6 9BY. Mr John Lambert, 01473 785248, jrlambert@talktalk.net. *3m NE of Ipswich. From Ipswich take B1077, go through village, take the Clopton Rd.* Home-made teas. **Adm £5, chd free. Sats 10 May; 14 June; 12 July; Sun 10 Aug (1-5). Visitors also welcome by appt May to Aug, for groups of 10+.**
The gardens of 8 acres comprise of woodland, field and more formal areas, and fall away from the house to the valley floor. A hill within a garden and in Suffolk at that! Hilly garden with a modern castle keep with an interesting and beautiful site overlooking the gentle Fynn valley and the village beyond.

28 LAVENHAM HALL
Hall Road, Lavenham, Sudbury CO10 9QX. Mr & Mrs Anthony Faulkner. *Next to Lavenham's iconic church & close to High St. From church turn off the main rd down the side of church (Potland Rd). Go down hill. Car Park on R after 100 metres.*
Adm £4, chd free.
Sun 8 June (11-5.30).
5-acre garden built around the ruins of the original ecclesiastical buildings

on the site and the village's 1-acre fishpond. The garden incl deep borders of herbaceous planting with sweeping vistas and provides the perfect setting for the sculptures which Kate makes in her studio at the Hall and exhibits both nationally and internationally. 40 garden sculptures on display. There is a gallery in the grounds which displays a similar number of indoor sculptures. Note large number of gravel paths and slopes within the garden.

29 NEW MILL HILL HOUSE

Bury Road, Brockley, Bury St. Edmunds IP29 4AG. Mr & Mrs Geoffrey Baber. *On the B1066 N of Brockley Green. Just over 1m N of Brockley Green on W side of rd.* Cream teas. **Adm £4, chd free (share to St Andrew's Church, Brockley). Sun 25 May (2-5.30).**
Charming 1-acre garden set in 4 acres of pasture with long views of rolling surrounding countryside. Formal box-edged beds, roses and herbaceous borders, new sunken gravel garden created from old pond, shaded planting around faux folly, ancient mulberry tree. Gravel areas.

30 MOAT HOUSE

Little Saxham, Bury St. Edmunds IP29 5LE. Mr & Mrs Richard Mason, 01284 810941, rnm333@live.com. *2m SW of Bury St Edmunds. Leave A14 at J42 - through Westley Village, at Xrds R towards Barrow/Saxham 1.3m L (follow signs).* Home-made teas. **Adm £4, chd free. Sun 6 July (1.30-5.30). Visitors also welcome by appt May to Aug, groups max 30.**
Set in a 2 acre historic and partially moated site. This tranquil mature garden has been developed by the present owners over 20yrs. Bordered by mature trees the garden is in various sections incl a sunken garden, rose and clematis arbours, herbaceous bordered by box hedging, small arboretum. Featured in Country Homes and Interiors.

31 NEW MULBERRY HOUSE

Church Hill, Pakenham, Bury St. Edmunds IP31 2LN. Keith & Rosemary Shelbourne. *Next to St Mary's Church Pakenham. 5m NE of Bury St Edmunds A143 at Great Barton take R turn to Thurston, L to Pakenham through village R up Church Hill parking behind church.* Tea. **Adm £3.50, chd free. Sun 13 July (1.30-5.30).**
Former vicarage garden recently extended to just over 1 acre. Many interesting features. Extensive mixed borders mature trees, 2 ancient mulberries, lawns, vegetable and herb garden, terrace and small pond. A false window in the house has an original painting by Rex Whistler of a Parson and his books. The house and garden was featured in some episodes of the television series Lovejoy. The garden lays on quite a steep slope up to the Church with many steps and gravel paths.

New sunken gravel garden created from old pond, shaded planting around faux folly . . .

32 428 NORWICH ROAD

Ipswich IP1 5DU. Robert & Gloria Lawrence, 01473 743673, globoblaw@talktalk.net. *1½ m W of Ipswich town centre. On A1156 Norwich Rd garden is 200yds W of railway bridge.* Cream teas. **Adm £2.50, chd free. Sun 15 June (2-5). Visitors also welcome by appt 15 June to July.**
⅓ acre garden with sunken terrace leading up to lawn with rose beds, herbaceous border and dry stone garden. Lawn leads to bog garden, island mixed bed and on to orchard (17 fruit trees), asparagus bed, small vegetable plot with composting area and greenhouse. Strawberry Cream Teas. Joint winner and joint award Ipswich in Bloom, Gold award Back Garden.

GROUP OPENING

33 OLD FELIXSTOWE GARDENS

41,Westmorland Road, Felixstowe IP11 9TJ. Mrs Diane Elmes. *Corner of Wrens Park & Westmorland Road. Enter Felixstowe on A154. At r'about take 1st exit then turn R - into Beatrice Av. L to High Road East. Proceed to Clifflands Car Park. Follow signs.* Home-made teas. **Combined adm £4, chd free. Sun 18 May (11-5).**

33 FERRY ROAD
Peter & Monica Smith

FERRYFIELDS
206 Ferry Road. Mr & Mrs Paul Smith.
Follow signs to Felixstowe Golf Club. Ferry Rd is opp Golf Club. Ferryfields (206 Ferry Rd) is about ¼ m on L

41 WESTMORLAND ROAD
Mrs Diane Elmes.
No. 41 is on the corner of Wrens Park
Visitors also welcome by appt May to Sept.
01394 284647
dianeelmes@talktalk.net

Three very different gardens either close to the sea or the R Deben. 33 Ferry Road is a large irregular shaped garden with established trees, shrubs, herbaceous borders and vegetables. It is well established but is constantly evolving. Ferryfields has mature gardens of ⅓ -acre with lawns, borders and informal island beds with shrubs and perennials, greenhouses, pond and gazebo with views across the Deben Estuary. The owners of 41 Westmorland Road moved into their house five years ago, since when they have recovered the garden by taking down 21 leylandii trees and various other dead trees. It is now full of perennials and has interesting and eclectic features.

34 NEW THE OLD RECTORY

Hulver Road, Henstead, Beccles NR34 7LA. Mr & Mrs Andrew Kendall. *Between Beccles & Southwold on the B1127. Between Henstead & Hulver on B1127. 1m from Henstead Church towards Beccles, on L.* Home-made teas. **Adm £3.50, chd free. Sat 28, Sun 29 June (1-5).**
A garden which is at its best in June and July. Spectacular roses in a walled garden designed to give colour and atmosphere. An allee of 54 pleached limes underplanted with hornbeam. The gardens surround a late C18 classical Georgian rectory and stableyard. Herb garden, parterre and cutting garden.

D

35 NEW **OLD RECTORY HOUSE**
Kedington Hill, Little Cornard, Sudbury CO10 0PD. Mrs Jane Mann. *2½ m outside Sudbury off B1508 Bures Rd. From Bures Rd follow signs to Little Cornard Parish Church. Garden is approx ½ m up the lane on L. Parking opp.* Home-made teas. **Adm £3.50, chd free. Sat 14 June (11-5).**
Large country garden surrounded by meadows. Approximately 3 acres of garden with some large specimen trees and interesting recent tree planting. Walled ornamental vegetable garden, greenhouse, herbaceous beds and bank. Roses, cottage garden, parterre, three ponds with waterside planting and woodland walk. Some slopes and uneven ground. Loose gravel in places.

GROUP OPENING

36 **ORFORD GARDENS**
High Street, Woodbridge IP12 2NW. *8m from Woodbridge. In Orford, follow B1084 past Kings Head bear L. L into High Street follow Yellow Signs.* Home-made teas at Brundish Lodge. **Combined adm £4, chd free. Sun 15 June (2-6).**

NEW **BELL HOUSE**
Quay Street. Tim & Jane Allen.
Leaving Wayside, turn R down Burnt Lane, R into Daphne Rd. Gate & drive into Bell House on L next to No 34

BRUNDISH LODGE D
High Street. Mrs Elizabeth Spinney.
In Orford, follow main rd to L keep going along church railings. Garden 3rd on R. Do not go down to the Quay

NEW **WAYSIDE**
Burnt Lane. Geoffrey & Anne Smeed.
From Market Sq, down Quay St approx 300yds; turn L at Xrds into Daphne Rd; approx 200yds Wayside on L

Three very different gardens with varied planting situated in the picturesque village of Orford.
Bell House: a small, sheltered, cottage garden with a rill, planned to give year-round interest. approx one third newly planted following building work in 2013. No lawn so as to give maximum room for plants.
Wheelchair accessible.
Brundish Lodge: is a garden of approx one third of an acre. It was completely redesigned, reconstructed and replanted in 2005. It has beds which are a mixture of shrubs, herbaceous plants and grasses grouped around a central lawn.
Wayside: a village garden of apprpox ¼ acre, comprising a series of 'rooms' surrounding the house (not open). A mixture of shrubs and perennials, chosen to suit the light, dry soil, and to cope with the cold easterly winds.

37 **POLSTEAD MILL**
Mill Lane, Polstead, Colchester CO6 5AB. Mrs Lucinda Bartlett, 01206 265969, lucyofleisure@hotmail.com. *Between Stoke by Nayland & Polstead on the R Box. From Stoke by Nayland take rd to Polstead - Mill Lane is 1st on L & Polstead Mill is 1st house on R.* Home-made teas. **Adm £5, chd £3. Sun 29 June (2-5). Visitors also welcome by appt June.**
The garden has formal and informal areas, a wild flower meadow and a large kitchen garden. The R Box runs through the garden and there is a mill pond, which gives opportunity for damp gardening, while much of the rest of the garden is arid and is planted to minimise the need for watering.

GROUP OPENING

38 **PRIORS HILL, ALDEBURGH**
Priors Hill Road, Aldeburgh IP15 5ET. *Turn R off A1094 into Park Rd 100yds after r'about with B1122. After 400yds, turn R into Priors Hill Rd.* Tea. **Combined adm £5, chd free. Sun 18 May (2-5).**

HERON HOUSE
Mr Jonathan Hale.
Last house on Priors Hill Rd on R, at the junction where it rejoins Park Rd
Visitors also welcome by appt Apr to Oct.
01728 452200
jonathanrhhale@aol.com

LONGCROFT
Dr & Mrs Charles Twort

STANNY
Kimberley & Angus Robertson

WESTCROFT
Mr & Mrs John Thompson

Four gardens situated in Priors Hill Road with enviable views over the River Alde and the sea. All gardens are on a slope which gives the opportunity for terracing and associated planting. Heron House consists of two acres with views over coastline, river and marshes. Unusual trees, herbaceous beds, shrubs and ponds with waterfall in large rock garden, stream and bog garden. Interesting attempts to grow half hardy plants in the coastal micro-climate. Longcroft has a terrace going down to a lawn with a herbaceous border and then on to an orchard and vegetable garden. Many roses, clematis and a heather bed. Stanny is terraced over three levels. There are many established camellias, hydrangea, grasses and mature trees, which include Holm Oaks, Scots Pine, Japanese Maples and Strawberry Trees. There is a waterfall, a large natural pond and a wild flower meadow along with some exotic planting. Westcroft is a town garden with views of the river and sea. Please note the garden has a pond and children must be supervised. Lovely views. Wheelchair access with difficulty in some instances.

The Laburnums

39 PRIORS OAK

Leiston Road, Aldeburgh IP15 5QE. Mrs Trudie Willis, 01728 452580, trudie.willis@dinkum.free-online.co.uk. *1m N of Aldeburgh on B1122. Garden on L opp RSPB Reserve.* Home-made teas. **Adm £4, chd free. Sun 29 June (2-6). Visitors also welcome by appt Mar to Sept.**

10-acre wildlife and butterfly garden. Ornamental salad and vegetable gardens with companion planting. Herbaceous borders, ferns and Mediterranean plants. Pond and wild flower acid grassland with a small wood. Skirting the wood are a 100 buddleia in around 30 varieties forming a perfumed tunnel. Very tranquil and fragrant garden with grass paths and yearly interest. Rich in animal and bird life. Specialist butterfly garden, as seen in SAGA magazine, renovated railway carriages, tortoise breeding, wildlife walks. Featured in Horticulture USA and SAGA magazine. Coaches or private visits by appointment only.

40 THE PRIORY

Stoke by Nayland, Colchester CO6 4RL. Mr & Mrs H F A Engleheart. *5m SW of Hadleigh. Entrance on B1068 to Sudbury (NW of Stoke by Nayland).* Home-made teas. **Adm £4, chd free. Sun 18 May (2-5).**

Interesting 9-acre garden with fine views over Constable countryside; lawns sloping down to small lakes and water garden; fine trees, rhododendrons and azaleas; walled garden; mixed borders and ornamental greenhouse. Wide variety of plants. Access over most of garden. Some steps.

41 RAVENSCROFT

Askins Road, East Bergholt, Colchester CO7 6SN. Mr D Milner. *1m E of A12,7m S of Ipswich. From A12 B1070 1st R (Hadleigh Rd) then 2nd L Askins Rd (no parking) 2nd R From Manningtree follow B1070 thro' village to Hadleigh Rd (last L before A12).* Tea. **Adm £3.50, chd free. Sun 8 June (11-5).**

Garden Designer and Plantaholic's very small walled garden. It is filled to capacity with many rare and unusual shrubs, trees and perennials. Interesting features incl a folly, large pond, an almost secret box-edged parterre, and studios with paintings for sale.

42 REDISHAM HALL

nr Beccles NR34 8LZ. The Palgrave Brown Family. *5m S of Beccles. From A145, turn W on to Ringsfield-Bungay rd. Beccles, Halesworth or Bungay, all within 5m.* Home-made teas. **Adm £4, chd free. Sun 6 July (2-6).**

C18 Georgian house (not open). 5-acre garden set in 400 acres parkland and woods. Incl 2-acre walled kitchen garden (in full production) with peach house, vinery and glasshouses. Lawns, herbaceous borders, shrubberies, ponds and mature trees. The garden has lots of gravel paths and there are lawned slopes. Wheelchair access is possible with assistance. Parking is on uneven parkland.

Water End Cottage

43 NEW RICHMOND HOUSE
20 Nethergate Street, Clare CO10 8NP. Dr Catherine Horwood Barwise, 07961 838598, catherine@richmondhouse-clare.com. *100 metres from centre of Clare. On L of Nethergate St (A1092) from direction of Stoke-by-Clare. Limited on-street parking. Please use Country Park car park off Well Lane.* Home-made teas. **Adm £4, chd free. Sun 27 July (2-5). Visitors also welcome by appt May to Aug.**
Romantic walled garden with emphasis on scented plants. Pleached-tree-framed steps lead to recently planted 'new perennial' parterre; Mediterranean terrace by swimming pool; informal wooded area with species roses and spring bulbs; vegetable/cutting garden, chickens, trained fruit trees, greenhouse; tender perennials; hellebore/hosta/fern path. Over 40 small-flowered clematis and 50+ roses.

44 RIVERSIDE HOUSE
Stoke Road, Clare, Sudbury CO10 8NS. Mr & Mrs A C W Bone, www.clare.bulbs.co.uk/garden. *On Haverhill side of Clare on A1092, 500yds from town centre.* **Adm £3.50, chd free. Sun 13 July (12-5).**
Peaceful walled country garden leading down to the R Stour. Bridge leads to Essex bank and glade. Fine lawns, trees, shrubs and mixed herbaceous beds. Annuals are a speciality. Some gravel paths.

45 ROSEDALE
40 Colchester Road, Bures CO8 5AE. Mr & Mrs Colin Lorking, 01787 227619, rosedale40@btinternet.com. *6m SE of Sudbury. From Colchester take B1508. After 10m garden on L as you enter the village, from Sudbury B1508 after 5m garden on R.* Home-made teas. **Adm £3, chd free. Suns 18 May; 13 July; 3 Aug (12-5). Visitors also welcome by appt Apr to Sept, preferably evenings and weekends.**
Approx 1/3 -acre plantsman's garden developed over the last 21 years, containing many unusual plants, herbaceous borders and pond. For the May opening see a super collection of peonies and for the August opening a stunning collection of approx 60 Agapanthus in full flower.

46 ROSEMARY
Rectory Hill, East Bergholt CO7 6TH. Mrs N E M Finch, 01206 298241, www.rosemarybnb.co.uk. *9m NE of Colchester. From A12 take B1070 to East Bergholt, first R Hadleigh Rd. At junction with village St turn R, past Red Lion PH, PO & Church. Garden 100 yards on L.* Home-made teas. **Adm £3.50, chd free. Sun 20 Apr (2-5.30).**
This romantic garden, which appeals particularly to artists, has been developed over 35yrs. Planted to reveal paths and vistas. Many flowering trees and shrubs, much admired 'tapestry' bed with mixed hellebores, bulbs and appropriate ground cover. 2 bog beds, and unusual trees. Planted for all seasons. Over 100 old-fashioned roses.

47 NEW 22 SHILLING STREET
Lavenham, Sudbury CO10 9RH. Dr Sue Hamilton Blyth, suehamb@googlemail.com. *In the heart of historic Lavenham. Shilling Street is the 3rd turning on L off Water St, which runs down the side of the famous Swan Hotel.* Home-made teas. **Adm £3.50, chd free. Mon 26 May (11-5). Visitors also welcome by appt May to July, for groups of 10+.**
A hidden garden in the centre of the medieval village of Lavenham, eclectically planted mixing a cottage garden style with grasses and interesting small trees. The garden has many different 'rooms', with several changes of level and perspective.

GROUP OPENING

48 SMALLWOOD GREEN GARDENS
Bradfield St George, nr Bury St Edmunds IP30 0AJ. *1/2 m from Bradfield Woods. On main rd between Hessett & Felsham. From A14 take Beyton turn off, S through Hessett. 2m from Hessett on Felsham rd. From A134 turn at Little Whelnetham, through Bradfield St George, past Bradfield Woods, turn L towards Hessett.* Home-made teas at Smallwood House (Martins Nursery). **Combined adm £4.50, chd free. Sun 22 June (11-5).**

SMALLWOOD FARMHOUSE
Widget & Tim Finn.
On main rd between Hessett & Felsham
Visitors also welcome by appt May to July.
01449 736358
widget.finn@gmail.com

SMALLWOOD HOUSE
Richard & Susan Martin.
Follow the brown signs to Bradfield Woods in Bradfield St George
www.martinsnurseries.co.uk

Two adjacent gardens with different styles of herbaceous gardening in the hamlet of Smallwood Green. Smallwood House has a relatively new garden full of herbaceous perennials with two distinctive styles of gardening on view. Smallwood Farmhouse, a C16 farmhouse is a backdrop to a romantic 3-acre garden with old roses, clematis, honeysuckle and an ancient meadow contrasting with a contemporary gravel garden.

49 SOUTHLEIGH
Valley Wash, Hundon CO10 8EJ. Paula Halson & Mike Laycock, www.southleighhouse.co.uk. *3 1/2 m NW of Clare. 5m NE of Haverhill, 10m S of Bury St Edmunds. A143 out of Haverhill, turn R at Grey's Lane to Hundon or take B1063 from Clare to Chilton St/Hundon.* Home-made teas. **Adm £3.50, chd free. Sun 13 July (11-4).**
Lovely 1/2 -acre cottage garden surrounding thatched cottage (not open) dating from 1640, and situated on the outskirts of the village. Garden restored in recent years to include both cottage-style planting and more formal borders. Music and Art display. Featured in 'Let's Talk' magazine by Thordis Fridriksson of BBC Radio Norfolk. Ramp up to main lawn.

50 STREET FARM
North Street, Freckenham IP28 8HY. David & Clodagh Dugdale. *3m W of Mildenhall. From Newmarket, follow signs to Snailwell, & Chippenham & then onto Freckenham.* Home-made teas. **Adm £4, chd free. Sun 11 May (11-5).**
Approx 1 acre of landscaped garden, with several mature trees. The garden incl a water cascade, pond with island and a number of bridges. Formal box garden, rose pergola, herbaceous borders and hornbeam walk. Gravel paths with steps and slopes.

Freeborn Memorial garden was designed,created and given to the village by Ray Freeborn. It's well maintained,colourful and teas will be served here . . .

51 UGGESHALL HALL
Uggeshall, Beccles NR34 8BG. Stevie & Bob Nicholson. *6m W of Southwold, 6.8m S of Beccles. A12 from S, turn L at Wangford bypass to Uggeshall, take 1st R then R again, garden 250 metres on L.* Home-made teas. **Adm £4, chd free. Sun 22 June (1-5).**
2 acre, relaxed style, country garden of contrasting areas, curved paths and circular lawn lead to a gravel garden at the front of the house, to the side a large pond with walkways and platform, walled garden with beds and trees, an orchard, avenue of lime trees, vegetable garden and formal area with box hedging and pergola covered in old fashioned roses.

GROUP OPENING

52 NEW WALSHAM-LE-WILLOWS BY THE STREET
The Street, Walsham-Le-Willows, Bury St. Edmunds IP31 3AA. *11m E of Bury St. Edmunds. A143 to Diss r'about, R to Walsham-le-Willows. 3 1/2 m into village.Yellow signs in The Street. Please park in the village hall car park.* Tea and cakes in the Memorial Hall and garden. **Combined adm £4, chd free. Suns 6 Apr; 6 July (1-6).**

BRIDGE HOUSE
David & Ann Daniels.
Open 6 July only. 250yds E of St Mary's church on The Street on R & opp congregational church

NEW FREEBORN MEMORIAL GARDEN
Joan Freeborn

MALTINGS HOUSE
Mrs P D Blyth

THE OLD BAKERY
Mr & Mrs R Barber.
200yds E of St Mary's church on The Street on R

NEW PRIOR'S CLOSE
Mr & Mrs Paul & Sue Leake

NEW WILLOW COTTAGE
Kevin Boardley

These are 6 quite different gardens.The walled garden at Willow Cottage is immaculate with imaginative hard landscaping and features roses, clematis, peonies, lavender and even a tiny chamomile lawn. The other walled garden is Priors Close recently planted with beds of shrubs and perennials with ornamental and fruit trees and a small formal pond. The one acre garden at Bridge House was the site of the village blacksmith and has been divided into manageable areas by the use of hedges, pathways and mature trees incl a mulberry. The Old Bakery has a long winding garden with a semi wild area with primroses and also features interesting decorative ironwork. Malting House has a large established garden with many interesting features incl a walled garden with well stocked borders. Freeborn Memorial garden was designed,created and given to the village by Ray Freeborn. It's well maintained,colourful and teas will be served here.

53 NEW WATER END COTTAGE

Cross Green, Cockfield, Bury St. Edmunds IP30 0LG. Terence Heath-Richardson, 01284 828927, whitewatch@aol.com. *On A1141, just off A134. From Bury St Edmunds on A134 Lavenham Rd, take L turn on A1141 after 300yds enter Cockfield, parking for garden 500yds on R.* Home-made teas. **Adm £4, chd free. Sat 2, Sun 3 Aug (12-6). Visitors also welcome by appt May to Aug parking. Normally available for a minibus or 5 cars.**

Water End Cottage offers various rooms set within a 2 acre garden. The owners have planted over 500 trees ranging from various types of acers, birches, willows and magnolias to Metasequoia. Formal rose gardens offer interest along with lavender borders, a regular lawn area adds some formality and there are hidden curiosities in and around the grounds with a mixture of plants you would not expect. An individually designed set of gardens in a rural setting. Step free access is available to over 90% of the gardens.

54 WHITE HOUSE FARM

Ringsfield, Beccles NR34 8JU. James & Jan Barlow, (gardener) 07780 901233, coppertops707@aol.com. *2m SW of Beccles. From Beccles take B1062 to Bungay, after 1¼ turn L signed Ringsfield. Continue for approx 1m. Parking opp church. Garden 300yds on L.* Home-made teas, we provide cakes and savoury flans. **Adm £3.50, chd free. Sat 12 July (10.30-5). Visitors also welcome by appt Tuesday - Friday, daytime or evening, not w/ends.**

Tranquil park-type garden approx 30 acres, bordered by farmland and with fine views. Comprising formal areas, copses, natural pond, ornamental pond, woodland walk, vegetable garden and orchard. Picnickers welcome. NB The ponds and beck are unfenced. Wheelchair access limited to the areas around the house.

55 WOOD FARM

Halesworth Road, Sibton, Saxmundham IP17 2JL. Andrew & Amelia Singleton. *4m S of Halesworth. Turn off A12 at Yoxford onto A1120. Turn R after Sibton Nursery towards Halesworth. Take the 2nd drive on R after the White Horse PH.* Home-made teas. **Adm £4, chd free. Sun 29 June (2-6).**

Country garden surrounding old farmhouse, divided into colour themed areas, incl white garden, hot courtyard and blue and yellow border. Large (unfenced) ponds, vegetable garden and mown walks. New for 2014, 'wild' white flowering shrub area. Garden designer owner. Featured in The English Garden. Some gravel paths which are not suitable for wheelchairs but which can be easily avoided by using alternative routes.

Curiosities in and around the grounds with a mixture of plants you would not expect . . .

56 WOODWARDS

Blacksmiths Lane, Coddenham, Ipswich IP6 9TX. Marion & Richard Kenward, 01449 760639, richardwoodwards@btinternet.com. *7m N of Ipswich. From A14 turn onto A140, after ¼ m take B1078 towards Wickham Market, Coddenham is on route. Ample parking for coaches.* Home-made teas. **Adm £2.50, chd free. Suns, Tues 6 Apr; 25 May; 10 June; 1, 20 July; 5, 24 Aug (10.30-5.30). Visitors also welcome by appt Mar to Sept groups 2-100+.**

Award winning S-facing gently sloping garden of 1½ acres, overlooking the rolling Suffolk countryside. Designed and maintained by owners for yr-round colour and interest, lots of island beds, well stocked with 1000s of bulbs, shrubs and perennials, vegetable plot, numerous hanging baskets for spring and summer. Well manicured lawns, with large mature trees. More than 25000 bulbs have been planted over the last 3yrs, for our spring display. Featured in W I Suffolk east magazine and on Radio suffolk.

57 ◆ WOOTTENS

Blackheath Road, Wenhaston IP19 9HD. Mrs E Loftus, 01502 478258, info@woottensplants.co.uk, www.woottensplants.co.uk. *18m S of Lowestoft. On A12 & B1123, follow signs to Wenhaston.* **Adm by donation. For NGS: Every Tue, Wed, Thur, Fri, Sat & Sun 1 Mar to 31 Oct (9.30-5). For other opening times and information, please phone or see garden website.**

Woottens Display Garden was redesigned in 2003 and consists of 27 raised display areas overflowing with hardy perennials to admire and inspire. The garden is inhabited with many rare and unusual cultivars and some of our traditional favourites. Spring Fair 4th May. Displays of Auriculas, Irises, Pelargoniums, Hemerocallis through the year. Regular art exhibitions. See website for dates.

58 ◆ WYKEN HALL

Stanton IP31 2DW. Sir Kenneth & Lady Carlisle, 01359 250287, www.wykenvineyards.co.uk. *9m NE of Bury St Edmunds. Along A143. Follow signs to Wyken Vineyards on A143 between Ixworth & Stanton.* Tea. **Adm £3.50, chd free. For NGS: Sat 7, Sun 8 June (2-6). For other opening times and information, please phone or see garden website.**

4-acre garden much developed recently; knot and herb garden; old-fashioned rose garden, wild garden, nuttery, pond, gazebo and maze; herbaceous borders and old orchard. Woodland walk, vineyard. Restaurant and shop.

28 Double Street

© Michael Warren

Suffolk County Volunteers

County Organiser

Jenny Reeve, 6a Church Walk, Mildenhall IP28 7ED, 01638 715289, j.reeve05@tiscali.co.uk

County Treasurer

David Reeve, 6a Church Walk, Mildenhall, Bury St. Edmunds IP28 7ED, 01638 715289, j.reeve05@tiscali.co.uk

Publicity & Booklet Coordinator

Catherine Horwood Barwise, Richmond House, 20 Nethergate Street, Clare, Sudbury CO10 8NP, 01787 279315, catherine@richmondhouse-clare.com

Assistant County Organisers:

Gilly Beddard, The Old School, School Road, Sudbourne IP12 2BE, 01394 450468, gbedd@btinternet.com
Frances Boscawen, Moat Farm, Dennington, Woodbridge IP13 8BZ, 01728 638768, francesboscawen@gmail.com
Yvonne Leonard, Crossbills, Field Road, Mildenhall IP28 7AL, 01638 712742, yj.leonard@btinternet.com
Barbara Segall, Primrose Cottage, Edgworth Road, Sudbury CO10 2TG, 01787 312046 barbara@bsegall.com
Adrian Simpson-James, Barracks Cottage, Bacons Green Road, Westhall, Halesworth IP19 8RA, 01502 575730, sjs@megenna.freeserve.co.uk
Dick Soper, Cobbs Hall, Cobbs Hall Lane, Great Saxham, Bury St Edmunds, IP29 5JN, 01284 850678, soperdoc@gmail.com

SURREY

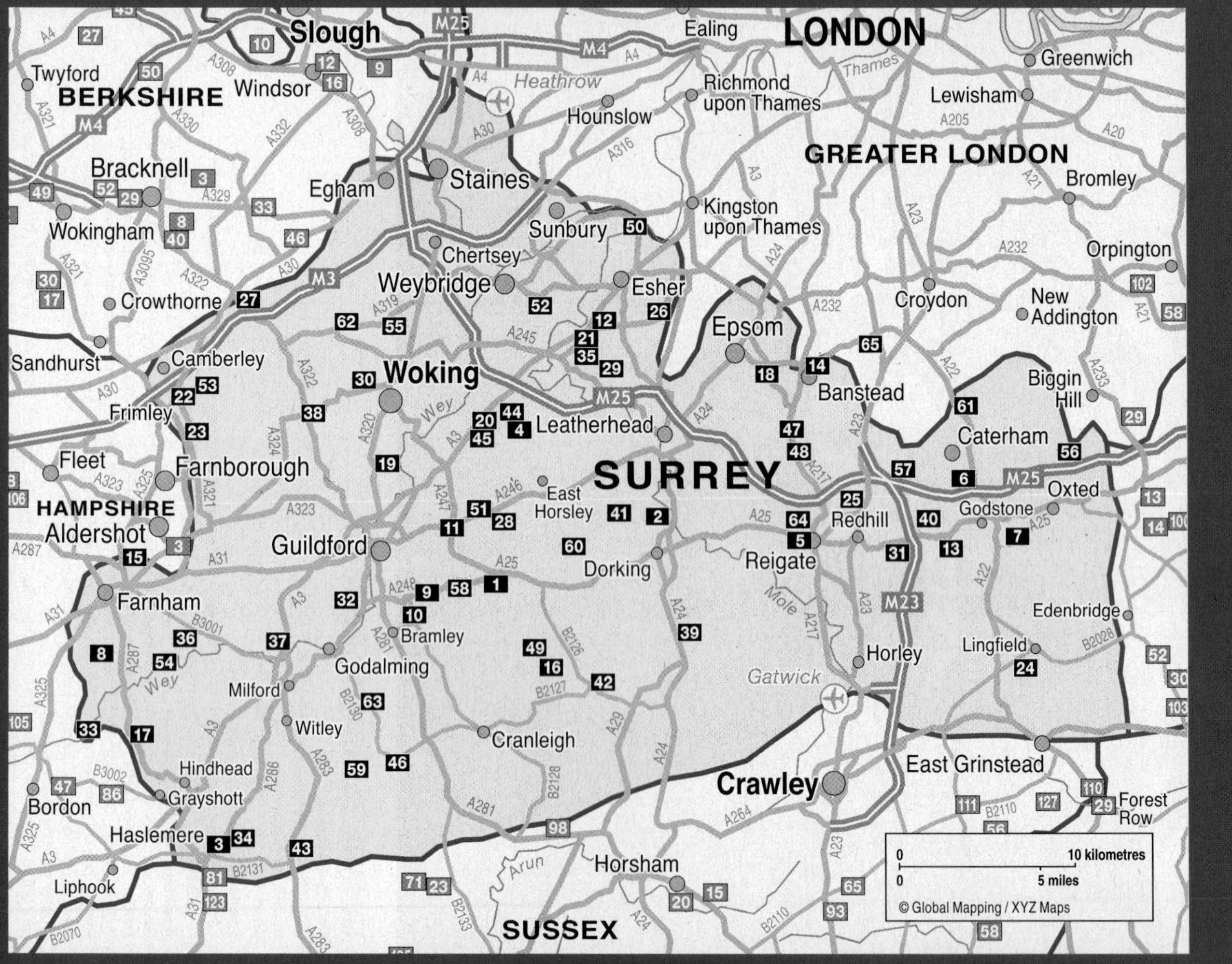

LONDON
GREATER LONDON
SURREY
BERKSHIRE
HAMPSHIRE
SUSSEX
Slough
Ealing
Greenwich
Twyford
Windsor
Heathrow
Richmond upon Thames
Lewisham
Hounslow
Bracknell
Egham
Staines
Bromley
Wokingham
Sunbury
Kingston upon Thames
Chertsey
Orpington
Weybridge
Esher
Crowthorne
Croydon
New Addington
Epsom
Sandhurst
Camberley
Woking
Banstead
Biggin Hill
Frimley
Leatherhead
Caterham
Fleet
Farnborough
Oxted
East Horsley
Godstone
Aldershot
Redhill
Guildford
Reigate
Dorking
Farnham
Edenbridge
Bramley
Lingfield
Godalming
Horley
Milford
Gatwick
Witley
Cranleigh
Hindhead
East Grinstead
Crawley
Bordon
Grayshott
Forest Row
Haslemere
Horsham
Liphook
Thames
Wey
Mole
Arun
M25
M4
M3
M23
A3
A23
A24
A25
A22
0
10 kilometres
0
5 miles
© Global Mapping / XYZ Maps

Opening Dates

All entries subject to change. For latest information check www.ngs.org.uk

February

Sunday 16
25 Gatton Park

March

Sunday 16
1 Albury Park

Sunday 23
11 Clandon Park

Saturday 29
59 Vann

Sunday 30
59 Vann

Monday 31
59 Vann

April

Tuesday 1
59 Vann

Wednesday 2
59 Vann

Thursday 3
59 Vann

Friday 4
59 Vann

Sunday 6
6 The Chalet

Sunday 13
6 The Chalet
16 Coverwood Lakes
63 Winkworth Arboretum

Sunday 20
5 Caxton House

Monday 21
16 Coverwood Lakes

Saturday 26
20 Dunsborough Park

Sunday 27
47 41 Shelvers Way

May

7 **Chauffeur's Flat (Open Daily Monday 19 to Sunday 25)**
59 **Vann (Open Daily Monday 5 to Sunday 11)**

Sunday 4
8 Chestnut Cottage
17 Crosswater Farm

Monday 5
16 Coverwood Lakes
17 Crosswater Farm
60 Walton Poor House

Saturday 10
27 Hall Grove School
62 Westways Farm

Sunday 11
12 Claremont Landscape Garden
16 Coverwood Lakes
62 Westways Farm

Saturday 17
15 56 Copse Avenue
53 NEW 26 The Fairway
56 Titsey Place Gardens

Sunday 18
9 Chilworth Manor
15 56 Copse Avenue
16 Coverwood Lakes
28 Hatchlands Park

Friday 23
43 Ramster

Sunday 25
8 Chestnut Cottage
16 Coverwood Lakes
34 The Manor House
39 The Old Croft
61 57 Westhall Road

Monday 26
39 The Old Croft
61 57 Westhall Road

Saturday 31
20 Dunsborough Park
53 NEW 26 The Fairway

June

7 **Chauffeur's Flat (Open Daily Monday 23 to Sunday 29)**
59 **Vann (Open Daily Sunday 8 to Saturday 14)**

Sunday 1
14 NEW 29 Commonfield Road
18 Culverkeys
44 Rose Cottage

Monday 2
14 NEW 29 Commonfield Road

Thursday 5
48 NEW Shieling (Evening)

Festival Weekend

Saturday 7
26 21 Glenavon Close

Sunday 8
21 Fairmile Lea
32 Loseley Park
35 Moleshill House

Saturday 14
24 NEW The Garth Pleasure Grounds
31 Little Priory (Evening)
45 7 Rose Lane
52 NEW Sunrise of Weybridge
56 Titsey Place Gardens

Sunday 15
4 Bridge End Cottage
23 Frimley Green Gardens
24 NEW The Garth Pleasure Grounds
26 21 Glenavon Close
31 Little Priory
48 NEW Shieling
60 Walton Poor House

Wednesday 18
23 Frimley Green Gardens

Friday 20
2 Ashleigh Grange (Evening)

Saturday 21
33 NEW Manor House
36 NEW Monksfield
54 Tilford Cottage

Sunday 22
2 Ashleigh Grange
10 Chinthurst Lodge
30 NEW Horsell Group Gardens
33 NEW Manor House
36 NEW Monksfield
37 Norney Wood
46 The Round House
54 Tilford Cottage
57 Tollsworth Manor

Wednesday 25
2 Ashleigh Grange
10 Chinthurst Lodge
46 The Round House

Friday 27
54 Tilford Cottage

Saturday 28
3 Bardsey
50 NEW Sterling House
54 Tilford Cottage

Sunday 29
3 Bardsey
14 NEW 29 Commonfield Road
40 The Old Rectory
50 NEW Sterling House
54 Tilford Cottage

Monday 30
14 NEW 29 Commonfield Road

Wander through fragrant herb and rose parterres with lavender and box . . .

July

Saturday 5
64 Woodbury Cottage

Sunday 6
42 Pratsham Grange
64 Woodbury Cottage

Saturday 12
56 Titsey Place Gardens

Sunday 13
18 Culverkeys
22 16 Farm Road
51 Stuart Cottage

Sunday 20
21 Fairmile Lea
35 Moleshill House
38 19 Oak Tree Road
47 41 Shelvers Way

Sunday 27
29 Heathside
41 Polesden Lacey
65 48 Woodmansterne Lane

August

Saturday 2
3 Bardsey

Sunday 3
3 Bardsey

Saturday 16
39 The Old Croft
56 Titsey Place Gardens

Sunday 17
39 The Old Croft

Sunday 24
42 Pratsham Grange

Wednesday 27
23 Frimley Green Gardens

Sunday 31
51 Stuart Cottage

September

Monday 1
14 NEW 29 Commonfield Road

Tuesday 2
14 NEW 29 Commonfield Road

Saturday 6
13 NEW Coldharbour House
64 Woodbury Cottage

Sunday 7
13 NEW Coldharbour House
64 Woodbury Cottage

Wednesday 10
64 Woodbury Cottage

Saturday 13
20 Dunsborough Park

October

Sunday 5
1 Albury Park
63 Winkworth Arboretum

Saturday 11
60 Walton Poor House

Sunday 12
12 Claremont Landscape Garden
60 Walton Poor House

Sunday 19
16 Coverwood Lakes

February 2015

Sunday 15
25 Gatton Park

Gardens open to the public

11 Clandon Park
12 Claremont Landscape Garden
17 Crosswater Farm
25 Gatton Park
28 Hatchlands Park
32 Loseley Park
41 Polesden Lacey
43 Ramster
56 Titsey Place Gardens
59 Vann
63 Winkworth Arboretum

By appointment only

19 Drybridge House
49 Spurfold
58 Vale End

Also open by appointment

2 Ashleigh Grange
3 Bardsey
5 Caxton House
10 Chinthurst Lodge
14 29 Commonfield Road
15 56 Copse Avenue
16 Coverwood Lakes
18 Culverkeys
24 The Garth Pleasure Grounds
26 21 Glenavon Close
29 Heathside
35 Moleshill House
36 Monksfield
40 The Old Rectory
42 Pratsham Grange
46 The Round House
47 41 Shelvers Way
48 Shieling
51 Stuart Cottage
54 Tilford Cottage
60 Walton Poor House
62 Westways Farm
64 Woodbury Cottage

A lovely place to wander . . .

The Gardens

1 ALBURY PARK

Albury GU5 9BH. Trustees of Albury Estate. *5m SE of Guildford. From A25 take A248 towards Albury for ¼ m, then up New Rd, entrance to Albury Park immed on L.* Home-made teas. **Adm £4, chd free. Sun 16 Mar, Sun 5 Oct (2-5).**
14-acre pleasure grounds laid out in 1670s by John Evelyn for Henry Howard, later 6th Duke of Norfolk. ¼ m terraces, fine collection of trees, lake and river. Gravel path and slight slope.

2 ASHLEIGH GRANGE

Off Chapel Lane, Westhumble RH5 6AY. Clive & Angela Gilchrist, 01306 884613, ar.gilchrist@btinternet.com. *2m N of Dorking. From A24 at Boxhill/Burford Bridge follow signs to Westhumble. Through village & L up drive by ruined chapel (1m from A24).* Home-made teas. **Adm £4, chd free (share to Barnardo's). Evening Opening £5.50, chd free, wine, Fri 20 June (6-8); Sun 22, Wed 25 June (2-5.30). Visitors also welcome by appt May to July.**
Plant lover's chalk garden on 3½ -acre sloping site in charming rural setting with delightful views. Many areas of interest incl rockery and water feature, raised ericaceous bed, prairie-style bank, foliage plants, woodland walk, fernery and folly. Large mixed herbaceous and shrub borders planted for dry alkaline soil and widespread interest.

3 BARDSEY

11 Derby Road, Haslemere GU27 1BS. Maggie & David Boyd, 01428 652283, maggie.boyd@live.co.uk, www.bardseygarden.co.uk. *¼ m N of Haslemere station. Turn off B2131 (which links A287 to A286 through town) 400yds W of station into Weydown Rd, 3rd R into Derby Rd, garden 400yds on R.* Home-made teas. **Adm £4.50, chd free. Sat 28, Sun 29 June, Sat 2, Sun 3 Aug (11-5). Visitors also welcome by appt June to July for groups 10+.**
Relax in this 2-acre garden in the heart of Haslemere. Wander through fragrant herb and rose parterres bordered by lavender and box. Enjoy the herbaceous borders, raised

vegetable beds and fruit garden. In the lower garden watch ducks and dragonflies in the natural ponds and the reflection of a tree carving. Classic MGs on view. First third of garden level, other two thirds sloping.

4 BRIDGE END COTTAGE

Ockham Lane, Ockham GU23 6NR. Clare & Peter Bevan. *Nr RHS Gardens, Wisley. At Wisley r'about turn L onto B2039 to Ockham/Horsley. After 1/2 m turn L into Ockham Lane. House 1/2 m on R. From Cobham go to Blackswan Xrds.* Home-made teas. **Adm £3.50, chd free. Sun 15 June (10.30-5).**

A 2-acre country garden with different areas of interest, incl perennial borders, mature trees, pond and streams, small herb parterre, fruit trees, soft fruit cage and a vegetable patch. In an adjacent 2-acre field, perennial wild flower seed was sown in May 2013 which started flowering in July. Large perennial wild flower meadow. Limited wheelchair access.

5 CAXTON HOUSE

67 West Street, Reigate RH2 9DA. Bob Bushby, 01737 243158, Bob.bushby@sky.com. *On A25 towards Dorking, approx 1/4 m W of Reigate on L. Parking on rd.* Cream teas. **Adm £4, chd free. Sun 20 Apr (2-5). Visitors also welcome by appt Apr to Sept for groups of 10+.**

Lovely large spring garden with wildlife wood, 2 well-stocked ponds, large collection of hellebores and spring flowers. Pots planted with colourful displays. Interesting plants in conservatory. Small Gothic folly built by owner. Herbaceous borders with grasses, perennials, spring bulbs and parterre. New bed with wild daffodils and wild flower meadow. Antique dog cart completes the picture.

6 THE CHALET

Tupwood Lane, Caterham CR3 6ET. Miss Lesley Manning & Mr David Gold. *1/2 m N of M25 J6. Exit J6 off M25 onto A22 to N. After 1/2 m take sharp 1st L, or follow signs from Caterham. Ample free parking. Disabled access via top gate.* Home-made teas. **Adm £5, chd free (share to St Catherine's Hospice). Sun 6, Sun 13 Apr (11-4.30).**

55 acres. Carpets of tens of thousands of daffodils; lakes, ornamental ponds, koi pond and waterfall. Ancient woodlands, grasslands and formal garden. Large planted terraces. Beautiful Victorian mansion (not open). Woodland and garden trail. On view, a limited edition 'Blue Train' Bentley, Silver Phantom Rolls Royce and various vintage and classic cars. Partial wheelchair access, some steep slopes. 3 large unfenced ponds.

7 CHAUFFEUR'S FLAT

Tandridge Lane, Tandridge RH8 9NJ. Mr & Mrs Richins. *2m E of Godstone. 1m W of Oxted. Turn off A25 for Tandridge. Take drive on L past church. Follow arrows to circular courtyard.* Home-made teas (Sat and Sun only). **Adm £4, chd free (share to Sutton & Croydon MS Therapy Centre). Mon 19 May to Sun 25 May incl (10-5); Mon 23 June to Sun 29 June incl (10-5).**

Enter a 1-acre tapestry of magical secret gardens with magnificent views. Touching the senses, all sure-footed visitors may explore the many surprises on this constantly evolving exuberant escape from reality. Imaginative use of recycled materials creates an inspired variety of ideas, while wild and specimen plants reveal an ecological haven.

8 CHESTNUT COTTAGE

15 Jubilee Lane, Boundstone, Farnham GU10 4SZ. Mr & Mrs David Wingent. *2 1/2 m SW of Farnham. At A31 r'about take A325 - Petersfield, 1/2 m bear L. At r'about into School Hill, 1/2 m over staggered X'rds into Sandrock Hill Rd, 4th turn R after PH.* Home-made teas. **Adm £3.50, chd free. Sun 4, Sun 25 May (2-5.30).**

1/2 -acre garden created by owners on different levels. Rhododendrons, azaleas, acers and conifers. Long pergola with wisteria and roses, attractive gazebo copied from the original at NT Hunting Lodge in Odiham. Peaceful setting. Plant expert John Negus will be in attendance.

9 CHILWORTH MANOR

Halfpenny Lane, Chilworth, Guildford GU4 8NN. Mia & Graham Wrigley. *3 1/2 m SE of Guildford. From centre of Chilworth village turn into Blacksmith Lane. 1st drive on R on Halfpenny Lane.* Home-made teas. **Adm £5, chd free. Sun 18 May (11-5).**

Extensive grounds of lawns and mature trees around C17/C18 manor on C11 monastic site. Substantial C18 terraced walled garden laid out by Sarah, Duchess of Marlborough, with herbaceous borders, topiary and fruit trees. Original stewponds integrated with new Japanese-themed garden and woodland garden and walk. Paddock home to alpacas. Ongoing restoration project aims to create a contemporary and practical garden sensitive to its historic context. Garden and tree walks at 12 noon, 1pm, 2pm and 3pm.

21 Glenavon Close

Vann

© Leigh Clapp

10 CHINTHURST LODGE
Wonersh Common Road, Wonersh, Guildford GU5 0PR. Mr & Mrs M R Goodridge, 01483 535108, michaelgoodridge@ymail.com. *4m S of Guildford. From A281 at Shalford turn E onto B2128 towards Wonersh. Just after Waverley sign, before village, garden on R.* Home-made teas. **Adm £5, chd free. Sun 22, Wed 25 June (12-5.30). Visitors also welcome by appt May to July (wine also available).**
1-acre yr-round enthusiast's atmospheric garden, divided into rooms. Herbaceous borders, white garden, specimen trees and shrubs, gravel garden with water feature, small kitchen garden, fruit cage, 2 wells, ornamental ponds, herb parterre and millennium parterre garden. Some gravel paths, which can be avoided.

11 ◆ CLANDON PARK
West Clandon, Guildford GU4 7RQ. National Trust, 01483 222482, www.nationaltrust.org.uk. *3m E of Guildford on A247. From A3 follow signs to Ripley to join A247 via B2215.* **Adm £5, chd £2.50. For NGS: Sun 23 Mar (10.30-5). For other opening times and information, please phone or see garden website.**
Garden around the house laid out informally, apart from parterre beneath South front. To the South a mid-C18 grotto. Principal front faces parkland, laid out in the style of Capability Brown around 1770. Created in 1901, Dutch garden modelled on the No.1 pond garden at Hampton Court Palace. Large bulb and daffodil field looks stunning in spring.

12 ◆ CLAREMONT LANDSCAPE GARDEN
Portsmouth Road, Esher KT10 9JG. National Trust, 01372 467806, www.nationaltrust.org.uk. *1m SW of Esher. On E side of A307 (no access from A3 bypass).* **Adm £7.70, chd £3.85. For NGS: Sun 11 May, Sun 12 Oct (10-5.30). For other opening times and information, please phone or see garden website.**
One of the earliest surviving English landscape gardens, begun by Vanbrugh and Bridgeman before 1720 and extended and naturalised by Kent and Capability Brown. Lake, island with pavilion; grotto and turf amphitheatre; viewpoints and avenues. Free guided walk at 2pm both NGS days with member of the gardening team. Cafe serving homemade cakes, light lunches and afternoon teas. Access maps available with recommended route.

13 NEW COLDHARBOUR HOUSE
Coldharbour Lane, Bletchingley, Redhill RH1 4NA. Mr Tony Elias. *Coldharbour Lane is off Rabies Heath Rd 1/2 m from A25 at Bletchingley and 0.9m from Tilburstow Hill Rd. Park in field & walk down to house.* Home-made teas. **Adm £4.50, chd free. Sat 6, Sun 7 Sept (1-5).**
This 1 1/2 -acre garden offers breathtaking views to the South Downs. Originally planted in the 1920's, it has since been adapted and enhanced. Several mature trees and shrubs incl a copper beech, a Canadian maple, magnolias, azaleas, rhododendrons, camellias, wisterias, fuschias, hibiscus, potentillas, mahonias, a fig tree and a walnut tree.

14 NEW 29 COMMONFIELD ROAD
Banstead SM7 2JR. Lynne Quick, 01737 357617, lynne.quick@virginmedia.com. *A217 from Reigate to Sutton. Turn on to Winkworth Rd A2022 at T-lights at Banstead Xrds towards Purley. Commonfield Rd 1st L.* Home-made teas. **Adm £3, chd free. Sun 1, Mon 2, Sun 29, Mon 30 June, Mon 1, Tue 2 Sept (12-4). Visitors also welcome by appt June to Sept for groups of 10.**
A plantswoman's small garden with a rich diversity of colourful shrubs, herbaceous perennials, roses, clematis and wisteria providing all round seasonal interest. A meandering garden providing vistas for acers, tree peonies, specimen trees and hosts beds with a clever use of foliage shape and colour. A magnificent display of unusual plants in containers cleverly link the patio with the garden.

15 56 COPSE AVENUE

Farnham GU9 9EA. Lyn & Jimmy James, 01252 323473, lynandjimmy@virginmedia.com. *Approx 1½ m N of Farnham. At Shepherd & Flock r'about take A325 to Farnborough. At 2nd r'about take Weybourne exit. At 2nd turn L. Take 2nd R at end of rd L.* Home-made teas. **Adm £4, chd free. Sat 17, Sun 18 May (12-5). Visitors also welcome by appt May to June.**

A fascinating and unusual 1-acre garden in a residential area. The garden was originally landscaped in the late 1960s following the plans of a Chelsea Flower Show garden, but was subsequently allowed to become very overgrown. The present owners have restored many of the original features and are adding innovative areas of planting and interest. Featured in interview by Amateur Gardening Magazine. Accessible for wheelchairs but some steep steps in garden and uneven paths.

Originally planted in the 1920's, it has since been adapted and enhanced . . .

16 COVERWOOD LAKES

Peaslake Road, Ewhurst GU6 7NT. The Metson Family, 01306 731101, coverwoodfarm@coverwoodlakes.co.uk, www.coverwoodlakes.co.uk. *7m SW of Dorking. From A25 follow signs for Peaslake; garden ½ m beyond Peaslake on Ewhurst rd.* Light refreshments. **Adm £5, chd £2. Sun 13, Mon 21 Apr, Mon 5, Sun 11, Sun 18, Sun 25 May (12-5); Sun 19 Oct (11-4.30). Visitors also welcome by appt May to Aug for groups 20+.**

14-acre landscaped garden in stunning position high in the Surrey Hills with 4 lakes and bog garden. Extensive rhododendrons, azaleas and fine trees. 3½ -acre lakeside arboretum. Marked trail through the 180-acre working farm with Hereford cows and calves, sheep and horses, extensive views of the surrounding hills.

17 ◆ CROSSWATER FARM

Crosswater Lane, Churt, Farnham GU10 2JN. Mrs E G Millais & Family, 01252 792698, www.rhododendrons.co.uk. *6m S of Farnham, 6m NW of Haslemere. From A287 turn E into Jumps Rd ½ m N of Churt village centre. After ¼ m turn acute L into Crosswater Lane & follow signs for Millais Nurseries.* **Adm £4, chd free. For NGS: Sun 4, Mon 5 May (10-5). For other opening times and information, please phone or see garden website.**

Idyllic 6-acre woodland garden. Plantsman's collection of rhododendrons and azaleas, incl rare species collected in the Himalayas, hybrids raised by the owners. Everything from alpine dwarfs to architectural large-leaved trees. Ponds, stream and companion plantings incl Sorbus, Magnolias and Japanese Acers. Trial gardens of new varieties. Woodland garden and specialist plant centre. Featured on BBC Gardener's World and BBC South Today TV (coverage of RHS Chelsea exhibit). Grass paths may be difficult for wheelchairs after rain.

18 CULVERKEYS

20A Longdown Lane North, Ewell, Epsom KT17 3JQ. Anne Salt, 020 8393 6861. *1m E of Epsom, 1m S of Ewell Village. Leave Ewell bypass (A24) by Reigate Rd (A240) to pass Nescot on L. Turn R in ¼ m.* **Adm £3, chd free. Sun 1 June, Sun 13 July (2-5). Visitors also welcome by appt May to Sept. No min, 20 max visitors.**

A romantic somewhat secret garden on the edge of Epsom Downs. Meandering paths pass borders planted to capacity with interesting and unusual plants. Arches smothered in climbers reveal secluded corners and running water soothes the spirit. Designed for yr-round interest, shrubs and trees play host to many clematis.

19 NEW DRYBRIDGE HOUSE

Pyle Hill, Woking GU22 0SR. Liz & Richard Summers, 01483 763264, lizsummers@f2s.com. *From Guildford, A3, take A320 to Woking. After 2.6m pass Garden Centre & PYO & take next R turn. Turn immed R into Pyle Hill.* Home-made teas. **Adm £5, chd free. Visitors welcome by appt Aug to Oct for groups 6+.**

Plantsman's garden with an extensive and colourful range of late summer perennials and grasses. 1½ acres incl formal areas, vegetable garden and courtyard.

20 DUNSBOROUGH PARK

Ripley GU23 6AL. Baron & Baroness Sweerts de Landas Wyborgh, www.dunsboroughpark.com. *6m NE of Guildford. Entrance across Ripley Green via The Milkway opp Wylie & Mar.* Home-made teas. **Adm £5, chd free. Sat 26 Apr, Sat 31 May, Sat 13 Sept (1-5.30).**

Extensive walled gardens of 6 acres redesigned by Penelope Hobhouse and Rupert Golby, structured with box hedging creating different garden rooms. Exciting herbaceous borders with beautiful standard wisterias. 70ft ginkgo hedge and ancient mulberry tree. Atmospheric water garden with life-size gunnera/rhododendrons. Festival of Tulips with 15,000 bulbs and large cut flower garden. Spectacular dahlias in September. Spectacular Festival of Tulips. 15,000 new bulbs planted and over 10,000 1yr old bulbs re-planted in grass to create a wild meadow. Sunday, 27 April: 1-5.30pm Saturday, 3 May: 1-5.30pm (Not for NGS).

21 FAIRMILE LEA

Portsmouth Road, Cobham KT11 1BG. Steven Kay. *2m NE of Cobham. On Cobham to Esher rd. Access by lane adjacent to Moleshill House & car park for Fairmile Common woods.* Home-made teas. **Combined adm £5.50, chd free. Sun 8 June, Sun 20 July (2-5). Combined with Moleshill House.**

Large Victorian sunken garden with pond. An old acacia tree stands in the midst of the lawn. Interesting planting on a large mound camouflages an old underground air raid shelter. Caged vegetable garden. Formality adjacent to wilderness.

22 16 FARM ROAD

Frimley, Camberley GU16 8TE. Norma & Bob Stephens. *1½ m from M3 J4. From Frimley Pk Hosp r'bout take Chobham Rd. At mini r'bout turn L into Bicknell Rd then 1st R into Farm Rd.* Light refreshments. **Adm £2.50, chd free. Sun 13 July (11-5).**
Small (60ft x 35ft) beautiful and well maintained, superbly structured on three levels with steps. Whilst the garden is small, it is a garden that should not be rushed. In addition to planting there are numerous quirky ornaments and features that add to this garden's charm incl a small pond with fish, frogs and newts.

Two lovely gardens and award winning allotments all within a few minutes walk of one another . . .

GROUP OPENING

23 FRIMLEY GREEN GARDENS

Frimley Green GU16 6HE. *3m S of Camberley. M3 J4 follow A325 to Frimley centre, towards Frimley Green on B3411 for 1m. Turn R by the green. R into The Hatches. Some parking at Frimley Green Recreation Ground on B3411 opp Elmcroft or The Hatches for on-street parking. Please be considerate of our neighbours.* Home-made teas at Wildwood. **Combined adm £5, chd free. Sun 15, Wed 18 June, Wed 27 Aug (2-5).**

ELMCROFT
Mrs Geraldine Huggon

OAKLEIGH
Mrs Angela O'Connell

TABOR
Susan Filbin

WILDWOOD
Annie Keighley

Visit four very different gardens in the delightful village of Frimley Green. Be inspired by designer chic and how to get the best from a small space at Tabor. Here you can admire a riot of hostas, colourful pots and an unusual water feature. Experience a romantic cottage garden at Wildwood with its tumbling roses, pond and ornamental potager. At Elmcroft, where no space is wasted, a huge *Buddleia alternifolia* forms a stunning backdrop for self-sown varieties of cottage classics, incl hardy geraniums and aquilegias. Look for surprises at charming Oakleigh, with a variety of plants creating a bright palette of colour and texture. A warm welcome awaits. Some old favourites and unusual plants for sale at Elmcroft. Tickets and map available at all gardens.

24 NEW THE GARTH PLEASURE GROUNDS

Newchapel Road, Lingfield RH7 6BJ. Mr Sherlock & Mrs Stanley, ab_post@yahoo.com, www.oldworkhouse.webs.com. *From A22 take B2028 by Mormon Temple to Lingfield. The Garth is on L after 1½ m, opp Barge Tiles. Parking: Barge Tiles or Gunpit Rd.* Cream teas. **Adm £5, chd free. Sat 14, Sun 15 June (1.30-5.30). Visitors also welcome by appt Apr to Nov. Please email at least 2 weeks in advance.**
Mature 9-acre Pleasure Grounds created by Walter Godfrey in 1919 present an idyllic setting surrounding the former parish workhouse refurbished in Edwardian-style. The formal gardens, enchanting nuttery, a spinney with many mature trees and a pond attract wildlife. Wonderful bluebells in spring. The woodland gardens and beautiful borders full of colour and fragrance for yr-round pleasure. Many areas of interest incl pond, woodland garden, formal gardens, spinney with large specimen plants incl 500yr old oak and many architectural features designed by Walter H Godfrey. Limited wheelchair access in woodland, Iris and Secret gardens.

25 ◆ GATTON PARK

Rocky Lane, Merstham RH2 0TW. Royal Alexandra & Albert School, 01737 649068, www.gattonpark.com. *3m NE of Reigate. 5 mins from M25 J8 (A217) or from top of Reigate Hill, over M25 then follow sign to Merstham. Entrance is off Rocky Lane accessible from Gatton Bottom or A23 Merstham.* **Adm £4.50, chd free. For NGS: Sun 16 Feb (11-4), Sun 15 Feb 2015. For other opening times and information, please phone or see garden website.**
Gatton Park is the core 250 acres of the estate originally laid out by Capability Brown. Gatton also boasts a Japanese garden, rock and water garden and Victorian parterre nestled within the sweeping parkland. Stunning displays of snowdrops and aconites in February and March. Free activities for children. Limited wheelchair access.

26 21 GLENAVON CLOSE

Claygate, Esher KT10 0HP. Selina & Simon Botham, 01372 210570, selina@designsforallseasons.co.uk, www.designsforallseasons.co.uk. *2m SE of Esher. A3 - A244 towards Esher. At T- lights turn R into Milbourne Lane, continue to Claygate village. Across at both mini r'abouts then R into Causeway.* Home-made teas. **Adm £3.50, chd free. Sat 7, Sun 15 June (1-6). Visitors also welcome by appt Apr to Oct.**
A relaxing 66ft x 92ft secluded garden created by garden designer Selina Botham and her husband Simon. Swathes of grasses and perennials surround a spacious lawn. Curving paths invite exploration. NEW curved seating area and 'secret' fruit garden. A magnificent willow is the setting for a pond, deck and garden office. Organic sculpture by Claire Knights. Guilded tours by RHS Gold medal winning designer. Featured in Real Homes magazine.

27 HALL GROVE SCHOOL

London Road (A30), Bagshot GU19 5HZ. Mr & Mrs A R Graham. *6m SW of Egham. M3 J3, follow A322 1m until sign for Sunningdale A30, 1m E of Bagshot, opp Long Acres garden centre, entrance at footbridge. Ample car park.* Home-made teas. **Adm £5, chd free. Sat 10 May (2-5).**
Formerly small Georgian country estate, now co-educational preparatory school. Grade II listed house (not open). Mature parkland with specimen trees. Historical features incl ice house, old walled garden, heated peach wall. New lake, woodland walks, rhododendrons and azaleas. Live music at 3pm.

28 ◆ HATCHLANDS PARK
East Clandon, Guildford GU4 7RT. National Trust, 01483 222482, www.nationaltrust.org.uk. *4m E of Guildford. Follow brown signs to Hatchlands Park (NT).* **Adm £4.70, chd £2.30. For NGS: Sun 18 May (10.30-5.30). For other opening times and information, please phone or see garden website.**
Garden and park designed by Repton in 1800. Follow one of the park walks to the stunning bluebell wood in spring (2.5km/1.7m round walk over rough and sometimes muddy ground). South of the house, a small parterre designed by Gertrude Jekyll in 1913 to flower in early June. In autumn enjoy the changing colours on the long walk. Partial wheelchair access to parkland, rough, undulating terrain, grass and gravel paths, dirt tracks, cobbled courtyard. Trampers available - booking essential.

29 HEATHSIDE
10 Links Green Way, Cobham KT11 2QH. Miss Margaret Arnott & Mr Terry Bartholomew, 01372 842459, m.a.arnott@btinternet.com. *1½ m E of Cobham. Through Cobham A245, 4th L after Esso garage into Fairmile Lane. Straight on into Water Lane. Links Green Way 3rd turning on L.* Home-made teas. **Adm £3.50, chd free. Sun 27 July (11-5). Visitors also welcome by appt. Afternoon tea or wine and canapes for evening visits.**
⅓ -acre terraced, plantsman's garden, designed for yr-round interest. There is a sumptuous collection of wonderful plants, all set off by harmonious landscaping. Many urns and obelisks aid the display. Two ponds and two water features add tranquil sound. A parterre with sundial and various topiary shapes add formality. Exciting colour combinations excite. Many inspirational ideas. 5m from RHS Wisley. Featured on ITV's Love Your Garden with Alan Titchmarsh.

GROUP OPENING

30 NEW HORSELL GROUP GARDENS
Horsell, Woking GU21 4XA. *1½ m W of Woking. From Woking follow signs to Horsell along High St towards Chobham.* Home-made teas. **Combined adm £5, chd free. Sun 22 June (1-6).**

BIRCH COTTAGE
Celia & Mel Keenan

NEW 3-4 BIRCH COTTAGES
Mr & Mrs Freeman

HORSELL ALLOTMENTS
Horsell Allotments Association www.horsellalots.wordpress.com

2 lovely gardens and award winning allotments all within a few minutes walk of one another nestled on the edge of Horsell Common, which is mentioned in HG Well's War of the Worlds. Both gardens are called Birch Cottage. 3 and 4 Birch Cottage is a new garden to the scheme full of charm with an interesting courtyard with rill. Walk down this long garden through into a series of rooms with topiary and attractive planting, and many specimen roses. Birch Cottage just over the road is a Grade II listed cottage with a box hedge knot garden feature in front, a Chinese slate courtyard with planted pots and hanging baskets, a canal water feature and active dovecot surrounded with an abundance of planting. Horsell allotments have over 100 individual plots growing a variety of unusual flowers and vegetables, many not seen in supermarkets. There are also 2 working beehives, with informative talks from the owners. Allotments and 3-4 Birch Cottage are flat, Birch Cottage, has gravel and steps but wheelchair visitors can see main garden.

31 LITTLE PRIORY
Sandy Lane, South Nutfield RH1 4EJ. Richard & Liz Ramsay. *1½ m E of Redhill. From Nutfield, on A25, turn into Mid St, following sign for South Nutfield. 1st R into Sandy Lane. Follow signs to parking, approx 300yds.* **Adm £4, chd free. Evening Opening £6, chd free, wine, Sat 14 June (5-8); Sun 15 June (11-5).**
Explore this 5-acre country garden where old blends with new. Wander the modern flower garden; lose yourself in the old orchard meadow; discover cherries and kiwi fruit in the greenhouses of the Victorian kitchen garden; relax beside the large pond, and be inspired everywhere by the views. Featured in Period Homes and Interiors. Partial wheelchair access.

32 ◆ LOSELEY PARK
Guildford GU3 1HS. Mr & Mrs M G More-Molyneux, 01483 304440/405112, www.loseley-park.com. *4m SW of Guildford. For SatNav please use GU3 1HS Stakescorner Lane.* Home-made teas. **Adm £5, chd £2.50. For NGS: Sun 8 June (11-5). For other opening times and information, please phone or see garden website.**
Delightful 2½ -acre walled garden. Award-winning rose garden (over 1,000 bushes, mainly old-fashioned varieties), extensive herb garden, fruit/flower garden, white garden with fountains, and spectacular organic vegetable garden. Magnificent vine walk, herbaceous borders, moat walk, ancient wisteria and mulberry trees. Wild flower meadow.

33 NEW MANOR HOUSE
Old Lane, Dockenfield, Farnham GU10 4HL. Mrs Pam Hibbert. *5m S of Farnham. From A287, through Frensham village to outskirts of Dockenfield. From A325 L at Halfway House PH. Old Lane 3rd L approx 1m. Ample parking.* Home-made teas. **Adm £4, chd free. Sat 21, Sun 22 June (1-5.30).**
2 acres of tranquility amidst wonderful countryside. Informally planted mixed beds incl climbing roses, alliums, flowering shrubs and masses of colourful and unusual plants. Contrasting plantings for wet, dry, sunny and shady areas. Lilly Pond, old orchard and ancient Oaks. Display of quilting by local craftswomen. Wheelchair access to most areas via lawns and paths.

34 THE MANOR HOUSE

Three Gates Lane, Haslemere GU27 2ES. Mr & Mrs Gerard Ralfe. *1m NE of Haslemere. From Haslemere centre take A286 towards Milford. Turn R after Museum into Three Gates Lane. At T-Junction turn R into Holdfast Lane. Car park on R.* Home-made teas. **Adm £5, chd free. Sun 25 May (12-5).**
Described by Country Life as 'The hanging gardens of Haslemere', The Manor House gardens are in a valley of the Surrey Hills. One of Surrey's inaugural NGS gardens, they are still under restoration. Fine views, six acres, water gardens.

35 MOLESHILL HOUSE

The Fairmile, Cobham KT11 1BG. Penny Snell, pennysnellflowers@btinternet.com, www.pennysnellflowers.co.uk. *2m NE of Cobham. On A307 Esher to Cobham Rd next to free car park by A3 bridge, at entrance to Waterford Close.* **Combined adm £5.50, chd free. Sun 8 June, Sun 20 July (2-5). Combined with Fairmile Lea. Visitors also welcome by appt May to Sept for groups of 15+.**
Romantic garden. Short woodland path leads from dovecote to beehives. Informal planting contrasts with formal topiary box and garlanded cisterns. Colourful courtyard and pots, conservatory, fountains, bog garden. Pleached avenue, new circular gravel garden replacing most of the lawn. Goodbye Victorian rockery - welcome new exciting feature! Music in the garden Sun 20 July. Garden 5 mins from Claremont Landscape Garden, Painshill Park & Wisley, also adjacent excellent dog-walking woods. Featured in Landscape Magazine.

36 NEW MONKSFIELD

Charles Hill (B3001), Tilford, Farnham GU10 2AL. Mr & Mrs Mark Reynolds, 01252 781377, Monksfieldhouse@gmail.com. *On B3001 Farnham to Elstead Rd, approx 800 metres S of junction with Crooksbury Rd. Car parking is opp house in field.* Home-made teas. **Adm £5, chd free. Sat 21, Sun 22 June (11-4.30). Visitors also welcome by appt May to Oct for groups 10+.**
Opening for the first time in 2014, a 10½ acre varied family garden. With Hampton Court show garden, orchard/walled garden, 300ft long border and formal garden, cottage garden, ½ acre pond and good selection of mature and newly planted specimen trees. Internal 'road' allowing wheelchair access to many parts of grounds.

The hanging gardens of Haslemere . . .

37 NORNEY WOOD

Elstead Road, Shackleford, Godalming GU8 6AY. Mr & Mrs R Thompson. *5m SW of Guildford. At Xrds of Elstead rd & Shackleford rd, ½ m towards Elstead from A3 Hurtmore/Shackleford junction.* Home-made teas. **Adm £5, chd free. Sun 22 June (11-5).**
Four years since its creation, the garden, in the style of Gertrude Jekyll, is set against a backdrop of mature trees and rhododendrons. The formal lawn terrace garden is surrounded by rose and herbaceous borders. Gertrude Jekyll's love of garden structures has been recreated with a Thunder house and paths linking the upper lawn terrace with the Tranquility water garden and pleached Lime tree walk. Long mixed herbaceous and rose borders; Multiple water features in the form of structured ponds and natural ponds; Woodland backdrop with mature trees and open grassland area; Kitchen garden; wild flower bank. New aspects of the garden under construction. Featured in Country Life and Surrey Life magazines. Wheelchair access possible on upper level only.

D

38 19 OAK TREE ROAD

Knaphill GU21 2RW. Barry & Pam Gray. *5m NW of Guildford. From A3 take A322 Bagshot Rd, continue through Worplesdon, straight over at Brookwood Xrds. 1st turn on L into Oak Tree Rd (opp Sainsbury's).* Home-made teas. **Adm £3, chd free. Sun 20 July (11-5).**
Colourful front garden of informal bedding, baskets and containers featuring tender perennials and annuals grown by owners. Back garden (approx 80ft x 35ft) has lawn, patio, small pond, trees, shrubs and perennials for foliage, texture, scent and yr-round interest. 3 greenhouses, fruit trees and vegetables. No wasted space in this delightful garden.

39 THE OLD CROFT

South Holmwood, Dorking RH5 4NT. David & Virginia Lardner-Burke, www.lardner-burke.org.uk. *3m S of Dorking. From Dorking A24 S for 3m, L to Leigh/Brockham into Mill Rd. ½ m on L, 2 free NT car parks on Holmwood Com. Access 500yds along woodland walk.* Home-made teas. **Adm £5, chd free. Sun 25, Mon 26 May, Sat 16, Sun 17 Aug (2-6).**
Beautiful 5-acre garden with many diverse areas of natural beauty, giving a sense of peace and tranquillity. Stunning vistas incl lake, bridge, pond fed by natural stream running over rocky weirs, bog gardens, roses, perennial borders, elevated viewing hide, tropical bamboo maze, curved pergola of rambling roses, unique topiary buttress hedge, many specimen trees and shrubs. Visitors return again and again. Featured in Period Living and Surrey Life magazine. **For direct access for disabled and elderly visitors please phone 01306 888224.**

40 THE OLD RECTORY

Sandy Lane, Brewer Street, Bletchingley RH1 4QW. Mr & Mrs A Procter, 01883 743388/07515 394506, trudie.y.procter@googlemail.com. *Top of village nr Red Lion PH, turn R into Little Common Lane then R Cross Rd into Sandy Lane. Parking nr house, disabled parking in courtyard.* Home-made teas. **Adm £5, chd free. Sun 29 June (11-4). Visitors also welcome by appt Mar to Sept. Please phone or email for appointments.**
Georgian Manor House (not open). Quintessential Italianate topiary garden, statuary, box parterres, courtyard with columns, water features, antique terracotta pots. Much of the 4-acre garden is the subject of ongoing reclamation. This incl the ancient moat, woodland with fine specimen trees and walled kitchen garden. Rill, sunken and exotic garden under construction. Featured in Country Living (Film location for BBC Emma). Gravel paths.

41 ◆ POLESDEN LACEY
Great Bookham, Dorking RH5 6BD. National Trust, 01372 452048, www.nationaltrust.org.uk. *Nr Dorking, off A246 Leatherhead to Guildford rd. 1½ m S of Great Bookham, well signed.* **Adm £7.75, chd £3.90. For NGS: Sun 27 July (10-5). For other opening times and information, please phone or see garden website.**
Designed as the perfect setting for Mrs Greville, a famous Edwardian hostess, to entertain royalty and the best of society, Polesden Lacey has beautiful formal gardens with something to offer for every season, as well as glorious views over the rolling Surrey Hills. Wheelchairs and battery cars available from Visitor Reception, it is advisable to pre-book.

42 PRATSHAM GRANGE
Tanhurst Lane, Holmbury St Mary RH5 6LZ. Alan & Felicity Comber, 01306 621116, alancomber@aol.com. *12m SE of Guildford, 8m SW of Dorking. From A25 take B2126. After 4m turn L into Tanhurst Lane. From A29 take B2126. Before Forest Green turn R on B2126 then1st R to Tanhurst Lane.* Home-made teas. **Adm £4.50, chd free. Sun 6 July, Sun 24 Aug (12-5). Visitors also welcome by appt June to Aug.**
4-acre garden around late Victorian house in a stunning setting overlooked by Holmbury Hill and Leith Hill. The garden is surrounded by mature oaks, laurels, rhododendrons and paddocks. Features incl herbaceous borders, cutting flower and kitchen gardens, 2 ponds joined by cascading stream and rose, hydrangea and fuchsia beds. The geometric beds highlighted in Surrey Life magazine. Some slopes and gravel paths. Deep ponds.

43 ◆ RAMSTER
Chiddingfold GU8 4SN. Mr & Mrs Paul Gunn, 01428 654167, www.ramsterevents.com. *1½ m S of Chiddingfold. On A283 1½ m S of Chiddingfold; large iron gates on R.* **Adm £6, chd free. For NGS: Fri 23 May (10-5). For other opening times and information, please phone or see garden website.**
A stunning, mature woodland garden set in over 20 acres, famous for its rhododendron and azalea collection and its carpets of bluebells in Spring.

The Old Croft
© Leigh Clapp

Enjoy a peaceful wander down the woodland walk, explore the bog garden with its stepping stones, or relax in the tranquil enclosed Tennis Court Garden. Tea house open every day while the garden is open, serving delicious cakes and sandwiches. Teahouse and WC wheelchair accessible, some paths in garden suitable for wheelchairs.

44 ROSE COTTAGE
Elm Corner, Ockham GU23 6PX. Helen Cowell. *Nr Wisley Gardens, on southbound side of A3 opp entrance to Wisley. From J10 on M25 travel S on A3 take 2nd turning off A3 signed 'Elm Corner' just before a footbridge over the A3. Single track road, park in field.* Home-made teas. **Adm £3.50, chd free. Sun 1 June (11-5).**
1-acre cottage garden starts with a vegetable garden enclosed in fan-trained fruit trees. Deep borders surround the C18 cottage and a rose arch takes you through to a tulip tree and laburnum walk with box balls and alliums. Next a large pond with resident terrapin and Koi carp. Finally the 12ft x 12ft knot garden with bird and frog topiary gives a formal ending to the garden journey. Rose Cottage is minutes from Wisley Gardens, close to Polesden Lacey (NT), Claremont Landscape Gardens (NT) and Painshill Park. Parking for disabled visitors reserved outside house.

45 7 ROSE LANE
Ripley, Woking GU23 6NE. Mindi McLean. *Ripley Village. Just off Ripley High St on Rose Lane, 3rd house on L next to shoe repair shop.* Cream teas. **Adm £3, chd free. Sat 14 June (10-4).**
7 Rose Lane is a small but perfectly formed village-centre garden behind an historic listed cottage. It has 3 'rooms' a traditional perennial flower garden laid to lawn; a vegetable and fruit garden with Agriframe orchard and a working garden with greenhouse, compost bins, shed and chicken run. It is a perfect example of how to make the most of a cottage garden. Monthly Ripley Farmers Market held on 14 June (9-1).

46 THE ROUND HOUSE
Dunsfold Road, Loxhill GU8 4BL. Mrs Sue Lawson, 01483 200375, roundhouseloxhill@gmail.com. *4m S of Bramley. Off A281, at Smithbrook Kilns turn R to Dunsfold. Follow to T-junction. Go R (B2130). After 1.2m Park Hatch on R, enter park, follow drive to garden.* Home-made teas. **Adm £4, chd free. 22, Wed 25 June (2-6). Visitors also welcome by appt May to July. Occasional visits accepted in September.**
2½ -acre walled Victorian garden with far-reaching views from the top of the garden. Continuing renewal programme since 2002. Colourful mixed beds with perennials, roses and interesting statuary. Water cascades. Apple and plum orchard. Serpentine paths between shrubs and wild flowers. 75 metre lavender walk. Ornamental fish pond and wild flower orchard. Gravel paths and steep slopes.

47 41 SHELVERS WAY
Tadworth KT20 5QJ. Keith & Elizabeth Lewis, 01737 210707, kandelewis@ntlworld.com. *6m S of Sutton off A217. 1st turning on R after Burgh Heath T-lights heading S on A217. 400yds down Shelvers Way on L.* Home-made teas. **Adm £3.50, chd free. Sun 27 Apr, Sun 20 July (2-5.30). Visitors also welcome by appt Apr to Aug. Groups 10+ required.**
Visitors say 'one of the most colourful back gardens in Surrey'. In spring, a myriad of small bulbs with specialist daffodils and many pots of colourful tulips. Choice perennials follow, with rhododendrons and azaleas. Cobbles and shingle support grasses and self-sown plants with a bubble fountain. Annuals, phlox and herbaceous plants ensure colour well into September. A garden for all seasons.

48 NEW SHIELING
The Warren, Kingswood, Tadworth KT20 6PQ. Dr Sarah Wilson, sarahwilson@doctors.org.uk. *Kingswood Warren Estate. Off A217 before Tadworth, gated entrance just past church. ¾ m walk from Station.* Home-made teas. **Adm £4, chd free. Evening Opening £5, chd free, wine, Thur 5 June (5.30-9); Sun 15 June (2-6). Visitors also welcome by appt May to Sept.**
A one acre garden restored to its original 1920's design. The front is a formal garden with island beds and shrub borders At the back there is a surprise with a large rock garden planted with bulbs, perennials and shrubs. The rest is a woodland garden with acid loving plants and some old and interesting trees and shrubs. Featured in local community magazine. Gravel drive and some narrow paths in back garden. Otherwise grass and paths easy for wheelchairs.

D

49 SPURFOLD
Radnor Road, Peaslake, Guildford GU5 9SZ. Mr & Mrs A Barnes, 01306 730196, spurfold@btinternet.com. *8m SE of Guildford. A25 to Shere. Turn R through village & up hill. Over railway bridge, 1st L to Peaslake. In Peaslake turn L after village stores Radnor Rd. Approx ½ m up single track lane fork L up steep drive & L at top, signs to car park.* **Adm £5, chd £2 (under 10s free). Visitors welcome by appt May to Aug. Home-made teas during day visits or glass of wine in evening if prefered.**
4 acres, large herbaceous and shrub borders, formal pond with Cambodian Buddha head, sunken gravel garden with topiary box and water feature, terraces, beautiful lawns, mature rhododendrons and azaleas, woodland paths, and gazebos. Garden contains unique collection of Indian elephants and other objets d'art. Topiary garden created 2010 and new formal lawn area created in 2012.

50 NEW STERLING HOUSE
65 Palace Road, East Molesey KT8 9DN. Mrs Deirdre Goddard. *Close to Hampton Court Palace. Take Hurst Rd from Hampton Court Way, take 3rd L (Church Rd) & then 1st R (Palace Rd).* **Adm £4, chd £2. Sat 28, Sun 29 June (2-6.30).**
The garden is set in just under one acre of ground and is a stunning quintessential English Country Garden but located moments from the hustle and bustle of Hampton Court. The garden truly comes into its own in June and July. Gentle planting schemes have been used throughout to provide a haven of tranquility, set off by beautifully tended lawns and mature trees. Although teas will not be served at Sterling House, the garden is just a short walk to Bridge Road where there are many lovely cafes and restaurants. All of the grounds can be access by wheelchair.

Gentle planting schemes have been used throughout to provide a haven of tranquility . . .

51 STUART COTTAGE
Ripley Road, East Clandon GU4 7SF. John & Gayle Leader, 01483 222689, gayle@stuartcottage.com, www.stuartcottage.com. *4m E of Guildford. Off A246 or from A3 through Ripley until r'about, turn L & continue through West Clandon until T-lights, then L onto A246. East Clandon 1st L.* Home-made teas. **Adm £3.50, chd free. Sun 13 July, Sun 31 Aug (2-6). Visitors also welcome by appt June to Sept for groups 15+.**
This much visited ½ -acre garden seems to please many, being planted to offer floral continuity through the seasons. In June, the romance of the rose walk combines with the sound of water, in July, flowerbeds are floriferous with soft coordinated colours and scented plants, in August, vibrant colours will lift the spirits and in September, tender perennials reach their zenith. Featured in The Countryside Magazine. Access to all the garden for wheelchairs.

52 NEW SUNRISE OF WEYBRIDGE
Ellesmere Road, Weybridge KT13 0HY. Mr Marcus Le Brocq, www.sunrise-care.co.uk/communities/weybridge. *1m E of Weybridge. From A3, 2½ m from Painshill r'about or M25 J11, approx 4m.* Light refreshments. **Adm £4, chd free. Sat 14 June (9-5).**
Situated on the outskirts of the town of Weybridge, Sunrise Senior living of Weybridge is a beautifully appointed purpose built care residence. The

community possesses extensive award winning private gardens with unique features, a beautiful lawn where garden parties and barbeques are held in the summer and a paved walkway surrounds the buildings under the mature trees overhead. Tea, coffee, soft drinks and patiserries will be served in the garden, with the provision of a marquee in case of poor weather. Fully compatible and accessible to all models of wheelchair and mobility devices.

53 NEW 26 THE FAIRWAY

Camberley GU15 1EF. Jacky Sheppard. *1½ m from M3 J4. Follow signs to Frimley Pk Hosp. At r'about take 3rd exit B311 Chobham Rd. Continue on B311 L at 2nd r'about. 1st L into Fairway.* **Adm £3, chd free. Sat 17, Sat 31 May (11-4).**
Spring and summer is the ideal time to see the azaleas, rhododendrons and heathers that surround the house. The hundreds of bulbs, primroses and winter anemones give ground cover beneath the shrubs. Climbers and a variety of plants continue a theme to make way for summer flowering.

54 TILFORD COTTAGE

Tilford Road, Tilford GU10 2BX. Mr & Mrs R Burn, 01252 795423, rodburn@tiscali.co.uk, www.tilfordcottagegarden.co.uk. *3m SE of Farnham. From Farnham station along Tilford Rd. Tilford Cottage opp Tilford House. Parking by village green.* Home-made teas. **Adm £6, chd free. Open for daytime and evening visits - Sat 21, Sun 22, Fri 27, Sat 28, Sun 29 June (10.30-4pm) and (6.30-9pm). Visitors also welcome by appt May to Aug. Refreshments by prior arrangement.**
Artist's garden designed to surprise, delight and amuse. Formal planting, herb and knot garden. Numerous examples of topiary combine beautifully with the wild flower river walk. Japanese and water gardens, hosta beds, rose, apple and willow arches, treehouse and fairy grotto all continue the playful quality especially enjoyed by children. Dogs on lead please! Beekeeper demonstrations. Holistic centre open for taster sessions. Art studio open for viewing. Some gravel paths and steep slopes.

56 ◆ TITSEY PLACE GARDENS

Titsey Hill, Oxted RH8 0SD. The Trustees of the Titsey Foundation, 01273 715356, www.titsey.org. *3m N of Oxted. A25 between Oxted & Westerham. Follow brown signs to Titsey Estate from A25 at Limpsfield or see website directions.* Light refreshments. **Adm £4.50, chd £1. For NGS: Sat 17 May, Sat 14 June, Sat 12 July, Sat 16 Aug (1-5). For other opening times and information, please phone or see garden website.**
One of the largest surviving historic estates in Surrey. Magnificent ancestral home and gardens of the Gresham family since 1534. Walled kitchen garden restored early 1990s. Golden Jubilee rose garden. Etruscan summer house adjoining picturesque lakes and fountains. 15 acres of formal and informal gardens in idyllic setting within the M25. Tearooms with delicious home-made teas served between 12:30-5 on open days. Last admissions to gardens at 4pm, gardens close at 5pm. Dogs allowed in picnic area, car park and woodland walks. Good wheelchair access and disabled car park alongside tearooms.

57 TOLLSWORTH MANOR

Rook Lane, Chaldon, Caterham CR3 5BQ. Carol & Gordon Gillett. *2m W of Caterham. From Caterham-on-the-Hill, take B2031 through Chaldon. 300yds out of Chaldon take concrete farm track on L. Parking in farmyard beyond house.* Home-made teas. **Adm £4, chd free. Sun 22 June (2-6).**
Surrounding a C14 rose/clematis covered house, an old-fashioned country garden, created from derelict site over 31yrs by present owners. Well-stocked herbaceous borders with old-fashioned roses, peonies, delphiniums. Wildlife pond and duck pond with ducks. Lovely views over surrounding farmland. Shetland pony. Friendly atmosphere. Some uneven paths.

58 VALE END

Chilworth Road, Albury GU5 9BE. Mr & Mrs John Foulsham, 01483 202594, daphnefoulsham@gmail.com. *4m SE of Guildford. From Albury take A248 W for ¼ m.* **Adm £5, chd free. Visitors welcome by appt May to Sept. Home-made teas and morning coffee available.**
1-acre walled garden arranged on many levels in idyllic setting overlooking mill pond. Spring garden and wild flower meadow give way to borders richly planted with roses, shrubs, perennials and annuals. Formal clipped yew walk with rope swags festooned with wisteria, roses and vines. Attractive hidden courtyard, gravel garden and steps by pantiled cascade lead up to fruit, vegetable and sunken herb garden. Delightful stream, lake and woodland walk from garden on public footpaths. Featured in Gardens Illustrated.

59 ◆ VANN

Hambledon GU8 4EF. Mrs M Caroe, 01428 683413, www.vanngarden.co.uk. *6m S of Godalming. A283 to Wormley. Turn L at Hambledon. On NGS days only, follow yellow Vann signs for 2m. Please park in field, not in road.* **Adm £5, chd free. For NGS: Sat 29 Mar to Fri 4 Apr incl (10-6); Mon 5 May (2-6); Tue 6 May to Sun 11 May incl (10-6); Sun 8 June to Sat 14 June incl (10-6). For other opening times and information, please phone or see garden website.**
5-acre English Heritage registered garden surrounding Tudor and William and Mary house (not open) with Arts and Crafts additions by W D Caröe incl a Bargate stone pergola. At the front, brick-paved original 'cottage' garden; to the rear, ¼ -acre pond, yew walk with rill and Gertrude Jekyll water garden. Snowdrops and hellebores, spring bulbs, Fritillaria meleagris in March. Island beds, crinkle crankle wall, orchard with wild flowers, vegetable garden. Centenary garden and woodland. Home-made teas (Mon 5 May only). Deep water. Water garden paths not suitable for wheelchairs, but many others are. Please ring prior to visit to request disabled parking.

60 WALTON POOR HOUSE

Ranmore RH5 6SX. Prue Calvert, 01483 282273, wnscalvert@btinternet.com. *6m NW of Dorking. From Dorking take rd to Ranmore, continue for approx 4m, after Xrds 1m on L. From A246 at E.Horsley go S into Greendene, 1st L Crocknorth Rd, 1m on R.* Home-made teas. **Adm £3.50, chd free. Mon 5 May, Sun 15 June, Sat 11, Sun 12 Oct (12-5). Visitors also welcome by appt Apr to Oct for groups 10+.**

Tranquil, almost secretive, 4-acre mostly wooded garden in North Downs AONB, planted to show contrast between colourful shrubs and mature trees. Paths wind through garden to pond, hideaway dell and herb garden, planted to show the use of aromatic plants and shrubs. Specialist nursery with wide variety of herbs, shrubs and aromatic plants. Herb talks, recipe leaflets and refreshments available for groups by appt. Featured in Surrey Life magazine. Grass paths.

61 57 WESTHALL ROAD

Warlingham CR6 9BG. Robert & Wendy Baston. *3m N of M25 on A22. M25, J 6, A22 London, at Whyteleafe r'about, take 3rd R, under railway bridge, turn immed R into Westhall Rd.* Home-made teas. **Adm £3.50, chd free (share to Warlingham Methodist Church). Sun 25, Mon 26 May (2-5). Also open Elm Tree Cottage (see London).**

Reward for the sure-footed - many steep steps to 3 levels! Swathes of tulips and alliums. Mature kiwi and grape vines. Mixed borders. Raised vegetable beds. Box, bay, cork oak and yew topiaries. 'Amphitheatre' of potted plants on lower steps. Stunning views of Caterham and Whyteleafe from top garden.

62 WESTWAYS FARM

Gracious Pond Road, Chobham GU24 8HH. Paul & Nicky Biddle, 01276 856163, nicolabiddle@rocketmail.com. *4m N of Woking. From Chobham Church proceed over r'about towards Sunningdale, 1st Xrds R into Red Lion Rd to junction with Mincing Lane.* Home-made teas. **Adm £4, chd free. Sat 10 May (11-5); Sun 11 May (11-4). Visitors also welcome by appt Apr to July.**

Open 6-acre garden surrounded by woodlands planted in 1930s with mature and some rare rhododendrons, azaleas, camellias and magnolias, underplanted with bluebells, erythroniums, lilies and dogwood; extensive lawns and sunken pond garden. Working stables and sandschool. Lovely Queen Anne House (not open) covered with listed *Magnolia grandiflora*. Victorian design glasshouse.

63 ◆ WINKWORTH ARBORETUM

Hascombe Road, Godalming GU8 4AD. National Trust, 01483 208477, www.nationaltrust.org.uk. *2m SE of Godalming on B2130. Car: nr Hascombe, 2m SE of Godalming on E side of B2130. Bus: 42/44 Guildford to Cranleigh (stops at Arboretum).* **Adm £7.20, chd £3.60. For NGS: Sun 13 Apr, Sun 5 Oct (10-5.30). For other opening times and information, please phone or see garden website.**

This dramatic hillside Arboretum perfectly demonstrates what Dr Fox, the Arboretum's creator, described as 'using trees and shrubs to paint a picture'. Impressive displays of daffodils, bluebells and azaleas await in spring. Picnic by the lake in summer. Don't miss the stunning autumnal display created by maples, cherries and tupelos. Guided walk with member of the garden team. Light refreshments available. Steep slopes.

64 WOODBURY COTTAGE

Colley Lane, Reigate RH2 9JJ. Shirley & Bob Stoneley, 01737 244235. *1m W of Reigate. M25 J8, A217 (Reigate). Immed before level Xing turn R into Somers Rd, continues as Manor Rd. At end turn R into Coppice Lane & follow signs to car park.* Home-made teas. **Adm £3.50, chd free. Sat 5 July (2-5); Sun 6 July (11-5); Sat 6 Sept (2-5); Sun 7 Sept (11-5); Wed 10 Sept (2-5). Visitors also welcome by appt July to Sept for groups 10+.**

Cottage garden of just under ¼ acre, made and maintained by owners. Garden is stepped on a slope, enhanced by its setting under Colley Hill and N Downs Way. We grow a rich diversity of plants, incl perennials, annuals and tender ones, with many plants in pots. The garden is colour-themed, and still looking great in September.

65 48 WOODMANSTERNE LANE

Wallington SM6 0SW. Joanne & Graham Winn, www.joannewinngardendesign.co.uk. *2.6m NE of Banstead. From A217 head E on A2022 for 2½, turn L. Park at Flitton's nursery or on rd. DO NOT park on grass verges (Traffic wardens).* Home-made teas. **Adm £4, chd free. Sun 27 July (12.30-4.30).**

Approx ⅓ acre. Part of former smallholding, converted by garden designer Joanne Winn and husband Graham. Built around the original orchard's remaining fruit trees, the bold, curvy design is softened by a sumptuous palette of perennials and grasses. Pop into the secluded kitchen garden, relax on the pond's deck amongst darting dragonflies and enjoy tea by the chicken run. Featured in Garden Style, Surrey Life and House Beautiful magazines. Partial wheelchair access, some gravel and narrow paths, raised deck and boardwalk.

D

Look out for the NGS yellow arrows ...

Moleshill House

© Nicola Stocken Tomkins

Surrey County Volunteers

County Organiser
Maggie Boyd, Bardsey, 11 Derby Road, Haslemere GU27 1BS, 01428 652283, maggie.boyd@live.co.uk

County Treasurer/Booklet Production
David Boyd, Bardsey, 11 Derby Road, Haslemere GU27 1BS, 01428 652283, dhboyd@live.co.uk

Publicity
Annie Keighley, Wildwood, 34 The Hatches, Frimley Green GU16 6HE, 01252 838660, annie.keighley12@btinternet.com

Booklet Coordimator
Keith Lewis, 41 Shelvers Way, Tadworth KT20 5QJ, 01737 210707, kandelewis@ntlworld.com

Group Tour Organiser
Margaret Arnott, Heathside, 10 Links Green Way, Cobham KT11 2QH, 01372 842459, m.a.arnott@btinternet.com

Assistant County Organisers
Margaret Arnott, Heathside, 10 Links Green Way, Cobham KT11 2QH, 01372 842459
Anne Barnes, Spurfold, Radnor Road, Peaslake, Guildford GU5 9SZ, 01306 730196
Di Grose, Three Farthings, 62 Hickmans Close, Godstone RH9 8EB, 01883 742983, di.grose@godstone.net
Annie Keighley, Wildwood, 34 The Hatches, Frimley Green GU16 6HE, 01252 838660, annie.keighley12@btinternet.com
Shirley Stoneley, Woodbury Cottage, Colley Lane, Reigate RH2 9JJ, 01737 244235
Jean Thompson, Norney Wood, Elstead Road, Shackleford, Godalming GU8 6AY, 01483 425633, norney.wood@btinternet.com

SUSSEX

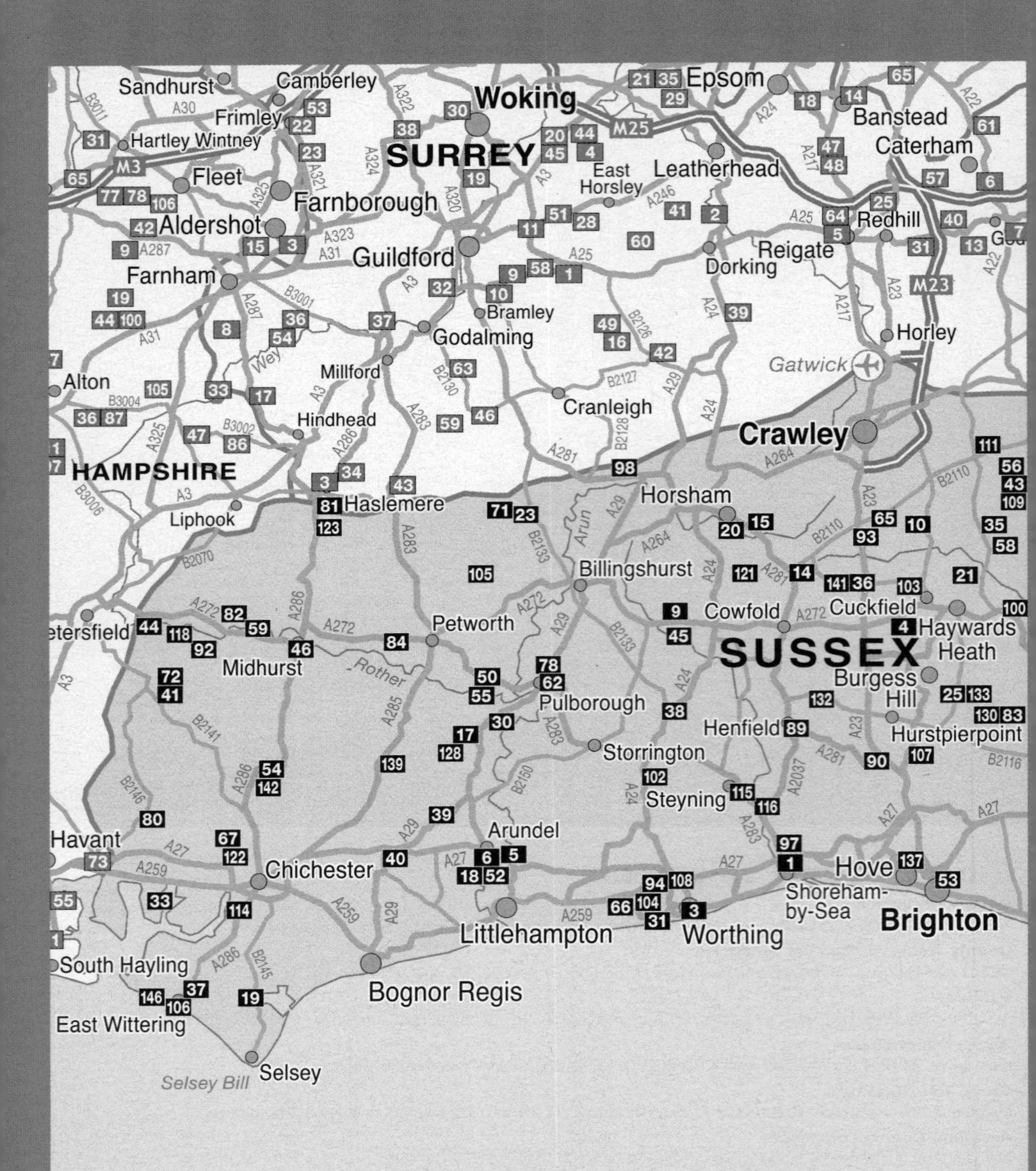

Sandhurst
Camberley
Woking
Epsom
Banstead
Frimley
Hartley Wintney
SURREY
Caterham
Fleet
Farnborough
East Horsley
Leatherhead
Aldershot
Guildford
Redhill
Reigate
Dorking
Farnham
Bramley
Godalming
Horley
Millford
Gatwick
Alton
Cranleigh
Hindhead
Crawley
HAMPSHIRE
Haslemere
Horsham
Liphook
Billingshurst
Cowfold
Cuckfield
Petworth
Haywards Heath
SUSSEX
Midhurst
Burgess Hill
Pulborough
Henfield
Hurstpierpoint
Storrington
Steyning
Arundel
Havant
Chichester
Hove
Shoreham-by-Sea
Brighton
Littlehampton
Worthing
South Hayling
Bognor Regis
East Wittering
Selsey
Selsey Bill

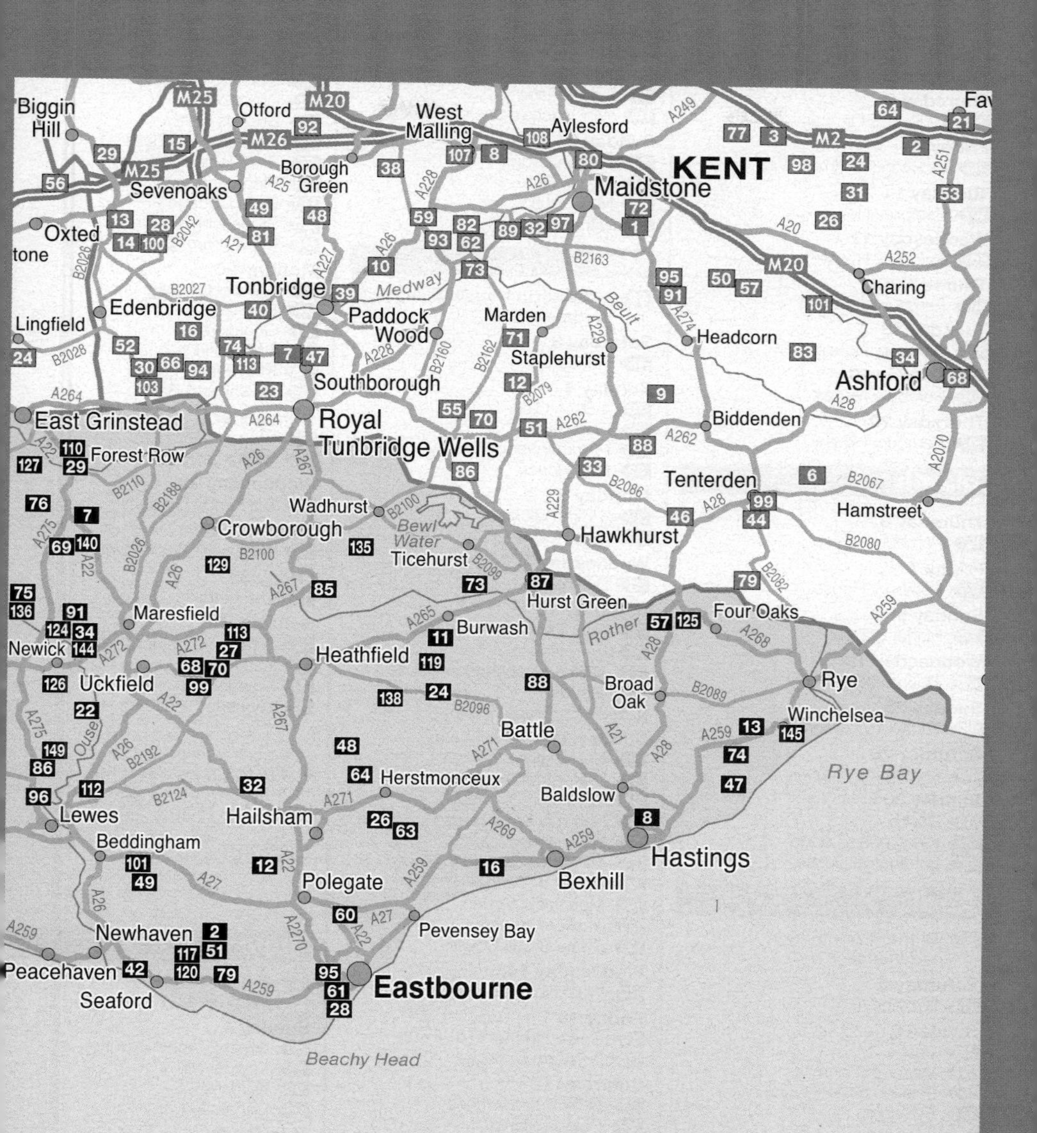
KENT
Maidstone
Royal Tunbridge Wells
Tonbridge
Sevenoaks
Ashford
East Grinstead
Crowborough
Uckfield
Heathfield
Lewes
Hailsham
Newhaven
Seaford
Peacehaven
Eastbourne
Bexhill
Hastings
Battle
Rye
Winchelsea
Tenterden
Hawkhurst
Rye Bay
Beachy Head
© Global Mapping / XYZ Maps

Opening Dates

All entries subject to change. For latest information check www.ngs.org.uk

February

Thursday 6
86 McBean's Orchids

Friday 7
86 McBean's Orchids

Tuesday 11
107 Pembury House

Wednesday 12
107 Pembury House

Thursday 13
107 Pembury House

Tuesday 18
107 Pembury House

Wednesday 19
107 Pembury House

Thursday 20
107 Pembury House

March

Thursday 6
107 Pembury House

Friday 7
107 Pembury House

Sunday 9
84 Manor of Dean

Wednesday 19
135 Tidebrook Manor

Sunday 23
102 The Old Vicarage

Saturday 29
80 Lordington House

Sunday 30
38 Dachs
73 King John's Lodge
80 Lordington House

April

17 Bignor Park (Every Wednesday)

Saturday 5
114 Rymans

Sunday 6
38 Dachs
84 Manor of Dean
104 Palatine School Gardens
114 Rymans

Saturday 12
26 Butlers Farmhouse
55 The Grange
118 Sandhill Farm House

Sunday 13
26 Butlers Farmhouse
53 The Garden House
55 The Grange
90 Newtimber Place
118 Sandhill Farm House

Sunday 20
23 Bradstow Lodge

Monday 21
102 The Old Vicarage

Saturday 26
41 Down Place
145 Winchelsea's Secret Gardens

Sunday 27
34 Clinton Lodge
41 Down Place
82 Malt House
96 Offham House

May

50 Fittleworth House (Every Wednesday)

Saturday 3
48 Fineoaks

Sunday 4
18 4 Birch Close
48 Fineoaks
59 Hammerwood House
82 Malt House

Monday 5
18 4 Birch Close
82 Malt House

Wednesday 7
11 Bateman's

Saturday 10
1 Adur Lodge
69 Holly House
74 NEW Knockbridge House
127 Standen
129 Stone Cross House

Sunday 11
14 Beedinglee
44 Durford Mill House
54 Gardeners' Cottage
59 Hammerwood House
69 Holly House
74 NEW Knockbridge House
84 Manor of Dean
88 Mountfield Court
123 Shalford House
129 Stone Cross House

Wednesday 14
142 West Dean Gardens

Friday 16
29 Caxton Manor
110 2 Quarry Cottages

Saturday 17
19 NEW The Birches
29 Caxton Manor
110 2 Quarry Cottages

Sunday 18
4 Ansty Gardens
19 NEW The Birches
76 Legsheath Farm

Saturday 24
28 51 Carlisle Road
43 Duckyls Holt
109 The Priest House

Sunday 25
6 Arundel Gardens Group
9 Bakers House
14 Beedinglee
20 Blue Jays
28 51 Carlisle Road
37 Cookscroft
43 Duckyls Holt
66 Highdown Gardens
73 King John's Lodge
112 Ringmer Park
113 Rose Cottage
130 Stonehealed Farm
139 Upwaltham Barns

Monday 26
6 Arundel Gardens Group
20 Blue Jays
37 Cookscroft
43 Duckyls Holt
73 King John's Lodge
139 Upwaltham Barns

Tuesday 27
130 Stonehealed Farm
149 NEW Woodside House

Wednesday 28
10 Balcombe Gardens

Thursday 29
149 NEW Woodside House

Friday 30
75 Latchetts

Saturday 31
8 NEW 96 Ashford Road
75 Latchetts
81 Lowder Mill
93 Nymans

Delicious home-made teas and cakes . . .

June

50 Fittleworth House (Every Wednesday)

Sunday 1
58 Great Lywood Farmhouse
81 Lowder Mill
93 Nymans
96 Offham House

Monday 2
34 Clinton Lodge
40 Denmans Garden

Tuesday 3
119 Sarah Raven's Cutting Garden

Thursday 5
66 Highdown Gardens
84 Manor of Dean (Evening)

Festival Weekend

Saturday 7
- 8 NEW 96 Ashford Road
- 46 54 Elmleigh
- 51 Follers Manor
- 68 Hobbs Barton
- 92 Nyewood House
- 114 Rymans
- 118 Sandhill Farm House
- 122 Sennicotts
- 124 Sheffield Park and Garden
- 127 Standen
- 137 11 Tredcroft Road

Sunday 8
- 16 Bexhill Gardens
- 17 Bignor Park
- 39 Dale Park House
- 46 54 Elmleigh
- 49 Firle Place Herb Garden
- 51 Follers Manor
- 61 Hardwycke
- 65 High Beeches
- 68 Hobbs Barton
- 92 Nyewood House
- 114 Rymans
- 118 Sandhill Farm House
- 127 Standen
- 137 11 Tredcroft Road

Tuesday 10
- 42 Driftwood

Wednesday 11
- 126 Sparrow Hatch

Thursday 12
- 126 Sparrow Hatch
- 136 Town Place

Friday 13
- 47 Fairlight End

Saturday 14
- 38 Dachs
- 41 Down Place
- 47 Fairlight End
- 58 Great Lywood Farmhouse
- 69 Holly House
- 100 Old Scaynes Hill House

Sunday 15
- 3 Ambrose Place Back Gardens
- 13 Beauchamps
- 38 Dachs
- 41 Down Place
- 63 Gardens & Grounds of Herstmonceux Castle
- 69 Holly House
- 85 Mayfield Gardens

Tuesday 17
- 2 Alfriston Clergy House

Wednesday 18
- 135 Tidebrook Manor

Friday 20
- 75 Latchetts

Saturday 21
- 22 Bradness Gallery
- 44 Durford Mill House

Bakers House

© Leigh Clapp

- 46 54 Elmleigh
- 52 70 Ford Road
- 64 NEW Herstmonceux Parish Trail
- 75 Latchetts
- 101 Old Vicarage
- 145 Winchelsea's Secret Gardens

Sunday 22
- 4 Ansty Gardens
- 9 Bakers House
- 22 Bradness Gallery
- 44 Durford Mill House
- 46 54 Elmleigh
- 52 70 Ford Road
- 64 NEW Herstmonceux Parish Trail
- 73 King John's Lodge
- 113 Rose Cottage
- 136 Town Place

Thursday 26
- 78 Little Hill (Evening)

Friday 27
- 105 Parsonage Farm

Saturday 28
- 10 Balcombe Gardens
- 15 4 Ben's Acre
- 31 Channel View
- 43 Duckyls Holt
- 91 North Hall
- 102 The Old Vicarage
- 109 The Priest House
- 144 1 Whites Cottages

Sunday 29
- 31 Channel View
- 43 Duckyls Holt
- 78 Little Hill
- 91 North Hall
- 102 The Old Vicarage
- 120 Seaford & Newhaven Group
- 121 Sedgwick Park House
- 136 Town Place
- 144 1 Whites Cottages

July

- 50 **Fittleworth House (Every Wednesday)**

Tuesday 1
- 42 Driftwood

Wednesday 2
- 121 Sedgwick Park House

Saturday 5
- 27 Cabbages & Kings
- 32 NEW Chiddingly Laughton Duo
- 48 Fineoaks
- 79 NEW The Long House
- 128 Stane House
- 128 Stane House (Evening)

Sunday 6
- 48 Fineoaks
- 87 NEW Merriments
- 94 Oak Grove College
- 104 Palatine School Gardens
- 128 Stane House
- 136 Town Place

Malthouse Farm

© Leigh Clapp

Friday 11
111 Ridge House

Saturday 12
35 NEW Cobb Cottage North
46 54 Elmleigh
89 NEW Moustows Manor
111 Ridge House

Sunday 13
46 54 Elmleigh
89 NEW Moustows Manor
100 Old Scaynes Hill House
106 33 Peerley Road
123 Shalford House
146 NEW Windhaven

Tuesday 15
117 8 Sandgate Close

Wednesday 16
125 South Grange

Thursday 17
42 Driftwood
63 Gardens & Grounds of Herstmonceux Castle

Friday 18
75 Latchetts
116 St Mary's House Gardens

Saturday 19
75 Latchetts
103 Orchard House
108 6 Plantation Rise
116 St Mary's House Gardens

Sunday 20
35 NEW Cobb Cottage North
70 The Hundred House
103 Orchard House
115 Saffrons
120 Seaford & Newhaven Group
141 Warninglid Gardens

Monday 21
70 The Hundred House

Wednesday 23
108 6 Plantation Rise
115 Saffrons

Saturday 26
69 Holly House

Sunday 27
25 Burgess Hill Gardens
67 4 Hillside Cottages
69 Holly House
93 Nymans (Evening)
99 NEW Old Pound Farm

Monday 28
25 Burgess Hill Gardens

Thursday 31
117 8 Sandgate Close

August

Saturday 2
26 Butlers Farmhouse

Sunday 3
26 Butlers Farmhouse
42 Driftwood

Monday 4
34 Clinton Lodge

Friday 8
75 Latchetts

Saturday 9
75 Latchetts

Sunday 10
84 Manor of Dean
85 Mayfield Gardens

Saturday 16
56 NEW Gravetye Manor
62 Heatherbank

Sunday 17
62 Heatherbank
83 Malthouse Farm

Tuesday 19
83 Malthouse Farm

Friday 22
45 Durrance Manor (Evening)

Saturday 23
15 4 Ben's Acre
60 Hankham Hall Cottage

Sunday 24
36 Colwood House
45 Durrance Manor
61 Hardwycke
93 Nymans (Evening)
98 The Old Farmhouse

Monday 25
98 The Old Farmhouse
132 Sussex Prairies

Wednesday 27
36 Colwood House

Sunday 31
123 Shalford House

September

Friday 5
133 NEW Sycamore Drive Evening Opening (Evening)

Saturday 6
55 The Grange

Sunday 7
7 Ashdown Park Hotel
55 The Grange
105 Parsonage Farm

Monday 8
21 Borde Hill Garden

Tuesday 9
21 Borde Hill Garden

Saturday 13
114 Rymans
125 South Grange

Sunday 14
71 Jacaranda
125 South Grange

Tuesday 16
140 Vachery Forest Garden

Wednesday 17
135 Tidebrook Manor

Sunday 21
17 Bignor Park
73 King John's Lodge
112 Ringmer Park

Tuesday 23
124 Sheffield Park and Garden

Saturday 27
118 Sandhill Farm House

Sunday 28
65 High Beeches
118 Sandhill Farm House

Visit a garden in your own time – look for by appointment gardens

October

Saturday 18
127 Standen

Sunday 19
102 The Old Vicarage

February 2015

Tuesday 10
107 Pembury House

Wednesday 11
107 Pembury House

Thursday 12
107 Pembury House

Sunday 15
84 Manor of Dean

Tuesday 17
107 Pembury House

Wednesday 18
107 Pembury House

Thursday 19
107 Pembury House

Gardens open to the public

2 Alfriston Clergy House
5 Arundel Castle & Gardens - The Collector Earl's Garden
11 Bateman's
21 Borde Hill Garden
34 Clinton Lodge
40 Denmans Garden
57 Great Dixter House, Gardens & Nurseries
63 Gardens & Grounds of Herstmonceux Castle
65 High Beeches
66 Highdown Gardens
73 King John's Lodge
86 McBean's Orchids
87 NEW Merriments
93 Nymans
109 The Priest House
116 St Mary's House Gardens
119 Sarah Raven's Cutting Garden
124 Sheffield Park and Garden
127 Standen
132 Sussex Prairies
142 West Dean Gardens

By appointment only

12 Bates Green
24 Brightling Down Farm
30 Champs Hill
33 Chidmere Gardens
72 Kent House
95 Ocklynge Manor
97 NEW Old Erringham Cottage
138 NEW Turners House

Also open by appointment

9 Bakers House
10 46 Westup Farm Cottages, Balcombe Gardens
10 Winterfield, Balcombe Gardens
14 Beedinglee
15 4 Ben's Acre
18 4 Birch Close
20 Blue Jays
25 47 Leylands Road, Burgess Hill Gardens
25 30 Sycamore Drive, Burgess Hill Gardens
26 Butlers Farmhouse
28 51 Carlisle Road
31 Channel View
32 2 Woodside, Chiddingly Laughton Duo
36 Colwood House
37 Cookscroft
38 Dachs
39 Dale Park House
41 Down Place
42 Driftwood
43 Duckyls Holt
44 Durford Mill House
45 Durrance Manor
46 54 Elmleigh
47 Fairlight End
50 Fittleworth House
52 70 Ford Road
53 The Garden House
59 Hammerwood House
60 Hankham Hall Cottage
61 Hardwycke
67 4 Hillside Cottages
68 Hobbs Barton
69 Holly House
71 Jacaranda
75 Latchetts
76 Legsheath Farm
79 NEW The Long House
80 Lordington House
81 Lowder Mill
82 Malt House
83 Malthouse Farm
84 Manor of Dean
91 North Hall
92 Nyewood House
98 The Old Farmhouse
100 Old Scaynes Hill House
102 The Old Vicarage
104 Palatine School Gardens
105 Parsonage Farm
106 33 Peerley Road
107 Pembury House
108 6 Plantation Rise
111 Ridge House
114 Rymans
115 Saffrons
117 8 Sandgate Close
118 Sandhill Farm House
120 NEW 4 Sunningdale Close, Seaford & Newhaven Group
121 Sedgwick Park House
125 South Grange
130 Stonehealed Farm
136 Town Place
139 Upwaltham Barns
149 NEW Woodside House

The Gardens

1 ADUR LODGE

The Street, Shoreham-by-Sea BN43 5NJ. Jeremy & Gilda Buckwell. *2m W of Southwick. From A27 on Shoreham bypass take A283 exit signed Shoreham. 1st L to Upper Shoreham Rd, immed L into St Nicholas Lane then R into The Street.* Light refreshments. **Adm £3.50, chd free. Sat 10 May (2-6).**
Walled garden with herbaceous beds, shrubs, vegetables and conservatory. Judas tree a feature in the spring.

2 ◆ ALFRISTON CLERGY HOUSE

Alfriston BN26 5TL. National Trust, 01323 871961, www.nationaltrust.org.uk/alfriston. *4m NE of Seaford. Just E of B2108, in Alfriston Village, adjoining The Tye & St Andrew's Church. Bus: RDH 125 from Lewes, Autopoint 126 from Eastbourne & Seaford.* **Adm £4.65, chd £2.35. For NGS: Tue 17 June (10.30-4.30). For other opening times and information, please phone or see garden website.**
Enjoy the scent of roses, admire the vegetable garden and orchard in a tranquil setting with views across the R Cuckmere. Visit this C14 thatched Wealden hall house, the first building to be acquired by the National Trust in 1896. Our gardener will be available to talk to you about this peaceful cottage garden. Limited wheelchair access.

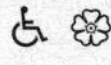

GROUP OPENING

3 AMBROSE PLACE BACK GARDENS

Richmond Road, Worthing BN11 1PZ. *Worthing Town Centre. Entry points: Ambrose Villa, corner Portland Rd and Richmond Rd; No 1, next to St Paul's Church; No 10, opp Worthing Library.* Teas available locally. **Combined adm £5, chd free.**
Sun 15 June (11-1 & 2-5).

1 AMBROSE PLACE
Tom & Helen Watson.
Entry point for visitors

3 AMBROSE PLACE
Tim & Fiona Reynoldson

4 AMBROSE PLACE
Graham & Terri Heald

5 AMBROSE PLACE
Pat & Sue Owen

6 AMBROSE PLACE
Sue Swanborough

7 AMBROSE PLACE
Mark & Susan Frost

8 AMBROSE PLACE
Claire & Steve Hughes

9 AMBROSE PLACE
Anna & Derek Irvine

10 AMBROSE PLACE
Alan & Marie Pringle.
Entry point for visitors

12 AMBROSE PLACE
Peter & Nina May

13 AMBROSE PLACE
Malcolm & Hilary Leeves

14 AMBROSE PLACE
Mr & Mrs A Marks

AMBROSE VILLA
122 Portland Road. Mark & Christine Potter.
Entry point for visitors

The highly acclaimed back gardens of Ambrose Place are indeed a 'horticultural phenomenon' in their rich panoply of styles, plantings and layouts. Behind a classic Regency Terrace, itself the architectural jewel of Worthing, the gardens draw inspiration from such exotic diversity as Morocco, Provence and the Alhambra to the more traditional sources of the English Cottage and Victorian gardens. All within the typically limited space of a terrace (NB seriously restricted disabled access), a variety of imaginative water features add to the charm and attraction for all gardeners and prove that small can be beautiful. Do come and enjoy our special spaces! Sunday 15 June (11am-1pm & 2pm-5pm). Featured on BBC Radio 'Dig-it' programme, in Worthing Herald, West Sussex Gazette and other local media.

A 'horticultural phenomenon' in their rich panoply of styles, plantings and layouts . . .

GROUP OPENING

4 ANSTY GARDENS

Ansty nr. Haywards Heath RH17 5AS. *3m W of Haywards Heath on A272. 1m E of A23. Park on L of A272 300yds W of r'about at junction of A272 and B2036, or if too wet try Council car park at Ansty end of Deaks Lane just W of r'about.* Home-made teas at Whydown Cottage (May) & Appletree Cottage (June). **Combined adm £5, chd free.**
Sun 18 May, Sun 22 June (1.30-6).

APPLETREE COTTAGE
Mr & Mrs G J Longfield

3 LAVENDER COTTAGES
Derry Baillieux

LITTLE ORCHARD
Cuckfield Road. Harry & Charlotte Lloyd Owen

SPRINGFIELD
Deaks Lane.
David & Julie Pyrah

WHYDOWN COTTAGE
Bolney Road. Mrs M Gibson & Lance Gibson.
Open May only

Ansty's gardens offer interesting contrast. **Whydown Cottage** covers an acre with water features and an atmospheric woodland including an Embothrium. **3 Lavender Cottages** has an attractive garden to the front and pretty brick courtyard to the rear with cottage flowers. Close by picturesque **Appletree Cottage** (C16) set in 2-acres with herbaceous beds, vegetable garden and fruit cage with wonderful views. **Springfield's** 1-acre offers mature trees and large pond, also camellias, azaleas, and rhododendrons plus herbaceous border. **Little Orchard** is a 3-acre garden with informal plantings of trees and shrubs, family friendly woodland and fine views. Limited wheelchair access at 3 Lavender Cottages, no wheelchair access at Springfield.

5 ◆ ARUNDEL CASTLE & GARDENS - THE COLLECTOR EARL'S GARDEN

Arundel BN18 9AB. Arundel Castle Trustees Ltd, 01903 882173, www.arundelcastle.org. *In the centre of Arundel, N of A27.* **For opening times and information, please phone or see garden website.**
Ancient castle. Family home of the Duke of Norfolk. 40-acres of grounds and gardens. The Collector Earl's Garden with hot subtropical borders and wild flowers. English herbaceous borders. 2 restored Victorian glasshouses with exotic fruit and vegetables. Walled flower and organic kitchen gardens. C14 Fitzalan Chapel white garden.

GROUP OPENING

6 ARUNDEL GARDENS GROUP

Arundel BN18 9HL. *¼ m W of Arundel town centre. Take Ford Rd exit off main A27 r'about by river then 1st L Torton Hill Rd. All 4 locations well signed and within easy walking distance.* Home-made teas at Torton Top. **Combined adm £5, chd free.**
Sun 25, Mon 26 May (2-5).

4 BIRCH CLOSE
Elizabeth & Mike Gammon
(See separate entry)

20 DALLOWAY ROAD
Mr Geoff Allen

TORTON TOP
36 Torton Hill Road. Barry & Lucy Hopkins

NEW **WOODPECKERS**
Dalloway Road. Mr & Mrs Richard & Jo Faggetter

Four gardens situated in Torton Hill, a residential area. Torton Top has mature gardens of ½-acre with ancient oak trees and large lawn areas interspersed with well stocked beds and borders full of specimen shrubs, acers, clematis, roses and annuals. Delightful natural pond feature with waterfall. 20 Dalloway Road is a charming split level woodland garden designed 14-yrs-ago, in a peaceful setting with many specimen shrubs and trees. Lovely summer house in the woodland corner with garden seating. 4 Birch Close; ¼-acre of woodland garden with a wide range of mature trees and shrubs with many hardy perennials. Extensive selection of spring flowers and over 100 clematis, all in a tranquil setting with meandering pathways and ample seating. New garden for 2014; Woodpeckers, 15 Dalloway Road is a small but pretty garden with a 'wow factor' of the view over the Arun Valley! A garden for all seasons to relax in and watch the wildlife. Partial wheelchair access.

A garden for all seasons to relax in and watch the wildlife . . .

7 ASHDOWN PARK HOTEL

Wych Cross, East Grinstead RH18 5JR. Mr Kevin Sweet, 01342 824988, reservations@ashdownpark.co.uk, www.elitehotels.co.uk. *6m S of East Grinstead. Turn off A22 at Wych Cross T-lights.* Teas (not for NGS). **Adm £5, chd free. Sun 7 Sept (2-5).**
186-acres of parkland, grounds and gardens surrounding Ashdown Park Hotel. Our 'Secret Garden' is well worth a visit with many new plantings. Large number of deer roam the estate and can often be seen during the day. Enjoy and explore the woodland paths, quiet areas and views. Featured in Sussex Life and local press. Some gravel paths and uneven ground with steps.

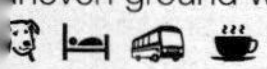

8 NEW 96 ASHFORD ROAD

Hastings TN34 2HZ. Lynda & Andrew Hayler. *From A21 (Sedlescombe Rd North) towards Hastings take 1st exit on r'about A2101 then 3rd on L.* **Adm £2.50, chd free. Sat 31 May, Sat 7 June (2-5).**
Small (100ft x 52ft) Japanese inspired front and back garden. Full of interesting planting. Many acers, azaleas and bamboos. Over 100 different hostas, many miniature. Lower garden with greenhouse and raised beds.

9 BAKERS HOUSE

Bakers Lane, Shipley RH13 8GJ. Mr & Mrs Mark Burrell, 01403 741215, margot@dragons.me.uk. *5m S of Horsham. Take A24 to Worthing, then A272 W, 2nd turn to Dragon's Green. L at George & Dragon PH, Bakers Lane then 300yds on L.* Home-made teas. **Adm £5, chd free. Sun 25 May, 22 Sun June (2-6). Visitors also welcome by appt May to June.**
Large parkland garden with great oaks, lake, laburnum tunnel, rose walks of old-fashioned roses, scented knot garden, olive and lemon walk, bog gardens and big kitchen garden with potager. Featured in many publications. Partial wheelchair access. Garden has gravel paths.

GROUP OPENING

10 BALCOMBE GARDENS

Balcombe RH17 6JJ. *3m N of Cuckfield on B2036. From J10A on M23, follow B2036 S for 2½ m.* Home-made teas at Krawden. **Combined adm £5, chd free. Wed 28 May, Sat 28 June (12-5).**

KRAWDEN
Victoria Road. Ann & Eddie Bryant

46 WESTUP FARM COTTAGES
Chris & Sarah Cornwell.
¼ m N of stn, turn L off B2036 immed before Balcombe Primary School (signed) ¾ m
Visitors also welcome by appt Apr to Sept for groups of 4+. 01444 811891 chris.westup@btinternet.com

WINTERFIELD
Sue & Sarah Howe.
Just N of stn, R into Newlands, follow road up hill. Garden on R once road has become Oldlands Avenue
Visitors also welcome by appt May to July for groups of 4+. 01444 811380 sarahjhowe_uk@yahoo.co.uk

Balcombe is in a designated AONB. Traceable back to the Saxons, the village contains 55 listed buildings incl C15 parish church of St Mary's. Nearby is the famous Ouse Valley Viaduct, ancient woodlands, lake, millpond and reservoir. The three gardens opening for the NGS will especially appeal to plant-lovers and are full of variety and interest. Hidden in the countryside of the High Weald, **Westup Farm Cottages'** garden contains unique and traditional features linked by intimate paths through lush and subtle planting, while **Winterfield** contains as many trees and shrubs as can be crammed into ½-acre with wild flowers, gravelled areas, alpine troughs, a secret garden, pond and borders. **Krawden** offers roses, herbaceous borders, fruit and vegetables, a Mediterranean area with gravel and water feature and provides the venue for teas. Wheelchair access at Winterfield and Krawden only.

11 ◆ BATEMAN'S

Burwash TN19 7DS. National Trust, 01435 882302, www.nationaltrust.org.uk. *6m E of Heathfield. ½ m S of A265 on road leading S at W-end of Burwash, or N from Woods Corner (B2096). Pick up and drop off point available.* **Adm £9.90, chd £4.45. For NGS: Wed 7 May (10-5.30). For other opening times and information, please phone or see garden website.**
Bateman's is an idyllic spot, loved by Rudyard Kipling until the end of his life. Nestled in a shallow valley, the house and garden were a joy and an inspiration to him, from the formal lawns and clipped yew hedges to the romantic meadow with the meandering river flowing through it. Highlights incl; Wild Garden carpeted with spring bulbs below flowering trees and shrubs, Orchard and Watermill. Water levels permitting, the mill will be grinding from 2pm. Most of the garden is accessible. There are some slopes and the paths are uneven.

12 ◆ BATES GREEN
Tye Hill Road, Arlington BN26 6SH. Carolyn & John McCutchan, 01323 485152, www.batesgreen.co.uk. *3½ m SW of Hailsham and of A22. Midway between the A22 and A27 2m S of Michelham Priory. Bates Green is in Tye Hill Rd (N of Arlington Village) 350yds S of Old Oak Inn.* **Adm £4, chd free. Visitors welcome by appt Mar to Oct excl August.**
Plantsman's 2-acre tranquil garden, of interest through the seasons. Springtime including narcissi, primroses, violets, early tulips and coloured stems of cornus. Summer progresses with alliums, hardy geraniums, kniphofias, hemerocallis, grasses, crocosmias and organic vegetables. Autumn peaks with asters, cyclamen, colchicum, dahlias, heleniums, miscanthus, and verbenas. Most areas are wheelchair accessible.

13 BEAUCHAMPS
Float Lane, Udimore, Rye TN31 6BY. Matty & Richard Holmes. *3m W of Rye. 3m E of Broad Oak Xrds. Turn S off B2089 down Float Lane ½ m.* Home-made teas. **Adm £4.50, chd free. Sun 15 June (2-6).**
With fine views of the beautiful Brede Valley, this lovely informal garden, maintained by its owners, displays a wide range of unusual herbaceous plants, shrubs and trees incl fine specimens of *Cornus controversa* 'Variegata', *Baptisia australis* and *Abutilon suntense*. Small orchard, kitchen garden and copse. Many home-propagated herbaceous plants for sale. Full wheelchair access, but difficult after any recent rainfall.

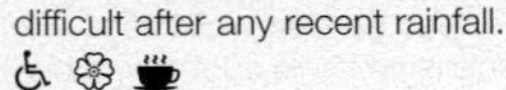

14 BEEDINGLEE
Brighton Road, Lower Beeding, Horsham RH13 6NQ. Mrs Jo Longley, 01403 891251, jolongley@tiscali.co.uk. *4m SE of Horsham on A281 to Cowfold. Beedinglee is approx ½ m N of South Lodge Hotel on A281 from Cowfold to Horsham. The entrance is almost opp a red post box on a stalk.* Light refreshments. **Adm £4, chd free. Sun 11, Sun 25 May (11.30-5). Visitors also welcome by appt June to Oct for groups of 10-25.**
Originally part of the Leonardslee Estate, the planting of the 6-acre Victorian/Edwardian garden disappeared during the hurricane of 1987, when over 100 mature trees blew down. The present garden has evolved since then with many interesting and unusual trees and shrubs. Still an informal garden, there are hidden paths and a secret garden.

Borders planted to capacity with interesting pot pourri of colour, texture and form . . .

15 4 BEN'S ACRE
Horsham RH13 6LW. Pauline Clark, 01403 266912, brian.clark8850@yahoo.co.uk, www.youtube.com, search Pauline & Brian's Sussex Garden. *NE of Horsham. From A281 via Cowfold after Hilliers Garden Centre on L, take 2nd R by Tescos into St Leonards Rd which runs into Comptons Lane. 5th R into Heron Way after mini-r'about, 2nd L Grebe Crescent, 1st L Ben's Acre.* Home-made teas. **Adm £3.50, chd free. Sat 28 June, Sat 23 Aug (1-5). Visitors also welcome by appt from late June to early Sept for groups of 15-40.**
On the edge of St Leonards Forest. Described as a little piece of heaven and a horticultural cornucopia with delights at every corner. Only 100ft x 45ft using steps and terraces to take you up gently to borders planted to capacity with interesting pot pourri of colour, texture and form. Secretive seating areas and top terrace to enjoy the garden while having your pot of tea and cake. Featured on the front cover of a garden book and in Woman's Weekly (under Gardening) Summer 2013.

GROUP OPENING

16 BEXHILL GARDENS
Bexhill TN39 4QB. *Bexhill and Little Common. Proceed to Little Common r'about on A259, then see directions for each garden.* Home-made teas at 6 Daresbury Close. **Combined adm £5, chd free. Sun 8 June (11-5).**

1 ASHCOMBE DRIVE
Richard & Liz Chown.
Exit r'about S into Cooden Sea Rd, 3rd L into Kewhurst Ave, 1st L into Ashcombe Drive, 400yds on R

89 COODEN DRIVE
Carole & Ian Woodland.
From Little Common r'about exit into Cooden Sea Rd. At Cooden Beach follow rd round to L into Cooden Drive, garden approx 1m on R

6 DARESBURY CLOSE
Ms M Carpenter.
From Little Common keep on A259 for approx 1.2m towards Hastings. Turn L just before lights and go across the down. R at T-junction, 2nd L, 1st L

NEW GARDEN FLAT 1, ELM TREE HOUSE
5 Hastings Road. Linda Exley.
From Little Common r'about follow A259 E, at the 2nd set of lights turn R into De La Warr Rd, 2nd L into car park yellow balloons opposite

NEW 6 KINGSWOOD AVENUE
Mr & Mrs Lal & Gloria Ratnayake.
Exit r'about E towards Hastings. After 1m turn L just before lights and over downs. At T-junction L, 1st R, then 3rd L, 2nd L

24 RIDERS BOLT
Margaret & Michael Steer.
½ m E of Little Common r'about on A259 turn L by bus shelter Broad Oak Lane, 1st R Courthope Drive, 1st R Riders Bolt

THE TULIP TREE
20 Chestnut Walk.
Pearse & Andrea Carty.
On r'about take exit skirting the RH side of The Wheatsheaf PH into Chestnut Walk. Halfway down on R

An attractive Edwardian residential seaside town famous for its De la Warr Pavilion arts centre. Also noted for the enthusiastic gardeners who open to the public. **Daresbury Close** is a secluded, partly-walled 80ft garden with mixed planting of acers, shrubs and perennials. Paintings for sale. **Riders Bolt** is a mix of trees, shrubs and herbaceous borders full of mixed perennials with dark and variegated foliage. **Cooden Drive** is a plant lover's garden with large numbers of herbaceous plants, shrubs and trees. Mixed borders with promontory and island beds. At **Ashcombe Drive** discover a delightful garden that is full of unusual plants. Original oil paintings available for purchase. Also an ever popular plant stall. **The Tulip Tree** has a wide variety of flowers, mainly from seed, shade plants and unusual trees. Wildlife, ornamental ponds, and wormery. **Kingswood Avenue** has mature trees, shrubs and herbaceous borders. Bonsai plants, fuschias and pelargoniums. Small pond with frogs, dragonflies etc. Plants for sale. **Hastings Road** is a pretty, cottage garden with a pergola featuring a variety of climbing plants. Some of the gardens have wheelchair access.

17 BIGNOR PARK

Pulborough RH20 1HG. The Mersey Family, www.bignorpark.co.uk. *5m S of Petworth and Pulborough. Well signed from B2138. Nearest villages Sutton, Bignor and West Burton. Approach from the E, directions and map available on website.* Teas at the stables. **Adm £4, chd free.** **Every Wed 2 Apr to 30 Apr (2-5); Sun 8 June, Sun 21 Sept (2-5).**

11-acres of garden to explore, with magnificent views of S Downs. Interesting trees, shrubs, wild flower areas, with swathes of daffodils in spring. The walled flower garden has been replanted with herbaceous borders. Temple, Greek loggia, Zen pond and unusual sculptures. A peaceful garden with no traffic noise. The stables, quadrangle and courtyard have recently been restored. Featured in the Saturday Telegraph, Sunday Times, Sussex Life and local press. Wheelchair access to shrubbery and croquet lawn, not so easy in rest of garden (gravel paths). Steps can be avoided except in stables quadrangle.

18 4 BIRCH CLOSE

Arundel BN18 9HN. Elizabeth & Mike Gammon, 01903 882722, e.gammon@toucansurf.com. *1m S of Arundel. From A27/A284 r'about at W end of Arundel take Ford Rd. After ½ m turn R into Maxwell Rd and follow signs.* Home-made teas. **Adm £3, chd free. Sun 4, Mon 5 May (2-5). Visitors also welcome by appt in May for groups of 10+.**

¼ -acre of woodland garden on edge of Arundel. Wide range of mature trees and shrubs with many hardy perennials. Emphasis on extensive selection of spring flowers and clematis (over 100 incl 11 montana). All in a tranquil setting with secluded corners, meandering paths and plenty of seating.

Caxton Manor

19 NEW THE BIRCHES

19 Selsey Road, Sidlesham, Chichester PO20 7NF. Monica Lucas & Anne Dobbins. *6m S of Chichester City Centre on the B2145 (off the A27 at Stockbridge r'about). Southern end of Sidlesham Village on the B2145, RH-side when heading S.* Home-made teas. **Adm £3.50, chd free. Sat 17, Sun 18 May (11-4.30).**

The garden was created from a 1¼ -acre field by the present owners over the last 12-yrs. The garden incorporates colour co-ordinated beds with grasses and herbaceous perennials and has been planted with wildlife in mind. A pond was created 2-yrs-ago and has added another dimension to the garden and a home for newts etc. There are beehives on site which thrive on the planting. Home-made teas will be provided by the Sussex Snowdrop Trust - a charity helping children at home with life threatening illnesses. The garden has grass paths.

20 BLUE JAYS

Chesworth Close, Horsham RH13 5AL. Stella & Mike Schofield, 01403 251065. *5 mins walk SE of St Mary's Church. From A281 (East St) L down Denne Rd, L to Chesworth Lane, R to Chesworth Close. Garden at end of close with 4 disabled parking spaces. Other parking in local streets and Denne Rd car park (free on Suns).* Home-made teas. **Adm £3.50, chd free (share to The Badger Trust). Sun 25, Mon 26 May (12-5). Visitors also welcome by appt Apr to Sept for groups of 8+ adults. Home-made teas or wine by arrangement.**

Wooded 1-acre garden with rhododendrons, camellias and azaleas. Candelabra primulas and ferns edge the R Arun. Primroses and spring bulbs border woodland path and stream. Cordylines, gunneras, flower beds, a pond, a fountain and new formal rose garden set in open lawns. Arch leads to a vegetable plot and orchard bounded by the river. Large WW2 pill box in the orchard; visits inside with short talk are available. Wheelchair access to most areas.

21 ◆ BORDE HILL GARDEN
Borde Hill Lane, Haywards Heath RH16 1XP. Borde Hill Garden Ltd, 01444 450326, www.bordehill.co.uk. *1½ m N of Haywards Heath. 20 mins N of Brighton, or S of Gatwick on A23 taking exit 10a via Balcombe and Cuckfield.* **Adm £8, chd £5. For NGS: Mon 8, Tue 9 Sept (10-6). For other opening times and information, please phone or see garden website.**
Explore 200-acres of English Heritage Listed Grade II* Garden nestled in an AONB. The Garden was created in the 1890's. The formal Garden is planted as distinctive garden 'rooms' including the Azalea Ring, the Rose & Italian Gardens. Discover the magical woodland, tranquil lakes and parkland. Largest private collection of Champion Trees in the British Isles. Special Offer: Visit again from 10 Sept to 21 Oct 2014 and enjoy 2-4-1 adult entry. Wheelchair access to formal garden (17-acres).

22 BRADNESS GALLERY
Spithurst Road, Spithurst, Barcombe BN8 5EB. Michael Cruickshank & Emma Burnett, www.emmaburnett.co.uk. *5m N of Lewes. Bradness Gallery lies midway between Barcombe and Newick in Spithurst. Free parking in field. Disabled parking will be available outside the gallery.* Home-made teas. **Adm £4, chd free. Sat 21, Sun 22 June (11-6).**
Delightful and tranquil mature, organic, wildlife garden with trees, scented shrubs, old roses, herbaceous borders and wild garden planting. A wooded stream flows along the bottom and two large ponds are home to wild ducks, dragonflies and frogs. Also raised beds for vegetables and cut flowers. Camomile patch. Delicious home-made teas and cakes. Lovely new tearoom for rainy days. Surrounded by fields and cows. Gallery will be open showing original paintings, prints and cards by owners. Featured in Country Living, Sussex Living, Sussex Life, Amateur Gardener and Garden News. Wheelchair access to the upper part of the garden, but the garden does slope down to the ponds and stream and the ground is uneven.

23 BRADSTOW LODGE
The Drive, Ifold, Billingshurst RH14 0TE. Ian & Elizabeth Gregory. *1m S of Loxwood. From B2133 ½ m S of Loxwood take Plaistow Rd, after 800 yds turn R into The Drive (by village shop). Follow signs. Parking in The Drive only.* Home-made teas. **Adm £3.50, chd free. Sun 20 Apr (2-5).**
A series of 'garden rooms' with a variety of planting for yr-round interest creates the effect of a much larger garden than ½ -acre. Bulbs, trees and shrubs, water features, formal topiary, raised beds and containers, greenhouses and vegetable garden give structure, texture and interest. Wheelchair access is possible but not to all areas of the garden due to narrow gravel paths. Unsuitable for powered wheelchairs.

A wooded stream flows along the bottom and two large ponds are home to wild ducks, dragonflies and frogs . . .

24 BRIGHTLING DOWN FARM
Observatory Road, Dallington TN21 9LN. Mr & Mrs P Stephens, 01689 852144/01435 831118, valstephens@icloud.com. *1m from Woods Corner. At Swan PH at Woods Corner, take road opp signed Brightling. Take 1st L, signed Burwash. Almost immed, turn into 1st driveway on L.* Home-made teas. **Adm £7, chd free. Visitors welcome by appt June to Oct for groups of 10-30.**
The garden has several different areas incl a Zen garden, water garden, walled vegetable garden with 2 large greenhouses, herb garden and herbaceous borders. The garden makes clever use of grasses and is set amongst woodland, with stunning countryside views. Winner of the Society of Garden Designers award.

D

GROUP OPENING

25 BURGESS HILL GARDENS
Burgess Hill. *10m N of Brighton. 5 gardens in town centre (park Marle Place), and 4 gardens off Folders Lane. Tickets from any garden.* Home-made teas at Marle Place Community Garden. **Combined adm £5, chd free. Sun 27, Mon 28 July (1-5).**

14 BARNSIDE AVENUE
RH15 0JU. Brian & Sue Knight.
From Folders Lane (B2113) take Kings Way and Barnside is on L

NEW 5 CROMWELL ROAD
RH15 8QH. Caroline Powell.
Cromwell Rd is off London Rd and within walking distance from parking at Marle Place

NEW 41 FAIRFIELD ROAD
RH15 8QB. Mrs Catriona Arnold.
Fairfield Rd runs parallel to London Rd. Park in road or at Marle Place

47 LEYLANDS ROAD
RH15 8AF. Diane & Stephen Rabson.
Leylands Rd lies between London Rd (B2036) and Wivelsfield Stn
Visitors also welcome by appt July to Aug. 01444 247937

MARLE PLACE COMMUNITY GARDEN
Leylands Road, RH15 8HZ. Steve Bridger.
Leylands Rd runs between London Rd and Wivelsfield Stn

THE OLD VICARAGE
27 Crescent Road, RH15 8EH. Martin & Tina Lucas

9 SYCAMORE DRIVE
RH15 0GG. Peter Machin & Martin Savage.
Off Folders Lane 1st house on LH-side at entrance to Sycamore Drive. Walk over gated bridge and follow signs

30 SYCAMORE DRIVE
RH15 0GH. John Smith & Kieran O'Regan.
Off Folders Lane (B2113) at Ditchling Common end
Visitors also welcome by appt June to Sept. 01444 871888

59 SYCAMORE DRIVE
RH15 0GG. Steve & Debby Gill

This diverse group of nine is a mixture of established and small new gardens. Three of the group are a great example of what can be achieved over a five year period from a blank canvas in a new development (Sycamore Drive) while close by is 14 Barnside, a wisteria (pruning advice given) clad house with a family lawn and borders. Next is Marle Place which is an adult community centre. Here local people including some with learning difficulties are actively involved in creating an amazing garden. Just down the road is a garden packed with an array of plants and a wildlife pond. The Victorian Old Vicarage is the oldest garden of the group with bay topiary, fig and jasmine along with statuary and greenhouses. At 5 Cromwell Road this long garden is imaginatively planted with perennials and at nearby 41 Fairfield Road the award winning back garden is home to free range bantams! Many useful ideas for people living in new build properties with small gardens and with heavy clay soil. Some gardens have partial wheelchair access.

26 BUTLERS FARMHOUSE

Butlers Lane, Herstmonceux BN27 1QH. Irene Eltringham-Willson, 01323 833770, irene.willson@btinternet.com. *3m E of Hailsham. Take A271 from Hailsham, go through village of Herstmonceux, turn R signed Church Rd then approx 1m turn R. Do not use SatNav!* Home-made teas (Apr) & Cream teas (Aug). **Adm £3.50 (Apr), £5 (Aug), chd free. Sat 12, Sun 13 Apr, Sat 2, Sun 3 Aug (2-5) with jazz in the garden in Aug. Visitors also welcome by appt Mar to Oct with refreshments provided, please ask for further information.**

Lovely rural setting for 1-acre garden surrounding C16 farmhouse (not open) with views of S Downs. Pretty in spring with primroses and hellebores. Mainly herbaceous with rainbow border, small pond with dribbling frogs and Cornish-inspired beach corners. Restored to former glory, as shown in old photographs, but with a few quirky twists such as a poison garden and a secret jungle garden. Relax and listen to live jazz in the garden in August. Featured on More 4 TV 'Four in a bed' and in Zeitlupe Magazine. Most of garden accessible by wheelchair.

27 CABBAGES & KINGS

Wilderness Barns, Wilderness Lane, Hadlow Down TN22 4HU. System Professional Ltd, www.sysprogardens.teamcreative.co.uk. *5m E of Uckfield. 1/2 m S of A272, centre of Hadlow Down, 1/2 m down Wilderness Lane from A272, turning on L, follow directional signs.* Light refreshments. **Adm £5, chd free. Sat 5 July (10-4).**

System Professional took proud ownership of Ryl Nowell's contemporary garden in September 2006 and started a major restoration exercise that is ongoing to this day to restore the garden back to its former glory. The garden comprises of semi-walled herbaceous and ornamental planting with stunning views overlooking open countryside. The garden also features undulating lawns leading down to a small tranquil lake. Limited wheelchair access.

28 51 CARLISLE ROAD

Eastbourne BN21 4JR. Mr & Mrs N Fraser-Gausden, 01323 722545, n.fg@sky.com. *200yds inland from seafront (Wish Tower), close to Congress Theatre.* Home-made teas. **Adm £3, chd free. Sat 24, Sun 25 May (2-5). Visitors also welcome by appt May to June.**

Walled, S-facing garden (82ft sq) with mixed beds intersected by stone paths and incl small pool. Profuse and diverse planting. Wide selection of shrubs, old roses, herbaceous plants and perennials mingle with specimen trees and climbers. Constantly revised planting to maintain the magical and secluded atmosphere. Art, cards & jewellery stalls.

29 CAXTON MANOR

Wall Hill, Forest Row RH18 5EG. Adele & Jules Speelman. *1m N of Forest Row, 2m S of E Grinstead. From A22 take turning to Ashurstwood, entrance on L after 1/3 m, or 1m on R from N.* Home-made teas. **Adm £4.50, chd free (share to St Catherine's Hospice, Crawley). Fri 16, Sat 17 May (2-5).**

Delightful 5-acre Japanese-inspired gardens planted with mature rhododendrons, azaleas and acers, surrounding large pond with boat house, massive rockery and waterfall, beneath the home of the late Sir Archibald McIndoe (house not open). Japanese tea house and Japanese-style courtyard. Featured in Sussex Living Magazine. **Also open 2 Quarry Cottages (separate admission).**

30 CHAMPS HILL

Waltham Park Road, Coldwaltham, Pulborough RH20 1LY. Mr & Mrs David Bowerman, 01798 831205, mary@thebct.org.uk. *3m S of Pulborough. On A29, turn R to Fittleworth into Waltham Park Rd, garden 400 metres on R.* **Visitors welcome by appt Mar to Oct. Adm by donation.**

27-acres of acid-loving plants around sand pits and woodland. Sculptures, superb views and yr-round interest.

31 CHANNEL VIEW

52 Brook Barn Way, Goring-by-Sea, Worthing BN12 4DW. Jennie & Trevor Rollings, 01903 242431, tjrollings@gmail.com. *1m W of Worthing, near seafront. Turn S off A259 into Parklands Avenue, L at T-junction into Alinora Crescent. Brook Barn Way is immed on L.* Home-made teas. **Adm £3.50, chd free. Sat 28, Sun 29 June (2-5). Visitors also welcome by appt May to Sept.**

Mature owner-designed garden by the sea, imaginatively blending traditional Tudor cottage garden with subtropical, Mediterranean and antipodean planting. Unusually designed structures, paths, arches and pond combine dense planting with shady viewpoints and sunny patios. Inter-connecting garden 'rooms' ensure multiple perspectives and hidden vistas. Great variety of home-grown plants for sale. Featured in Worthing Herald and West Sussex Gazette in 2013. Limited wheelchair access.

GROUP OPENING

32 NEW CHIDDINGLY LAUGHTON DUO

Chiddingly, Lewes BN8 6HS. *6m S of Uckfield. On A22, at the junction with B2124, watch for yellow signs at junction (Woodside) and just S of junction (Netherwood).* Home-made teas at Netherwood Lodge. **Combined adm £3.50, chd free.** **Sat 5 July (2-5).**

NETHERWOOD LODGE 
Muddles Green. Margaret Clarke
01825 872512

2 WOODSIDE
Dick & Kathy Boland.
On B2124 through Laughton E of Roebuck PH
Visitors also welcome by appt June to Aug.
01323 811507
k.boland01@tiscali.co.uk

2 gardens set in small villages. Netherwood Lodge is a small romantic garden and rural retreat created by the present owner over 20 years. A sunny garden with traditional herbaceous borders stocked with mixed perennial plants, roses and a raised bed. Seasonal pots and interesting use of colourful climbing plants. 2 Woodside is a small but inspiring garden that comprises a herb garden, rockeries and a pond with fish, lawn and herbaceous borders, a shade garden, a small stream and pond, fruit trees, rose garden and vegetables in raised beds.

33 CHIDMERE GARDENS

Chidham Lane, Chidham, Chichester PO18 8TD. Jackie & David Russell, 01243 572287, info@chidmere.com, www.chidmerefarm.com. *6m W of Chichester at SE end of Chidham Lane by pond in village.* **Adm £5, chd free. Visitors welcome by appt Apr to Sept. Adm incl a cup of tea.**
Wisteria-clad C15 house surrounded by yew and hornbeam hedges situated next to Chidmere pond. Garden incl white garden, formal rose garden, well-stocked herbaceous borders and springtime woods. 8-acres of orchards with wide selection of heritage and modern varieties of apples, pears and plums incl 200-yr-old varieties of Blenheim Orange and Bramley Seedling. Chidmere pond (approx 5-acres) is a natural wildlife preserve. Chidmere Farm apple juice available. Limited wheelchair access.

34 ◆ CLINTON LODGE

Fletching, Uckfield TN22 3ST. Lady Collum, 01825 722952, www.clintonlodgegardens.co.uk. *4m NW of Uckfield. Clinton Lodge is situated in Fletching High St, N of Rose & Crown PH. Please park on site, not on road.* Home-made teas. **Adm £5, chd free (share to local charities). For NGS: Sun 27 Apr, Mon 2 June, Mon 4 Aug (2-5.30). For other opening times and information, please phone or see garden website.**
6-acre formal and romantic garden, overlooking parkland, with old roses, William Pye water feature, double white and blue herbaceous borders, yew hedges, pleached lime walks, copy of C17 scented herb garden, medieval-style potager, vine and rose allée, wild flower garden. Canal garden, small knot garden, shady glade and orchard. Caroline and Georgian house (not open).

Orchards with wide selection of heritage and modern varieties of apples, pears and plums. . .

35 NEW COBB COTTAGE NORTH

Selsfield Road, Ardingly, Haywards Heath RH17 6TH. Peter & Marlene Holter. *B2028 N of Village. Opposite S gate of South of England showground, 1m S of Wakehurst Place (National Trust). Drive into gravel car park.* Home-made teas. **Adm £3, chd free.** **Sat 12, Sun 20 July (11-6).**
½ -acre edge of village garden with mixed shrubs, perennials, and annuals set off by flowing lawns, 3 wildlife ponds with cascades, patio with seating, terracotta pots and hanging baskets. Come and see Peter's giant show onions in raised beds along with an extensive range of other vegetables, soft fruit, and well stocked greenhouse. Plants and soft fruit for sale. Public WC 150yds away in village. The garden is mostly accessible by wheelchair, but sloping site and grass paths.

36 COLWOOD HOUSE

Cuckfield Lane, Warninglid RH17 5SP. Mr & Mrs Patrick Brenan, 01444 461831, rbrenan@me.com. *6m W of Haywards Heath, 6m SE of Horsham. Entrance on B2115 (Cuckfield Lane). From E, N & S, turn off A23, turn W towards Warninglid for ¾ m. From W come through Warninglid Village.* **Adm £5, chd free (share to Seaforth Hall). Sun 24, Wed 27 Aug (2-5). Visitors also welcome by appt May to Aug for groups of 10+.**
12-acres of garden, with mature and specimen trees from the late 1800s, lawns and woodland edge. Formal parterre, rose and herb gardens. 100ft terrace and herbaceous border overlooking flower-rimmed croquet lawn. Cut turf labyrinth and forsythia tunnel. Water features, statues and gazebos. Pets' cemetery. Giant chessboard. Lake with island and temple. Featured in Sussex Life. The garden has gravel paths, and some slopes.

37 COOKSCROFT

Bookers Lane, Earnley, nr Chichester PO20 7JG. Mr & Mrs J Williams, 01243 513671, williams.cookscroft@virgin.net, www.cookscroft.co.uk. *6m S of Chichester. At end of Birdham Straight A286 from Chichester, take L fork to E Wittering B2198. 1m on, before sharp bend, turn L into Bookers Lane. 2nd house on L. Parking available.* Cream teas. **Adm £4, chd free. Sun 25, Mon 26 May (1-5). Visitors also welcome by appt Feb to Nov. Coaches by prior arrangement.**
This is a garden for all seasons which delights the visitor. Started in 1988, it features a cottage, woodland and Japanese gardens, water features and borders of perennials, with a particular emphasis on S Hemisphere plants. Unusual plants for the plantsman to enjoy, many grown from seed. The garden has grass paths, and unfenced ponds.

38 DACHS

Spear Hill, Ashington RH20 3BA. Bruce Wallace, 01903 892466, wallacebuk@aol.com. *Approx 6m N of Worthing. From A24 at Ashington onto B2133 Billingshurst Rd, R into Spear Hill. We are 1st house, garden runs along Billingshurst Rd.* Home-made teas. **Adm £4, chd free. Sun 30 Mar, Sun 6 Apr, Sat 14, Sun 15 June (2-5.30). Visitors also welcome by appt Apr to Sept.**

A waterlogged field turned into a beautiful garden of about 2-acres. Incl white garden, bog area, stream and unusual design of bridges. Several other themed beds with perennials of different textures and colours. Wide range of daffodils, narcissi, some snowdrops, fritillaria and iris in the spring. Photgraphed 2013 by Leigh Clapp for Country Life.

39 DALE PARK HOUSE

Madehurst BN18 0NP. Robert & Jane Green, 01243 814260, robertgreen@farming.co.uk. *4m W of Arundel. Take A27 E from Chichester or W from Arundel, then A29 (London) for 2m, turn L to Madehurst and follow red arrows.* Home-made teas. **Adm £4, chd free. Sun 8 June (2-5). Visitors also welcome by appt May to July. Wine available by arrangement.**

Set in parkland on S Downs with magnificent views to the sea. Large walled garden with 200ft herbaceous border, mixed borders and small rose garden. Gravel sunken garden. Rose and clematis arches, interesting collection of hostas, foliage plants and shrubs, orchard and kitchen garden.

40 ◆ DENMANS GARDEN

Denmans Lane, Fontwell BN18 0SU. Michael Neve & John Brookes, 01243 542808, www.denmans-garden.co.uk. *5m from Chichester and Arundel. Off A27, ½ m W of Fontwell r'about.* **Adm £4.95, chd £3.95. For NGS: Mon 2 June (10-4). For other opening times and information, please phone or see garden website.**

Denmans is a unique 4-acre garden designed for yr-round interest through use of form, colour and texture. Owned by Michael Neve and John Brookes MBE, renowned garden designer and writer. It is a garden full of ideas to be interpreted within

Follers Manor

© Marianne Majerus

smaller home spaces. Award-winning café and plant centre.

41 DOWN PLACE

South Harting, Petersfield GU31 5PN. Mr & Mrs D M Thistleton-Smith, 01730 825374, selina@downplace.co.uk. *1m SE of South Harting. B2141 to Chichester, turn L down unmarked lane below top of hill.* Home-made teas. **Adm £3.50, chd free (share to Friends of Harting Church). Sat 26, Sun 27 Apr, Sat 14, Sun 15 June (2-6). Groups of 15+ also welcome by appt, adm includes refreshments.**

7-acre hillside, chalk garden on the N side of S Downs with fine views of surrounding countryside. Extensive herbaceous, shrub and rose borders on different levels merging into natural wild flower meadow renowned for its collection of native orchids. Fully stocked vegetable garden and greenhouses. Spring flowers and blossom. Substantial top terrace and borders accessible to wheelchairs.

42 DRIFTWOOD

4 Marine Drive, Bishopstone, Seaford BN25 2RS. Geoff Stonebanks & Mark Glassman, 01323 899296, geoffstonebanks@gmail.com, www.driftwoodbysea.co.uk. *A259 between Seaford and Newhaven. Turn L into Marine Drive from Bishopstone Rd, 2nd on R. Please park carefully in road but NOT on bend beyond house.* Light refreshments. **Adm £4, chd free. Tue 10 June, Tue 1, Thur 17 July, Sun 3 Aug (11-5). Visitors also welcome by appt June to Aug for groups of 25 max.**

An exuberant yet immaculate seaside garden (112 x 48ft) split into several garden rooms. It has an eclectic palette, creating a layered tapestry of coloured plantings and fully embraces its location, beautifully integrating wooden and rusted metal features with the landscape. The heavy, dense plantings (over 400 plants) with no lawn and no exposed soil create an illusion of a much bigger garden. Holder of coveted Daily Mail National Garden competition blue plaque and winner of the Best Small Garden in the UK for Garden News magazine, both 2012. Plant supports and garden decorations for sale. In 2013, featured garden in Mail On Sunday, Sussex Life and featured in 360° Panorama in 'Mail Plus', Weekend Magazine's on line version. Monthly article in Garden News magazine about the garden, written by owner. Featured extensively in local press. Steep drive and narrow paths but help readily available on site or call ahead before visit.

43 DUCKYLS HOLT

Selsfield Road, West Hoathly RH19 4QN. Mrs Diana Hill & Miss Sophie Hill, 01342 810282, sophie@duckylsholt.fsnet.co.uk. *4m SW of East Grinstead, 6m E of Crawley. At Turners Hill take B2028. After 1m fork L to West Hoathly. Garden on R immed beyond 30 mph sign. Some parking at garden, other parking in village.* Home-made teas. **Adm £3.50, chd free.** **Sat 24, Sun 25, Mon 26 May, Sat 28, Sun 29 June (11-5.30). Also open 24 May & 28 June The Priest House, combined adm £4. Visitors also welcome by appt May to June.**

Delightful cottage garden of approx 2-acres on many different levels. Small herb garden, colourful formal and informal plantings, herbaceous borders, rose border and formal rose garden, lots of pots and baskets - a riot of colour. Mature azaleas and rhododendrons in season.

44 DURFORD MILL HOUSE

West Harting, Petersfield GU31 5AZ. Mrs Sue Jones, 01730 821125, sdurford@tiscali.co.uk. *3m E of Petersfield. Just off A272 between Petersfield and Rogate, signed Durford Mill and the Hartings. From S Harting past village shop first L to West Harting.* Home-made teas. **Adm £3.50, chd free.** **Sun 11 May, Sat 21, Sun 22 June (2-5.30). Visitors also welcome by appt May to July for groups of 10+.**

Come and relax in our peaceful mill garden with it's meandering stream and quiet places to sit. Wander along the paths and over the bridges among the flowers, shrubs and beautiful trees. Finishing up with delicious home-made cakes and tea. Wheel chair access to main garden and tea area.

45 DURRANCE MANOR

Smithers Hill Lane, Shipley RH13 8PE. Gordon & Joan Lindsay, 01403 741577, jlindsay@dsl.pipex.com. *7m SW of Horsham. A24 to A272 (S from Horsham, N from Worthing), turn W towards Billingshurst. 1.7m, 2nd L Smithers Hill Lane signed to Countryman PH. Garden 2nd on L.* Home-made teas. **Adm £4.50, chd free.** **Evening Opening with wine available on Fri 22 Aug (6-8.30); Sun 24 Aug (2-6). Visitors also welcome by appt Apr to Sept.**

2-acre site surrounding medieval hall house (not open) with Horsham stone roof. Uninterrupted views to S Downs and Chanctonbury Ring over ha-ha. Many different gardens incl colourful long borders, Japanese-style gardens, shade gardens, large pond, wild flowering meadow and orchard, greenhouse and vegetable garden.

Large walled garden set in parkland on South Downs with magnificent views to the sea . . .

46 54 ELMLEIGH

Midhurst GU29 9HA. Wendy Liddle, 07796 562275, wendyliddle@btconnect.com. *1/4 m W of Midhurst, off A272. Wheelchair users please use designated parking spaces at top of drive, phone on arrival for assistance.* Home-made teas. **Adm £3, chd free.** **Sat 7, Sun 8, Sat 21, Sun 22 June, Sat 12, Sun 13 July (10-5). Visitors and groups also welcome by appt May to Sept.**

Come and walk around this beautiful, award-winning garden on the edge of Midhurst. Planted with majestic Scots pines, shrubs, perennials and annuals, packed with interest, a tapestry of unusual plants giving all-season colour. Many raised beds and numerous statues. A child-friendly garden. New attraction is a wildlife pond and bog garden.

47 FAIRLIGHT END

Pett Road, Pett, Hastings TN35 4HB. Chris & Robin Hutt, 07774 863750, chrishutt@btopenworld.com. *4M E of Hastings. From Hastings take A259 to Rye. At White Hart Beefeater turn R into Friars Hill. Descend into Pett Village. Park in village hall car park, opp house.* Home-made teas, pimms, wine & beer (in village hall if wet). **Adm £4.50, chd free (share to Pett Village Hall).** **Fri 13, Sat 14 June (11-5). Visitors also welcome by appt May to Sept for groups of 10+.**

3-acre sloping garden with lovely views. Kitchen garden with 30 raised beds, wild flower meadow with mown paths, large orchard, two natural ponds joined by a stream and terraced herbaceous borders; Ian Kitson designed split level garden in front of house with corten steel wall and plant supports, topiary, and decking, all around ancient cherry tree. New decorative fruit garden this year. Fine hay meadows. Model kitchen garden. Featured in the English Garden, June 2013. Steep paths, gravelled areas, unfenced ponds.

D

48 FINEOAKS

Hammer Lane, Cowbeech, Heathfield TN21 9HF. Brian & Brenda Taylor. *5m S of Heathfield, 5m N of Hailsham. From Cowbeech 1m, on LH-side.* Light refreshments. **Adm £4, chd £2 (under 12s free).** **Sat 3, Sun 4 May, Sat 5, Sun 6 July (1-5).**

An immaculate 3½ -acre garden in lovely countryside. Along the northern boundary runs a trout stream, flowing in spring, trickling in summer. The lawns are punctuated with island beds planted idiosyncratically with a mixture of shrubs, herbaceous and bedding plants. Further afield an orchard, large vegetable and fruit garden, greenhouse and woodland. Nearer the house a pond, fountain and pretty rockery. Home-made organic jams and marmalades for sale.

49 FIRLE PLACE HERB GARDEN

Firle Place, Firle, Lewes BN8 6LP. Lady Gage, firleplaceherbgarden.co.uk. *Located within main grounds of Firle Place, making up part of its walled gardens. Signed before entering main village of Firle approx 300yds from A27 turn, 4m from Lewes, free parking with a short walk to garden.* **Adm £3, chd free.** **Sun 8 June (12-5).**

Lady Gage's fascinating walled wilderness, 130ft x 200ft, originally part of the kitchen gardens for Firle Place, being transformed into newly planted tranquil herb garden. A unique work in progress, started in the winter of 2011, already home to a wide range of unusual medicinal, culinary and native wild herbs, planted organically in zones of colour. Herbal teas, a selection of fresh infusions made from the plants in the garden.

50 FITTLEWORTH HOUSE

Bedham Lane, Fittleworth, Pulborough RH20 1JH. Edward & Isabel Braham, 01798 865074, www.marksaunders66.com. *3m E, SE of Petworth. Just off A283, midway between Petworth and Pulborough, 200yds along lane signed Bedham*. Home-made teas. **Adm £5, chd free. Every Wed 7 May to 30 July (2-5). Visitors also welcome by appt May to July for groups of 5+.**

3-acre tranquil garden with working walled kitchen garden growing a wide range of fruit, vegetables and flowers. Large glasshouse and old potting shed. Rhododendrons, roses, fountain, mixed borders. Magnificent cedar overlooks wisteria-covered Georgian house (not open) and croquet lawn. Wild garden, long grass areas, wildlife pond, spring bulbs. Head gardener with 30-yrs experience on hand to answer questions. The garden sits on a gentle slope but is accessible for wheelchairs/buggies.

A wonderfully lush sanctuary in which to relax . . .

51 FOLLERS MANOR

Seaford Road, Alfriston, Polegate BN26 5TT. Geoff & Anne Shaw, www.facebook.com/FollersManorGarden. *1/2 m S of Alfriston. From Alfriston uphill towards Seaford. Park on L in paddock before garden. Garden next door to Alfriston Youth Hostel immed before road narrows*. Light refreshments. **Adm £5, chd free. Sat 7, Sun 8 June (2-5.30).**

Contemporary garden designed by Ian Kitson attached to C17 listed historic farmhouse. Entrance courtyard, sunken garden, herbaceous displays, wildlife pond, wild flower meadows, woodland area and beautiful views of the S Downs. Winner of Sussex Heritage Trust Award and three awards from the Society of Garden Designers; Best Medium Residential Garden, Hard Landscaping and, most prestigious, the Judges Award. Featured on Gardeners World, C4's Landscape Man and in numerous publications as far afield as Shanghai! Limited wheelchair access to some areas.

52 70 FORD ROAD

Arundel BN18 9EX. Tony & Lizzie Gilks, 01903 884981, timespan70@tiscali.co.uk. *1m S of Arundel. At Chichester r'about take exit to Ford/Bognor Regis*. Home-made teas. **Adm £3.50, chd free. Sat 21, Sun 22 June (2-5). Visitors also welcome by appt from 4 May to 15 Sept.**

An immaculate town garden with ingenious ideas of how to incorporate well stocked flower beds with yr-round colour and texture, herbs, fruit and vegetable beds producing a wonderfully lush sanctuary in which to relax. A small exhibition of artefacts covering the Great War 1914-1918.

53 THE GARDEN HOUSE

5 Warleigh Road, Brighton BN1 4NT. Bridgette Saunders & Graham Lee, 07729 037182 or 01273 702840, contact@gardenhousebrighton.co.uk. *1 1/2 m N of sea front. 1st turning L off Ditchling Rd, heading N from sea front*. Home-made teas. **Adm £3.50, chd free. Sun 13 Apr (11-4). Visitors also welcome by appt Apr to July for groups of 10+.**

Tucked away in the heart of the city this really is a secret garden, in Victorian times a market garden. The garden is organic and gives interest all year, supporting cut flowers, vegetables, fruit, old climbing roses and a pond. Many of the plants have been propagated by the garden owner, and the garden has unique features using many recycled materials. Garden produce and plants for sale.

54 GARDENERS' COTTAGE

West Dean, nr Chichester PO18 0RX. Jim Buckland & Sarah Wain. *6m N of Chichester. Follow signs to West Dean Gardens and park in gardens car park. Follow signs to cottage*. Home-made teas. **Adm £3, chd free. Sun 11 May (11-5).**

Small serene and secluded theatrical retreat with strong emphasis on texture, foliage and good structure created by trees, topiary, labyrinthine paths, interesting spaces. Separate courtyard garden with pond.

55 THE GRANGE

Fittleworth RH20 1EW. Mr & Mrs W Caldwell. *3m W of Pulborough on A283. In Fittleworth turn S onto B2138 then W at Swan PH. From the S turn L off A29 onto B2138 at Bury Gate then L again at Swan PH. Do NOT use Satnav*. Home-made teas. **Adm £4, chd free. Sat 12, Sun 13 Apr, Sat 6, Sun 7 Sept (2-5.30).**

3-acre garden gently sloping to R Rother. Formal areas enclosed by yew hedges comprising colour-themed beds and herbaceous borders around pretty C18 house (not open). Small potager and orchard.Tulips and other spring flowering bulbs and snakeshead fritillaries a feature in April. Late summer colour provided by sedums, dahlias, hydrangeas persicarias and asters. Plants for sale September only. Featured in Ten Landscapes by Michael Balston and in the April 2014 issue of The English Garden. The garden has gravel paths.

56 NEW GRAVETYE MANOR

West Hoathly RH19 4LJ. Jeremy & Elizabeth Hosking, www.gravetyemanor.co.uk. *From M23, J10 E Grinstead, A264 Dukes Head, B2028 Turner's Hill. After Turner's Hill take L fork for Sharpthorne, then take first L into Vowels Lane*. **Adm £20 incl refreshments. Sat 16 Aug (2-5). Advanced booking only. For tickets please visit www.ngs.org.uk or phone 01483 211535.**

The gardens at Gravetye Manor can be considered amongst the most influential in English gardening history. The manor was the home of revolutionary gardener, William Robinson from 1884-1935. Thanks to the backing of new owners, a major restoration project is under way. Overseeing the project is head gardener, Tom Coward, who has come from working 3 years alongside Fergus Garrett at Great Dixter. Parts of the garden are accessible via ramps.

57 ◆ GREAT DIXTER HOUSE, GARDENS & NURSERIES

Northiam TN31 6PH. Great Dixter Charitable Trust, 01797 252878, www.greatdixter.co.uk. *8m N of Rye. 1/2 m NW of Northiam off A28.* **For opening times and information, please phone or see garden website.**

Designed by Edwin Lutyens and Nathaniel Lloyd whose son, Christopher, officiated over these gardens for 55yrs, creating one of the most experimental and constantly changing gardens of our time. Wide variety of interest from clipped topiary, wild meadow flowers, natural ponds, formal pool and the famous long border and exotic garden. A long and varied season is aimed for. A wide range of educational study days and workshops held. Some areas of the garden are accessible for wheelchairs, a map is available from the ticket kiosk.

58 GREAT LYWOOD FARMHOUSE

Lindfield Road, Ardingly RH17 6SW. Richard & Susan Laing. *21/2 m N of Haywards Heath. Between Lindfield and Ardingly on B2028. 2m N of Lindfield, turn L (west) down paved track. 1st house on R, car park beyond house.* Home-made teas. **Adm £5, chd free. Sun 1, Sat 14 June (2-5.30).**

Approx 11/2 -acre terraced garden surrounding C17 Sussex farmhouse (not open). Terracing and lovely views to S Downs. Featuring lawns and grass walks, mixed borders, rose garden, kitchen garden and orchard, walled garden with dovecote. Wheelchair access possible, some slopes and short grass.

59 HAMMERWOOD HOUSE

Iping, Midhurst GU29 0PF. Mr & Mrs M Lakin, 07785 776222, amandalakin@me.com. *3m W of Midhurst. Take A272 from Midhurst, approx 2m outside Midhurst, turn R for Iping. From A3, leave for Liphook, follow B2070. Turn L for Iping.* Home-made teas. **Adm £5, chd free. Sun 4, Sun 11 May (1.30-5). Visitors also welcome by appt in May for groups of 10+.**

Large S-facing garden with lots of mature shrubs, incl camellias, rhododendrons and azaleas. An arboretum with a variety of flowering and fruit trees. The old yew and beech hedges give a certain amount of formality to this traditional English garden. Tea on the terrace is a must with the most beautiful view of the S Downs. For the more energetic, there is a woodland walk. Wheelchair access limited, garden set on slope.

60 HANKHAM HALL COTTAGE

Hankham, nr Stone Cross BN24 5AH. Mr & Mrs Simon Buller, 01323 763348, simon.buller@btinternet.com. *4m N of Eastbourne. 3m S of Hailsham. At Stone Cross take B2104 Hailsham Rd, after 100yds turn R, then fork R. At T junction turn R. Hankham Hall Cottage is 200yds on R.* **Adm £4, chd free. Sat 23 Aug (11-5). Visitors also welcome by appt.**

Keen gardeners' 2-acre informal country garden, featuring island beds of individual varieties and colours. Large collection of different plants. Spectacular 'hot' border in August. Natural pond and wood encouraging wildlife. Kitchen garden and propagating greenhouse.

61 HARDWYCKE

Southfields Road, Eastbourne BN21 1BZ. Lois Machin, 01323 729391, loisandpeter@yahoo.co.uk. *Centre of Eastbourne, Upperton. A259 towards Eastbourne, Southfields Rd on R just before junction with A2270 (Upperton Rd). Limited parking, public car park (pay) in Southfields Rd.* **Adm £3.50, chd free. Sun 8 June, Sun 24 Aug (11-5). Visitors also welcome by appt May to Sept for 12 max. Refreshments by arrangement.**

Delightful S-facing town garden mainly of chalky soil, with many usual and unusual plants. Separate vegetable garden with restored 1920's summer house. Wide selection of shrubs including 50 types of clematis. L shaped garden that has 2 spaces 70ft x 50ft and 18ft x 50ft. 2 slight steps to rear garden area, accessible with care.

62 HEATHERBANK

20 London Road, Pulborough RH20 1AS. Colin & Dee Morley. *On A29 opp BP garage in Pulborough, large eucalyptus tree in front garden.* Home-made teas. **Adm £3.75, chd free. Sat 16, Sun 17 Aug (2-5).**

Appletree Cottage, Ansty Gardens

A real oasis in a most unexpected location. A Mediterranean-style suburban garden (200ft x 40ft), with interesting features and well stocked with many unusual plants, incl several tropical species.

63 ◆ GARDENS & GROUNDS OF HERSTMONCEUX CASTLE

Herstmonceux, Hailsham BN27 1RN. Bader International Study Centre, Queen's University (Canada), 01323 833816, www.herstmonceux-castle.com. *Located between Herstmonceux and Pevensey on the Wartling Rd. From Herstmonceux take A271 to Bexhill, 2nd R signed Castle. Do not use SatNav.* Light refreshments in licenced tearooms. **Adm £6, chd £3, concessions £4.95.** **For NGS: Sun 15 June, Thur 17 July (10-6). For other opening times and information, please phone or see garden website.**

Herstmonceux is renowned for its magnificent moated castle set in beautiful parkland and superb Elizabethan walled gardens, leading to delightful discoveries such as our rhododendron, rose and herb gardens and onto our woodland trails. Take a slow stroll past the lily covered lakes to the 1930s folly and admire the sheer magnificence of the castle. The Gardens & Grounds first opened for the NGS in 1927. Limited wheelchair access to formal gardens.

GROUP OPENING

64 NEW HERSTMONCEUX PARISH TRAIL

Hailsham BN27 4JF. *2m N of Herstmonceux Village off A271. See directions for each garden.* Cream teas on the lawn at Lime Cross Nursery Pinetum. **Combined adm £4, chd free.**
Sat 21, Sun 22 June (10-5).

NEW 2 ACRES
Mr Jon Tate.
1 min E of Herstmonceux Village (A271) on LH-side

NEW THE ALLOTMENTS - STUNTS GREEN
George Taylor.
E on A271, take L at Woolpack PH onto West End Rd, then next R towards Cowbeech Village. Allotments on RH-side

NEW COWBEECH HOUSE
Cowbeech. Mr Anthony Hepburn.
In the centre of Cowbeech Village opp the Merrie Harriers PH

NEW LIME CROSS NURSERY PINETUM
Herstmonceux. Vicky Tate.
1 min E of Herstmonceux Village A271 on LH-side
www.limecross.co.uk

Herstmonceux Parish lies in 1066 country. It is a working rural community with an impressive history incl trug making. Both Herstmonceux Castle and Science Centre (once home to Greenwich Observatory) are worth visiting. Along with these, the parish has some gardens and allotments showing an abundance of enthusiasm. Starting at Cowbeech House with its tranquil setting, relaxing water features and maybe a few stunning surprises. Then, heading down to the 54 allotments set in the picturesque fruit farm at Stunts Green showing community spirit aplenty. Moving onto Two Acres, with its splendid selection of trees and shrubs sloping to the beautiful garden pond. The trail then ends with delicious cream teas on the lawn at Lime Cross Nursery Pinetum. This will give you a chance to sit down, relax and take in the view over the pinetum and soak up the shapes, colours and different sizes of planting looking over the nursery reservoir. Please note some of the gardens have limited wheelchair access.

65 ◆ HIGH BEECHES

Handcross, Haywards Heath RH17 6HQ. High Beeches Gardens Conservation Trust, 01444 400589, www.highbeeches.com. *5m NW of Cuckfield. On B2110, 1m E of A23 at Handcross.* Light refreshments. **Adm £7, chd free. For NGS: Sun 8 June, Sun 28 Sept (1-5). For other opening times and information, please phone or see garden website.**

25-acres of enchanting landscaped woodland and water gardens with spring daffodils, bluebells and azalea walks, many rare and beautiful plants, wild flower meadows and glorious autumn colours. Picnic area. National Collection of Stewartias.

66 ◆ HIGHDOWN GARDENS

33 Highdown Rise, Littlehampton Road, Goring-by-Sea, Worthing BN12 6FB. Worthing Borough Council, 01903 501054, www.highdowngardens.co.uk. *3m W of Worthing. Off A259. Approx 1m from Goring-by-Sea Railway Station.* **Adm by donation. For NGS: Sun 25 May, Thur 5 June (10-6). For other opening times and information, please phone or see garden website.**

Famous garden created by Sir Frederick Stern situated in chalk pit and downland area, containing a wide collection of plants. Many plants were raised from seed brought from China by great collectors like Wilson, Farrer and Kingdon-Ward. Open all yr-round. Wheelchair access limited. Hillside garden with mainly grass paths.

NCH

Imaginatively blending traditional Tudor cottage garden with subtropical, Mediterranean and antipodean planting . . .

67 4 HILLSIDE COTTAGES

Downs Road, West Stoke PO18 9BL. Heather & Chris Lock, 01243 574802, chlock@btinternet.com. *3m NW of Chichester. From A286 at Lavant, head W for 1½ m, nr Kingley Vale.* **Adm £3, chd free. Sun 27 July (2-5). Visitors also welcome by appt June to Aug.**

Garden 120ft x 27ft in a rural setting. Densely planted with mixed borders and shrubs. Large collection of roses, mainly New English shrub roses; walls, fences and arches covered with mid and late season clematis; baskets overflowing with fuchsias. A profusion of colour and scent in a well maintained small garden.

68 HOBBS BARTON

Streele Lane, Framfield, nr Uckfield TN22 5RY. Mr & Mrs Jeremy Clark, 01825 732259, hobbsbarton@btinternet.com. *3m E of Uckfield. Signed from Framfield (near church) and Buxted (A272 mini-r'about near Railway Station).* Home-made teas in C17 Barn Room. **Adm £5, chd free (share to The Friends of Sussex Hospices). Sat 7, Sun 8 June (11.30-5). Visitors also welcome by appt June to July for groups of 10+.**

Peaceful pastoral setting, typical of rural Sussex. Far from traffic noise, this is a mature garden of 2³/₄ -acres developed by present owners over past 40yrs. Sweeping lawns lead to areas with many types of rose, shrubberies and herbaceous borders; numerous specimen trees incl *M'sequoia glyptostroboides*, liriodendron, giant prostrate junipers; water features; part-walled vegetable/fruit garden. Developing woodland garden. Delightful 10 min circular lakeside stroll. Picnics and dogs in car park field only (some shady areas).

69 HOLLY HOUSE

Beaconsfield Road, Chelwood Gate, Haywards Heath RH17 7LF. Mrs Deirdre Birchell, 01825 740484, db@hollyhousebnb.demon.co.uk, www.hollyhousebnb.co.uk. *7m E of Haywards Heath. From Nutley Village on A22 turn off at RajRani signed Chelwood Gate 2m. Chelwood Gate Village Hall on R, Holly House is opp.* Home-made teas. **Adm £3.50, chd free. Sat 10, Sun 11 May, Sat 14, Sun 15 June, Sat 26, Sun 27 July (2-5). Visitors also welcome by appt May to July. Coaches can drop off only.**

An acre of English garden providing views and cameos of plants and trees round every corner with many different areas giving constant interest. A fish pond and a wildlife pond beside a grassy area with many shrubs and flower beds. Among the trees and winding paths there is a cottage garden which is a profusion of colour and peace. Exhibition of paintings and cards by owner. Garden accessible by wheelchair in good weather, but it is not easy.

70 THE HUNDRED HOUSE

Pound Lane, Framfield TN22 5RU. Dr & Mrs Michael Gurney. *4m E of Uckfield. From Uckfield take B2102 through Framfield. 1m from centre of village turn L into Pound Lane, then ³/₄ m on R. Disabled parking is close by the entrance gate.* Home-made teas. **Adm £4, chd free. Sun 20, Mon 21 July (2-5.30).**

Delightful garden with panoramic views set in the grounds of the historic The Hundred House. Fine stone ha-ha. 1¹/₂ -acre garden with mixed herbaceous borders, productive vegetable garden, greenhouse, ancient yew tree, pond area with some subtropical plants, secret woodland copse and orchard. Beech hedge, field and butterfly walk, wild flower meadow under development.

A garden full of ideas to be interpreted within smaller home spaces . . .

71 JACARANDA

Chalk Road, Ifold, Loxwood RH14 0UE. Brian & Barbara McNulty, 01403 751532, bam101@btinternet.com. *1m S of Loxwood. From A272/A281 take B2133 (Loxwood). ¹/₂ m S of Loxwood take Plaistow Rd. 3rd R into Chalk Rd. Follow signs for parking and garden.* Home-made teas. **Adm £3, chd free. Sun 14 Sept (2-5). Visitors also welcome by appt May to Sept.**

Tranquil wildlife-friendly ¹/₄ -acre garden created from scratch over past 14-yrs. Sweeping borders with many interesting trees, shrubs and perennials give colour and interest throughout the yr. Delightful seating areas allow you to sit and enjoy the garden. Wide variety of roses and clematis plus over 70 hostas in pots. Large raised bed in the kitchen garden. Greenhouse, potting and compost areas. Wheelchair users can park in the driveway.

72 KENT HOUSE

East Harting, nr Petersfield GU31 5LS. Mr & Mrs David Gault, 01730 825206. *4m SE of Petersfield. On B2146 at South Harting take Elsted to Midhurst Rd E for ¹/₂ m. Just W of Turkey Island, turn N up no through road for 400yds.* **Adm £4, chd free. Visitors welcome by appt May to Aug.**

The garden of about 1¹/₂ -acres is designed around 4 areas, each with quite a different feeling. A shaded garden for spring with bulbs and woodlanders, 2 summer gardens; 1 based on the square, and the other on the circle, and an area of open spaces bringing in lovely views of the Downs and surrounding countryside.

73 ◆ KING JOHN'S LODGE

Sheepstreet Lane, Etchingham TN19 7AZ. Jill Cunningham, 01580 819232, www.kingjohnsnursery.co.uk. *2m W of Hurst Green. A265 Burwash to Etchingham. Turn L before Etchingham Church into Church Lane which leads into Sheepstreet Lane after ¹/₂ m. L after 1m.* Home-made teas. **Adm £4, chd free. For NGS: Sun 30 Mar (2-4); Sun 25, Mon 26 May (11-5); Sun 22 June, Sun 21 Sept (2-5). For other opening times and information, please phone or see garden website.**

4-acre romantic garden for all seasons surrounding an historic listed house (not open). Formal garden with water features, rose walk and wild garden and pond. Rustic bridge to shaded ivy garden, large herbaceous borders, old shrub roses and secret garden. Further 4-acres of meadows, fine trees and grazing sheep. Nursery and shop. Garden is mainly flat. Stepped areas can usually be accessed from other areas. No disabled WC.

74 NEW KNOCKBRIDGE HOUSE

Laurel Lane, Icklesham, Winchelsea TN36 4AN. Jo & Charles Sandeman-Allen. *A259 to village of Icklesham. Knockbridge is S of village.* Light refreshments. **Adm £3.50, chd free. Sat 10, Sun 11 May (11-5).**

Knockbridge House enjoys 7-acres of mature gardens arranged in discrete areas around the house with lawns, herbaceous borders, pond, swimming pool with tropical garden of tree ferns and a potager with intricately laid brick paths and box hedging. Paths are tightly mown through clouds of cow parsley; terraces are dominated by a Magnolia grandiflora, two huge figs and a wisteria.

75 LATCHETTS

Freshfield Lane, Danehill, Haywards Heath RH17 7HQ. Laurence & Rebeka Hardy, 01825 790237, rebekahardy@gmail.com. *5m NE of Haywards Heath, 7m S of East Grinstead. SW off A275. In Danehill turn into Freshfield Lane at War Memorial. 1m on R (not Latchetts Farmhouse).* Cream teas. **Adm £5, chd free (share to Danehill Parish Church). Fri 30, Sat 31 May, Fri 20, Sat 21 June, Fri 18, Sat 19 July, Fri 8, Sat 9 Aug (1.30-5). Visitors also welcome by appt May to Aug for groups of 20-60.**

'In Top 10 of 600 gardens visited' as quoted by a coach organiser. 8-acres of variety, design, and imagination. Lovely setting, fine lawns, colourful planting, walled Christian millennium garden, heuchera tapestry, ponds, ducks, geese, unusual water features. Raised bed vegetables, woodland, prairie, wild flowers. Scary path for all ages! New sensory garden. Features incl Safari Hunt for children, delicious home-made teas, enlarged fern stumpery and reworked water garden. Wheelchair access can be difficult in wet weather. Some slopes in garden to avoid steps. Disabled WC.

76 LEGSHEATH FARM

nr Forest Row RH19 4JN. Mr & Mrs M Neal, 01342 810230, legsheath@btinternet.com. *4m S of East Grinstead. 2m W of Forest Row, 1m S of Weirwood Reservoir.* Home-made teas. **Adm £5, chd free (share to Holy Trinity Church, Forest Row). Sun 18 May (2-5). Visitors also welcome by appt Mar to Oct.**

Panoramic views over Weirwood reservoir. Exciting 10-acre garden with woodland walks, water gardens and formal borders. Of particular interest, clumps of wild orchids, fine davidia, acers, eucryphia and rhododendrons. Mass planting of different species of meconopsis on the way to ponds. Featured in Sussex Living and on the cover of The Yellow Book 2014.

78 LITTLE HILL

Hill Farm Lane, Codmore Hill, Pulborough RH20 1BW. Barbara & Derek James. *1m N of Pulborough. Hill Farm Lane off A29 by The India Resturant, garden 10th on L. Overflow parking in field before garden entrance, follow signs.* **Adm £4, chd free. Evening Opening with wine available on Thur 26 June (5-7); Sun 29 June (2-4).**

4-acres of formal gardens with shaded areas and countryside views. The garden incl a sunken rose garden and pond, tiered rock garden with waterfall and pond, rose and grape arbour in middle of box-hedged beds, and hidden rhododendron dell. There are also some annuals, perennials, shrubs, trees and small orchard, vegetable plot and fruit cage. Wild flowers and wildlife. The garden has gravel and stone paths, but many areas accessible for wheelchairs.

♿ ☕

79 NEW THE LONG HOUSE

The Lane, Westdean, Seaford BN25 4AL. Robin & Rosie Lloyd, 01323 870432, rosie.lloyd@dsl.pipex.com. *3m E of Seaford, 6m W of Eastbourne. From A27 follow signs to Alfriston then Litlington. Westdean 1m on L. From A259 at Exceat L on Litlington Rd 1/4 m on R.* Home-made teas. **Adm £4, chd free. Sat 5 July (2-5). Visitors also welcome by appt June to July for groups of 15+. Coaches can drop off only.**

If you enjoyed Bankton Cottage in Crawley Down, we hope you like our new garden here in the tiny hamlet of Westdean: a cottage garden on a chalk slope with colour themes. There's a perennial border the entire length of the house at the rear, a paddock of wild flowers indigenous to chalk and many 'rooms' with slopes and steps surrounding our C17 flint cottage. Situated on The South Downs Way. Gravel forecourt at entrance, some slopes and steps.

80 LORDINGTON HOUSE

Lordington, Chichester PO18 9DX. Mr & Mrs John Hamilton, 01243 375862, hamiltonjanda@btinternet.com. *7m W of Chichester. On W side of B2146, 1/2 m S of Walderton, 6m S of South Harting. Ask for directions at gate.* Home-made teas. **Adm £4, chd free. Sat 29, Sun 30 Mar (1.30-4.30). Visitors also welcome by appt Apr to Sept.**

Early C17 house (not open) and walled gardens. Clipped yew and box, lawns, borders and fine views. Vegetables, fruit and poultry in old kitchen garden. Carpet of daffodils in spring. Nearly 100 roses planted since 2008. Various trees both mature and young. Lime avenue planted in 1973 to replace elms. Overlooks farmland, Ems Valley and wooded slopes of S Downs, all in AONB and S Downs National Park. Wheelchair access possible to all areas of the garden, although there are gravel paths, uneven paving, and slopes.

Paths are tightly mown through clouds of cow parsley . . .

81 LOWDER MILL

Bell Vale Lane, Fernhurst, Haslemere GU27 3DJ. Anne & John Denning, 01428 644822, anne@denningconsultancy.co.uk, www.lowdermill.com. *1 1/2 m S of Haslemere. Follow A286 out of Midhurst towards Haslemere, through Fernhurst and take the 2nd R after Kingsley Green into Bell Vale Lane.* Home-made teas. **Adm £3.50, chd £1.50. Sat 31 May (11-5.30); Sun 1 June (10.30-5.30). Groups also welcome by appt only, close to opening dates.**

C17 mill house and former mill set in 3-acre garden. The garden has been restored with the help of Bunny Guinness. Interesting assortment of container planting forming a stunning courtyard between house and mill. Streams, waterfalls, innovative and quirky container planting around the potting shed and restored greenhouse. Raised vegetable garden. Rare breed chicken and ducks, as well as resident kingfishers. Renowned for superb home-made teas, served overlooking the mill lake. Extensive plant stall, mainly home propagated. Choir singing on Sunday 1st June at 11am. Featured in Country Life, Country Living, Sussex Life, Chichester Observer.

82 MALT HOUSE

Chithurst Lane, Rogate, Petersfield GU31 5EZ. Mr & Mrs G Ferguson, 01730 821433, g.ferguson34@btinternet.com. *3m W of Midhurst. On A272, turn N signed Chithurst for 1½ m, narrow lane; or off A3 at Liphook to old A3 (B2070) for 2m, L to Milland following signs to Chithurst for 1½ m.* Home-made teas. **Adm £5, chd free. Sun 27 Apr, Sun 4, Mon 5 May (2-6). Visitors also welcome by appt Apr to Sept. Refreshments by arrangement.**

6-acres; flowering shrubs incl exceptional rhododendrons and azaleas, leading to 50-acres of arboretum and lovely woodland walks plus many rare plants and trees. Special access can be made at the entrance, to part of the garden only.

83 MALTHOUSE FARM

Streat Lane, Streat, Hassocks BN6 8SA. Richard & Helen Keys, 01273 890356, helen.k.keys@btinternet.com. *2m SE of Burgess Hill. From r'about between B2113 and B2112 take Folders Lane/Middleton Common Lane E; after 1m, R into Streat Lane; garden is ½ m on R.* Home-made teas. **Adm £4, chd free. Sun 17, Tue 19 Aug (2-5.30). Visitors also welcome by appt Apr to Sept.**

Rural 5-acre garden with stunning views to S Downs. Garden divided into separate 'rooms', box parterre, newly planted border with glass sculpture, herbaceous and shrub borders, kitchen garden. Orchard leading to partitioned areas with grass walks, stream of summer flowers, snail mound, birch maze. Wildlife farm pond. Featured in Sussex Living. Wheelchair access possible although some steps. Caution if wet as much access is across grass.

84 MANOR OF DEAN

Tillington, Petworth GU28 9AP. Mr & Mrs James Mitford, 07887 992349, emma@mitford.uk.com. *3m W of Petworth. From Petworth go through Tillington and follow yellow signs N from A272.* Home-made teas. **Adm £3.50, chd free (share to Tillington Church Repair Fund on evening opening only). Sun 9 Mar, Sun 6 Apr, Sun 11 May (2-5). Evening Opening with wine available on Thur 5 June (5-8); Sun 10 Aug (2-5); Sun 15 Feb 2015 (2-4.30). Visitors also welcome by appt Mar to Sept for groups of 10+.**

Approx 3-acres. Traditional English garden, herbaceous borders, a variety of early-flowering bulbs and snowdrops, spring bulbs, grass walks and steps. Walled kitchen garden partly in use for household. Lawns, rose garden and informal areas with views of S Downs. Garden under a long-term programme of improvements. The garden has uneven steps and slopes.

GROUP OPENING

85 MAYFIELD GARDENS

Mayfield TN20 6TE. *10m S of Tunbridge Wells. Turn off A267 into Mayfield. Parking available in village and a detailed map will be available from each of the gardens.* Home-made teas. **Combined adm £5, chd free. Sun 15 June (11-5); Sun 10 Aug (2-5).**

HOOPERS FARM
Andrew & Sarah Ratcliffe.
Open June & Aug dates

NEW LONGCROFT HOUSE
The Warren. Mr & Mrs Alex & Sue Grieve.
Open June date

NEW MAY COTTAGE
Fletching Street. M Prall.
Open June date

MAYFIELD PRIMARY SCHOOL
Fletching Street. Ms Teresa Cass.
Open June date

MEADOW COTTAGE
Adrian & Mo Hope.
Open June date

NEW THE MIDDLE HOUSE
High Street. Mr Johnny Marsh.
Open June & Aug dates
01435 872146
info@themiddlehousemayfield.co.uk

NEW THE OAST
Fletching Street. Mrs Tessa Crowe.
Open Aug date

TEW COTT
Jon & Sue Barnes.
Open June date

WARREN HOUSE
Chris Lyle & Pat Robson.
Open June date

Mayfield is a beautiful Wealden village with several old pubs and interesting historical connections. There are eight gardens to visit in June and three in August. All are in the village centre, except for two which are within walking distance. The gardens vary in size and style including a formal parterre, colour-themed and cottage-style planting, wild flower meadows, woodland and vegetables and incl the Mayfield Primary School Garden planted and maintained by the pupils. Many have far-reaching, panoramic views over beautiful countryside. There are four new gardens this year: Longcroft House, May Cottage, The Middle House PH and The Oast.

86 ◆ MCBEAN'S ORCHIDS

Resting Oak Hill, Cooksbridge, Lewes BN8 4PR. Mr Jim Durrant, 01273 400228, www.mcbeansorchids.co.uk. *A275 1m N of Cooksbridge Stn, 4m N of Lewes.* **Adm £4, chd free. For NGS: Thur 6, Fri 7 Feb (10-3.30). For other opening times and information, please phone or see garden website.**

A selection of orchids bred by McBeans since 1879 on this site. Includes tropical plants award winning cymbidium and oncidium orchids plus other plants of interest from around the world. Working nursery tour throughout the day plus exotic growing house display with shop full of plants to buy. One of the very few nurseries exhibiting at every Chelsea Flower Show - numerous gold medals - extensive press and TV coverage. Wheelchair access to shop and display house. Flight of 4 steps for nursery tour.

87 NEW ◆ MERRIMENTS
Hawkhurst Road, Hurst Green TN19 7RA. Peggy & David Weeks, 01580 860666, www.merriments.co.uk. *Off A21, 1m N of Hurst Green. On A229 Hawkhurst Rd. Situated between Hurst Green and Hawkhurst.* Home-made teas. **Adm £6, chd £3.**
For NGS: Sun 6 July (10.30-5.30).
For other opening times and information, please phone or see garden website.
Behind the tall green hedges lies a well-kept secret, a stunning 4-acre garden, the South East's hidden gem. The garden has deep meandering borders, many formal and informal focal points and a rich tapestry of colour, texture and scent. There are also many benches to pause and enjoy the atmosphere of this ever evolving garden. Nursery, restaurant and wildlife centre. Featured in Which? Gardening, Sussex Life, Country Living and local publications.

88 MOUNTFIELD COURT
nr Robertsbridge TN32 5JP. Mr & Mrs Simon Fraser. *3m N of Battle. On A21 London-Hastings; ½ m from Johns Cross.* Home-made teas. **Adm £3.50, chd free. Sun 11 May (2-5).**
3-acre wild woodland garden; walkways through exceptional rhododendrons, azaleas, camellias and other flowering shrubs; fine trees and outstanding views. Small paved herb garden.

89 NEW MOUSTOWS MANOR
High Street, Henfield BN5 9DD. Lyn & Nick Peacock. *Centre of Henfield. Located at junction of A2037 and A281 at the S-end of Henfield High St. Parking in Henfield Village Hall or Library car parks.* **Adm £4, chd free. Sat 12, Sun 13 July (2-5).**
1-acre newly designed garden which beautifully compliments the Georgian house (not open). Reclaimed york stone and clay pavers path, leads through pleached Pyrus calleryana 'Chanticleer' to colour themed borders, from white through to pastels and leads up steps to hot border and summer house. Attractive water feature, gazebo, sculptures and sunken seating area. Refreshments available in Henfield High St. Partial wheelchair access only as steps to top lawn.

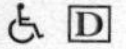

Fairlight End

90 NEWTIMBER PLACE
Newtimber BN6 9BU. Mr & Mrs Andrew Clay, 01273 833104, andy@newtimberholidaycottages.co.uk, www.newtimberplace.co.uk. *7m N of Brighton. From A23, take A281 towards Henfield. Turn R at small Xrds signed Newtimber in approx ½ m. Go down Church Lane, garden is at end of lane on L.* Home-made teas. **Adm £4, chd free.**
Sun 13 Apr (2-5.30).
Beautiful C17 moated house (not open). Gardens and woods full of bulbs and wild flowers in spring. Herbaceous border and lawns. Moat flanked by water plants. Mature trees. Wild garden, ducks, chickens and fish. Wheelchair access across lawn to some of garden, tea room and WC.

91 NORTH HALL
North Hall Lane, Sheffield Green, Uckfield TN22 3SA. Celia & Les Everard, 01825 791103, indigodogs@yahoo.co.uk. *1½ m NW of Fletching Village. 6m N Uckfield. From A272 turn N at Piltdown or N Chailey. From A275 turn E at Sheffield Green into North Hall Lane.* Home-made teas.
Combined Adm £4, chd free with 1 Whites Cottages. Sat 28, Sun 29 June (2-5.30). Visitors also welcome by appt June to July for groups of 10+.
A romantic garden surrounding a C16 house (not open) planted to please the senses. Roses tumble, clematis scramble and the dense perennial planting needs little support - a palette of soft colours and heady scent. Themed island beds and a moated terrace add to the many cottage garden features. Wildlife and self seeding encouraged. Home grown plants and delicious teas.

92 NYEWOOD HOUSE
Nyewood, nr Rogate GU31 5JL. Mr & Mrs C J Wright, 01730 821563, s.warren.wright@gmail.com. *4m E of Petersfield. From A272 at Rogate take South Harting Rd for 1½ m. Turn L at pylon towards South Downs Hotel. Nyewood House 2nd on R over cattle grid.* Cream teas. **Adm £3.50, chd free. Sat 7, Sun 8 June (2-5.30). Visitors also welcome by appt May to June for groups of 18+. Refreshments by arrangement.**
Victorian country house garden with stunning views of S Downs. 3-acres comprising formal gardens with rose walk and arbours, pleached hornbeam, colour-themed herbaceous borders, shrub borders, lily pond and fully stocked kitchen garden with greenhouse. Wooded area featuring spring flowers followed by wild orchids and wild flowers. Gravel drive.

Lemon drizzle cake, Victoria sponge ... yummy!

93 ◆ NYMANS

Handcross RH17 6EB. National Trust, 0844 2491895, www.nationaltrust.org.uk. *4m S of Crawley. On B2114 at Handcross signed off M23/A23 London-Brighton road. Metrobus 271 and 273 stop nearby.* **Adm £10.50, chd £5. For NGS: Sat 31 May, Sun 1 June (10-5). Jazz in the Garden £12, chd £6, Sun 27 July, Sun 24 Aug (6-8). For other opening times and information, please phone or see garden website.**

In the late 1800's Ludwig Messel bought Nymans estate in the Sussex High Weald to make a dream country home. Inspired by its woodland setting he created a garden with plants collected from around the world. Here he entertained family and friends and enjoyed relaxing and picnicking in the garden and woods. Today Nymans is still a garden lovers' home - a place to relax in a peaceful country garden. Jazz in the Garden. Enjoy a relaxed evening of Jazz sounds set against the stunning backdrop of Nymans gardens. Gates open 5pm for picnics. 50% of proceeds go to NGS charities. For more details visit Nymans website. Booking essential through www.nationtrust.org.uk/nymans or 0844 2491895 (booking fees apply). Numbers are strictly limited.

Many gardening ideas to take away for everyone! . . .

94 OAK GROVE COLLEGE

The Boulevard, Worthing BN13 1JX. Oak Grove College. *1m W of Worthing. Turn S off A2032 at r'about onto The Boulevard, signed Goring. School entrance 1st on L (shared entrance with Durrington High School).* Teas at Palatine School. **Combined Adm £4, chd free with Palatine School. Sun 6 July (2-5).**

An inspiring example of how special needs children have transformed their school grounds into a green oasis. Extensive and unusual planting, features incl water-wise, memorial and herb gardens, large sensory courtyard, sculptures, mosaics, and large food growing area. Living willow, reclaimed woodland, outdoor textiles and outdoor performance area.

95 OCKLYNGE MANOR

Mill Road, Eastbourne BN21 2PG. Wendy & David Dugdill, 01323 734121, ocklyngemanor@hotmail.com, www.ocklyngemanor.co.uk. *Close to Eastbourne District General Hospital. Take A22 (Willingdon Rd) towards Old Town, turn L into Mill Rd just before parade of shops.* Home-made teas. **Adm £4, chd free. Visitors welcome by appt May to Aug for groups of 10-20.**

Hidden oasis behind an ancient, flint wall. Informal and tranquil, 1/2 -acre chalk garden with sunny and shaded places to sit. Use of architectural and unusual trees. Rhododendrons, azaleas and acers in containers. Garden evolved over 20yrs, maintained by owners. Georgian house (not open), former home of Mabel Lucie Attwell.

96 OFFHAM HOUSE

The Street, Offham, Lewes BN7 3QE. Mr S Goodman & Mr & Mrs P Carminger. *2m N of Lewes on A275. Offham House is on the main road (A275) through Offham between the filling stn and the Blacksmiths Arms.* Home-made teas. **Adm £4.50, chd free. Sun 27 Apr, Sun 1 June (1-5).**

Romantic garden with fountains, flowering trees, double herbaceous border, long peony bed. 1676 Queen Anne house (not open) with well-knapped flint facade. Herb garden. Walled kitchen garden with glasshouses, coldframes, chickens guinea fowl and friendly pigs. Teas on lawn/conservatory.

97 NEW OLD ERRINGHAM COTTAGE

Steyning Road, Shoreham-By-Sea BN43 5FD. Fiona & Martin Phillips, 01273 462285, fiona.h.phillips@btinternet.com. *2m N of Shoreham by Sea. From A27 Shoreham flyover take A283 towards Steyning. Take 2nd R into private lane. Follow sharp LH-bend at top, house on L. Limited parking.* **Adm £4.50, chd free. Visitors welcome by appt May to June for groups of 10-25.**

1-acre plant lover's garden, developed over past 25-yrs. Sited on a hillside, internal yew hedging provides wind protection and allows for different styled areas. Highly productive fruit and vegetable area with greenhouses. Beautiful views of the S Downs at the front with colourful mixed borders, and small pond. Wild flower area.

98 THE OLD FARMHOUSE

Hermongers Lane, Rudgwick RH12 3AL. Caspian Robertson, 01403 824034, surreygardens@googlemail.com, www.musicmindspirit.org. *Between Horsham and Cranleigh. 1/4 m N of Rudgwick on B2128 at Cox Green turn R (E) into Hermongers Lane. 1/2 m, parking signed. Disabled parking available.* Home-made teas. **Adm £4, chd free (share to Mind Music Spirit Trust). Sun 24, Mon 25 Aug (1-6). Visitors also welcome by appt Apr to Sept.**

1/4 -acre traditional garden set about C16 Grade II listed farmhouse (not open), and barns open as tea-room and concert hall. Features incl knot garden, rose garden, espalier avenue of fruit trees, water features and walks. Fine views and live music events in magnificent C17 converted barn. As featured in the BBC's Hampton Court Program 2013. Wheelchair access to main garden and concert hall.

99 NEW OLD POUND FARM

Pound Lane, Framfield, East Sussex TN22 5RT. Alan & Beryl Henderson. *4m E of Uckfield take B2102 through Framfield. 1m from centre of village turn L into Pound Lane. Parking in field behind Pound Cottage next door.* Home-made teas. **Adm £4, chd free. Sun 27 July (11-5).**

Typical Sussex farmhouse - part dating back to 1480, with attractive terrace and 2-acre garden consisting of long herbaceous perennial border; area with many ancient rhododendrons and fruit trees; attractive hedges and trees; pond area which incl an ancient cattle watering hole. Wheelchair access to most areas.

Cookscroft

100 OLD SCAYNES HILL HOUSE

Clearwater Lane, Scaynes Hill RH17 7NF. Sue & Andy Spooner, 01444 831602, a_spooner@btopenworld.com. *2m E of Haywards Heath. 50yds down Sussex Border Path beside BP garage shop. NO PARKING at garden (drop-off only). Please park considerately in the village.* Home-made teas. **Adm £4, chd free. Sat 14 June, Sun 13 July (2-5). Visitors also welcome by appt June to July for groups of 30 max.**

In memory of Sarah Robinson. Entrance archway with steps leading to peaceful 1-acre naturalistic garden on S-facing slope of clay. Mature trees and shrubs, several colourful herbaceous borders and island beds. Many roses, hemerocallis and ornamental grasses, small wild flower meadow with orchids, fruit and vegetable area and natural-looking pond.

101 OLD VICARAGE

The Street, Firle, Lewes BN8 6NR. Mr & Mrs Charlie Bridge. *Off A27 5m E of Lewes. Signed from main road.* Home-made teas. **Adm £4, chd free. Sat 21 June (2-5).**

Garden originally designed by Lanning Roper in the 1960's. Previously opened under NGS in 1970's 80's and 90's. 4-acre garden set around a Regency vicarage (not open). Features a walled garden with vegetable parterre and flower borders, wild flower meadow, pond, pleached limes. Over 100 roses. Wonderful Downland views.

102 THE OLD VICARAGE

The Street, Washington RH20 4AS. Sir Peter & Lady Walters, 07766 761926, meryl.walters@me.com. *2½ m E of Storrington, 4m W of Steyning. From Washington r'about on A24 take A283 to Steyning. 500yds R to Washington. Pass Frankland Arms, R to St Mary's Church.* Home-made teas. **Adm £4.50, chd free. Sun 23 Mar, Mon 21 Apr (10.30-4); Sat 28, Sun 29 June (10.30-4.30); Sun 19 Oct (10.30-4). Visitors also welcome by appt Mar to Oct for groups of 10+.**

3½ -acre garden, set around 1832 Regency-style house (not open). Front is formally laid out with topiary, a large lawn and mixed border. To the rear some mature trees dating back to C19, herbaceous border, new large pond and stunning uninterrupted 20-mile view to the N Downs. Stream and woodland area with log cabin. Featured in the Sussex Life, and Period Living.

103 ORCHARD HOUSE

Staplefield Road, Cuckfield, Haywards Heath RH17 5HY. Dr & Mrs Andrew Winskill. *Approx 1m W of Cuckfield. Garden is approx 400 metres W of Haywards Heath Rugby Club on B2114 Cuckfield to Staplefield road.* Home-made teas. **Adm £4, chd free. Sat 19, Sun 20 July (2-5).**

Large family garden with greenhouses, herbaceous borders, vegetable plot, grasses bed, a small North American prairie meadow, shrubberies, heather bed, rhododendron walk, an orchard, a walled courtyard and wild area which incl a childrens play area. There is also an extensive compost area. The courtyard has container planting and a part raised, part sunk pond.

104 PALATINE SCHOOL GARDENS

Palatine Road, Worthing BN12 6JP. Mrs N Hawkins, 01903 242835, nhawkins@wsgfl.org.uk, www.palatineschool.org/. *Turn S off A2032 at r'about onto The Boulevard, signed Goring. Take R turn at next r'about into Palatine Rd. School approx 100yds on R.* **Adm £4, chd free. Sun 6 Apr, Sun 6 July (2-5). Combined Adm £4.00, chd free with Oak Grove College on Sun 6 July only. Visitors also welcome by appt Apr to July not during school hours.**

This is a many-roomed mature garden with varied planting. Constructed by teachers, volunteers and children with special needs, it never ceases to surprise visitors. Wildlife corner, large and small ponds, themed gardens and children's outdoor art features, along with rockeries, living willow, labyrinth, mosaics and interesting tree collection.

105 PARSONAGE FARM

Kirdford RH14 0NH. David & Victoria Thomas, 01403 820295, davidandvictoria.thomas@gmail.com. *5m NE of Petworth. From centre of Kirdford (before church) turn R, through village, past Forresters PH on R. Entrance on L, just past R turn to Plaistow.* Home-made teas. **Adm £5, chd free (share to Churchers College - Walter Olsen School, Kenya). Fri 27 June, Sun 7 Sept (2-6). Visitors also welcome by appt.**

Major garden in beautiful setting developed over 20-yrs with fruit theme and many unusual plants. Formally laid out on grand scale with long vistas; C18 walled garden with borders in apricot, orange, scarlet and crimson; topiary walk; pleached lime allée; tulip tree avenue; rose borders; large vegetable garden with trained fruit; turf amphitheatre; lake; informal autumn shrubbery and jungle walk.

Large collection of culinary and medicinal herbs in a small formal garden . . .

106 33 PEERLEY ROAD

East Wittering PO20 8PD. Paul & Trudi Harrison, 01243 673215, stixandme@aol.com. *7m S of Chichester. From A286 take B2198 to Bracklesham. Turn R into Stocks Lane, L at Royal British Legion into Legion Way. Follow road round to Peerley Rd ½ -way along.* **Adm £2.50, chd free. Sun 13 July (12-4). Visitors also welcome by appt Apr to Oct.**

Small seaside garden 65ft x 32ft, 110yds from sea. Packed full of ideas and interesting plants using every inch of space to create rooms and places for adults and children to play. A must for any suburban gardener. Specialising in unusual plants that grow well in seaside conditions with advice on coastal gardening.

107 PEMBURY HOUSE
Ditchling Road (New Road), Clayton, nr Hassocks BN6 9PH. Nick & Jane Baker, 01273 842805, jane.baker47@btinternet.com, www.pemburyhouse.co.uk. *6m N of Brighton, off A23. On B2112, 110 metres from A273. Disabled parking at the house, otherwise parking at village green (BN6 9PJ) clearly signed. Good public transport service.* Home-made teas & light refreshments. **Adm £5, chd free.** **Tue 11, Wed 12, Thur 13, Tue 18, Wed 19, Thur 20 Feb, Thur 6, Fri 7 Mar, Tue 10, Wed 11, Thur 12, Tue 17, Wed 18, Thur 19 Feb 2015 (11-4). Visitors also welcome by appt Feb to Mar for groups of 15+.**
Depending on the vagaries of the season, winter-flowering shrubs, hellebores and drifts of snowdrops are at their best in February. Special Hellebore Days on 6 & 7 March. Winding paths give a choice of walks through over 2-acres of garden, which is in and enjoys views of, the S Downs National Park. Small 29-yr-old woodland. Wellies, macs and winter woollies advised. Hellebores and snowdrops for sale. Limited disabled access in wet weather.

108 6 PLANTATION RISE
Worthing BN13 2AH. Nigel & Trixie Hall, 01903 262206, trixiehall@btinternet.com. *2m from seafront on outskirts of Worthing BN13 2AH. A24 meets A27 at Offington r'about. Turn into Offington Lane, 1st R into The Plantation, 1st R again into Plantation Rise.* Home-made teas. **Adm £4, chd free.** **Sat 19, Wed 23 July (2-5). Visitors also welcome by appt Mar to Sept for groups of 4-25. Refreshments by arrangement.**
Our garden is 70ft x 80ft with pond, summerhouse, patio areas with pergolas, 9 silver birches, plus evergreen shrubs, azaleas, rhododendrons and acers; heathers in spring, roses, clematis and perennials in August all to ensure yr-round colour and interest. WC available on request. The garden has some steps.

109 ◆ THE PRIEST HOUSE
North Lane, West Hoathly RH19 4PP. Sussex Archaeological Society, 01342 810479, www.sussexpast.co.uk. *4m SW of East Grinstead. Turn E to West Hoathly 1m S of Turners Hill at Selsfield Common junction on B2028. 2m S turn R into North Lane. Garden ¼ m.* **Adm £2, chd free. For NGS: Sat 24 May, Sat 28 June (10.30-5.30). For other opening times and information, please phone or see garden website.**
C15 timber-framed farmhouse with cottage garden on fertile acid clay. Large collection of culinary and medicinal herbs in a small formal garden and mixed with perennials and shrubs in exuberant borders. Long-established yew topiary, box hedges and espalier apple trees provide structural elements. Traditional fernery and small secluded shrubbery. Adm to Priest House Museum £1 for NGS visitors.

110 2 QUARRY COTTAGES
Wall Hill Road, Ashurst Wood, East Grinstead RH19 3TQ. Mrs Hazel Anne Archibald. *1m S of East Grinstead. From N turn L off A22 from East Grinstead, garden adjoining John Pears Memorial Ground. From S turn R off A22 from Forest Row, garden on R at top of hill.* Home-made teas. **Adm £3, chd free.** **Fri 16, Sat 17 May (2-5).**
Peaceful little garden that has evolved over 40yrs in the present ownership. A natural sandstone outcrop hangs over an ornamental pond; mixed borders of perennials and shrubs with specimen trees. Many seating areas tucked into corners. Highly productive vegetable plot. Terrace round house revamped 2013. Florist and gift shop in barn. **Also open Caxton Manor (separate admission).**

🏵 ☕

111 RIDGE HOUSE
East Street, Turners Hill RH10 4PU. Mr & Mrs Nicholas Daniels, 01342 715344, nickanwyn@supanet.com. *4m SW of East Grinstead. 3m E of Crawley. On B2110, 5m SE of J10 M23. Via A264 and B2028. 30yds E of Crown PH on Turners Hill Xrds. Parking at recreation ground E of Ridge House.* Home-made teas. **Adm £3.50, chd free.** **Fri 11, Sat 12 July (2-5). Visitors also welcome by appt May to July.**
A magical view of the High Weald greets the visitor, with all-yr interest being offered by Nigel's Garden in its quiet corner together with the mixed borders, dell with its pond and the productive vegetable garden. Large beautifully manicured bi-coloured Leylandii hedge plus other shrubs. Paths lead to unexpected vistas, and the large compost heaps and Victorian greenhouse with its reservoir should not be missed. Solar panels and 5,000 gallon underground reservoir with water collected from roof. Mainly flat, some steep slopes.

Fittleworth House

© Leigh Clapp

112 RINGMER PARK

Ringmer, Lewes BN8 5RW. Deborah & Michael Bedford, www.ringmerpark.com. *On A26 Lewes to Uckfield road. 1½ m NE of Lewes, 5m S of Uckfield.* Home-made teas. **Adm £5, chd free. Sun 25 May, Sun 21 Sept (2-5).**
Densely-planted 8-acre formal garden with soft edges and outstanding views of S Downs. Emphasis is on continuous flowering with bold and dramatic blocks of colour. Features incl a striking hot garden, white garden, rose gardens, pergola covered with roses and clematis, double herbaceous borders, a new grasses garden and much more. Featured in GGG (Highly Recommended), The Most Amazing Gardens of Britain, Country Life, Period Homes and Interiors, Sussex Life and Magnet.

113 ROSE COTTAGE

Hall Lane, Hadlow Down TN22 4HJ. Ken & Heather Mines. *6m NE of Uckfield. After entering village on A272, turn into Hut Lane next to the New Inn. Follow signs.* Home-made teas. **Adm £4, chd free. Sun 25 May, Sun 22 June (2-5.30).**
Plantsman's 2/3 -acre garden with views across an Area of Outstanding Natural Beauty. Old roses, exuberant planting and luxuriance within a strong design create a garden that visitors refer to as harmonious, tranquil and evoking memories of childhood. Self-seeding is encouraged, so constantly changing. David Newman sculptures are integral to the design, further enhanced by Victorian church stonework. Bug hunt and fact sheet for children. Some gravel paths.

114 RYMANS

Apuldram, Chichester PO20 7EG. Mrs Michael Gayford, 01243 783147, suzanna.gayford@btinternet.com. *1m S of Chichester. Take Witterings Rd, at 1½ m SW turn R signed Dell Quay. Turn 1st R, garden ½ m on L.* Home-made teas. **Adm £4, chd free. Sat 5, Sun 6 Apr, Sat 7, Sun 8 June, Sat 13 Sept (2-5). Visitors also welcome by appt Mar to Sept for groups of 8+.**
Walled and other gardens surrounding lovely C15 stone house (not open); bulbs, flowering shrubs, roses, ponds, potager. Many unusual and rare trees and shrubs. In late spring the wisterias are spectacular. The heady scent of hybrid musk roses fills the walled garden in June. In late summer the garden is ablaze with dahlias, sedums, late roses, sages and Japanese anemones. Featured in Period Homes and Interiors in Sept 2013.

A stylish garden of textural contrasts and rich colour . . .

115 SAFFRONS

Holland Road, Steyning BN44 3GJ. Tim Melton & Bernardean Carey, 01903 810082, tim.melton@btinternet.com. *6m NE of Worthing. Exit r'about on A283 at S-end of Steyning bypass into Clays Hill Rd. 1st R into Goring Rd, 4th L into Holland Rd. Parking in Goring Rd and Holland Rd.* Home-made teas. **Adm £4, chd free. Sun 20, Wed 23 July (2-5.30). Visitors also welcome by appt July to Aug for groups of 10+. Teas by arrangement.**
A stylish garden of textural contrasts and rich colour. The herbaceous beds are filled with agapanthus, spiky eryngium and fragrant lilies, alliums and salvias. A broad lawn is surrounded by borders with Japanese maples, rhododendrons, hydrangeas and specimen trees interspersed with ferns and grasses. Fruit cage, vegetable beds and fruit trees. Featured garden in Garden Answers, September 2013.

116 ◆ ST MARY'S HOUSE GARDENS

Bramber BN44 3WE. Peter Thorogood & Roger Linton, 01903 816205, www.stmarysbramber.co.uk. *1m E of Steyning. 10m NW of Brighton in Bramber Village off A283.* Home-made teas. **Adm £4, chd free. For NGS: Fri 18, Sat 19 July (2-5.30). For other opening times and information, please phone or see garden website.**
Five acres incl charming formal topiary, ivy-clad 'Monks' Walk, large *Ginkgo biloba*, and magnificent Magnolia grandiflora around charming timber-framed medieval house. Victorian 'Secret' gardens incl splendid 140ft fruit wall, Rural Museum, terracotta garden, delightful Jubilee Rose Garden, pineapple pits and English Poetry Garden. In the heart of the S Downs National Park. All parts of the gardens are accessible by wheelchair.

117 8 SANDGATE CLOSE

East Sussex, Seaford BN25 3LL. Aideen & Denis Jones, 01323 899452, deniswjones@gmail.com, www.sandgateclosegarden.co.uk. *From A259 follow signs to Alfriston, E of Seaford, turn R into Hillside Ave, L into Hastings Ave, R into Deal Close and R into Sandgate Close.* Light refreshments. **Adm £3.50, chd free. Tue 15, Thur 31 July (11-5). Visitors also welcome by appt June to Aug for groups of 25 max.**
8 Sandgate Close is a green and tranquil haven, with a delightful mix of trees, shrubs and perennial borders in different themed beds, with courtyard garden, gazebo, summerhouse, water features, sweet pea arches, huge range of plants in all seasons, plenty of places to sit and enjoy. Plants, jams and books for sale. Featured in Amateur Gardening, Galloping Gardener and Sussex Life in 2014.

118 SANDHILL FARM HOUSE

Nyewood Road, Rogate, Petersfield GU31 5HU. Rosemary Alexander, www.rosemaryalexander.co.uk. *4m SE of Petersfield. From A272 Xrds in Rogate, take road S signed Nyewood/Harting. Follow road for approx 1m over small bridge. Sandhill Farm House on R, over cattle grid.* Home-made teas. **Adm £3.50, chd free. Sat 12, Sun 13 Apr, Sat 7, Sun 8 June, Sat 27, Sun 28 Sept (2-5). Visitors also welcome by appt Mar to Oct for groups of 10+.**
Front and rear gardens are broken up into garden rooms, incl small kitchen garden. Front garden incl small woodland area planted with early spring flowering shrubs and bulbs, white garden and hot dry terraced area. Rear garden has mirror borders, small decorative vegetable garden and 'red' border. Grit and grasses garden. Organic and environmentally

friendly. Home of author and Principal of The English Gardening School. Gardening Club bookings welcome. The garden has gravel paths, and a few steps.

119 ◆ SARAH RAVEN'S CUTTING GARDEN
Perch Hill Farm, Willingford Lane, Robertsbridge, Brightling TN32 5HP. Sarah Raven, www.sarahraven.com. *7m SW of Hurst Green. From Burwash, turn off A265 by church/memorial follow road for 3m. From Woods Corner, take road opp Swan Inn. Take 1st L go up hill take 1st L again.* Light refreshments. **Adm £5, chd free.** **For NGS: Tue 3 June (9.30-4). For other opening times and information, please see garden website.**
Sarah's inspirational, productive 2-acre working garden with different garden rooms including large cut flower garden, vegetable and fruit garden, salads and herbs area plus two ornamental gardens. Parking is in a field - possible uneven ground.

3D landscaping to create mood and enclosure and yet preserve views and openness . . .

GROUP OPENING

120 SEAFORD & NEWHAVEN GROUP
BN25 3LL, www.sandgateclosegarden.co.uk. *Start at 8 Sandgate Close, BN25 3LL. See individual entries for directions to other gardens. Map will be available at all gardens.* Cream teas at 8 Sandgate Close and Windover. **Combined adm £5, chd free. Sun 29 June, Sun 20 July (11-5).**

1 BUCKTHORN CLOSE
Seaford, BN25 4NY. Roger & Jane Bullock.
From A259 towards Eastbourne turn R into Sutton Ave. 1st L at mini r'about into Kingston Ave. Follow road L (becomes Kingston Way), Buckthorn Close 2nd L

ELIZABETH COTTAGE
22 Sherwood Road, Seaford, BN25 3EH. Sue Wright.
A259 turn L from Brighton or R from Eastbourne at War Memorial down Avondale Rd. R at pond into Sutton Drove, 1st L Vale Rd, 1st L Sherwood Rise, L at T-junction

NEW 5 OLD COASTGUARD COTTAGES
Gill Weaver.
A259 into Newhaven, keep R follow ring road. Turn L into South Rd. Continue into Fort Rd past Fire Station. Geneva Rd is 1st on R. Park in Fort Rd

8 SANDGATE CLOSE
Aideen & Denis Jones
(See separate entry)

NEW 4 SUNNINGDALE CLOSE
Mick & Debbie Hibberd.
From E or W use A259 coast road, follow NGS signs, turn R or L down Southdown Rd
Visitors also welcome by appt June to July.
01323 899385
sunningdale.garden4thof9@gmail.com

NEW WINDOVER
Chyngton Lane North, Seaford. Dave & Helen Roberts.
Just off A259. House on RH-side of road which leads to Dymock Farm Shop on Eastbourne side of Seaford. Follow NGS signs

6 totally unique gardens. **Sandgate Close**, a green and tranquil haven with a delightful mix of trees, shrubs and perennial borders, water features, sweet pea arches, and courtyard garden. Huge range of plants. **1 Buckthorn Close** is an integrated combination of flowers, fruits and vegetables. The garden majors on 3D landscaping to create mood and enclosure and yet preserve views and openness. **Elizabeth Cottage** is a small delightful garden stocked with cottage plants mature ginkgo and silver birch. **Windover** has stunning coastal views and **Old Coast Guard Cottages**, winner of Newhaven in Bloom 2012, harbour views. **Sunningdale Close** was winner of Seaford in Bloom Plantsman's Cup 2013 and best front garden. Delightful mix of plants and colour. Home-made jam and plant sales at Sandgate Close. Plant sales at Sunningdale Close. Featured in local and gardening press. Wheelchair access at 1 Buckthorn Close, Sunningdale Close and Windover.

121 SEDGWICK PARK HOUSE
Horsham, RH13 6QQ. John & Clare Davison, 01403 734930, clare@sedgwickpark.com, www.sedgwickpark.co.uk. *1m S of Horsham off A281. Take A281 towards Cowfold/Brighton. Hillier Garden Centre on R, then 1st R into Sedgwick Lane. After Sedgwick sign, enter N gates of Sedgwick Park, or enter W gates via Broadwater Lane, from Copsale or Southwater off A24.* Home-made teas. **Adm £5, chd free. Sun 29 June (1-5); Wed 2 July (2-6.30). Visitors also welcome by appt May to Sept. Ground floor of house is also available for tours.**
Parkland, meadows and woodland. Formal gardens by Harold Peto featuring 20 interlinking ponds, impressive water garden known as 'The White Sea'. Large Horsham stone terraces and lawns look out onto clipped yew hedging and specimen trees. Original secluded rosewalk and herbaceous borders, set in the grounds of Grade II listed Ernest George Mansion. One of the finest views of S Downs, Chanctonbury Ring and Lancing Chapel. Turf labyrinth and organic vegetable garden with chickens. The grounds incl uneven paving, slippery when wet; unfenced ponds and swimming pool.

122 SENNICOTTS
West Broyle, Chichester PO18 9AJ. Mr & Mrs James Rank, www.sennicotts.com. *2m NW of Chichester. White gates diagonally opp and W of the junction between Salthill Rd and the B2178.* Home-made teas. **Adm £4, chd free. Sat 7 June (2-6).**
Historic gardens set around a Regency villa (not open). Extensive rhododendron and azalea borders. Working walled kitchen and cutting garden. Avenues and walks. Fountain. Views across mature Sussex parkland to S Downs. Lots of space for children. A warm welcome for all. The grounds incl gravel paths.

Borde Hill Garden

Bring a bag for plants – help us give more to charity

123 SHALFORD HOUSE

Square Drive, Kingsley Green GU27 3LW. Sir Vernon & Lady Ellis. *2m S of Haslemere. Just S of border with Surrey on A286. Square Drive is at brow of hill, to the E. Turn L after 0.2m and follow road to R at bottom of hill.* Home-made teas. **Adm £5, chd free. Sun 11 May, Sun 13 July (2-6); Sun 31 Aug (2-5.30).**

Highly regarded 10-acre garden designed and created from scratch over last 22-yrs. Beautiful hilly setting with streams, ponds, waterfall, sunken garden, good late borders, azaleas, walled kitchen garden, wild flower meadow with orchids, prairie-style plantation and stumpery merging into further 7-acre woodland. Additional 30-acre arboretum with beech, rhododendrons, bluebells, ponds and specimen trees. Children's woodland trail. Cover feature for Period Homes and Interiors Sept 2013.

D

124 ◆ SHEFFIELD PARK AND GARDEN

Sheffield Park TN22 3QX. National Trust, 01825 790231, www.nationaltrust.org.uk. *10m S of East Grinstead. 5m NW of Uckfield; E of A275.* Home-made teas in Coach House Restaurant. **Adm £9, chd free. For NGS: Sat 7 June, Tue 23 Sept (10.30-5.30, last admission 4.30). For other opening times and information, please phone or see garden website.**

Magnificent 120-acres (40 hectares) landscaped garden laid out in C18 by Capability Brown and Humphry Repton. Further development in early yrs of this century by its owner Arthur G Soames. Centrepiece is original lakes, with many rare trees and shrubs. Beautiful at all times of the year, but noted for its spring and autumn colours. National Collection of Ghent azaleas. Natural play trail for families on South Park. Large number of Champion Trees - 87 in total. Garden largely accessible for wheelchairs - please call for information.

NCH

125 SOUTH GRANGE

Quickbourne Lane, Northiam, Rye TN31 6QY. Linda & Michael Belton, 01797 252984, belton.northiam@virgin.net. *Between A268 and A28, 1km E of Northiam. From Northiam centre follow Beales Lane into Quickbourne Lane, or Quickbourne Lane leaves A286 approx ²/₃km S of A28/A286 junction.* Light refreshments. **Adm £3.50, chd free. Wed 16 July (2-5); Sat 13, Sun 14 Sept (11-5). Visitors also welcome by appt May to Oct.**

Hardy Plant Society members' garden for all year interest combining grasses, herbaceous perennials, shrubs, trees, raised beds, wildlife pond, vegetable plot. Orchard incl meadow flowers, fruit cage with willow windbreak, rose arbour, polytunnel. Woodland is left wild. House roof runoff diverted to pond and bulk storage. Home propagated plants for sale. We are becoming older folk who garden without assistance and like to think that visitors can see what they too might achieve. We hope that our September opening will feature our collection of asters.

126 SPARROW HATCH

Cornwell's Bank, nr Newick BN8 4RD. Tony & Jane Welfare. *5m E of Haywards Heath. From A272 turn R into Oxbottom Lane (signed Barcombe), ½ m fork L into Narrow Rd, continue to T-junction & park in Chailey Lane (no parking at house).* Cold drinks available only. **Adm £3, chd free. Wed 11, Thur 12 June (2-5).**

Delightful ⅓-acre plantsman's cottage garden, wholly designed, made and maintained by owners. Many features incl 2 ponds, formal and wildlife, herbaceous borders, shady dell, vegetables, herbs, alpines. Planned for owners' enjoyment and love of growing plants, both usual and unusual. Plants for sale, propagated and grown by garden owner. Featured in Sussex Living, Sussex Express and Magnet Magazine.

127 ◆ STANDEN

West Hoathly Road, East Grinstead RH19 4NE. National Trust, 01342 323029, www.nationaltrust.org.uk/standen. *2m S of East Grinstead. Signed from B2110 Turners Hill Rd and from East Grinstead Town Centre.* Light refreshments in Barn Cafe. **Adm £10.50, chd £5.25. For NGS: Sat 10 May, Sat 7, Sun 8 June, Sat 18 Oct (10-5). For other opening times and information, please phone or see garden website.**

This arts and crafts inspired garden, with spectacular views across Weirwood reservoir to Ashdown Forest beyond, was created by Mrs Margaret Beale at the end of the C19. The collection of plants that she gathered here were of horticultural significance and included many unique plants brought back from the family's travels abroad and also collected by plant hunters of that day. Plant sales area. Kitchen garden produce available to buy. Specialist garden tours available on NGS days in spring and autumn (proceeds to NGS). Hillside garden with steps, slopes and gravel paths; wheelchair map available.

Organic garden with water features, kitchen and herb garden including music, candles and garden lighting at evening opening . . .

128 STANE HOUSE

Bignor RH20 1PQ. Mr & Mrs Nicholas Symes, 01798 869454, www.stanehouse.co.uk. *Equidistant Arundel, Petworth and Pulborough, each approx 6m. Follow signs for Roman Villa off A29 at Bury or A285 4m S of Petworth. Garden next to Bignor Roman Villa.* Cream teas. **Adm £4, chd free (share to Sussex Air Ambulance). Sat 5 July (10.30-5.30) & Evening Opening £5 with wine available from (6.30-10); Sun 6 July (11-5).**

Beautiful country location overlooking S Downs with tremendous views. Classic English 1-acre organic garden with water features, herbaceous borders, kitchen and herb garden. Flowing structure in the romantic style. Features incl music, candles and garden lighting at evening opening. Garden orientated poetry. The garden has some gentle slopes, gravel and grass paths.

129 STONE CROSS HOUSE

Alice Bright Lane, Crowborough TN6 3SH. Mr & Mrs D A Tate. *1½ m S of Crowborough Cross. At Crowborough T-lights (A26) turn S in to High St, and shortly R on to Croft Rd. Over 3 mini-r'abouts to Alice Bright Lane. Garden on L at next X-rds*. Home-made teas. **Adm £4, chd free. Sat 10, Sun 11 May (2-5).**

Beautiful 9-acre country property with gardens containing a delightful array of azaleas, acers, rhododendrons and camellias, interplanted with an abundance of spring bulbs. The very pretty cottage garden has interesting examples of topiary and unusual plants. Jacob sheep graze the surrounding pastures. Featured on Local TV news and radio reports. Featured in Courier and Sussex Express. Mainly flat, no steps. Gravel drive.

130 STONEHEALED FARM

Streat Lane, Streat BN6 8SA. Lance & Fiona Smith, 01273 891145, afionasmith@hotmail.com. *2m SE of Burgess Hill. From Ditchling B2116, 1m E of Westmeston, turn L (N) signed Streat, 2m on R immed after railway bridge*. Home-made teas. **Adm £4, chd free (share to St Peter & St James Hospice). Sun 25, Tue 27 May (2-5). Visitors also welcome by appt Apr to Sept for groups of 10+.**

C17 house (not open) in beautiful rural setting. Sheltered garden 'rooms' link with areas open to views of the S Downs. Paths wind through relaxed informal planting of trees, shrubs, climbers and unusual perennials, around ponds, through a vegetable garden and extending out into surrounding fields. Wonderful overview from a raised platform in an ancient oak tree. Delicious home-made teas served under cover. Featured in Period Living May 2013. Some gravel paths and steps.

132 ◆ SUSSEX PRAIRIES

Morlands Farm, Wheatsheaf Road, Henfield BN5 9AT. Paul & Pauline McBride, 01273 495902, www.sussexprairies.co.uk. *2m NE of Henfield on B2116 Wheatsheaf Rd (also known as Albourne Rd). Look out for pink buffalo sign with Sussex Prairie garden written on it*. Home-made teas. **Adm £6, chd free. For NGS: Mon 25 Aug (11-5). For other opening times and information, please phone or see garden website.**

Exciting prairie garden of approx 6-acres planted in the naturalistic style using 30,000 plants and over 600 different varieties. A colourful garden featuring a huge variety of unusual ornamental grasses. Expect layers of colour, texture and architectural splendour. Surrounded by mature oak trees with views of Chanctonbury Ring and Devil's Dyke on the S Downs. Permanent sculpture collection and exhibited sculpture throughout the season. Rare breed sheep and pigs. Featured in many magazines and books incl The RHS Garden; Gardens Illustrated, Country Life, Homes and Gardens, Country Homes and Interiors, Sunday Times and Sunday Telegraph. Woodchip paths may be difficult for wheelchairs. No disabled WC available.

Qni
The Queen's Nursing Institute
Garden visiting is good for you – and helps others too!

133 NEW SYCAMORE DRIVE EVENING OPENING

Burgess Hill RH15 0GH. John Smith & Kieran O'Regan. *8m N of Brighton. Sycamore Drive is off Folders Lane (B2113) in Burgess Hill.* **Evening Opening £5, chd free, wine, Fri 5 Sept (7-9.30).**

With a glass of wine, see how the delightful garden at number 30 is transformed at night with clever lighting and candles. Please register your intention to visit in advance by email: jsarastroo@aol.com or call 01444 871888.

135 TIDEBROOK MANOR

Tidebrook, Wadhurst TN5 6PD. *Between Wadhurst and Mayfield. From Wadhurst take B2100 towards Mark Cross, L at Best Beech PH, down-hill, 200 metres past church on R, then a drive on L.* **Adm £5, chd free. Wed 19 Mar, Wed 18 June, Wed 17 Sept (10-4).**

4-acre garden developed over the last decade with outstanding views of the Sussex countryside. In the 'Arts and Crafts' tradition the garden features large mixed borders, intimate courtyards, meadows, hydrangea walk, kitchen garden with raised beds, a willow platt and a wild woodland of particular interest in the spring. A lively and stimulating garden throughout the year. Tours with Head Gardener, Edward Flint, at 11am and 2pm, £2 extra. Wheelchair access possible, not in woodland area.

136 TOWN PLACE

Ketches Lane, Freshfield, nr Sheffield Park RH17 7NR. Dr & Mrs Anthony McGrath, 01825 790221, www.townplacegarden.org.uk. *5m E of Haywards Heath. From A275 turn W at Sheffield Green into Ketches Lane for Lindfield. 1¾ m on L*. Cream teas. **Adm £5, chd free. Thur 12, Sun 22, Sun 29 June, Sun 6 July (2-6). Visitors also welcome by appt June to July for groups of 20+.**

3-acres with over 600 roses, 150ft herbaceous border, walled herb garden, ornamental grasses, ancient hollow oak, orchard and potager. 'Green' Priory Church and Cloisters. C17 Sussex farmhouse (not open).

137 11 TREDCROFT ROAD

Hove BN3 6UH. Barbara Kennington. *E of Hove Park. Tredcroft Rd runs between Woodruff Avenue and Shirley Drive. Free on-street parking*. Home-made teas. **Adm £3, chd free. Sat 7, Sun 8 June (11-5).**

110ft x 50ft town garden on 4 levels facing NW, on clay soil. Designed and landscaped 6-yrs-ago, the garden is now well established and boasts many creative features incl sculptures, a pebble mosaic, an exotic pool garden, shaded walk, many perennials and grasses and a working vegetable garden. Featured in The English Garden magazine.

138 NEW TURNERS HOUSE

Turners Green, Heathfield TN21 9RB. Christopher Miscampbell & Julia Padbury, 01435 831191, chris-joolz@zen.co.uk. *4m E of Heathfield. S off B2096 at Middle Lane, 3 Cups Corner signed Rushlake Green, Hailsham, for ⅓m. Look for big clock face on L. Park on*

green, not roads. **Adm £3.50, chd free.** **Visitors welcome by appt Apr to July for individuals and groups of 15 max. Refreshments by prior arrangement.**
2/3 -acre country garden of lush, densely-planted, colour-themed shrubaceous borders, developed and maintained by owners battling against the combined challenges of exposure and drought. Catenary rose walk leading to summerhouse, displaying photos showing the development of the garden. Scrubbed birch grove, small underplanted orchard. WC on request. Limited wheelchair access following wet weather. Grass and old brick paths, stepping stones, some gravel.

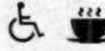

139 UPWALTHAM BARNS

Upwaltham GU28 0LX. Roger & Sue Kearsey, 01798 343145. *6m S of Petworth. 6m N of Chichester on A285.* Light refreshments. **Adm £4, chd free (share to St Mary's Church).** **Sun 25, Mon 26 May (11-5.30).** **Visitors also welcome by appt May to July, Mon-Wed only. Refreshments by arrangement.**
Unique farm setting transformed into a garden of many rooms. Entrance is a tapestry of perennial planting to set off C17 flint barns. At the rear, walled terraced garden redeveloped and planted with an abundance of unusual plants. Extensive vegetable garden. Landscaping in walled garden in progress. Roam at leisure, relax and enjoy in all seasons. Lovely views of S Downs and C12 Shepherds Church (open to visitors). The grounds have some gravel paths.

140 VACHERY FOREST GARDEN

Wych Cross TN22 3HR. Conservators of Ashdown Forest, www.ashdownforest.org. *2/3 m W of A22 between Wych Cross and Nutley. Park 1 1/2 m S of Wych Cross on A22 at Trees, Long or Vachery car parks. Access along rides, across heath and down steepish bridleway. Round trip 2 1/2 m, no facilities.* **Adm £4, chd free.** **Tue 16 Sept (11-4).**
The Vachery Garden, a hidden gem of Ashdown Forest, is being part restored. It comprises a string of lakes, sluices and weirs with a Folly Bridge; a 'gorge' of Cheddar Gorge limestone landscaped by Gavin Jones in 1925; and fine stands of rhododendrons and native and

Shalford House

© Leigh Clapp

introduced trees. Guided tours at 11am and 2.30pm, starting from the Trees Car Park on A22. The circular walk is approx 2-hrs, over steep and rugged terrain and will only take place weather permitting - please phone on the day by 10am for confirmation or check our website. Pre-booking for tours is essential, please phone or email by 15 Sept.

GROUP OPENING

141 WARNINGLID GARDENS

Warninglid, Haywards Heath RH17 5TR. *Midway between Haywards Heath and Horsham, both 6m. From A23 W towards Warninglid for 3/4 m. S at B2115 Xrds (Cuckfield/ Warninglid Lane). From W through Warninglid Village. Parking at recreation ground next to pavilion. Street parking limited for disabled access, drop off for elderly visitors.* Cream teas in the pavilion.
Combined adm £5, chd free.
Sun 20 July (2-6).

APRIL COTTAGE
Alan Griffin

BEECHES
Mr & Mrs C Steel

GLENWOOD COTTAGE
Mr & Mrs Peter & Susanna Lye

1 HERRINGS COTTAGES
Mr A L Brown

OLD BARN COTTAGE
Alison & David Livesley

OLD PLACE
Carey Phelan

OLD POST
Mariola & Bob Clark

NEW **7 THE STREET**
Mrs Angela Buckton

NEW **YEOVENENY HOUSE, CUCKFIELD LANE**
Mr & Mrs Bill & Joan Hill

Warninglid is a pretty medieval village set in a conservation area of outstanding natural beauty. The village architecture provides a perfect back drop to the gardens on view. Several of the gardens are sited in The Street and on Spronketts Lane; part of the old coach and horses smuggling route along the south coast towards Shoreham, through Wineham. The gardens are of remarkable variety and in different ways reflect the distinctive approach of each gardener. Terraces, shrubs and water features are used to enhance the natural landscapes and offer variety and contrast stimulating thoughts and ideas for you as the visitor. We have many gardening ideas to take away for everyone! Partial wheelchair access.

Merriments

142 ◆ WEST DEAN GARDENS

West Dean PO18 0QZ. Edward James Foundation, 01243 818221, www.westdean.org.uk. *5m N of Chichester. On A286, midway between Chichester and Midhurst.* Light refreshments. **Adm £7.70, chd £0.90 (adm quoted, provisional for 2014). For NGS: Wed 14 May (10.30-5). For other opening times and information, please phone or see garden website.**

35-acre historic garden in tranquil downland setting. 300ft long Harold Peto pergola, mixed and herbaceous borders, rustic summerhouses, water and spring garden, and specimen trees. 2½ -acre walled garden contains fruit collection, 13 Victorian glasshouses, apple store, large working kitchen garden, and an extensive plant collection. Circuit walk (2¼ m) climbs through parkland to 45-acre St Roche's Arboretum. Most areas of the walled garden and grounds are accessible.

144 1 WHITES COTTAGES

Fletching, Uckfield TN22 3SP. Gillian & Colin Smith. *4m NW of Uckfield. From A272 turn N at Piltdown or North Chailey 1m. From A275 turn E at Sheffield Green 2m.* Home-made teas at North Hall. **Combined Adm £4, chd free with North Hall. Sat 28, Sun 29 June (2-5.30).**

Located in the picturesque village of Fletching this enchanting little garden is delightfully crammed with everything synonymous with a true cottage garden. Small in space but huge in interest it features amongst the lovely perennial planting and unique paths, a child's gipsy caravan and free running ducks. Reasonably priced home propagated plants for sale.

GROUP OPENING

145 WINCHELSEA'S SECRET GARDENS

Winchelsea TN36 4EJ. *2m W of Rye, 8m E of Hastings. Purchase ticket for all gardens at first garden visited; a map will be provided, also showing the location of teas.* Home-made teas in village hall (1-5). **Combined adm £5, chd free. Sat 26 Apr, Sat 21 June (1-5.30).**

ALARDS
John & Vicky Jessup.
Open April only

ALARDS PLAT
1 High Street. Richard & Cynthia Feast.
Open June only

THE ARMOURY
Mr & Mrs A Jasper

NEW BACKFIELDS END
Rectory Lane. Sandra & Peter Mackenzie Smith.
Open June only

NEW 1 BARRACK SQUARE
Andy & Maureen Pemble.
Open June only

NEW 2 BARRACK SQUARE
Melvyn & Jan Pett.
Open June only

NEW 3 BARRACK SQUARE
Ms Deborah Upton.
Open June only

CLEVELAND HOUSE
Mr & Mrs J Jempson

CLEVELAND PLACE
Sally & Graham Rhodda

FIVE CHIMNEYS
Tony & Sue Davis

PERITEAU HOUSE
Dr & Mrs Lawrence Youlten.
Open April only

RYE VIEW
Howard Norton & David Page

SOUTH MARITEAU
Robert & Sheila Holland.
Open June only

THE WELL HOUSE
Alice Kenyon.
Open June only

Winchelsea is a beautiful medieval town founded in 1288 by Edward I. For nearly 200 years, as a Cinque Port, it was a major trading centre. Now all that remains of that time are the medieval merchants' cellars and the old streets, built on a grid system, behind whose old walls are the Secret Gardens. There are 14 gardens in the group this year, including 4 that haven't opened before and 4 returning to the list after a break. Guided tours of medieval cellars both dates at 10.30am, £5, booking essential, 01797 229525 (mornings) or cellars@winchelsea.com. Beautiful church of St Thomas open to visitors. Town information at www.winchelsea.com and www.winchelsea.net. Wheelchair access to most gardens; see map for details.

146 NEW WINDHAVEN
Longlands Road, East Wittering, Chichester PO20 8DD. Mr & Mrs Cedric Marshall. *Turn L at the end of Shore Rd, East Wittering (if you don't, you're in the sea), 150yds on L.* **Adm £3, chd free.** **Sun 13 July (10-5).**
Newly retired garden designer has downsized and faced the challenge of moving to windswept and salt laden air 100-metres from sea. Three very different gardens; front seaside garden; side courtyard garden and rear garden with mixed planting of salt resistant shrubs, herbaceous plants and grasses in two parts (700-sq-metre). Teas available in East Wittering Village.

Relax and listen to live jazz in the garden . . .

149 NEW WOODSIDE HOUSE
Cooksbridge Road, Barcombe BN8 5TJ. Christopher & Joanna Newman, 01273 401060, CWSNewman@aol.com. *4m N of Lewes. A275. Turn by Rainbow PH. Next R to Barcombe. From E, A26 towards Barcombe. L at village r'about. 1/2 m W out of village.* Home-made teas. **Adm £4, chd free.** **Tue 27, Thur 29 May (11-5).**
Visitors also welcome by appt May to Sept for small groups.
Approx 2-acres of informal country garden with mixed borders, vegetable garden and meadows in idyllic setting.

Sussex County Volunteers

East & Mid Sussex

County Organiser
Irene Eltringham-Willson, Butlers Farmhouse, Butlers Lane, Herstmonceux BN27 1QH, 01323 833770, irene.willson@btinternet.com

Treasurer
Peter Willson, Butlers Farmhouse, Butlers Lane, Herstmonceux BN27 1QH, 01323 833770, peter.willson2@btopenworld.com

Publicity Officer and ACO
Geoff Stonebanks, Driftwood, 4 Marine Drive, Bishopstone BN25 2RS, 01323 899296, ngseastsussex@gmail.com

Assistant County Organisers
Jane Baker, Pembury House, Ditchling Road (New Road), Clayton, Hassocks BN6 9PH, 01273 842805, jane.baker47@btinternet.com
Lynne Brown, 26 Cornwall Gardens, Brighton BN1 6RJ, 01273 556439, brown.lynne@ntlworld.com
Diane Gould, Heronbrook, Perrymans Lane, High Hurstwood, nr Uckfield TN22 4AG, 01825 732253, heron.brook@btinternet.com
Jasmine Hart, Roundstone House, Town Littleworth, Cooksbridge BN8 4TH, 01273 400427, jasminehart111@yahoo.co.uk
Richard & Matty Holmes, Beauchamps, Float Lane, Udimore TN31 6BY, 01797 223055, mrholmes@rye.hivetelecom.net
Philippa Hopkins, Birchover Cottage, 10 Maypole Road, Ashurstwood RH19 3QN, 01342 822090, piphop@btinternet.com
Jean Kendrick, Brinkers, Brinkers Lane, Wadhurst TN5 6LS, jm.kendrick1@btinternet.com
Susan Laing, Great Lywood Farmhouse, Lindfield Road, Ardingly RH17 6SW, 01444 892500, splaing@btinternet.com
Jan Newman, Millcroft, 25 Mill Lane, East Hoathly, Lewes BN8 6QB, 01825 840916
Sara Turner, 9 Terminus Avenue, Bexhill TN39 3LS, 01424 210716, sara.kidd@virgin.net
Liz Warner, 10 Roundhay Avenue, Peacehaven BN10 9TQ, 01273 586050, elizabeth55warner@btinternet.com

West Sussex

County Organiser
Jane Allen, Dyers House, Pickhurst Road, Chiddingfold GU8 4TG, 01428 683130, jane.allen01@talktalk.net

Treasurer
Position vacant, please contact NGS Head Office, 01483 213909, lgrainger@ngs.org.uk

Assistant County Organisers
Sanda Belcher, The Courtyard, Linchmere GU27 3NG, 01428 723259, sandabelcher@tiscali.co.uk
Jane Burton, Church Farmhouse, Ford Water Road, Lavant, Chichester PO18 0AL, 01243 527822
Diana Cave, Old Barkfold, Plaistow RH14 0PU, 01403 871254
Lesley Chamberlain, Clare Cottage, 4 Lime Road, Findon, Worthing, BN14 0UL, chamberlain_lesley@hotmail.com
Patty Christie, Garden House, Guillards Oak, Midhurst, GU29 9JZ, 01730 813323, patty@christieuk.co.uk
Sue Foley, The Well House, School Hill, Slindon, Arundel, BN18 0RS, 01243 814452, suefoley@mac.com
Jane Lywood, Battlehurst Farm, Kirdford, Billingshurst RH14 0LJ, 01403 820225, jmlywood@aol.com
Claudia Pearce, 11 Beaumont Road, Worthing BN14 8HF, 07985 648216, claudiapearce17@gmail.com
Fiona Phillips, Old Erringham Cottage, Steyning Road, Shoreham-by-Sea BN43 5FD, 01273 462285, fiona.h.phillips@btinternet.com
Susan Pinder, 30 Townfield, Kirdford RH14 0LZ, 01403 820430, nasus.rednip@virgin.net
Caroline & Adrian Skeates, 2 Churchyard Cottages, Clapgate Lane, Slinfold, Horsham, RH13 0QU, 07743 505392, as13cs@btinternet.com

WARWICKSHIRE

(for Birmingham & West Midlands see Staffordshire)

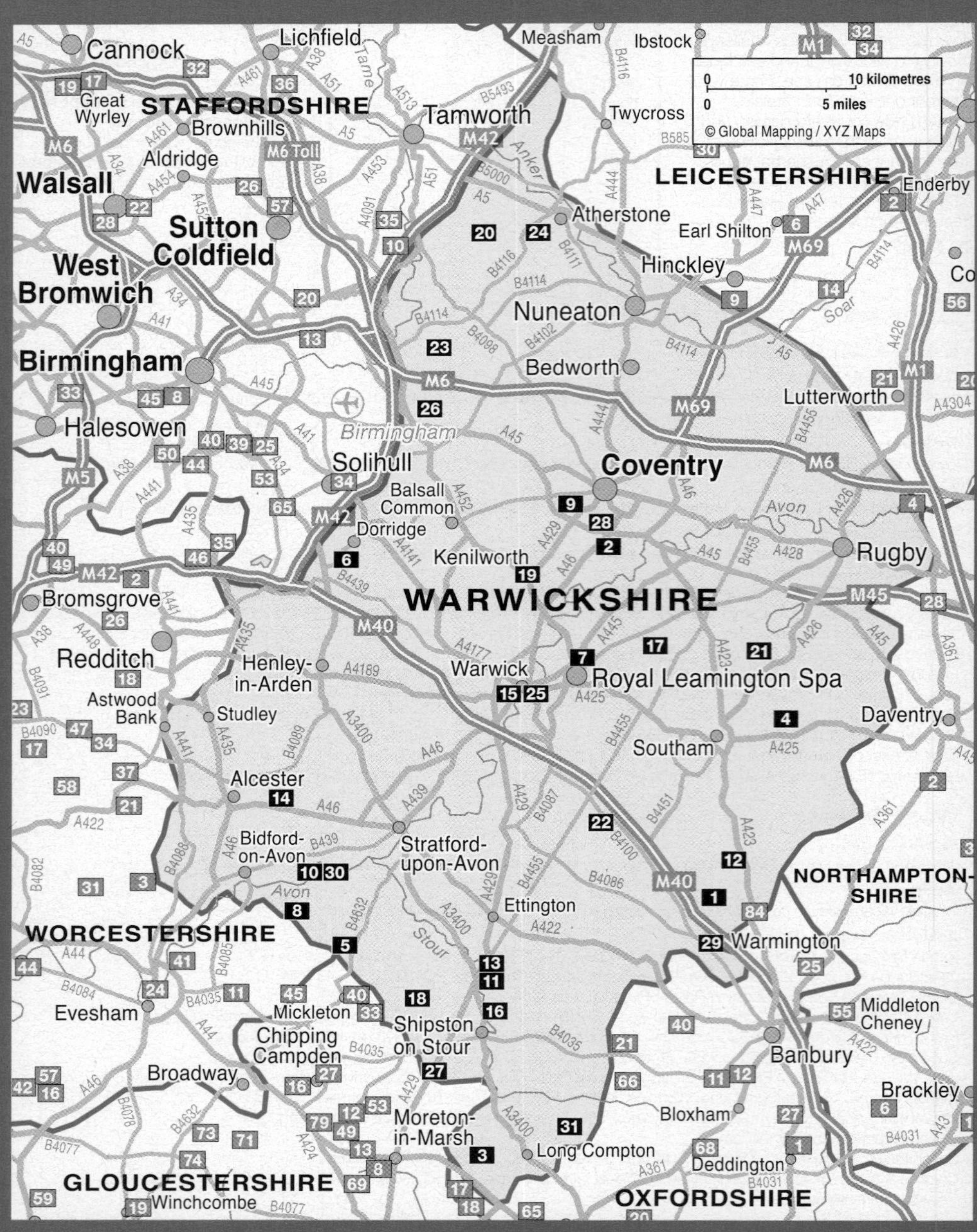

Opening Dates

All entries subject to change. For latest information check www.ngs.org.uk

February

Saturday 22
15 Hill Close Gardens

April

Every day (from Saturday 5)
4 **Bridge Nursery**
Every day
25 **The Mill Garden**
Sunday 20
6 Broadacre
Sunday 27
7 19 Church Lane
27 Stretton-on-Fosse Gardens

May

Every day
4 **Bridge Nursery**
25 **The Mill Garden**
Monday 5
9 Earlsdon Gardens
Sunday 18
24 Merevale Hall
Wednesday 21
11 Folly Lodge
Sunday 25
3 Barton House
5 Broad Marston & Pebworth Gardens
Monday 26
5 Broad Marston & Pebworth Gardens

June

Every day
4 **Bridge Nursery**
25 **The Mill Garden**

Festival Weekend

Sunday 8
7 19 Church Lane
14 NEW Haselor Gardens
26 Packington Hall
Saturday 14
12 The Granary
17 Hunningham Village Gardens
Sunday 15
8 Dorsington Gardens
12 The Granary
16 Honington Village Gardens
17 Hunningham Village Gardens
23 Maxstoke Castle

16 Delaware Road, Styvechale Gardens

31 Whichford & Ascott Gardens
Sunday 22
19 Kenilworth Gardens
28 Styvechale Gardens
29 Warmington Village Gardens
Saturday 28
30 Welford-on-Avon & District Gardens
Sunday 29
13 Halford Gardens
22 NEW Lighthorne Gardens
30 Welford-on-Avon & District Gardens

July

Every day
4 **Bridge Nursery**
25 **The Mill Garden**
Sunday 6
7 19 Church Lane
20 Latimers Rest
Saturday 12
18 Ilmington Gardens
Sunday 13
1 Avon Dassett Gardens
18 Ilmington Gardens
Saturday 19
12 The Granary
Sunday 20
12 The Granary
27 Stretton-on-Fosse Gardens

August

Every day
4 **Bridge Nursery**
25 **The Mill Garden**
Sunday 3
2 Avondale Nursery
Saturday 23
12 The Granary
Sunday 24
2 Avondale Nursery
12 The Granary
Monday 25
2 Avondale Nursery
12 The Granary
Sunday 31
19 Kenilworth Gardens

September

Every day (until Sunday 14)
4 **Bridge Nursery**
Every day
25 **The Mill Garden**
Saturday 27
15 Hill Close Gardens

October

Every day (until Thursday 30)
25 **The Mill Garden**

Gardens open to the public

- 2 Avondale Nursery
- 4 Bridge Nursery
- 15 Hill Close Gardens
- 25 The Mill Garden

By appointment only

- 10 Elm Close
- 21 NEW The Lawns

Also open by appointment

- 3 Barton House
- 6 Broadacre
- 7 19 Church Lane
- 11 Folly Lodge
- 12 The Granary
- 14 NEW The Croft House, Haselor Gardens
- 19 Fieldgate, Kenilworth Gardens
- 20 Latimers Rest
- 27 Court House, Stretton-on-Fosse Gardens

The Gardens

GROUP OPENING

1 AVON DASSETT GARDENS

Southam CV47 2AE. *7m N of Banbury. From M40 J12 turn L and L again B4100. 2nd L into village. Park in village and at top of hill.* Home-made teas at Old Mill Cottage. **Combined adm £5, chd free. Sun 13 July (2-6).**

THE COACH HOUSE
Diana & Peter Biddlestone

HILL TOP FARM
Mrs N & Mr D Hicks

THE LIMES
John & Diane Anderson

OLD MILL COTTAGE
Mike & Jill Lewis

THE OLD RECTORY
Lily Hope-Frost

POPPY COTTAGE
Bob & Audrey Butler

Pretty Hornton stone village sheltering in the lee of the Burton Dassett hills, well wooded and with parkland setting, The Old Rectory mentioned in Domesday Book. Wide variety of gardens incl kitchen gardens, gravel and tropical gardens. Range of plants incl alpines, herbaceous, perennials, roses, climbers and shrubs. Art Exhibition. Two churches open. Wheelchair access to most properties.

Exotic garden with palms, cypresses, olive trees and vineyard . . .

2 ◆ AVONDALE NURSERY

at Russell's Nursery, Mill Hill, Baginton CV8 3AG. Mr Brian Ellis, 02476 673662, www.avondalenursery.co.uk. *3m S Coventry. At junction of A45/A46 take slip road to Baginton, 1st L to Mill Hill. Opp Old Mill Inn.* Light refreshments in Potting Shed Cafe at Russell's Nursery. **Adm £3, chd free. For NGS: Sun 3, Sun 24, Mon 25 Aug (11-4). For other opening times and information, please phone or see garden website.**

Vast array of flowers and ornamental grasses, including National Collections of *Anemone nemorosa, Sanguisorba and Aster novae-angliae*. Technicolor cornucopia of plants, our 'Library Garden' is a well-labelled reference book illustrating the unusual, exciting and even some long-lost treasures. Adjacent nursery is a plantaholic's delight. Visitors often remark 'Why have I not visited this garden before?'. On Sunday 3rd August at 2-3pm, Brian hopes you'll join him for an enthusiastic 'Talk Around the Library Garden', when he'll show you all of his current late-flowering plant obsessions, including big collections of *Helenium, Crocosmia, Sanguisorba* and ornamental grasses, and the garden will be looking at its best! Admission £5 incl tea/coffee and biscuits. All proceeds to NGS. Featured on Gardener's World, in House & Garden and The English Garden.

NCH

3 BARTON HOUSE

Barton-on-the-Heath GL56 0PJ. Mr & Mrs I H B Cathie, 01608 674303, hamish.cathie@thebartonfarms.com. *2m W of Long Compton. 2m W off A3400 Stratford-upon-Avon to Oxford road; 1¼ m N off A44 Chipping Norton to Moreton-in-Marsh road.* Home-made teas. **Adm £5, chd free. Sun 25 May (2-6). Visitors also welcome by appt spring to autumn.**

6½-acres with mature trees, azaleas, species and hybrid rhododendrons, magnolias, mountain tree peonies. National collections of *Arbutus* and *Catalpa*. Japanese garden, rose garden, secret garden and many rare and exotic plants. Victorian kitchen garden. Exotic garden with palms, cypresses and olive trees established 2002. Vineyard planted 2000 - free wine tasting. Manor house by Inigo Jones (not open). Some gravel paths and some steps. Can be slippery but generally wheelchair friendly. Dogs strictly only on leads.

NCH

4 ◆ BRIDGE NURSERY

Tomlow Road, Napton, nr Southam CV47 8HX. Christine Dakin & Philip Martino, 01926 812737, www.bridge-nursery.co.uk. *3m E of Southam. Brown tourist sign at Napton Xrds on A425 Southam to Daventry road.* **Adm £2.50, chd free. For NGS: Sat 5 Apr to Sun 14 Sept incl (10-4). For other opening times and information, please phone or see garden website.**

Be inspired by the range of rare and unusual plants thriving in heavy clay soil. Our 1½ -acre garden is a fine example of mind over matter! Large pond and bamboo grove. Hedgerow walk, butterfly border, cutting garden. Wildlife abounds.

GROUP OPENING

5 BROAD MARSTON & PEBWORTH GARDENS

Stratford-upon-Avon CV37 8XZ. *9m SW of Stratford-upon-Avon. On B439 at Bidford turn S towards Honeybourne, after 3m turn L at Xrds signed Pebworth.* Home-made teas at Pebworth Village Hall. **Combined adm £6, chd free. Sun 25, Mon 26 May (2-6).**

NEW ASHLOW
Rachel & Dudley Jarrett

BANK HOUSE
Clive & Caroline Warren

1 ELM CLOSE
Mr & Mrs G Keyte

FELLY LODGE
Maz & Barrie Clatworthy

ICKNIELD BARN
Sheila Davies

IVYBANK NCH
Mr & Mrs R Davis

NEW **JASMINE COTTAGE**
Ted & Veronica Watson

THE KNOLL
Mr & Mrs K Wood

THE MOUNT
Mr & Mrs J Ilott

NOLAN COTTAGE
Gill & Ron Thomas

ORCHARD HOUSE
David & Susan Lees

PETTIFER HOUSE
Mr & Mrs Michael Veal

NEW **3 ST PETER'S COURT**
Michael & Jana Foist

Broad Marston, a small hamlet with a priory and manor (not open), modern houses and thatched cottages, lies at the lowest point of the parish and the gardens are all on the level. Pebworth received a Silver-gilt in the Heart of England in Bloom. The gardens in Pebworth, run down the hill topped by St. Peter's C13 church (open). At the bottom of the hill lies the primary school with a thriving garden. The children grow vegetables and then cook them. Among the houses here you will find the village hall and two small but interesting gardens very different in character. This is another area with old thatched cottages, and properties of various ages. On the outskirts of the village is Fibrex Nursery, holders of the National *Pelargonium* and ivy collections; Ivybank, their private garden, is open. This year we have new gardens and some that have not opened for some years. No wheelchair access to The Knoll.

6 BROADACRE

Grange Road, Dorridge, Solihull B93 8QA. Mr John Woolman, 07818 082885, john@jgwoolman.plus.com, www.broadacregarden.org. *Approx 3m SE of Solihull. On B4101 opp the Railway PH.* Home-made teas. **Adm £3, chd free. Sun 20 Apr (2-6). Visitors also welcome by appt.**
Broadacre is a semi-wild garden attractively landscaped with pools, lawns and trees and with two adjoining wild flower meadows. The garden is at its best when the fruit trees are blossoming in the spring. Bring stout footwear to follow the nature-trail around the meadows. Lovely venue for a spring picnic. Pets welcome. Dorridge Cricket Club is in the grounds.

7 19 CHURCH LANE

Lillington, Leamington Spa CV32 7RG. David & Judy Hirst, 01926 422591. *1½ m NE of Leamington Spa. Take A445 towards Rugby. Church Lane on R just beyond r'about junction with B4453. Garden on corner of Hill Close. Enter via driveway in Church Lane.* **Adm £2.50, chd free. Sun 27 Apr, Sun 8 June, Sun 6 July (2-5.30). Visitors also welcome by appt Mar to Aug for groups of 16 max.**
Camellias, spring bulbs and hellebores greet the early visitor to this plantsperson's cottage-style garden. Many unusual plants in all seasons, with pleasingly combined herbaceous areas, clematis, raised beds and alpine containers. A country atmosphere, satisfying to the horticultural connoisseur as well as to the general gardener.

6 DINGLE END
See Worcestershire

GROUP OPENING

8 DORSINGTON GARDENS

Dorsington CV37 8AR. *6m SW of Stratford-upon-Avon. On B439 from Stratford turn L to Welford-on-Avon, then R to Dorsington. Free shuttle bus service and map incl.* Tea in the marquee at The Old Manor Garden. **Combined adm £7, chd free. Sun 15 June (10-5).**

THE BARN
Mr & Mrs P Reeve

CEDAR BARN
Pat & Derek Hudson

COLLETTS FARM
Mr & Mrs D Bliss

CRABTREE FARM COTTAGE
Mr & Mrs David Boulton

DORSINGTON ARBORETUM
Mr F Dennis

DORSINGTON HOUSE
Mr & Mrs I Kolodotschko

2 DORSINGTON MANOR
Mr & Mrs C James

3 DORSINGTON MANOR
Mr & Mrs E Rusling

1 GLEBE COTTAGES
Mr & Mrs A Brough

MANOR FARM HOUSE
Mr F Dennis

NEW **MILFIELD**
Mr & Mrs Roger & Lorraine Johnson

THE OLD MANOR
Mr F Dennis

THE OLD RECTORY
Mr & Mrs Nigel Phillips

SAPPHIRE HOUSE
Mrs D Sawyer

THE WELSHMAN'S BARN
Mr F Dennis

NEW **WINDRUSH HOUSE**
Mr Alastair & Dr Claire Manning

Dorsington is a Domesday hamlet with a secret… it is revealed one magic day in June - a spectacle of glorious gardens, tea and cake, plants, vintage Rolls Royces, statues and farm animals. These gardens offer an array of different styles such as young cottage gardens, productive kitchen gardens, stone terracing and climbing roses, orchards and gurgling brooks, ultra modern, futuristic and minimal. You can wander among the life-size statues at Welshman's Barn together with Oz maze and Japanese garden.

Overflowing beds and borders are a patchwork of colour and shape . . .

Barton House

© Mandy Bradshaw

Bring a bag for plants – help us give more to charity

A relaxing, informal country garden with hidden corners and special spaces . . .

GROUP OPENING

9 EARLSDON GARDENS

Coventry CV5 6FS. *Turn towards Coventry at A45/A429 T-lights. Take 3rd L into Beechwood Ave, continue ½ m to St. Barbara's Church at Xrds with Rochester Rd. Maps and tickets at St Barbara's Church Hall.* Light refreshments at St Barbara's Church Hall. **Combined adm £3.50, chd free. Mon 5 May (11-4).**

43 ARMORIAL ROAD
Gary & Jane Flanagan

3 BATES ROAD
Victor & Judith Keene

NEW **177 BEECHWOOD AVENUE**
Terry & Lisa Cornwall

40 HARTINGTON CRESCENT
Viv & George Buss

114 HARTINGTON CRESCENT
Liz Campbell & Denis Crowley

36 PROVIDENCE STREET
Rachel Culley & Steve Shiner

54 SALISBURY AVENUE
Peter & Pam Moffit

2 SHAFTESBURY ROAD
Ann Thomson & Bruce Walker

23 SPENCER AVENUE
Susan & Keith Darwood

Varied selection of town gardens from small to more formal with interest for all tastes incl a mature garden with deep borders bursting with spring colour, a large garden with extensive lawns and an array of rhododendrons, azaleas and large mature trees; densely planted town garden with sheltered patio area and wilder woodland and surprisingly large garden offering interest to all ages! There is also a pretty garden set on several levels with hidden aspects, large peaceful garden with water features and vegetable plot and a large mature garden in a peaceful surrounding. Plantaholic's garden with a large variety of plants, clematis and small trees, some unusual and a woodland setting providing the backdrop to a garden of many contrasts incl a terrace of subtropical plants.

10 ELM CLOSE

Welford on Avon CV37 8PT. Eric & Glenis Dyer, 01789 750793, glenisdyer@gmail.com. *5m SW of Stratford, off B4390. Elm Close is between Welford Garage and The Bell Inn.* **Adm £3, chd free. Visitors welcome by appt for groups 15-50 (a coach load). Teas can be supplied by, and in aid of British Red Cross if required.**
Drifts of snowdrops, aconites, erythroniums and hellebores in spring are followed by species peonies, sumptuous tree peonies, herbaceous peonies and delphiniums. Colourful Japanese maples, daphnes and cornus are underplanted with hostas, heucheras, and brunneras. Then agapanthus, phlox, asters, salvias and hydrangeas extend the seasons, with hundreds of clematis providing yr-round colour. Sloping gravel front drive.

11 FOLLY LODGE

Idlicote Road, Halford CV36 5DG. Mike & Susan Solomon, 01789 740183, ss@follylodge.eclipse.co.uk. *3m NE of Shipston-on-Stour. On A429 (Fosse Way). In Halford take turning to Idlicote, garden 200yds on R.* Home-made teas. **Adm £3.50, chd free. Wed 21 May (2-5.30). Also open with Halford Gardens on Sun 29 June (2-5.30). Visitors also welcome by appt May to Aug for groups of 8+.**
A relaxing, informal country garden with hidden corners and special spaces. Overflowing beds and borders are a patchwork of colour and shape. In addition there are a variety of sculptures, including Susan's ceramics. Mostly level with gravel paths.

12 THE GRANARY

Wharf Road, Fenny Compton, Southam CV47 2FE. Lucy & Mike Davies, 01295 770033, bookings@the-granary.co.uk, www.the-granary.co.uk. *7m S of Southam. On A423 Southam to Banbury road. 200yds S of turning to Fenny Compton turn R into service road signed Fenny Compton Wharf. Follow NGS signs.* Home-made teas and light lunches. **Adm £4, chd free. Sat 14, Sun 15 June, Sat 19, Sun 20 July, Sat 23, Sun 24, Mon 25 Aug (11-4.30). Visitors also welcome by appt June to Sept.**
Attractive 1-acre canal-side garden with views of the Oxford canal and Dassett Hills. Recent additions incl herbaceous beds, water feature and herb garden. Beyond is a ⅓ -acre kitchen plot comprising a vegetable area (grown on organic principles), a poly-tunnel for propagation and salad crops, fruit-cage and orchard. There is also a copse of native British trees in the 3-acre paddock. Steps down to the herb garden and up to the vegetable area and gravel paths.

GROUP OPENING

13 HALFORD GARDENS

Halford, Shipston-on-Stour CV36 5DJ. *3m NE of Shipston-on-Stour. On A429 (Fosse Way). In Halford take turning to Idlicote.* Home-made teas. **Combined adm £5, chd free. Sun 29 June (2-5.30).**

1 AYLWORTH COTTAGES
Sue Lyons

NEW **15 THE CLOSE**
Vaughan Booth

NEW **17 THE CLOSE**
David Brook & Rose Whelan

19 THE CLOSE
Amanda & Henry Probert

FOLLY LODGE
Mike & Susan Solomon
(See separate entry)

Following an enjoyable first opening in 2013, this year we have persuaded more gardeners to join in the fun. Five beautiful village gardens, all within 200yds walk, and all different. With Three small, colourful gardens next door to each other in The Close, planted specifically for wildlife. The very small garden at 1 Aylworth Cottages shows what can be done in such a small place. A larger garden at Folly Lodge incl a potted garden and many artworks.

GROUP OPENING

14 NEW HASELOR GARDENS

Haselor, Alcester B49 6LU. *6m W of Stratford upon Avon, 2m E of Alcester, off A46. From A46 take Haselor turn. From Alcester take old Stratford Rd, L turn for Haselor then R at Xrds. Gardens are in centre of village.* **Combined adm £4, chd free. Sun 8 June (12-6).**

NEW BEXLEY COTTAGE
Andy & Sue Roake

NEW THE CROFT HOUSE
Isobel & Patrick Somers
Visitors also welcome by appt May to July.
01789 488881

Haselor is a picturesque village with many historic buildings. Bexley Cottage aka The Old Post Office appeared in the Guinness Book of Records as the smallest Post Office in England. An informal 1/2 -acre cottage garden planted with perennials, cheeky annuals, shrubs and mature trees plus a kitchen garden. Rear open fields invite a myriad of wildlife whilst views of St Mary and All Saints Church to the front bring peace and tranquillity. The Croft House offers an acre of trees, shrubs and herbaceous borders planted with a designer's passion for colour and texture. Gorgeous scented wisteria on two sides of the house. Organically managed, providing a haven for birds and other wildlife. Frog pond, small vegetable plot and a few venerable old fruit trees from its days as a market garden. Complete your visit with a stroll up the hill to admire our C11 church and the far-reaching views. Art and crafts exhibition at the Croft House, donating to the NGS.

15 ◆ HILL CLOSE GARDENS

Bread & Meat Close, Warwick CV34 6HF. Hill Close Gardens Trust, 01926 493339, www.hillclosegardens.com. *Town centre. Entry from Friars St by Bread & Meat Close. Car park by entrance next to racecourse. 2hrs free parking. Disabled parking outside the gates.* Light refreshments in Visitor Centre. **Adm £3.50, chd £1. For NGS: Sat 22 Feb (11-4.30); Sat 27 Sept (10.30-5). For other opening times and information, please phone or see garden website.**

Restored Grade II* Victorian leisure gardens comprising 16 individual hedged gardens, 8 brick summerhouses. Herbaceous borders, heritage apple and pear trees, C19 daffodils, many varieties of asters and chrysanthemums. Heritage vegetables. Plant Heritage border, auricula theatre, Victorian style glasshouse. Children's garden. Gardener's walk 2nd Fri in month. Visitors can admire our many varieties of snowdrop, large collection of asters and wide range of other late flowering plants and the unusual fruit trees.The listed Victorian brick summerhouses have great views. Tender plants in glasshouse. Wheelchair available which can be booked in advance by phone. Access route indicated on plan of the gardens.

GROUP OPENING

16 HONINGTON VILLAGE GARDENS

Shipston-on-Stour CV36 5AA. *1 1/2 m N of Shipston-on-Stour. Take A3400 towards Stratford-upon-Avon then turn R signed Honington.* Home-made teas. **Combined adm £5, chd free. Sun 15 June (2-6).**

HONINGTON GLEBE
Mr & Mrs J C Orchard

HONINGTON HALL
B H E Wiggin

MALT HOUSE RISE
Mr & Mrs M Underhill

THE OLD COTTAGE
Liz Davenport

THE OLD HOUSE
Mr & Mrs I F Beaumont

ORCHARD HOUSE
Mr & Mrs Monnington

SHOEMAKERS COTTAGE
Christopher & Anne Jordan

C17 village, recorded in Domesday, entered by old toll gate. Ornamental stone bridge over the R Stour and interesting church with C13 tower and late C17 nave after Wren. Seven super gardens. 2-acre plantsman's garden consisting of rooms planted informally with yr-round interest in contrasting foliage, texture, lily pool and parterre. Extensive lawns and fine mature trees with river and garden monuments. Small garden that is well stocked with interesting established shrubs and container plants and a structured cottage garden formally laid out with box hedging and small fountain. Small, developing garden created by the owners with informal mixed beds and borders. Wheelchair access to most gardens.

GROUP OPENING

17 HUNNINGHAM VILLAGE GARDENS

Hunningham, Leamington Spa CV33 9DS. *6m NE of Leamington Spa, 8m SW of Rugby, 7m S of Coventry. Just off the Fosseway-B4455, or take B4453 from Leamington through Weston-under-Wetherley and turn off R to Hunningham. Park in village.* Home-made teas. **Combined adm £4, chd free. Sat 14, Sun 15 June (12.30-5.30).**

BIRKDALE COTTAGE
Dean & Rose Woodford

NEW THE DORMERS
Irene & Oliver Ryan

NEW 5 LEIGH TERRACE
Rob & Lynn Parsons

THE MOTTE
Margaret & Peter Green

SNOWFORD HALL COTTAGES
Mark Hancock

Five gardens in contrasting styles with more gardens likely to be open on the day. Amongst the gardens on view are two well stocked plant lover's gardens brimming with woodland plants, tender perennials, unusual shrubs and trees, some exotic. Two recently redesigned gardens with attractive herbaceous borders and hard landscaping, and a cottage garden specialising in vegetables. Lovely views across the R Leam can be seen from some of the gardens. There is a good plant sale. Teas and homemade cakes will be available in the parish room which is attached to the quaint village church dating from the C13. More substantial refreshments are available at Hilltop Farm Cafe on the Fosse Way and the renowned Red Lion PH. Hunningham Open Gardens has been a very popular event over the years and we look forward to seeing you again. Teas and plant sales from 2pm. One garden without wheelchair access.

GROUP OPENING

18 ILMINGTON GARDENS

Ilmington CV36 4LA. *8m S of Stratford-upon-Avon. 8m N of Moreton in Marsh. 4m NW of Shipston-on-Stour off A3400. 3m NE of Chipping Campden.* Teas and refreshments at village hall. **Combined adm £6, chd free (share to Warwickshire and Northamptonshire Air Ambulance). Sat 12, Sun 13 July (2-6).**

THE BEVINGTONS
Mr & Mrs N Tustain

CHERRY ORCHARD
Mr Angus Chambers

CRAB MILL
Mr & Mrs D Brown

FROG ORCHARD
Mr & Mrs Jeremy Snowden

THE GRANGE
Mr & Mrs M Markham

GRUMP COTTAGE
Mr & Mrs Martin Underwood

ILMINGTON MANOR
Mr Martin Taylor

PARK FARM HOUSE
Mike & Lesley Lane

Ilmington is an ancient hillside Cotswold village 2m from the Fosse Way with two good pubs and splendid teas at the village hall. Buy your ticket at the Ilmington Manor (next to the Red Lion PH), wander the 3-acres of clipped yews, rose gardens, long borders and fish ponds. Proceed to Crab Mill's hillside gardens, then to Grump Cottage, a small stone-terraced garden planted in 2010. Walk to nearby Frog Lane, view cottage gardens of Park Farm House, Cherry Orchard and Frog Orchard. Cross the village to The Bevingtons, a large cottage garden in Valanders Lane between the Manor ponds and the Norman church. Walk up Back Street to The Grange with its large hill-top terraced gardens. Morris Men will perform around the village on Sunday afternoon only.

GROUP OPENING

19 KENILWORTH GARDENS

Kenilworth CV8 1BT. *Fieldgate Lane. Tickets and maps available at all gardens. Parking is available at Abbey Fields and Hollis Lane, and street parking at Malthouse Lane and Beehive Hill.* Home-made teas at Fieldgate. **Combined adm £5 (June), £4 (Aug), chd free. Sun 22 June, Sun 31 Aug (1-5).**

NEW BEEHIVE HILL ALLOTMENTS
Mr Keith Rocket.
Open 22 June only

NEW DUNNS PITTS BARN
Maggie Curley & Geoff Litterick.
Open 22 June only

FIELDGATE
Liz & Bob Watson.
Open 22 June and 31 August
Visitors also welcome by appt May to Sept.
01926 512307
bob.watson@lineone.net

14C FIELDGATE LANE
Mrs Sandra Aulton.
Open 22 June and 31 August

NEW 7 FIELDGATE LAWN
Mr Simon Cockell.
Open 22 June and 31 August

25 MALTHOUSE LANE
David & Linda Pettifor.
Open 22 June only

NEW ST AUGUSTINE'S CATHOLIC SCHOOL
Mrs Angela Scull.
Open 22 June only

Kenilworth was historically a very important town in Warwickshire, which now has one of England's best castle ruins and plenty of pubs and good restaurants. This year we welcome four new gardens, the Beehive Hill Allotments, Dunns Pilts Barn, 7 Fieldgate Lawn and St Augustine's Catholic School to the group. This makes seven in all, providing great variety; the group incl small and large gardens, formal and informal, and floral and vegetable gardening. All the gardens have won gold awards in the Kenilworth in Bloom garden competition with three attaining Best in Class. All seven are open in June and three (Fieldgate, 14c Fieldgate Lane and 7 Fieldgate Lawn) will open again in August.

20 LATIMERS REST

Hipsley Lane, Baxterley, Atherstone CV9 2HS. Gerald & Christine Leedham, 01827 875526, christine_leedham@yahoo.co.uk. *3m S of Atherstone on B4116. Next to Baxterley Church.* Home-made teas. **Adm £5, chd free. Sun 6 July (12-5). Visitors also welcome by appt May to Sept.**

2½ -acres of wonderful contrasts. Formal lawns and ponds with colourful flower beds and giant hanging baskets give way to hostas and ferns with Medieval moat backdrop. Feature rose gardens with over 40 standard roses. Small arboretum with specimen trees, vegetable gardens, greenhouses and chickens.

This group of gardens nestle within a dramatic landscape of hills, pasture and woodland, which is used to picturesque effect by the garden owners . . .

Avondale Nursery

21 NEW THE LAWNS
Birdingbury Road, Leamington Hastings, Rugby CV23 8EB. Mr & Mrs Graham Rice, 01926 632291, sandra@alexandrarice.plus.com. *Rugby 6m, Southam 6m. From A426 Leamington Hastings on a sharp bend. From A423, Marton, to Birdingbury to Leamington Hastings.* Home-made teas. **Adm £3, chd free. Visitors welcome by appt Feb to Oct.**
A developing 1-acre garden growing a wide range of plants with yr-round interest - the plantaholic owners are trying to fit in as many of their favourites from their previous 2-acre garden to create a garden which is easier to manage. Favourites incl snowdrops, daphne, clematis, salvias and asters, plus much more. As wandering around the garden is mainly on lawn, wheelchair users may need help to move about easily.

GROUP OPENING

22 NEW LIGHTHORNE GARDENS
Lighthorne, Warwick CV35 0AR. *10m S of Warwick. Lighthorne will be signed from the Fosse Way and B4100.* Home-made teas at The Old Rectory. **Combined adm £6, chd free. Sun 29 June (2-6).**

NEW BANK COTTAGE
Maggie Woodhouse

NEW BISHOPS FARM HOUSE
Sheila Barrett

NEW 1 CHURCH HILL COURT
Irene Proudman

NEW 4 CHURCH HILL COURT
Carol Pready

NEW THE OLD FORGE
Penny Neave

THE OLD RECTORY
The Hon Lady Butler

NEW THE PADDOCK
Martin & Lesley Thornton

NEW ROBIN COTTAGE
Martin & Mel Ryan

NEW ROSEMARY COTTAGE
Jane & Edward Stroud

NEW SMITHY COTTAGE
Josette Tait

NEW TAWTON
David Copson & Maureen Thomson

Lighthorne is a compact, pretty village between the Fosse Way and the B4100, with a charming church (open), pub and village hall. Park and buy your tickets at The Old Rectory and when you have visited that garden - sheltered by old stone walls clothed with roses and dominated by two magnificent copper beeches - the eleven gardens to be open are within easy reach on foot. Some are very small, particularly the tiny one beside the village green - 12ft by 6 ft! - but all are interesting and different. When you finish your tour come back to The Old Rectory for a delicious home-made tea. Limited wheelchair access.

23 MAXSTOKE CASTLE
Coleshill B46 2RD. Mr & Mrs M C Fetherston-Dilke. *2½ m E of Coleshill. E of Birmingham, on B4114. Take R turn down Castle Lane, Castle drive 1¼ m on R.* Home-made teas. **Adm £7, chd £4.50. Sun 15 June (11-5).**
Approx 5-acres of garden and grounds with herbaceous, shrubs and trees in the immed surroundings of this C14 moated castle. No wheelchair access to house.

MEADOW FARM
See Worcestershire

74 MEADOW ROAD
See Worcestershire

24 MEREVALE HALL
Atherstone CV9 2HG. Matthew & Paige Dugdale. *¾ m SW of Atherstone. Sat Nav: Merevale Rd, Atherstone. Entrance is 300yds SE of r'about on A5 at Merevale Lane, between 2 single storey gate houses. Garden 1m up drive.* Light refreshments. **Adm £5, chd free. Sun 18 May (2-4).**
Good mixture of formal and wilderness over 29-acres. Incl a parterre by Nesfield, stumpery, bog garden and walled garden. In May it is a riot of bluebells, azaleas and rhododendrons.

25 ◆ THE MILL GARDEN
55 Mill Street, Warwick CV34 4HB. Julia (née Measures) Russell & David Russell, 01926 492877. *Off A425 beside old castle gate, at the bottom of Mill St. Use St Nicholas car park.* **Adm £1.50, chd free. For NGS: Tue 1 Apr to Thur 30 Oct incl (9-6). For other opening times and information, please phone.**
This garden lies in a magical setting on the banks of the R Avon beneath the walls of Warwick Castle. Winding paths lead round every corner to dramatic views of the castle and ruined Medieval bridge. This informal cottage garden is a profusion of plants, shrubs and trees. Beautiful all-yr. Limited wheelchair access. Unsuitable for electric wheelchairs.

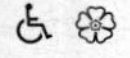

MORTON HALL
See Worcestershire

26 PACKINGTON HALL
Meriden, nr Coventry CV7 7HF. Lord & Lady Aylesford. *Midway between Coventry and Birmingham on A45. Entrance 400yds from Stonebridge island towards Coventry. CV7 7HE for SatNav.* Home-made teas. **Adm £5, chd free. Sun 8 June (2-5.30).**
Packington is the setting for an elegant Capability Brown landscape. Designed from 1750 in 100-acres of parkland which sweeps down to a lake incl.1762 Japanese bridge. Mirrored terrace beds glow with perennials. Nearby is the Millennium Rose Garden planted with old fashioned roses complete with flowers, hips and haws. Delicious W.I. tea on the terrace! Wheelchair access is not that easy but possible. The Garden is all grass and the terrace, up steps from grass, is gravel.

4 PODEN COTTAGES
See Worcestershire

PUMP COTTAGE
See Worcestershire

GROUP OPENING

27 STRETTON-ON-FOSSE GARDENS
Stretton on Fosse, Moreton-in-Marsh GL56 9SD. *Off A429 between Moreton-in-Marsh and Shipston-on-Stour. Two gardens in the centre of the village. Court House is next to the church, Old Beams a few doors away.* Home-made teas at Court House. **Combined adm £5, chd free. Sun 27 Apr, Sun 20 July (2-6).**

COURT HOUSE
Christopher White
Visitors also welcome by appt Jan to Sept.
01608 663811
mum@star.co.uk

OLD BEAMS
Mrs Hilary Fossey

Court House is a continually evolving, 4-acre garden with yr-round interest and colour. Extensive and varied spring bulbs. Herbaceous borders, fernery, recently redesigned and restored walled kitchen garden. Rose garden, newly planted winter garden, pond area and paddocks which are gradually being established with wild flowers. Old Beams is a walled cottage garden on a slope with traditional cottage garden plants, small lawn, rockery, fruit cage and vegetable garden.

GROUP OPENING

28 STYVECHALE GARDENS
Knoll Drive, Coventry CV3 5DE. *The gardens are located on the S-side of Coventry close to A45. Tickets and map available on the day from St Thomas More's Church. Advance tickets available from suepountney@btinternet.com.* Home-made teas. **Combined adm £3.50, chd free (share to Zoe's Place Baby Hospice, Exhall, Coventry). Sun 22 June (11-5).**

43 ARMORIAL ROAD
Gary & Jane Flanagan

164 BAGINTON ROAD
Fran & Jeff Gaught

166 BAGINTON ROAD
Wilf & Ann Hawes

16 DELAWARE ROAD
Val & Roy Howells

2 THE HIRON
Sue & Graham Pountney

A collection of lovely, mature, suburban gardens, each one different in style and size. Come and enjoy the imaginatively planted herbaceous borders, spectacular roses, water features, fruit and vegetable patches, cottage garden planting and shady areas - something for everyone and plenty of ideas for you to take home. Relax in the gardens and enjoy the warm, friendly welcome you will receive from us all. There will be refreshments available and plants for sale in some of the gardens. Other gardens will be open on the day.

Organically managed, providing a haven for birds and other wildlife. . .

GROUP OPENING

29 WARMINGTON VILLAGE GARDENS

Banbury OX17 1BU. *5m NW of Banbury. Take the B4100 N from Banbury after 5m turn R across short dual carriageway into Warmington. From the N take J12 off M40 onto B4100.* Home-made teas at village hall. **Combined adm £5, chd free. Sun 22 June (2-5.30).**

AGDON HOUSE
Mr & Mrs P Grenet

GROVE FARM HOUSE
Richard & Kate Lister

KIRK LEE
Mr & Mrs L Albrighton

THE MANOR HOUSE
Mr & Mrs G Lewis

OLD RECTORY FARMHOUSE
Dr & Mrs J Deakin

SPRINGFIELD HOUSE
Jenny & Roger Handscombe
01295 690286
jenny.handscombe@virgin.net

WESTERING
Mr & Mrs R Neale

1 THE WHEELWRIGHTS
Ms E Bunn

Warmington, at the edge of the Cotswolds is an exceptionally attractive village with its C17 Hornton stone houses set around the village green. In front of the pond is The Manor House with its Elizabethan knot garden, and topiary. Kirk Lee on 3 levels with its cascade has panoramic views across the valley. Wheelwrights features a small pond surrounded by many varieties of heuchera and allium. Springfield House with its gravel garden is terraced and informal. A garden of many parts is to be found at the Old Rectory Farmhouse, incl rosebeds, a slate and heather garden and a small wooded area. A knot garden and a pleached hornbeam pathway are to be found in the lovely garden at Grove Farm. Agdon House and Westering have colourful herbaceous borders with many unusual plants. Do visit St Michael's Church at the top of the village containing the Millennium Tapestry. The village is on a hill and so some gardens are not easy for wheelchairs.

Something for everyone and plenty of ideas for you to take home . . .

GROUP OPENING

30 WELFORD-ON-AVON & DISTRICT GARDENS

Welford-on-Avon CV37 8PT. *5m SW of Stratford-upon-Avon. Off B4390.* Home-made teas in the village hall. **Combined adm £5, chd free. Sat 28, Sun 29 June (2-6).**

ARDENCOTE
Mike & Sally Luntley

NEW **AVONCOT**
Emma & Shaun Baker

2 CHAPEL STREET
Mr Rod Scarrott

DUNELM
Mr & Mrs Paul & Colleen King

NEW **6 QUINEYS LEYS**
Mr & Mrs Gordon & Penny Whitehead

9 QUINEYS LEYS
Ann Raff

RIVERCOT
Mrs Elaine Selby

SOUTHLAWNS
Mr & Mrs Guy & Amanda Kitteringham

WATERMILL COTTAGE
Martin & Sheila Greenwood

In addition to its superb position on the river, with serene swans, dabbling ducks and resident herons, Welford-on-Avon has a beautiful church, an excellent family butcher's shop, a very convenient general store and selection of PHs serving great food. Just down the road is a highly popular farm-shop where seasonal fruit and vegetables are much in demand. With its great variety of house styles, incl an abundance of beautiful cottages with thatched roofs and chocolate-box charisma, Welford also has an army of keen gardeners (6yr old garden club has over 100 members!) The gardens open for the NGS range from a plot with fantastic topiary, herb knot and live willow weaving, to a walled garden, gardens with fun sculptures, flowerpot men, prairie planting and water features, all with a glorious array of containers and hanging baskets. Fruit and vegetable areas are also integral to these gardens for all seasons.

GROUP OPENING

31 WHICHFORD & ASCOTT GARDENS

Whichford & Ascott, Shipston-on-Stour CV36 5PP. *6m SE of Shipston-on-Stour. Turn E off A3400 at Long Compton for Whichford. Car park opp church.* Home-made teas at Knights Place, opp church. **Combined adm £5, chd free. Sun 15 June (2-5.30).**

ASCOTT LODGE
Charlotte Copley

BROOK HOLLOW
John & Shirley Round

NEW **KNIGHT'S PLACE**
Mr & Mrs Derek Atkins

MURTON COTTAGE
Hilary & David Blakemore

THE OLD RECTORY
Peter & Caroline O'Kane

PLUM TREE COTTAGE
Janet Knight

WHICHFORD HILL HOUSE
Mr & Mrs John Melvin

THE WHICHFORD POTTERY
Jim & Dominique Keeling
www.whichfordpottery.com

This group of gardens reflects a range of several garden types and sizes. The two villages are in an area of outstanding natural beauty. They nestle within a dramatic landscape of hills, pasture and woodland, which is used to picturesque effect by the garden owners. Fine lawns, mature shrub planting and much interest to plantsmen provide a peaceful visit to a series of beautiful gardens. Many incorporate the inventive use of natural springs, forming ponds, pools and other water features. Classic cottage gardens contrast with other larger gardens which adopt variations on the traditional English garden of herbaceous borders, climbing roses, yew hedges and walled enclosures. Other amenities are the C12 church, the internationally renowned pottery and a PH serving meals. Some gardens are not appropriate for wheelchair users.

7 Fieldgate Lawn, Kenilworth Gardens

Warwickshire Volunteers

County Organiser
Julia Sewell, Dinsdale House, Baldwins Lane, Upper Tysoe, Warwick CV35 0TX, 01295 680234, seweljulia@btinternet.com

County Treasurer
Susan Solomon, Folly Lodge, Idlicote Road, Halford, Shipston-on-Stour CV36 5DG, 01789 740183, SS@follylodge.eclipse.co.uk

Publicity
Peter Pashley, Millstones, Mayfield Avenue, Stratford upon Avon CV37 6XB, 01789 294932, peter@peterpash.mail1.co.uk
Lily Farrah, The Elms, Tiddington, Stratford-upon-Avon CV37 7AG, 01789 204858, dipsy25@hotmail.com

Booklet Coordinator
Janet Neale, Westering, The Green, Warmington, Banbury OX17 1BU, 01295 690515, janetneale5@gmail.com

Assistant County Organiser
Emma Burbidge, Chadley House, Loxley Road, Wellesbourne, Warwick CV35 9JL, 01789 842650, emmaburbidge@hotmail.co.uk
Elspeth Napier, 17 Simpson Road, Shipston-on-Stour CV36 4JT, 01608 666278, elspeth@cherryvilla.demon.co.uk
Sal Renwick, 75 Blue Lake Road, Dorridge, Solihull B93 8BH, 01564 770215, sal.renwick@blueyonder.co.uk
Eleni Tovey, 8 The Spinney, off Kenilworth Road, Coventry CV4 7AG, 02476 419049, elenitovey@aol.com

WILTSHIRE

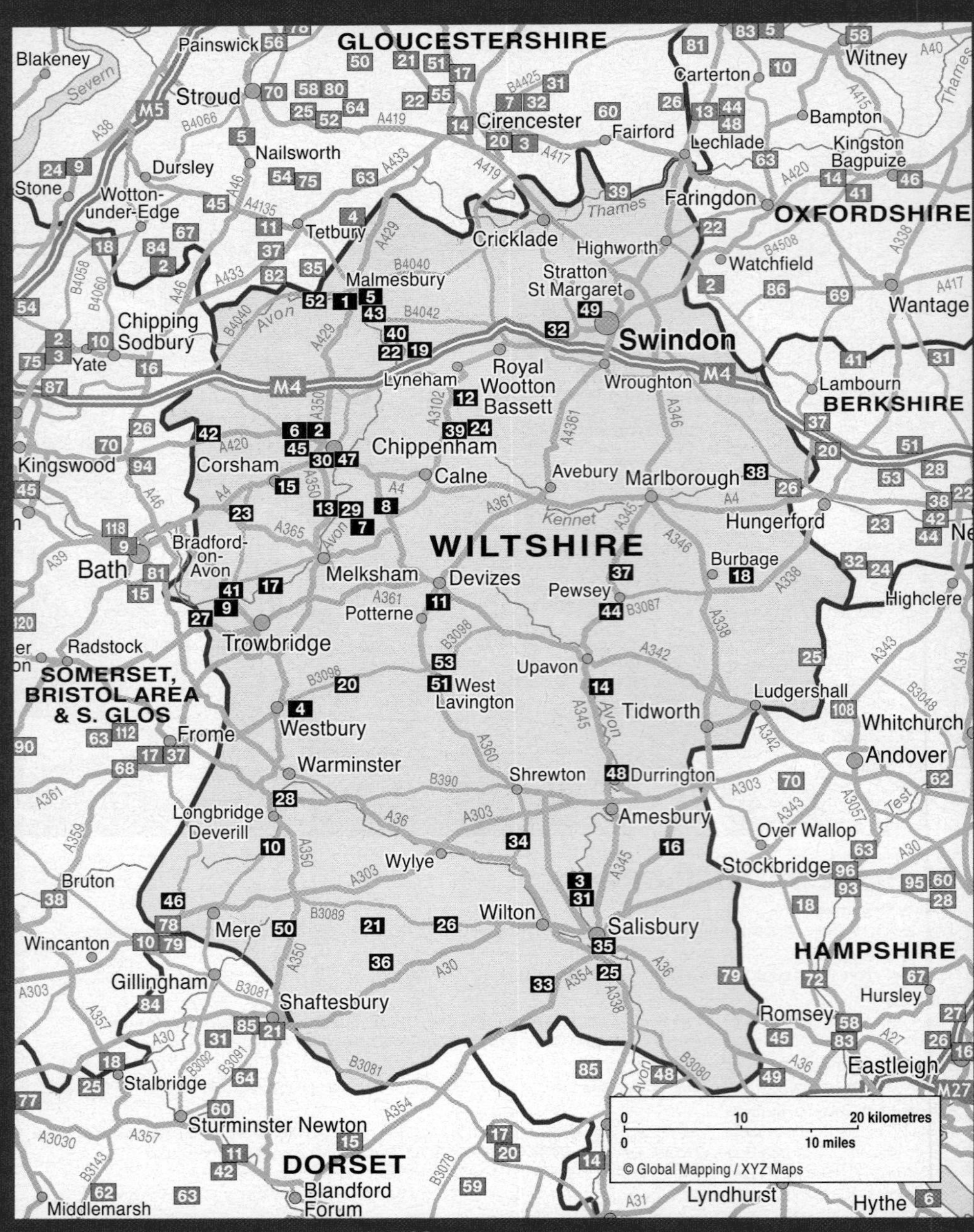
GLOUCESTERSHIRE
OXFORDSHIRE
BERKSHIRE
WILTSHIRE
SOMERSET, BRISTOL AREA & S. GLOS
HAMPSHIRE
DORSET
Blakeney
Painswick
Stroud
Nailsworth
Dursley
Stone
Wotton-under-Edge
Tetbury
Cirencester
Fairford
Lechlade
Carterton
Witney
Bampton
Kingston Bagpuize
Faringdon
Cricklade
Highworth
Watchfield
Wantage
Malmesbury
Stratton St Margaret
Swindon
Chipping Sodbury
Yate
Lyneham
Royal Wootton Bassett
Wroughton
Lambourn
Chippenham
Kingswood
Corsham
Calne
Avebury
Marlborough
Hungerford
Bath
Bradford-on-Avon
Melksham
Devizes
Pewsey
Burbage
Highclere
Potterne
Trowbridge
Radstock
Upavon
West Lavington
Ludgershall
Westbury
Tidworth
Whitchurch
Frome
Andover
Warminster
Shrewton
Durrington
Longbridge Deverill
Amesbury
Over Wallop
Wylye
Stockbridge
Bruton
Wilton
Salisbury
Wincanton
Mere
Gillingham
Hursley
Shaftesbury
Romsey
Eastleigh
Stalbridge
Sturminster Newton
Blandford Forum
Lyndhurst
Middlemarsh
Hythe
Thames
Avon
Kennet
Severn
0 10 20 kilometres
0 10 miles
© Global Mapping / XYZ Maps

Opening Dates

All entries subject to change.
For latest information check
www.ngs.org.uk

February

Saturday 8
29 Lacock Abbey Gardens

Sunday 9
29 Lacock Abbey Gardens

Saturday 15
29 Lacock Abbey Gardens

Sunday 16
29 Lacock Abbey Gardens

Sunday 23
3 Avon Cottage

March

Sunday 16
1 Abbey House Gardens

Sunday 23
21 Fonthill House

April

Wednesday 2
44 Sharcott Manor

Sunday 6
11 Broadleas House Gardens
15 Corsham Court
44 Sharcott Manor

Sunday 13
31 Little Durnford Manor

Wednesday 23
23 Hazelbury Manor Gardens

Friday 25
53 Windmill Cottage

Saturday 26
28 Job's Mill
41 Priory House

Sunday 27
2 Allington Grange
27 Iford Manor
37 Oare House

May

Sunday 4
16 Cottage in the Trees
50 Waterdale House

Wednesday 7
44 Sharcott Manor

Sunday 11
11 Broadleas House Gardens
25 Horatio's Garden

Wednesday 14
7 NEW Bowden Park

Friday 16
35 Mompesson House

Sunday 18
2 Allington Grange
9 NEW Bradford on Avon Gardens
15 Corsham Court
49 Twigs Community Garden

Wednesday 21
7 NEW Bowden Park
23 Hazelbury Manor Gardens

Friday 23
53 Windmill Cottage

Sunday 25
26 Hyde's House
38 The Old Mill

June

Sunday 1
10 NEW Brixton Deverill Gardens
13 Cantax House
36 North Cottage

Wednesday 4
44 Sharcott Manor

Friday 6
53 Windmill Cottage

Inspirational 1-acre garden . . . mosaic pavements wind around ponds and rocks . . .

Festival Weekend

Saturday 7
28 Job's Mill
46 Stourhead Garden

Sunday 8
18 Crofton Lock House
31 Little Durnford Manor
39 The Old Vicarage
42 Ridleys Cheer

Tuesday 10
17 The Courts

Wednesday 11
39 The Old Vicarage
45 Sheldon Manor

Saturday 14
51 West Lavington Manor

Sunday 15
11 Broadleas House Gardens
14 Chisenbury Priory
19 Dauntsey Gardens
23 Hazelbury Manor Gardens
36 North Cottage

Wednesday 18
48 Trantor House

Thursday 19
52 Whatley Manor

Friday 20
53 Windmill Cottage

Saturday 21
22 Great Somerford Gardens

Sunday 22
12 33 Calne Road
16 Cottage in the Trees
20 Edington Gardens
22 Great Somerford Gardens
24 Hilmarton Group Gardens
48 Trantor House

Wednesday 25
12 33 Calne Road

Sunday 29
5 Blicks Hill House
6 Bolehyde Manor
34 The Mill House
37 Oare House

July

Wednesday 2
44 Sharcott Manor

Friday 4
53 Windmill Cottage

Saturday 5
18 Crofton Lock House

Sunday 6
11 Broadleas House Gardens

Sunday 13
43 River Barn

Friday 18
53 Windmill Cottage

Saturday 19
4 Beggars Knoll Chinese Garden

Sunday 20
4 Beggars Knoll Chinese Garden
49 Twigs Community Garden

Sunday 27
30 130 Ladyfield Road and Allotments
32 Lydiard Park Walled Garden
47 Sweet Briar Cottage

August

Sunday 3
16 Cottage in the Trees
18 Crofton Lock House
41 Priory House

Wednesday 6
44 Sharcott Manor

Sunday 17
38 The Old Mill

September

Wednesday 3
44 Sharcott Manor

Sunday 14
44 Sharcott Manor

Sunday 21
13 Cantax House

Wednesday 24
23 Hazelbury Manor Gardens

February 2015

Wednesday 25
29 Lacock Abbey Gardens

Saturday 28
29 Lacock Abbey Gardens

Gardens open to the public

1 Abbey House Gardens
8 Bowood Rhododendron Walks
15 Corsham Court
17 The Courts
27 Iford Manor
29 Lacock Abbey Gardens
32 Lydiard Park Walled Garden
34 The Mill House
35 Mompesson House
45 Sheldon Manor
46 Stourhead Garden
49 Twigs Community Garden
50 Waterdale House

By appointment only

33 Manor House
40 The Pound House

Also open by appointment

2 Allington Grange
3 Avon Cottage
4 Beggars Knoll Chinese Garden
5 Blicks Hill House
6 Bolehyde Manor
14 Chisenbury Priory
16 Cottage in the Trees
18 Crofton Lock House
23 Hazelbury Manor Gardens
36 North Cottage
39 The Old Vicarage
41 Priory House
47 Sweet Briar Cottage
48 Trantor House
51 West Lavington Manor
53 Windmill Cottage

The Gardens

1 ◆ ABBEY HOUSE GARDENS

Malmesbury Town Centre SN16 9AS. Ian & Barbara Pollard, 01666 827650, www.abbeyhousegardens.co.uk. *5m N of J17 M4. Beside C12 Abbey. Parking in town centre (short stay) or follow brown signs to long stay (via steps to gardens).* **Adm £8, chd £3. For NGS: Sun 16 Mar (11-5.30). For other opening times and information, please phone or see garden website.**

Beside Malmesbury Abbey, straddling the R Avon, this spectacular 5-acre garden, home to The Naked Gardeners, has brought praise from around the world. Spring bulbs begin the display; 70,000 tulips bloom from March to May. 20th anniversary of the current ownership.

2 ALLINGTON GRANGE

Allington, Chippenham SN14 6LW. Mrs Rhyddian Roper, 01249 447436, rhyddianroper@hotmail.co.uk, www.allingtongrange.com. *2m W of Chippenham. Take A420 W from Chippenham. 1st R signed Allington Village, entrance 1m up lane on L.* Home-made teas. **Adm £3.50, chd free. Sun 27 Apr, Sun 18 May (2-5). Groups also welcome by appt Apr to June.**

Informal country garden of approx 1½ acres, around C17 farmhouse (not open) with a diverse range of plants. Mixed and herbaceous borders, colour themed; white garden with water fountain. Pergola lined with clematis and roses. Walled potager. Small orchard with chickens. Wildlife pond with natural planting. Many spring bulbs. Featured in The English Garden and Wiltshire Magazine. Mainly level with ramp into potager. Dogs on leads.

3 AVON COTTAGE

Lower Woodford, Salisbury SP4 6NQ. Mr & Mrs Trevor Shepherd, 01722 782295, dotty.sas@gmail.com, www.avoncottagegarden.wordpress.com. *4m N of Salisbury. Off Woodford Valley Rd, between A360 & A345.* Home-made teas. **Adm £4, chd free. Sun 23 Feb (10-3). Visitors also welcome by appt Feb to Sept on Weds and Fris only.**

Garden planted for year round interest incl bulbs, large drifts of snowdrops and narcissi, flowering shrubs and perennials in woodland, along stream and in borders. Mature evergreen hedges break up the level site which is under continual development. Lovely views and abundant wildlife. Mentioned in Saturday Gardening section of Daily Telegraph. Gravel drive and tree roots on woodland paths.

4 BEGGARS KNOLL CHINESE GARDEN

Newtown, Westbury BA13 3ED. Colin Little & Penny Stirling, 01373 823383, silkendalliance@talktalk.net. *1m SE of Westbury. Turn off B3098 at White Horse Pottery, up hill towards the White Horse for ¾ m. Disabled parking at end of drive. Main parking 300 yds up hill.* Home-made teas. **Adm £3.50, chd free. Sat 19, Sun 20 July (2-6). Visitors also welcome by appt June to July.**

This inspirational 1-acre garden is filled with colourful plantings set against a backdrop of Chinese pavilions, gateways, statues and dragons. Pathways and mosaic pavements wind around ponds and rocks. Rare Chinese shrubs, mature trees, and flower-filled borders form a haven of serenity. A large potager houses chickens, and pigs live in the woods. Spectacular views too! Art exhibition.

5 BLICKS HILL HOUSE

Blicks Hill, Malmesbury SN16 9HZ. Alan & Valerie Trotman, 01666 829669, vat@timberwright.co.uk. *½ m E of Malmesbury. On A429 Malmesbury bypass, turn off ½ way between r'abouts.* Home-made teas. **Adm £4, chd free. Sun 29 June (11-5.30). Visitors also welcome by appt May to July for groups of 10+.**

Stunning, and having the wow factor is how visitors describe this garden situated on a 1-acre stepped and sloping site. Mature trees give a backdrop to the colourful beds and borders which have all been created since 2004. Unique pergola leading to a woodland glade, water feature and stream constructed in green slate, hanging baskets, tubs and bedding plants add extra impact. Very much a plantsman's garden. Gradual slope.

6 BOLEHYDE MANOR
Allington SN14 6LW. The Earl & Countess Cairns, 01249 443056, amandamcairns@gmail.com. *1½ m W of Chippenham. On Bristol Rd (A420). Turn N at Allington Xrds. ½ m on R. Parking in field.* Home-made teas. **Adm £4, chd free. Sun 29 June (2.30-6). Visitors also welcome by appt May to June (weekdays preferred).**
Series of gardens around C16 manor house (not open), enclosed by walls and topiary. Formal framework densely planted with many interesting shrubs and climbers, especially roses. Mixed borders. Blue walk of alliums and agapanthus. Inner courtyard with troughs full of tender plants. Collection of tender pelargoniums. Vegetable/fruit garden and greenhouse.

7 NEW BOWDEN PARK
Lacock, Chippenham SN15 2PP. Bowden Park Estate. *10 mins from Chippenham. Entrance via Top Lodge at top of Bowden Hill, between A342 at Sandy Lane and A350 in Lacock.*
Adm £5, chd free.
Wed 14, Wed 21 May (1-5).
A 22 acre private garden within surrounding parkland. Pleasure garden, water garden, a working kitchen garden with formal lawns and a Grotto. Rhododendrons & Azaleas in flower.

8 ◆ BOWOOD RHODODENDRON WALKS
Calne SN11 9PG. The Marquis of Lansdowne, 01249 812102, www.bowood.org. *3½ m SE of Chippenham. Located off J17 M4 nr Bath & Chippenham. Entrance off A342 between Sandy Lane & Derry Hill Villages. Follow brown signs.* **Adm £6.25, chd free. For opening times and information, please phone or see garden website.**
This 60-acre woodland garden of azaleas and rhododendrons is one of the most exciting of its type in the country. From the individual flowers to the breathtaking sweep of colour formed by hundreds of shrubs, surrounded by carpets of bluebells, this is a garden not to be missed. Planting began in 1850 and some of the earliest known hybrids feature among the collection. The Rhododendron Walks are located 2m from Bowood House and Gardens.

Allington Grange
© Lynn Keddie

GROUP OPENING

9 NEW BRADFORD ON AVON GARDENS
Pound Lane, Bradford on Avon BA15 1LF. *Near centre of Bradford on Avon. From Bradford on Avon take B3109 Frome Rd, Pound Ln is on R, signed Tythe Barn, or on L if approaching from Frome. Parking limited, drop off only. Park at Stn and walk L along River at end of Car Park for Barton Farm, R for Horton's House.* Home-made teas at Horton's House. **Combined adm £5, chd free. Sun 18 May (2-5.30).**

NEW BARTON FARM
Pound Lane. Simon & Amanda Relph

NEW HORTON'S HOUSE
15 Church Street. Annette Seekings

NEW 1 ROSEMARY WALK
Penny Hopwood & Sally Wilson

Barton Farm: C14 home which looks across to the Tythe Barn. Walled garden at rear planted principally with flowering shrubs and underplanted with bulbs, primroses and herbaceous plants particularly those tolerant of dry shade. Recently redesigned, re-structured and re-planted by owner. Horton's House (1496): Until 15 yrs ago the house and land was a commercial property with a huge copper beech, numerous sycamore saplings, wild undergrowth and no garden. The steeply sloping land of approx 1 acre is now terraced and planted by the owners with orchard and fig trees, roses and plants that love sunny S-facing aspect. 1 Rosemary Walk: Walled, terraced garden, landscaped and planted in 2008. Colour-themed beds with a variety of plants and shrubs.

GROUP OPENING

10 NEW BRIXTON DEVERILL GARDENS

Brixton Deverill, Warminster BA12 7EJ. Mr Nigel Hawkins. *6m S of Warminster, 5m N of Mere. A350, exit at Longbridge Deverill onto B3095, signed The Deverills. After 1m in Brixton Deverill, immed after bridge over R Wylye, R through gates into paddock for parking. All gardens within easy walking distance.* Home-made teas at Longmead. **Combined adm £5, chd free (share to Deverill Churches). Sun 1 June (2-5.30).**

NEW **BRIDGE COTTAGE**
Nigel & Shouanna Hawkins

NEW **LITTLE DOWN HOUSE**
Peter & Penny Marsh

NEW **LONGMEAD**
Mary Stewart-Cox

NEW **MANOR FARM COTTAGE**
Patricia Armstrong

4 gardens set in picturesque Domesday Book village in Conservation Area with wide downland views. The stone cottages, several thatched, and masonry arched bridge over the river lie beside C11 church. Bridge Cottage is set in 2 acres with large herbaceous borders, pergolas hung with roses and wisteria, riverside walk, variety of trees and fruit and vegetable cages. Little Down House was a stone barn, converted some 20 yrs ago. The garden, once a field, now includes a wide range of trees and shrubs, borders, rose trellis, pergola, yew arbour and topiary, water features and patios. It enjoys a peaceful location on the edge of the village with views to the downs. Long Mead, adjoining the church, has approx ½ acre of perennial garden on chalk soil, including herbaceous beds and roses. Manor Farm Cottage has a mature, meandering, unsophisticated ½ -acre cottage garden. Clothed throughout the year with trees and shrubs, enhanced by water, topiary, bulbs and herbaceous beds.

11 BROADLEAS HOUSE GARDENS

Devizes SN10 5JQ. Mr & Mrs Cardiff. *1m S of Devizes. From Hartmoor Rd turn into Broadleas Park, follow rd for 350 metres then turn R into estate. PLEASE NOTE, NO ACCESS from A360 Potterne Rd.* Home-made teas. **Adm £5, chd free. Suns 6 Apr, 11 May, 15 June, 6 July (2-5.30).**

A 6 acre garden of hedges, herbaceous borders, rose arches, bee garden and orchard stuffed with good plants. It is overlooked by the house and arranged above the small valley garden which is crowded with magnolias and rhododendrons, cornus and hydrangeas.

12 33 CALNE ROAD

Lyneham, Chippenham SN15 4PT. Sue & Sam Wright. *7m N of Calne. Next to MOD Lyneham entrance.* Home-made teas. **Adm £2.50, chd free. Sun 22, Wed 25 June (1-5).**

Approx ¾ -acre informal garden comprising modest collection of hostas, clematis and roses. Small kitchen garden, pond and mature orchard with bantams, chickens, doves and dovecote. Wheelchairs only, not mobility scooters.

13 CANTAX HOUSE

Lacock SN15 2JZ. Andrew & Deborah van der Beek, www.deborahvanderbeek.com. *3m S of Chippenham. Off A350 between Chippenham & Melksham. Please use signed public car park (except disabled). Entrance to garden in Cantax Hill; satnav unhelpful.* **Adm £4, chd free (share to Amnesty International).**
Sun 1 June, Sun 21 Sept (2-6).

Queen Anne former vicarage (not open). Medium-sized garden of colour, pattern and scent straddling the Bide Brook. Designed and maintained by sculptor owner for 25yrs; both common and unusual plants including wildflower sports; hornbeam spire, yew castle and other topiary; old orchard wild garden; sculpture by owner and friends.

14 CHISENBURY PRIORY

East Chisenbury SN9 6AQ. Mr & Mrs John Manser, john.peter.manser@live.com. *3m SW of Pewsey. Turn E from A345 at Enford then N to E Chisenbury, main gates 1m on R.* Home-made teas. **Adm £4, chd free. Sun 15 June (2-6). Visitors also welcome by appt May to July.**

Medieval Priory with Queen Anne face and early C17 rear (not open) in middle of 5-acre garden on chalk. Mature garden with fine trees within clump and flint walls, herbaceous borders, shrubs, roses. Moisture-loving plants along mill leat, carp pond, orchard and wild garden, many unusual plants. Front borders redesigned in 2009 by Tom Stuart-Smith.

15 ◆ CORSHAM COURT

Corsham SN13 0BZ. Mr James Methuen-Campbell, 01249 701610, www.corsham-court.co.uk. *4m W of Chippenham. Signed off A4 at Corsham.* **Adm £5, chd £2.50. For NGS: Sun 6 Apr, Sun 18 May (2-5.30). For other opening times and information, please phone or see garden website.**

Park and gardens laid out by Capability Brown and Repton. Large lawns with fine specimens of ornamental trees surround the Elizabethan mansion. C18 bath house hidden in the grounds. Spring bulbs, beautiful lily pond with Indian bean trees, young arboretum and stunning collection of magnolias. Wheelchair (not motorised) access to house, gravel paths in garden.

16 COTTAGE IN THE TREES

Tidworth Rd, Boscombe Village, nr Salisbury SP4 0AD. Karen & Richard Robertson, 01980 610921, robertson909@btinternet.com. *7m N of Salisbury. Turn L of A338 just before Social Club. Continue past church, turn R after bridge to Queen Manor, cottage 150yds on R.* Home-made teas. **Adm £2.50, chd free. Suns 4 May, 22 June, 3 Aug (2-5). Also open 22 June Trantor House. Visitors also welcome by appt Mar to Sept.**

Enchanting ½ -acre cottage garden, immaculately planted with a water feature, raised vegetable beds, small wildlife pond and gravel garden. Spring bulbs, hellebores and pulmonarias give a welcome start to the season, with pots and baskets, roses and clematis. Mixed borders of herbaceous plants, dahlias, grasses and shrubs giving all-yr interest. Featured in Wiltshire Society and Amateur Gardening.

17 ◆ THE COURTS
Holt, Trowbridge BA14 6RR. National Trust, 01225 782875, www.nationaltrust.org.uk. *2m E of Bradford-on-Avon. S of B3107 to Melksham. In Holt follow NT signs, park at village hall and at overflow car park when signed.* Cream teas. **Adm £6.55, chd £3.25. For NGS: Tue 10 June (11-5.30). For other opening times and information, please phone or see garden website.**
Beautifully kept but eclectic garden. Yew hedges divide garden compartments with colour themed borders and organically shaped topiary. Water garden with 2 pools, temple, conservatory and small kitchen garden split by an apple allée, all surrounded by 3½ acres of arboretum with specimen trees. Wheelchair access map available.

18 CROFTON LOCK HOUSE
Crofton, Great Bedwyn, Marlborough SN8 3DW. Michael & Jenny Trussell, 01672 870674, jennytrussell@hotmail.com. *Lock 62, K&A Canal, Crofton, 1m W of Great Bedwyn. 4m W of Hungerford. Signs from A4 at Great Bedwyn turning, and from A338 at East Grafton. Limited parking. Garden 8 - 10 mins walk along towpath.* Home-made teas. **Adm £2.50, chd free (share to Wiltshire Air Ambulance). Sun 8 June, Sat 5 July, Sun 3 Aug (2-6). Visitors also welcome by appt June to Aug for groups of 20 max.**
¾ -acre garden in idyllic setting around 200 yr old lock keeper's cottage. Garden comprises herbaceous beds designed with a painter's eye to provide riotous colour, sculptural form, and an abundance of wildlife from spring to autumn; at rear a small orchard, collection of apple and soft fruit trees and raised vegetable beds. Artist's studio open. Off grid house relying on sun and wind for electricity, own water supply. Unusual plants for sale. Crofton steam pumping station and Wilton Windmill close by.

GROUP OPENING

19 DAUNTSEY GARDENS
Chippenham SN15 4HW. *5m SE of Malmesbury. Approach via Dauntsey Rd from Gt Somerford, 1¼ m from Volunteer Inn.* Home-made teas at Idover House. **Combined adm £5, chd free. Sun 15 June (1.30-5).**

THE COACH HOUSE
Col & Mrs J Seddon-Brown

DAUNTSEY PARK
Mr & Mrs Giovanni Amati

THE GARDEN COTTAGE
Miss Ann Sturgis

IDOVER HOUSE
Mr & Mrs Christopher Jerram

THE OLD POND HOUSE
Mr & Mrs Stephen Love

This group of 5 gardens, centred around the historic Dauntsey Park Estate, ranges from the Classical C18 country house setting of Dauntsey Park, with spacious lawns, old trees and views over the R Avon, to mature country house gardens and traditional walled gardens. Enjoy the formal rose garden in pink and white, old fashioned borders and duck ponds at Idover House, and the quiet seclusion of The Coach House with its thyme terrace and gazebos, climbing roses and clematis. Here, mop-headed pruned crataegus prunifolia line the drive. The Garden Cottage has a traditional walled kitchen garden with organic vegetables, apple orchard, woodland walk and yew topiary. Meanwhile the 2 acres at The Old Pond House are both clipped and unclipped! Large pond with lilies and fat carp, and look out for the giraffe and turtle.

GROUP OPENING

20 EDINGTON GARDENS
Edington, nr Westbury BA13 4QF. *4m NE of Westbury. On B3098 between Westbury and West Lavington. Park on B3098 in church car park, or car park nr B3098 and Monastery Rd junction. Overflow Monastery Rd.* Home-made teas in Parish Hall close to The Old Vicarage. **Combined adm £5, chd free. Sun 22 June (2-6).**

THE OLD VICARAGE NCH
Westbury Road. Mr J N d'Arcy

THE PLOUGH
Lower Road. Mr & Mrs Nicholas Buckman

2 varied gardens on greensand, both with lovely views, are open in this historic village. Both gardens are full of colour, interest and ideas. Among the highlights are an arboretum with a growing range of unusual trees and an avenue of fastigiate hornbeams, herbaceous borders, gravel garden, wide range of interesting bulbs, magnolias, roses, fruit and vegetables - and even some long-established Japanese knotweed. The Old Vicarage is home to a National Collection of evening primroses, with over 20 species. The Plough is on 4 levels, with a camomile lawn the size of a handkerchief. Grade I C14 church open.

Wild flower drive from butterfly rich common . . .

21 FONTHILL HOUSE
nr Tisbury SP3 5SA. The Lord Margadale of Islay, www.fonthill.co.uk/gardens. *13m W of Salisbury. Via B3089 in Fonthill Bishop. 3m N of Tisbury.* Light refreshments. **Adm £6, chd free. Sun 23 Mar (2-6).**
Large woodland garden. Daffodils, rhododendrons, azaleas, shrubs, bulbs; magnificent views; formal gardens. The gardens have been extensively redeveloped recently under the direction of Tania Compton and Marie-Louise Agius. The formal gardens are being continuously improved with new designs, exciting trees, shrubs and plants. Limited wheelchair access.

© Heather Edwards

Barton Farm, Bradford on Avon Gardens

GROUP OPENING

22 GREAT SOMERFORD GARDENS

The Old Maltings, Great Somerford, Chippenham SN15 5JB. Doreen Jevons. *4m SE of Malmesbury. 4m N of M4 between J16 and J17. 2m S of B4042 Malmesbury to Royal Wootton Bassett Rd; 3m E of A429 Cirencester to Chippenham Rd. Cross river bridge in Great Somerford. Park opp The Mount, additional parking on Dauntsey Rd opp allotments.* Home-made teas at The Mount. **Combined adm £5, chd free. Sat 21, Sun 22 June (1.30-5).**

GREAT SOMERFORD'S FREE GARDENS & ALLOTMENTS
In trust to Great Somerford Parish Council

NEW **MANOR HOUSE**
West Street. Mr & Mrs Davis

THE MOUNT
Mr & Mrs McGrath

THE OLD POLICE HOUSE
Diane Hunt

SOMERFORD HOUSE
Mr & Mrs Hyde.
Opening on Sat 21 Jun only

Great Somerford is a medium-sized village, with a lovely walk by R Avon. Maintained by very active gardeners, there are three well-established large gardens and a charming smaller one and Gt Somerford's Free Gardens and Allotments. Limited wheelchair access.

23 HAZELBURY MANOR GARDENS

Wadswick, Box SN13 8HX. Mr L Lacroix, 07813 452008. *5m SW of Chippenham, 5m NE of Bath. From A4 at Box, A365 to Melksham, at Five Ways junction L onto B3109 toward Corsham, 1st L at top of hill, drive immed on R.* **Adm £5, chd free. Wed 23 Apr, Wed 21 May (11-3); Sun 15 June (2-5.30); Wed 24 Sept (11-3). Visitors also welcome by appt Mar to Oct.**
8 Acres of Grade II landscaped organic gardens around C15 fortified manor (not open). Edwardian garden with yew hedges and topiary, beech stilt hedges, laburnum tunnel and pleached lime avenue. A large variety of plants, shrubs fill 5000 sq metres of planting, many herbal and native species. Productive vegetable gardens, orchards and a circle of megaliths. Wild flower drive from butterfly rich common.

GROUP OPENING

24 HILMARTON GROUP GARDENS

Church Road, Hilmarton, Calne SN11 8SE. *On A3102 between Calne and Lyneham. Turn off A3102, opp The Duke PH, into village, follow signs to car park. Directions to gardens will be provided.* Home-made teas in Hilmarton Community Room, Poynder Place. **Combined adm £5, chd free. Sun 22 June (1-5).**

HAMLYN HOUSE
Mr & Mrs John & Brenda Reeves

10 POYNDER PLACE
Mrs Marion Jeary

WEAVERS
Sheron & Mel Wilkins

3 gardens with their own individual charm. An interesting tiered garden, previous winner of the BBC Points West 'Garden of the Year' competition. An informal family garden with established trees, shrubs and herbaceous borders, a fun garden to visit. A cottage garden set out with different 'rooms' and lawns linked by a leafy pergola. Gravel drive at 10 Poynder Place & Weavers. No wheelchair access at Hamlyn House.

25 HORATIO'S GARDEN

Duke of Cornwall Spinal Treatment Centre, Salisbury Hospital NHS Foundation Trust, Odstock Road, Salisbury SP2 8BJ. Tina Crossley (Head Gardener), www.horatiosgarden.org.uk. *Salisbury Hospital. Please park in car park 8 or 10.* Home-made teas. **Adm £3, chd free (share to Horatio's Garden). Sun 11 May (2-5). Volunteers will be available to talk to visitors to give details about the design and information about the patients' therapeutic garden activities.**

Horatio's Garden is a small garden which opened in September 2012 and was designed by Cleve West for patients with spinal cord injury at the Duke of Cornwall Spinal Treatment Centre. It was built from donations given in memory of Horatio Chapple who was a volunteer at the centre in his school holidays. Low limestone walls, which represent the form of the spine divide the densely planted beds and double as seating. Everything in the garden has been designed to benefit patients during their long stays in hospital. The Garden is run by a Head Gardener and a team of volunteers, called Horatio's Garden Friends. Cleve West has seven RHS gold medals, including Best in Show at the Chelsea Flower Show in 2011 and 2012. Extensive press coverage including The Guardian colour supplement and Sunday Telegraph. Fully accessible.

D

26 HYDE'S HOUSE

Dinton SP3 5HH. Mr George Cruddas. *9m W of Salisbury. Off B3089 nr Dinton Church on St Mary's Rd.* Home-made teas at Thatched Old School Room. **Adm £4.50, chd free. Sun 25 May (2-5).**

3 acres of wild and formal garden in beautiful situation with series of hedged garden rooms. Numerous shrubs, flowers and borders, all allowing tolerated wild flowers and preferred 'weeds'. Large walled kitchen garden, herb garden and C13 dovecote (open). Charming C16/18 Grade I listed house (not open), with lovely courtyard. Free walks around park and lake. Steps, slopes and gravel paths.

27 ◆ IFORD MANOR

Lower Westwood, Bradford-on-Avon BA15 2BA. Mrs Cartwright-Hignett, 01225 863146, www.ifordmanor.co.uk. *7m S of Bath. Off A36, brown tourist sign to Iford 1m. Or from Bradford-on-Avon or Trowbridge via Lower Westwood Village (brown signs).* Cream teas. **Adm £5, chd £4.50, under 10s free. For NGS: Sun 27 Apr (2-5). For other opening times and information, please phone or see garden website.**

Very romantic award-winning, Grade I listed Italianate garden famous for its tranquil beauty. Home to the Edwardian architect and designer Harold Peto 1899-1933. The garden is characterised by steps, terraces, sculpture and magnificent rural views. (House not open). Housekeeper's cream teas and home made cakes. Please see website for wheelchair access details.

28 JOB'S MILL

Five Ash Lane, Crockerton BA12 8BB. Lady Silvy McQuiston. *1½ m S of Warminster. Down lane E of A350, S of A36 r'about.* Home-made teas. **Adm £3.50, chd free. Sat 26 Apr (2-5); Sat 7 June (2-6).**

Surrounding an old converted water mill, a delightful terraced garden through which the River Wylye flows. Riverside and woodland walks, vegetable garden, orchard, herbaceous border and water garden.

29 ◆ LACOCK ABBEY GARDENS

Lacock, Chippenham SN15 2LG. National Trust, 01249 730459, www.nationaltrust.org.uk/lacock. *3m S of Chippenham. Off A350. Follow NT signs. Use public car park just outside Abbey.* **Adm £5.50, chd £2.75. For NGS: Sat 8, Sun 9 Feb (11-4); Sat 15, Sun 16 Feb (10.30-4); Wed 25, Sat 28 Feb 2015 (10.30-4). For other opening times and information, please phone or see garden website.**

Woodland garden with carpets of aconites, snowdrops, crocuses and daffodils. Botanic garden with greenhouse, mediaeval cloisters and magnificent trees. Mostly level site, some gravel paths.

30 130 LADYFIELD ROAD AND ALLOTMENTS

Ladyfield Road, Chippenham SN14 0AP. Philip & Pat Canter and Chippenham Town Council. *1m SW of Chippenham. Between A4 Bath and A420 Bristol rds. Signed off B4528 Hungerdown Lane which runs between A4 & A420.* **Adm £3, chd free. Sun 27 July (1.30-5.30).**

Very pretty small garden with more than 30 clematis, climbing roses and a small fish pond. Curved neat edges packed with colourful herbaceous plants and small trees. 2 patio areas with lush lawn, pagoda and garden arbour. Also Hungerdown Allotments, 15 allotments owned by Chippenham Town Council. Garden featured as Garden of the Week in Garden News; also in Amateur Gardener and Garden Answers. Wheelchair access to allotments on main drive only.

31 LITTLE DURNFORD MANOR

Salisbury SP4 6AH. The Earl & Countess of Chichester. *3m N of Salisbury. Just beyond Stratford-sub-Castle.* Home-made teas. **Adm £3.50, chd £1. Sun 13 Apr, Sun 8 June (2-5).**

Extensive lawns with cedars, walled gardens, fruit trees, large vegetable garden, small knot and herb gardens. Terraces, borders, sunken garden, water garden, lake with islands, river walks, labyrinth walk. Gravel paths, some narrow. Steep slope and some steps.

32 ◆ LYDIARD PARK WALLED GARDEN

Lydiard Tregoze, Swindon SN5 3PA. Swindon Borough Council, 01793 466 664, www.lydiardpark.org.uk. *3m W Swindon, 1m from J16 M4. Follow brown signs from W Swindon.* Light refreshments in Tea Rooms by Walled Garden. **Adm £2.50, chd £1. For NGS: Sun 27 July (11-5). For other opening times and information, please phone or see garden website.**

Beautiful ornamental C18 walled garden. Trimmed shrubs alternating with individually planted flowers and bulbs incl rare daffodils and tulips, sweet peas, annuals and wall-trained fruit trees. Park and children's playground. Unique features including well and sundial. Wide level paths, no steps.

33 MANOR HOUSE

Stratford Tony, Salisbury SP5 4AT. Mr & Mrs Hugh Cookson, 01722 718496, lucindacookson@stratfordtony.co.uk, www.stratfordtony.co.uk. *4m SW of Salisbury. Take minor rd W off A354 at Coombe Bissett. Garden on S after 1m. Or take minor rd off A3094 from Wilton signed Stratford Tony and racecourse.* Light refreshments. **Adm £5, chd free. Visitors welcome by appt.**

Varied 4-acre garden with all yr interest. Formal and informal areas. Small lake fed from R Ebble, waterside planting, herbaceous borders with colour from spring to late autumn. Pergola-covered vegetable garden, formal parterre garden, orchard, shrubberies, roses, specimen trees, winter colour and structure, many original contemporary features and places to sit and enjoy the downland views. Some gravel.

34 ◆ THE MILL HOUSE

Berwick St James, Salisbury SP3 4TS. Diana Gifford Mead, 01722 790331, www.millhouse.org.uk. *8m NW of Salisbury. S of A303, N of A36, on B3083, S end of village.* Cream teas in Village Hall. **Adm £3, chd free. For NGS: Sun 29 June (2-6). For other opening times and information, please phone or see garden website.**

Surrounded by the R Till, millstream and a 10-acre traditional wet water meadow, this garden of wildness supports over 300 species of old fashioned roses rambling from the many trees. It is filled with butterflies, moths and insects. Birdsong is phenomenal in spring and summer. Herbaceous borders crammed with plants of yesteryear, unforgettable scents. Glorious spring bulbs. SSSI. Open all yr-round.

We can guarantee scrumptious home-made food. Pottery and handicrafts all made by garden owners . . .

35 ◆ MOMPESSON HOUSE

The Close, Salisbury SP1 2EL. National Trust, 01722 335659, www.nationaltrust.org.uk. *Central Salisbury. Enter Cathedral Close via High St Gate, Mompesson House on R.* Cream teas. **Adm £1, chd free. For NGS: Fri 16 May (11-4.30). For other opening times and information, please phone or see garden website.**

The appeal of this comparatively small but attractive garden is the lovely setting in Salisbury Cathedral Close, with a well-known Queen Anne house (not open). Planting as for an old English garden with raised rose and herbaceous beds around the lawn. Climbers on pergola and walls, shrubs and small lavender walk. Cake stall.

36 NORTH COTTAGE

Tisbury Row, Tisbury SP3 6RZ. Jacqueline & Robert Baker, 01747 870019, robert.baker@pearceseeds.co.uk. *12m W of Salisbury. From A30 turn N through Ansty, L at T-junction, towards Tisbury. From Tisbury take Ansty road. Car park entrance nr junction signed Tisbury Row.* Home-made teas. **Adm £3, chd free. Sun 1, Sun 15 June (11-5). Visitors also welcome by appt June to July.**

A cottage garden set in a quiet vale in a beautiful part of South Wiltshire. Views over meadow towards Castle Ditches. Of course it's lovely, so there is no need to wax lyrically about the intriguing beauty therein. It will be a memorable visit and we can guarantee scrumptious home-made food. Pottery and handicrafts all made by garden owners. Ceramics featured in and part of the Wylye Valley Arts Trail.

37 OARE HOUSE

Rudge Lane, Oare, Nr Pewsey SN8 4JQ. Sir Henry Keswick. *2m N of Pewsey. On Marlborough Rd (A345).* Home-made teas. **Adm £4, chd free (share to The Order of St John). Sun 27 Apr, Sun 29 June (2-6).**

A 1740s Mansion house later extended by William Clough Ellis in the 1920s. The formal gardens originally created around the house have been developed over the years to create a wonderful garden full of many unusual plants. The current owner is very passionate and has developed a fine collection of rarities. The garden today is undergoing a renaissance but still maintains the split compartments each with its own individual charm; the traditional walled garden with its fine herbaceous borders, vegetable areas, trained fruit, roses and the grand mixed borders surrounding the formal lawns. The Magnolia garden is wonderful in spring with some trees dating from the 1920s, together with strong bulb plantings. There is a large arboretum and woodland walks with many unusual and champion trees. In spring and summer there is always something of interest, with the glorious Pewsey Vale as a backdrop. Limited wheelchair access.

38 THE OLD MILL

Ramsbury SN8 2PN. Annabel & James Dallas. *8m NE of Marlborough. From Marlborough head to Ramsbury. At The Bell PH follow sign to Hungerford. Garden behind yew hedge on R 100yds beyond The Bell.* **Adm £4.50, chd free. Sun 25 May, Sun 17 Aug (2-6).**

Water running through multitude of channels no longer drives the mill but provides backdrop for whimsical garden of pollarded limes, colour themed borders and naturalistic planting. Paths meander by streams and over small bridges. Vistas give dramatic views of downs beyond. New kitchen/herb garden and cutting bed give added interest.

39 THE OLD VICARAGE
Swindon Road, Hilmarton SN11 8SB. Lesley & George Hudson, 07802 741293, lesleyhudson@outlook.com. *4m S of Royal Wootton Bassett on A3102 between Lyneham & Calne. On main rd next to the Duke PH. Follow signs to park in paddock behind house.* Home-made teas. **Adm £3.50, chd free. Sun 8, Wed 11 June (12-5). Visitors also welcome by appt June to Aug for groups, day and evening appts.**
7-acre plot incl a Victorian walled garden, ornamental pond, wisteria-covered pergola, blue and white herbaceous border, Italianate secret garden, woodland garden, colourful herbaceous borders flanked by lawns and a herb garden. Adjacent to the formal garden are two paddocks incorporating a wild flower meadow (in June), orchard and kitchen garden. Featured in WI Life July 2013. Limited wheelchair access, some gravel paths.

40 THE POUND HOUSE
Little Somerford SN15 5JW. Mr & Mrs Michael Baines, 01666 823212, squeezebaines@yahoo.com. *2m E of Malmesbury on B4024. In village turn S, leave church on R. Car park on R before railway bridge.* Home-made teas. **Adm £4, chd free. Visitors welcome by appt Apr to Oct.**
Large well planted garden surrounding former rectory attached to C17 house. Mature trees, hedges and spacious lawns. Well-stocked herbaceous borders, roses, shrubs, pergola, parterre, swimming pool garden, water, ducks, chickens, alpacas and horses. Raised vegetable garden and lots of places to sit. A very beautiful english garden! Featured in Wiltshire Life.

41 PRIORY HOUSE
Market Street, Bradford-on-Avon BA15 1LH. Mr & Mrs Tim Woodall, trwwoodall@yahoo.com. *Town centre. Park in town centre. Take A363 signed Bath up Market St. House 500yds.* Home-made teas. **Adm £3, chd free. Sat 26 Apr, Sun 3 Aug (2-5.30). Visitors also welcome by appt Apr to Aug.**
¾ -acre town garden, mostly formal. Spring garden of narcissi, tulips and hellebores. Late summer borders planted in a traditional manner using asters, heleniums, dahlias, daylilies and others, but with a modern twist using grasses. Knot garden in front of part Georgian house is an interpretation of the sash windows. Feature in Period Living (spring 2013) and Gardens Illustrated (August 2013). Steep slopes and steps at bottom of garden.

Surrounding an old converted water mill, a delightful terraced garden . . .

42 RIDLEYS CHEER
Mountain Bower SN14 7AJ. Mr & Mrs A J Young, 01225 891204, sueyoung@ridleyscheer.co.uk, www.ridleyscheer.co.uk. *9m WNW of Chippenham. At The Shoe, on A420 8m W of Chippenham, turn N then take 2nd L & 1st R.* Home-made teas. **Adm £4, chd free. Sun 8 June (2-5).**
Largely informal garden; mixed borders, lawns, interesting collection of shrubs and trees incl acers, magnolias, liriodendrons, tree peonies, deutzias, daphnes, oaks, beech, birch and hollies. Some 130 rose varieties; old-fashioned and modern shrub roses, and magnificent tree ramblers. Potager, miniature box garden, arboretum, 3-acre wild flower meadow, plus new ½ -acre meadow. Dew pond. Featured in Country Living (March/April 2014).

43 RIVER BARN
Cowbridge Farm, Swindon Road, Malmesbury SN16 9LZ. Finn and Nicki Spicer, www.riverbarn.org.uk. *1m SE of Malmesbury. From Malmesbury r'about, take Wootton Bassett road (B4042) for 1km. Turn L immed after Sir Bernard Lovell turning.* Home-made teas. **Adm £4, chd free. Sun 13 July (11-5.30).**
3 acre garden in a sublime river setting as part of former model farm. Planting commenced in 2007 to create an arboretum with wild flower areas and wildlife pond. Walled courtyard garden with koi pond, rose pergola, mosaics and rich planting. Formal terraced lawn overlooking Avon, pygmy pinetum, stone circle, fruit and vegetable garden. Dragonflies breeding in wildlife pond. Wildflower areas teeming with butterflies, moths, honey bees, solitary bees and bumblebees. R Avon with swans, ducks, moorhens, dabchicks and kingfishers.

44 SHARCOTT MANOR
Pewsey SN9 5PA. Captain & Mrs D Armytage. *1m SW of Pewsey. Via A345 from Pewsey towards Salisbury. Turn R signed Sharcott at grass triangle. 400yds up lane, garden on L over cattle-grid.* Home-made teas. **Adm £4, chd free. Wed 2 Apr (11-5); Sun 6 Apr (2-6); Weds 7 May, 4 June, 2 July, 6 Aug, 3 Sept (11-5); Sun 14 Sept (2-6).**
6-acre plantsman's garden on greensand, planted for yr-round interest. Wide range of trees and shrubs, densely planted mixed borders with many unusual plants and climbers. Magnificent tree ramblers. Woodland walk carpeted with spring bulbs around ½ -acre lake. Good autumn colour. Small collection of ornamental water fowl. Gravel and narrow grass paths, grass slope.

45 ◆ SHELDON MANOR
Chippenham SN14 0RG. Kenneth & Caroline Hawkins, 01249 653120, www.sheldonmanor.co.uk. *1½ m W of Chippenham. Take A420 W. 1st L by Allington Farm Shop, signed Chippenham RFC, entrance approx ½ m on R up a tree lined drive way.* Home-made teas. **Adm £4.50, chd £2.50. For NGS: Wed 11 June (2-5). For other opening times and information, please phone or see garden website.**
Wiltshire's oldest inhabited manor house with C13 porch and C15 chapel. Gardens with ancient yews, mulberry tree and profusion of old-fashioned roses blooming in May and June. There is the opportunity to have a private tour of house and historical gardens. House open, £3.50 per person.

46 ◆ STOURHEAD GARDEN
Stourton, Warminster BA12 6QD. National Trust, 01747 841152, www.nationaltrust.org.uk/stourhead. *3m NW of Mere on B3092. Follow NT signs, the property is very well signed from all main roads incl A303.* **Adm £8.80, chd £4.80. For NGS: Sat 7 June (9am-7pm). For other opening times and information, please phone or see garden website.**
One of the earliest and greatest landscape gardens in the world, creation of banker Henry Hoare in 1740s on his return from the Grand Tour, inspired by paintings of Claude and Poussin. Planted with rare trees, rhododendrons and azaleas over last 250yrs. Wheelchair accessible and buggy available.

47 SWEET BRIAR COTTAGE
19 Gladstone Road, Chippenham, Wiltshire SN15 3BW. Paul & Joy Gough, 01249 656005, paulgough@btopenworld.com. *Chippenham town centre. In town centre, turn off A4 Ave La Fleche into Gladstone Rd. Park in Borough Parade car parks. Garden just above car park opp Angel Hotel.* Home-made teas. **Adm £3, chd free. Sun 27 July (1.30-5). Visitors also welcome by appt May to Sept.**
Nearly an acre of walled garden restored in 2006, visitors are still amazed that such a large garden can exist within a town centre location. Low box-edged herbaceous borders planted to encourage wildlife. Slate paths. Vegetables grown organically in 4ft beds. Large collection of roses, ornamental and fruit trees. Featured in Wiltshire Wildlife Trust Golden Gardens, Wiltshire Life Magazine and Western Daily Press.

48 TRANTOR HOUSE
Hackthorne Road, Durrington SP4 8AS. Mrs Jane Turner, 01980 655101, sjcturner@talktalk.net. *10m N of Salisbury. Turn off A345 (signed Village Centre) onto Hackthorne Rd. Approx 200 yds. on L.* **Adm £3, chd free. Wed 18, Sun 22 June (2-5.30). Also open 22 June Cottage In The Trees. Groups of 10+ also welcome by appt.**
Border Oak timber framed house on country lane surrounded by approx 2/3 acre of both formal and informal gardens. Attractive mixed and herbaceous colour themed borders, rose garden, wildlife pond and stream. Summerhouse, raised veg beds and new wildflower meadow. Chickens. Sloping garden with steps. Plants for sale.

Italianate secret garden . . .

49 ◆ TWIGS COMMUNITY GARDEN
Manor Garden Centre, Cheney Manor, Swindon SN2 2QJ. RF TWIGS, 01793 523294, www.twigscommunitygardens.org.uk. *From Gt Western Way, under Bruce St Bridges onto Rodbourne Rd. 1st L at r'about, Cheney Manor Industrial Est. Through estate, 2nd exit at r'about. Opp Pitch & Putt. Signs on R to Manor Garden Centre.* Home-made teas. **Adm £3, chd free. For NGS: Sun 18 May, Sun 20 July (1-5). For other opening times and information, please phone or see garden website.**
Twigs is a delightful 2-acre community garden, created and maintained by volunteers. Features incl seven individual display gardens, ornamental pond, plant nursery, Iron Age round house, artwork, fitness trail, separate 1-acre organic allotment site, Swindon beekeepers and the haven, overflowing with wild flowers. Live folk music on patio. Willow working demonstration. Most areas wheelchair accessible. Disabled WC.

50 ◆ WATERDALE HOUSE
East Knoyle SP3 6BL. Mr & Mrs Julian Seymour, 01747 830262. *8m S of Warminster. N of East Knoyle, garden signed from A350. DO NOT use Sat Nav.* Home-made teas. **Adm £5, chd free. For NGS: Sun 4 May (2-6). For other opening times and information, please phone.**
4-acre mature woodland garden with rhododendrons, azaleas, camellias, maples, magnolias, ornamental water, bog garden, herbaceous borders. Bluebell walk. Shrub border created by storm damage mixed with agapanthus and half hardy salvias. Limited wheelchair access.

51 WEST LAVINGTON MANOR
1 Church Street, West Lavington SN10 4LA. Mr & Mrs Andrew Doman, andrewdoman01@gmail.com. *6m S of Devizes, on A360. House opp White St, where parking available.* Home-made teas. **Adm £6, chd free (share to West Lavington Youth Club). Sat 14 June (11-6). Visitors also welcome by appt.**
A 5-acre walled garden first established in C17 by John Danvers who brought Italianate gardens to the UK. Herbaceous border, Japanese garden, rose garden, orchard and arboretum with some outstanding specimen trees all centered around a trout stream and duck pond. This year our opening coincides with our biennial contemporary sculpture exhibition, see www.friendsofthegarden.org.uk for details.

52 WHATLEY MANOR
Easton Grey SN16 0RB. Christian Landolt & Alix Landolt, www.whatleymanor.com. *4m W of Malmesbury. From A429 at Malmesbury take B4040 signed Sherston. Manor 2m on L.* **Adm £5.50, chd free. Thur 19 June (4-8).**
12 acres of English country gardens with 26 distinct rooms each with a strong theme based on colour, scent or style. Original 1920s plan inspired the design and combines classic style with more contemporary touches. Specially commissioned sculptures.

53 WINDMILL COTTAGE
Kings Road, Market Lavington SN10 4QB. Rupert & Gill Wade, 01380 813527. *5m S of Devizes. Turn E off A360 1m N of West Lavington, 2m S of Potterne. At top of hill turn L into Kings Rd, L into Windmill Lane after 200yds. Limited parking.* Home-made teas. **Adm £3, chd free. Fris 25 Apr, 23 May, 6, 20 June, 4, 18 July (2-5). Visitors also welcome by appt May to July.**
1-acre cottage-style, wild-life friendly garden on greensand. Mixed beds and borders with long season of interest. Roses on pagoda, large vegetable patch for kitchen and exhibition at local shows, polytunnel and greenhouse. Whole garden virtually pesticide free for last 18yrs. Small bog garden by wildlife pond. Secret glade with prairie.

The Old Mill

Wiltshire County Volunteers

County Organisers

Sean & Kena Magee, Byams House, Willesley, Tetbury GL8 8QU, 01666 880009, spbmagee@googlemail.com

Publicity/Booklet Coordinator

Tricia Duncan, Chapel Cottage, Easton Royal, Pewsey SN9 5RU, 01672 810443, tricia@windward.biz

Assistant County Organisers

Suzie Breakwell, West Holm House, Sherrington, Warminster BA12 0SW, 01985 850297, suzievb@me.com
Sarah Coate, Colts Corner, Upper Woodford, Salisbury SP4 6PA, 01722 782365
Jo Hankey, Mill Cottage, Burcombe, Wilton SP2 0EJ, 01722 742472, rbhankey@gmail.com
Shirley Heywood, Brook House, Kingston Deverill, Warminster BA12 7HF, 01985 844486
Diana Robertson, Broomsgrove Lodge, New Mill, nr Pewsey SN9 5LE, 01672 810515, diana@broomsgrovelodge.co.uk

WORCESTERSHIRE

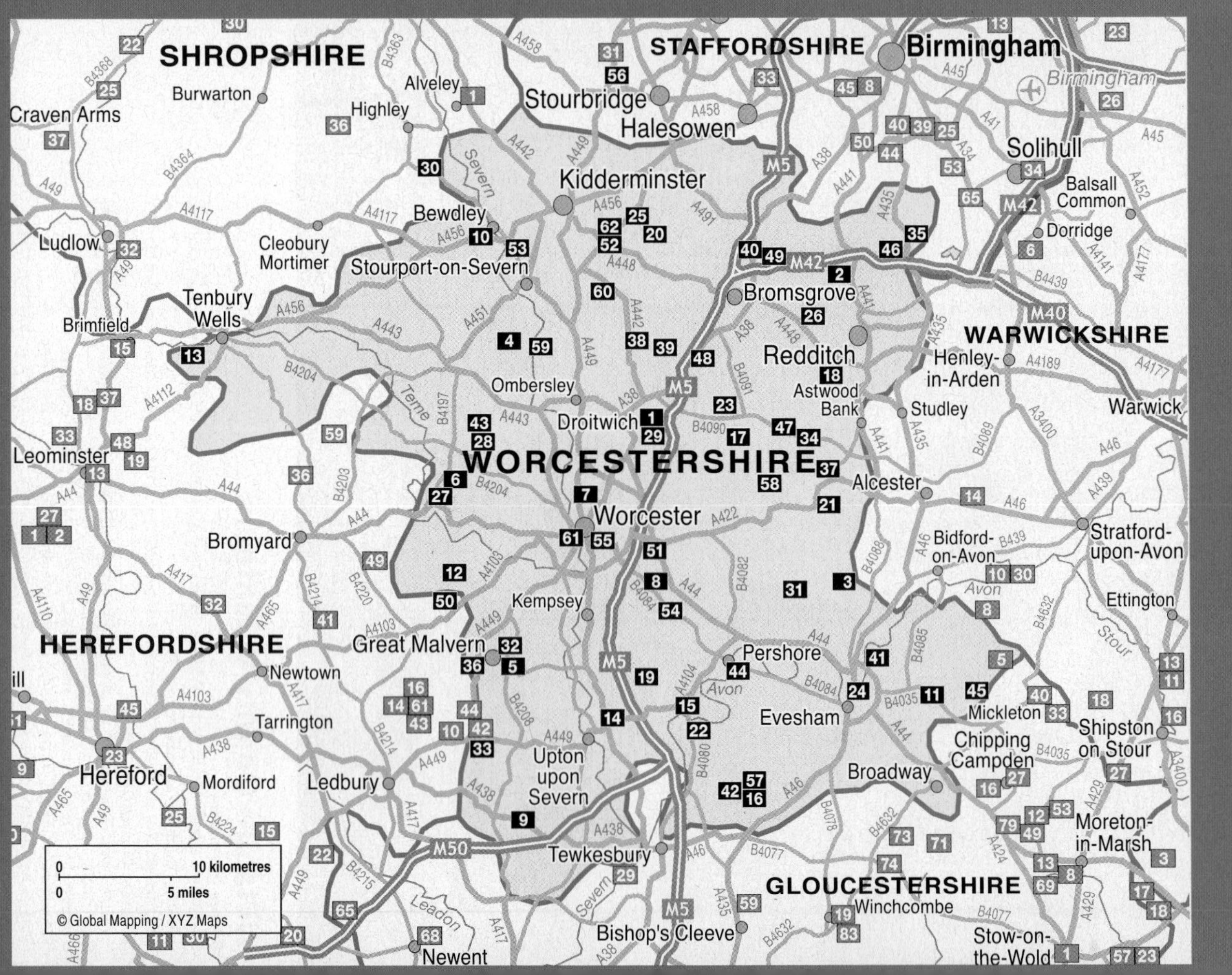

Opening Dates

All entries subject to change. For latest information check www.ngs.org.uk

February

Saturday 22
60 Whitlenge Gardens

Sunday 23
60 Whitlenge Gardens

March

Sunday 16
33 Little Malvern Court

Thursday 27
47 Red House Farm

April

47 Red House Farm (Every Thursday)

Saturday 12
55 The Walled Garden

Sunday 13
58 White Cottage

Wednesday 16
55 The Walled Garden

Friday 18
51 Spetchley Park Gardens

Sunday 20
1 24 Alexander Avenue

Saturday 26
60 Whitlenge Gardens

Sunday 27
5 Barnard's Green House
60 Whitlenge Gardens

May

47 Red House Farm (Every Thursday)

Saturday 3
15 1 Church Cottage

Sunday 4
12 Bridges Stone Mill
15 1 Church Cottage

Monday 5
15 1 Church Cottage
33 Little Malvern Court

Wednesday 7
29 Hiraeth

Saturday 10
39 New House Farm, Elmbridge
50 Shuttifield Cottage

Sunday 11
39 New House Farm, Elmbridge
50 Shuttifield Cottage

Saturday 17
26 Hewell Grange
32 22 Layton Avenue

Sunday 18
26 Hewell Grange
32 22 Layton Avenue
36 Model Farm

Tuesday 20
19 Croome Park

Wednesday 21
7 5 Beckett Drive

Saturday 24
3 NEW Ashley
14 Bylane

Sunday 25
3 NEW Ashley
15 1 Church Cottage
40 Oak Tree House

Monday 26
15 1 Church Cottage

Saturday 31
50 Shuttifield Cottage
60 Whitlenge Gardens

To paraphrase the lovely Eric Morecambe 'They're all the right plants, just not necessarily in the right order . . .

June

47 Red House Farm (Every Thursday)

Sunday 1
57 Whitcombe House
58 White Cottage
60 Whitlenge Gardens

Festival Weekend

Saturday 7
6 The Barton
28 NEW Highfield Cottage
44 Pershore Gardens
55 The Walled Garden

Sunday 8
6 The Barton
9 Birtsmorton Court
28 NEW Highfield Cottage
29 Hiraeth
32 22 Layton Avenue
44 Pershore Gardens

Wednesday 11
55 The Walled Garden

Saturday 14
61 68 Windsor Avenue

Sunday 15
18 NEW The Cottage, 3 Crumpfields Lane
36 Model Farm
45 4 Poden Cottages
61 68 Windsor Avenue

Friday 20
46 Pump Cottage

Saturday 21
2 Alvechurch Gardens
8 NEW Beechwood House
22 Eckington Gardens
43 Pear Tree Cottage
46 Pump Cottage

Sunday 22
2 Alvechurch Gardens
5 Barnard's Green House
8 NEW Beechwood House
22 Eckington Gardens
43 Pear Tree Cottage
46 Pump Cottage
62 The Woodlands

Saturday 28
13 Brook Farm (Evening)
50 Shuttifield Cottage

Sunday 29
4 Astley Towne House
13 Brook Farm
28 NEW Highfield Cottage

July

47 Red House Farm (Every Thursday)

Wednesday 2
29 Hiraeth

Saturday 5
14 Bylane
25 Harvington Hall

Sunday 6
25 Harvington Hall
30 Hunters End
31 NEW Jasmine Cottage
40 Oak Tree House
49 Round Hill Garden
51 Spetchley Park Gardens

Saturday 12
23 Hanbury Hall & Gardens

Sunday 13
1 24 Alexander Avenue
7 5 Beckett Drive
23 Hanbury Hall & Gardens
24 Harrells Hardy Plants Nursery Garden
28 NEW Highfield Cottage
62 The Woodlands

Saturday 19
38 New House Farm, Cutnall Green
56 Westacres

Sunday 20
38 New House Farm, Cutnall Green
53 Toll House Cottage
56 Westacres

Saturday 26
18 NEW The Cottage, 3 Crumpfields Lane
50 Shuttifield Cottage

Sunday 27
4 Astley Towne House
29 Hiraeth
31 NEW Jasmine Cottage

August

47 **Red House Farm (Every Thursday)**

Saturday 2
14 Bylane

Thursday 7
7 5 Beckett Drive (Evening)

Sunday 10
58 White Cottage

Saturday 16
41 Offenham Gardens

Sunday 17
41 Offenham Gardens

Sunday 24
21 6 Dingle End
40 Oak Tree House
49 Round Hill Garden

Monday 25
21 6 Dingle End
43 Pear Tree Cottage (Evening)

Saturday 30
50 Shuttifield Cottage
60 Whitlenge Gardens

Sunday 31
4 Astley Towne House
60 Whitlenge Gardens

September

47 **Red House Farm (Every Thursday)**

Sunday 7
58 White Cottage

Saturday 13
39 New House Farm, Elmbridge

Sunday 14
39 New House Farm, Elmbridge

Sunday 21
5 Barnard's Green House

October

Sunday 12
58 White Cottage

Gardens open to the public

19 Croome Park
23 Hanbury Hall & Gardens
24 Harrells Hardy Plants Nursery Garden
25 Harvington Hall
33 Little Malvern Court
47 Red House Farm
48 Riverside Gardens at Webbs
51 Spetchley Park Gardens
52 Stone House Cottage Gardens
60 Whitlenge Gardens

By appointment only

10 Bowcastle Farm
11 Bretforton Manor
16 Conderton Manor
17 The Cottage
20 Dial Park
27 High View
34 Meadow Farm
35 74 Meadow Road
37 Morton Hall
42 Overbury Court
54 The Tynings
59 The White House

Also open by appointment

1 24 Alexander Avenue
7 5 Beckett Drive
13 Brook Farm
14 Bylane
15 1 Church Cottage
22 Eckington Gardens
22 Mantoft, Eckington Gardens
26 Hewell Grange
29 Hiraeth
30 Hunters End
38 New House Farm, Cutnall Green
39 New House Farm, Elmbridge
40 Oak Tree House
45 4 Poden Cottages
46 Pump Cottage
49 Round Hill Garden
50 Shuttifield Cottage
53 Toll House Cottage
56 Westacres
57 Whitcombe House
58 White Cottage
62 The Woodlands

The Gardens

1 24 ALEXANDER AVENUE

Droitwich Spa WR9 8NH. Malley & David Terry, 01905 774907, terrydroit@aol.com. *1m S of Droitwich. Droitwich Spa towards Worcester A38.Or from M5 J6 to Droitwich Town centre.* **Adm £3.50, chd free. Suns 20 Apr; 13 July (2-5.30). Visitors also welcome by appt Mar to Sept.**
Beautifully designed giving feeling of space and tranquillity. 100+ clematis varieties interlacing high hedges. Borders with rare plants and shrubs. Sweeping curves of lawns and paths to woodland area with shade-loving plants. Drought-tolerant plants in S-facing gravel front garden. Alpine filled troughs. April spring bulbs, June clematis. Partial wheelchair access.

GROUP OPENING

2 ALVECHURCH GARDENS

Alvechurch B48 7LP, 0121 4453895. *3m N of Redditch, 3m NE of Bromsgrove. NGS Gardens are signposted from all roads into Alvechurch village. Pick up your map when you pay at your first garden.* Light refreshments at Old Rectory Cottage. **Combined adm £5, chd free. Sat 21, Sun 22 June (1-6).**

NEW THE ALLOTMENTS
Old Rectory Lane. Tony Ellis

11 BEAR HILL DRIVE
Margaret Haste.
Bear Hill Drive is located at rear of The Red Lion Inn

HILL COTTAGE
Scarfield Hill. Philip & Elisabeth Aubury.
Use Alvechurch Station car park (signed) as only disabled parking at Hill Cottage

SUNNYMEAD
Station Road. Anne & Andy Humphries

THE OLD SWAN
9 Swan Street. Ray & Norma Yarnell.
Opp The Swan PH

RECTORY COTTAGE
Old Rectory Lane. Celia Hitch.
From A441 at Alvechurch, turn into Old Rectory Lane, continue along, after sharp R bend, next house on L

0121 445 4824
celiaandsteve@reccott.
freeserve.co.uk

THE SHRUBBERY
Bear Hill. Chris & Stephanie Miall

NEW **76 TANYARD LANE**
Dianne & Barry Court

8 TRANTER AVENUE
Kevin Baker

TUDOR COTTAGE
5 Meadow Lane. Jill Green

Large village - much new development but interesting core - buildings spanning medieval to Edwardian church on hill with a selection of lovely gardens ranging from a large natural pond with jetty, to rose beds, a professionally landscaped terraced garden, herbaceous beds and waterfall, fruit and vegetable gardens and meadow. A cottage garden with lots of colour in pots and a wrap-around informal garden. Sloped garden with potted plants and shrubs, and a garden with wooden bridge, decking and pebbled areas. Last but not least rockery and sculptures. Not all gardens are wheelchair accessible.

3 NEW ASHLEY

Low Road, Church Lench, Evesham WR11 4UH. Roy & Betty Bowron. *6m N of Evesham. At Church Lench 4th property on L from T-junction (Low Rd & Main St).* Home-made teas. **Adm £3, chd free. Sat 24, Sun 25 May (2-6).**
Sloping garden with steps down to lawn, garden pond with plants and fish. Mixed flower beds, greenhouse and vegetable garden. Large pergola with climbing roses, and shaded section with semi-exotic plants which incl tree ferns, other ferns, banana plants, etc. Plants on the large patio incl sago palms, bird of paradise (strelitzia), Hawaiian Palm, agarves and various other plants. Dogs allowed on a lead.

4 ASTLEY TOWNE HOUSE

Astley DY13 0RH. Tim & Lesley Smith, www.astleytownehousesubtropicalgarden.co.uk. *3m W of Stourport-on-Severn. On B4196 Worcester to Bewdley Road.* Home-made teas. **Adm £4, chd free. Suns 29 June; 27 July; 31 Aug (1-5).**

The Barton

2½ acres garden of a Grade II listed timber building (not open) incl sub-tropical planting. Stumpery garden with tree ferns and woodland temple. Mediterranean garden, tree house, revolving summerhouse and underground grotto with shell mosaics and water features. Teas/cakes and plant stall within the garden. Featured on Gardeners' World and in various newspapers & magazines. Limited wheelchair access.

5 BARNARD'S GREEN HOUSE

Hastings Pool, Poolbrook Road, Malvern WR14 3NQ. Mrs Sue Nicholls, 01684 574446. *1m E of Malvern. At junction of B4211 & B4208.* Home-made teas. **Adm £4, chd free. Suns 27 Apr; 22 June; 21 Sept (2-6).**
With a magnificent backdrop of the Malvern Hills, this 2 acre old-fashioned English garden is a plantsman's paradise. The main feature a magnificent cedar. The garden contains a woodland area, 3 herbaceous and 2 shrub borders, rose garden, white and red borders, pond, sculptures and vegetable garden all surrounding 4 separate lawns. In summer and autumn the herbaceous borders are ablaze with colour incl two rockeries, white and red borders. Vegetable plot surrounding a rose-covered gazebo, known as the Millennium Dome. Dogs on leads.

6 THE BARTON

Berrow Green, Martley WR6 6PL. David & Vanessa Piggott, v.piggott@btinternet.com. *1m S of Martley. On B4197 between Martley & A44 at Knightwick, corner of lane to Broadheath. Parking & lunches (12.30 to 2.30) at Admiral Rodney PH opp.* Home-made teas. **Adm £3, chd free. Sat 7, Sun 8 June (1-5).**
Started in 2003 this ½ -acre colourful cottage-style garden contains unusual trees, shrubs and herbaceous planting. Large pond with herbaceous terracing, wildlife pond, colour-themed gardens, gravel and grass beds. Roses, clematis and uncommon climbers decorate pergola, arbour and trellises. Vegetable garden. Ornamental features and sculptures. Book sale.

7 5 BECKETT DRIVE

Northwick, Worcester WR3 7BZ. Jacki & Pete Ager, 01905 451108, peteandjacki@tiscali.co.uk. *1½ m N of Worcester city centre. Cul-de-sac off A449 Ombersley Rd directly opp Grantham's garage, 1m S of Claines r'about on A449.* Home-made teas. **Adm £3, chd free. Wed 21 May (2-5); Sun 13 July (10-5). Evening Opening £4, chd free, wine, Thur 7 Aug (6-9). Visitors also welcome by appt May to Aug.**

A plantsman's garden with a wide variety of colourful planting in distinctly different settings. Hot borders give way to a raised alpine area and sun-loving bed before moving into a shade garden with hostas and ferns. A walk through this long, narrow garden reveals a number of surprising features, a recent garden visitor describing it as 'a magical mystery tour'. New bed planned for 2014. Compost advisors in attendance. Featured in Worcestershire Life.

8 NEW BEECHWOOD HOUSE

High Park, Whittington, Worcester WR5 2RS. Martin & Gill Rowley. *0.6m from J7 on Pershore to Worcester Rd. From J7 enter on to Pershore Rd for 0.6m. Pull L into lay-by (High Park) follow signs for parking.* Home-made & cream teas. **Adm £4, chd free. Sat 21, Sun 22 June (11-4.30).**

'A Dynamic Living Space'. Beechwood House Gardens offer 3 acres of gardens with a huge variety of functional garden rooms incl a productive garden kitchen; extensive and diverse borders, rockeries, patio areas, decked seating areas, fountains and more. With our small holding situated beyond our gardens come and enjoy an afternoon stroll, cup of tea and a slice of homemade cake with us!

9 BIRTSMORTON COURT

Birtsmorton, nr Malvern WR13 6JS. Mr & Mrs N G K Dawes. *7m E of Ledbury. Off A438 Ledbury/Tewkesbury rd.* Home-made teas. **Adm £5, chd free. Sun 8 June (2-5.30).**

Fortified manor house (not open) dating from C12; moat; Westminster pool laid down in Henry VII's reign at time of consecration of Westminster Abbey. Large tree under which Cardinal Wolsey reputedly slept in shadow of ragged stone. White garden, potager; topiary.

10 BOWCASTLE FARM

Tanners Hill, Bewdley DY12 2LN. Thelma & Cedric Quayle, 01299 403585, Quayle@phonecoop.coop. *1m W of Bewdley town centre. OS ref: SO769752. At 3rd r'about on Bewdley by-pass (or 1st if coming from Ludlow) take the B4190 signed 'Town Centre'. In about ½m turn off at Hop Pole Inn, bear L in 100 yds down Tanners Hill. Follow single track rd approx 500 yds. Farm on L(signed).* Home-made teas. **Adm £5, chd free. Visitors welcome by appt May to July adm incl refreshments.**

½ -acre garden,set among C18 farm buildings and old cherry, pear and apple orchards (SSSI), with fine long views. Informal planting of interesting trees, shrubs and herbaceous, around a lawn, old cider press and stone troughs, pond and seating. An ever-growing collection of clematis and beginnings of a new orchard/arboretum. Some narrow paths of bark and gravel. Stout shoes recommended in orchard.

Holding situated beyond our gardens come and enjoy an afternoon stroll, cup of tea and homemade cake with us! . . .

11 BRETFORTON MANOR

Main Street, Bretforton, Evesham WR11 7JH. Mr & Mrs M L Chambers, 01386 832148, angela-m-chambers@hotmail.co.uk. *4m E of Evesham, 6½ m N of Broadway. Centre of Bretforton village, next to the church.* Light refreshments. **Adm £5, chd free. Visitors welcome by appt Apr to Oct groups of 10+.**

An outstanding garden of 5 acres recently redesigned and replanted. The immaculately maintained garden contains mixed and herbaceous borders, an exotic border, scented walk and many tender and unusual plants. Hedges and topiary both old and new, several water features and many listed buildings and structures. The orchard has been extended and now contains a wide variety of fruit and specimen trees. The dovecote, aviary, apiary, cider barn and old village stocks are all listed. Waterfall and ponds. Featured in Cotswold Life, Cotswold Gardens Section article entitled 'Maintaining Standards' The English Garden,, Worcestershire Gardens article entitled 'Beauty reborn'. Gravel paths, unfenced ponds.

12 BRIDGES STONE MILL

Alfrick Pound WR6 5HR. Sir Michael & Lady Perry. *6m NW of Malvern. A4103 from Worcester to Bransford r'about, then Suckley Rd for 3m to Alfrick Pound.* Home-made teas. **Adm £5, chd free. Sun 4 May (2-5.30).**

Formerly a cherry orchard adjoining the mainly C19 water mill, this is now a 2½ -acre garden laid out with trees, shrubs, mixed beds and borders. Small lake, stream and brook. The garden is bounded by 200yd stretch of Leigh Brook (an SSSI), and a mill stream from the mill's own weir. Extensive all-yr round planting. Ornamental vegetable parterre completes the picture. Wheelchair access by car to courtyard.

13 BROOK FARM

Berrington, nr Tenbury Wells WR15 8TJ. Sarah & William Wint, 01584 819868, sarah@brookfarmberrington.com, www.brookfarmberrington.com. *2m W of Tenbury Wells. From Tenbury take A4112 towards Leominster. After about 3m, pass St Michael's church on L, continue for a further mile. Turn R down Hayes Lane, signed Berrington, and continue 1½ m to T-junction. Brook Farm on L. If using satnav, the garden is approx 500 metres N along Hayes Lane from post code destination.* Home-made teas in Conservatory: Glass of wine/soft drink on Sat, tea & cake on Sun. **Adm £3.50, chd free. Evening Opening, wine, Sat 28 June (5.30-8.30); Sun 29 June (12-5.30). Visitors also welcome by appt, max 30.**

A relaxed country garden. It's been described as a cottage garden, wildlife garden and chaotic garden. To paraphrase the lovely Eric

Morecambe 'They're all the right plants, just not necessarily in the right order'. 1½ -acre garden, 7 acres woodland and wilderness. His and her guides, teas, some weeds. Limited wheelchair access to the garden over gravel and grass, which is passable unless it's very wet.

14 BYLANE

Worcester Road, Earls Croome WR8 9DA. Shirley & Fred Bloxsome, 01684 592489, shirleymay70@hotmail.co.uk. *1m N of Upton on Severn turning. On main A38 directly past Earls Croome Garden Centre, signed Bridle Way. Directly behind Earls Croome Garden Centre.* Light refreshments. **Adm £3, chd free. Sats 24 May; 5 July; 2 Aug (1-5). Visitors also welcome by appt May to Sept, please give one months notice. Adm £5 incl tea.**
Herbaceous garden, paddock with pond (wildlife), small vegetable garden, chickens, wood with mature trees and bluebells. Sensible shoes needed. Picnic area, private parties welcome.

15 1 CHURCH COTTAGE

Defford WR8 9BJ. John Taylor, 01386 750863, ann98sheppard@btinternet.com. *3m SW of Pershore. A4104 Pershore to Upton rd, turn into Harpley Rd, Defford, black & white cottage at side of church. Parking in village hall car park.* Home-made teas. **Adm £3, chd free. Sat 3, Sun 4, Mon 5, Sun 25, Mon 26 May (11-5). Visitors also welcome by appt May to Sept.**
True countryman's ⅓-acre garden. Interesting layout. Japanese -style feature with new 'dragons den'. Specimen trees; water features; vegetable garden; poultry and cider making. New perennial garden under construction. Featured in Amateur Gardener.

16 CONDERTON MANOR

Conderton, nr Tewkesbury GL20 7PR. Mr & Mrs W Carr, 01386 725389, carrs@conderton.wanadoo.co.uk. *5½ m NE of Tewkesbury. On Bredon - Beckford rd or from A46 take Overbury sign at Beckford turn.* Tea in the house. **Adm £5, chd free. Visitors welcome by appt Mar to Oct, small numbers welcome.**
7-acre garden, recently replanted in a contemporary style with magnificent views of Cotswolds. Flowering cherries and bulbs in spring. Formal terrace with clipped box parterre; huge rose and clematis arches, mixed borders of roses and herbaceous plants, bog bank and quarry garden. Many unusual trees and shrubs make this a garden to visit at all seasons. Visitors are particularly encouraged to come in spring and autumn. This is a garden/small arboretum of particular interest for tree lovers. Some gravel paths and steps - no disabled WC.

17 THE COTTAGE

Broughton Green, nr Hanbury, Droitwich WR9 7EF. Terry Dagley, 01905 391670. *5m E of Droitwich. 8m S of Bromsgrove. Nr Hanbury. From Droitwich take B4090 4m towards Feckenham. Turn R at sign Broughton Green & Earls Common. 1m (just before T junction). Cottage up track on R, 300yds.* **Adm £3.50, chd free. Visitors welcome by appt Feb to Sept.**
Plantsmans ½-acre garden, structured by formal hedges, topiary and mature fruit trees. Yr round colour and interest provided by unusual plants and shrubs. Special 9 month coloured grass area Sept to May by bulbs and tubers, plus crocus lawns in spring and autumn. Track not suitable for coaches.

18 NEW THE COTTAGE, 3 CRUMPFIELDS LANE

Webheath, Redditch B97 5PN. Victor Johnson. *From A448 through Redditch take slip rds signed to Headless Cross, at r'about take 3rd exit then follow NGS signs.* Tea. **Adm £4, chd free. Sun 15 June, Sat 26 July (10-5).**
Newly established 1½ - acre garden landscaped to provide 5 rooms on 4 levels stepped into a hillside. From the 2nd level are stunning views over Vale of Evesham. 2 water features, (1 in a cave) and places to sit and enjoy the wildlife. Wonderland can be found in meadow area of wild flowers. Partial wheelchair access to levels 2 and 3 are accessible with able body escort (help available).

19 ◆ CROOME PARK

nr High Green WR8 9DW. National Trust, 01905 371006, www.nationaltrust.org.uk/main/w-croome. *4m W of Pershore. Signed from A38 & B4084.* Light refreshments in the 1940's RAF Visitor Centre. **Adm £7, chd £3.50. For NGS: Tue 20 May (10-5). For other opening times and information, please phone or see garden website.**
730 acre landscape park designed by Capability Brown in mid C18. Restored pleasure grounds, with shrubberies, flowering studs, garden buildings and statuary, ornamental lake and restored parkland. Gardens, lake, parkland, cafe, playarea, den building, kids' trails,. Featured in local press and television news, national television 'Garden Revival' programme. Ask at reception for transport and alternative parking for wheelchair users to access the garden.

20 DIAL PARK

Chaddesley Corbett DY10 4QB. David & Olive Mason, 01562 777451, olivemason75@btinternet.com. *4½ m from Kidderminster, 4½ m from Bromsgrove. On A448 midway between Kidderminster & Bromsgrove. Parking by arrangement with the owner.* **Adm £3, chd free. Visitors welcome by appt individuals or groups. Refreshments by arrangement.**
Approx ¾ acre garden in rural setting. Planted with a wide variety of plants providing interest throughout the year. Specialities incl a large collection of snowdrops, old daffodils and hardy ferns. Small collection of country tools and bygones. Featured in Garden Answers, Gardens Illustrated & Weekend Telegraph.

21 6 DINGLE END

Inkberrow, Worcester WR7 4EY. Mr & Mrs Glenn & Gabriel Allison, 01905 391670. *12m E of Worcester. A422 from Worcester. At the 30mph sign in Inkberrow turn R down Appletree Lane then 1st L up Pepper St. Dingle End is 4th on R of Pepper St. Limited parking in Dingle End but street parking on Pepper St.* Light refreshments. **Adm £3, chd free. Sun 24, Mon 25 Aug (11-5).**

Over 1 acre garden with formal area close to the house opening into a flat area featuring a large pond, stream and weir with apple orchard and woodland area. Large vegetable garden incl an interesting variety of fruits. Garden designed for wildlife. Croquet on the Lawn. Giant Redwood Tree. Slopes alongside every terrace.

GROUP OPENING

22 ECKINGTON GARDENS

Eckington WR10 3BH. Coordinator, Lynn Glaze, 01386 751924, lynnglaze@cmail.co.uk. *5 gardens - 2 in Manor Rd, 3 in or close to New Rd/Nafford Rd. A4104 Pershore to Upton & Defford, L turn B4080 to Eckington. In centre, by war memorial turn R for Brook House & turn L for other gardens.* Home-made teas at Brook House. Wine & soft drinks at Mantoft. **Combined adm £5, chd free. Sat 21, Sun 22 June (11-5). Visitors also welcome by appt Apr to Sept.**

BROOK HOUSE
Manor Road. George & Lynn Glaze

COURT GATE COTTAGE
Manor Road. Mr & Mrs David & Yvonne Walton

HILLTOP
Nafford Road. Richard & Margaret Bateman.
Park on road - easy walk from Mantoft. Disabled drivers can drive right to house/garage for parking

MANTOFT
Mr & Mrs M J Tupper.
Was The Croft. Park on road - garden has electric gates, admission requires pressing a button on a VDU screen to obtain entrance
Visitors also welcome by appt Apr to Sept.
01386 750819

NAFFORD HOUSE
Nafford Road. Janet & John Wheatley.
Enter village of Eckington over river bridge at t-lights on B4080 from Pershore to Tewkesbury At xrds in centre of Eckington (by war memorial): Turn L into New Rd (signed the Combertons) & follow for 3m, on L at top of hill.
01386 750233

5 very diverse gardens; traditional open cottage garden with koi pond; cottage garden broken into smaller areas; formal and structured walled garden with topiary; garden enhanced by magnificent views through hedging windows; natural wooded garden sloping down to the riverside. Set in/close to lovely village of Eckington with riverside parking and picnic site. Brook House 1 acre cottage garden with herbaceous beds and koi pond surrounded by rockery. Court Gate Cottage 2/3 acre cottage garden, broken into 'rooms', with wildlife pond, summer house and vegetable garden. Mantoft - formal walled garden with fish pond, topiary and dew pond, with ducks and geese. Hedges and stone paths, gazebo overlooking garden. Dovecote planned for 2014.
Hilltop 1 acre garden with sunken garden/pond, rose garden, herbaceous borders and formal hedging having 'windows' linking to extensive countryside views.
Nafford House 2 acre mature natural garden/wood with slopes to R Avon, formal gardens, magnificent wisteria and orangery planned for 2014.
Featured in Amateur Gardening-Hilltop. Limited wheelchair access at Nafford House to wooded area and slopes to river.

23 ◆ HANBURY HALL & GARDENS

School Road, Hanbury, Droitwich WR9 7EA. National Trust, 01527 821214, www.nationaltrust.org.uk/hanbury-hall. *4m E of Droitwich. From M5 exit 5 follow A38 to Droitwich; from Droitwich 4m along B4090.* Light refreshments. **Adm £7, chd £3.50. For NGS: Sat 12, Sun 13 July (10.30-5). For other opening times and information, please phone or see garden website.**

Highfield Cottage

Every garden visit makes a difference

Re-creation of early 18th century formal garden by George London. Parterre, fruit garden and wilderness. Mushroom house, orangery and ice house, William and Mary style house dating from 1701. Opportunity to meet the gardeners and to see behind the scenes in the Walled Garden. Featured in a special episode of BBC Doctors and in local media. Buggy available to bring visitors from the car park to the front of the property and wheelchairs are available from the Hall.

24 ◆ HARRELLS HARDY PLANTS NURSERY GARDEN
Rudge Road, Evesham WR11 4JR. Liz Nicklin & Kate Phillips, 01386 443077, www.harrellshardyplants.co.uk. *1/4 m from centre of Evesham. From A4184 turn into Queens Rd R at end, then L, Rudge Rd. 150 yds on R down lane. Sat Nav WR11 4LA.* Home-made teas. **Adm £3, chd free. For NGS: Sun 13 July (2-5). For other opening times and information, please phone or see garden website.**
This garden is naturalistic in style and informally planted with a glorious array of hardy perennials, grasses and a large range of hemerocallis. The 1-acre site consists of beds and borders accessed by bark paths, with several seating areas giving views over the garden.

25 ◆ HARVINGTON HALL
Harvington, Kidderminster DY10 4LR. The Roman Catholic Archdiocese of Birmingham, 01562 777846, www.harvingtonhall.com. *3m SE of Kidderminster. 1/2 m E of A450 Birmingham to Worcester Rd & approx 1/2 m N of A448 from Kidderminster to Bromsgrove.* Light refreshments. **Adm £3.50, chd £1.50. For NGS: Sat 5, Sun 6 July (11.30-4). For other opening times and information, please phone or see garden website.**
Romantic Elizabethan moated manor house with island gardens, small Elizabethan-style herb garden, all tended by volunteers. Tours of the Hall, which contains secret hiding places and rare wall paintings, are also available. Access to gardens, Malt House Visitor Centre, tea room and shop.

A real picture book cottage garden with traditional borders overflowing with delphiniums, roses and geraniums etc . . .

26 HEWELL GRANGE
Hewell Lane, Tardebigge, Redditch B97 6QS. HMP Hewell, 01527 785050, alison.bramham@hmps.gsi.gov.uk. *2m NW of Redditch. HMP Hewell is situated on B4096. Sat Nav postcode B97 6QQ. Follow signs to Grange Resettlement Unit.* Home-made teas. **Adm £5, chd £2.50. Sat 17, Sun 18 May (9.30-4.30). Visitors by appointment only on specified days and times. All visitors must follow a booking procedure and due to Prison environment, must follow security procedures. Booking via email only to Alison Bramham-Smith, OLASS manager (email address above).**
Hewell Grange is an C18 landscape park and lake laid out by Lancelot Brown and modified around 1812 by Humphery Repton. The grounds of this prison feature rhododendrons and azaleas, restored repton bridge, formal garden, water tower, and rock garden. Grounds have mature woodland. Not a flower garden. Please note - Visitors to the garden will be shown the garden features in escorted small groups. The garden tour may be over 60 minutes. Therefore, visitors must be physically able to walk for this length of time. There are uneven surfaces in the grounds so sensible walking footwear is essential. Lakeside walk and bluebell walk Please Note - All visits have to have been booked prior to date.

27 HIGH VIEW
Martley WR6 6PW. Mike & Carole Dunnett, 01886 821559, mike.dunnett@btinternet.com. *1m S of Martley. On B4197 between Martley & A44 at Knightwick.* Tea. **Adm £4, chd free. Visitors welcome by appt June to Sept, groups of 10+.**
Intriguing and mature 2 1/2 acre garden developed over 40yrs. Visitors have described the garden as magical, inspirational and one of the best kept horticultural secrets of Worcestershire! With its superb views over the Teme valley, vast range of plants and many interesting features, it is a garden not to be missed. Steps and steep slopes so appropriate foot wear required.

28 NEW HIGHFIELD COTTAGE
Kings Green, Wichenford, Worcester WR6 6YG. Valerie Mills. *7m from Worcester. Take B4204 from Worcester to Martley turn R at the Masons Arms PH. Follow yellow NGS signs from here. Parking available.* Home-made teas. **Adm £3.50, chd free. Sat 7, Suns 8, 29 June; 13 July (2-6).**
A real picture book cottage garden with traditional borders overflowing with delphiniums, roses and geraniums etc. Mature trees, shrubs and large water garden. New raised vegetable beds, gravel paths and seating areas. Small woodland with live ornamental pheasants. Collection of old garden implements. Exhibition of local artists' paintings and sculptures.

29 HIRAETH
30 Showell Road, Droitwich WR9 8UY. Sue & John Fletcher, 07752 717243 / 01905 778390, jfletcher@inductotherm.co.uk. *1m S of Droitwich. On The Ridings estate. Turn off A38 r'about into Addyes Way, 2nd R into Showell Rd, 500yds on R. Follow the yellow signs!* Home-made teas. **Adm £3, chd free. Wed 7 May (1.30-5.30); Sun 8 June (2-5.30); Wed 2 July (1.30-5.30); Sun 27 July (2-5.30). Visitors also welcome by appt May to Aug.**
'A haven on the way to heaven' - description in Visitors Book. Front, rear gardens contain unusual plants, traditional cottage garden, herbaceous, hostas, ferns, 300yr-old Olive Tree, arches, pool, waterfall, 200yr-old stile, oak sculptures, metal animals, birds etc incl, giraffes, elephant. An oasis of colours in a garden not to be missed.

30 HUNTERS END

Button Bridge Lane, Button Bridge. Kinlet, Bewdley DY12 3DW. Norma & Colin Page, 01299 841055, norma_and_colin@hotmail.co.uk. *6m NW of Bewdley. A4194 from Bewdley at Button Bridge, turn R down Button Bridge Lane, garden ¾ m on L (look for horses heads).* Home-made teas. **Adm £3.50, chd free. Sun 6 July (11-5). Visitors also welcome by appt Apr to Sept.**

This ¾ -acre garden with plants and decorative features will create a smile and a laugh from beginning to end of your tour. Soak up the atmosphere and tranquillity of the garden. Relax in one of the many seating areas and enjoy your tea and cake. Some gravel. Partly sloping.

31 NEW JASMINE COTTAGE

Broad Lane, Bishampton, Pershore WR10 2LY. David & Lesley Miller. *4m S of Inkberrow, 4m NE of Pershore. At Bishampton join Broad Lane after 200yds track on L, property on L up track. Parking village hall, Broad Lane on R.* Home-made teas. **Adm £3, chd free. Sun 6, Sun 27 July (11-4).**

A haven of delight nestled in this rural Worcestershire village, a pretty ⅓ acre garden, packed with interest to complement the Grade II listed black and white cottage. The plot has been transformed in the past two years from a plain lawn to incl ponds, colourful mixed borders, arbours, trees, and vegetable patch, and is testimony to what can be achieved in a relatively small space.

32 22 LAYTON AVENUE

Malvern WR14 2ND. Brian & Jenny Bradford. *From Worcester/Ledbury approach Malvern on A449. Route signed from 'Countrywide'. From Upton approach Malvern on B4211. Signed from Barnards Green.* Home-made teas. **Adm £3, chd free. Sat 17, Sun 18 May, Sun 8 June (11-4.30).**

Developed over 7 years and now maturing this is a garden to linger in. The entrance is via a wisteria and clematis draped pergola opening onto lawns with beds and borders packed full of interesting plants and trees. Like all gardens this one changes from year to year. All plants on sale are from cuttings or seeds from the garden. A stream side garden and ornamental pond complete its attractions. Exhibition in the conservatory of paintings, carvings and ceramic sculptures by Jenny. There are three steps at the garden entrance and a further four steps to access the stream side. Wheelchair access can be achieved with assistance.

33 ◆ LITTLE MALVERN COURT

Little Malvern WR14 4JN. Mrs T M Berington, 01684 892988, www.littlemalverncourt.co.uk. *3m S of Malvern. On A4104 S of junction with A449.* Home-made teas. **Adm £6, chd £0.50. For NGS: Sun 16 Mar, Mon 5 May (2-5). For other opening times and information, please phone or see garden website.**

10 acres attached to former Benedictine Priory, magnificent views over Severn valley. Garden rooms and terrace around house designed and planted in early 1980s; chain of lakes; wide variety of spring bulbs, flowering trees and shrubs. Notable collection of old-fashioned roses. Topiary hedge and fine trees. The May Bank Holiday - Flower Festival in the Priory Church. Very limited wheelchair access.

34 MEADOW FARM

33 Droitwich Road, Feckenham B96 6RU. Robert & Diane Cole, 01527 821156, meadowfarm33@aol.com, www.meadowfarm33.co.uk. *½ m W of Feckenham. On B4090, Droitwich Rd, opposite Berrow Hill Lane.* **Adm £5, chd free. Visitors welcome by appt May to Sept.**

1-acre plantsmans garden created since 1999 by enthusiastic husband and wife team, and intensively planted with herbaceous perennials. Particularly colourful between June and Sept, but planted for all season interest. 1¼ -acre wild flower meadow, and ¾ -acre nursery not normally open to the public.

35 74 MEADOW ROAD

Wythall B47 6EQ. Joe Manchester, 01564 829589, joe@cogentscreenprint.co.uk. *4m E of Alvechurch. 2m N from J3 M42. On A435 at Beckets Farm r'about take rd signed Earlswood/Solihull. Approx 250 metres turn L into School Drive, then L into Meadow Rd.* Tea. **Adm £2.50, chd free. Visitors welcome by appt May to Sept.**

Has been described one of the most unusual urban garden dedicated to woodland, shade-loving plants. 'Expect the unexpected' in a few tropical and foreign species. Meander through the garden under the majestic pine, eucalyptus and silver birch. Sit and enjoy the peaceful surroundings and see how many different ferns and hostas you can find.

A haven of delight nestled in this rural Worcestershire village, a pretty ⅓ acre garden . . .

36 MODEL FARM

Montpelier Road, West Malvern WR14 4BP. Deirdre & Phil Drake. *W side of Malvern Hills. B4232 at Elim Pentecostal H.Q.(Stately stone building).Turn down Croft Bank 200yds and park. Walk left down Montpelier Rd to Model Farm.* Home-made teas. **Adm £4.50, chd free. Suns 18 May; 15 June (2-5.30).**

Stunning 2-acre tranquil garden in the Malvern Hills. Victorian tudor-style house (not open) surrounded by well-stocked borders, patio and courtyard. Picturesque contours of garden complemented by natural stream, ponds, mixed borders, orchard, bog garden, meadow. Ancient oaks, specimen trees, acers, panoramic views to Hay Bluff. Steep in some areas. Wonderful spring bulbs, wisteria and clematis. New for 2014 a high level circular folly and a 60x10ft. new border. Featured in the Worcestershire Life. Cover featured in The Little Book of Worcestershire Gardens.

Pump Cottage

37 MORTON HALL

Morton Hall Lane, Holberrow Green, Redditch B96 6SJ. Mrs A Olivieri, 01386 791820, mortonhall61@hotmail.co.uk. *Between B4090 & A422 signed Inkberrow, then signed Holberrow Green. At circular wooden bench around tree in center of hamlet, turn up Morton Hall Lane. You will reach the main gates to Morton Hall on your RH-side. Press intercom to be admitted..* Home-made teas. **Adm £5, chd free. Visitors welcome by appt Apr to Oct, adm incls tea & cake.**

An elegant stroll garden around a late Georgian house (not open), with potager, hot coloured borders, formalised flower garden, wisteria arbour, large rock garden leading to soft plantings around pools and teahouse, into fritillary meadows with wild roses and towering redwoods. Living roof, Mediterranean plantings, and Ha-Ha with views over vale of Evesham'.

38 NEW HOUSE FARM, CUTNALL GREEN

Kidderminster Road, Cutnall Green, Droitwich Spa WR9 0PW. Mrs Rachel Barnes, 01299 851013, barnes.p7@sky.com. *N of Droitwich Spa. S of Kidderminster. From either Droitwich or Kidderminster follow A442 until you reach the village of Cutnall Green. Yellow signs indicate separate parking and gardens.* Light refreshments, tea room within grounds. **Adm £4, chd free. Sat 19 July (10-5); Sun 20 July (11-3). Visitors also welcome by appt June to July.**

1 acre country garden surrounding Victorian farmhouse (not open), offering many old features, with new planting schemes and views over open countryside giving this garden a wealth of interest. The creativity is abundant due to resident designer who runs an interior design/craft shop and tea room. Plenty of flat ground and lawned areas, some gravel pathways and steps.

39 NEW HOUSE FARM, ELMBRIDGE

Elmbridge Lane, Elmbridge WR9 0DA. Charles & Carlo Caddick, 01299 851249, Carlocaddick@hotmail.com. *2½ m N of Droitwich Spa. From Droitwich take A442 to Cutnall Green. Take lane opp The Chequers PH and proceed 1m to T-junction, turning L towards Elmbridge Green & Elmbridge. Continue along lane passing church and church hall. At T-junction turn R into Elmbridge Lane, garden on L.* Tea. **Adm £4, chd free. Sats, Sun 10, 11 May; 13, 14 Sept (2-4.30). Visitors also welcome by appt May to Sept.**

This charming garden surrounding an early C19 red brick house, (not open) has a wealth of rare trees and shrubs under planted with unusual bulbs and herbaceous plants. Special features are the 'perry wheel', ornamental vegetable gardens. Water garden, dry garden, rose garden, mews, the retreat, potager and greenhouse. Topiary and tropical. plants complete the effect. New plant nursery with many exotics for sun and shade. Plant clearance sale.

40 OAK TREE HOUSE

504 Birmingham Road, Marlbrook, Bromsgrove B61 0HS. Di & Dave Morgan, 0121 445 3595, meandi@btinternet.com. *On A38 midway between M42 J1 & M5 J4. Park old A38 - R fork 250yd N or in front of Marlbrook/Toby PH car park 200yd S. If visiting Round Hill Garden (July/Aug) use Braces Lane car park.* Tea. **Adm £3, chd free. Sun 25 May (11-5); Sun 6 July, Sun 24 Aug (1.30-5.30). If combined with Round Hill Garden (approx 500 yds) in July & Aug, adm £5. Visitors also welcome by appt May to Aug groups of 10+.**

Plantsman's cottage garden (ex Marlbrook Gardens), overflowing with plants, pots and interesting artifacts. Secluded patio with plants and shrubs for Spring, small pond and waterfall. Plenty of seating, separate wildlife pond, water features, alpine area, rear open vista. Many scented plants, hostas, dahlias and lilies. Conservatory with art by owners. Visitor HS said: 'Such a wonderful peaceful oasis'.

GROUP OPENING

41 OFFENHAM GARDENS

Main Street, Offenham WR11 8QD, 01386 424880, asjames@btinternet.com. *Approaching Offenham on B4510 from Evesham, L into village signed Offenham and ferry ¾ m. Follow road round into village & to church. Park in Village Hall car park opp church. NO PARKING AVAILABLE IN VILLAGE OTHER THAN CAR PARK. Gardens 5 mins walk from car park. R out of car park down to maypole. L at maypole into Church St. Keep L in Church St, gardens next to each other on R. Combined ticket at each garden.* Tea. **Combined adm £3, chd free. Sat 16, Sun 17 Aug (11-5).**

LANGDALE
Sheila & Adrian James
www.adrianjames.org.uk

WILLOWAY
Stephen & Linda Pitts

Offenham is a picturesque village in the heart of the Vale of Evesham, with thatched cottages and traditional maypole. Two gardens of diverse interests from woodland and wildlife to herbaceous and exotic. Langdale, a recently developed plantsman's garden, is designed for all year round interest. Surrounding a formal rill are relaxed lawns and borders in a variety of styles, from woodland to hot exotic, leading down to a productive vegetable garden. Willoway, an oasis of sound and colour, is initially hidden by the traditional front garden. A corridor of Hostas leads the visitor to the patio, a lush carpet of lawn, and then, via the bamboo curtain, to the oriental area with ponds and waterfalls. Acers and a stunning Silver Birch Tree. The Streptocarpus House is an additional feature containing many varieties especially from Eastern Europe & Japan.

42 OVERBURY COURT
nr Tewkesbury GL20 7NP. Mr & Mrs Bruce Bossom, 01386 725111(office), garden@overburyestate.co.uk. *5m NE of Tewkesbury. Village signed off A46, Turn off village rd beside the church. Park by gates & walk up drive.* **Adm £4, chd free. Also open by appt Whitcombe Garden. Visitors welcome by appt Mar to Oct, groups of 10+.**
Georgian house 1740 (not open); landscape garden of same date with stream and pools; daffodil bank and grotto. Plane trees, yew hedges; shrubs; cut flowers; coloured foliage; gold and silver, shrub rose borders. Norman church adjoins garden. Some slopes, while all the garden can be viewed, parts are not accessible to wheelchairs.

43 PEAR TREE COTTAGE
Witton Hill, Wichenford, Worcester WR6 6YX. Pamela & Alistair Thompson, 01886 888295, peartree.pam@gmail.com, www.peartreecottage.me. *13m NW of Worcester & 2m NE of Martley. From Martley, take B4197. Turn R into Horn Lane then first L signed Prickley Green. Keep R & Pear Tree Cottage is on L at top of hill.* Tea. **Adm £3.50, chd free. Sat 21, Sun 22 June (11-6). Evening Opening £4.50, chd free, wine, Mon 25 Aug (5-10).**
A Grade II listed black and white cottage (not open) with SW-facing gardens and far reaching views across orchards to Abberley clock tower. The gardens extend to approx. ¾ acre and comprise of gently sloping lawns with mixed and woodland borders, shade and plenty of strategically placed seating. The garden exudes a quirky and humorous character with the odd surprise! The 'Gardeners' Loo' is available to visitors. Evening Opening 25 Aug. Featured in Worcestershire Life Magazine & Worcester News. Most areas are accessible by wheelchair.

GROUP OPENING

44 PERSHORE GARDENS
Pershore WR10 1BG, Coordinator Jan Garrett, www.visitpershore.co.uk. *On B4084 between Worcester & Evesham, & 6m from exit 7 on M5. There is also a train station.* Tea at The Primary School & Number 8 Community Arts Centre, 8 High Street. **Combined adm £5, chd free. Sat 7, Sun 8 June (1-5).**
Tickets valid both days. Tickets available in advance from Tourist Information and 'Blue' in Broad Street and on the day at an open garden. Explore 20 large and small gardens in the attractive market town of Pershore. These incl gardens tucked away behind Georgian town houses, gardens which sweep down to the R Avon, tiny courtyards and walled gardens and a Primary School garden. Holy Redeemer has a selection of raised beds growing a variety of fruit and vegetables. We are fortunate to be a Breathing Places School and with our Lottery Funding, we have invested in a large outdoor classroom equipped with a propagator, microscopes, a variety of child friendly tools and electricity for inclement days. We have a natural pond which has many newts and frogs and where pond dipping is a great favourite with the children. Tomatoes are grown in our two green houses and we have had grapes on our vine. Produce is either eaten enthusiastically by the children who particularly enjoy the strawberries and baking the potatoes straight from the ground and some is sold. Wheelchair access to some gardens.

45 4 PODEN COTTAGES
Honeybourne WR11 7PS. Patrick & Dorothy Bellew, 01386 438996, pots@poden.freeserve.co.uk. *6m E of Evesham. At the Gate Inn take the Pebworth, Long Marston Rd, turn R at end of the Village for Mickleton. 1m on Mickleton Rd.* Home-made teas. **Adm £3, chd free. Sun 15 June (2-5). Visitors also welcome by appt June to July groups welcome.**
⅓ acre cottage garden which has been planted by the owners. Paths wind through mixed herbaceous borders. Roses old and modern, shrubs, small terrace and pond. Fine views over the Cotswold Hills. All-yr colour. Gravel drive at entrance.

46 PUMP COTTAGE
Hill Lane, Weatheroak, nr Alvechurch B48 7EQ. Barry Knee & Sue Hunstone, 01564 826250, barryknee.1947@btinternet.com, www.pumpcottage.org.uk. *3m E of Alvechurch. 1½ m from J3 M42 off N-bound c'way of A435 (signed Alvechurch). Parking in adjacent field.* Home-made teas, all home-made cakes, incl gluten free on request before visit. **Adm £3, chd free. Fri 20, Sat 21, Sun 22 June (11-5). Visitors also welcome by appt, adm £6 (incl home-made teas) May to Sept, for individuals or groups. Introductory talk and guided tour can be provided.**
Described by visitors as 'A secret wonderland, surprises at every turn'. C19 cottage, rural setting. Enchanting, romantic 1 acre plantaholic's garden with yr-round interest. Colourful borders, roses, rockery, fernery, water features, bog garden, natural pond, water lilies and wildlife area. Victorian styled greenhouse, creative features, artefacts and ornaments. Continually evolving. Limited wheelchair access.

The garden exudes a quirky and humorous character with the odd surprise . . . !

47 ◆ RED HOUSE FARM
Flying Horse Lane, Bradley Green, nr Redditch B96 6QT. Mrs M M Weaver, 01527 821269, www.redhousefarmgardenandnursery.co.uk. *7m W of Redditch, 7m E of Droitwich. On B4090 Alcester to Droitwich Spa. Ignore sign to Bradley Green. Turn opp The Red Lion PH.* **Adm £2.50, chd free. For NGS: Every Thur 27 Mar to 25 Sept (12-5). For other opening times and information, please phone or see garden website.**
Created as a peaceful haven from its working farm environment, this mature country garden offers yr-round interest. In densely planted borders a wide range of traditional favourites rub shoulders with the newest of introductions and make each visit a pleasurable and rewarding experience. Adjacent nursery open daily 10-5.

Pear Tree Cottage

48 ◆ RIVERSIDE GARDENS AT WEBBS

Wychbold, nr Droitwich WR9 0DG. Webbs of Wychbold, 01527 860000, www.webbsdirect.co.uk. *2m N of Droitwich Spa. 1m N of M5 J5 on A38. Follow tourism signs from M5.* **For opening times and information, please phone or see garden website.**

2½ acres. Themed gardens incl Colour spectrum, tropical and dry garden, New David Austin Rose collection, new vegetable garden area, grassery and bamboozelum. New Wave gardens opened 2004, designer Noel Kingsbury, to create natural seasonal interest with grasses and perennials.This area is now home to beehives which produce honey for our own food hall. The New Wave Garden is being slightly changed over 2014 to become more of a natural wildlife area. There are two willow wigwams made for children to play in with more planned for later in the year. Open all yr except Christmas, Boxing Day and Easter Sunday. Our New Wave Gardens area has grass paths which are underlaid with mesh so people with heavy duty wheelchairs can be taken around.

49 ROUND HILL GARDEN

24 Braces Lane, Marlbrook, Bromsgrove B60 1DY. Lynn & Alan Nokes, 0121 445 5520, alyn.nokes@btinternet.com. *2m N of Bromsgrove. 1m N of M42 J1, follow B4096 signed Rednal, turn L at Xrds into Braces Lane. 1m S of M5 J4, follow A38 signed Bromsgrove, turn L at T-lights into Braces Lane. Parking available.* Home-made teas. **Adm £3, chd free. Suns 6 July; 24 Aug (1.30-5.30). If combined with Oak Tree House (approx 500yds) adm £5. Visitors also welcome by appt July to Sept, groups of 10+.**

Recently created front garden.
S - facing rear garden with planting in abundance, from exotics and unusual through to traditional. Shady areas, hot beds, water features, sculptures and artefacts. Garden ascends from the house, landscaped and built by enthusiastic owners into four rooms: Mediterranean area, patio and pond area, lawn with herbaceous borders and raised bed vegetable garden with greenhouses. Previously part of Marlbrook Gardens.

50 SHUTTIFIELD COTTAGE

Birchwood, Storridge WR13 5HA. Mr & Mrs David Judge, 01886 884243, judge.shutti@btinternet.com. *8m W of Worcester. Turn R off A4103 opp Storridge Church to Birchwood. After 1¼ m L down steep tarmac drive. Please park on roadside but drive down if walking is difficult.* Tea. **Adm £4, chd free. Sat 10, Sun 11, Sat 31 May; Sats 28 June; 26 July; 30 Aug (1.30-5). Visitors also welcome by appt Apr to Oct.**

Superb position and views. Unexpected 3-acre plantsman's garden, extensive herbaceous borders, primula and stump bed, many unusual trees, shrubs, perennials, colour-themed for all-yr interest. Walks in 20-acre wood with ponds, natural wild areas, anemones, bluebells, rhododendrons, azaleas are a particular spring feature. Large old rose garden with many spectacular mature climbers. Good garden colour throughout the yr. Small deer park, vegetable garden. Wildlife ponds, wild flowers and walks in 20 acres of ancient woodland. Featured in Cotswold Life and Gardeners World (programme to be shown before Malvern Spring Show).

Look out for the NGS yellow arrows ...

51 ◆ SPETCHLEY PARK GARDENS

Spetchley WR5 1RS. Mr John Berkeley, 01453 810303, www.spetchleygardens.co.uk. *2m E of Worcester. On A44, follow brown signs.* Light refreshments. **Adm £6.50, chd free. For NGS: Fri 18 Apr, Sun 6 July (11-6). For other opening times and information, please phone or see garden website.**

Surrounded by glorious countryside lays one of Britain's best-kept secrets. Spetchley is a garden for all tastes containing one of the biggest private collections of plant varieties outside the major botanical gardens. Spetchley is not a formal paradise of neatly manicured lawns or beds but rather a wondrous display of plants, shrubs and trees woven into a garden of many rooms and vistas. Gravel paths.

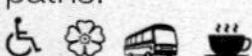

52 ◆ STONE HOUSE COTTAGE GARDENS

Stone DY10 4BG. James & Louisa Arbuthnott, 01562 69902, www.shcn.co.uk. *2m SE of Kidderminster. Via A448 towards Bromsgrove, next to church, turn up drive.* **Adm £4, chd free. For opening times and information, please phone or see garden website.**

A beautiful and romantic walled garden adorned with unusual brick follies. This acclaimed garden is exuberantly planted and holds one of the largest collections of rare plants in the country. It acts as a shop window for the adjoining nursery. Open Wed to Sat late March to early Sept 10-5. Limited wheelchair access.

53 TOLL HOUSE COTTAGE

Stourport Road, Bewdley DY12 1PU. Joan & Rob Roberts, 01299 402331, joanroberts7@live.co.uk. *1m S of Bewdley, 2m N of Stourport, 3m W of Kidderminster. On A456 between Bewdley & Stourport, Opp Blackstone car park & picnic site (free parking). Disabled parking on drive.* Home-made teas. **Adm £3, chd free. Sun 20 July (10-5). Visitors also welcome by appt 18 May to end Aug, min 10 max 30.**

Developing ½ acre garden started in 2008 in 2 sections. Cottage garden with a collection of bulbs, herbaceous and shrubs for year round colour incl lawn. A small arboretum with grass walkways and summerhouse. A large pool with waterfall and beach for wildlife. Vegetable garden with raised beds in large fruit cage. A painters garden. Gallery for Woodturning and Paintings also open for viewing.

> Described by a visitor in the visitors book as 'A garden which we all wished we could have, at least in our lifetime' . . .

54 THE TYNINGS

Church Lane, Stoulton, nr Worcester WR7 4RE. John & Leslie Bryant, 01905 840189, johnlesbryant@btinternet.com. *5m S of Worcester; 3m N of Pershore. On the B4084 (formerly A44) between M5 J7 & Pershore. The Tynings lies beyond the church at the extreme end of Church Lane. Ample parking.* Light refreshments. **Adm £3, chd free. Visitors welcome by appt May to Sept.**

Acclaimed plantsman's ½ -acre garden, generously planted with a large selection of rare trees and shrubs. Features incl specialist collection of lilies, many unusual climbers and rare ferns. The colour continues into late summer with dahlia, berberis, euonymus and tree colour. Surprises around every corner. You will not be disappointed. Lovely views of adjacent Norman Church and surrounding countryside. Plants labelled and plant lists available. Further info and photos on NGS website.

55 THE WALLED GARDEN

6 Rose Terrace, off Fort Royal Hill, Worcester WR5 1BU. William & Julia Scott, 01905 354629, herbgarden@onetel.com. *Close to the City centre. ½ m from Cathedral. Via Fort Royal Hill, off London Rd (A44). Park on 1st section of Rose Terrace & walk the last 20yds down track.* Tea. **Adm £3, chd free. Sats, Weds 12, 16 Apr; 7, 11 June (1-5).**

In this peaceful oasis of scent and colour, a tapestry of culinary and medicinal herbs, vegetables, flowers and fruit grow organically. History, symmetry and historic tributes are the foundation of this C19 walled kitchen garden which is seasonally evolving with new projects and planting schemes. Featured on BBC Hereford and Worcester Radio, Garden Show and in Cotswold Gardens Magazine.

56 WESTACRES

Wolverhampton Road, Prestwood, Stourbridge DY7 5AN. Mrs Joyce Williams, 01384 877496. *3m W of Stourbridge. A449 in between Wall Heath (2m) & Kidderminster (6m). Ample parking Prestwood Nurseries (next door).* Home-made teas. **Adm £4, chd free. Sat 19, Sun 20 July (11-4). Visitors also welcome by appt May to Sept.**

¾ -acre plant collector's garden, many different varieties of acers, hostas, shrubs. Woodland walk, large koi pool. Covered tea area with home-made cakes. Come and see for yourselves, you won't be disappointed. Described by a visitor in the visitors book as 'A garden which we all wished we could have, at least in our lifetime'. Plants for Sale. Large collection of hostas and acers.

57 WHITCOMBE HOUSE

Overbury, nr Tewkesbury GL20 7NZ. Faith & Anthony Hallett, 01386 725206, faith@whitcombeassocs.co.uk. *9m S of Evesham. Leave A46 at Beckford to Overbury (2m). Or B4080 from Tewkesbury through Bredon/Kemerton (5m). Approx 5m from J9 on M5.* Home-made teas. **Adm £3.50, chd free. Sun 1 June (2-5). Visitors also welcome by appt Apr to Sept, evenings visits possible (with wine).**

1 acre planted for every season in an idyllic Cotswold stone setting. Spring bulbs give way to cool blue and white, allium and flowering shrubs are followed by cascading roses, summer pastels and fiery oranges, red and yellows. The spring-fed stream flows through colourful moisture loving plants. Asters, cosmos and yet more roses provide late summer colour. Lots of seats for relaxation. For wheelchair access please contact us in advance for details.

5 Beckett Drive

58 WHITE COTTAGE
Earls Common Road, Stock Green, nr Inkberrow B96 6SZ. Mr & Mrs S M Bates, 01386 792414, smandjbates@aol.com. *2m W of Inkberrow, 2m E of Upton Snodsbury. A422 Worcester to Alcester, turn at sign for Stock Green by Red Hart PH, 1½ m to T- junction, turn L 500 yds on the L.* **Adm £3, chd free. Suns 13 Apr; 1 June; 10 Aug; 7 Sept; 12 Oct (11-4.30). Visitors also welcome by appt Mar to Oct, adm £3.75.**
2-acres, herbaceous and shrub beds, stream and spring wild flower area, rose garden, raised woodland bed, New raised vegetable bed. Featured in Period Living. Gravel drive to the gate but it is manageable.

59 THE WHITE HOUSE
Seedgreen Lane, Astley Burf, Stourport on Severn DY13 0SA. John & Joanna Daniels, 01299 879290, whcountrygarden@hotmail.co.uk. *3m SW of Stourport on Severn. Off B4196 Holt Heath to Stourport Rd.* Light refreshments. **Adm £3, chd free. Visitors welcome by appt May to June, individuals and small groups (max 20).**
An informal half acre country garden in a peaceful location surrounding a period property (not open). The garden is constantly evolving with large mixed borders planted with shrubs and cottage garden plants. Hostas in containers, vegetable beds, herbs and greenhouse. Adjoining recently planted half acre orchard with fruit and ornamental trees. Chickens and beehives.

60 ◆ WHITLENGE GARDENS
Whitlenge Lane, Hartlebury DY10 4HD. Mr & Mrs K J Southall, 01299 250720, www.whitlengegardens.co.uk. *5m S of Kidderminster, on A442. A449 kidderminster to Worcester L at T-lights, A442 signed Droitwich, over island, ¼ m, 1st R into Whitlenge Lane. Follow brown signs.* Light refreshments. **Adm £3.50, chd £1. For NGS: Sats, Suns 22, 23 Feb, 26, 27 Apr; 31 May; 1 June; 30, 31 Aug. (Sat 9-4), (Sun 10-4). For other opening times and information, please phone or see garden website.**
3 acre show garden of professional designer with over 800 varieties of trees, shrubs etc. Twisted pillar pergola, camomile lawn, waterfalls and pools. Mystic features of the Green Man, 'Sword in the Stone' and cave fernery. Walk the labyrinth and take refreshments in The Garden 'Design Studio' tearoom. 400 sq metre grass labyrinth, 2½ metre high brick and oak moongate with 4 cascading waterfalls, deck walk through giant Gunnera leaves, Camomile paths through herb gardens, childrens play and pet corner. Locally sourced homemade food in tearoom, plant nursery. Featured on BBC Hereford and Worcester Radio.

61 68 WINDSOR AVENUE
St Johns, Worcester WR2 5NB. Roger & Barbara Parker, 01905 428723, robarpark@googlemail.com. *W area of Worcester. Off the A44 to Bromyard Rd into Comer Rd, 3rd L into Laugherne Rd, 3rd L into Windsor Ave.* Tea. **Adm £4, chd free. Sat 14, Sun 15 June (11-4).**
In a cul-de-sac, behind a 1930s semi-detached house is almost 1 acre of garden with 4 ponds in very different styles. Split into 3 areas, the garden has flower beds, bog gardens, an 'oriental' area and vegetable patch. Plus 4 greenhouses and chickens and ornamental pheasants!

62 THE WOODLANDS
Dunclent, Stone, Kidderminster DY10 4AY. Pat & Phil Gaskin, 01562 740795, thewoodlands1@yahoo.co.uk. *2m SE of Kidderminster. A448 Bromsgrove Rd. Turn into Dunclent Lane, follow signs down narrow lane onto unadopted rd, short distance. Parking in adjoining field.* Home-made teas. **Adm £3.50, chd free. Suns 22 June; 13 July (11.30-4). Visitors also welcome by appt June to July, groups of 10+.**
Intriguing approx ¾ -acre garden in rural woodland, open fields haven. Developed last 9yrs, designed on various levels, with secret winding paths, steps to coloured themed herbaceous/shrub borders, large vegetable garden, tomato/cucumber greenhouses. Courtyard, waterfall, pergola walk, pond, swimming pool, hanging baskets and tubs of flowers, a very attractive colourful garden. Featured in Kidderminister Shuttle.

Worcestershire County Volunteers

County Organiser
David Morgan, Oak Tree House, 504 Birmingham Road, Marlbrook B61 0HS, 0121 445 3595, meandi@btinternet.com

County Treasurer
Cliff Woodward, 11 Trehernes Drive, Pedmore, Stourbridge DY9 0YX, 01562 886349

Publicity
Pamela Thompson, Pear Tree Cottage, Witton Hill, Wichenford WR6 6YX, 01886 888295, peartree.pam@gmail.com

Booklet & Advertising Coordinator
Alan Nokes, 24 Braces Lane, Marlbrook, Bromsgrove B60 1DY, 0121 445 5520, alyn.nokes@btinternet.com

Assistant County Organisers
Richard Armitage, 11 Myatts Field, Harvington, Evesham WR11 8NG, 01386 871211
Mike George, 55 Hawkwood Crescent, Worcester WR2 6BP, 01905 427567
Lynn Glaze, Brook House, Manor Road, Eckington, nr Pershore WR10 3BH, 01386 751924 lynnglaze@cmail.co.uk

YORKSHIRE

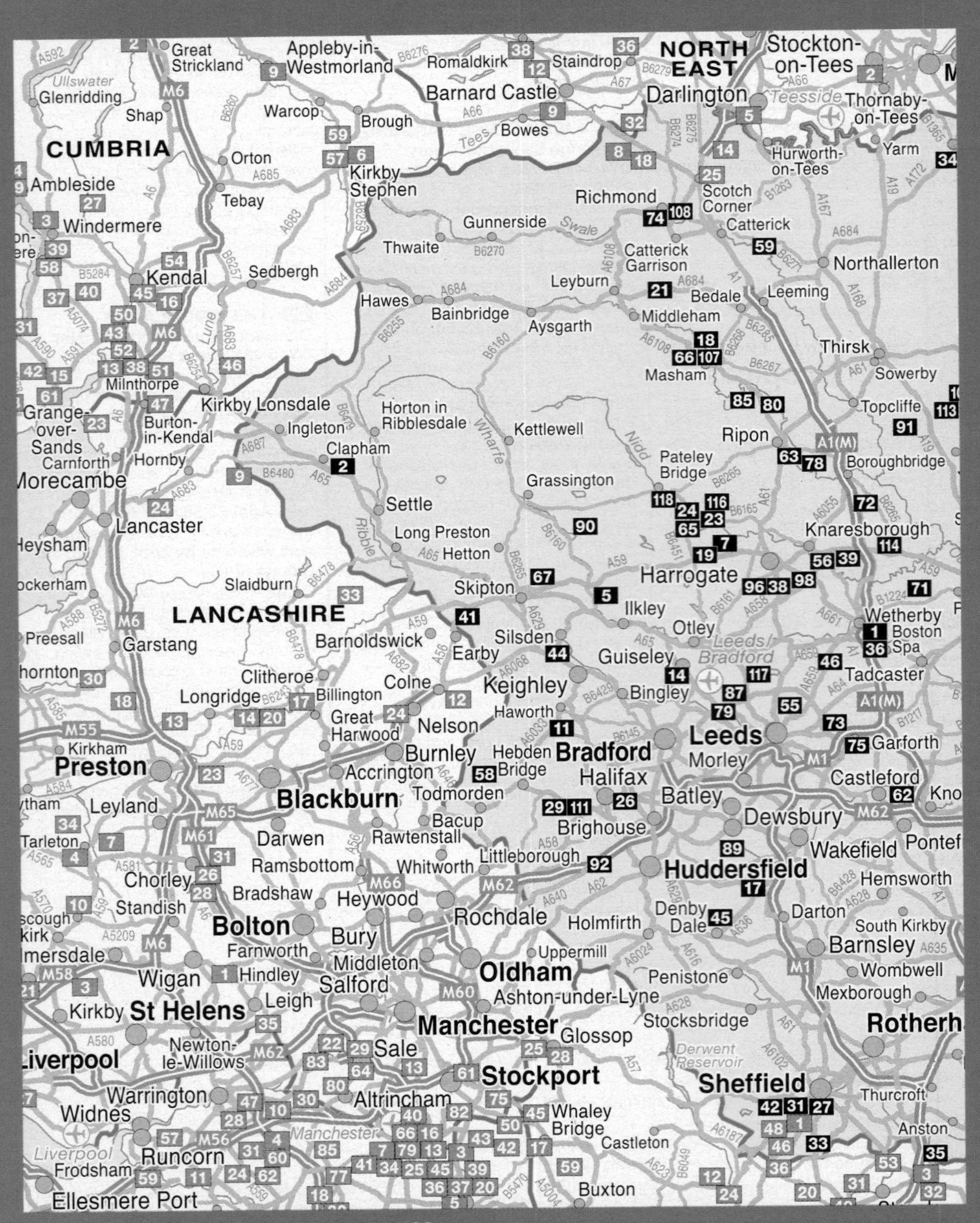
CUMBRIA
NORTH EAST
LANCASHIRE
Great Strickland
Appleby-in-Westmorland
Romaldkirk
Staindrop
Stockton-on-Tees
Ullswater
Glenridding
Shap
Warcop
Brough
Barnard Castle
Darlington
Teesside
Thornaby-on-Tees
Bowes
Tees
Orton
Kirkby Stephen
Hurworth-on-Tees
Yarm
Ambleside
Tebay
Richmond
Scotch Corner
Windermere
Gunnerside
Swale
Catterick
Thwaite
Catterick Garrison
Northallerton
Kendal
Sedbergh
Leyburn
Bedale
Leeming
Hawes
Bainbridge
Middleham
Aysgarth
Lune
Thirsk
Masham
Sowerby
Milnthorpe
Kirkby Lonsdale
Horton in Ribblesdale
Topcliffe
Grange-over-Sands
Burton-in-Kendal
Ingleton
Kettlewell
Wharfe
Nidd
Ripon
Clapham
Pateley Bridge
Boroughbridge
Carnforth
Hornby
Morecambe
Grassington
Settle
Knaresborough
Lancaster
Long Preston
Heysham
Ribble
Hetton
Harrogate
Slaidburn
Skipton
Ilkley
Wetherby
Boston Spa
Preesall
Garstang
Barnoldswick
Silsden
Otley
Earby
Guiseley
Leeds/Bradford
Tadcaster
Clitheroe
Colne
Keighley
Bingley
Longridge
Billington
Great Harwood
Nelson
Haworth
Leeds
Kirkham
Burnley
Hebden Bridge
Bradford
Garforth
Preston
Accrington
Morley
Halifax
Castleford
Blackburn
Todmorden
Batley
Leyland
Bacup
Dewsbury
Tarleton
Darwen
Rawtenstall
Brighouse
Wakefield
Whitworth
Littleborough
Ramsbottom
Chorley
Huddersfield
Hemsworth
Bradshaw
Heywood
Standish
Denby Dale
Darton
Rochdale
Holmfirth
South Kirkby
Bolton
Bury
Farnworth
Uppermill
Barnsley
Middleton
Wombwell
Wigan
Hindley
Oldham
Penistone
Salford
Ashton-under-Lyne
Mexborough
Kirkby
St Helens
Leigh
Stocksbridge
Manchester
Glossop
Rotherham
Newton-le-Willows
Sale
Derwent Reservoir
Liverpool
Stockport
Sheffield
Warrington
Altrincham
Thurcroft
Widnes
Whaley Bridge
Anston
Manchester
Castleton
Liverpool
Runcorn
Frodsham
Buxton
Ellesmere Port

0 10 20 kilometres
0 10 miles
© Global Mapping / XYZ Maps
YORKSHIRE
LINCOLNSHIRE
Middlesbrough
Saltburn-by-the-Sea
Hinderwell
Guisborough
Sandsend
Whitby
Great Ayton
Stokesley
Danby
Sleights
Robin Hood's Bay
Goathland
Burniston
Scalby
West Ayton
Scarborough
Eastfield
Kirkbymoorside
Helmsley
Pickering
Oswaldkirk
Snainton
Filey
Filey Bay
Hovingham
Hunmanby
Brandsby
Malton
Norton
Flamborough Head
Flamborough
Easingwold
North Grimston
Sledmere
Langtoft
Bridlington
Burton Agnes
Bridlington Bay
Shipton
Stamford Bridge
Haxby
Fridaythorpe
Driffield
Skipsea
York
Bainton
Hutton Cranswick
Pocklington
Rufforth
Fulford
Hayton
Market Weighton
Brandesburton
Hornsea
Beverley
Cawood
Holme-on-Spalding-Moor
Aldbrough
Barlby
Bubwith
Cottingham
Selby
North Cave
South Cave
Bilton
Kingston upon Hull
Howden
Hessle
Hedon
Withernsea
Goole
North Ferriby
Snaith
Barton-upon-Humber
Patrington
Easington
Winterton
Askern
Thorne
Crowle
Immingham
River Humber
Hatfield
Scunthorpe
Humberside
Grimsby
Spurn Head
Bentley
Bottesford
Cleethorpes
Epworth
Brigg
Laceby
Humberston
Doncaster
Caistor
Waltham
Bawtry
Blyton
Kirton in Lindsey
Binbrook
Ludborough
North Somercotes
Maltby
Market Rasen
Gainsborough
Louth
Mablethorpe
Retford
Worksop
Newton on Trent
Saxilby
Dunholme
Nettleham
Wragby
Maltby le Marsh
Alford
Milton

Opening Dates

All entries subject to change. For latest information check www.ngs.org.uk

February

Sunday 16
25 Devonshire Mill

Wednesday 26
2 Austwick Hall

March

Sunday 2
9 Bridge Farm House

Sunday 16
75 Millrace Nursery

Sunday 23
39 Goldsborough Hall

April

Thursday 3
50 Hotham Hall

Sunday 13
18 Clifton Castle
47 Holly Croft

Thursday 17
50 Hotham Hall

Saturday 19
30 Ellerker House

Sunday 20
45 Highfields
75 Millrace Nursery

Wednesday 23
45 Highfields
90 Parcevall Hall Gardens

Friday 25
102 Shandy Hall Gardens (Evening)

Sunday 27
1 Acorn Cottage
36 Four Gables
59 Langton Farm
91 3 Pilmoor Cottages
96 RHS Garden Harlow Carr

May

19 **Cold Cotes (Every Saturday)**

Sunday 4
35 Firvale Allotment Garden
69 Manor House
95 Rewela Cottage

Sunday 11
65 Low Hall
106 Stillingfleet Lodge
109 Terrington House
111 Warley House Garden
116 Woodlands Cottage

Wednesday 14
5 Beacon Hill House

Saturday 17
34 Fir Trees Cottage
94 The Red House

Sunday 18
17 The Circles Garden
46 Hillbark
94 The Red House

Sunday 25
27 34 Dover Road
42 16 Hallam Grange Croft
75 Millrace Nursery
97 The Ridings

Monday 26
9 Bridge Farm House

Saturday 31
60 Linden House

Overlooking the Wolds on a limestone ridge this site has a bronze age burial mound . . .

June

19 **Cold Cotes (Every Saturday)**
26 **Dove Cottage Nursery Garden (Every Friday)**

Sunday 1
11 Brookfield
22 The Court
53 Jackson's Wold
60 Linden House

Wednesday 4
11 Brookfield

Festival Weekend

Saturday 7
13 Burton Agnes Hall & Gardens
16 NEW Churchside
51 Hunmanby Grange
85 Old Sleningford Hall
103 Shiptonthorpe Gardens
119 NEW The Yorkshire Arboretum

Sunday 8
13 Burton Agnes Hall & Gardens
16 NEW Churchside
18 Clifton Castle
28 Dowthorpe Hall & Horse Pasture Cottage
49 Hornsea Gardens
51 Hunmanby Grange
61 Linden Lodge
85 Old Sleningford Hall
88 NEW Orchard House
98 Rudding Park
103 Shiptonthorpe Gardens

Wednesday 11
104 Skipwith Hall

Thursday 12
50 Hotham Hall

Friday 13
32 Fawley House

Sunday 15
32 Fawley House
40 The Granary
56 Kelberdale
64 Lockington Gardens
71 NEW Marston Grange
74 Millgate House
80 Norton Conyers
91 3 Pilmoor Cottages
108 Swale Cottage
109 Terrington House

Monday 16
32 Fawley House

Tuesday 17
32 Fawley House

Wednesday 18
32 Fawley House
114 Whixley Gardens

Thursday 19
32 Fawley House

Friday 20
32 Fawley House
102 Shandy Hall Gardens (Evening)

Saturday 21
16 NEW Churchside
86 Omega

Sunday 22
7 Birstwith Hall
16 NEW Churchside
31 NEW Endcliffe Mount (Evening)
54 Jasmine House
61 Linden Lodge
62 Little Eden
66 Low Sutton
75 Millrace Nursery
84 Old Rectory Cottage
86 Omega
92 Prospect House
107 NEW Sutton Grange
112 Westfield Farm
118 Yorke House

Wednesday 25
72 Marton Cum Grafton Gardens

Friday 27
110 NEW Tickton CE Primary

Saturday 28
6 Beverley Hidden Town Gardens
83 NEW The Old Rectory

Sunday 29
4 NEW Basin Howe Farm
6 Beverley Hidden Town Gardens
33 Fernleigh
46 Hillbark
74 Millgate House
76 Millview Cottage

You are always welcome at an NGS garden!

77 Neakins House
87 The Orchard
114 Whixley Gardens

July

19 **Cold Cotes (Every Saturday)**
26 **Dove Cottage Nursery Garden (Every Friday)**

Wednesday 2
56 Kelberdale
87 The Orchard

Friday 4
102 Shandy Hall Gardens (Evening)

Saturday 5
16 NEW Churchside

Sunday 6
16 NEW Churchside
47 Holly Croft
53 Jackson's Wold
97 The Ridings

Friday 11
92 Prospect House (Evening)

Saturday 12
12 NEW Bugthorpe Gardens
15 Cawood Gardens
52 Hunmanby School
59 Langton Farm (Evening)

Sunday 13
12 NEW Bugthorpe Gardens
15 Cawood Gardens
24 Dacre Banks & Summerbridge Gardens
29 Edgeholme
43 Havoc Hall
59 Langton Farm
82 Oatmill Cottage
89 Overthorpe J I & N School
111 Warley House Garden
115 NEW Windsong

Saturday 19
44 High Hall

Sunday 20
39 Goldsborough Hall
44 High Hall
48 54 Hollym Road
66 Low Sutton
75 Millrace Nursery
81 The Nursery
95 Rewela Cottage
99 Rudston House
105 Stamford Bridge Gardens

Wednesday 23
20 Combe Hay
41 The Grange
81 The Nursery

Friday 25
73 Mere'stead (Evening)

Sunday 27
33 Fernleigh
55 NEW The Jungle Garden
91 3 Pilmoor Cottages
93 Queensgate & Kitchen Lane Allotments

Havoc Hall

August

19 **Cold Cotes (Every Saturday)**
26 **Dove Cottage Nursery Garden (Every Friday)**

Wednesday 6
41 The Grange

Saturday 9
70 Mansion Cottage

Sunday 10
70 Mansion Cottage

Wednesday 13
14 Butterfield Heights
41 The Grange
79 NEW 2 Newlay Grove

Saturday 16
38 6 Fulwith Avenue

Sunday 17
38 6 Fulwith Avenue
62 Little Eden
75 Millrace Nursery

Sunday 31
33 Fernleigh
69 Manor House

September

19 **Cold Cotes (Every Saturday)**
26 **Dove Cottage Nursery Garden (Every Friday)**

Saturday 6
57 23 Lambert Road

Sunday 7
8 Boundary Cottage
9 Bridge Farm House
57 23 Lambert Road
68 Manor Farm
91 3 Pilmoor Cottages
106 Stillingfleet Lodge

Sunday 21
75 Millrace Nursery

February 2015

Wednesday 25
2 Austwick Hall

Gardens open to the public

13 Burton Agnes Hall & Gardens
21 Constable Burton Hall Gardens
53 Jackson's Wold
58 Land Farm
78 Newby Hall & Gardens
80 Norton Conyers
90 Parcevall Hall Gardens
96 RHS Garden Harlow Carr
101 Scampston Walled Garden
102 Shandy Hall Gardens
106 Stillingfleet Lodge
117 York Gate
119 The Yorkshire Arboretum

By appointment only

3 3 Bainton Close
10 Brook Farm
23 Cow Close Cottage
37 Friars Hill
63 Littlethorpe Manor
67 Lower Heugh Cottage Garden
100 Rustic Cottage
113 The White House

Also open by appointment

- **4** Basin Howe Farm
- **5** Beacon Hill House
- **7** Birstwith Hall
- **9** Bridge Farm House
- **11** Brookfield
- **12** Bugthorpe Gardens
- **12** 3 Church Walk, Bugthorpe Gardens
- **12** The Old Rectory, Bugthorpe Gardens
- **14** Butterfield Heights
- **15** 9 Anson Grove, Cawood Gardens
- **15** 21 Great Close, Cawood Gardens
- **19** Cold Cotes
- **22** The Court
- **24** Dacre Banks & Summerbridge Gardens
- **24** Riverside House, Dacre Banks & Summerbridge Gardens
- **31** Endcliffe Mount
- **32** Fawley House
- **33** Fernleigh
- **35** Firvale Allotment Garden
- **38** 6 Fulwith Avenue
- **39** Goldsborough Hall
- **41** The Grange
- **42** 16 Hallam Grange Croft
- **50** Hotham Hall
- **54** Jasmine House
- **55** The Jungle Garden
- **56** Kelberdale
- **59** Langton Farm
- **60** Linden House
- **61** Linden Lodge
- **62** Little Eden
- **65** Low Hall
- **66** Low Sutton
- **70** Mansion Cottage
- **71** Marston Grange
- **75** Millrace Nursery
- **76** Millview Cottage
- **86** Omega
- **87** The Orchard
- **91** 3 Pilmoor Cottages
- **92** Prospect House
- **95** Rewela Cottage
- **97** The Ridings
- **99** Rudston House
- **104** Skipwith Hall
- **105** Daneswell House, Stamford Bridge Gardens
- **105** Stamford Bridge Gardens
- **109** Terrington House
- **114** Ash Tree House, Whixley Gardens
- **114** Cobble Cottage, Whixley Gardens
- **114** Lydiate House, Whixley Gardens
- **116** Woodlands Cottage
- **118** Yorke House

The Gardens

1 ACORN COTTAGE

50 Church Street, Boston Spa LS23 6DN. Andrew Froggatt & Tim Froggatt. *1m SE of Wetherby. Off A1 on A659 Church St opp Central Garage.* **Adm £2, chd free. Sun 27 Apr (12.30-5). Combined with Four Gables adm £4.**
Small, well-established alpine garden full of spring delights. Three generations of the family have collected the plants and bulbs, and these have recently been rearranged and the garden significantly altered for ease of maintenance and access without losing the character and uniqueness of this fine collection.

Qni
The Queen's Nursing Institute
Garden visiting is good for you – and helps others too!

2 AUSTWICK HALL

Town Head Lane, Austwick, nr Settle LA2 8BS. James E Culley & Michael Pearson, 015242 51794, austwickhall@austwick.org, www.austwickhall.co.uk. *5m W of Settle. Leave the A65 to Austwick. Pass the PO on R, Gamecock Inn on L. Take first L onto Town Head Lane. Parking on Town Head Lane.* Home-made teas. **Adm £3.50, chd free. Wed 26 Feb (12-4), Wed 25 Feb 2015.**
Set in the dramatic limestone scenery of the Dales the garden nestles into a steeply wooded hillside. Extensive drifts of common single and double snowdrops are an impressive sight with examples of over 50 other varieties. Sculptures along the trail add further interest.Woodland paths may be slippery in wet weather so sensible footwear is recommended.

3 NEW 3 BAINTON CLOSE

Beverley HU17 7DL. Mrs Elaine Thornton, 01482 861643. *Located off New Walk opp Police Station. If using SAT NAV, please use address and not the postcode, as this will take you to next lane.* **Adm £2.50, chd free. Visitors welcome by appt 16 to 23 Feb.**
Small town garden with a variety of spring flowers incl hellebores and a collection of approx 150 varieties of snowdrop which will be of particular interest to 'Galanthophiles'.

4 NEW BASIN HOWE FARM

Cockmoor Road, Sawdon, Scarborough YO13 9EG. Mr & Mrs Richard & Heather Mullin, 01723 850180, info@basinhowefarm.co.uk, www.basinhowefarm.co.uk. *Turn off A170 between Scarborough & Pickering at Brompton by Sawdon follow sign to Sawdon. Basin Howe Farm 1½ m above Sawdon village on the LH-side.* Home-made teas. **Adm £4, chd free. Sun 29 June (11-5). Visitors also welcome by appt May to July, not Saturdays.**
Overlooking the Wolds on a limestone ridge this site has a bronze age burial mound. These gardens have a lovely atmosphere. 3 acres of garden with box parterre with seasonal planting, rose garden, 2 ponds, herbaceous bedding and elevated viewing deck with Pod summer house. Orchard and woodland shelter belt, lawns and shrubs. Paved seating areas but gravel paths. Maintained by owners. Wheelchair Access is possible to most areas but a helper is required. Paths are gravel and grass.

5 BEACON HILL HOUSE

Langbar, nr Ilkley LS29 0EU. Mr & Mrs H Boyle, 01943 607544, humphrey@humphreyboyle.co.uk. *4m NW of Ilkley. 1¼ m SE of A59 at Bolton Bridge.* Home-made teas. **Adm £3.50, chd free (share to Riding for the Disabled). Wed 14 May (1.30-5). Visitors also welcome by appt Apr to June.**
Look over the garden wall onto a grouse moor. This 7-acre 'intake', steeply sloping but gardened since 1848, is a spring paradise with early rhododendrons, magnolias and bulbs. Roses, large scented rhododendrons and borders take over, some unusual trees, an established liriodendron, pterostyrax, hoherias and several species of eucryphia. Small kitchen garden, orchard and pond.

Visit a garden in your own time – look for by appointment gardens

Marston Grange

Mansion Cottage

GROUP OPENING

6 BEVERLEY HIDDEN TOWN GARDENS

Beverley HU17 8JH. *Centre of Beverley.* **Combined adm £3.50, chd free. Sat 28, Sun 29 June (10-5).**

30 RAILWAY STREET
Wendy Munday

32 RAILWAY STREET
M Williamson

34 RAILWAY STREET
Sharon Clay

16 ST MATTHEWS COURT
Annegret Aveyard

Four town gardens. 16 St Matthews Court: front garden overlooking spectacular West Towers of Beverley Minster. A rich collection of hellebores, tulips, grasses and other spring flowers. Hidden garden at back features many perennials, roses, climbers, annuals and grasses, Mediterranean area with different succulents and small pond with water plants. Has been described as giving a Continental feel with its modern art work. 30 Railway Street: through spectacular 'triumphal arch' is an amazing display of climbers, pots and water feature. 32 Railway Street: after extensive building work, a newly planted garden. 34 Railway Street: paved, creatively planted courtyard. All 3 Railway Street gardens have a S aspect and tender plants thrive. The town has many tearooms.

7 BIRSTWITH HALL

High Birstwith, Harrogate HG3 2JW. Sir James & Lady Aykroyd, 01423 770250, info@birstwithhall.co.uk. *5m NW of Harrogate. Between Hampsthwaite & Birstwith villages, close to A59 Harrogate/Skipton Rd.* Home-made teas. **Adm £4, chd free. Sun 22 June (2-5). Visitors also welcome by appt May to July, groups and coaches welcome.**
Large 8 acre garden nestling in secluded Yorkshire dale with formal garden and ornamental orchard, extensive lawns, picturesque stream, large pond and Victorian greenhouse.

8 BOUNDARY COTTAGE

Seaton Ross, York YO42 4NF. Roger Brook, www.nodiggardener.co.uk. *5m SW of Pocklington. From A64 York take Hull exit and immed. B1228, Approx 10m to Seaton Ross. From M62 Howden N on B1228. From A1079 follow Seaton Ross.* Light refreshments. **Adm £4, chd free. Sun 7 Sept (11-4).**
Lecturer and creator of Bolton Percy churchyard garden, Roger Brook's own no-dig garden. 1500 different plant varieties, many rare, provide colour all yr round. The acre garden has numerous and varied intimate features, visually connected in sweeping views. Horticulturally unorthodox, especially the fruit and vegetables, the overall effect is dramatic. The garden holds the National Collection of Dicentra. Very friendly rheas in the field next door! Artist in the garden. Access to all parts of the garden. Some pushing required on fescue lawns. WC access up a step.
NCH

9 BRIDGE FARM HOUSE

Long Lane, Great Heck, nr Selby DN14 0BE. Barbara & Richard Ferrari, 01977 661277, barbaraferrari@mypostoffice.co.uk. *6m S of Selby, 3m E M62 J34. At M62 J34 take A19 to Selby, at r'about turn E to Snaith on A645. R at T-lights, L at T-junction onto Main St, past Church, to T-junction, cross to car park.* Tea in church opp. **Adm £3, chd free. Sun 2 Mar, Mon 26 May, Sun 7 Sept (12-4.30). Visitors also welcome by appt Feb to June.**
2-acre garden on sandy soil, divided by hedges, to house a varied collection of plants, many rare and unusual, providing year round interest, starting in Spring with a large collection of named snowdrops. Including mature trees, bog, gravel, ponds, long double mixed borders, hens, compost heaps and wildlife.

10 NEW BROOK FARM

Elstronwick, Hull HU12 9BP. Mrs Janet Dolling, 01964 670191. *10m E of Hull city centre. Go N on Hedon to Withernsea Rd. Turn off L before Burton Pidsea. Go down Back Lane. Garden at junction of Elstronwick & Danthorpe, next to beck bridge.* **Adm £3, chd free. Visitors welcome by appt Feb to May, for groups between 4 and 25.**
Plantsman's garden with large collection of Hellebores. 3/4 acre with borders, gravel and formal areas. Many species of snowdrops, hellebores and narcissus, tulips and peonies. Large vegetable and fruit garden. Wooded area with large collection of woodland plants. Flowering and ornamental trees.

11 BROOKFIELD

Jew Lane, Oxenhope, nr Keighley BD22 9HS. Mrs R L Belsey, 01535 643070. *5m SW of Keighley. From Keighley take A629 (Halifax) Fork R A6033 towards Haworth & Oxenhope turn L at Xrds into village. Turn R (Jew Lane) at bottom of hill.* Home-made teas. **Adm £3, chd free. Sun 1, Wed 4 June (1.30-5). Visitors also welcome by appt May to July.**
1-acre, intimate garden, incl large

pond with island and mallards. Many varieties of primula, candelabra and florindae; azaleas and rhododendrons. Unusual trees and shrubs, screes, greenhouses and conservatory. Series of island beds. Children's quiz and garden notes 'A walk round the garden'.

A hidden treasure in Betjeman's 'prettiest suburb' . . .

GROUP OPENING

12 NEW BUGTHORPE GARDENS

York YO41 1QG. Natalie Verow, 01759 368444, natalieverow@aol.com. *4m E of Stamford Bridge, A166, village of Bugthorpe.* Light refreshments The Old Rectory. **Combined adm £5, chd free. Sat 12, Sun 13 July (10.30-4.30). Visitors also welcome by appt July (for both gardens), dates near weekend opening, max 15.**

NEW 3 CHURCH WALK
York. Barrie Creaser & David Harding
Visitors also welcome by appt, July near weekend opening, max 15.
01759 358152
barriecreaser@gmail.com

THE OLD RECTORY
Dr & Mrs P W Verow.
House 1st on R from A166 (York direction)
Visitors also welcome by appt July, near weekend opening, max 15.
01759 368444
natalieverow@aol.com

Two contrasting gardens situated in the small village of Bugthorpe.
The Old Rectory is a ¾ acre garden with views of the Yorkshire Wolds. Mixed borders, ponds, stumpery, terrace,summerhouse, courtyard and many mature trees. Raised vegetable beds. Artist in the garden and herbaceous perennials for sale.
3 Church Walk a cottage garden with herbaceous borders, wildlife pond, trees, shrubs and kitchen garden designed by the current owners.

13 ◆ BURTON AGNES HALL & GARDENS

Burton Agnes, Driffield YO25 4NB. Mrs S Cunliffe-Lister, 01262 490324, www.burtonagnes.com. *Burton Agnes. Between Driffield and Bridlington on A614 in village of Burton Agnes. Parking signposted.* Light refreshments. **Adm to Gardeners Fair incl adm to gardens. Sat 7, Sun 8 June (11-5) Gardeners Fair. Donation to NGS. For other opening times and information, please phone or see garden website.**

Beautiful award-winning gardens of Burton Agnes Hall are home to 3,000 different plant species, herbaceous borders, a jungle garden, potager, coloured gardens, giant games, a maze and collection of campanulas. Surrounded by lawns, topiary yews, fountains and a woodland walk. Collections of hardy geraniums, clematis, penstemons and unusual perennials..

14 BUTTERFIELD HEIGHTS

4 Park Crescent, Guiseley, Leeds LS20 8EL. Vicky & Trevor Harris, 07852 163733, vicky.harris2@btinternet.com. *11m NW of Leeds. From Guiseley A65 (Otley-Leeds) A6038 towards Shipley (Bradford Rd). Park Crescent ½ m on L. Park on Bradford Rd or surrounding streets.* Home-made teas. **Adm £3, chd free. Wed 13 Aug (11-5). Visitors also welcome by appt Aug, for groups of 8+.**

Hardy plantswoman's garden with view towards Otley Chevin. Restoration of this dark, damp plot since 1998 revealed 1930s landscape on 3 levels linked by steps. Sumptuous planting for late summer colour, unusual herbaceous plants, shrubs and trees. Winding gravel paths and tall perennials, secluded Japanese corner. Small pond, box parterre, new thugs border and steep steps to paved area. Featured in Amateur Gardening and the Yorkshire Post.

GROUP OPENING

15 CAWOOD GARDENS

Cawood, Nr Selby YO8 3UG. *On B1223 5m N of Selby & 7m SE of Tadcaster. Between York & A1 on B1222. Village maps given at all gardens.* Home-made teas at 9 Anson Grove and 21 Great Close. **Combined adm £5, chd free. Sat 12, Sun 13 July (12-5).**

9 ANSON GROVE
Tony & Brenda Finnigan
Visitors also welcome by appt June to Aug.
01757 268888
beeart@btinternet.com

21 GREAT CLOSE
David & Judy Jones
Visitors also welcome by appt June to Aug.
01757 268571
dave-judyjones@hotmail.co.uk

NEW THE PIGEONCOTE
2a Wistowgate. Maria Parks & Angela Darlington

These three contrasting gardens in an attractive historic village are linked by a pretty riverside walk to the C11 church and Memorial garden and across the Castle Garth to the remains of Cawood Castle.
9 Anson Grove is a small garden with tranquil pools and secluded sitting places. Narrow winding paths and raised areas give views over oriental-style pagoda, bridge and Zen garden.
21 Great Close is a flower arranger's garden, designed and built by the owners. Interesting trees and shrubs combine with herbaceous borders incl many grasses. Two ponds are joined by a stream, winding paths take you to the vegetable garden and summerhouse, then back to the colourful terrace for views across the garden and countryside beyond. The small walled garden, Pigeoncote at 2 Wistowgate is surrounded by historic C17 buildings. A balanced design of formal box hedging, cottage garden planting and creative use of grasses. Angled brick pathways lead to shaded seating areas with all day sunny views. Crafts and paintings on sale at 9 Anson Grove. Limited wheelchair access to all gardens.

Millview Cottage

© Suzie Gibbons

16 NEW CHURCHSIDE
41 Station Road, Wressle, Selby YO8 6ES. Suzanne York. *5m from J37 M62, 6½ m from A19/A63 junction. From the A63 Loftsome Bridge Coaching House, travel towards Wressle/Breighton. Churchside is directly in front on 1st sharp RH-bend.* Tea. **Adm £3, chd free. Sats, Suns 7, 8, 21, 22 June; 5, 6 July (1-5).**
Four year old cottage garden. ¼ acre full of herbaceous perennials and several garden areas to create interest for every family member. Rose rope, large cottage front garden, raised vegetable beds, small wildlife pond and new raised fish pond. Wooded retreat planted with yellow and white scheme. Summerhouse, Wendy house and sitting areas. The path amongst the front flower border cannot be accessed by wheelchair users. WC facilities are across a 20cm step and with limited space.

17 THE CIRCLES GARDEN
8 Stocksmoor Road, Midgley, nr Wakefield WF4 4JQ. Joan Gaunt. *Equidistant from Huddersfield, Wakefield & Barnsley, W of M1. Turn off A637 in Midgley at the Black Bull PH (sharp bend) onto B6117 (Stocksmoor Rd). Please park on L adjacent to houses.* Home-made teas. **Adm £3, chd free. Sun 18 May (1.30-5).**
First May opening of this organic and self-sustaining plantswoman's ½ - acre garden on gently sloping site overlooking fields, woods and nature reserve opposite. Designed and maintained by owner. Interesting herbaceous, bulb and shrub plantings linked by grass and gravel paths, a woodland area with mature trees, spring and summer meadows, fernery, greenhouse, fruit trees, viewing terrace with pots. Also, around 100 hellebores grown from my own seed. South African plants, hollies, small bulbs are particular interests also many hellebores grown from own seed.

18 CLIFTON CASTLE
Ripon HG4 4AB. Lord & Lady Downshire. *2m N of Masham. On rd to Newton-le-Willows & Richmond. Gates on L next to red telephone box.* Home-made teas. **Adm £4, chd free. Suns 13 Apr; 8 June (2-5).**
Fine views, river walks, wooded pleasure grounds with bridges and follies. Cascades, wild flower meadow and C19 walled kitchen garden. Gravel paths and steep slopes to river.

19 COLD COTES
Cold Cotes Road, nr Kettlesing, Harrogate HG3 2LW. Penny Jones, Ed Loft, Doreen & Joanna Russell, 01423 770937, info@coldcotes.com, www.coldcotes.com. *7m W of Harrogate. Off A59. After Black Bull PH turn R to Menwith Hill/Darley.* Light refreshments. **Adm £3.50, chd free. Every Sat 3 May to 27 Sept (11-5). Visitors also welcome by appt May to Sept, for groups of 20+.**
This large peaceful garden with expansive views is at ease in its rural setting. Year round interest moves through a series of discrete gardens incl formal areas, stream-side walk, bog garden. Oudolf-influenced sweeping herbaceous borders peak in late summer. Chatto-influenced woodland garden underplanted with masses of bulbs and perennials for spring to autumn interest. Tearoom and nursery specialising in shade and moisture-loving perennials.

Herbaceous perennials and several garden areas to create interest for every family member . . .

20 COMBE HAY
Stepney Drive, Scarborough YO12 5DJ. The George Edward Smart Homes. *1m W of Scarborough. From Whitby take A171. After Scarborough Hospital follow sign for A170 onto Stepney Drive. From Thirsk follow A170 to sixth form college, L at r'about 150 metres on R. A64 into Scarborough L onto A171 follow signs for Thirsk A170. At r'about L Stepney Drive..* Tea. **Adm £3.50, chd free. Wed 23 July (10-4).**
Situated in attractive and tranquil landscape grounds of approx 4½ acres. The award-winning garden is designed for relaxation, with summerhouses and seating areas to admire the large variety of trees and shrubs/colourful herbaceous/annual borders. Other features of interest incl orchard, vegetable garden and pond.

21 ◆ CONSTABLE BURTON HALL GARDENS
Constable Burton, nr Leyburn DL8 5LJ. Mr Charles Wyvill, 01677 450428, www.constableburton.com. *3m E of Leyburn. Constable Burton Village. On A684, 6m W of A1.* **Adm £4, chd 50p (5-16). For opening times and information, please phone or see garden website.**
Large romantic garden with terraced woodland walks. Garden trails, shrubs, roses and water garden. Display of daffodils and over 6,500 tulips planted annually amongst extensive borders. Fine John Carr house (not open) set in splendour of Wensleydale countryside. Tulip Festival each year on the first May Bank Holiday weekend, Constable Burton Hall Gardens plays host to a magnificent Tulip Festival. Sponsored by Chelsea award winning nursery Bloms Bulbs, over 6,500 traditional and new variant tulips are planted throughout the gardens. Opening 22 March - 14 Sept 9am - 6pm.

22 THE COURT
Humber Road, North Ferriby HU14 3DW. Guy & Liz Slater, 01482 633609, liz@guyslater.karoo.co.uk. *7m W of Hull. Travelling E on A63 towards Hull, follow sign for N Ferriby. Through village to Xrds with war memorial, turn R & follow rd to T-junction with Humber Rd. Turn L & immed R into cul-de-sac, last house on L.* Home-made teas. **Adm £3, chd free. Sun 1 June (1-5). Visitors also welcome by appt Jan to Sept.**
Romantic and restful with hidden seating areas offering different vistas. Roses and clematis scrambling up walls and trees. 2 summerhouses, small pond and waterfall with secluded arbours and historical items. A long tunnel of wisteria, clematis and laburnum leads to a little path with Betula jacquemontii, small stumpery, and grown up swing.

Littlethorpe Manor

23 COW CLOSE COTTAGE

Stripe Lane, Hartwith, Harrogate HG3 3EY. William Moore & John Wilson, 01423 779813, cowclose1@btinternet.com. *8m NW of Harrogate. From A61(Harrogate-Ripon) at Ripley take B6165 to Pateley Bridge. 1m beyond Burnt Yates turn R signed Hartwith onto Stripe Lane. Parking available.* **Adm £5, chd free. Visitors welcome by appt July to Sept, refreshments available on request.**

2/3 -acre recently redeveloped country garden on sloping site with stream and far reaching views. Large borders with drifts of interesting, well-chosen, later flowering summer perennials and some grasses contrasting with woodland shade and streamside plantings. Gravel path leading to vegetable area. Terrace and seating with views of the garden and beyond. New orchard and meadow walk to view-point.

GROUP OPENING

24 DACRE BANKS & SUMMERBRIDGE GARDENS

Nidderdale HG3 4EW, 01423 780456, pat@yorkehouse.co.uk. *4m SE of Pateley Bridge, 10m NW of Harrogate, 10m N of Otley on B6451 & B6165. Parking at each garden. Maps available to show garden locations.* Home-made teas at Yorke House & Low Hall. **Combined adm £7, chd free. Sun 13 July (11-5). Visitors also welcome by appt June to Aug, for groups of 10+.**

LOW HALL
Mrs P A Holliday
(See separate entry)

RIVERSIDE HOUSE
Joy Stanton
Visitors also welcome by appt June to July, adm £4 per person, groups of 10+.
01423 780596
joy.stanton21@gmail.com

WOODLANDS COTTAGE
Mr & Mrs Stark
(See separate entry)

YORKE HOUSE
Tony & Pat Hutchinson
(See separate entry)

Dacre Banks and Summerbridge Gardens are situated in the beautiful countryside of Nidderdale and designed to take advantage of the scenic Dales landscape. The gardens are linked by an attractive walk along the valley and may be accessed individually by car. Low Hall has a romantic walled garden set on different levels around the historic C17 family home (not open) with extensive herbaceous borders, shrubs, climbing roses and tranquil water garden. Riverside House is a mysterious waterside garden on many levels, supporting shade-loving plants and incorporates a Victorian folly, fernery, courtyard and naturalistic riverside plantings. Woodlands Cottage is designed to harmonise with boulder-strewn woodland whilst also having varied areas of formal and informal planting, a wild flower meadow and productive fruit and vegetable garden. Yorke House has colour-themed borders, attractive waterside plantings and secluded millennium garden full of fragrant plants and rambling roses. Visitors welcome to use orchard picnic area at Yorke House. Featured in Harrogate Advertiser.

25 DEVONSHIRE MILL

Canal Lane, Pocklington, York YO42 1NN. Sue & Chris Bond, www.devonshiremill.co.uk. *1m S of Pocklington. Situated on Canal Lane, Pocklington off A1079 at The Wellington Oak PH.* Home-made teas. **Adm £3, chd free. Sun 16 Feb (11-4.30).**

Early spring features double snowdrops (mainly galanthus flore pleno) in old orchards, hellebores and ferns in a woodland setting. The house (not open) is a 200yr old Grade II listed watermill. An intimate garden with different areas and mill stream. Organic principles used to encourage wildlife. Productive vegetable gardens with raised beds, polytunnel, greenhouses, hen run and well-stocked herbaceous borders.

26 DOVE COTTAGE NURSERY GARDEN

Shibden Hall Road, nr Halifax HX3 9XA. Kim & Stephen Rogers, www.dovecottagenursery.co.uk. *1m E Halifax. From Halifax take A58 turn L signed Claremount, cont over bridge, cont 1/2 m. J26 M62- A58 Halifax. Drive 4m. L turn at Pet Shop down Tanhouse Hill, cont 1/2 m.* Tea. **Adm £3, chd free. Every Fri 6 June to 26 Sept (10-5).**

Hedges and green oak gates enclose 1/3 -acre sloping garden, generously planted by nursery owners over 16yrs. A beautiful mix of late summer perennials and grasses. Winding paths and plenty of seats incl a romantic tulip arbour. Plants for sale in nursery. Wildlife friendly. Featured in Gardens Illustrated and on BBC Great British Garden Revival.

27 34 DOVER ROAD

Hunters Bar, Sheffield S11 8RH. Marian Simpson. *1½ m SW of city centre. From A61 (ring rd) A625 Moore St/Eccleshall Rd for approx 1m. Dover Rd on R.* Home-made teas. **Adm £3, chd free. Sun 25 May (10.30-4.30). Also open 16 Hallam Grange Croft.**

Colourful, small town garden packed with interest and drama, combining formality with exotic exuberance. Attractive alpine area replacing old driveway, many interesting containers and well-stocked borders. Conservatory, seating areas and lawns complement unusual plants and planting combinations. Featured in Yorkshire Post, Sheffield Telegraph and on BBC Radio Sheffield.

28 DOWTHORPE HALL & HORSE PASTURE COTTAGE

Skirlaugh, Hull HU11 5AE. Mr & Mrs J Holtby, 01964 562235, john.holtby@farming.co.uk, www.dowthorpehall.com. *6m N of Hull, 8m E of Beverley. From Hull A165 towards Bridlington. Through Ganstead & Coniston. 1m S of Skirlaugh on R, (long drive white railings & sign at drive end).* **Adm £5, chd free. Sun 8 June (10-5).**

Dowthorpe Hall: 3½ acres, large herbaceous borders, lawns, shady area, pond with bridge, scree garden, hardy garden, orchards and vegetable potager. Horse Pasture Cottage:small cottage garden, herbaceous border and woodland water feature. Gravel, lawns, no steps.

29 EDGEHOLME

Stock Lane, Warley, Halifax HX2 7RW. Mrs S L Ryan. *2m W of Halifax. From Halifax take A546 (Burnley). 1m after A58/A646 Junction (King Cross) turn R (Windleroyd Lane) Park on rd before Warley Village.* Home-made teas. **Combined adm £5, chd free with Warley House. Sun 13 July (1-5).**

Terraced country house garden complementing 1910 Arts and Crafts house (not open). Colourful mixed herbaceous borders, paths and steps link the lower and upper areas. Natural hillside stream enters via stone trough, flowing into formal pond and rill then descending to large informal bog garden in a shrub and woodland setting.

30 ELLERKER HOUSE

Everingham, York YO42 4JA. Mrs R Los & Mr M Wright, www.ellerkerhouse.weebly.com. *15m SE of York. 5½ m from Pocklington. On rd towards Harswell on R.* Home-made teas. **Adm £4, chd free. Sat 19 Apr (12-5).**

5 acres of garden on sandy soil. Lots of spring bulbs, mature trees, formal lawn and extensive grass area. Woodland walkway around lake. Traditional oak and thatched breeze hut. Several seating areas with views of the garden. Rose archway, herbaceous borders. Garden open and Rare Plant Fair.

Oak seating placed throughout the garden invites quiet contemplation a place to 'lift the spirit' . . .

31 NEW ENDCLIFFE MOUNT

89 Endcliffe Vale Road, Sheffield S10 3ET. Dr Lyn Challands, challands3kids@aol.com. *1m W of Sheffield city centre nr Botanical Gardens. From ring rd, A625 Ecclesall Rd to Hunters Bar r'about, then Brocco Bank & take 6th L turn. From A57 Manchester Rd, take Fulwood Rd then 4th L.* **Evening Opening £3, chd free, Home-made teas, Sun 22 June (5-7). Visitors also welcome by appt Apr to June, mornings or evenings only, max 30.**

A hidden treasure in Betjeman's 'prettiest suburb'. From a shady wooded area with a natural bog and wildlife pond, this garden opens out to sweeping lawns, a striking deep herbaceous border beside the drive and a sunny butterfly-friendly terrace. In contrast, the Lutyens inspired walled rear garden is intimate and romantic with lush planting within formal structures. Ground floor of house opens for the day as an art gallery. Pond dipping (under adult supervision) encouraged. Also open adjacent gardens under Broomhill Festival. The limestone chipping drive may cause problems for light wheelchairs, but is accessible to heavy or motorised chairs.

32 FAWLEY HOUSE

7 Nordham, North Cave HU15 2LT. Mr & Mrs T Martin, 01430 422266, louisem200@hotmail.co.uk, www.nordhamcottages.co.uk. *15m W of Hull. M62 E, J38 turn L to North Cave Wetlands, then R where rd bends to L. Car park on L after bend, beyond Fawley House, along Nordahm.* **Adm £4, chd free. Fri 13 June (2-7); Sun 15 June (12-5); Mon 16 to Fri 20 June (10-4). Visitors also welcome by appt Feb to Mar.**

Tiered, 2½ -acre garden with lawns, mature trees, formal hedging and gravel pathways. Lavender beds, mixed shrub/herbaceous borders, hot borders. Apple espaliers, pears, soft fruit, vegetable and herb gardens. Terrace with pergola and vines. Sunken garden with white border. Woodland with naturalistic planting and spring bulbs. Quaker well, stream and spring area. New stone bed in the hot coloured garden and new wildlife hide in secret garden. For accomodation please see website. **Exhibition of art from East Riding Artists 'Art in the Garden' in June.** The art displayed will be from artists in the NGS East Yorkshire gardens from 2013. Featured in The Journal. Partial wheelchair access, pea gravel on terrace and at top of garden.

33 FERNLEIGH

9 Meadowhead Avenue, Meadowhead, Sheffield S8 7RT. Mr & Mrs C Littlewood, 01142 747234, christine@fernleighs8.plus.com. *4m S of Sheffield city centre. From Sheffield city centre. A61, A6102, B6054 r'about,exit B6054. 1st R Greenhill Ave, 2nd R. From M1 J33, A630 to A6102, then as above.* Light refreshments. **Adm £2.50, chd free. Suns 29 June; 27 July; 31 Aug (1-7). Visitors also welcome by appt Apr to Aug, coach drop-off only.**

Plantswoman's ⅓ -acre cottage style garden. Large variety of unusual plants set in differently planted sections to provide all-yr interest. Auricula theatre and paved area for drought resistant plants in pots. Seating areas to view different aspects of garden. Patio, gazebo and greenhouse. Miniature log cabin with living roof. Sempervivum, alpine displays and wildlife 'hotel'. 'Animal Search' for children. Featured in Sheffield Star, Telegraph and Gazette.

34 FIR TREES COTTAGE

Stokesley TS9 5LD. Helen & Mark Bainbridge, www.firtreespelargoniums.co.uk. *1m S of Stokesley. On A172, signed Pelargonium Exhibition.* Home-made teas. **Adm £3.50, chd free. Sat 17 May (2-4).**

1-acre mixed shrubaceous borders, large rockeries, spring bulbs, species tulips, mature conifers, fritillaries, erythroniums and secluded ornamental pond. Hosta collection and garden sculpture. Tranquil garden surrounded by farmland with views to Cleveland Hills and Roseberry Topping. Designed and maintained by owners since 1992 with low maintenance in mind. Pelargonium Exhibition - features mature award-winning show plants. Over 85 RHS gold medals on display around glass house. Gravel drive.

35 FIRVALE ALLOTMENT GARDEN

Winney Hill, Harthill, nr Worksop S26 7YN. Don & Dot Witton, 01909 771366, donshardyeuphorbias @btopenworld.com, www.euphorbias.co.uk. *12m SE of Sheffield, 6m W of Worksop. M1 J31 A57 to Worksop. Turn R to Harthill. Allotments at S end of village, 26 Casson Drive at N end on Northlands Estate.* Home-made teas at 26 Casson Drive. **Adm £2.50, chd free. Sun 4 May (1-4). Visitors also welcome by appt Apr to July.**

Large allotment containing 13 island beds displaying 500+ herbaceous perennials incl the National Collection of hardy Euphorbias with approx 100 varieties in flower. Organic vegetable garden. Refreshments, WC, plant sales at 26 Casson Drive - small garden with mixed borders, shade and seaside garden.

NCH

36 FOUR GABLES

Oaks Lane, Boston Spa, nr Wetherby LS23 6DS. David & Anne Watts, 01937 845592, info@fourgables.co.uk, www.fourgables.co.uk. *2m SE of Wetherby off A659 in Boston Spa on the R 300yds before the Church. Please park in the Church car park 200 meters away from the garden. Please do not park on main rd.* Home-made teas. **Adm £3, chd free. Sun 27 Apr (12.30-5). Combined with Acorn Cottage, adm £4.**

Many surprises in this ½ -acre garden surrounding Grade II listed Arts and Crafts home (not open). View 7 different gardens in one visit. Fine specimen trees, hellebores, wood anemone, dicentra, tree peony, aquilegia and fritillaria. Ponds, deep well, 30ft. wood sculpture, and various garden features. Teas indoors if raining. Attractive courtyard with seating areas and raised beds.

37 FRIARS HILL

Sinnington YO62 6SL. Mr & Mrs C J Baldwin, 01751 432179, friars.hill@abelgratis.co.uk. *4m W of Pickering. On A170.* **Adm £3, chd free. Visitors welcome by appt Mar to Aug.**

Plantswoman's 1¾ -acre garden containing over 2500 varieties of perennials and bulbs, with yr-round colour. Early interest with hellebores, bulbs and woodland plants. Herbaceous beds. Hostas, delphiniums, old roses and stone troughs. Excellent Autumn colour.

38 6 FULWITH AVENUE

Harrogate HG2 8HR. Vanda & David Hartley, 01423 815412, vandahartley100@yahoo.co.uk. *1½ m S of Harrogate. A61 (Harrogate-Leeds). From town centre straight over 2 r'abouts & main T-lights. 3rd L (Fulwith Mill Lane), Ist R.* Light refreshments. **Adm £2.50, chd free. Sat 16 Aug (1-5); Sun 17 Aug (12-4). Visitors also welcome by appt Aug to Sept groups of 10+.**

From wall fountain to gothic folly, waterfall to Japanese topiary, this small town garden has interest at every turn. The multi-layered planting provides a constantly changing tapestry of texture and colour which is at its best in late summer.

39 GOLDSBOROUGH HALL

Church Street, Goldsborough HG5 8NR. Mr & Mrs M Oglesby, 01423 867321, info@goldsboroughhall.com, www.goldsboroughhall.com. *2m SE of Knaresborough. 3m W of A1M. Off A59 (York-Harrogate) carpark 300yds past PH on R.* Cream teas. **Adm £5, chd free (share to St Mary's Church, Goldsborough). Sun 23 Mar (12-4); Sun 20 July (12-5). Visitors and groups also welcome by appt Feb to Oct.**

Previously opened for NGS from 1928-30 and now beautifully restored by present owners (re-opened in 2010). 11-acre garden and formal landscaped grounds in parkland setting and Grade II*, C17 house, former residence of the late HRH Princess Mary, daughter of George V and Queen Mary. Gertrude Jekyll inspired replanted 120ft double herbaceous borders and rose garden. ¼ -m lime tree walk planted by royalty circa 1920 underplanted with 50,000 naturalised daffodils. Woodland walk and specimen trees. St Mary's Church also open. Featured in local and national newspapers and magazines. Gravel paths and some steep slopes.

40 THE GRANARY

Langbaurgh Grange, Great Ayton, Middlesbrough TS9 6QQ. Helen Jones. *¼ m W of Great Ayton. Entrance to Langbaurgh Grange in trees on S side of B1292 ¼ m from junction with A173, (Sat Navs sometimes misleading) The Granary is furthest building from rd. Follow signs for parking..* Home-made teas. **Adm £3.50, chd free. Sun 15 June (2-5).**

A plantswoman's much-loved country garden reclaimed from ⅙ -acre brown field site over the last 20 yrs. Narrow paths lead through distinct areas separated by windbreak hedges, each having its own mood. Varied planting is influenced by local conditions as well as the owner's interest in plant-hunting and photography.

41 THE GRANGE

Carla Beck Lane, Carleton in Craven, Skipton BD23 3BU. Mr & Mrs R N Wooler, 07740 639135, margaret.wooler@hotmail.com. *1½ m SW of Skipton. Turn off A56 (Skipton-Clitheroe) into Carlton. Keep L at Swan PH, continue to end of village then turn R into Carla Beck Lane*. Home-made teas. **Adm £5, chd free (share to Sue Ryder Care Manorlands Hospice). Weds 23 July; 6, 13 Aug (12.30-4.30). Visitors also welcome by appt July to Aug for groups of 20+, adm incl guided tour and refreshments.**

Over 4 acres set in the grounds of Victorian house (not open) with mature trees and panoramic views towards The Gateway to the Dales. The garden has been restored by the owners over the last 2 decades with many areas of interest being added to the original footprint. Bountiful herbaceous borders with many unusual species, rose walk, parterre, mini-meadows and water features. Large greenhouse and raised vegetable beds. Oak seating placed throughout the garden invites quiet contemplation, a place to 'lift the spirit'. Gravel paths and steps.

42 16 HALLAM GRANGE CROFT

Fulwood, Sheffield S10 4BP. Tricia & Alistair Fraser, 0114 230 6508, tricia.fraser@talktalk.net. *Approx 4m SW of Sheffield city centre. Follow A57 (Glossop). 1½ m after University turn L after petrol station. After 1m turn L (at top of hill) and follow signs*. Tea. **Adm £2.50, chd free. Sun 25 May (12.30-4.30). Also open 34 Dover Road. Visitors also welcome by appt May to Sept, min entry charge for 10 people applies.**

Developed over 20yrs, a plantswoman's SE-facing sloping wildlife-friendly garden. Backed by mature trees with established perennial and shrub planting including many unusual hardy geraniums. Shady areas, pond, summerhouse, greenhouse and vegetable plots. Raised bed, rockery and decking area feature alpines and sun-loving perennials. Featured in Sheffield Profile Magazine, Yorkshire Post and Yorkshire Ridings Magazine.

Bridge Farm House

43 HAVOC HALL

York Rd, Oswaldkirk, York YO62 5XY. David & Maggie Lis, www.havochall.co.uk. *21m N of York. On B1363, 1st house on R as you enter Oswaldkirk from S and last house on L as you leave village from N*. Home-made teas. **Adm £4, chd free. Sun 13 July (1-5).**

Started in 2009, comprising 8 areas incl knot, herbaceous, mixed shrub and flower gardens, courtyard, vegetable area and orchard, woodland walk and large lawned area with hornbeam trees and hedging. To the S is a 2-acre wild flower meadow and small lake. Some steps but these can be avoided.

44 HIGH HALL

St Stephen's Road, Steeton, nr Keighley BD20 6SB. Roger & Christine Lambert, 01535 657060. *3m W of Keighley. Enter Steeton from A629. Turn R at lights & R after 100yds & down St St Rd. No parking at house except disabled. Follow signs for parking in village*. Home-made teas. **Adm £3.50, chd free. Sat 19, Sun 20 July (11-5).**

2-acre surprising suburban Arts and Crafts garden and historic house (not open) adjacent to St Stephen's Church. Formal walled garden with tanks, pond, belvedere, pergola, dovecote, summerhouse and ancient yew, herbaceous planting in formal beds connected by gravel paths. Walled kitchen garden with vegetable beds and fruit trees. Natural woodland area and small croquet lawn. Historical notes available. Exhibition of Alexander Keighley photographs and pottery display by local potter, Barbara Miskin. Also opening with Flower Festival at St Stephen's Church next door.

45 HIGHFIELDS

Manorstead, Skelmanthorpe, Huddersfield HD8 9DW. Julie & Tony Peckham. *8m SE of Huddersfield. M1 (J39) A636 towards Denby Dale. Turn R in Scissett village (B6116). Turn L (Barrowstead) just before zebra crossing*. Tea. **Adm £2.50, chd free. Sun 20, Wed 23 Apr (1-4).**

Small garden which shows creativity within metres rather than acres! Re-opened last year after refurbishment and upgrading of hard landscaping and planting. New summerhouse and patio area with alpine beds. Larger of two ponds has been replanted and has boardwalk. New acer woodland border. Spring/early summer garden with bulbs, woodland plants and alpines. Summerhouse and lots of intimate seating areas.

46 HILLBARK
Church Lane, Bardsey, nr Leeds LS17 9DH. Tim Gittins & Malcolm Simm, www.hillbark.co.uk. *4m SW of Wetherby. Turn W off A58 into Church Lane, garden on L before church.* Tea. **Adm £4, chd free. Suns 18 May; 29 June (11-5).**
Award-winning 1-acre country garden. 3 S-facing levels, hidden corners; surprise views. Formal topiary, relaxed perennial planting. Dramatic specimen yew. Ornamental ponds, summerhouse overlooking gravel, rock and stream gardens, large natural pond with ducks. Marginal planting incl bamboo. Woodland area. Large rambling roses. Unusual ceramics.

Elevated 'Jungle Lodge' and aerial walkway with views over the garden . . .

47 HOLLY CROFT
28 Station Road, Scalby, Scarborough YO13 0QA. Mrs Christine Goodall, 01723 375376, christine.goodall@tesco.net. *From Scarborough take Whitby Road A171. At Scalby Xrds turn by tennis court into Station Rd. Garden is approx 400 metres on R.* **Adm £3, chd free. Suns 13 Apr; 6 July (2-5).**
2/3 -acre sloping garden leading from house to Scalby Beck. Lawned formal area near house has circular pond, pergola, large beech tree and clipped box. Sundial garden has mixed borders, fruit bushes, raised vegetable beds, original Edwardian potting shed leading to wild flower area with steps, mown path to rustic hut. Gate and steps lead steeply down through woodland area to bench by river. Wheelchair access to terrace overlooking garden.

48 54 HOLLYM ROAD
Withernsea HU19 2PJ. Mr Matthew Pottage. *23m E of Hull, 16m S of Hornsea. Enter Withernsea from A1033 onto Hollym Rd. From Hornsea, B1242 through town onto Hollym Rd.* Light refreshments. **Adm £3, chd free. Sun 20 July (12-6).**
Matthew Potage works at RHS Wisley as Garden Manager and his garden is bursting with plants! Traditional favourites and less well known treats all grow side by side here in a creative layout. There is a small exotic walled garden, pond area with alpines, mixed borders, small meadow and vegetable garden. Plants incl succulents, hostas, exotic shrubs and choice conifers. Family home of Matthew Pottage, Garden Manager at RHS Garden Wisley.

GROUP OPENING

49 HORNSEA GARDENS
Hornsea HU18 1UR. *12 NE of Beverley. On B1242 S-side of Hornsea between Freeport & golf course. Directions to New House from Nutkins signed.* Home-made teas At Nutkins. **Combined adm £5, chd free. Sun 8 June (11-4).**

NEW HOUSE
Belvedere Park. Mrs Kate Willans.
N end of Cliff Rd, opp bus garage. Garden is halfway down L fork

NUTKINS
72 Rolston Road. Alan & Janet Stirling

Two gardens set in the popular seaside town. One large garden divided into different areas with a sense of fun, and a smaller garden, a real gem with plants for the enthusiast. Hornsea has seaside attractions, as well as the Mere, Museum, Freeport and Honeysuckle Farm nearby. Nutkins covers 3/4 acre with herbaceous borders, bog garden, streamside walk and woodland garden with pergolas and gazebo. Plenty of seating to linger and enjoy different views of the garden and see light play on many pieces of stained glass. New House is a compact plant enthusiasts garden, close to the sea with island beds and borders containing hardy and tender herbaceous and shrubs, some unusual, wildlife ponds, greenhouse with a succulent collection and a seating area. New experimental vertical garden this year. Wheelchair access at Nutkins.

50 HOTHAM HALL
Hotham YO43 4UA. Stephen & Carolyn Martin, 01430 422054, carolynandstephenmartin@btinternet.com. *15m W of Hull. J38 of M62 turn towards North Cave, follow signs for Hotham.* Light refreshments. **Adm £5, chd £2. Thurs 3, 17 Apr (11-2.30); 12 June (11-3.30). Visitors also welcome by appt Feb to Aug.**
C18 Grade II house (not open), stable block and clock tower in mature parkland setting with established gardens. Lake with bridge over to island walk (arboretum). Garden with Victorian pond and mixed borders. Many spring flowering bulbs. Children's play area, garden games. FREE Easter treasure hunt. Toddler Teddy Bears picnic in June, garden games, Easter decoration making. LIGHT REFRESHMENTS AND CHILDRENS PICINIC BASKET INCLUDED IN THE TICKET.

51 HUNMANBY GRANGE
Wold Newton YO25 3HS. Tom & Gill Mellor. *12½ m SE of Scarborough. Hunmanby Grange home of Wold Top Brewery, between Wold Newton & Hunmanby on rd from Burton Fleming to Fordon.* Light refreshments Wold Top Brewery bar area. **Adm £4, chd free. Sat 7, Sun 8 June (11-5).**
3-acre garden created over the last 30 yrs from exposed open field, on top of Yorkshire Wolds nr coast. Hedges and fences now provide shelter from wind, making series of gardens with yr-round interest and seasonal highlights. Wold Top Brewery open with garden. Picnics welcome and bring your Teddy Bears! Steps can be avoided by using grass paths and lawns. Pond garden not completely accessible to wheelchairs but can be viewed from gateway.

52 HUNMANBY SCHOOL
Priest Close, Hunmanby, Filey YO14 0QH. Mrs Lisa Woolridge. *9m S of Scarborough A64 At r'about 1st exit A1039 toward Filey take R fork to Hunmanby 2nd exit at r'about. 9m N of Bridlington A165 R to Hunmanby.* Home-made teas. **Adm £3, chd free. Sat 12 July (10-4).**
Grounds incl a sensory bed, vegetable garden, rivers of wildflowers, wildlife garden, living willow classroom, sculpture, Japanese courtyard, and orchard.

3 times winners of Yorkshire in Bloom (Gold) and best in category. Some areas of rough terrain may not be suitable for wheelchairs.

Various seating areas allow viewing from different perspectives . . .

53 ◆ JACKSON'S WOLD
Sherburn, Malton YO17 8QJ. Mr & Mrs Richard Cundall, 07966 531995, www.jacksonswoldgarden.com. *11m E of Malton, 10m SW of Scarborough. T-lights take the Weaverthorpe rd after 100 metres R fork to Helperthorpe & Luttons. 1m to top of hil, turn L at garden sign.* Home-made teas. **Adm £3, chd free. For NGS: Suns 1 June; 6 July (1-5). For other opening times and information, please phone or see garden website.**
2-acre garden with stunning views of the Vale of Pickering. Walled garden with mixed borders, numerous old shrub roses underplanted with unusual perennials. Woodland paths lead to further shrub and perennial borders. Lime avenue with wild flower meadow. Traditional vegetable garden with roses, flowers and box edging framed by Victorian greenhouse. Adjoining nursery. Featured on BBC radio York.

54 JASMINE HOUSE
145 The Grove, Wheatley Hills, Doncaster DN2 5SN. Ray & Anne Breame, 01302 361470, raybreame@hotmail.co.uk. *2m E of Doncaster. 1m E of Doncaster Royal Infirmary off A18. Turn R into Chestnut Ave (Motor Save on corner).* Home-made teas. **Adm £2.50, chd free. Sun 22 June (1-5). Visitors also welcome by appt June to Sept, for groups of 10+.**
Colourful tropical to traditional, plant-packed haven. A real surprise awaits you on entering this town 'garden for all seasons'. Climbers festoon archways that lead to enclosed gardens displaying the gardener's love of rare and unusual plants, from ferns and alpines to bonsai and tender perennials. Winner Doncaster in Bloom.

55 NEW THE JUNGLE GARDEN
76 Gledhow Wood Avenue, Leeds LS8 1NX. Nick & Gill Wilson, 0113 266 5196, nick.wilson@software4hr.co.uk. *4m NE of Leeds. A58 from Leeds for 3½ m to Oakwood. Turn L onto Gledhow Lane & follow NGS signs.* **Adm £3, chd free. Sun 27 July (11-5). Visitors also welcome by appt July to Sept.**
Multi level garden with jungle style planting and accents of hot tropical colour. Boardwalks and bark paths. Crown lifted trees create overhead canopy. Walk under mad, huge Gunnera leaves. 2 ponds, walkway over lower pond and raised deck with seating overlooks upper pond. Elevated 'Jungle Lodge' and aerial walkway with views over the garden. Tea room at Tropical World at Roundhay Park (1m). Featured in National Press and on 'The Great British Garden Revival' BBC2.

56 KELBERDALE
Wetherby Road, Knaresborough HG5 8LN. Stan & Chris Abbott, 01423 862140, kelberdale@gmail.com. *1m S of Knaresborough. On B6164 Wetherby rd. House on L immed after ring rd (A658) r'about.* **Adm £3, chd free. Sun 15 June (10-6); Wed 2 July (10-4). Visitors also welcome by appt May to Aug, group of 10 +.**
Winner of 3 national awards, this owner-made and maintained plantsman's garden overlooking the R Nidd has a bit of everything. Full of yr round interest with large traditional herbaceous border, colour themed beds, pond and bog garden, alpine house and troughs and vegetable garden. The wild garden with large pond and meadow is a haven for wildlife. Wheelchair access limited but help will be given.

57 23 LAMBERT ROAD
Bridlington YO16 6RD. S Earnshaw. *North Bridlington. A614 or A165 to Bridlington. Scarborough Rd double r'about follow signs to Flamborough. Next r'about turn R. Across next r'about to T-lights, turn L.* **Adm £2.50, chd free. Sat 6, Sun 7 Sept (11-4).**
Recently created small town garden on clay soil. Shaded areas planted with ferns, hostas and heucheras contrast with sunny beds of herbaceous perennials and colourful containers of bedding plants. The planting area has been designed to provide year-round interest culminating in a blaze of colour in late summer. A tranquil garden with seating areas where shade loving ferns, hostas and heucheras contrast with beds of sun-loving phlox, dahlias, helenium and day lilies and a bank of containers provides a riot of colour.

58 ◆ LAND FARM
Edge Lane, Colden, Hebden Bridge HX7 7PJ. Mr J Williams, 01422 842260, www.landfarmgardens.co.uk. *8m W of Halifax. At Hebden Bridge (A646) after 2 sets of T-lights take turning circle to Heptonstall and Colden. After 2¾ m turn R at Edge Lane 'no through rd'.* **For opening times and information, please phone or see garden website.**
6 acres incl alpine, herbaceous, formal and newly developing woodland garden, meconopsis varieties in June, cardiocrinum giganteum in July. Elevation 1000ft N-facing. C17 house (not open). Art Gallery and garden sculpture. Garden listed on Lap Map as being one of the best 80 gardens of England and Wales. Look for sculptures on Google Earth. Open weekends and Bank Hol Mons May to end Aug. Limited wheelchair access.

59 LANGTON FARM
Great Langton, Northallerton DL7 0TA. Richard & Annabel Fife, 01609 748446, annabelfife@fsmail.net. *5m W of Northallerton. B6271 in Great Langton between Northallerton & Scotch Corner.* Home-made teas. **Adm £4, chd free. Sun 27 Apr (12-6). Evening Opening wine, Sat 12 July (5.30-8); Sun 13 July (11-5.30). Visitors also welcome by appt Apr to Sept, groups 10+.**
Riverside garden comprising formal and informal gravel areas, nuttery, romantic flower garden with mixed borders and pebble pool. Organic. Featured in The English Garden.

60 LINDEN HOUSE

16 Northgate, Cottingham HU16 4HH. Eric Nicklas & Mrs Pat Plaxton, 01482 847788. *4m NW of Hull. A164, onto B1233 to Cottingham. Garden on L 50yds before rail Xing. From A1079, take B1233, past bowling club, over Xing. 50 yds on R.* Light refreshments. **Adm £2.50, chd free (share to Hospice in Hull). Sat 31 May; Sun 1 June (11-5). Visitors also welcome by appt.**

This interesting small garden with a thoughtfully curved lawn, numerous shrubs, pond and aviary which blend well together. Homebrew demonstration and wine tasting.

61 LINDEN LODGE

Newbridge Lane, nr Wilberfoss, York YO41 5RB. Robert Scott & Jarrod Marsden, 07900 003538, rdsjsm@gmail.com. *10m E of York. Do not enter the village of Wilberfoss from the A1079, take the turning towards Bolton.* Cream teas in the marquee. **Adm £4, chd free. Suns 8, 22 June (1-5). Visitors also welcome by appt May to July, min group 15.**

1 acre garden, owner-designed and constructed since 2000, with many choice, unusual plants and trees. Gravel paths edged with box and lavender lead to herbaceous/mixed borders, wildlife pond and summerhouse. Kitchen garden, glasshouse, orchard and woodland area and formal garden with pond and water feature. A further 5 acres of developing meadow, trees, pathways and Shetland sheep. Plants and local craft stalls. Featured in 100 Inspirational Garden of England, Yorkshire Post, Amateur Gardening and East Riding Journal. Gravel paths and shallow steps.

62 LITTLE EDEN

Lancaster Street, Castleford WF10 2NP. Melvyn & Linda Moran, 01977 558653, melvynmoran@btinternet.com, ngs little eden facebook. *2½ m NW of M62 J32. A639 (Castleford) 1st r'about 2nd exit B6136. At hill top turn L T-lights, next r'about straight on, then 3rd R (Elizabeth Drive) then 2nd L, then 3rd.L.* Home-made teas. **Adm £3, chd free. Suns 22 June; 17 Aug (10-4.30). Also open Millrace Nursery. Visitors also welcome by appt June to Aug.**

Plant lovers' small hidden oasis of unusual, tender, exotic and tropical plants in the midst of large housing estate. Trellis and archway festooned with climbers, colourful pots and hanging baskets. Herbaceous perennials, succulents, tree ferns, palms, bananas, pond and a decorative summerhouse.

63 LITTLETHORPE MANOR

Littlethorpe Road, Littlethorpe, Ripon HG4 3LG. Mr & Mrs J P Thackray, thackray@littlethorpemanor.com, www.littlethorpemanor.com. *Outskirts of Ripon by racecourse. Ripon bypass A61. Follow Littlethorpe Rd from Dallamires Lane r'about to stable block with clock tower. Map supplied on application.* Light refreshments. **Adm £6, chd free. Visitors welcome by appt May to Oct, incl guided tour £8.**

11 acres. Walled garden based on cycle of seasons with box, herbaceous, roses, gazebo. Sunken garden with white rose parterre and herbs. Brick pergola with white wisteria, blue and yellow borders. Terraces with ornamental pots. Formal lawns with fountain pool, hornbeam towers and yew hedging. Box headed hornbeam drive with Aqualens water feature. Extensive perennial borders. Parkland with lake, late summer plantings and classical pavilion. Cut flower garden. Spring bulbs and winter garden. Featured in Northern Echo Weekend edition and Living magazine (North East). Gravel paths, some steep steps.

GROUP OPENING

64 LOCKINGTON GARDENS

Driffield YO25 9SR. *7m N of Beverley. Lockington is on Thorpe Rd between A164 & B1248. Park in church car park and follow signs to gardens.* Home-made teas. **Combined adm £4, chd free. Sun 15 June (1-6).**

PENNY COTTAGE
42 Thorpe Road. Sue & John Rowson

THORPE LODGE
Dead Lane. Mrs Jane Warburton

Two small gardens in the village of Lockington. Penny Cottage is a small, well-maintained garden on different levels with conifers, selection of herbaceous perennials and climbers. Small raised vegetable plot.
Thorpe Lodge a cottage garden on the site of an old orchard. Interesting shrubs and trees creating contrast and shade. Wildlife pond, summer house and vegetable patch.

65 LOW HALL

Dacre Banks, Nidderdale HG3 4AA. Mrs P A Holliday, 01423 780230, pamela@pamelaholliday.co.uk. *10m NW of Harrogate. On B6451 between Dacre Banks and Darley.* Home-made teas. **Adm £3, chd free. Sun 11 May (1-5). Also open with Dacre Banks & Summerbridge Gardens, 13 July. Visitors also welcome by appt.**

A romantic walled garden set on differing levels designed to complement historic C17 family home (not open). Spring bulbs, rhododendrons; azaleas round tranquil water garden. Asymmetric rose pergola underplanted with auriculas and lithodora links orchard to the garden. Extensive herbaceous borders, shrubs and climbing roses give later interest.

Recycle – bring a bag for your plant purchases

Sutton Grange

66 LOW SUTTON

Sutton Lane, Masham HG4 4PB. Steve & Judi Smith, 01765 688565, info@lowsutton.co.uk, www.lowsutton.co.uk. *1½ m W of Masham. From Masham towards Leyburn (A6108). L into Sutton Lane, single track tarmac rd. Low Sutton ¼ m on L.* Home-made teas. **Adm £3, chd free. Sun 22 June (11-5); Sun 20 July (1-5). Combined with Sutton Grange, adm £5 (22 June). Visitors also welcome by appt June to Aug.**

Developing since 2007 a fresh approach to cottage gardening. Concentric circular floral colour wheel surrounded by scented roses and clematis. Abundant variety of fruit and vegetables decoratively grown in raised beds, fruit cage, greenhouse and coldframe. Perennial border, grasses, fernery and courtyard surround the house, all set within 6-acre smallholding.

67 LOWER HEUGH COTTAGE GARDEN

14 Kirk Lane, Eastby, nr Skipton BD23 6SH. Trevor & Marian Nash, 01756 793702, mnash862@btinternet.com. *2½ m NE of Skipton (Do not use satnav). Follow A59/65 N ringroad around Skipton, turn at sign for Skipton, Embsay (railway) and Eastby. In Embsay turn to Eastby & Barden (Kirk Lane).* Light refreshments. **Adm £7, chd free. Visitors welcome by appt only, a tour is followed by appropriate refreshments incl in the adm.**

Japanese Kaiyushiki stroll through Garden. Hosting Professor Fukuhara, one of the world's leading Japanese Garden Designers for a workshop led by him in late 2011, was a privilege. His Emperor Garden design for the outer Roji extension within this one acre stroll garden has proved inspirational for the many visitors during 2012/13. Uniquely, this little piece of the Orient, high in the Yorkshire Dales is all Japanese in style. Its many gardens are explained during the 90 minute conducted tour enhancing the understanding of the history, religion, philosophy and concepts behind Japanese garden design. This all year round garden, created and maintained by the owners, is perhaps best seen from March to October yet can be spectacular in the winter. Featured in Yorkshire Ridings Magazine. Limited wheelchair access.

68 MANOR FARM

Thixendale, Malton YO17 9TG. Charles & Gilda Brader, 01377 288315, manorfarmthixendale@hotmail.com. *10m SE of Malton. Unclassified rd through Birdsall, ½ m up hill, turn L at Xrds for Thixendale - 3m, 1st farm on R. 17m E of York, turn off A166 rd at top of Garrowby Hill, follow signs for Thixendale, 4m turn into village, drive through to end, farm on L. Yellow signs will be on route.* Home-made teas. **Adm £4, chd free. Sun 7 Sept (12-5).**

Main lawn surrounded by shrub and herbaceous borders. Ruined shed, small knot garden, little arbour, running water and rocks. Topiary and pots throughout garden. Central pergola to new bespoke summerhouse, formal pool with sphere, set in stone flagged trellised area. Through curved pergola to alpines planted among farm stones, small courtyard, into garden room overflowing with plants.

69 MANOR HOUSE

Church Street, North Cave, Brough HU15 2LW. Mr & Mrs Christian Carver, 01430 421418, christiancarver@btinternet.com. *1½ m from M62, J38. B1230 E of North Cave, leaving village next to church*. Home-made teas. **Adm £4, chd free. Suns 4 May; 31 Aug (1-5).**

Next generation of family in situ. 2-acre garden surrounding C18 farmhouse with octagonal dovecote, stream and lake. Parterre for late-summer interest; herbaceous border, glasshouse with productive garden and small orchard. Naturalistic planting at rear running into 20yr-old arboretum with spring bulbs and wild flowers and woodland walk by lakeside. Coaches by arrangement Accommodation at www.estateescapes.co.uk.

70 MANSION COTTAGE

8 Gillus Lane, Bempton, Bridlington YO15 1HW. Polly & Chris Myers, 01262 851404, bemptonsupperclub@hotmail.co.uk. *2m NE of Bridlington. From Bridlington take B1255 to Flamborough. 1st L at T lights - Bempton Lane, turn 1st R into Short Lane then L at end. Continue - L fork at Church*. Light refreshments. **Adm £3, chd free. Sat 9, Sun 10 Aug (10-4). Visitors also welcome by appt July to Aug, individuals and groups 10+.**

Exuberant, lush, vibrant perennial planting highlighted with grasses in this hidden, peaceful and surprising garden offering many views and features. Visitors book comments 'A truly lovely garden and a great lunch', 'The garden is inspirational, the food delicious', 'A veritable oasis! New for 2014, more bee and butterfly planting. Delicious home-made lunches, produce stalls incl jams, chutneys, pickles and hand-made soaps.

71 NEW MARSTON GRANGE

Tockwith Road, Long Marston, York YO26 7PL. Mrs Joanne Smakman, 01423 358283, david.smakman@unicombox.com. *5m W of York 5m E of Wetherby. From B1224 in Long Marston turn to Tockwith. Turn R after Battlefield Monument*. Home-made teas. **Adm £3, chd free. Sun 15 June (11-5). Visitors also welcome by appt May to July, home-made teas for groups of 10+ and conducted tours.**

2 acre garden, with views over the Battlefield of Marston Moor, designed to blend into the arable landscape and planted with many native and wild flower species with a traditional ha-ha, wildlife pond and small walled garden. The summerhouse garden, shaded by mature trees leads to an orchard with vegetables and cutting garden. Walks through and round large perennial wild flower meadow. Bees.

GROUP OPENING

72 MARTON CUM GRAFTON GARDENS

nr Boroughbridge, York YO51 9QJ. *2½ m S of Boroughbridge. A1m J48 off A168, nr Boroughbridge*. Tea at Well House. **Combined adm £3.50, chd free. Wed 25 June (2-5).**

SPRINGFIELD
Chris Woods & Molly Naish

WELL HOUSE
Glen Garnett

Marton cum Grafton are adjacent villages overlooking the York Plain. The two Grafton cottage gardens are away from the village centre and nestle into the hillside with long views to the White Horse and Hambleton Hills. Well House extends to over 1½ acres and has evolved over 35 years and continues to change. Flowing colourful borders, climbers and rambling roses and ornamental shrubs of interest. Orchard with geese, ducks and chickens. Adjacent below lies Springfield with box parterre to the front and a rear paved garden overflowing with cottage garden plants, ramblers and shrub old roses. Narrow box lined paths lead to vegetable garden and orchard with copper marans and silky bantams.

73 MERE'STEAD

28 Kelmscott Garth, Manston Crossgates, Leeds LS15 8LB. Mr Roberto Renzi. *6m E of Leeds. 1m from M1 J46 follow A63 towards Leeds. Take ring rd (A6120) then follow signs to Barwick-in-Elmet. At 2nd T-lights turn R (Penda's Way), then 1st L. No parking in cul-de-sac. Parking nearby at community centre.* **Evening Opening Fri 25 July (5-9).**

A small enclosed English town garden with an Italian twist lovingly developed and cared for by owners. Mature trees, magnolia and cedar deodara, underplanted with interesting perennials and bulbs giving colour and foliage interest throughout the year. Arches festooned with climbers, small wildlife pond, pots with succulents, colourful summer bulbs and alpine troughs. Winner of Leeds in Bloom for past 8 years.

Plenty of seats and interesting corners and features; children love to explore . . .

74 MILLGATE HOUSE

Millgate, Richmond DL10 4JN. Tim Culkin & Austin Lynch, 01748 823571, oztim@millgatehouse.demon.co.uk, www.millgatehouse.com. *Centre of Richmond. House located at bottom of Market Place opp Barclays Bank. Just off corner of Market Place*. **Adm £3.50, chd free. Suns 15, 29 June (8-8.30). Also open 15 June, Swale Cottage.**

SE walled town garden overlooking R Swale. Although small, the garden is full of character, enchantingly secluded with plants and shrubs. Foliage plants incl ferns and hostas. Old roses, interesting selection of clematis, small trees and shrubs. RHS associate garden. Immensely stylish, national award-winning garden. Featured in GGG and on BBC Gardeners' World.

75 MILLRACE NURSERY

84 Selby Road, Garforth, Leeds LS25 1LP. Mr & Mrs Carthy, 01132 869233, carol@millrace-plants.co.uk, www.millrace-plants.co.uk. *5m E of Leeds. On A63 in Garforth. 1m from M1 J46, 3m from A1.* Home-made teas. **Adm £4, chd free. Suns 16 Mar; 20 Apr; 25 May; 22 June; 20 July; 17 Aug; 21 Sept (1-5). Also open Little Eden 22 June; 17 Aug. Visitors also welcome by appt Mar to Sept, 10+ needed for conducted tours.**

Overlooking a secluded valley, garden incl large herbaceous borders containing over 3000 varieties of perennials, shrubs and trees, many of which are unusual and drought tolerant. Ornamental pond, vegetable garden and walled terraces leading to wild flower meadow, small woodland, bog garden and wildlife lakes. 17 Aug seed collecting opportunity. Art Exhibition, specialist nursery.

76 MILLVIEW COTTAGE

21 Church Street, North Cave, Brough HU15 2LJ. Emma Jackson, 01430 421064, jackson5@jackson5.karoo.co.uk. *15m W of Hull. J38 M62E turn L to North Cave B1230 E of village on R of Church St. No parking on Church St.* Home-made teas. **Adm £2.50, chd free. Sun 29 June (10.30-5). Visitors also welcome by appt June to Aug.**

Inspirational cottage garden, long and narrow, split into different styled sections. Rear extension, of Scandinavian influence links the house to contemporary outdoor room with terrace, raised beds, wooden walkway, water feature and exotic planting. More traditional area leads to family garden, with vegetables and greenhouse. Please be aware hidden step near back of house. Featured in House Beautiful and on Alan Titchmarsh TV series 'Love Your Garden'.

77 NEAKINS HOUSE

North Leys Road, Hollym, Withernsea HU19 2QN. David & Trish Smith. *2m S of Withernsea. Enter Hollym on A1033 Hull to Withernsea Rd. Turn E at Xrds. Garden on R after double bend. Strictly no roadside parking, please park in grounds.* Home-made teas. **Adm £3, chd free. Sun 29 June (11-5).**

Quiet country garden with shrubs and choice herbaceous plantings. Specimen evergreens complement formal box topiary and hedging. Enter log arch to shady hosta walk and emerge through rose arch. Gravelled area with seating overlooks large wildlife pond. Folly wall, clothed in clematis, features iron gate leading on to bee and butterfly border. Classic cars on display. Hosta walk too narrow for wheelchairs but can be viewed from entrance.

78 ◆ NEWBY HALL & GARDENS

Ripon HG4 5AE. Mr R C Compton, 01423 322583, www.newbyhall.com. *4m SE of Ripon. (HG4 5AJ for Sat Nav). Follow brown tourist signs from A1 & Ripon town centre.* **For opening times and information, please phone or see garden website.**

40 acres extensive gardens laid out in 1920s. Full of rare and beautiful plants. Formal seasonal gardens, stunning double herbaceous borders to R Ure and National Collection holder - Cornus. Miniature railway and adventure gardens for children. Contemporary sculpture exhibition (open June - Sept). Wheelchair map available.

NCH

79 NEW 2 NEWLAY GROVE

Horsforth, Leeds LS18 4LH. Mrs Kate van Heel. *4m NW Leeds city centre. From A65 turn down Newlay Lane then 2nd R onto Newlay Grove. House is 25 metres on L, limited parking near house.* Light refreshments. **Adm £3, chd free. Wed 13 Aug (1-5).**

Large rear family garden within third acre plot in quiet conservation area close to R Aire. Landscaped over past 20 years, featuring late summer perennials, shrubs, pond and shade loving plants. Steps and slopes link lawns and paved terracing and various seating areas allow viewing from different perspectives.

80 ◆ NORTON CONYERS

Wath, Nr Ripon HG4 5EQ. Sir James & Lady Graham, 01765 640333, www.weddingsatnortonconyers.co.uk. *4m N of Ripon. Take Melmerby & Wath sign off A61 Ripon-Thirsk. Go through both villages to boundary wall. Signed entry 300 metres on R.* Home-made teas by MCCC. **Adm £5.50, chd free. For NGS: Sun 15 June (2-5). For other opening times and information, please phone or see garden website.**

Large C18 walled garden of interest to garden historians. Interesting iron entrance gate; herbaceous borders, yew hedges and Orangery (open to the public) with an attractive little pond in front. Small sales area specialising in unusual hardy plants, fruit in season. House, visited by Charlotte Brontë and inspiration for Thornfield Hall in 'Jane Eyre' is closed for major repairs. The garden retains the essential features of its original design, combined with sympathetic replanting in the English style. Borders of gold and silver plants, of old-fashioned peonies, and irises in season. Visitors frequently comment on its tranquil atmosphere. Most areas wheelchair accessible along gravel paths.

A big, very wild pond, grassy paths, hidden corners . . .

81 THE NURSERY

15 Knapton Lane, Acomb, York YO26 5PX. Tony Chalcraft & Jane Thurlow. *2½ m W of York. From A1237 take B1224 direction Acomb. At r'about turn L (Beckfield Ln.), after 150 metres Turn L.* Home-made teas. **Adm £3, chd free. Sun 20 July (1-5). Afternoon and evening opening Wed 23 July (2-8).**

Hidden attractive and productive 1-acre organic garden behind suburban house. Wide range of top and soft fruit (incl 50+ varieties apples and pears). Many different vegetables grown both outside and under cover including a large 20m greenhouse. Productive areas interspersed with informal ornamental plantings providing colour and habitat for wildlife. Tomato tasting on 23 July.

Cow Close Cottage

82 OATMILL COTTAGE

Lealholm, nr Whitby YO21 2AG. Sue Morgan. *9m W of Whitby. Turn from A171 to Lealholm. Parking in centre of village or by station. Garden just below station across railway line.* Home-made teas. **Adm £3, chd free. Sun 13 July (11-4.30).**
Cottage-style garden with a variety of herbaceous borders with drought-tolerant plants, terrace, range of mature trees and shrubs set on the hillside overlooking the picturesque village of Lealholm. Features incl sculpture, fountain, bog garden and summerhouse. Plant sales in village nursery adjacent to the garden. Art Exhibition of garden-inspired art.

83 NEW THE OLD RECTORY

Scrayingham, York YO41 1JD. Peter & Urszula Pace. *12m N E of York. From York A64, take A166, after Gate Helmsley turn L to Buttercrambe, once crossed the two small (narrow) river bridges, take sharp L to Scrayingham.* Tea. **Adm £5, chd free. Sat 28 June (10.30-6.30).**
6¼ acre, with mature trees, and developed over last 15 years with a good variety of flowering plants and shrubs from Spring to late Summer. Extensive Lawns, parterre, terraces, large pond with island, woodland, large meadow and river walk. Short walk to Saxon Church. Paths gravelled. Sloping grass lawns, wheelchair access to upper part of garden only.

84 OLD RECTORY COTTAGE

Rectory Lane, Tunstall, Hull HU12 0JE. Mrs P Garbutt. *6m NW of Withensea. On coast 1½ m off B1242 between Withernsea & Aldbrough via Roos. Sharp L bend into village. After church on R take 1st turn R into Rectory Lane.* Home-made teas at Tunstall village hall. **Adm £3, chd free. Sun 22 June (1-5).**
Pretty cottage garden in peaceful seaside location, featuring arched walk with roses, clematis and honeysuckle, gravel garden and water feature. Perennial island beds and borders, clipped box with roses and lavender. Separate wildlife area with a small vegetable plot, greenhouse/work area. Public footpath to sea/cliffs. WC facilities at village hall.

85 OLD SLENINGFORD HALL

Mickley, nr Ripon HG4 3JD. Jane & Tom Ramsden. *5m NW of Ripon. Off A6108. After N Stainley turn L, follow signs to Mickley. Gates on R after 1½ m opp cottage.* Home-made teas. **Adm £5, chd free. Sat 7, Sun 8 June (12.30-4.30).**
A large English country garden and developing 'Forest Garden'. Early C19 house (not open) and garden with original layout; wonderful mature trees, woodland walk and Victorian fernery; romantic lake with islands, watermill, walled kitchen garden; beautiful long herbaceous border, yew and huge beech hedges. Award winning permaculture forest garden. Several plant and other garden stalls. Picnics welcome and bring your Teddy Bears. Reasonable wheelchair access to most parts of garden. Disabled WC at Old Sleningford Farm next to the garden.

86 OMEGA
79 Magdalen Lane, Hedon HU12 8LA. Mr & Mrs D Rosindale, 01482 897370, mavirosi@hotmail.co.uk. *6m E of Hull. Through to E Hull onto A1033. L into St Augustine's Gate through Market Place, immediately R to Magdalen Gate, ahead to Magdalen Lane.* Home-made teas. **Adm £2.50, chd free. Sat 21, Sun 22 June (12-5.30). Visitors also welcome by appt June to July, for groups of 10 to 20.**
Front garden formalised by box hedging has densely planted borders. Small shady side garden which leads leads to patio with pots. Herbaceous borders are followed by shady areas and a large area of plant sales,greenhouses and newly planted orchard. The mini-meadow is a work in progress. A garden with diverse range of perennials, hostas, ferns and trees. Wildlife friendly. Cream Teas, beverages and cakes available. Afternoon Tea can be booked in advance by telephone. Large range of perennial plants for sale incl hostas, succulents and some bedding plants.

Many places to sit and enjoy the views or have a game of croquet or boules . . .

87 THE ORCHARD
4a Blackwood Rise, Cookridge, Leeds LS16 7BG. Carol & Michael Abbott, 0113 2676764, michael.john.abbott@hotmail.co.uk. *5m N of Leeds centre. Off A660 (Leeds-Otley) N of A6120 Ring Rd. Turn L up Otley Old Road. At top of hill turn L at T-lights (Tinshill Lane). Please park in Tinshill Lane.* Home-made teas. **Adm £2.50, chd free. Sun 29 June (12.30-5.30); Wed 2 July (1-5). Visitors also welcome by appt June to July groups of 10+ Refreshments included.**
1/3 -acre hidden suburban oasis of peace and tranquillity. Differing levels made by owners using old stone, found on site, planted for yr-round interest. Long rockery, unusual fruit tree arbour and sheltered oriental style seated area linked by narrow grass lawns and steps. Mixed perennials,shrubs, bulbs and pots amongst paved and pebbled areas. Tombola in aid of Yorkshire Air Ambulance.

88 NEW ORCHARD HOUSE
Sandholme Lane, Leven HU17 5LW. Mrs Frances Cooper. *In Leven turn between Hare & Hounds PH & PO. Continue for 400yds then onto Carr Lane picking up yellow signs to Orchard House.* Light refreshments. **Adm £3.50, chd free. Sun 8 June (10-5).**
An informal country garden begun in 1985. Part acidic Carr land, wet in winter, part neutral dry sandy land. Areas of woodland with associated planting, a big, very wild pond, grassy paths, hidden corners.

89 OVERTHORPE J I & N SCHOOL
Edge Top Road, Thornhill, Dewsbury WF12 0BH. Overthorpe J I & N School, www.arcadialandscapes.com. *1m S of Dewsbury town centre. Follow signs to Whitley & Briestfield on Edgetop Rd.* Home-made teas. **Adm £2.50, chd free. Sun 13 July (2-5).**
A rare opportunity to visit the grounds of a primary school that are managed for outdoor learning, play and wildlife. Large kitchen and vegetable garden, orchard, wildlife garden and ponds, meadows, WW2 themed garden. Woodland and natural play areas, all richly planted to create opportunities for play and learning in a natural setting. Drama and music in the grounds. Refreshments provided by children from school-grown produce.

90 ◆ PARCEVALL HALL GARDENS
Skyreholme, nr Skipton BD23 6DE. Walsingham College, 01756 720311, www.parcevallhallgardens.co.uk. *9m N of Skipton. Signs from B6160 Bolton Abbey-Burnsall rd or off B6265 Grassington-Pateley Bridge.* Light refreshments. **Adm £6, chd free. For NGS: Wed 23 Apr (10-5). For other opening times and information, please phone or see garden website.**
The only garden open daily in the Yorkshire Dales National Park. 24 acres in Wharfedale sheltered by mixed woodland; terrace garden, rose garden, rock garden, fish ponds. Mixed borders, spring bulbs, tender shrubs (desfontainea, crinodendron, camellias); autumn colour. Bird watching, old apple orchard for picnics. CafË.

91 3 PILMOOR COTTAGES
Pilmoor YO61 2QQ. Wendy & Chris Jakeman, 01845 501848, cnjakeman@aol.com. *20m N of York. From A1M J48. N end B'bridge follow rd towards Easingwold. From A19 follow signs to Hutton Sessay then Helperby. Garden next to mainline railway.* Light refreshments. **Adm £3.50, chd free. Suns 27 Apr; 15 June; 27 July; 7 Sept (11-5). Visitors also welcome by appt Mar to Sept.**
2-acre garden round C19 cottages. Developed by 2 avid garden visitors unable to visit a garden without buying a new plant, leading to an informal cottage style, but always with something to look at from bulbs in spring to colchicum and cyclamen in autumn. Clock-golf putting green. 71/4' Gauge railway around the garden, ponds and rockery.

92 PROSPECT HOUSE
2 Prospect Place, Outlane, nr Huddersfield HD3 3FL. Carol & Andy Puszkiewicz, 01422 376408, carol-puszkiewicz@talktalk.net. *5m N of Huddersfield. 1m N of M62. J24 (W) take A643 to J23 (E) follow A640 to Rochdale. Turn R immed before 40mph sign (Gosport Lane). Parking in field at top of the lane.* Light refreshments. **Adm £3.50, chd free. Sun 22 June (12-5). Evening Opening wine, Fri 11 July (5.30-8). Visitors also welcome by appt June to July, groups of 6+.**
1-acre intimate garden, created by owners, high in the Pennines (900ft). Cottage herbaceous borders lead to shaded areas and secret garden with chamomile lawn, colour themed borders surrounding circular bed and kitchen garden with trained fruit and herbs. Wild area with raised wooden pathway to summerhouse, large pond, narrow stream and meadow. Featured on BBC Great British Garden Revival. Some parts of the garden are accessible for wheelchairs.

ALLOTMENTS

93 QUEENSGATE & KITCHEN LANE ALLOTMENTS

Beverley HU17 8NN. Beverley Town Council. *Outskirts of Beverley Town Centre. On A164 towards Cottingham, allotment site is before Victoria Rd, after double mini r'about & opp Beverley Grammar School.* Cream teas. **Adm £2.50, chd free. Sun 27 July (12-4).**

Varied allotment site of 85 plots, plus another 35 on Kitchen Lane, growing a wide variety of fruit, vegetables and flowers. Some allotment holders will be present to discuss their plots. Path for easy viewing and plots either side. Dogs on leads.

94 THE RED HOUSE

17 Whin Hill Road, Bessacarr, Doncaster DN4 7AF. Rosie Hamlin, www.pyjamagardenersyorks.com. *2m S of Doncaster. A638 South, L at T-lights for B1396, Whin Hill Rd is 2nd R. A638 North, R signed Branton B1396 onto Whin Hill.* Home-made teas. **Adm £3, chd free. Sat 17, Sun 18 May (2-5).**

Mature 2/3 acre garden. Dry shade a challenge but acid loving plants a joy. Fine acers, camellia, daphne, rhododendrons, kalmia and eucryphia. Terrace and rockery stepping stones lead past and through new wave and cloud pruned shrubs to lawn with modern orb-shaped rotating summerhouse and young trees. White border conceals pond, compost and hens.

95 REWELA COTTAGE

Skewsby YO61 4SG. John Plant & Daphne Ellis, 01347 888125, plantjohnsgarden@btinternet.com. *4m N of Sheriff Hutton, 15m N of York. After Sheriff Hutton, towards Terrington, turn L towards Whenby & Brandsby. Turn R just past Whenby to Skewsby. Turn L into village. 400yds on R.* Home-made teas. **Adm £3.50, chd free. Suns 4 May; 20 July (11-5). Visitors also welcome by appt May to July, please phone or email. None in June.**

3/4 -acre ornamental garden, designed by current owner, featuring unusual trees, shrubs, and architectural plants. Other features include a pond, pergola, natural stone sunken garden, breeze house, raised vegetable garden. May for rhododendrons, azaleas, magnolias and spring bulbs. July for summer flowering plants, year round interest. Over 130 heucheras, 40 penstemons and 40 hostas in the garden. All unusual trees and shrubs have labels giving full descriptions, picture, and any cultivation notes incl propagation. Plant sales are specimens from garden. Many varieties of Heuchera, Heucherella and Tiarelas, Penstemon. Hostas and herbs for sale. Access to all parts of the garden for wheelchair users.

96 ◆ RHS GARDEN HARLOW CARR

Crag Lane, Harrogate HG3 1QB. Royal Horticultural Society, 01423 565418, www.rhs.org.uk/harlowcarr. *1 1/2 m W of Harrogate town centre. On B6162 (Harrogate - Otley).* **Adm £7.95, chd £3.95. For NGS: Sun 27 Apr (9.30-5). For other opening times and information, please phone or see garden website.**

One of Yorkshire's most relaxing yet inspiring locations! Highlights incl spectacular herbaceous borders, streamside garden, alpines, scented and kitchen gardens. 'Gardens Through Time', woodland and wild flower meadows. Betty's Tearoom, gift shop and childrens play area incl tree house. Wheelchairs and mobility scooters available, advanced booking recommended.

97 THE RIDINGS

South Street, Burton Fleming, Driffield YO25 3PE. Roy & Ruth Allerston, 01262 470489. *11m NE of Driffield. 11m SW of Scarborough. 7m NW of Bridlington. From Driffield B1249, before Foxholes turn R to Burton Fleming. From Scarborough A165 turn R to Burton Fleming.* Home-made teas. **Adm £3, chd free. Suns 25 May; 6 July (1-5). Visitors also welcome by appt Apr to Sept.**

Tranquil cottage garden designed by owners in 2001 on reclaimed site. Brick pergola and arches covered with climbers lead to secret garden with lavender edged beds. Colour-themed mixed borders with old English roses. Paved terrace with water feature and farming bygones, small potager; summerhouse and greenhouse.

98 RUDDING PARK

Follifoot, nr Harrogate HG3 1JH. Mr & Mrs Simon Mackaness, www.ruddingpark.co.uk. *3m S of Harrogate off A658. Follow brown tourist signs. Use hotel entrance.* NGS Teas £2 - £3.50. **Adm £3.50, chd free. Sun 8 June (12.30-5).**

20 acres of attractive gardens and lawns around a Grade I Regency house extended and used as a hotel. Original parkland planting to designs of Humphry Repton. Formal gardens known for their collection of rhododendrons and azaleas. Planting adjacent to hotel is more modern with grasses and perennials, designed by Matthew Wilson.

99 RUDSTON HOUSE

Long Street, Rudston, nr Driffield YO25 4UH. Mr & Mrs Simon Dawson, 01262 420400. *5m W of Bridlington. On B1253. S at Bosville Arms for approx 300yds.* Home-made teas. **Adm £5, chd free. Sun 20 July (11-5). Visitors also welcome by appt July to Aug.**

Birthplace of authoress Winifred Holtby. Victorian farmhouse (not open) and 3 acres of exuberant garden with fine old trees, lawns, paths with clipped box hedges, conifers, shrubs, greenhouses, roses, interesting potager with named vegetable varieties, hosta beds with lilies, and short woodland walk, with pond. Plenty of seats and interesting corners and features; children love to explore. The rose garden has been redesigned with seats to sit and enjoy. Natural wildlife area with birds, bees and butterflies has been grown where three large old tree were blown down in a tornado in November 2011. Partial wheelchair access with assistance.

100 RUSTIC COTTAGE
Front Street, Wold Newton, nr Driffield YO25 3YQ. Jan Joyce, 01262 470710. *13m N of Driffield. From Driffield take B1249 to Foxholes (12m), take R turning signed Wold Newton. Turn L onto Front St, opp village pond, continue up hill, garden on L.* **Adm £3, chd free. Visitors welcome by appt Apr to Oct.**
Plantswoman's cottage garden of much interest with many choice and unusual plants. Hellebores and bulbs are treats for colder months. Old-fashioned roses, fragrant perennials, herbs and wild flowers, all grown together provide habitat for birds, bees, butterflies and small mammals. It has been described as 'organised chaos'! The owner's 2nd NGS garden. Small dogs only.

101 ◆ SCAMPSTON WALLED GARDEN
Scampston Hall, Scampston, Malton YO17 8NG. The Legard Family, 01944 759111, www.scampston.co.uk/gardens. *5m E of Malton. ½ m N of A64, near the village of Rillington & signed Scampston only.* **For opening times and information, please phone or see garden website.**
An exciting modern garden designed by Piet Oudolf. The 4-acre walled garden contains a series of hedged enclosures designed to look good throughout the year. The garden contains many unusual species and is a must for any keen plantsman. The Walled Garden is set within the grounds and parkland surrounding Scampston Hall. The Hall opens to visitors for a short period during the summer months.

102 ◆ SHANDY HALL GARDENS
Coxwold YO61 4AD. The Laurence Sterne Trust, 01347 868465, www.laurencesternetrust.org.uk/shandy-hall-garden.php. *N of York. From A19, 7m from both Easingwold & Thirsk, turn E signed Coxwold.* **For NGS: Evening Openings £3, chd free, Fris 25 Apr; 20 June; 4 July (6.30-8). For other opening times and information, please phone or see garden website.**
Home of C18 author Laurence Sterne. 2 walled gardens, 1 acre of unusual perennials interplanted with tulips and old roses in low walled beds. In old quarry, another acre of trees, shrubs, bulbs, climbers and wild flowers encouraging wildlife, incl over 300 recorded species of moths. Moth trap, identification and release. Wheelchair access to wild garden by arrangement.

GROUP OPENING

103 SHIPTONTHORPE GARDENS
York YO43 3PQ. *2m NW of Market Weigton. From Market Weigton on A1079, take 2nd turn off to Shiptonthorpe Cairngorm on R is start point with car parking opp.* Light refreshments at Cairngorm.
Combined adm £5, chd free. Sat 7, Sun 8 June (11-5).

6 ALL SAINTS
Di Thompson

CAIRNGORM
Station Road. Peter & Ann Almond

EAST VIEW
Town Street. Maureen Almond

FIELD VIEW
5 Sandsfield Avenue. Mrs L Wollaston

Four contrasting gardens offering different approaches to gardening style.- A contemporary garden; a small garden making a big impression with good use of vertical height; a more traditional garden with mixed and evergreen planting; and lastly a cottage garden, tucked out of sight. 6 All Saints is planned like a maze with a mixture of contemporary and cottage garden features; hidden corners, water features and pond. Cairngorm has gravelled areas and paths, conifers, ferns, hostas, a vegetable plot, log cabin and greenhouse and new feature for this year. East View, hidden away, is a long narrow garden with cottage herbaceous planting. Hostas and ferns set off a water feature near the cottage and a wildlife pond can be found at the bottom of the garden. Field View is a small garden intensively planted with a mix of evergreen and deciduous small trees, shrubs and herbaceous perennials to provide a tranquil and private space with all-year-round interest and colour.

Through moon gate to secluded late summer border and seating area with countryside view . . .

104 SKIPWITH HALL
Skipwith, nr Selby YO8 5SQ. Mr & Mrs C D Forbes Adam, 01757 288381, rosalind@escrick.com, www.escrick.com/hall-gardens. *9m S of York, 6m N of Selby. From York A19 Selby, L in Escrick, 4m to Skipwith. From Selby A19 York, R onto A163 to Market Weighton, then L after 2m to Skipwith.* Home-made teas. **Adm £5, chd free. Wed 11 June (1-4). Visitors also welcome by appt June to July, groups of 10+.**
4-acre walled garden of Queen Anne house (not open). Ancient mulberry, extensive mixed borders and Cecil Pinsent designed 'Richard's Garden'. Recreated working kitchen garden with 15' beech hedge, pleached fruit walks, herb maze and pool. Woodland with specimen trees and shell house. Decorative orchard with trained fruit on walls. Secret Italian garden - hopefully reopened in 2014. Gravel paths.

GROUP OPENING

105 STAMFORD BRIDGE GARDENS

Stamford Bridge YO41 1PD, 01759 373838, dmt9245@hotmail.co.uk. *Stamford Bridge. Approx 7m E of York on A166 to Bridlington. Please use main car park in village or station car park on Church Rd.* **Combined adm £5, chd free. Sun 20 July (12-5). Visitors also welcome by appt July to Aug, groups of 10+.**

DANESWELL HOUSE
Brian & Pauline Clayton
01759 371446

GROVE LODGE
2 Butts Close, off High Catton Rd. Mr & Mrs G Tattersall

MILL TIMBER
2 Viking Close, off Viking Road. Mr & Mrs K Chapman

Three interesting and contrasting gardens situated in the historic village of Stamford Bridge. Grove Lodge is a plantsman's garden with a large collection of plants grown from seed or propagated from cuttings. There are small number of vegetables grown in planters, fruit trees and greenhouse that contains a variety of salad vegetables. Mill Timber has a good collection of perennials in a large sloping border. The garden is sheltered on one side by mature trees. Patio planters with summer flowers and hanging baskets displaying a kaleidoscope of colour. Daneswell House is a ³/₄ -acre terraced garden that sweeps down to the R Derwent. Pond and water feature with walk over bridge. Large lawned area with mixed borders and shrubs. Attracts wildlife.

106 ◆ STILLINGFLEET LODGE

Stewart Lane, Stillingfleet, nr York YO19 6HP. Mr & Mrs J Cook, 01904 728506, www.stillingfleetlodgenurseries.co.uk. *6m S of York. From A19 York-Selby take B1222 towards Sherburn in Elmet. In village turn opp church.* Home-made teas. **Adm £5, chd £1. For NGS: Suns 11 May; 7 Sept (1-5). For other opening times and information, please phone or see garden website.**

Plantsman's garden subdivided into smaller gardens, each based on colour theme with emphasis on use of foliage plants. Wild flower meadow and natural pond. 55yd double herbaceous borders. Modern rill garden. Rare breeds of poultry wander freely in garden. Adjacent nursery. Featured in Daily Mail and York Press. Gravel paths and lawn. Ramp to cafe if needed.

Children will be involved in a variety of activities to demonstrate the use of the grounds . . .

107 NEW SUTTON GRANGE

Masham, Ripon HG4 4PB. Mr & Mrs Robert Jameson. *1¹/₂ m W of Masham. From Masham towards Leyburn (A6108) L into Sutton Lane single track tarmac rd, parking & entry at Low Sutton ¹/₄ m on L.* Wine and ice cream in the garden. **Adm £5, chd free. Sun 22 June (11-5). Combined with Low Sutton.**

1¹/₂ acre established garden and orchard with woodland walk incl greenhouse with tomatoes and fig tree, walled vegetable garden with cutting flower beds and gazebo, summerhouse lawns surround by herbaceous borders with iris, roses, peonies, wisteria, and clematis, laburnum and honeysuckle arches, many places to sit and enjoy the views or have a game of croquet or boules.

108 SWALE COTTAGE

Station Road, Richmond DL10 4LU. Julie Martin & Dave Dalton. *Richmond town centre. On foot, facing bottom of Market Place, turn L onto Frenchgate, then R onto Station Rd. House 1st on R.* Home-made teas. **Adm £3, chd free. Sun 15 June (1-5). Also open Millgate House.**

¹/₂ -acre urban oasis on steep site, with sweeping views and hidden corners. Several enclosed garden rooms on different levels. Mature herbaceous, rose and shrub garden with some areas of recent improvement. Magnificent yew and cedar. Organic vegetables and soft fruit and pond. Adjacent orchard and paddock with sheep and hens. Featured in Amateur Gardening. Some rough paths and inaccessible areas.

109 TERRINGTON HOUSE

Terrington YO60 6PU. Mr & Mrs James Fenwick, 01653 648470, lindatex7@yahoo.com, Www.lindafenwickshelldesign.com. *15m NE of York. Last house in village on R if coming from Sheriff Hutton or 1st on L coming from A64 & Castle Howard rd.* Home-made teas. **Adm £4, chd free. Suns 11 May; 15 June (11-4). Visitors also welcome by appt May to June, for groups of 10+.**

Formal garden set in 3 acres with exquisite Shell House, herbaceous and mixed borders. Spring: mixed beds of brunnera, narcissi, tulips, azaleas, daffodils, bluebells, rhododendrons, roses, peonies, hostas. Summer: delphiniums. Impressive trees including split-leaf beech, herb garden parterre and vegetable garden. The Shell House. Featured in Yorkshire Post Saturday Magazine, The Lady Magazine Country and Homes and Interiors.

110 NEW TICKTON CE PRIMARY

Main Street, Tickton, Beverley HU17 9RZ. Miss C Brown. *E of Beverley. Tickton is signed from A1035.* Light refreshments. **Adm £2.50, chd free. Fri 27 June (10-3).**

At Tickton school we actively encourage outdoor learning including gardening. The aim is to provide a stimulating environment for play and educational activities whilst creating habitats for wildlife. Children will be involved in a variety of activities to demonstrate the use of the grounds. Many of the refreshments will have been prepared by the children. Wheelchair access to most of the garden including the refreshment area.

111 WARLEY HOUSE GARDEN

Stock Lane, Warley, Halifax HX2 7RU. Dr & Mrs P J Hinton, www.warleyhousegardens.com. *2m W of Halifax. Take A646 (Burnley) from Halifax. Go through large intersection after approx 1m. Approx 1m further take a R turn up Windle Royd Lane.* Light refreshments. **Adm £4, chd free. Suns 11 May; 13 July**

(1-5). **Combined adm £5 with Edgeholme 13 July.**
Partly walled 2½ -acre garden of demolished C18 House, renovated by the present owners. Rocky paths and Japanese style planting leads to lawns and lovely S-facing views. Alpine ravine planted with ferns and fine trees give structure to the developing woodland area. Drifts of shrubs, herbaceous plantings, wild flowers and heathers maintain constant seasonal interest. WC available to accommodate wheelchairs. Limited wheelchair access to Japanese garden. Disabled parking on site is permitted but limited.

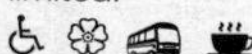

112 WESTFIELD FARM

Melbourne, York YO42 4SX. Carol & Howard Wilson. *10m SE of York. From York follow B1228 from Grimston r'about, through Elvington & Sutton on Derwent to Melbourne. Garden is ½ m before village on L.* Light refreshments. **Adm £3, chd free. Sun 22 June (1-6).**
A 1½ -acre garden partly situated in original farm fold yard. Features incl, herb garden with box hedging, vegetable garden with raised beds and greenhouse; fruit trees, shrubs and numerous borders and beds. Ornamental fish pond with reedbed filter, wildlife pond, footbridge over stream to woodland area. Rare breed pigs and sheep in field. limited wheelchair access.

113 THE WHITE HOUSE

Husthwaite YO61 4QA. Mrs A Raper, 01347 868688, audrey.husthwaite@btinternet.com. *5m S of Thirsk. Turn R off A19 signed Husthwaite. 1½ m to centre of village opp parish church.* Light refreshments. **Adm £5, chd free. Visitors welcome by appt, any size group.**
Meet an enthusiastic plantswoman. Exchange ideas and visit a 1-acre country garden. Walled garden, conservatory, herbaceous borders, fresh lavender and purple palette in late spring and hot summer border. Unusual plants and shrubs. Collections of pÊonies, clematis and hemerocallis (in season), landscaping, planting and bed of English and shrub roses in the old orchard. A garden for all seasons.

Butterfield Heights

GROUP OPENING

114 WHIXLEY GARDENS

nr York YO26 8AR. *8m W of York, 8m E of Harrogate, 6m N of Wetherby. 3m E of A1(M) off A59 York-Harrogate. Signed Whixley.* Home-made teas at The Old Vicarage. **Combined adm £6, chd free. Wed 18, Sun 29 June (11-5).**

ASH TREE HOUSE
Mr & Mrs E P Moffitt
Visitors also welcome by appt May to July with other Whixley gardens.
01423 331424
epmoff@btinternet.com

COBBLE COTTAGE
John Hawkridge & Barry Atkinson
Visitors also welcome by appt May to Aug groups of 10+.
01423 331419
johnbarry44@talktalk.net

NEW **LYDIATE HOUSE**
Roger & Sheila Lythe
Visitors also welcome by appt May to July open with other Whixley gardens.
01423 330178
sheila.lythe@hotmail.co.uk

THE OLD VICARAGE
Church Street. Mr & Mrs Roger Marshall

Attractive rural yet accessible village nestling on the edge of the York Plain with beautiful historic church and Queen Anne Hall (not open). The gardens are spread throughout the village with good footpaths. A plantsman's and flower arranger's garden at Cobble Cottage has views to the Hambleton Hills. Further towards the village centre are two small well designed gardens on sloping sites. Ash tree House with extensive rock garden and borders full of established herbaceous plants, shrubs and roses creating a tapestry of soft colour and textures achieving a cottage garden effect and Lydiate House, recently redesigned, with sloping alpine rockeries, naturalistic borders, foliage plants and unusual perennials. Close to the church, The Old Vicarage, with a ¾ -acre walled flower garden, overlooks the old deer park. The walls, house and various structures are festooned with climbers. Gravel and old brick paths lead to hidden seating areas creating the atmosphere of a romantic English garden.

16 St Matthews Court, Beverley Hidden Town Gardens

115 NEW WINDSONG
Sand Lane, Osgodby, Selby YO8 5HT. Mr & Mrs Alan Gladwin. *1m N of Selby. From A19 take A63 (Hull). After Garden Centre fork L into village at telephone box.* Light refreshments. **Adm £3, chd free. Sun 13 July (1-4).**
Small south facing bungalow cottage garden. Large mixed borders giving yr-round interest, collection of hemerocallis, salvias and some tropical planting. Patios, pergola, rill and brick path lead through moon gate to secluded late summer border and seating area with countryside view. Featured in Yorkshire Post. Limited wheelchair access, narrow paths.

116 WOODLANDS COTTAGE
Summerbridge, Nidderdale HG3 4BT. Mr & Mrs Stark, 01423 780765, www.woodlandscottagegarden.co.uk. *10m NW of Harrogate. On the B6165 W of Summerbridge.* Light refreshments. **Adm £3, chd free. Sun 11 May (1.30-5). Also open 13 July with Dacre Banks & Summerbridge Gardens. Visitors also welcome by appt May to Aug.**
A one-acre country garden created by its owners and making full use of its setting, which includes natural woodland with wild bluebells and gritstone boulders. There are several gardens within the garden, from a wild flower meadow and woodland rock-garden to a formal herb garden and herbaceous areas; also a productive fruit and vegetable garden. Gravel paths with some slopes.

117 ◆ YORK GATE
Back Church Lane, Adel, Leeds LS16 8DW. Perennial, 0113 2678240, www.yorkgate.org.uk. *5m N of Leeds. 2¼ m SE of Bramhope, signed from A660. Park in Church Lane in lay-by opp church and take public footpath through churchyard to garden.* **For opening times and information, please phone or see garden website.**
One-acre masterpiece and outstanding example of late C20 garden design. A series of smaller gardens with different themes and in

contrasting styles are linked by a succession of delightful vistas. Striking architectural features play a key role throughout the garden which is also noted for its exquisite detailing.

118 YORKE HOUSE

Dacre Banks, Nidderdale HG3 4EW. Tony & Pat Hutchinson, 01423 780456, pat@yorkehouse.co.uk, www.yorkehouse.co.uk. *4m SE of Pateley Bridge, 10m NW of Harrogate, 10m N of Otley. On B6451 near centre of Dacre Banks. Car park.* Cream teas. **Adm £4, chd free. Sun 22 June (1-5). Also open with Dacre Banks & Summerbridge Gardens. Visitors also welcome by appt June to Aug, coaches welcome, for groups of 10+.**

Award-winning flower arranger's 2-acre garden with colour-themed borders full of flowering and foliage plants. Water feature incl large ornamental ponds and stream with attractive waterside plantings. Other features incl nut walk, rose walk, patios, gazebo, millennium garden and wildlife areas. Large collection of hosta. The garden enjoys beautiful views across Nidderdale. Orchard picnic area. Winner Harrogate's Glorious Gardens. Featured in Harrogate Advertiser. All main features accessible to wheelchair users.

119 NEW ◆ THE YORKSHIRE ARBORETUM

Castle Howard, York YO60 7BY, 01653 648598, www.yorkshirearboretum.org. *15m NE of York. Off A64. Follow brown signs to Castle Howard then look for Yorkshire Arboretum signs at the obelisk r'about.* Light refreshments. **Adm £6, chd £3 (12-16) under 12 free. For NGS: Sat 7 June (10-6). For other opening times and information, please phone or see garden website.**

A glorious, 120 acre garden of trees from around the world set in a stunning landscape of parkland, lakes and ponds. With woodland walks and lakeside trails, tours, family activities, cafË and gift shop we welcome visitors of all ages wanting to enjoy the space, serenity and beauty of this sheltered valley as well as those with an interest in our extensive collection of trees and shrubs. Internationally renowned collection of trees in a beautiful setting, accompanied by a diversity of wild flowers, birds, insects and other wildlife. Not suitable for wheelchairs. Motorised buggies available on loan, please book 24hrs in advance.

Yorkshire County Volunteers

County Organisers

East Yorks Louise Martin, Fawley House, 7 Nordham, North Cave HU15 2LT, 01430 422266, louisem200@hotmail.co.uk

North Yorks - Districts of Hambleton, Richmond, Ryedale, Scarborough & Cleveland Josephine Marks, Carlton Hall, Carlton Husthwaite, Thirsk YO7 2BR, 01845 501626, carlton331@btinternet.com

West & South Yorks & North Yorks District of Craven, Harrogate, Selby & York Bridget Marshall, The Old Vicarage, Whixley, York YO26 8AR, 01423 330474, biddymarshall@btopenworld.com

County Treasurer

Angela Pugh, Savage Garth, Nun Monkton, York YO26 8ER, 01423 330456, amjopugh@clannet.co.uk

Publicity

Felicity Bowring, Lawkland Hall, Austwick, Lancaster LA2 8AT, 01729 823551, diss@austwick.org

County Booklet Advertising – Clubs and Societies Secretary

John Plant, Rewela Cottage, Main Street, Skewsby YO61 4SG, 01347 888125, plantjohnsgarden@btinternet.com

Assistant County Organisers

East Yorks Ian & Linda McGowan, 36 Weghill Road, Preston, Hull HU12 8UN, 01482 896492, adnil_magoo@yahoo.com

East Yorks Natalie Verow, The Old Rectory, Bugthorpe, York YO41 1QG, 01759 368444, natalieverow@aol.com

East Yorks Kate Willans, New House, Belvedere Park, Hornsea HU18 1JJ, 01964 534502, kwkatewillans32@googlemail.com

North Yorks Gill Mellor, Hunmanby Grange, Wold Newton, Driffield YO25 3HS, gill.mellor@btconnect.com

North Yorks Judi Smith, Low Sutton, Sutton Lane, Marsham HG4 4PB, 01765 688565, lowsutton@hotmail.co.uk

West & South Yorks Deborah Bigley, The Old Rectory, Great Langton, Northallerton DL7 0TA, 01609 748915, debsandbobbigley@btinternet.com

West & South Yorks Veronica Brook, Church House, Moor Lane, Arkendale, Knaresborough HG5 0QU, 01423 340845, veronicabowring@me.com

West & South Yorks Jane Cooper, The Old Vicarage, 14 Marsh Lane, Shepley, Huddersfield, West Yorkshire HD8 8AE 01484 604232 coopers_shepley@btinternet.com

West & South Yorks Rosie Hamlin, The Red House, 17 Whin Hill Road, Bessacarr, Doncaster DN4 7AF, 01302 535135, rosiehamlin@aol.com

West & South Yorks Jane Hudson, Lower Crawshaw, Emley, Huddersfield HD8 9SU, 01924 840980, janehudson42@btinternet.com

Mead Lodge, Carmarthenshire & Pembrokeshire

WALES

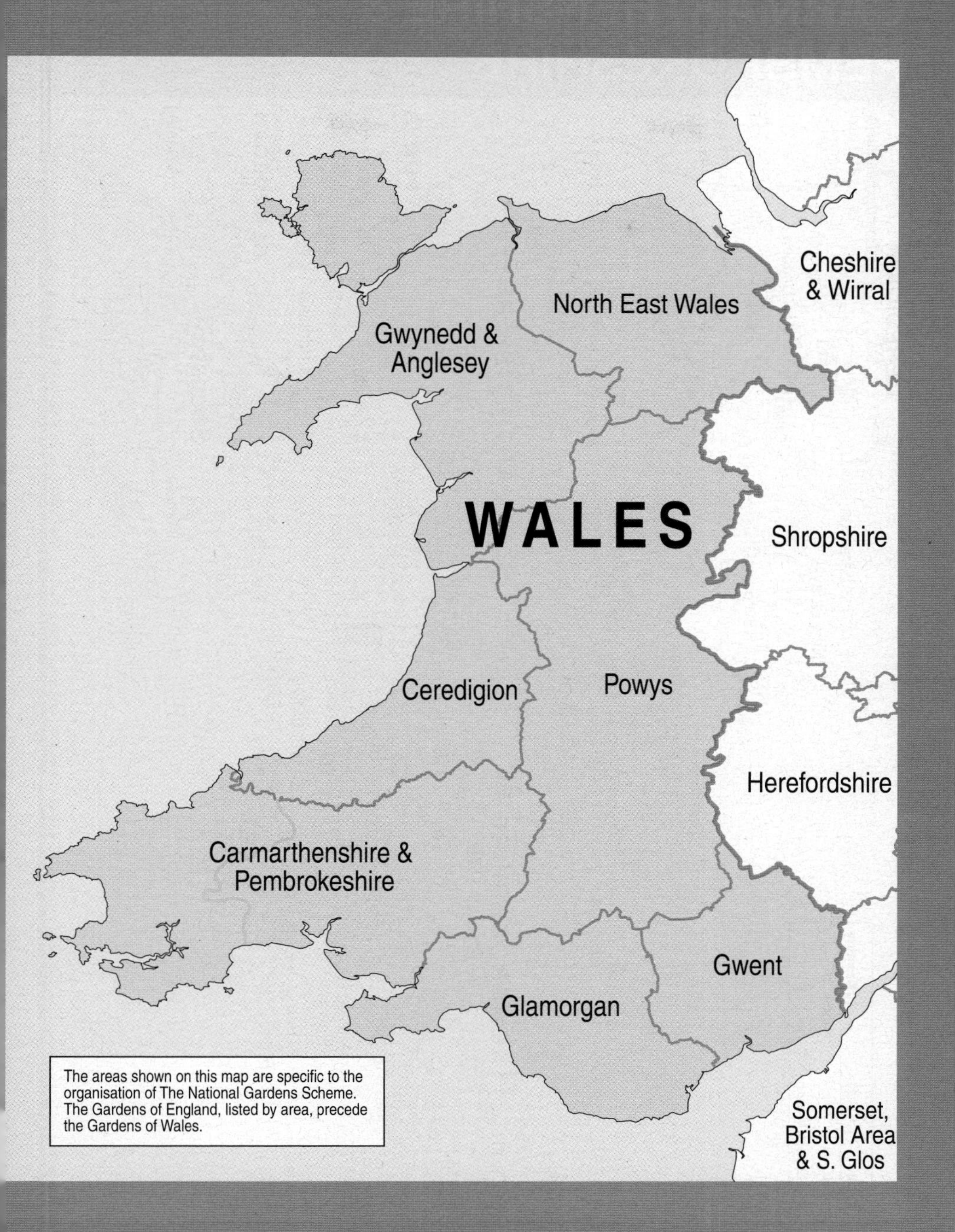
Cheshire
& Wirral
North East Wales
Gwynedd &
Anglesey
WALES
Shropshire
Ceredigion
Powys
Herefordshire
Carmarthenshire &
Pembrokeshire
Gwent
Glamorgan
The areas shown on this map are specific to the organisation of The National Gardens Scheme. The Gardens of England, listed by area, precede the Gardens of Wales.
Somerset,
Bristol Area
& S. Glos

CARMARTHENSHIRE & PEMBROKESHIRE

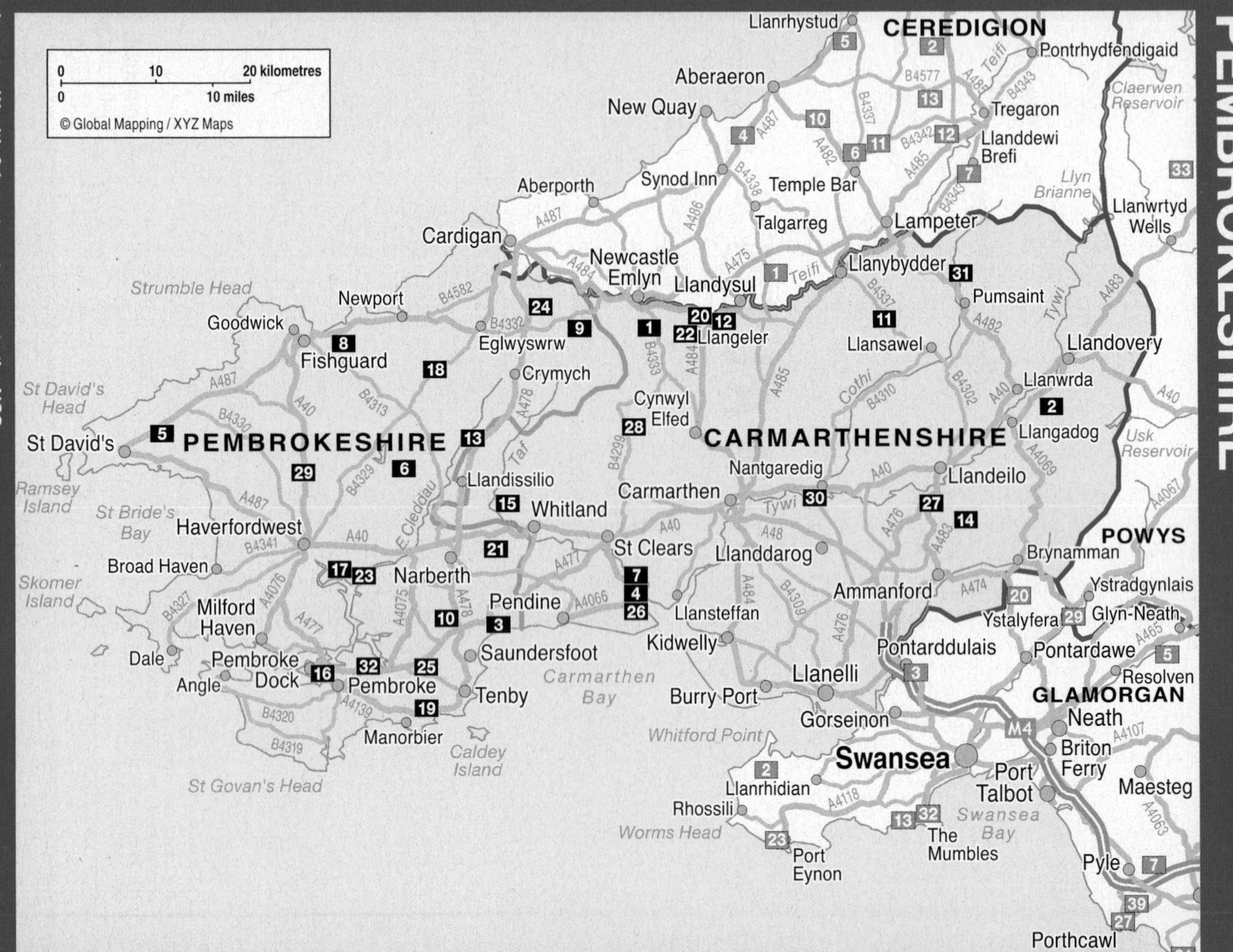

Opening Dates

All entries subject to change. For latest information check www.ngs.org.uk

April

Open daily 1 April to 15 April
5 **The Crystal Garden**

Saturday 19
15 Llwyngarreg

Sunday 20
15 Llwyngarreg

May

Open Daily 1 May to 15 May
5 **The Crystal Garden**

Open daily (excl Weds) 10 May onwards
18 **Moorland Cottage Plants**

Sunday 4
29 Treffgarne Hall

Sunday 11
9 Ffynone

Saturday 17
3 Colby Woodland Garden

Sunday 18
3 Colby Woodland Garden
8 Dyffryn Fernant

Sunday 25
15 Llwyngarreg
21 Panteg
23 Picton Castle & Gardens

Saturday 31
22 Pant-y-Fedwen

June

Open daily 1 June to 15 June
5 **The Crystal Garden**

Open daily (excl Weds)
18 **Moorland Cottage Plants**

Sunday 1
27 Talardd

Festival Weekend

Sunday 8
1 Blaenfforest

Sunday 15
1 Blaenfforest

Saturday 21
13 NEW Glyn Bach

Sunday 22
13 NEW Glyn Bach
32 Upton Castle Gardens

Saturday 28
28 Tradewinds

Sunday 29
10 Foxways
15 Llwyngarreg
28 Tradewinds

July

Open daily 1 July to 15 July
5 **The Crystal Garden**

Open daily (excl Weds)
18 **Moorland Cottage Plants**

Saturday 5
12 Glandwr
19 Norchard (Evening)

Sunday 6
12 Glandwr

Sunday 13
29 Treffgarne Hall

Sunday 20
25 Rosewood
26 Swan Cottage

Friday 25
16 Mead Lodge

Saturday 26
16 Mead Lodge

Sunday 27
16 Mead Lodge

Monday 28
16 Mead Lodge

August

Open daily 1 Aug to 15 Aug
5 **The Crystal Garden**

Open daily (excl Weds)
18 **Moorland Cottage Plants**

Sunday 3
8 Dyffryn Fernant
31 Ty'r Maes

Saturday 9
13 NEW Glyn Bach
15 Llwyngarreg

Sunday 10
13 NEW Glyn Bach
15 Llwyngarreg
28 Tradewinds

Saturday 16
13 NEW Glyn Bach

Sunday 17
13 NEW Glyn Bach
23 Picton Castle & Gardens

September

Open daily 1 Sept to 15 Sept
5 **The Crystal Garden**

Open daily (excl Weds)
18 **Moorland Cottage Plants**

Sunday 7
8 Dyffryn Fernant

Gardens open to the public

3 Colby Woodland Garden
8 Dyffryn Fernant
23 Picton Castle & Gardens
32 Upton Castle Gardens

By appointment only

2 Cilgwyn Lodge
4 The Cors
6 Cwm Pibau
7 Delacorse
11 Gelli Uchaf
14 Llwyn Cyll
17 Millinford
20 The Old Vicarage
24 Rhosygilwen Mansion
30 Ty Castell

A place to write poetry . . . !

Also open by appointment

1 Blaenfforest
5 The Crystal Garden
12 Glandwr
13 Glyn Bach
15 Llwyngarreg
16 Mead Lodge
18 Moorland Cottage Plants
21 Panteg
22 Pant-y-Fedwen
25 Rosewood
27 Talardd
29 Treffgarne Hall
31 Ty'r Maes

The Gardens

1 BLAENFFOREST

Newcastle Emlyn, Carmarthenshire SA38 9JD. Sally & Russell Jones, 01559 371264, enquiries@blaenfforest.co.uk, www.cottageholidayswales.com. *2m S of Newcastle Emlyn. From Newcastlle Emlyn take A484 to Carmarthen, Turn R on B4333. From Carmarthen take A484 to Cardigan, L on B4333 at Cynwyl Elfed.* Light refreshments. **Adm £3.50, chd free. Sun 8, Sun 15 June (11-5). Visitors also welcome by appt May to July.**
Relaxed and tranquil gardens incl stunning views from the patio, lush planting by the wildlife ponds, interesting, tucked away corners, bees in the orchard and Woodland Walk, deep in the valley of the R Arad. Peacocks roam freely. Children to be supervised. A place to write poetry! Limited wheelchair access to some parts of gardens.

2 CILGWYN LODGE

Llangadog, Carmarthenshire SA19 9LH. Keith Brown & Moira Thomas, 01550 777452, keith@cilgwynlodge.co.uk, www.cilgwynlodge.co.uk. *3m NE of Llangadog village. Turn off A40 into Llangadog. Bear L in front of village shop then 1st R to Myddfai. After 2½ m pass Cilgwyn Manor on L then 1st L. Garden ¼ m on L.* **Adm £4, chd free. Visitors welcome by appt June to Sept. Teas available on request when booking for 16+.**

A well established and much-admired 1-acre garden with something for everyone. Wide variety of plants displayed in extensive colour-themed borders, large collection of hostas, many herbaceous perennials, hardy, and tender, common, rare or unusual. Traditional vegetable and fruit garden and large waterlily pond and Koi Pond. 'A Welsh Wonderland'. One of the first gardens to be featured in Daily Mail App. Mail Plus. Partial wheelchair access.

Marie Curie
Cancer Care
Mare Curie is the leader in end of life care research

3 ◆ COLBY WOODLAND GARDEN

Narberth, Amroth, Pembrokeshire SA67 8PP. National Trust, 01834 811885, www.nationaltrust.org.uk. *6m N of Tenby. 5m SE of Narberth. Follow brown tourist signs on coast rd & A477.* **Adm £5.40, chd £2.70. For NGS: Sat 17, Sun 18 May (10-5). For other opening times and information, please phone or see garden website.**

8-acre woodland garden in a secluded valley with fine collection of rhododendrons and azaleas. Wildflower meadow and stream with rope swings and stepping stones for children to explore and play. Ornamental walled garden incl unusual gazebo, designed by Wyn Jones, with internal tromp l'oeil. Incl in the *Register of Historic Parks and Gardens: Pembrokeshire*. Extensive play area for children incl den building and log climbing. Free family activities incl duck racing, pond dipping, campfire lighting etc. Limited access for wheelchair users.

4 THE CORS

Newbridge Road, Laugharne, Carmarthenshire SA33 4SH. Nick Priestland, 01994 427219, nickpriestland@hotmail.com, www.thecors.co.uk. *12m SW of Carmarthen. From Carmarthen, turn R in centre of Laugharne at The Mariners PH. At bottom of Newbridge Rd on R. Please use public car parks, 5 mins walk.* Light refreshments. **Adm £3.50, chd free. Visitors welcome by appt Apr to Sept. Please request refreshments when booking.**

Approx 2½ acres set in beautiful wooded valley bordering river. Large bog garden with ponds, *Gunnera*, bamboos and tree ferns. Exceptional, elegant plantsman's garden with unusual architectural and exotic planting incl *Tetrapanax papyrifer*, *Blechnum chilense* chusan palms and sculptures. Wheelchair access to garden dependent on weather conditions.

5 THE CRYSTAL GARDEN

Golwg yr Ynys, Carnhedryn, St Davids, Pembrokeshire SA62 6XT. Mrs Sue Clark, 01437 721082, sueclark132@gmail.com, www.golwgyrynys.com. *4m E of St Davids, 11m SW of Fishguard, 2m N of Solva. Village of Carnhedryn, off A487 between Fishguard & St Davids.* **Adm £3, chd free. Tue 1 Apr to Tue 15 Apr incl; Thur 1 May to Thur 15 May incl; Sun 1 June to Sun 15 June incl; Tue 1 July to Tue 15 July incl; Fri 1 Aug to Fri 15 Aug incl; Mon 1 Sept to Mon 15 Sept incl (1-6). Visitors also welcome by appt Mar to Oct.**

A ¾ acre garden for plantaholics with yr-round floral colour and foliage interest. Intriguing layout of sheltered 'rooms' full of surprises packed with unusual shrubs, perennials and garden favourites. Ever-changing outer garden. The garden never stands still. Specialities incl hebes and hydrangeas. A warm welcome awaits. Art Wall, Glazed visitor room.

6 CWM PIBAU

New Moat, Haverfordwest, Pembrokeshire SA63 4RE. Mrs Duncan Drew, 01437 532454. *10m NE of Haverfordwest. 3m SW of Maenclochog. Off A40, take B4313 to Maenclochog, follow signs to New Moat, pass church, then 2nd concealed drive on L, ½ m rural drive.* **Adm by donation. Visitors welcome by appt. Please telephone first to ensure a warm welcome.**

5-acre woodland garden surrounded by old deciduous woodland and streams. Created in 1978, contains many mature, unusual shrubs and trees from Chile, New Zealand and Europe, set on S-facing sloping hill. More conventional planting nearer house.

7 DELACORSE

Laugharne, Carmarthenshire SA33 4QP. Annie Hart, 01994 427728, annie.hart@ymail.com, www.buntysblog.co.uk. *13m SW of Carmarthen. A4066 from St Clears 1st L after Cross Inn at 'No Footway' sign. At bend (1/2m) straight down farm track. On foot, riverside path from Dylan Thomas Museum (20mins).* **Adm £4, chd free. Visitors welcome by appt Apr to Oct. Discount for groups 10+.**

3-acre garden beside Taf Estuary in peaceful, beautiful landscape with fine views. Scented walled garden with chamomile lawn; sheltered courtyard; fernery; mixed borders with all-yr interest; living willow work; lawns; specimen trees; millpond; orchard. Carefully managed informal areas merging into woodland, reed beds and salt marsh. Extensive organic kitchen garden. Comprehensive information available on how to grow fruit, vegetables and herbs. Managed 6 acre woodland providing fuel for biomass/solar heating installation. Wheelchair access to all of garden except millpond and orchard.

8 ◆ DYFFRYN FERNANT

Llanychaer, Fishguard, Pembrokeshire SA65 9SP. Christina Shand & David Allum, 01348 811282, christina@dyffrynfernant.co.uk, dyffrynfernant.co.uk. *3m E of Fishguard, then ½ m inland. Off A487 towards Llanychaer, on L.* **Adm £5,**

chd free. For NGS: Sun 18 May, Sun 3 Aug, Sun 7 Sept (11-6). For other opening times and information, please phone or see garden website.
'The gardens ambitions are many: to be colourful at all seasons, to provide a fascinating journey through a score of different spaces and atmospheres, to create some rich and surprising planting' Stephen Anderton in Discovering Welsh Gardens. 6 acres incl ornamental grasses, a marsh packed with wild flowers, wide views of the Preseli landscape as well as many highly cultivated areas made 'With a drama and flair rarely seen' Noel Kingsbury in The Garden. Teas on NGS days and for pre-booked groups of 10 or more. Featured in The Garden,'Cultivating a sense of Place', and filmed for BBC Gardener's World.

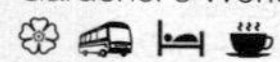

9 FFYNONE

Newchapel, Boncath, Pembrokeshire SA37 0HQ. With the kind permission of the Honourable Robert Lloyd George, 01239 841610, ffynone.wales@gmail.com, www.ffynone.org. *9m SE of Cardigan. 7m W of Newcastle Emlyn. From Newcastle Emlyn take A484 to Cenarth, turn L on B4332, turn L again at X'rds just before Newchapel.* Light refreshments in tearoom. **Adm £3.50, chd free.**
For NGS: Sun 11 May (1-5).
Large woodland garden designated Grade I on Cadw Register of Historic Parks and Gardens in Wales. Lovely views, fine mature specimen trees; formal garden nr house with massive yew topiary; rhododendrons, azaleas, woodland walks and bluebells. House (also Grade I) by John Nash (1793). Later additions and garden terraces by F Inigo Thomas c1904. House open for guided tours by appointment until Oct. House & Garden adm £10, Garden only adm £5 main season, chd over 6 yrs £2. (Donation to NGS 2nd & 4th Sunday pm monthly). New exhibition at Ffynone opening July re history of house and garden with particular reference to collections of rhododendrons and azaleas. Limited wheelchair access. Some steep paths and steps.

10 FOXWAYS

Thomas Chapel, Begelly, Kilgetty, Pembrokeshire SA68 0XH. Roy & Angela Weston. *From S A478 to Narberth. L after 1m by Regent Garage. Continue 1m & round R bend (ignore satnav). Foxways 2nd on R. Parking past house to 1st lane on R.* Home-made teas. **Adm £3, chd free. Sun 29 June (1-5).**.
Recently developed the 3-acre garden has a wide range of plants from dry shade, cottage-garden beds to sunny bog gardens. There are waterfalls and wildlife and ornamental ponds. The garden is for fun and relaxation so seats abound, as do hidden corners to get the most from our plants and their peace and quiet. The planting is textural to complement leaf-colour, size and forms for all-season enjoyment. Limited wheelchair access.

11 GELLI UCHAF

Rhydcymerau, Llandeilo, Pembrokeshire SA19 7PY. Julian & Fiona Wormald, 01558 685119, thegardenimpressionists@gmail.com, www.thegardenimpressionists.co.uk. *5m SE of Llanybydder. 1m NW of Rhydcymerau. In Rhydcymerau on B4337 turn up Mountain Rd for Llanllwni (by BT phone Box). After about 300yds turn R up farm track, cont ½ m bearing R up hill.* **Adm £3, chd free. Visitors welcome by appt 20 Feb - 22 March (11.30-3) Thurs, Fris, Sats only and everyday from Sun 23 March - Fri 31 Oct (10.30-4). Cream teas and light refreshments available by prior arrangement.**
Complementing a C17 longhouse and 11 acre smallholding. Beautiful 1-acre garden. Stunning views, meadow walks and masses of flowers from Feb to Nov. Unique fruit/vegetable garden with 50+ fruit trees. Comments from visitors: 'Magic around every corner'; 'Truly wonderful. Gardens within a garden and amazing plants and natural effects'. For photos through the year see our blog http://www.thegardenimpressionists.wordpress.com. Exhibition of images and artwork created from photographs of moths and butterflies taken in the garden; and of the restoration of the house and creation of the garden. Featured in Amateur Gardening, Finalist at Hay Festival in The English Garden & Wiggly Wigglers 'Green and Gorgeous Garden' Competition.

Glyn Bach

12 GLANDWR

Pentrecwrt, Llandysul, Carmarthenshire SA44 5DA. Mrs Jo Hicks, 01559 363729, leehicks@btinternet.com. *15m N of Carmarthen, 2m S of Llandysul, 7m E of Newcastle Emlyn. On A486. At Pentrecwrt village, take minor rd opp Black Horse PH. After bridge keep L for 1/4 m. Glandwr is on R.* **Adm £3, chd free. Sat 5, Sun 6 July (11-5). Visitors also welcome by appt Apr to Sept. Please telephone first.**
Delightful 1-acre cottage garden, bordered by a natural stream with country views. Some single coloured beds, a rockery and many shrubs and climbers. Walk in the mature woodland transformed into an adventurous intriguing place, with shade loving shrubs and plants, ground covers and many surprises.

13 NEW GLYN BACH

Efailwen, Clunderwen, Carmarthenshire SA66 7JP. Peter & Carole Whittaker, 01994 419104, carole.whittaker7@btinternet.com, www.glynbachgardens.co.uk. *Efailwen 8m N of Narberth, 15m S of Cardigan. W off A487 at Glandy Cross garage, follow signs for 1m towards Llangolman.* Home-made teas. **Adm £3, chd free. Sat 21, Sun 22 June, Sat 9, Sun 10, Sat 16, Sun 17 Aug (11-5). Visitors also welcome by appt May to Sept. Please arrange teas when booking.**
6 acre holding; 4 acres woodland and 2 acres of garden with herbaceous and tropical borders, large pond, bog garden and monarda collection. Emphasis on nectar-rich plants for pollinators. Limited wheelchair access on grass pathways.

14 LLWYN CYLL

Llandeilo, Trap, Carmarthenshire SA19 6TR. Liz & John Smith, 01558 822398. *3m SE of Llandeilo. In Trap turn towards Glanaman & Llandybie (at The Cennen Arms). Llwyn Cyll is 1/2 m on L adjoining Llwyn Onn. Coach parking nearby.* Home-made teas. **Adm £3, chd free. Visitors welcome by appt Mar to June. Home-made teas available on request.**
3½ -acre country garden of yr-round interest. Abundant, colourful terraced and walled borders, orchard, highly productive vegetable garden. Sun and shade areas with sympathetic planting. An Enthusiast's garden with many rarities and specimen trees. Up to 30 different magnolias in the arboretum, many in flower late Apr to early June. Scenic views. Limited wheelchair access around house.

Visit in spring, summer and early autumn you will be most welcome . . . !

15 LLWYNGARREG

Llanfallteg, Whitland, Carmarthenshire SA34 0XH. Paul & Liz O'Neill, 01994 240717, lizpaulfarm@yahoo.co.uk. *19m W of Carmarthen. A40 W from Carmarthen, turn R at Llandewi Velfrey, 2½ m to Llanfallteg. Go through village, garden 1/2 m further on: 2nd farm on R.* Home-made teas. **Adm £3.50, chd free. Sat 19, Sun 20 Apr, Sun 25 May, Sun 29 June, Sat 9, Sun 10 Aug (2-6). Combined with Panteg (Llandewi Velfrey) Sun 25 May, adm £6, chd free. Visitors also welcome by appt most days: please check our phone message.**
3-acre plantaholic's haven with yr-round impact, from spring bulbs through to glorious autumn colour; tapestries of colour and texture in the many trees, interspersed with unusual shrubs and perennial underplantings. Willow tunnel welcomes visitors into a maturing shelter belt, beyond which lies the main garden with wide mixed borders. Closely planted areas in front of the house, gravel gardens behind. Woodland garden leads down to the potager. Plantsmen will linger to find many gems. Several deep ponds - children to be closely supervised. Wildlife ponds, twig piles for overwintering insects, composting, numerous living willow structures. Limited wheelchair access. Disabled car park in bottom yard.

16 MEAD LODGE

Imble Lane, Pembroke Dock, Pembrokeshire SA72 6PN. John & Eileen Seal, 01646 682504, eileenseal@aol.com. *From A4139 between Pembroke & Pembroke Dock take B4322 signed Pennar & Leisure Centre. After 1/2 m turn L into Imble Lane. Mead Lodge at end.* Home-made teas. **Adm £3, chd free. Fri 25, Sat 26, Sun 27, Mon 28 July (11-5). Visitors also welcome by appt Apr to Sept. Please request teas when booking.**
Unexpected, secluded country garden, a relaxing oasis on S-facing slope overlooking the Pembroke River estuary. Varied 3/4 acre garden reflects the owners' keen interest in ferns, grasses and herbs. Incl terraces with Chinese and Mediterranean influences, colour-themed beds, small arboretum underplanted for spring colour, Fernery, vegetable garden, pond and bog garden.

17 MILLINFORD

The Rhos, Haverfordwest, Pembrokeshire SA62 4AL. Drs B & A Barton, 01437 762394. *3m E of Haverfordwest. From Haverfordwest on A40 to Carmarthen, turn R signed The Rhos, take turning to Millin. Turn R at Millin Chapel then immed L over river bridge.* **Adm £3, chd free. Visitors welcome by appt throughout the year. Please request teas when booking.**
Beautiful, spacious, and peaceful garden of 5 acres on bank of Millin Creek. Varied collection of over 125 trees; horse chestnuts, rowans, catalpas, many unusual conifers, plus shrubs, herbaceous plants and bulbs. Impressive terracing and water features. Visit in spring, summer and early autumn you will be most welcome!

18 MOORLAND COTTAGE PLANTS

Rhyd-y-Groes, Brynberian, Pembrokeshire SA41 3TT. Jennifer & Kevin Matthews, 01239 891363, jenny@moorlandcottageplants.co.uk, www.moorlandcottageplants.co.uk. *12m SW of Cardigan. 16m NE of Haverfordwest, on B4329, 3/4 m downhill from cattlegrid (from Haverfordwest) & 1m uphill from signpost to Brynberian (from Cardigan).* **Adm £3, chd £0.50 (share to Paul Sartori Foundation). Every Mon, Tue, Thur, Fri, Sat & Sun 10 May to 30 Sept (10.30-5.30). Visitors also welcome by appt May to Sept.**
1½ -acres at 700ft on NE hillside overlooking a vast wilderness.

Exuberant and diverse plantings provide propagating material for the adjacent nursery. Secretive, enclosed areas where carpets of spring flowers give way to jungly perennials, grasses, bamboos and ferns contrast with formal herbaceous borders and extensive shrubberies. Stunning mountain and moorland vistas. Garden entirely organic. Mollusc-proof plantings.

19 NORCHARD

The Ridgeway, Manorbier, Tenby, Pembrokeshire SA70 8LD. Ms H E Davies. *4m W of Tenby. From Tenby, take A4139 for Pembroke. 1/2 m after Lydstep, take R at X'rds. Proceed down lane for 3/4 m. Norchard on R.* **(share to The Little Princess Trust). Evening Opening £12, chd £3, wine, Sat 5 July (5-8). For advanced tickets please call 07790 040278 or 01437 741115.**

Historic gardens at medieval residence. Nestled in tranquil and sheltered location with ancient oak woodland backdrop. Strong structure with formal and informal areas incl early walled gardens with Elizabethan parterre and potager (currently undergoing restoration). 1 1/2 acre orchard with old (many local) apple varieties. Mill and millpond. Extensive collections of roses, daffodils and tulips. Live music, wine and canapes, exhibition of paintings, licensed bar! Limited wheelchair access due to gravel paths. Access to potager via steps only.

20 THE OLD VICARAGE

Llangeler, Carmarthenshire SA44 5EU. Mr & Mrs J C Harcourt, 01559 371168. *4m E of Newcastle Emlyn. 15m N of Carmarthen on A484. From N Emlyn turn down lane on L in Llangeler before church.* Home-made teas. **Adm £2.50, chd free. Visitors welcome by appt May to Aug. Please request teas when booking!**

A garden gem created since 1993. Less than 1 acre divided into 3 areas of roses, shrubs and a semi-formal pool with an interesting collection of unusual herbaceous plants. Ever changing scene. The last 2 winters have taken their toll so some re-invention has been needed. Optimum colour, mid-June onwards. Gravel yard - temporary ramp available.

21 PANTEG

Llanddewi Velfrey, Narberth, Pembrokeshire SA67 8UU. Mr & Mrs D Pryse Lloyd, 01834 860081, d.pryselloyd@btinternet.com. *Situated off main A40 in the village of Llanddewi Velfrey. A40 from Carmarthen, after garage take 1st L. At next T- junction turn L. On R gateway with stone gate pillars which is 1/2 m drive to Panteg.* **Adm £3, chd free. Sun 25 May (2-6). Combined with Llwyngarreg (Llanfallteg), Sun 25 May, adm £6, chd free. Visitors also welcome by appt Mar to Sept please telephone first!**

Approached down a woodland drive, this tranquil, S-facing, large garden, surrounding a Georgian house (not open), has been developed since early 1990s. A Plantsman's garden set off by lawns on different levels. Walled garden, wisteria covered pergola. Vegetable garden, camellia and azalea bank, wild flower woodland. Many rare shrubs and plants incl, Embothrium, Eucryphia and Hoheria.

22 PANT-Y-FEDWEN

Drefelin, Drefach Felindre, Llandysul SA44 5XB. Steven & Viki Harwood, 01559 371807, steven@harwoodsartsandcrafts.co.uk, www.harwoodsartsandcrafts.co.uk. *Drefach Felindre is signed from A484 approx 16m from Carmarthen & Cardigan, 5m from Newcastle Emlyn. Check website for detailed directions.* Home-made teas. **Adm £2.50, chd free. Sat 31 May (11-4). Visitors also welcome by appt.**

Small front garden with stream, surrounded by lush architectural plantings. Hillside garden on 6 terraces behind house, informally managed, with unusual plants and various seating areas giving views over the valley. Quirky garden of about 1/3 acre, on 5 levels, culminating in a tranquil woodland garden. For the physically adept only. Arts and Crafts for sale in Workshop.

23 ◆ PICTON CASTLE & GARDENS

The Rhos, Haverfordwest, Pembrokeshire SA62 4AS. Picton Castle Trust, 01437 751326, info@pictoncastle.co.uk, www.pictoncastle.co.uk. *3m E of Haverfordwest. On A40 to Carmarthen, signed off main rd.* Light refreshments. **Adm £6.50, chd £4. For NGS: Sun 25 May, Sun 17 Aug (10.30-5). For other opening times and information, please phone or see garden website.**

Mature 40-acre woodland garden with unique collection of rhododendrons and azaleas, many bred over 42yrs, producing hybrids of great merit and beauty; rare and tender shrubs and trees incl *Magnolia*, myrtle, *Embothrium* and *Eucryphia*. Wild flowers abound. Walled garden with roses; fernery; herbaceous and climbing plants and large clearly-labelled collection of herbs. Exciting art exhibitions and a wide range of seasonal events. Please see website for details. Some woodland walks unsuitable for wheelchair users.

24 RHOSYGILWEN MANSION

Rhoshill, Cilgerran, Cardigan, Pembrokeshire SA43 2TW. Glen Peters & Brenda Squires, 01239 841387, enquiries@retreat.co.uk, www.rhosygilwen.co.uk. *6m S of Cardigan. From Cardigan follow A478 signed Tenby. After 6m turn L at Rhoshill towards Cilgerran. After 1/4 m turn R signed Rhosygilwen. Mansion gates 1/2 m.* Light refreshments. **Adm £3, chd free. Visitors welcome by appt Apr to Sept. Light Refreshments on request when booking.**

20 acres of garden in 55 acre estate. Pretty 1/2 m drive through woodland planting. Spacious lightly wooded grounds for leisurely rambling, superb 1-acre walled garden fully productive of fruit, vegetables and flowers; authentically restored Edwardian greenhouses, many old and new trees, small formal garden. Children must be supervised please. Gravel paths around garden. Full disabled facilities.

25 ROSEWOOD

Redberth, nr Tenby, Pembrokeshire SA70 8SA. Jan & Keith Treadaway, 01646 651405. *3m SW of Kilgetty. On W side of village on old A477, now bypassed. Parking by side of rd or in field if dry.* Home-made teas. **Adm £3, chd free. Sun 20 July (1-5). Visitors also welcome by appt Apr to Sept, groups of 10+.**
Intimate well-maintained 1/4 -acre garden, cleverly designed in different areas. Abundant colourful mixed plantings with many exotic species and a collection of clematis in bloom all yr, but especially in Summer. A new pergola with clematis and other climbers, as well as a growing collection of grasses and ferns. In the field opposite a fruit and vegetable area with raised beds has been redeveloped. Featured in Pembrokeshire Life and Tenby Observer. Limited wheelchair access to parts of garden.

26 SWAN COTTAGE

20 Gosport Street, Laugharne, Carmarthenshire SA33 4SZ. Geoffrey Brown, 01994 427409. *Laugharne town centre. A4066 to Laugharne & park in central car park by castle. Swan Cottage is a short, uphill, walk towards Pendine on A4066 (500yds).* Home-made teas. **Adm £2.50, chd free. Sun 20 July (2-6).**
A small well-maintained town garden packed with great variety of plants, shrubs, trees and bamboos as well as ponds, rockeries and gravel area. Plantings show how small areas can provide colour and structure for yr long interest. Fine views overlooking the Taf estuary and the castle.

27 TALARDD

Golden Grove, Carmarthen, Carmarthenshire SA32 8NN. Mr Steve Bryan, 01558 822418, steve@stevebryan.org.uk. *Off A476 between Crosshands & Llandeilo. R 6m N of Crosshands, L 1 1/2 m S of Llandeilo on A476 nr Z bends. Lane marked by Renault garage sign. Turn L at T junction follow signs to Talardd.* **Adm £4, chd free (share to Robert Dickie Charitable Trust). Sun 1 June (2-6). Visitors also welcome by appt Apr to Oct. Please request teas when booking!**
The historic house is set above the stream with its banks of primulas, astilbes, *Gunnera* and diverse bog garden plants. Nearby is the productive walled kitchen garden, surrounded by beds of herbaceous plants and grasses. Elsewhere, extensive grassed areas are planted with unusual trees, shrubs and spring bulbs. There is also a riverside walk and boules court! The garden covers some 5 acres. Guided tours if requested. Wheelchair access to kitchen garden and part of woodland areas on bound gravel paths.

28 TRADEWINDS

Ffynnonwen, Pen-y-Bont, nr Trelech, Carmarthen, Carmarthenshire SA33 6PX. Stuart & Eve Kemp-Gee. *10m NW of Carmarthen. From A40 W of Carmarthen, take B4298 to Meidrim, then R onto B4299 towards Trelech. After 5m turn R at Tradewinds sign.* **Adm £3, chd free. Sat 28, Sun 29 June, Sun 10 Aug (11.30-5).**
2 1/2 -acre plantsman's garden with abundance of herbaceous perennials, shrubs and trees giving yr-round interest. Mixed borders, natural streams and pond. Picturesque garden in tranquil setting. 100' grass, 100' herbaceous and 80' conifer borders. The arboretum incl *Quercus cerris* 'Argenteovariegata', *Aralia elata* 'Variegata', *Salix fargesii* plus numerous rhododendrons and azaleas. Stream banks planted with many moisture loving plants. Vegetable plot. Many rare and unusual plants to be seen.

29 TREFFGARNE HALL

Treffgarne, Haverfordwest, Pembrokeshire SA62 5PJ. Martin and Jackie Batty, 01437 741115, bathole2000@aol.com. *7m N of Haverfordwest, signed off A40. Proceed up through village & follow rd round sharply to L, Hall 1/4 m further on L.* Home-made teas. **Adm £3.50, chd free. Sun 4 May, Sun 13 July (1-5). Visitors also welcome by appt.**
Stunning hilltop location with panoramic views: handsome Grade II listed Georgian house (not open) provides formal backdrop to garden of four acres with wide lawns and themed beds. A walled garden, with double rill and pergolas, is planted with a multitude of borderline hardy exotics. Also large-scale sculptures, summer broadwalk, meadow patch, gravel garden, heather bed and stumpery. Planted for yr-round interest. The planting schemes are the owner's, and seek to challenge the boundaries of what can be grown in Pembrokeshire.

Delightful riverside walks with otters, kingfishers, jumping salmon and more to be seen along the way with stunning sunsets . . .

30 TY CASTELL

Station Road, Nantgaredig, Carmarthen SA32 7LQ. Paul & Steve, 01267 290034, tycm@ty-castell.co.uk, www.ty-castell.co.uk. *5m E of Carmarthen town. 10m W of Llandeilo. A40 W from Llandeilo heading to Carmarthen for 10.3m until the village of Nantgaredig L into Station Rd R after the Railway Inn. Sat Nav not accurate.* Light refreshments. **Adm £3, chd free. Visitors welcome by appt Apr to Sept. Lunch menu available.**
1/4 -acre of tranquil garden on the banks of the river Towy with walks and wildlife. Gardens segmented into chill out rooms featuring a pond and waterfall with herbaceous borders, trees, shrubs, rockery, lawned areas boasting panoramic views of the Towy valley and on the doorstep of the National Botanic and Aberglasney Gardens. Delightful riverside walks with otters, kingfishers, jumping salmon and more to be seen along the way with stunning sunsets.

31 TY'R MAES

Ffarmers, Llanwrda, Carmarthenshire SA19 8JP. John & Helen Brooks, 01558 650541, johnhelen@greystones140.freeserve.co.uk. *7m SE of Lampeter. 8m NW of Llanwrda. 1 1/2 m N of Pumsaint on A482, opp turn to Ffarmers.* Home-made teas. **Adm £3, chd free. Sun 3 Aug (1-5). Visitors also welcome by appt Mar to Oct. Please request teas when booking!**

3-acre garden with splendid views. Herbaceous and shrub beds - formal design, exuberantly informal planting, full of cottage garden favourites and many unusual plants. Burgeoning arboretum (200+ types of tree); formal and wildlife ponds, pergola, gazebos, post and rope arcade covered in climbers. Gloriously colourful; spring (rhododendrons, azaleas, primulas, 1000's bulbs); late summer (tapestry of annuals/perennials). Craft, produce, books and jewellery stalls. Some gravel paths.

32 ◆ UPTON CASTLE GARDENS

Cosheston, Pembroke Dock SA72 4SE. Prue & Stephen Barlow, 01646 689996, info@uptoncastle.com, www.uptoncastlegardens.com. *4m E of Pembroke Dock. 2m N of A477 between Carew & Pembroke Dock. Follow brown signs to Upton Castle Gardens through Cosheston.* Light refreshments. **Adm £4, chd free. For NGS: Sun 22 June (10-4.30). For other opening times and information, please phone or see garden website.**

Lovely location in a tranquil valley leading to the upper reaches of the Cleddau estuary. 35 acres of mature gardens & arboretum; many rare trees and shrubs surrounding the C13 castle (not open) and C12 century chapel.. Formal rose gardens, herbaceous borders, productive walled kitchen garden, wild flower meadow, woodland walks to estuary. Walk on the Wild Side: New woodland walks funded by Countryside Council for Wales and Welsh Assembly Government. Featured in The Times:Twenty Best Gardens with Cottages and on Channel 4: The Time Team. Limited wheelchair access.

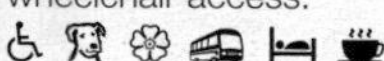

Moorland Cottage Plants

Carmarthenshire & Pembrokeshire County Volunteers

County Organiser

Mrs Jane Stokes, Llyshendy, Llandeilo SA19 6YA, 01558 823233, jane.h.stokes@btinternet.com

County Treasurer

Mrs Christine Blower, Glangwilli Lodge, Llanllawddog, Carmarthen SA32 7JE, 01267 253334, cheahnwood@toucansurf.com

Publicity

Carms Mrs Jane Stokes, Llyshendy, Llandeilo SA19 6YA, 01558 823233, jane.h.stokes@btinternet.com

Assistant County Organisers

Mrs Jackie Batty, Treffgarne Hall, Treffgarne, Haverfordwest, Pembs SA62 5PJ, 01437 741115, bathole2000@aol.com
Mr Ivor Stokes, Llyshendy, Llandeilo SA19 6YA, 01558 823233, ivor.t.stokes@btopenworld.com

CEREDIGION

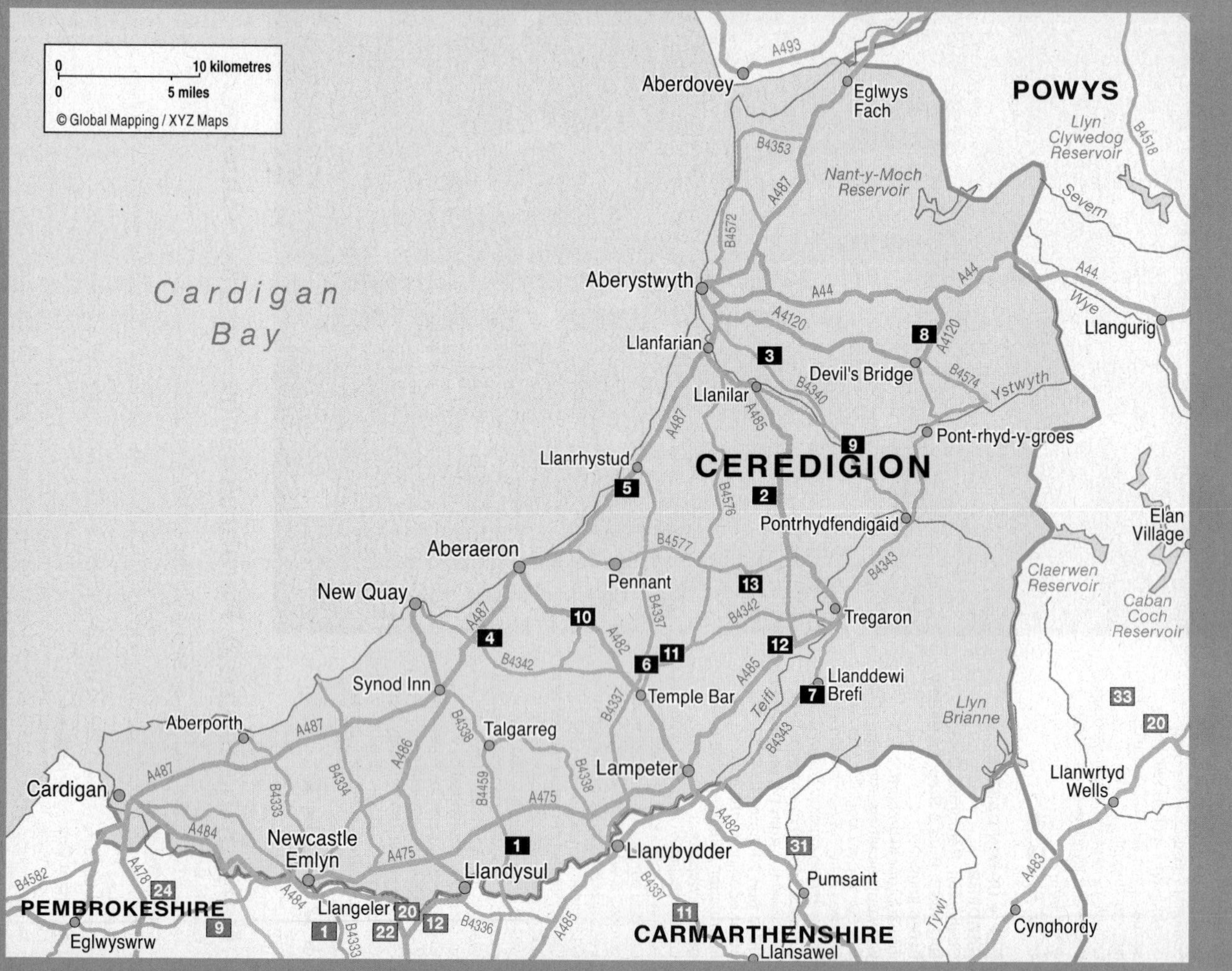
10 kilometres
5 miles
© Global Mapping / XYZ Maps
Cardigan Bay
POWYS
CEREDIGION
CARMARTHENSHIRE
PEMBROKESHIRE
Aberdovey
Eglwys Fach
Llyn Clywedog Reservoir
Nant-y-Moch Reservoir
Severn
Wye
Llangurig
Aberystwyth
Llanfarian
Devil's Bridge
Ystwyth
Llanilar
Pont-rhyd-y-groes
Llanrhystud
Pontrhydfendigaid
Elan Village
Claerwen Reservoir
Caban Coch Reservoir
Aberaeron
Pennant
New Quay
Tregaron
Synod Inn
Temple Bar
Llanddewi Brefi
Teifi
Llyn Brianne
Aberporth
Talgarreg
Lampeter
Llanwrtyd Wells
Cardigan
Newcastle Emlyn
Llandysul
Llanybydder
Pumsaint
Tywi
Llangeler
Eglwyswrw
Cynghordy
Llansawel

Opening Dates

All entries subject to change. For latest information check www.ngs.org.uk

May

Sunday 18
3 Bwlch y Geuffordd

Sunday 25
1 Alltyrodyn Mansion

June

Festival Weekend

Sunday 8
11 Winllan Wildlife Garden

Sunday 15
8 NEW Pantygorlan

Sunday 22
6 Llanllyr
11 Winllan Wildlife Garden

Sunday 29
7 Pantyfod
13 Ysgoldy'r Cwrt

July

Sunday 20
7 Pantyfod
12 Yr Efail

Saturday 26
9 NEW Penybont

Sunday 27
9 NEW Penybont
10 Ty Glyn Walled Garden

August

Sunday 3
13 Ysgoldy'r Cwrt

Sunday 10
5 Gwynfryn

Sunday 17
7 Pantyfod

Gardens open to the public

10 Ty Glyn Walled Garden

By appointment only

2 Bwlch y Geuffordd
4 Castell Pigyn

Also open by appointment

1 Alltyrodyn Mansion
5 Gwynfryn
6 Llanllyr
12 Yr Efail
13 Ysgoldy'r Cwrt

The Gardens

1 ALLTYRODYN MANSION

Capel Dewi SA44 4PS. Mr & Mrs Donald Usher, 01545 590206. *8m W of Lampeter, off A475. Take B4459 at Rhydowen to Capel Dewi. Entrance on R by South Lodge.* Home-made teas. **Adm £4, chd free (share to Capel Dewi Village Church). Sun 25 May (11-5). Visitors also welcome by appt May to Sept.**

Early C19 garden. Approx 8 acres, mostly mature woodland with many fine trees. Rare stone-built gothic cold bathhouse. Early C20 lake, Dutch garden and rhododendron plantings. Garden is best in spring when rhododendrons and azaleas are in bloom. Large and interesting plant stall. A garden with interesting walks. Limited wheelchair access due to slopes and steps.

2 BWLCH Y GEUFFORDD

Bronant, Aberystwyth SY23 4JD. Mr & Mrs J Acres, 01974 251559, gayacres@aol.com. *6m NW of Tregaron. 12m SE of Aberystwyth, 6m NW of Tregaron off A485. Take turning opp Bronant school for 1½ m then L up ½ m track.* **Adm £3.50, chd 50p. Visitors are welcome anytime, but advisable to phone first.**

1000ft high, 3-acre, constantly evolving wildlife garden featuring a lake and several pools. There are a number of themed gardens, incl Mediterranean, cottage garden, woodland, oriental, memorial and jungle. Plenty of seating. Unique garden sculptures and buildings, incl a cave, gazebo and jungle hut. Developing as a healing garden for those dealing with cancer. Pond dipping available by appointment. 'Treasure' hunt available for children. Unique garden art and buildings. Featured in - 'The Holy Wells of Wales' by Phil Cope, and 'Mynydd Bach - Ei Hanes Its History' by Eirian Jones.

3 BWLCH Y GEUFFORDD

New Cross, Aberystwyth SY23 4LY. Manuel & Elaine Grande, 01974 261196. *4½ m SE of Aberystwyth. Off A487, onto A4120 Devil's Bridge Rd. & immed R on B4340 Trawsgoed rd. Garden 3m on R at bottom of small dip. Park in lay-bys.* Home-made teas. **Adm £3.50, chd free. Sun 18 May (10.30-4.30).**

1-acre hillside garden, with lovely views of the surrounding countryside. Herbaceous borders, bog garden, ponds with waterfall, azaleas, rhododendrons and bluebells in May. New courtyard area. Some steep paths and steps make parts of the garden unsuitable for those with mobility problems.

4 CASTELL PIGYN

Llanarth SA47 0PT. Mrs Wendy Thacker, 01545 580014. *1m N of Llanarth, 3m S of Aberaeron. On A487 midway Cardigan-Aberystwyth. White cottage close to rd, on L when travelling N. Parking for 1 minibus & 1 car on drive.* Light refreshments. **Adm £3.50, chd free. Visitors welcome by appt Apr to Aug 11am - dusk (excl Weds & Suns). Max group 12.**

Knowledgable plantswoman's garden developed from old orchard. Paths wind through herbaceous borders full of hardy geraniums, roses, shrubs and trees. Many varieties of clematis and hellebores. Bog garden, incl gunnera. Fernery, dry river bed, grasses, hostas. 4 wildlife ponds with frogs, newts and dragonflies. Old apple varieties. Seating.

Stunning views over Cardigan Bay . . .

5 GWYNFRYN

Llanrhystud SY23 5BY. Sue Pester, 01974 200948, sueruffles123@gmail.com. *Between Llanrhystud & Llanon, on A487. 1m S of Llanrhystud, after 'Hidden Dip' rd sign. Entrance to garden where rd sign indicates L turn.* Home-made teas. **Adm £3.50, chd free. Sun 10 Aug (2-6). Visitors also welcome by appt July to Sept.**

Large garden of 11 acres with woodland, incl over 20 varieties of cherries, paddocks, large vegetable and soft fruit areas. Lawns, herbaceous borders, pond, fuchsia hedges, poultry and other livestock. Stunning views over Cardigan Bay. Level garden, but with gravel and grass paths.

6 LLANLLYR

Talsarn, Lampeter SA48 8QB. Mr & Mrs Robert Gee, 01570 470900, lgllanllyr@aol.com. *6m NW of Lampeter. On B4337 to Llanrhystud.* Home-made teas. **Adm £4, chd free.** Sun 22 June (2-6). **Visitors also welcome by appt May to Sept.**
Large early C19 garden on site of medieval nunnery, renovated and replanted since 1989. Large pool, bog garden, formal water garden, rose and shrub borders, gravel gardens, laburnum arbour, allegorical labyrinth and mount, all exhibiting fine plantsmanship. Yr-round appeal, interesting and unusual plants. Specialist plant fair by Ceredigion Growers Association. Garden Owner has been selected by The National Botanic Garden of Wales as one of only six present-day Inspirational Horticulturists of Wales.

7 PANTYFOD

Llanddewi Brefi, Tregaron SY25 6PE. David & Susan Rowe, www.pantyfodgarden.co.uk. *About 3m S of Tregaron. From Llanddewi Brefi village square, take R fork past Community Centre. Go up hill, past Ffarmers turning for approx ¾ m. Pantyfod is on R.* Home-made teas. **Adm £3.50, chd free.** Sun 29 June, Sun 20 July, Sun 17 Aug (12-5.30).
Peaceful well-established 3½ -acre garden with lots of pathways through a wide variety of perennials, trees and shrubs, many unusual. Varying habitats incl terraces, woodland, mature trees, natural ponds. Hardy geraniums, Iris sibirica, grasses and rugosa roses. Wildlife friendly. Stunning, panoramic views of the Teifi Valley and mountains beyond. We are developing a new Sensory Garden. We have a grand Woodfired pizza oven in the garden in which we bake authentic Italian-style thin crust pizzas (available Sun 17 Aug). Gravel paths, steps and steep slopes, but level around the house.

8 NEW PANTYGORLAN

Ystumtuen, Aberystwyth SY23 3AE. Mr & Mrs Winter. *12m E of Aberystwyth. On A44, 1m W of Ponterwyd, turn L for Ystumtuen. At top of hill turn R by parking areas. Disabled parking close to house.* Home-made teas. **Adm £3.50, chd free.** Sun 15 June (10.30-5.30).
3½ acre garden high in Cambrian mountains, comprising small formal garden with pond, rockery, vegetable plot and shrubbery, encompassed by large mixed woodland with walks, carefully sited sculptures and seating. 2 established lakes with waterfalls accommodating a variety of water plants. Steep slopes make part of the garden unsuitable for those with mobility issues.

9 NEW PENYBONT

Llanafan, Aberystwyth SY23 4BJ. Norman & Brenda Jones. *9m SW of Aberystwyth. In Ystwyth valley off B4340. From Aberystwyth, stay on B4340 for 9m, via Trawscoed. R over stone bridge. ¼ m up hill, turn R past row of cream houses.* **Adm £3.50, chd free.** Sat 26, Sun 27 July (11-6).
'Starting with a clean sheet and maturing fast'. Penybont shows what can be achieved from a green field sloping site in just a few years. This exciting and beautifully planted garden has been designed to compliment the modern building, its forest backdrop and panoramic views. Country location with stunning views of the Ystwyth valley. Good level paths around the house, but parts of the garden inaccessible to wheelchair users.

10 ◆ TY GLYN WALLED GARDEN

Ciliau Aeron, Lampeter SA48 8DE. Ty Glyn Davis Trust, 01970 832268, www.tyglyndavistrust.co.uk. *3m SE of Aberaeron. Turn off A482 Aberaeron to Lampeter at Ciliau Aeron signed to Pennant. Entrance 700 metres on L.* Home-made teas. **Adm £3.50, chd free.** For NGS: Sun 27 July (11-5). **For other opening times and information, please phone or see garden website.**
Secluded walled garden in beautiful woodland setting alongside R Aeron, developed specifically for special needs children. Terraced kitchen garden overlooks herbaceous borders, orchard and ponds with child-orientated features and surprises amidst unusual shrubs and perennials. Planted fruit trees selected from former gardener's notebook of C19. Access paths and lower garden are accessible to wheelchairs.

11 WINLLAN WILDLIFE GARDEN

Talsarn, Lampeter SA48 8QE. Joy Silvester & Martin Gillard. *8m NNW of Lampeter. On B4342, Talsarn - Llangeitho, 1m E of Talsarn.* Light refreshments. **Adm £3.50, chd free.** Sun 8, Sun 22 June (11-5).
A 6 acre wildlife garden with 4 acre hay meadow, over 10,000 wild orchids incl the rare Greater Butterfly Orchid. The meadows are subject to SSSI status and in 2013 has been designated as a Coronation Meadow to celebrate the Queens jubilee. The gardens incl a riverbank walk, a small wood, and formal area with large pond.

12 YR EFAIL

Llanio Road, Tregaron SY25 6PU. Mrs Shelagh Yeomans, 01974 299370, shelaghyeo@hotmail.com. *3m SW of Tregaron. Lampeter: A485 - Tregaron. L at Llanio to B4578, Aberystwyth: A487, A485 - Tregaron. At Tyncelyn B4578, 4m on R.* Home-made teas. **Adm £3.50, chd free.** Sun 20 July (11-5). **Visitors also welcome by appt Feb to Oct.**
A vegetable growers paradise, with newly-developed beds growing a wide variety of hardy vegetables in addition to glasshouse and poly tunnels full of tender crops and fruit garden. Established ornamental area of nearly 1 acre with large pond, herbaceous borders, bog and gravel gardens and shaded areas. Quiz sheet for children. Gravelled paths accessible to wheelchairs but grass paths difficult when wet.

Woodfired pizza oven in the garden in which we bake authentic Italian-style thin crust pizzas . . .

13 YSGOLDY'R CWRT
Llangeitho, Tregaron SY25 6QJ. Mrs Brenda Woodley, 01974 821542. *1½ m N of Llangeitho. Llangeitho, turn L at school signed Penuwch. Garden 1½ m on R. From Cross Inn take B4577 past Penuwch Inn, R after brown sculptures in field. Garden ¾ m on L.* Home-made teas. **Adm £3.50, chd free. Sun 29 June, Sun 3 Aug (11-5). Visitors also welcome by appt Apr to Aug 2pm - dusk.**

1 acre hillside garden, with 4 natural ponds which are a magnet for wildlife. Areas of wild flower meadow, bog, dry and woodland gardens. Newly established rose walk. Rare trees, large herbaceous beds, acer collection, bounded by a mountain stream, with 2 natural cascades, and magnificent views. Children must be supervised because of steeply sloping ground.

Bwlch y Geuffordd

Ceredigion County Volunteers

County Organiser
Pat Causton, Plas Treflys, Llangwyryfon, Aberystwyth SY23 4HD, 01974 272619, dandpcauston@btinternet.com

County Treasurer
Steve Yeomans, Yr Efail, Llanio Road, Tregaron SY25 6PU, 01974 299370, s.j.yeomans@btinternet.com

Assistant County Organiser
Lisa Raw-Rees, The Old Mill, Water Street, Aberaeron SA46 0DG, 01545 570107, hywelrawrees@hotmail.com

Bring a bag for plants – help us give more to charity

GLAMORGAN

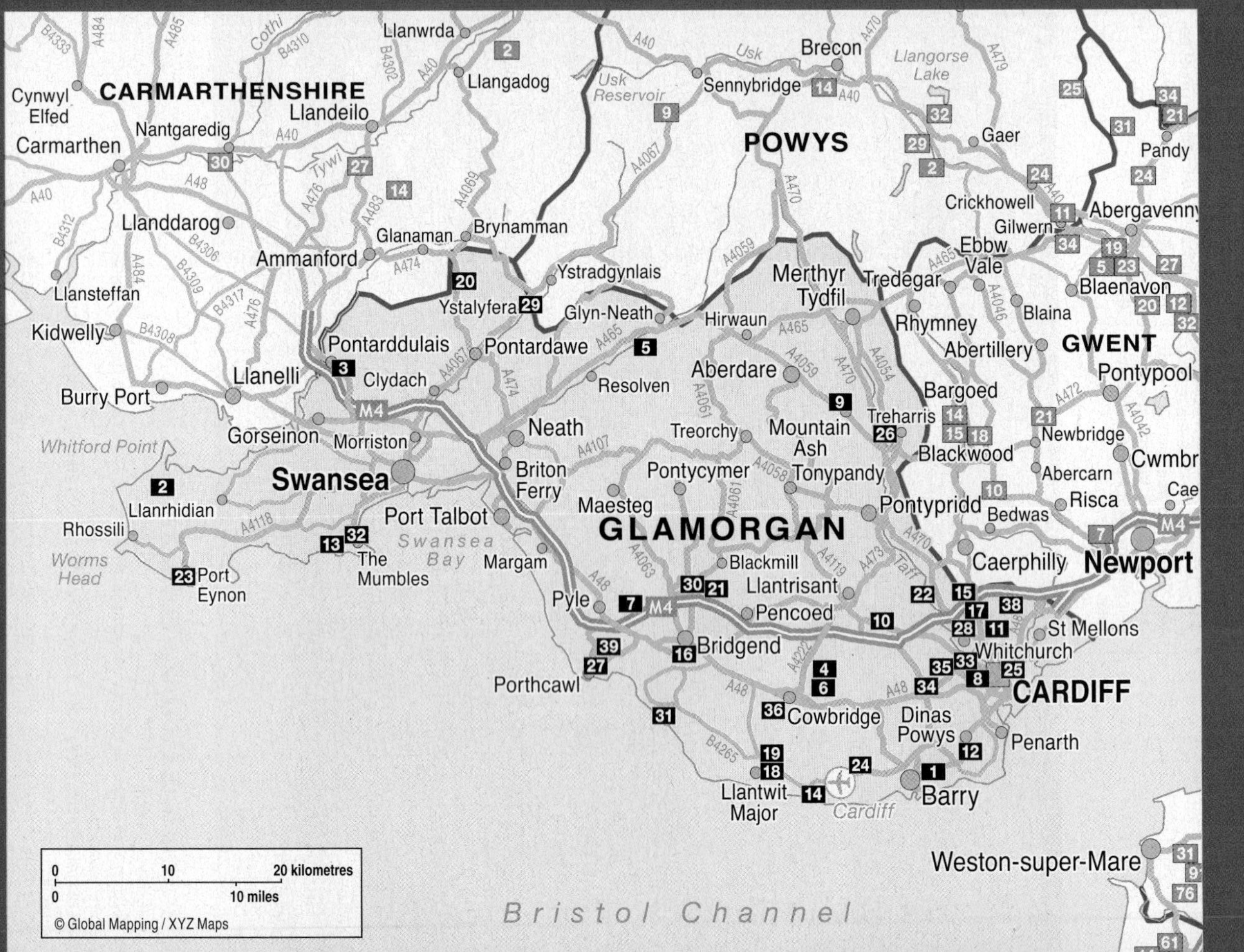

CARMARTHENSHIRE
POWYS
GWENT
GLAMORGAN
CARDIFF
Newport
Swansea
Bristol Channel
Swansea Bay
Cynwyl Elfed
Carmarthen
Nantgaredig
Llandeilo
Llanwrda
Llangadog
Usk Reservoir
Sennybridge
Brecon
Llangorse Lake
Gaer
Pandy
Crickhowell
Abergavenny
Gilwern
Ebbw Vale
Blaenavon
Blaina
Tredegar
Rhymney
Abertillery
Pontypool
Merthyr Tydfil
Hirwaun
Glyn-Neath
Ystradgynlais
Brynamman
Glanaman
Ammanford
Llanddarog
Llansteffan
Kidwelly
Burry Port
Llanelli
Pontarddulais
Clydach
Pontardawe
Ystalyfera
Resolven
Aberdare
Mountain Ash
Treharris
Bargoed
Blackwood
Newbridge
Abercarn
Cwmbran
Risca
Bedwas
Caerphilly
Pontypridd
Tonypandy
Treorchy
Pontycymer
Maesteg
Neath
Briton Ferry
Gorseinon
Morriston
Whitford Point
Llanrhidian
Rhossili
Worms Head
Port Eynon
The Mumbles
Port Talbot
Margam
Pyle
Porthcawl
Bridgend
Blackmill
Llantrisant
Pencoed
Cowbridge
Llantwit Major
Cardiff
Barry
Dinas Powys
Penarth
Whitchurch
St Mellons
Weston-super-Mare
0 10 20 kilometres
0 10 miles
© Global Mapping / XYZ Maps

Opening Dates

All entries subject to change. For latest information check www.ngs.org.uk

April

Saturday 26
31 Slade

Sunday 27
31 Slade

May

Saturday 10
38 Ty'n Y Berllan

Sunday 11
38 Ty'n Y Berllan

Sunday 18
20 22 Llwyn Road

Saturday 24
26 Pontygwaith Farm

Sunday 25
17 Japanese Garden
18 NEW Knightsbridge
19 Llanmaes Gardens
26 Pontygwaith Farm
36 St. Quintins Cottage

Monday 26
6 Bryn-y-Ddafad
26 Pontygwaith Farm

Wednesday 28
4 Bordervale Plants
6 Bryn-y-Ddafad

Saturday 31
29 Rhos y Bedw

June

Sunday 1
14 Gileston Manor
29 Rhos y Bedw
39 Tyn-y-Caeau Farm

Festival Weekend

Saturday 7
1 Barry Gardens
22 The Old Post Office
29 Rhos y Bedw
31 Slade

Sunday 8
20 22 Llwyn Road
31 Slade
32 19 Slade Gardens

Sunday 15
26 Pontygwaith Farm
27 Porthcawl Gardens

Monday 16
26 Pontygwaith Farm

Wednesday 18
4 Bordervale Plants

Saturday 21
28 Rhiwbina Open Gardens

Sunday 22
2 Big House Farm
7 Cefn Cribwr Garden Club
16 Heronsbridge School
21 Maes-y-Wertha Farm
28 Rhiwbina Open Gardens

Saturday 28
24 Penmark Village Gardens

Sunday 29
25 Penylan Gardens
30 NEW Rose Cottage
34 NEW St. Fagans Church Primary School

July

Saturday 5
15 Hafod y Milgi
33 St Michael's College

Sunday 6
6 Bryn-y-Ddafad
15 Hafod y Milgi

Sunday 13
11 Cyncoed & Llanishen Gardens

Friday 18
5 Brynheulog

Saturday 19
5 Brynheulog
35 NEW St. Peter's Community Garden

Sunday 20
10 Creigiau Village Gardens
35 NEW St. Peter's Community Garden

Saturday 26
1 Barry Gardens
3 NEW Bolgoed Gardens
12 Dinas Powys Village Gardens
23 NEW Overton and Port Eynon Gardens

Sunday 27
3 NEW Bolgoed Gardens
12 Dinas Powys Village Gardens
20 22 Llwyn Road

Tuesday 29
4 Bordervale Plants
6 Bryn-y-Ddafad

August

Sunday 3
13 NEW The Dingle

Monday 25
4 Bordervale Plants

Sunday 31
30 NEW Rose Cottage

September

Tuesday 9
4 Bordervale Plants

Saturday 13
8 NEW Chapter Community Garden

Sunday 14
20 22 Llwyn Road

Gardens open to the public

4 Bordervale Plants

By appointment only

9 The Cottage

Also open by appointment

2 Big House Farm
5 Brynheulog
6 Bryn-y-Ddafad
16 Heronsbridge School
18 Knightsbridge
20 22 Llwyn Road
25 7 Cressy Road, Penylan Gardens
25 5 Southcourt Road, Penylan Gardens
26 Pontygwaith Farm
31 Slade
38 Ty'n Y Berllan

This keen plantswoman's hillside garden perfectly reflects the dramatic setting and surrounding natural beauty . . .

The Gardens

GROUP OPENING

1 BARRY GARDENS

CF63 4PP. *6m SW of Cardiff. From J33 on M4 take A4232 towards Cardiff following signs for Airport. Take 2nd slip rd then at r'about take A4050 & follow signs for Barry.* Home-made teas. **Combined adm £5, chd free. Sat 7 June, Sat 26 July (1-5.30).**

47 ANEURIN ROAD
Dave Bryant

CAE GWYN
Kay & Crandon Villis

28 PORT ROAD EAST
Mrs Lorna Tinsley

76 PORT ROAD EAST
Ms Michele Van Duval

4 gardens of differing styles.
47 Aneurin Rd is an ever changing small vertical garden with a collection of over 30 clematis. Cae Gwyn is a large secret garden with many attractive features incl a large pond, gravel garden, pergolas and sweeping lawns. 28 Port Rd is a mini smallholding with lots of creative, eccentric touches, lush, unmanicured, jungly feel with meandering paths. 76 Port Rd is a newly developed garden with stunning views over the Vale, a wonderful old greenhouse and newly planted borders with more to come.

2 BIG HOUSE FARM

Llanmadoc, Gower, Swansea SA3 1DE. Mark & Sheryl Mead, 07831 725753, sherylandmark@tiscali.co.uk. *15m W of Swansea. M4 J47, L A483 for Swansea, 2nd r'about R, A484 Llanelli 3rd r'about L, B4296 Gowerton T-lights, R B4295, pass Bury Green R to Llanmadoc.* Home-made teas. **Adm £4, chd free. Sun 22 June (1-5.30). Visitors also welcome by appt June to Aug for groups 10+.**

Award winning inspirational garden of just under an acre combines colour form and texture in this beautiful much loved Gower village, described by one visitor as 'the best I've seen this season'. Large variety of interesting plants and shrubs, with ambient cottage garden feel, Mediterranean garden, kitchen garden, beautiful views. Most of garden is accessible to wheelchairs.

4 acres and 35 years of amateur muddling have produced this enchanting garden . . .

GROUP OPENING

3 NEW BOLGOED GARDENS

Bolgoed Road, Pontarddulais, Swansea SA4 8JP. *On A48. N of Pontarddulais. M4 J48 join A4138 to Pontarddulais. Take A48 Swansea. Opp Fountain Inn PH.* Home-made teas. **Combined adm £3, chd free. Sat 26, Sun 27 July (1-5).**

NEW BOLGOED GANOL FARM
Mrs Susan Goss

NEW 146 BOLGOED RD
Mrs Jean Bolton

NEW CAEGLAS
Keith & Christine Stephens

Caeglas garden borders Bolgoed Ganol Farm. The planting is on many levels and incl streams with a lake and a woodland and bog garden. A short stroll along the lake is Bolgoed Ganol Farm cottage garden with its circular lawn and pretty borders. 146 Bolgoed Road is a charming pretty garden with interesting planting.

4 ◆ BORDERVALE PLANTS

Sandy Lane, Ystradowen, Cowbridge CF71 7SX. Mrs Claire Jenkins, 01446 774036, www.bordervale.co.uk. *8m W of Cardiff. 10 mins from M4 or take A4222 from Cowbridge. Turn at Ystradowen postbox, then 3rd L & proceed ½ m, follow brown signs. Garden on R. Parking in rd.* **Adm £3, chd free. For NGS: Wed 28 May, Wed 18 June, Tue 29 July, Mon 25 Aug, Tue 9 Sept (10-5). For other opening times and information, please phone or see garden website.**

Within mature woodland valley (semi-tamed), with stream and bog garden, extensive mixed borders; mini wild flower meadow, providing diverse wildlife habitats. Children must be supervised. The Nursery specialises in unusual perennials and cottage garden plants. Nursery open: Fri - Sun (10-5), (and often open Mon - Thurs) Mar - Sept, when garden is also open May - Sept. NOT FOR NGS. Silver Medal RHS Flower Show Cardiff for Unusual Welsh grown trees and perennials. Wheelchairs can access the top third of garden as well as the Nursery.

5 BRYNHEULOG

45 Heol y Graig, Cwmgwrach, Neath SA11 5TW. Lorraine Rudd, 01639 722593, lorrainejrudd@sky.com. *8m W of Neath. Turn off A465 at McDonalds r'about & take exit for Cwmgwrach. (Yellow NGS sign visible on main r'about). Turn R at mini r'about.* Home-made teas. **Adm £3.50, chd free. Fri 18, Sat 19 July (2-5). Visitors also welcome by appt May to Sept.**

This keen plantswoman's hillside garden perfectly reflects the dramatic setting and surrounding natural beauty. ¾ -acre plot on many levels with cottage style planting, tropical greenhouse, 2 other greenhouses showing Begonias and Carnations, wildflower areas, large rockery and ponds. Polytunnel houses all yr-round vegetables. Lots of scent and colour with roses and lilies. Wildflower planting.

6 BRYN-Y-DDAFAD

Welsh St Donats, Cowbridge CF71 7ST. Glyn & June Jenkins, 01446 774451, junejenkins@bydd.co.uk, www.bydd.co.uk/home/garden *10m W of Cardiff. 3m E of Cowbridge. From A48 follow signs to Welsh St Donats. Follow brown tourist signs from X'rds, Bryn-y-Ddafad is approx 1m from this point.* **Adm £4, chd free. Mon 26, Wed 28 May, Sun 6, Tue 29 July (11-5). Visitors also welcome by appt Apr to Sept.**

Small courtyard garden with raised beds informally planted using pastel shades of annuals, perennials and small shrubs. The terraced rear garden has colourful raised beds and borders, mature trees and shrubs. Lily pond with water feature. Recently constructed and planted pergola of roses leads to a bridge crossing the natural stream. New bog garden and small bank of rhododendrons and azaleas. Most of the garden is accessible by wheelchair.

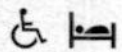

GROUP OPENING

7 CEFN CRIBWR GARDEN CLUB

Cefn Cribwr, Bridgend CF32 0AP. *5m W of Bridgend. Cefn Cribwr is located 5m W of Bridgend on B4281.* Teas at Green Hall Community Centre. **Combined adm £4, chd free. Sun 22 June (11-5).**

6 BEDFORD ROAD
Carole & John Mason

2 BRYN TERRACE
Alan & Tracy Birch

CEFN CRIBWR PRIMARY SCHOOL & ALLOTMENTS
Cefn Cribwr Primary School & Allotments

77 CEFN ROAD
Peter & Veronica Davies & Mr Lee

25 EAST AVENUE
Mr & Mrs D Colbridge

NEW **15 GREEN MEADOW**
Thomas Noble

HILL TOP
Mr & Mrs W G Hodges

6 TAI THORN
Mr Kevin Burnell

21 WEST AVENUE
Mr Martin Morgan

Cefn Cribwr gardening club is the heart of a friendly community. The 9 diverse gardens vary from the local school allotments, an exposed mature garden, a recycled garden, a garden that has its own composting system, a children's garden, a rustic garden, an artists' garden, a productive vegetable garden and lastly a small fascinating garden. Just about something for everyone. Craft stalls, games, raffles, teas, plant stall, local school competition and table top sale, all in Green Hall Community Centre.

The Dingle

8 NEW CHAPTER COMMUNITY GARDEN

Market Road, Canton, Cardiff CF5 1QE. Mr Michael Goode (co-ordinator), www.cantoncommunitygardens.co.uk. *At the front of Chapter Arts Centre. Chapter is situated in Canton, behind Cowbridge Rd East (A4161), between Llandaff Rd (B4267) & Market Rd.* Light refreshments, adm incl tea/coffee and a cake. **Adm £2.50. Sat 13 Sept (10.30-4.30).**
Canton Community Gardens was established in July 2009, with the intention of bringing local people together for a range of gardening, recycling and environmental projects in the area. The Chapter Community Garden is an ongoing project involving members and volunteers of Canton Community Gardens. It was shortlisted for a Big Lunch award organised by the Eden Project for Chapter's Big Lunch in 2012. Featured in South Wales Echo, Federation of City Farms & Community Gardens, on Radio Cymru and S4C's Byw yn yr Ardd. Flat site with excellent wheelchair access.

9 THE COTTAGE

Cwmpennar, Mountain Ash CF45 4DB. Helen & Hugh Jones, 01443 472784, hhjones1966@yahoo.co.uk. *18m N of Cardiff. A470 from N or S. Then follow B4059 to Mountain Ash. Follow signs for Cefnpennar then Cwmpennar.* Home-made teas. **Adm £3.50, chd free. Visitors welcome by appt May to Aug 12.**
4 acres and 35yrs of amateur muddling have produced this enchanting garden incl bluebell wood, rhododendron and camellia shrubbery, herbaceous borders, rose garden, small arboretum, many uncommon trees and shrubs. Garden slopes NE-SW. Featured in 'My Garden' pages of South Wales Echo.

GROUP OPENING

10 CREIGIAU VILLAGE GARDENS

Maes Y Nant, Creigiau CF15 9EJ. *W of Cardiff (J34 M4). From M4 J34 follow A4119 to T-lights, turn R by Castell Mynach PH, pass through Groes Faen & turn L to Creigiau. Follow NGS signs.* Home-made teas 28 Maes-y-Nant and Waunwyllt. **Combined adm £5, chd free.**
Sun 20 July (11-5).

28 MAES Y NANT
Mike & Lesley Sherwood

31 MAES Y NANT
Frances Bowyer

WAUNWYLLT
John Hughes & Richard Shaw

Three interesting and colourful gardens; Waunwyllt is 1m from Maes y Nant. Waunwyllt has been developed over the last 4yrs, taking it from a state of neglect to a tranquil garden with several colour co-ordinated rooms. 28 Maes y Nant is surrounded on 3 sides by cottage style planting, with an area to the side of the house surrounded by native hedging incl a wildlife patch and area of informal mixed planting. 31 Maes y Nant is a unique architect designed garden linked by water to garden room, strong architectural elements supplemented by colourful planting. Incl a colourful 'prairie style' area alongside the property. Waunwyllt featured in SW Echo.

GROUP OPENING

11 CYNCOED & LLANISHEN GARDENS

Cyncoed, Cardiff CF23 6NA. *From Hollybush Rd follow yellow NGS signs to Cyncoed Crescent & Danycoed Rd. Alternatively from Cyncoed Rd, Fidlas Rd or Rhydypenau Rd follow NGS signs.* Home-made teas at 22 Dan y Coed Rd, 8 Cyncoed Cresent and Rhydypenau School. **Combined adm £4, chd free.**
Sun 13 July (12-6).

8 CYNCOED CRESCENT
Alistair & Teresa Pattillo

22 DAN Y COED
Alan & Miranda Workman

KINSLEY, 3 LLYSWEN ROAD
Ms Jill Davey

MOUNT COTTAGE, 166 FIDLAS ROAD
Robert Davies

RHYDYPENAU PRIMARY SCHOOL
Mr Richard Melhuish

This interesting group has rapidly expanded from two to five gardens. Three of the four suburban gardens were carved out of woodland in the 1930's when the houses were built and they are surrounded by trees. The fourth house was originally a Victorian cottage. These gardens have a multitude of shrubs, climbing roses, clematis, hostas, succulents and ferns and many unusual plants. The owners incl sculptures and features in their gardens and spend time on landscaping. 2 of the gardens have been maintained by the same family owners for nearly half a century. The latest addition to the group was Rhydypenau school which has a vibrant array of features incl vegetable and edible flower gardening, ponds and several wildlife areas. The school is providing inspiration to educators nationally and internationally. Not all gardens within walking distance.

GROUP OPENING

12 DINAS POWYS VILLAGE GARDENS

Dinas Powys CF64 4TL. *Dinas Powys is approx 6m SW of cardiff. Exit M4 at J33, follow A4232 to Leckwith, onto B4267& follow to Merry Harrier T-lights. Turn R & enter Dinas Powys. Follow yellow NGS signs.* Home-made teas at most gardens. **Combined adm £4, chd free (share to Dinas Powys charities). Sat 26, Sun 27 July (12-5).**

1 ASHGROVE
Sara Bentley

NEW **BROOKLEIGH**
Mr Duncan Syme

18 MILL ROAD
Edward Jenkins

NEW **30 MILLBROOK ROAD**
Mr & Mrs R Golding

NEW **32 MILLBROOK ROAD**
Mr & Mrs G Marsh

Five gardens in this friendly village, all with something different to offer. 1 Ashgrove is a plantaholic's garden based on permaculture principles, with many unusual perennials growing together with fruit, vegetable, a pond, woodland garden. Brookleigh is a large garden, many specimen trees, 3 colourful herbaceous borders, plus a large established pond and a bog area.18 Mill Rd is an urban garden created 6yrs ago, from what was substantially a vegetable garden. Completely replanted, although still work in progress (isn't that always the case) it is reaching a very pleasant state of maturity.
30 Millbrook Rd is a large beautiful family garden developed over 25yrs with established pond plus several seating areas to relax in. Planting in sun and shade, mature trees and shrubs. Carport for rain refuge!
32 Millbrook Rd is a large garden consisting of many 'rooms' with quirky design features, incl a caravan playhouse. Good wheelchair access at 30 and 32 Millbrook Rd but limited elsewhere.

13 NEW THE DINGLE

Caswell, Swansea SA3 4RT. Paul & Linda Griffiths. *4m W Swansea. Swansea A4067 to Mumbles. Mini r'bout in Mumbles R B4593 L at 2nd T-lights pass Church then follow yellow NGS signs. Park in Caswell Dr.* **Adm £4, chd free. Sun 3 Aug (10.30-3.30).**

The Dingle is a secret garden in Caswell. We have been hard at work for 8 yrs restoring what was an overgrown jungle of weeds, roots and ruins of ancient trees to what is now a blooming and restful oasis.

14 GILESTON MANOR

Gileston, Barry CF62 4HX. Joshua Llewelyn & Lorraine Garrad-Jones, www.gilestoncoachhouse.co.uk. *From Cardiff airport take B4265 to Llantwit Major. After 3m turn L at petrol station. Go under bridge, turn L follow yellow NGS signs. No turning at Cenotaph*. Cream teas. **Adm £5, chd free. Sun 1 June (1-5).**
C18 walled garden and summer house. C19 kitchen garden and woodland/ herbaceous borders in restoration. Lawns and views across the Bristol Channel. Gardens surround the Grade II* listed manor house. Woodland and secret wall garden. Walled garden has flat gravel paths, gravel drive.

15 HAFOD Y MILGI

Heol y Wenallt, Thornhill CF83 1ND. Eric & Angharad Roberts. *4m from Cardiff centre. From Cardiff take A469 to Caerffili, past Thornhill crematorium. House at junction with Wenallt Rd opp Travellers Rest PH. From Caerffili A470 signed*. Home-made teas. **Adm £3, chd free. Sat 5, Sun 6 July (2-5).**
We love our garden and have enjoyed finding plants that survive in this elevated and sometimes windy position. The aim has been to create sheltered places to sit and enjoy the pond, flowers and views of Nofydd Valley and Garth Mountain. Come and enjoy it with us. Short ramp, some sloping paths in addition to flat patio.

16 HERONSBRIDGE SCHOOL

Ewenny Road, Bridgend CF31 3HT. Heronsbridge School, 01446 710423, broadclose1@btinternet.com. *In Bridgend, from A48 turn R onto B4265 Ewenny Rd. School on R*. Home-made teas. **Adm £3, chd free. Sun 22 June (12-4). Visitors also welcome by appt Apr to July for any size group.**
The special needs school which won silver at Chelsea 2011 and gold and Best in Show in RHS Cardiff 2013. You are welcome to visit our sensory kitchen and formal gardens and our heritage orchard, with swings and a willow tunnel. Fantastic homemade cakes made by our children, display of slides from our sister schools in Botswana and Tanzania; imaginative projects for the gardens. Home grown plants for sale. Playground with swings. Beehives, chickens, wild areas, willow tunnel to play in. Disability friendly, as almost all our gardens are purpose built for the disabled. Full access to our afternoon teas and WC.

17 JAPANESE GARDEN

Cardiff CF14 6EE. Mr B A Harding. *Rhiwbina garden village. 1st L after Rhiwbina village shops, on L almost to end of Lon Isa*. **Adm £4. Sun 25 May (11.30-6).**
Typical Japanese style garden with undulating ground, small stream, pond and tea house. Seeks to evoke and imitate nature with the elements being tranquillity, simplicity and harmony. Featured on 'A Little Piece of Paradise' HTV Wales. Maples and pine trees shaped in japanese tradition.

The aim has been to create sheltered places to sit and enjoy the pond, flowers and views . . .

18 NEW KNIGHTSBRIDGE

21 Monmouth Way, Boverton, Llantwit Major CF61 2GT. Don & Ann Knight, 01446 794529, anncknight@hotmail.co.uk. *At Llanmaes rd T- lights turn onto Eagleswell Rd, next L into Monmouth Way, garden half way down on R.* Home-made teas. **Sun 25 May (1-6). Combined with Llanmaes Gardens, combined adm £5, chd free. Visitors also welcome by appt Mar to Sept.**
Japanese garden with a large collection of Bonsai, which incl an English elm, oak, larch etc., pagoda and two water features. Entrance via rear garden.

GROUP OPENING

19 LLANMAES GARDENS

Llanmaes, Llantwit Major CF61 2XR. *5m S of Cowbridge. From West Winds travel S via Church to Church House, continue down lane for 1m to Old Froglands*. Home-made teas incl cakes at Old Froglands and Church House. **Combined adm £5, chd free. Sun 25 May (1-6).**

NEW BROWN LION HOUSE
Mrs Wendy Hewitt-Sayer

NEW CHURCH HOUSE
Kathryn Crook

GADLYS FARM HOUSE
Dot Williams

OLD FROGLANDS
Dorne & David Harris

WEST WINDS
Jackie & Richard Simpson

Llanmaes, a mile from Llantwit Major, is a pretty village with attractive village green, stream running through and C13 church. Old Froglands is an historic farmhouse with streams and woodland areas linked by bridges. Ducks swim and chickens roam free. The vegetable plot is now productive. Plantings are varied with interesting foliage. West Winds is a work in progress. It was a beautiful and much loved garden that sadly became overgrown and is now being reclaimed. Pathways weave through terraces with balustrades, wooded areas and lawns with views over the village and open fields. The garden has a full range of aspects from deep shade to full sun, and is shared and enjoyed with a diverse collection of wildlife. Church House has an extremely pretty cottage garden and has seen significant work and much talking over the past two years. Brown Lion House is a newly renovated garden around mature trees and shrubs with patios and pathways. Gadlys farm House is 1-acre of informal family garden surrounding a C17 farmhouse. Various sitting areas to relax amongst mature trees, herbaceous borders, summerhouse water feature and courtyard with planters. Old Froglands featured in the South Wales Echo.

20 22 LLWYN ROAD

Cwmgors, Ammanford SA18 1RD. Terri Darnbrook, 01269 824635, terriinwales@yahoo.co.uk, www.darnbrookgarden.com. *Cwmgors. From M4 - J45 take A4067 to Pontardawe. Turn L to Ammanford/Gwaun cae Gurwen on A474.Signed from A474.* Light refreshments. **Adm £3, chd free. Sun 18 May, Sun 8 June, Sun 27 July, Sun 14 Sept (2-5.30). Visitors also welcome by appt May to Sept.**
A well established garden with mature trees, with newer elements added. The history garden is the latest edition and incl a stone circle! Two ponds, herbaceous borders, an alpine garden with cairn, woodland areas as well as fruit and vegetable plots provide lots of interest. There is even a little secret garden hidden away with a quiet seating area. Perennials for sale.

A separate herb garden provides plants for hedgerow medicine . . .

21 MAES-Y-WERTHA FARM

Bryncethin CF32 9YJ. Stella & Tony Leyshon. *3m N of Bridgend. Follow sign for Bryncethin, turn R at Masons Arms. Follow sign for Heol-y-Cyw garden about 1m outside Bryncethin on R.* Home-made teas. **Adm £4, chd free. Sun 22 June (2-6).**
A 3-acre garden. Informal mixed beds with large selection of perennial plants, shrubs, conifers and trees. Water garden fed by natural spring. Large grass area under new planting.

22 THE OLD POST OFFICE

Main Road, Gwaelod-Y-Garth, Cardiff CF15 9HJ. Ms Christine Myant. *N of Cardiff nr Radyr & Pentyrch. Garden on L of rd, 4 houses pass PH. Parking in school car park further down hill.* Home-made teas. **Adm £3, chd free. Sat 7 June (12-5).**
Situated in the popular village of Gwaelod-y-Garth on the northern edge of Cardiff this informal terraced garden provides some splendid views of the green valley and hills opposite.

GROUP OPENING

23 NEW OVERTON AND PORT EYNON GARDENS

Overton Lane, Porteynon, Swansea SA3 1NR. *16.8m W of Swansea on Gower Peninsula. From Swansea follow A 4118 to Port Eynon. Overton, turn R just before Port Eynon village then follow yellow NGS signs/arrows.* Home-made teas at The Bays Farm, Overton. **Combined adm £4, chd free. Sat 26 July (2-5.30).**

NEW BOX BOAT COTTAGE
Ms Christine Williams

NEW OLD FORT FARM
Mr Dick Metcalfe

NEW 6 THE BOARLANDS
Robert & Annette Dyer

NEW TY'R GWYNT
Mr Richard Morris

On the beautiful Gower Peninsula 4 very different gardens. One a flat cottage garden, one a steep sloping garden, one a plants man's garden, and one a garden created from a deeply excavated site. Enjoy views over The Bristol Channel while having teas at The Bays Farm in Overton.

GROUP OPENING

24 PENMARK VILLAGE GARDENS

Penmark CF62 3BP. *4m W of Barry. Take B4265 from Barry to Penmark.* **Combined adm £5, chd free. Sat 28 June (11-5).**

GILESTON HOUSE
Clive & Kath Linton

GWAL EIRTH
Gwyneth Grisley

PENMARK PLACE
Mr & Mrs Julian Radcliffe

SEFTON BUNGALOW
Cynthia John

4 wonderfully different gardens. From an original medieval 'strip' garden designed by the current owners with abundantly stocked flower beds and shrubberies presenting an ever changing vista, to a beautiful terraced garden that is described as a plantaholic's paradise and displaying a range of the owners pottery throughout the garden. C13 manor house walled gardens with 100yr-old varieties of apple and pear and large vegetable plot, mixed terrace garden with shrubs, bulbs and perennials to give all yr round interest, and cottage garden with a walk along a meandering stream. A healthy walk between some of the gardens!! Transport available.

GROUP OPENING

25 PENYLAN GARDENS

Penylan, Cardiff CF23 5BY. *1½ m NE of Cardiff city centre. M4 J29, Cardiff E A48, then Llanedeyrn/Docks junction, towards Cyncoed. L down Penylan Rd. Marlborough is L at T-lights at bottom of hill.* Home-made teas. **Combined adm £4, chd free. Sun 29 June (2-6).**

7 CRESSY ROAD
Victoria Thornton
Visitors also welcome by appt July to Aug. Groups max 15. 02920 311215 thornton.victoria@me.com

102 MARLBOROUGH ROAD
Mrs Judith Griffiths

128 PENYLAN ROAD
John & Judi Wilkins

5 SOUTHCOURT ROAD
Pat & Mel Griffiths
Visitors also welcome by appt July to Aug for small groups. 02920 490420 David.griffiths12@sky.com

Penylan is a Victorian suburb of mostly terraced houses with small gardens and many parks. The gardens open show a variety of ways of adding interest and individuality to a small space incl Mediterranean-style sunny patio areas, informal mix of cottage plants, a riot of exotic foliage, stone walled SE facing cottage garden offering colour and peace away from the busy main rd and a bijou terrace garden profusely planted with an abundance of unusual and exotic plants. Victoria Thornton and Pat and Mel Griffiths are regular winners in the Cardiff in Bloom competition. Maps showing the gardens will be available.

5 Southcourt Rd, awarded Gold, 'Best Senior Citizen Gardener' (Penylan area) and 2nd place (in same category) for City of Cardiff as a whole.

26 PONTYGWAITH FARM
Edwardsville, nr Treharris CF46 5PD. Mrs D Cann, 07784 871502. *2m NW of Treharris. N from Cardiff on A470. At r'about take A4054 N towards Aberfan. 1m after Edwardsville turn sharp L by black bus shelter. Garden at bottom of hill.* **Adm £3.50, chd free. Sat 24, Sun 25, Mon 26 May, Sun 15, Mon 16 June (10-5). Visitors also welcome by appt May to Aug.**
4½ acre garden surrounding C17 farmhouse adjacent to Trevithick's Tramway. Situated in picturesque wooded valley. Fish pond, lawns, perennial borders, new lakeside walk, rose garden, Japanese garden. Grade II listed humpback packhorse bridge in garden, spanning R Taff. A lovely day out for all the family. Welcome to visitors on the Taff Trail (April - Sept, 10am - 5pm). Limited wheelchair access due to steep slope to river, gravel paths.

GROUP OPENING

27 PORTHCAWL GARDENS
Porthcawl CF36 5EB. *Porthcawl. M4 J37, follow the A4229 towards Porthcawl. On arriving at r'about follow yellow NGS signs.* Home-made teas. **Combined adm £5, chd free. Sun 15 June (12-6).**

3 LIAS COTTAGES
Bryn Davies

NEWTON COTTAGE
Mr & Mrs J David

SHORTLANDS
Mr Mike James

TYTHEGSTON POTTERY
Joanna Howells
www.joannahowells.co.uk

Shortlands has recently been refurbished and the garden is now being tackled and restored to its former glory. The garden is approx 2 acres and divided into four areas. Front garden is laid to lawns and shrubs together with mature trees, a formal Walled Garden with Central Water feature, two further large lawns surrounded by mature trees and shrubs with summer house. Tythegston Pottery is a developing natural varied garden (⅓ acre) with borders, rockery, lawn, vegetable garden, soft fruit cages and fruit trees, and a shady bank with ferns. 3 Lias Cottage garden is delightful with a profusion of colour all yr-round, a real secret. Newton Cottage has a large informal cottage garden. Mixed borders, good variety of shrubs, climbers and herbaceous plants. Box garden. Kitchen garden.

GROUP OPENING

28 RHIWBINA OPEN GARDENS
Rhiwbina CF14 6EL. *N Cardiff. M4 J32. 1st L to mini r'about, turn R into village at T-lights, turn R to Pen Y Dre.* **Combined adm £3, chd free. Sat 21, Sun 22 June (11-5).**

9 GERNANT
Pat Morrey

7 PEN Y DRE
Christine Lewis

7 Pen y Dre is a charming garden approached from a bridge over a babbling brook. 9 Gernant is an 8yr old garden still in the making, both gardens a must to be seen.

29 RHOS Y BEDW
4 Pen y Wern Rd, Ystalyfera, Swansea SA9 2NH. Robert & Helen Davies. *13m N of Swansea. M4 J45 take A4067. Follow signs for Dan yr Ogof caves across 5 r'abouts. After T-lights follow yellow NGS signs. Parking above house on rd off to R.* Home-made teas. **Adm £2, chd free. Sat 31 May, Sun 1, Sat 7 June (12-5).**
This constantly evolving garden provides a haven of peace and tranquility with spectacular views. Wander through this glorious compact garden with its array of planting areas. Perennial, herb, bog, vegetable and a new knot garden are sure to provide inspiration. A garden to be savoured slowly, relax and enjoy. Gluten free cakes available.

Mount Cottage, 166 Fidlas Road, Cyncoed & Llanishen Gardens

Knightsbridge

30 NEW ROSE COTTAGE
32 Blackmill Road, Bryncethin, Bridgend CF32 9YN. Maria & Anne Lalic, www.cobwebs.uk.net/simplecountryfolk. *1m N of M4 J36 on A4061. Follow A4061 to Bryncethin. Straight on at mini r'about for approx 400metres. Just past Used Car Garage, turn R onto side rd at grassed area.* **Adm £3.50, chd free.**
Sun 29 June, Sun 31 Aug (12-5).
Rose Cottage has been a working cottage garden for 250yrs. We borrow ideas from Permaculture and No Dig methods, mix with companion planting and old-fashioned gardening to give us vegetables all yr-round and fit our simple, nearly self sufficient lifestyle. Bentwood fences and reclaimed Victorian bricks edge paths and flower beds. A separate herb garden provides plants for hedgerow medicine. A raised terrace area alongside the conservatory allows viewing of the field where the goats, chickens and ducks graze. Flowers will be at their best in June, Vegetables in August. Main paths and gateways are suitable for wheelchairs. Narrower, bark chip paths around the vegetable beds and the polytunnel interior are not.

31 SLADE
Southerndown CF32 0RP. Rosamund & Peter Davies, 01656 880048, ros@sladewoodgarden.plus.com, www.sladeholidaycottages.co.uk. *5m S of Bridgend. M4 J35 Follow A473 to Bridgend. Take B4265 to St. Brides Major. Turn R in St. Brides Major for Southerndown, then follow yellow NGS signs*. Home-made teas. **Adm £4, chd free. Sat 26, Sun 27 Apr, Sat 7, Sun 8 June (2-6). Visitors also welcome by appt Apr to July.**
Set in 8 acres, Slade garden is an unexpected gem with masses of spring flowers. The terraced lawns, mature specimen trees, living willow arbours, rose and clematis pergola, orchard and herbaceous borders, create a very natural garden that also has extensive views over the Bristol Channel. Heritage Coast wardens will give guided tours of adjacent Dunraven Gardens with slide shows every hour from 2pm. Limited wheelchair access.

32 19 SLADE GARDENS
Norton, Swansea SA3 5QP. Norma & Peter Stephen. *5m SW of Swansea. At mini r'about on Mumbles Rd A4067 take 2nd exit (Fairwood Rd), 1st L onto West Cross Lane & follow yellow NGS signs*. Light refreshments. **Adm £3, chd free. Sun 8 June (2-5.30).**
A small enclosed front and rear garden designed to lead you around its informal planting of over 200 species. Somewhere to sit and relax. Narrow paths make access difficult for less mobile visitors.

Lemon drizzle cake, Victoria sponge ... yummy!

Pupils, parents and staff have worked together to develop 'The Secret Garden' . . .

33 ST MICHAEL'S COLLEGE
54 Cardiff Road, Llandaff, Cardiff CF5 2YJ. Representative Body of the Church in Wales, www.stmichaels.ac.uk. *1m N of Cardiff. Follow signs for Llandaff (A48). In village turn L down Ely Rd at Malsters PH then L into St Michael's College car park.* Home-made teas. **Adm £3.50, chd free.**
Sat 5 July (12-5).
The attractive gardens which won 'Cardiff in Bloom' in 2011 provide a haven of peace and tranquillity in what is a busy part of Llandaff. Musical entertainment will be provided in the Pace Chapel and teas and light refreshments served from our reputable college Servery. Come and enjoy 'a little bit of heaven'.

34 NEW ST. FAGANS CHURCH PRIMARY SCHOOL
Drope Road, Cardiff CF5 4SZ. Alison Price, www.stfaganscwprimary.com. *1m from A4232 at Culverhouse Cross r'about, West Cardiff. At r'about, take A48 towards Cardiff & Ely. Turn L at T- lights into Michaelston Rd & L at PH into Drope Rd. Parking available on site.* Home-made teas. **Adm £3, chd free. Sun 29 June (1-5).**
Pupils, parents and staff have worked together to develop 'The Secret Garden' from a piece of wasteland to a stimulating learning environment and beautiful garden. Features incl vegetable beds, a wildlife pond, log circle, woodland area and a fruit forest garden. Tours of the garden by the children will be on offer. The School has received a special award from Cardiff Healthy Schools for the development of the garden.

35 NEW ST. PETER'S COMMUNITY GARDEN
St Fagans Road, Cardiff CF5 3DW. Father Colin Sutton, www.stpeterschurchfairwater.org.uk. *A48 to Culverhousecross r'bout take A48 Cowbridge Rd West to Ely r'bout 1st L. At T-lights go L B4488 to Fairwater Green, follow yellow NGS signs.* Home-made teas. **Adm £5, chd free.**
Sat 19, Sun 20 July (10-5).
'Secret Garden' in city suburb. Unusual combination of flower beds, raised vegetable beds and nature reserve, all created by volunteers. Features incl a large natural pond surrounded by wild plants, Welsh heritage apple trees, long herb border and wild flower meadow. Planted to encourage birds, butterflies and bees. Full wheelchair access and disabled WC.

36 ST. QUINTINS COTTAGE
St. Quintins Hill, Llanblethian, Cowbridge CF71 7JT. Dr Malcolm & Dr Lorna Callaghan. *15 W of Cardiff. From Cardiff follow bypass A48 to Cowbridge. Turn at T-lights in Cowbridge for Llanbleddian. 1st R into Broadway, then follow yellow NGS signs.* **Adm £3, chd free.**
Sun 25 May (2-6).
The garden of St Quintin's Cottage was designed by renowned garden designer Ralph Hancock and features stone terraces and sloping lawns, linked by winding paths and steps between ornamental ponds. A 1940's garden providing an intimacy of place rather than exotic planting. Some unlevel paving and unfenced ponds.

38 TY'N Y BERLLAN
Graig Llwyn Road, Lisvane, Cardiff CF14 0RP. Jeffrey Morgan, 02920 752443. *1m NE Lisvane village. From Lisvane Village take Rudry Rd. After M/W bridge turn R into Graig Llwyn Rd & follow yellow NGS signs.* Home-made teas. **Adm £4, chd free.**
Sat 10, Sun 11 May (2-6). Visitors also welcome by appt May to June.
A 2-acre garden set around an ancient farmhouse. Beds of azaleas, rhododendrons, camellia and mixed shrubs, set in undulating lawns designed to blend with the fields and woodlands around. The lawns are planted with trees such as oak, beech, hornbeam, ginkgo and tulip which provide interest and yr-round colour. Spring bulbs, primula and stream give natural informality to sit and dream as well as a courtyard garden and pool, Wollemi pine.

39 TYN-Y-CAEAU FARM
Porthcawl CF36 5SY. Ian John. *1m N Porthcawl. M4 J39 Follow A4229 to r'about follow yellow NGS signs. From A48 follow A4106 to r'about then follow yellow NGS signs.* Home-made teas. **Adm £3, chd free.**
Sun 1 June (1-5).
Established garden with herbaceous borders, vegetable garden, ponds, wild flower meadow, orchard with fruit trees and hens. Wonderful panoramic view of Bristol Channel, a delight to be seen.

Glamorgan County Volunteers

County Organiser/Booklet Coordinator
Rosamund Davies, Slade, Southerndown, Glamorgan CF32 0RP, 01656 880048, ros@sladewoodgarden.plus.com

County Treasurer
Dr Trevor Humby, 1 Ashgrove, Dinas, Vale of Glamorgan CF64 4TL, 02920 512709, humbyt@cardiff.ac.uk

Publicity
Sara Bentley, 1 Ashgrove, Dinas, Vale of Glamorgan CF64 4TL, 02920 512709, sarajanebentley@googlemail.com

Assistant County Organiser
Sol Blytt Jordens, The Bays Farm, Overton Lane, Port Eynon, Swansea SA3 1NR, 01792 391676, solinge22@yahoo.co.uk
Melanie Hurst, Wolf House, Llysworney, Cowbridge, Vale of Glamorgan CF71 7NQ, 01446 773659, melanie@hurstcreative.co.uk
Ceri Macfarlane, 5 Moorside Road, West Cross, Swansea SA3 5EY, 01792 404906, ceri@mikegravenor.plus.com

GWENT

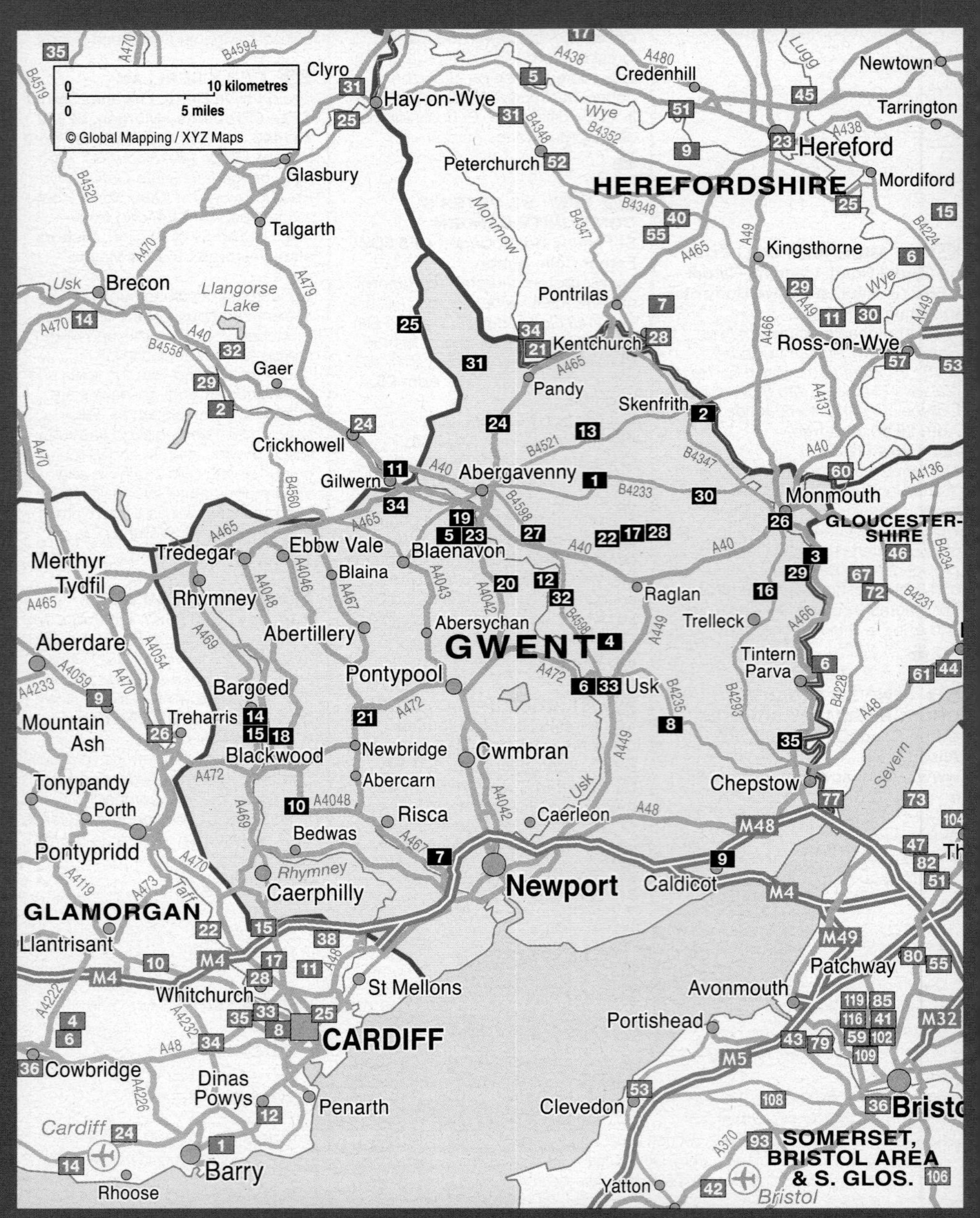

10 kilometres
5 miles
© Global Mapping / XYZ Maps
HEREFORDSHIRE
GLOUCESTERSHIRE
GWENT
GLAMORGAN
SOMERSET, BRISTOL AREA & S. GLOS.
Hay-on-Wye
Hereford
Brecon
Abergavenny
Monmouth
Ross-on-Wye
Newport
CARDIFF
Chepstow
Usk
Pontypool
Cwmbran
Caerphilly
Barry

Opening Dates

All entries subject to change. For latest information check www.ngs.org.uk

March

Sunday 30
20 Llanover

April

Sunday 13
9 Dewstow Gardens & Grottoes

Saturday 26
12 Glebe House

Sunday 27
12 Glebe House

May

Sunday 4
17 High House
28 NEW Penrhos Gardens

Monday 5
28 NEW Penrhos Gardens

Sunday 11
16 High Glanau Manor

Saturday 17
27 Penpergwm Lodge

Sunday 18
27 Penpergwm Lodge

Tuesday 20
35 NEW Wyndcliffe Court

Saturday 24
18 Hillcrest

Sunday 25
18 Hillcrest
26 NEW The Nelson Garden

Monday 26
11 Glangrwyney Court
18 Hillcrest

June

Friday 6
21 Llwyn-y-Wen Farm (Evening)

Festival Weekend

Saturday 7
21 Llwyn-y-Wen Farm

Sunday 8
19 Llanfoist Village Gardens
21 Llwyn-y-Wen Farm
22 Longhouse Farm

Thursday 12
10 NEW Forest House

Saturday 14
32 Trostrey Lodge

Sunday 15
29 Pentwyn Farm
32 Trostrey Lodge
34 NEW Wenallt Isaf

Friday 20
24 Mione

Sunday 22
1 NEW Baileau
5 Castell Cwrt
13 Glen Trothy
23 NEW Middle Ninfa Farm & Bunkhouse

Friday 27
24 Mione

Saturday 28
33 Usk Open Gardens

Sunday 29
33 Usk Open Gardens

July

Friday 4
24 Mione

Friday 11
24 Mione

Saturday 12
14 NEW 10 Gwerthonor Lane
15 NEW 14 Gwerthonor Lane

Sunday 13
3 Birch Tree Well
4 Brynderi
14 NEW 10 Gwerthonor Lane
15 NEW 14 Gwerthonor Lane

Saturday 19
25 Nant y Bedd

Sunday 20
25 Nant y Bedd

Saturday 26
31 Tair-Ffynnon, 'The Garden in the Clouds'.

August

Saturday 2
18 Hillcrest

Sunday 3
18 Hillcrest

Sunday 17
7 Croesllanfro Farm
8 Curlews

September

Tuesday 2
35 NEW Wyndcliffe Court

Sunday 14
9 Dewstow Gardens & Grottoes

Gardens open to the public

2 The Bell at Skenfrith
9 Dewstow Gardens & Grottoes

By appointment only

6 Castle House
30 Sunnyside

Also open by appointment

3 Birch Tree Well
4 Brynderi
7 Croesllanfro Farm
8 Curlews
10 Forest House
18 Hillcrest
20 Llanover
25 Nant y Bedd
28 Woodlands Farm, Penrhos Gardens
32 Trostrey Lodge

Explore the terracing, folly and grotto, let the children try the quiz . . . !

The Gardens

1 NEW BAILEAU

Llantilio Crossenny, Abergavenny NP7 8TA. Peter & Elizabeth Miln. *Between Abergavenny (7m) & Monmouth (9m). Between Llantilio Crossenny & Treadam on lane from B4521 near Lane's garage, Llanvetherine to B4233 at Llantilio Crossenny.* Home-made teas. **Adm £4, chd free. Sun 22 June (2-6).**
A cottage style garden planted over the last 5yrs around an ancient farmhouse (not open). Packed with fruit and vegetables, the garden incl a rose walk, a crab apple walk, herbaceous borders, a circular ornamental vegetable garden and an old orchard. Geese, chickens and friendly pigs to entertain children. Views to Blorenge and Sugarloaf mountains.

2 ◆ THE BELL AT SKENFRITH

Skenfrith NP7 8UH. William & Janet Hutchings, 01600 750235, www.skenfrith.co.uk. *In village of Skenfrith on B4521, opp Norman castle. Parking in field adjacent to garden as indicated.* **Entry by donation (£3.50 suggested). For opening times and information, please phone or see garden website.**

Productive kitchen garden with formal area of raised beds edged with edible delights. Less formal area where more space consuming plants are grown. Produce grown incl herbs, salads, vegetables, flowers (edible and cutting), soft and hard fruits. All produce grown used in the restaurant at The Bell. Limited wheelchair access. Please call beforehand so we can assist you (this would be accessed across an open field).

3 BIRCH TREE WELL

Upper Ferry Road, Penallt, Monmouth NP25 4AN. Jill Bourchier, gillian.bourchier@btinternet.com. *4m SW of Monmouth. Approx 1m from Monmouth on B4293, turn L for Penallt & Trelleck. After 2m turn L to Penallt. On entering village turn L at Xrds.* Cream teas. **Adm £3.50, chd free. Sun 13 July (2-6). Visitors also welcome by appt Apr to Sept.**

Situated in the heart of the Lower Wye Valley this garden is gradually evolving amongst the ancient habitat of woodland, rocks and streams. 3 acres shared with deer, badger and fox so careful planting is constantly under review. A woodland setting with streams and boulders which can be viewed from a look-out tower.

4 BRYNDERI

Wainfield Lane, Gwehelog, Usk NP15 1RG. Dr Ann Benson, 01291 672976, mail@brynderi.co.uk, www.brynderi.co.uk. *3m N of Usk. From Usk follow Monmouth Rd signed Gwehelog. L at Hall Inn onto Wainfield Lane. Parking for 5 cars at house & 40 cars in field (100 metres away).* Home-made teas. **Adm £4, chd free. Sun 13 July (1-6). Visitors also welcome by appt June to Sept.**

2 acres of garden 'rooms' and areas of fruit, vegetables and specimen trees. Fountains, lawns, topiary, and colour-themed borders are linked with pergolas, arbours and a knot garden to provide formal, tranquil spaces. Fruit tree topiary incl a Belgian-trained fruit 'wall'. Birches, liquidambers, acers and a crabapple avenue are under-planted with bulbs. Ann is an academic garden historian and can arrange talks and garden tours. Some gravel paths and slopes but main features can be viewed. Ramp available for wheelchair users.

Informal, pretty country garden, with borders overflowing with colour . . .

5 CASTELL CWRT

Llanelen, Abergavenny NP7 9LE. Lorna & John McGlynn. *1m S of Abergavenny. From Abergavenny/Llanfoist take B4269 signed Llanelen. Pass Grove Farm turn R up single track rd. Approx 500yds past canal garden entrance 2nd on L.* Home-made teas. **Combined adm £4, chd free. Sun 22 June (2-6). Combined with Middle Ninfa Farm & Bunk House.**

Large informal wildlife friendly family garden on 10-acre small holding with fine views overlooking Abergavenny. Lawns with established trees, shrubs and perennial borders. Organic soft fruit and vegetable gardens. Woodland and haymeadow walks, chickens and geese, livestock in fields and family pets. Children very welcome, animals to see and space to let off steam. Hay meadow in full bloom. Some gravel paths.

6 CASTLE HOUSE

Castle Parade, Usk NP15 1SD. Mr & Mrs J H L Humphreys, 01291 672563, www.uskcastle.com. *200yds NE from Usk centre. Signed to Usk Castle, 300yds E from town square on Castle Parade in Usk. Disabled parking is available in stableyard.* **Adm £4, chd free. Visitors welcome by appt, refreshments for groups by prior arrangement.**

Overlooked by the romantic ruins of Usk Castle, the gardens date from early C20, with yew hedges and topiary, long herbaceous border, croquet lawn and pond. The herb garden has plants that would have been used when the castle was last lived in c.1469. Castle House is part of the Usk Open Gardens event on Sat 29, Sun 30 June (10-5). Most areas easily accessible to wheelchair users.

7 CROESLLANFRO FARM

Groes Road, Rogerstone, Newport NP10 9GP. Barry & Liz Davies, 01633 894057, lizplants@gmail.com. *3m W of Newport. From M4 J27 take B4591 towards Risca. Take 3rd R, Cefn Walk (also signed 14 Locks Canal Centre). Proceed over bridge, continue ½ m.* Home-made teas. **Adm £4.50, chd free. Sun 17 Aug (1.30-5). Visitors also welcome by appt May to Sept any size group welcome.**

Celebrate the end of summer by visiting this 2 acre country garden. Informal, mass planted perennial borders concentrate on late summer colour also a formal courtyard garden on 6 different levels leading to a tithe barn (open). Explore the terracing, folly and grotto, let the children try the quiz! Owner co-author of Designing Gardens on Slopes.

8 CURLEWS

Llangwm, Usk NP15 1HD. Mr & Mrs M Hatfield, 01291 652972, margarethatfield@madasafish.com. *5m E of Usk. Midway between Usk (5m) & Chepstow (8m) on B4235. From Usk continue through Llangwm village for 1m.* Home-made teas, sandwiches between 1pm - 2pm. **Adm £4, chd free. Sun 17 Aug (1-5). Visitors also welcome by appt June to Aug, min group 10.**

Situated in Monmouthshire countryside this 1½ acre garden has many areas of mature and recent planting and offers delightful changes in perspective from the numerous ways it can be explored. Since 2011 the owners have made changes incl transforming one of the vegetable plots into a stunning bed of late flowering perennials and grasses. Plant stall, mature cactus collection and vintage cars. Gravel paths and slopes so wheelchair access difficult in parts of garden.

Llanover

9 ◆ DEWSTOW GARDENS & GROTTOES

Caerwent, Caldicot NP26 5AH. John Harris, 01291 431020, www.dewstowgardens.co.uk. *Dewstow House, 6m W of Chepstow - 8m E of Newport. A48 Newport to Chepstowrd rd, drive into village of Caerwent. Follow brown tourist daisy signs to Gardens*. Light refreshments. **Adm £5, chd free. For NGS: Sun 13 Apr, Sun 14 Sept (10.30-4). For other opening times and information, please phone or see garden website.**

5-acre Grade 1 listed unique garden which was buried and forgotten after World War II and rediscovered in 2000. Created around 1895 by James Pulham & Sons, the garden contains underground grottoes, tunnels and ferneries and above ground stunning water features. You will not be disappointed. Various events throughout the season. No wheelchair access to underground areas.

10 NEW FOREST HOUSE

Commercial Street, Ynysddu NP11 7JN. Mrs Joy Beacham, 01495 200333, clivebeacham315@btinternet.com. *9m N of J28, M4. At J28 follow A467 for Brynmawr, then B4251 via Wattsville. At Xrds in Ynysddu turn R then R again. 2m S of Blackwood on B4251, L at Xrds then R*. Home-made teas. **Adm £3.50, chd free. Thur 12 June (1-5). Visitors also welcome by appt Apr to July, max group 10.**

Informal, pretty country garden, with borders overflowing with colour. Gravel garden and mixed borders to the front. Sloping back garden with terraces leading to small waterfall, shady areas and wildlife pond. Small lawn and borders with seating to rest awhile. Productive vegetable plot, fruit cage and cold frames.

11 GLANGRWYNEY COURT

Glangrwyney, Crickhowell NP8 1ES. Warwick & Christina Jackson, 01873 811288. *3m W of Abergavenny. A40 (W) from Abergavenny. 200 metres after Powys County sign, turn R along the 200 metre drive to house. Small coaches only permitted*. Home-made teas. **Adm £4, chd free. Mon 26 May (2-6.30).**

Grade II listed 2-acre gardens in grounds of Regency house (not open) surrounded by 33 acres of parkland. Set in the Usk Valley at foot of the Black Mountains. Variety of mature rhododendrons, azaleas, magnolias, Japanese acers, catalpa and davidia. Walled garden (partly under restoration) with spacious lawns, roses and herbaceous borders. 2 cottage gardens under construction.

12 GLEBE HOUSE

Llanvair Kilgeddin NP7 9BE. Mr & Mrs Murray Kerr, 01873 840422, joanna@amknet.com. *Midway between Abergavenny (5m) & Usk (5m) on B4598*. Home-made teas. **Adm £4, chd free. Sat 26, Sun 27 Apr (2-6).**

Borders and orchard bursting with bulbs in 1½ acre garden in picturesque Usk Valley. S-facing terrace with climbers and ornamental vegetable garden. Old Rectory of St Mary's Llanvair Kilgeddin with famous Victorian Scraffito Murals which will also be open.

13 GLEN TROTHY

Llanvetherine, Abergavenny NP7 8RB. Mr & Mrs Ben Herbert. *5m NE of Abergavenny. 6m from Abergavenny off B4521 (Old Ross Rd)*. Home-made teas. **Adm £4.50, chd free. Sun 22 June (2-6).**

Victorian house (not open) in the Scottish Baronial style, set in mature parkland with a small pinetum and arboretum. The walled garden has been renovated over the past 5yrs, incorporating blue and white herbaceous borders, a rose garden and ornamental vegetable garden with pear tunnel as well as an Italianate loggia.

Nant y Bedd

14 NEW **10 GWERTHONOR LANE**

Gilfach, Bargoed CF81 8JT. Mr Paul Spearman. *8m N of Caerphilly. A469 to Bargoed. Through T-lights next to school, then L filter lane at next T-lights to turn onto Cardiff Rd. Follow yellow NGS signs.* Cream teas. **Combined adm £3.50, chd free. Sat 12, Sun 13 July (11-6). Combined with 14 Gwerthonor Lane.**

A Japanese Garden with over 80 mature Bonsai Trees, Alpines and Stone Garden Features.

15 NEW **14 GWERTHONOR LANE**

Gilfach, Bargoed CF81 8JT. Suzanne & Philip George. *8m N of Caerphilly. A469 to Bargoed. Through T-lights next to School, then L filter lane at next T-lights to turn onto Cardiff Rd. Follow yellow NGS signs.* Cream teas. **Combined adm £3.50, chd free. Sat 12, Sun 13 July (11-6). Combined with 10 Gwerthonor Lane.**

The garden has a beautiful panoramic view of the Rhymney Valley and is in a semi rural setting. It is a real plantswoman's garden with over 400 varieties of trees, shrubs, perenials, bulbs and annuals. There are numerous rare and unusual plants (many available for sale) combined with more traditional and well loved favourites. A pond with a small waterfall adds to the tranquil feel of the garden.

16 **HIGH GLANAU MANOR**

Lydart, Monmouth NP25 4AD. Mr & Mrs Hilary Gerrish, 01600 860005, helenagerrish@gmail.com. *4m SW of Monmouth. Situated on B4293 between Monmouth & Chepstow. Turn R into Private Rd, ¼ m after Craig-y-Dorth turn on B4293.* Home-made teas. **Adm £5, chd free. Sun 11 May (2-6).**

Listed Arts and Crafts garden laid out by H Avray Tipping in 1922. Original features incl impressive stone terraces with far-reaching views over the Vale of Usk to Blorenge, Skirrid, Sugar Loaf and Brecon Beacons. Pergola, herbaceous borders, Edwardian glasshouse, rhododendrons, azaleas, tulips, orchard with wild flowers and woodland walks. Owners book 'Edwardian Country Life - the story of H Avray Tipping' by Helena Gerrish for sale. Featured in Country Life, The English Garden and Gardener's World.

17 **HIGH HOUSE**

Penrhos NP15 2DJ. Mr & Mrs R Cleeve. *4m N of Raglan. From r'about on A40 at Raglan take exit to Clytha. After 50 yds turn R at Llantilo Crossenny. Follow garden open signs - 10mins through lanes.* Home-made teas. **Adm £4, chd free. Sun 4 May (2-6).**

3-acres of spacious lawns and trees surrounding C16 house (not open) in a beautiful, hidden part of Monmouthshire. Large extended pond, orchard with chickens and ducks. S-facing terrace and extensive bed of old roses. Areas of grass with tulips, camassias, wild flowers and far reaching views.

18 **HILLCREST**

Waunborfa Road, Cefn Fforest, Blackwood NP12 3LB. Mr M O'Leary & Mr B Price, 01443 837029, bev.price@mclweb.net, www.hillcrestgarden.co.uk. *3m W of Newbridge. On open days follow A4048 to Blackwood town centre or A469 to Pengam (Glan-y-Nant) T-lights, then NGS signs.* Cream teas. **Adm £4, chd free. Sat 24, Sun 25, Mon 26 May, Sat 2, Sun 3 Aug (11-6). Visitors also welcome by appt Apr to Sept, max group 25.**

A cascade of secluded gardens, each having established a distinct character over the years, all within 1½ acres. With choices at every turn, visitors exploring the gardens are well-rewarded as hidden delights and surprises are revealed. Numerous, well-placed seats encourage the unhurried pace at which the gardens are best appreciated. Delicious cream teas to be enjoyed. Woodland area not accessible to wheelchairs.

19 **LLANFOIST VILLAGE GARDENS**

Llanfoist, Abergavenny NP7 9NF. *1m SW of Abergavenny on B4246. Map provided with ticket. Most gardens within easy walking distance of village centre. Free minibus to others.* Fantastic home-made teas, cakes and lunches in village hall. **Combined adm £5, chd free. Sun 8 June (10.30-5.30).**

Make this a great day out. Visit around 15 exciting and contrasting village gardens, both large and small, set just below the Blorenge Mountain on the edge of the Black Mountains. A number of new gardens opening along with many regulars. This is our

12th annual event. Canal boat trips. Featured in local press. Wheelchair access not available at all gardens.

20 LLANOVER

nr Abergavenny NP7 9EF. Mr & Mrs M R Murray, 07753 423635, elizabeth@llanover.com, www.llanovergarden.co.uk. *4m S of Abergavenny, 15m N of Newport, 20m SW Hereford. On A4042 Abergavenny - Pontypool rd, in village of Llanover.* Home-made teas. **Sun 30 Mar (2-5). Visitors also welcome by appt Mar to Oct, groups 15+ for conducted tours.**

15-acre listed garden and arboretum with well preserved water features and a circular walled garden. The Rhyd-y-meirch stream tumbles into ponds, down cascades and beneath flagstone bridges suitable for playing poo-sticks. Lawns for children to run around on or play hide and seek. Given a fine March, many of the spring bulbs and 30+ Magnolias will be in flower. Delicious home-made teas. The House (not open) is the birthplace of Augusta Waddington, Lady Llanover, C19 patriot and supporter of the Welsh Language Descendants. The flock of Welsh Black Mountain Sheep which she introduced, can be seen grazing in the park. Gravel and grass paths, lawns.

21 LLWYN-Y-WEN FARM

Hafodyrynys Road, Crumlin NP11 5AX. Mrs Helen Lewy. *11m NW of Newport, 6m W of Pontypool. M4 J28, take A467 to Risca. 11m to Crumlin T-lights, turn R on A472 to Pontypool. Entrance 1/4 m on R. Limited parking; lay-bys on main rd.* Cream teas. **Adm £4.50, chd free. Evening Opening £4.50, chd free, wine, Fri 6 June (6-9); Sat 7, Sun 8 June (2-5).**

3 acres of Welsh hillside with spring creating ponds and bog garden. A plantswoman's paradise, of great interest to those in search of the unusual. Auriculas, primulas, hellebores and shade and damp-loving plants a speciality. Informal mass of flowers in orchard setting. 12 metre-long rockery. Newly landscaped areas and planting on cleared hillside with many new trees and shrubs. Many areas accessible by wheelchair but will require some effort in places.

22 LONGHOUSE FARM

Penrhos, Raglan NP15 2DE. Mr & Mrs M H C Anderson. *Midway between Monmouth & Abergavenny. 4m from Raglan. Off Old Raglan/Abergavenny rd signed Clytha. At Bryngwyn/Great Oak Xrds turn towards Great Oak - follow yellow NGS signs from red phone box down narrow lane.* Home-made teas. **Adm £4, chd free. Sun 8 June (2-6).**

21yrs (ongoing) of developing this hidden 2 acre garden with a south facing terrace, millrace wall, pond, spacious lawns. Colourful and unusual plants varying from blossom, irises, summer bulbs, roses, vegetables to asters, grasses and a malus avenue of autumn colour. Unspoilt vistas of Monmouthshire. Possible to push wheelchairs around garden and into barn for tea.

23 NEW MIDDLE NINFA FARM & BUNKHOUSE

Llanelen, Abergavenny NP7 9LE. Richard Lewis, www.middleninfa.co.uk. *2 1/2 m SSW Abergavenny. At A465/ B4246 Junction, S for Llanfoist, L at mini r'about, B4269 towards Llanelen, 1/2 m R turn up steep lane, over canal. 3/4 m to Middle Ninfa on R.* Light refreshments. **Combined adm £4, chd free. Sun 22 June (2-6). Combined with Castel Cwrt.**

Large terraced eco-garden on east slopes of the Blorenge mountain. Vegetable beds, polytunnel, 3 greenhouses, orchard, flower borders, wild flowers. Great views, woodland walks, cascading water and ponds. Paths steep in places, unsuitable for less able. Campsite and small bunkhouse on farm. 5min walk uphill to the scenic Punchbowl Lake and walks on the Blorenge.

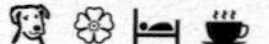

24 MIONE

Old Hereford Road, Llanvihangel Crucorney, Abergaveny NP7 7LB. Yvonne & John O'Neil. *5m N of Abergavenny. From Abergaveny take A465 to Hereford. After 4.8m turn L - signed Pantigelli. Mione is 1/2 m on L.* Home-made teas. **Adm £3, chd free. Every Fri 20 June to 11 July (11-7).**

Beautiful garden with a wide variety of established plants, many rare and unusual. Pergola with climbing roses and clematis. Wildlife pond with many newts, insects and frogs. Numerous containers with diverse range of planting. Several seating areas, each with a different atmosphere. Summerhouse. Featured as an inspirational wildlife garden on ITV's Love Your Garden.

25 NANT Y BEDD

Grwyne Fawr, Abergavenny NP7 7LY. Sue & Ian Mabberley, 01873 890219, ian.mabberley@btconnect.com, http://nantybedd,com. *In Grwyne Fawr valley. From Llanv Crucorney, direction Llanthony, then L to Fforest Coal Pit. At grey telephone box continue on for 4 1/2 m towards Reservoir.* **Adm £4, chd free. Sat 19, Sun 20 July (12-6). Visitors also welcome by appt May to Oct.**

The Garden in the Forest, Nant y Bedd comes as a complete surprise with wonderful mix of organic vegetables, imaginative planting, water, stone and timber features giving something for everyone. A hillside site with mature trees and open spaces, this is a garden to take time exploring. New for 2014 are a wonderful river walk and a natural swimming pond. See the NGS website for pictures. In addition to plants, some garden accessories, made on the premises, will be available for sale. See garden website for details. As featured in Saga Magazine.

26 NEW THE NELSON GARDEN

Monnow Street, Monmouth NP25 3EE. Penny Thomas (Convenor of U3A Practical Gardening Group). *Garden is accessed via Blestium St, follow yellow NGS signs. There are also tourist signs indicating the Nelson Garden*. Home-made teas. **Adm £3.50, chd free. Sun 25 May (2-5.30).**
This ancient town garden was the site of a real tennis court in C17 and a bowling green by 1718. Roman and Norman remains lie deep beneath the lawn. Admiral Lord Nelson and his entourage took tea here on 19th August 1802. Planting throughout the garden is designed around species that would have been popular in informal gardens of the late C18, early C19.

27 PENPERGWM LODGE

Nr Abergavenny NP7 9AS. Mr & Mrs Simon Boyle, www.penplants.com. *3m SE of Abergavenny, 5m W of Raglan. On B4598. Turn opp King of Prussia Inn. Entrance 150yds on L*. **Adm £4.50, chd free. Sat 17, Sun 18 May (2-6).**
3-acre garden with Jubilee tower overlooking terraced ornamental garden containing canal, cascading water and new loggia at head of canal. S-facing terraces planted with rich profusion and vibrant colours all surrounded by spacious lawns and mature trees. Brick waisted tower built 2011. Some gravel paths.

GROUP OPENING

28 NEW PENRHOS GARDENS

Penrhos, Raglan, Usk NP15 2LE. *3m from Raglan. From A449 take Raglan exit, join A40 & move immed into RH lane & turn R across dual carriageway. Follow yellow NGS signs*. Teas at Woodlands Farm. **Combined adm £6, chd free. Sun 4, Mon 5 May (2-6).**

THE OLD VICARAGE, PENRHOS
Professor & Mrs Luke Herrmann

WOODLANDS FARM
Craig Loane & Charles Horsfield
Visitors also welcome by appt Mar to Oct.
01600 780203

Two contrasting gardens in a glorious rural setting. If you are looking for a conventional country garden but also enjoy creative garden design, then the Old Vicarage and Woodlands Farm combination is an unmissable treat. The Old Vicarage has a mature series of skilfully crafted gardens surrounding a beautiful house (not open). Sweeping lawns, a summer house and formal garden, two charming ponds and immaculate kitchen garden all enhanced by imaginatively placed pots. Woodlands Farm is quirky in its design and built to entertain with nooks, paths and water features that invite you into 'rooms' within the garden. Don't miss the hidden Acers, climb on to the viewing platform, enjoy the new parterre garden and pavilion with its eco credentials; all combine to make this garden truly unique and will give returning visitors lots more to enjoy.

29 PENTWYN FARM

Penallt, Monmouth NP25 4SE. Gwent Wildlife Trust, www.gwentwildlife.org/reserves. *3m SW of Monmouth. From Monmouth take B4233 towards Trellech, at top of hill turn L towards Penallt & follow yellow NGS signs*. **Adm £3.50, chd free (share to Gwent Wildlife Trust). Sun 15 June (10-4).**
A wild garden with meadows as beautiful as anything under cultivation. Gwent Wildlife Trust invites you to view the wildflowers of Pentwyn Farm, famous for its orchids, teeming with butterflies and with spectacular views over the Wye Valley. Guests can also visit Wyeswood Common, a 100 acre grassland and woodland restoration project home to the trusts flock of Hebridean sheep and lambs. Guided walks through the meadows at 11am, 1pm and 3pm.

30 SUNNYSIDE

The Hendre, Monmouth NP25 5HQ. Helen & Ralph Fergusson-Kelly, 01600 714928, helen_fk@hotmail.com. *4m W of Monmouth. On B4233 Monmouth to Abergavenny rd. Parking in field 50 metres from garden*. Home-made teas. **Adm £3.50, chd free. Visitors welcome by appt only May to Oct.**
Late summer colour: The last soft blooms of summer perennials and shrubs give way to the biscuit and russet tones of grasses and then bold injections of scarlet, cerise, violet and gold from bulbs, perennials and trees. All this in a sloping ⅓ acre garden on the old Rolls estate. Seating areas to enjoy views of the Monmouthshire countryside. Some gravel paths.

Wildlife pond with many newts, insects and frogs . . .

31 TAIR-FFYNNON, 'THE GARDEN IN THE CLOUDS'.

Nr Llanvihangel Crucorney, Abergavenny NP7 7NR. Antony & Verity Woodward, www.thegardenintheclouds.com. *8m N of Abergavenny. Follow yellow NGS signs from Llanvihangel Crucorney. Challenging, steep single-track lanes - reversing may be necessary. If wet, parking 15 mins away*. Home-made teas. **Adm £4.50, chd free. Sat 26 July (12-6).**
'The Garden in the Clouds' of Antony Woodward's award-winning memoir. One of the highest in the NGS, this 6-acre smallholding in mountain landscape (reaching to over 1,800 ft) sits on Offa's Dyke footpath in the Brecon Beacons National Park. For anyone who sees beauty in wild places: box balls 'rolling' through upland flower meadows, fading poetry on wrinkly tin barns and gateways framing 70 mile views. 'The pinnacle of beauty' Sunday Times; 'Untamed but stunningly beautiful' Reader's Digest. Featured in 'Is Wales the new Sussex?' Daily Telegraph and 'The Gardens of England, Treasures of the National Gardens Scheme'.

32 TROSTREY LODGE

Bettws Newydd, Usk NP15 1JT. Roger & Frances Pemberton, 01873 840352, trostrey@googlemail.com. *4m W of Raglan. 7m E of Abergavenny. Off old A40 (unnumbered) Abergavenny - Raglan. 1m S of Clytha Gates & 1½ m N of Bettws Newydd.* Home-made teas. **Adm £4, chd free.**
Sat 14, Sun 15 June (2-6). Visitors also welcome by appt May to June.
Come over the ha-ha to be greeted by a tall Tulip tree in exotic flower. Inside the walled garden you will find colourful, fragrant flowers and herbs, with ribbons of honeysuckle and climbing roses - for Bees, Butterflies and Birds. Also an orchard. Good range of home grown plants and packets of Trostrey poppy seeds to buy to help bees in need.

33 USK OPEN GARDENS

Usk NP15 1HN, www.uskopengardens.com. *From M4 J24 take A449, proceed 8m to Usk exit. Good free parking in town. Map of gardens provided with ticket bought in car park.* **Combined adm £7.50, chd free.**
Sat 28, Sun 29 June (10-5).
Proud winner of Wales in Bloom for many years, with colourful hanging baskets and boxes - a sight not to be missed! The town is a wonderful backdrop to the 25+ gardens from small cottages packed with colourful and unusual plants to large gardens with brimming herbaceous borders. Wonderful romantic garden around the ramparts of Usk Castle. Gardeners' Market with wide selection of interesting plants. Wonderful day out for all the family with lots of places to eat and drink incl picnic places down by the R Usk. Unmissable. Various cafes, PH and restaurants available for refreshments. Not all the gardens are wheelchair accessible.

34 NEW WENALLT ISAF

Twyn Wenallt, Gilwern, Abergavenny NP7 0HP. Tim & Debbie Field. *3m W of Abergavenny. From Gilwern r'about follow A465 towards Merthyr Tydfil take 1st L & follow signs.* Home-made teas. **Adm £4, chd free. Sun 15 June (2-6).**
2½ acre garden 650ft up on a north facing hillside with magnificent views of the Black Mountains. Mature trees, flowering shrubs, borders, productive vegetable garden, small polytunnel, orchard, pigs, chickens, and plenty of space to run about.

35 NEW WYNDCLIFFE COURT

St Arvans NP16 6EY. Mr H A P Clay, www.wyndcliffecourt.co.uk. *3m N of Chepstow. Off A466, turn at Wyndcliffe signpost. Bus: Chepstow-Monmouth, alight at St Arvans, Wyndcliffe stop, then ¼ m.* Cream teas. **Adm £5, chd free.**
Tue 20 May, Tue 2 Sept (11-5).
Medium-sized garden designed by H. Avray Tipping and Eric Francis; herbaceous borders; views, topiary, sunken garden and walled garden. One of the historic gardens of Wales. Please visit the press area of our website: http://www.wyndcliffecourt.co.uk/press.html. Wheelchair access to the lower gardens and terrace (map provided) Take care with uneven surfaces of original flooring and steep inclines.

Mione

Gwent County Volunteers

County Organiser
Joanna Kerr, Glebe House, Llanvair Kilgeddin, Abergavenny NP7 9BE, 01873 840422, joanna@amknet.com

County Treasurer
Helen Fergusson-Kelly, Sunnyside, The Hendre, Monmouth NP25 5HQ, 01600 714928, helen_fk@hotmail.com

Assistant County Organiser
Sue Torkington, Trewyscoed Mill, Fforest Coal Pit, Abergavenny NP7 7LW, 01873 890045, sue@torkington.myzen.co.uk

Spread the word about the NGS: tell your family and friends

GWYNEDD, ANGLESEY & CONWY

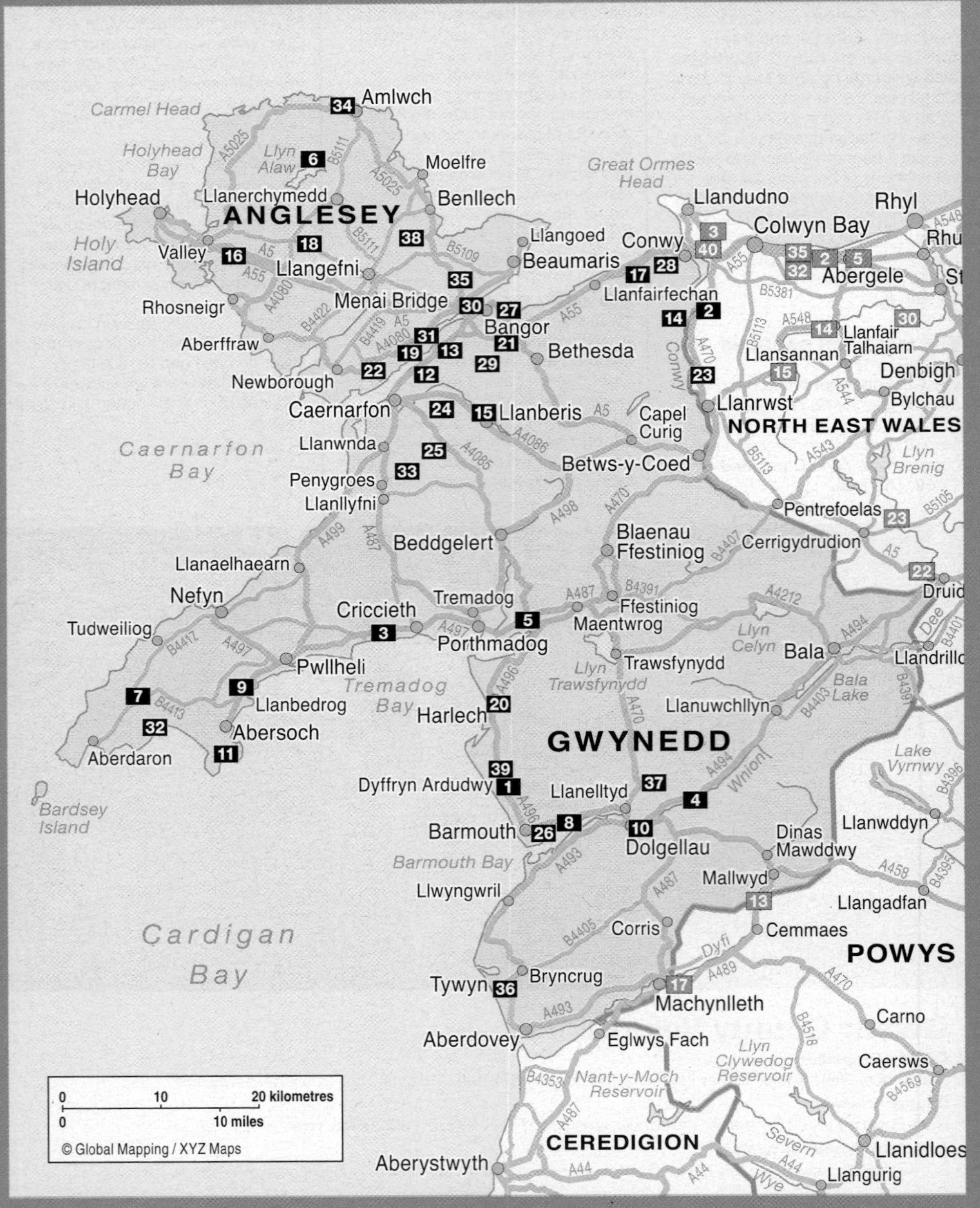

Opening Dates

All entries subject to change. For latest information check www.ngs.org.uk

February

Sunday 9
32 Plas Yn Rhiw

Saturday 22
27 Penrhyn Castle

April

Sunday 6
5 Bwlch y Fedwen

Friday 18
20 Llyn Rhaeadr
31 Plas Newydd Country House & Gardens

Saturday 19
20 Llyn Rhaeadr

Sunday 20
3 Bont Fechan Farm
20 Llyn Rhaeadr

Monday 21
3 Bont Fechan Farm
20 Llyn Rhaeadr

Sunday 27
23 Maenan Hall
40 41 Victoria Drive

Wednesday 30
30 Plas Cadnant Hidden Gardens

Superb autumn colours in September . . .

May

Sunday 4
14 Gilfach
20 Llyn Rhaeadr
34 Sunningdale

Monday 5
20 Llyn Rhaeadr

Sunday 11
10 Craig y Ffynnon
26 Pen y Bryn

Saturday 17
9 Coron

Sunday 18
4 Bryn Gwern
9 Coron
21 Llys-y-Gwynt

Saturday 24
20 Llyn Rhaeadr

Sunday 25
3 Bont Fechan Farm
20 Llyn Rhaeadr

Monday 26
3 Bont Fechan Farm
20 Llyn Rhaeadr
25 NEW Parc Newydd

Tuesday 27
20 Llyn Rhaeadr

Wednesday 28
20 Llyn Rhaeadr

Saturday 31
12 Crûg Farm

June

Sunday 1
5 Bwlch y Fedwen

Festival Weekend

Saturday 7
6 Cae Newydd
15 Groeslon

Sunday 8
1 An Artist's Garden
6 Cae Newydd
15 Groeslon
28 Pensychnant
36 NEW Ty Cadfan Sant

Tuesday 10
8 Coedmor

Saturday 14
11 Crowrach Isaf
22 Maen Hir

Sunday 15
3 Bont Fechan Farm
11 Crowrach Isaf
14 Gilfach
22 Maen Hir
35 Treffos School
38 Ty Gwyn, Llanbedrgoch

Sunday 22
34 Sunningdale

Saturday 28
19 Llanidan Hall

Sunday 29
36 NEW Ty Cadfan Sant

July

Wednesday 2
18 Gwyndy Bach

Saturday 5
29 Pentir Gardens

Sunday 6
28 Pensychnant

Tuesday 8
8 Coedmor

Saturday 12
2 Bodnant Garden
19 Llanidan Hall

Sunday 13
21 Llys-y-Gwynt

Saturday 19
24 NEW Pant Ifan

Friday 25
33 St John the Baptist & St George

Saturday 26
7 Coed Ty Mawr

Sunday 27
4 Bryn Gwern
7 Coed Ty Mawr

August

Sunday 17
23 Maenan Hall

Saturday 23
20 Llyn Rhaeadr

Sunday 24
14 Gilfach
20 Llyn Rhaeadr

Monday 25
20 Llyn Rhaeadr

Friday 29
17 Gwel Yr Ynys

Saturday 30
17 Gwel Yr Ynys

September

Sunday 7
1 An Artist's Garden

Tuesday 16
8 Coedmor

October

Tuesday 14
8 Coedmor

February 2015

Sunday 8
32 Plas Yn Rhiw

Saturday 14
27 Penrhyn Castle

Gardens open to the public

2 Bodnant Garden
12 Crûg Farm
27 Penrhyn Castle
28 Pensychnant
31 Plas Newydd Country House & Gardens
32 Plas Yn Rhiw

You are always welcome at an NGS garden!

By appointment only

Also open by appointment

The Gardens

1 AN ARTIST'S GARDEN

Ty Llwyd, Dyffryn Ardudwy LL44 2EP. Karen Hall, 01341 242623, karen.artistsgarden@gmail.com, www.artistsgarden.co.uk. *5m N of Barmouth on A496. From Barmouth garden is on L, after 20mph sign. From Harlech drive through Dyffryn Ardudwy, garden on R after 20mph sign.* Home-made teas. **Adm £3, chd free. Sun 8 June, Sun 7 Sept (11-5.30). Visitors also welcome by appt May to Sept. 48 hours prior notice required.**

A 140ft village garden. In June roses and peonies feature amongst interesting and unusual perennial plants. In September ornamental grasses and colourful late season perennials take centre stage. Paths meander through abundant planting, with seating areas, 2 ponds, cutting garden polytunnel and greenhouses. A Textile Studio at the bottom of the garden will be open for visitors to view. The propagating area will be accesible to view and the plant sales area will be open.

2 ◆ BODNANT GARDEN

Tal-y-Cafn, nr Colwyn Bay LL28 5RE. National Trust, 01492 650460, www.nationaltrust.org.uk. *8m S of Llandudno. From A55 exit at J19. Follow brown signs to Garden. Just off A470 on B rd to Eglwysbach.* **Adm £10.45, chd £5.23. For NGS: Sat 12 July (10-5). For other opening times and information, please phone or see garden website.**

Among the finest gardens in the country with rhododendrons, magnolias, camellias and the famous laburnum arch. Summer colours incl roses, water lilies, herbaceous borders and hydrangeas. Superb autumn colours in October. Formal Italianate-style terraces contrast with steeply sided shrub borders and the dell. Dogs welcome on short leads. Thurs - Sat, Nov - Feb, and from 5pm on Weds evenings May - Aug. Light refreshments. The garden is steep in places and has many steps. Please ensure motorised wheelchairs have a fully charged battery.

NCH

> A maturing country garden which blends seamlessly into the open landscape with stunning views . . .

3 BONT FECHAN FARM

Llanystumdwy LL52 0LS. Mr & Mrs J D Bean, 01766 522604. *2m W of Criccieth. On A497 to Pwllheli on L of main rd.* Home-made teas. **Adm £2.50, chd free. Sun 20, Mon 21 Apr, Sun 25, Mon 26 May, Sun 15 June (11-5). Visitors also welcome by appt Apr to July.**

Cottage garden with rockery, fish pond, herbaceous border, steps to river. Large variety of plants. Nicely planted tubs; good vegetable garden and poultry. Rhododendrons and azaleas.

4 BRYN GWERN

Llanfachreth, Dolgellau, Gwynedd LL40 2DH. H O & P D Nurse, 01341 450255, antique_pete@btinternet.com. *5m NE of Dolgellau. Do not go to Llanfachreth village, stay on A494 Bala-Dolgellau rd: 13m from Bala. Take 1st R Llanfachreth. From Dolgellau 4m Llanfachreth turn L, follow signs. No coach parking.* Cream teas. **Adm £3, chd free. Sun 18 May, Sun 27 July (10-5). Visitors also welcome by appt Apr to Oct.**

Sloping 2 acre garden in the hills overlooking Dolgellau with views to Cader Idris, originally wooded but redesigned to enhance its natural features with streams, ponds and imaginative and extensive planting and vibrant colour. The garden is now a haven for wildlife with hedgehogs and 27 species of birds feeding last winter as well as being home to ducks, dogs and cats. Wheelchair access to main area of garden but only when dry.

5 BWLCH Y FEDWEN

Penrhyndeudraeth LL48 6BT. David & Gillian Surman. *22m N of Dolgellau, 3m E of Porthmadog. Opp Griffin PH, take A4085 along High St to village car park. Walking from there, follow signs to garden approx 150yds.* Home-made teas. **Adm £3.50, chd free. Sun 6 Apr, Sun 1 June (11-4).**

With views towards the Rhinogs and Moelwyns, ½ acre of neglected, rocky hillside has been transformed, providing terraced gardens with inter-twining paths, many steps with handrails, seating and all yr-round interesting plants, a proliferation of spring bulbs, hellebores, roses, clematis and trees incl embothrium, halesia, koelreuteria, camellias, azaleas, magnolias.

6 CAE NEWYDD

Rhosgoch, Anglesey LL66 0BG. Hazel & Nigel Bond, 01407 831354, nigel@cae-newydd.co.uk. *3m SW of Amlwch. A5025 from Benllech to Amlwch, follow signs for leisure centre & Lastra Farm. Follow yellow NGS signs (approx 3m), car park on L.* Light refreshments. **Adm £3.50, chd free. Sat 7, Sun 8 June (11-4.30).**

A maturing country garden which blends seamlessly into the open landscape with stunning views of Snowdonia and Llyn Alaw. Good variety of shrubs and trees, large wildlife pond, meadow areas, polytunnel, greenhouse, vegetable garden and chicken run. Adjacent sheltered paddock garden. Formal pond and patio area, raised beds. All yr-round interest, Apr for spring bulbs, June for aquilegias, roses etc. Hay meadow best seen in June. Garden area closest to house suitable for wheelchairs.

Sunningdale

7 COED TY MAWR

Ty Mawr, Bryncroes, Pwllheli LL53 8EH. Nonni & David Goadby, 01758 730359, nonni@goadby.net, www.coed-tymawr.co.uk. *12m W of Pwllheli. Take B4413 Llanbedrog to Aberdaron. 1 3/4 m past Sarn Meyllteyrn. Turn R at Penygroeslon sign. From Nefyn take B4417, at Xrds with B4413 turn L.* Home-made teas. **Adm £4, chd free. Sat 26, Sun 27 July (10.30-5). Visitors also welcome by appt Apr to Oct.**

Outstanding 5-acre woodland garden created from wilderness and situated among some of the most beautiful scenery of Wales. Over 3,000 trees and shrubs incl growing collections of magnolia, rhododendron, hydrangea and cornus. Also large pond, orchard, fernery, vegetable, oriental and sea-view gardens. Plenty of seating. Sit on the raised deck, take in the sea views and enjoy a homemade tea. Grass paths.

8 COEDMOR

Caerdeon, Barmouth LL42 1TL. Zarina & Chris Lamb, 01341 430332, coedmorenquiry@hotmail.co.uk, www.coedmor.com. *Take A496 from Dolgellau - Barmouth, through village of Bontddu then follow yellow NGS signs. Just beyond garden, on corner, there is a small car park.* Cream teas. **Adm £3, chd free. Tue 10 June, Tue 8 July, Tue 16 Sept, Tue 14 Oct (9.30-3).**

Coedmor was built in late 1800's, set in an acre of landscaped gardens overlooking the Mawddach Estuary with magnificent views to the Cader Idris mountain range.

9 CORON

Llanbedrog LL53 7NN. Mr & Mrs B M Jones. *3m SW of Pwllheli. Turn R off A499 opp Llanbedrog Village sign, before garage, up private drive.* Cream teas. **Adm £3.50, chd free. Sat 17, Sun 18 May (10.30-5).**

6-acre mature garden featuring Davidia involucrata, overlooking Cardigan Bay. Pathways leading through extensively planted areas with rhododendrons, embothrium, azaleas, camellias, bluebell walks, wooded slopes and rock outcrops providing shelter for tender plants. Lakes and bog gardens; orchards, walled vegetable and formal garden.

10 CRAIG Y FFYNNON

Ffordd y Gader, Dolgellau LL40 1RU. Jon & Sh,n Lea. *Take Tywyn rd from Dolgellau main sq. Park on rd by Penbryn Garage. Walk up rd signed Cader Idris. Garden entrance on L 50yds from junction.* Home-made teas. **Adm £4, chd free (share to Papur Llafar y Deillion Dolgellau a'r Cylch). Sun 11 May (10-4.30).**

N-facing 2-acre Victorian garden set out in 1870s. Majority of garden planted with mature specimen trees, rhododendrons and azaleas predominate. More formal herbaceous borders and greenhouse enclosed by box hedges. Wildlife pond; bees and call ducks; unusual shade-loving plants and ferns. '...refreshing to find something different from the manicured gardens of today.' Frances Denby.

11 CROWRACH ISAF

Bwlchtocyn LL53 7BY. Margaret & Graham Cook, 01758 712860, crowrach_isaf@hotmail.com. *1½ m SW of Abersoch. Follow rd through Abersoch & Sarn Bach, L at sign for Bwlchtocyn for ½ m until junction & no-through rd - Cim Farm. Turn R, parking 50 metres on R.* Cream teas. **Adm £3, chd free.**
Sat 14, Sun 15 June (1-5).
2-acre plot incl 1 acre fenced against rabbits, developed from 2000, incl island beds, windbreak hedges, vegetable garden, wild flower area and wide range of geraniums, shrubs and herbaceous perennials. Views over Cardigan Bay and Snowdonia. Grass and gravel paths, some gentle slopes.

12 ◆ CRÛG FARM

Griffiths Grossing, Caernarfon LL55 1TU. Mr & Mrs B Wynn-Jones, 01248 670232, www.crug-farm.co.uk. *2m NE of Caernarfon. ¼ m off main A487 Caernarfon to Bangor rd. Follow signs from r'about.* **Adm £3, chd free. For NGS: Sat 31 May (10-5). For other opening times and information, please phone or see garden website.**
3 acres; grounds to old country house (not open). Gardens filled with choice, unusual plants collected by the Wynn-Jones. Woodland garden with shade loving plants, many not seen in cultivation before. Walled garden with more wonderful collections growing. Gold Medal winner, Chelsea Flower Show. Home-made teas. Limited wheelchair access.

13 FOXBRUSH

Felinheli LL56 4JZ. Mr & Mrs B S Osborne, 01248 670463. *3m SW of Bangor. On Bangor to Caernarfon rd, entering village opp Felinheli signpost.* **Adm £3, chd free. Visitors welcome by appt Mar to June, refreshments by prior arrangement.**
Fascinating country garden created over 40yrs, from waste land. Still cared for solely by the same lady. Rare and interesting plant collections incl rhododendrons, ferns, hydrangea, clematis and roses cover a 45ft long pergola. Fan-shaped knot garden, 3 bridges and new plantings replace those lost in the floods of 2004. Wildlife mill pond created 2011 full of amphibians and wild ducks, wildflowers abound. Very relaxed wildlife garden.

14 GILFACH

Rowen LL32 8TS. James & Isoline Greenhalgh, 01492 650216, isolinegreenhalgh@btinternet.com. *4m S of Conwy. At Xrds 100yds E of Rowen S towards Llanrwst, past Rowen School on L, turn up 2nd drive on L.* Home-made teas. **Adm £3, chd free. Suns 4 May, 15 June, 24 Aug (2-5.30). Visitors also welcome by appt May to Aug. Coffee and biscuits (am); tea and cake (pm).**
1-acre country garden on S-facing slope with magnificent views of the R Conwy and mountains; set in 35 acres of farm and woodland. Collection of mature shrubs is added to yearly; woodland garden, herbaceous border and small pool. Spectacular view of the Conwy Valley and the mountain range of the Carneddau.

15 GROESLON

Caenarfon Road, Llanberis LL55 4EL. Mr Robert Vaughan. *On A4086 ¾ m W of Llanberis. On A4086 travelling W into Llanberis turn R 200 metres before Lakeview Hotel.* **Adm £3, chd free.**
Sat 7, Sun 8 June (11-5).
2 acres comprising of woodland, fish pond, wildlife pond, stream, wildflower areas, many exotic trees and shrubs and a variety of ducks and chickens. Views over Llyn Padarn. Some steps.

16 GWAELOD MAWR

Caergeiliog, Anglesey LL65 3YL. John & Tricia Coates, 01407 740080. *6m E of Holyhead. ½ m E of Caergeiliog. From A55 J4. r'about 2nd exit signed Caergeiliog. 300yds, Gwaelod Mawr is 1st house on L.* Tea, coffee & biscuits/bara brith. **Adm £3, chd free. Visitors welcome by appt May to Aug.**
2½ -acre garden created by owners over 20yrs with lake, large rock outcrops and palm tree area. Spanish style patio and laburnum arch lead to sunken garden and wooden bridge over lily pond with fountain and waterfall. Peaceful Chinese orientated garden offering contemplation. Separate Koi carp pond. Abundant seating throughout. Many flat areas, gravel and stone paths.

17 GWEL YR YNYS

Parc Moel Lus, Penmaenmawr LL34 6DN. Mr Dafydd Lloyd-Borland, 07968 243119, garden@gwelyrynys.com, www.gwelyrynys.com. *Take J16 from A55. At Mountain View PH take sharp L onto Conwy Old Rd. In ½ m take sharp R into Graiglwyd R.* Home-made teas. Light lunches available 12 -2pm. **Adm £3.50, chd free. Fri 29 Aug (12-4.30); Sat 30 Aug (12-3.30). Visitors also welcome by appt Apr to Sept for 20+ visitors.**
A ¾ -acre challenging hillside garden in an elevated position some 650ft above sea level. Features with Joe Swift on BBC Gardener's World.

18 GWYNDY BACH

Tynlon, Llandrygarn LL65 3AJ. Keith & Rosa Andrew, 01407 720651, keithandrew.art@gmail.com. *5m W of Llangefni. From Llangefni take B5109 towards Bodedern, cottage exactly 5m out on L.* Home-made teas. **Adm £3, chd free. Wed 2 July (11-4.30). Visitors also welcome by appt May to July.**
¾ -acre artist's garden, set amidst rugged Anglesey landscape. Romantically planted in informal intimate rooms with interesting rare plants and shrubs, box and yew topiary, old roses and Japanese garden with large Koi pond. National Collection of Rhapis miniature Japanese palms. Studio attached. Gravel entrance to garden.

19 LLANIDAN HALL
Brynsiencyn LL61 6HJ. Mr J W Beverley (Head Gardener), 07759 305085, beverley.family@btinternet.com. *5m E of Llanfair Pwll. From Llanfair PG follow A4080 towards Brynsiencyn for 4m. After Hooton's farm shop on R take next L, follow lane to gardens*. Light refreshments. **Adm £3.50, chd free (share to CAFOD). Sat 28 June, Sat 12 July (10-4). Visitors also welcome by appt May to Aug.**
Walled garden of 1¾ acres. Physic and herb gardens, ornamental vegetable garden, herbaceous borders, water features and many varieties of old roses. Sheep, rabbits and hens to see. Children must be kept under supervision. Llanidan Church will be open for viewing. Hard gravel paths, gentle slopes.

20 LLYN RHAEADR
Parc Bron-y-Graig, Centre of Harlech LL46 2SR. Mr D R Hewitt & Miss J Sharp, 01766 780224. *Centre of Harlech. From A496 take B4573 into Harlech, take turning to main car parks S of town, L past overspill car park, garden 75yds on R.* **Adm £3, chd free (share to WWF UK). Fri 18, Sat 19, Sun 20, Mon 21 Apr, Sun 4, Mon 5, Sat 24, Sun 25, Mon 26, Tue 27, Wed 28 May, Sat 23, Sun 24, Mon 25 Aug (2-5). Visitors also welcome by appt Mar to Oct, max 30+.**
Hillside garden blending natural wildlife areas with garden plants, shrubs, vegetables and fruit. Small lake with 20 species of waterfowl, fish and wildlife ponds, waterfalls, woodland, rockeries, lawns, borders, snowdrops, daffodils, heathers, bluebells, ferns, camellias, azaleas, rhododendrons, wild flowers, views of Tremadog Bay, Lleyn Peninsula. Good paths and seating with gazebos. Waterfowl collection.

21 LLYS-Y-GWYNT
Pentir Road, Llandygai, Bangor LL57 4BG. Jennifer Rickards & John Evans, 01248 353863. *3m S of Bangor. 300yds from Llandygai r'about at J11, A5 & A55, just off A4244. Follow signs for services (Gwasanaethau). 'No through rd' 50yds beyond. Do not use SatNav*. Cream teas. **Adm £3, chd free. Sun 18 May, Sun 13 July (11-4). Visitors also welcome by appt.**
Rambling 2-acre garden in harmony with and incl magnificent views of Snowdonia. Bronze Age burial cairn. Exposed site incl wandering paths, levels and planting to create shelter, interest and micro climates and lead to varied 'rooms'. Ponds, waterfall, bridge, N-facing rockery and well organised compost. Local materials and crafts used. Yr-round interest and wildlife. Good family garden.

Spectacular views over Irish sea, Snowdon and Caernarfon Castle . . .

22 MAEN HIR
Dwyran, Anglesey LL61 6UY. Mr & Mrs K T Evans. *6m SE of Llanfairpwll. From Llanfair P.G (Anglesey) follow A4080 through village Brynsiencyn. Continue on this rd for approx 2m. Maen Hir on R.* Home-made teas. **Adm £3.50, chd free. Sat 14, Sun 15 June (11-5).**
Set in 7 acres incl beautiful walled garden with gazebo, old roses and mixed herbaceous borders replanted 2007. Courtyard, outer garden, woodland walks, greenhouse, potting shed, cutting patch and hay meadow. Maen Hir enjoys magnificent views of Snowdonia range.

23 MAENAN HALL
Maenan, Llanrwst LL26 0UL. The Hon Mr & Mrs Christopher Mclaren, 01492 640441, cmmclaren@gmail.com. *2m N of Llanrwst. On E side of A470, ¼ m S of Maenan Abbey Hotel*. Home-made teas. **Adm £4, chd free (share to St Davids Hospice). Sun 27 Apr, Sun 17 Aug (10.30-5.30). Visitors also welcome by appt Apr to Oct.**
Superbly beautiful garden (about 4 hectares) on the slopes of the Conwy Valley, with dramatic views of Snowdonia, set amongst mature hardwoods. Both upper part, with sweeping lawns, ornamental ponds and retaining walls, and bluebell carpeted woodland dell contain copious specimen shrubs and trees, many originating at Bodnant. In spring Magnolias, Rhododendrons, Camellias, Pieris and Cherries amongst many others make a breathtaking display. Treasure Hunt (£1) on both open days. Upper part of garden accessible but with fairly steep slopes.

24 NEW PANT IFAN
Ceunant, LLanrug, Caernarfon LL55 4HX. Mrs Delia Lanceley. *2m E of Caernarfon. From Llanrug take rd opp PO between Premier Store & Monumental Mason. Straight across at next X'rds. Then 3rd turn on L at X'rds. Pant Ifan 2nd house on L (Grid Ref: SH 52452 61700).* Home-made teas. **Adm £3.50, chd free. Sat 19 July (1-5).**
2 acre mix of formal and wildlife garden set around farmhouse and yard. Herbaceous borders, shrubs, vegetable, fruit, ponds and recently planted woodland. Field walks, sitting areas in the sun or shade. Poultry, ducks, geese, donkeys, horse and greenhouses. Deep water, children must be supervised at all times.

25 NEW PARC NEWYDD
Rhosgadfan, Caernarfon LL54 7LF. Grace & Geraint Meirion-Jones, 01286 831195. *4½ m SE of Caernarfon. On 4085 through Waunfawr, at derestricted sign turn R, signed Rhosgadfan. Follow lane 1m uphill, cross gattle grid onto mountain. Satnav not suitable*. Home-made teas. **Adm £3.50, chd free. Mon 26 May (11-5).**
Recently developed garden on former Quarryman's smallholding at 900ft. On slopes of Moel Smythaw surrounded by open mountain, subject to strong winds, high rainfall and poor soil. A variety of small 'gardens' incl shrubbery, herbaceous borders, herb garden and vegetable plot. Spectacular views over Irish sea, Snowdon and Caernarfon Castle. Home-made teas at Tal y Briach a listed Quarryman's cottage in a historic field system used for filming the BBC production 'Snowdonia 1890'. The Kate Roberts Trail nearby, famous Welsh writer.

Cae Newydd

26 PEN Y BRYN

Glandwr, Barmouth LL42 1TG. Phil & Jenny Martin. *2m E of Barmouth. On A496 7m W of Dolgellau, 2m E of Barmouth, situated on N side of Mawddach Estuary. Park in or nr layby & walk L up narrow lane.* Cream teas. **Adm £3.50, chd free (share to Gwynedd Hospice at Home).**
Sun 11 May (11-5).
A glorious hillside garden with panoramic views of The Mawddoch Estuary. Woodland walks awash with Bluebells in the spring. Lawns on different levels with vibrant rhododendrons and azaleas, arches of clematis, honeysuckle and roses. Heather filled natural rocks, unusual conifer feature, a rock cannon and a pond for wildlife.

27 ◆ PENRHYN CASTLE

Bangor LL57 4HN. National Trust, 01248 353084, www.nationaltrust.org.uk. *3m E of Bangor. On A5122. Buses from Llandudno, Caernarfon, Betws-y-Coed; alight: Grand Lodge Gate. J11 A55, signed from thereon. Sat Nav LL57 4HT.* **Adm £5.75, chd £2.87.**
For NGS: Sat 22 Feb (12-3), Sat 14 Feb 2015. For other opening times and information, please phone or see garden website.
Large grounds incl Victorian walled garden; fine trees, shrubs, wild garden, good views, snowdrop walks. Coffee shop open, light refreshments. Gravelled and grassed paths, some steps, exposed tree roots, some surfaces bark and chippings.

28 ◆ PENSYCHNANT

Sychnant Pass, nr Conwy LL32 8BJ. Pensychnant Foundation; Wardens Julian Thompson & Anne Mynott, 01492 592595, www.pensychnant.co.uk. *2½ m W of Conwy at top of Sychnant Pass. From Conwy: L into*

Upper Gate St; after 2½ m Pensychnant's drive signed on R. From Penmaenmawr: fork R, up Pass, after walls U-turn L into drive. **Adm £3.50, chd £0.50.** **For NGS: Sun 8 June, Sun 6 July (11-5).** **For other opening times and information, please phone or see garden website.**
Wildlife Garden. Diverse herbaceous 'cottage garden' borders surrounded by mature shrubs, banks of rhododendrons, ancient and Victorian woodlands. 12 acre woodland walks with views of Conwy Mountain and Sychnant. Woodland birds. Picnic tables, archaeological trail on mountain. A peaceful little gem. Large Victorian gothic house (open) with art exhibition. Home-made teas. Partial wheelchair access, please phone for advice.

GROUP OPENING

29 PENTIR GARDENS

Pentir, Bangor LL57 4UY. *Take A4244 from J11 of A55/A5, continue for 3m to Pentir. Turn R signed Caerhun/Vaynol PH, into Pentir Square.* Light refreshments at Bryn Meddyg. **Combined adm £5, chd free.** **Sat 5 July (12-5).**

BRYN MEDDYG
Mr Wyn James

2 RHYD Y GROES
Mr & Mrs IwanThomas

NEW **TAN RALLT**
John Lewis & Gary Carvalho

TAN Y BRYN
Mrs Eliz Battle

TY UCHAF
Miss Belinda Thompson

Ty Uchaf A small densely packed garden with a wide variety of cottage favourites, plus unusual planting schemes. It enjoys a romantic-feel, prioritizing colour and texture. A secret gate takes visitors to neighbouring **Bryn Meddyg**, serving refreshments. A 10 min walk takes you to **Tan y Bryn**, a garden with mature shrubs, a lawned area with herbaceous planting. There is also a vegetable plot, paddock with stunning views, pond and a dwarf conifer collection. Continue along road to the secluded garden **2 Rhyd y Groes** to enjoy views of Moel y Ci and Menai Strait. This immaculate garden has a a number of 'rooms' with a variety of planted areas, seating, pond and summerhouse and sculptures. Further along the lane, a 5 mins walk to **Tan Rallt**, backing onto Moel y Ci, the 0.8 acre garden includes a range of mature trees and shrubs, veg and soft fruit, herbaceous borders and areas of lawn. A diversely planted pond with tree ferns, bog plants and giant gunnera.

30 PLAS CADNANT HIDDEN GARDENS

Cadnant Road, Menai Bridge, Anglesey LL59 5NH. Mr A J Tavernor, 01248 717174, plascadnantgardens@gmail.com, www.plascadnantgardens.co.uk. *½ m E of Menai Bridge. Take A545 & leave Menai Bridge heading for Beaumaris, then follow brown tourist information signs.* Home-made teas in traditional tea room. **Adm £6.50, chd free.** **Wed 30 Apr (1-5).**
Early C19 Picturesque garden undergoing restoration since 1996. Valley gardens with waterfalls, large ornamental walled garden, woodland and early pit house. Visitor centre. Limited wheelchair access to gardens. Some steps, gravel paths, slopes. Access statement available. Disabled WC.

31 ◆ PLAS NEWYDD COUNTRY HOUSE & GARDENS

Llanfairpwll, Anglesey LL61 6DQ. National Trust, 01248 714795, www.nationaltrust.org.uk. *2m S of Llanfairpwll on A4080. A55 J7 & J8 on A4080.* **Adm £7.35, chd £3.70.** **For NGS: Fri 18 Apr (10.30-5.30).** **For other opening times and information, please phone or see garden website.**
Plas Newydd is a beautiful C18 country house with spectacular panoramic views across the Menai Strait to Snowdonia. Set in beautiful gardens, there are tranquil walks, an Australasian arboretum and a pretty Italianate Terrace Garden. The house (not open on NGS day), is the family home of the Marquess of Anglesey. Light refreshments in Old Dairy Tea Room. Some slopes and gravel paths.

32 ◆ PLAS YN RHIW

Rhiw, Pwllheli LL53 8AB. National Trust, 01758 780219, www.nationaltrust.org.uk. *4m E of Aberdaron. 12m from Pwllheli, signed from B4413 to Aberdaron.* **Adm £2, chd £1.** **For NGS: Sun 9 Feb (11-3), Sun 8 Feb 2015.** **For other opening times and information, please phone or see garden website.**
Essentially a cottage garden of ¾ acre laid out around C17 manor house (not open) overlooking Porth Neigwl. Flowering shrubs and trees flourish in compartments framed by formal box hedges and paths. On summer days, scented plants infuse the air. A place of romance and charm. Snowdrops in spring.

33 ST JOHN THE BAPTIST & ST GEORGE

Lon Batus, Carmel LL54 7AR. Bishop Abbot Demetrius. *7m SE of Caernarfon. On A487 Porthmadog Rd, at Dinas r'about exit 1st L to Groeslon, turn L at PO for 1½ m. At village centre turn L & L again at Xrds.* Home-made teas. **Adm £2, chd free.** **Fri 25 July (2-4).**
Holy community in the making under the authority of The Orthodox Catholic and Holy Synod of Milan. This is not a garden in the traditional sense but it and the monastery are a spiritual retreat from the stresses and strains of modern life, surrounded on all sides by space and rural tranquillity. We are privileged to share a glimpse of a more contemplative life. Monastery antique collection.

34 SUNNINGDALE

Bull Bay Road, Bull Bay, Amlwch LL68 9SD. Michael Cross & Gill Boniface, 01407 830753, mikeatbb@aol.com. *1½ m NW of Amlwch. On A5025 through Amlwch towards Cemaes. No parking at house but parking will be signed.* Home-made teas and sandwiches. **Adm £3, chd £1. Sun 4 May, Sun 22 June (11-5). Visitors also welcome by appt May to July, adm £5, chd £3.**

An evolving seaside garden. Headland has cliffs, steps, wild flowers and seating, spectacular views and sheer drops! Front garden has raised pond and planting to cope with hostile weather. The relatively sheltered rear garden is cottage style; no large lawn here! Lots of different plants, paths, seats, pots and raised bed vegetable area. Star is the 50yr old laburnum.

Areas devoted to fruit and vegetable growing and the so called Diamond apple tree . . .

35 TREFFOS SCHOOL

Llansadwrn, Anglesey LL59 5SD. Stuart & Joyce Humphreys. *2½ m N of Menai Bridge. A5025 Amlwch/Benllech exit from the Britannia Bridge onto Anglesey. Approx 3m turn R towards Llansadwrn. Entrance to Treffos School is 200yds on L.* Cream teas. **Adm £3, chd free. Sun 15 June (12-3).**

7 acres, child-friendly garden, in rural location, surrounding C17 house now run as school. Garden consists of mature woodland, underplanted with spring flowering bulbs and rhododendrons, ancient beech avenue leading down to rockery, herbaceous borders and courtyards. Art and Craft activities for children. Also face painting.

36 NEW TY CADFAN SANT

National Street, Tywyn LL36 9DD. Mrs Katie Pearce. *A493 going S & W. L into on-way, garden ahead. Bear R, parking 2nd L. A493 going N, 1st R in 30 mph zone, L at bottom by garden, parking 2nd L.* Cream teas. **Adm £3, chd free. Sun 8, Sun 29 June (10-4).**

Large eco-friendly garden. In the front, shrubbery, mixed flower beds and roses surround a mature copper beech. Up six steps the largely productive back garden has chickens in the orchard, fruit, vegetables, flowers and a poly tunnel. Crafts. Limited wheelchair access due to steps to rear garden.

37 TY CAPEL FFRWD

Llanfachreth, nr Dolgellau LL40 2NR. Revs Mary & George Bolt, 01341 422006, georgebolt@talktalk.net. *4m NE of Dolgellau, 18m SW of Bala. From Dolgellau 4m up hill to Llanfachreth. Turn L at War Memorial. Follow lane ½ m to chapel on R. Park & walk down lane past chapel to cottage.* Home-made teas. **Adm £3, chd free. Visitors welcome by appt May to Sept. Art Groups and Gardening Clubs welcome, max 10 visitors.**

True cottage garden in Welsh mountains. Azaleas, rhododendrons, acers; large collection of aquilegia. Many different hostas give added strength to spring bulbs and corms. Stream flowing through the garden, 10ft waterfall and on through a small woodland bluebell carpet. For summer visitor's there is a continuous show of colour with herbaceous plants, roses, clematis and lilies, incl cardiocrinum giganteum.

38 TY GWYN, LLANBEDRGOCH

Llanbedrgoch, Anglesey LL76 8NX. Keith & Anna Griffiths. *2m inland W of Red Wharf Bay. A5025 from Menai Bridge through Pentraeth. Turn L to Llanbedrgoch. At village centre follow NGS signs.* Home-made teas. **Adm £4, chd free. Sun 15 June (12-5).**

Wildish 9-acres incl wild flower meadow, limestone pavement and hazel copses together with landscaped formal lawns and gardens separated into a number of 'green rooms' of different interest incl gazebo and pond, small walled garden, topiary yews and box hedging. Adjacent to several SSSI's, incl Cors Goch, an International Wetlands Nature Reserve. Anglesey Beekeepers' Association apiary within the grounds, escorted visits to view hives and be introduced to the craft of beekeeping.

39 TY NEWYDD

Ffordd Clwt Glas, Dyffryn Ardudwy LL44 2DB. Guy & Margaret Lloyd, 01341 247357, guylloyd@btinternet.com. *5½ m N of Barmouth, 4½ m S of Harlech. Situated just off A496 Barmouth to Harlech rd ½ m N of Dyffryn village centre.* Home-made teas. **Adm £3, chd free. Visitors welcome by appt Feb to Dec.**

3½ -acre maritime garden diversley planted with trees and shrubs to provide yr-round interest through contrasting foliage colours and forms as well as floral displays. Plants incl a number of more tender subjects such as echium, grevillea and pittosporum. Areas devoted to fruit and vegetable growing and the so called Diamond apple tree. Limited wheelchair access, uneven surfaces, granite chip driveway.

40 41 VICTORIA DRIVE

Llandudno Junction LL31 9PF. Allan Evans. *Llandudno Junction. A55 J18. From Bangor 1st exit, from Colwyn Bay 2nd exit, A546 to Conwy. Next r'about 3rd exit then 1st L.* Light refreshments. **Adm £3, chd free. Sun 27 Apr (1-4).**

An interesting small urban garden, offering so much to see, colourful spring bulbs, polyanthus, pansy, violas, spring flowering shrubs - seed sowing in progress- young sweet pea plants, dahlias, cuttings and gladioli growing on ready for planting, plenty to interest visitors. Featured in Daily Post and Weekly News.

Foxbrush

Gwynedd County Volunteers

County Organisers

North Grace Meirion-Jones, Parc Newydd, Rhosgadfan, Caernarfon LL54 7LF, 01286 831195
South Hilary Nurse, Bryn Gwern, Llanfachreth, Dolgellau LL40 2DH, 01341 450255

County Treasurers

South Michael Bishton, Bronclydwr, Rhoslefain, Tywyn LL36 9LT, 01654 710882, m.bishton@btopenworld.com
North Nigel Bond, Cae Newydd, Rhosgoch, Amlwch, Anglesey LL66 0BG, 01407 831354, nigel@cae-newydd.co.uk

Assistant County Organisers

North Hazel Bond, Cae Newydd, Rhosgoch, Amlwch, Anglesey LL66 0BG, 01407 831354, nigel@cae-newydd.co.uk
North Janet Jones, Coron, Llanbedrog, Pwllheli LL53 7NN, 01758 740296 coron@hotmail.co.uk

NORTH EAST WALES

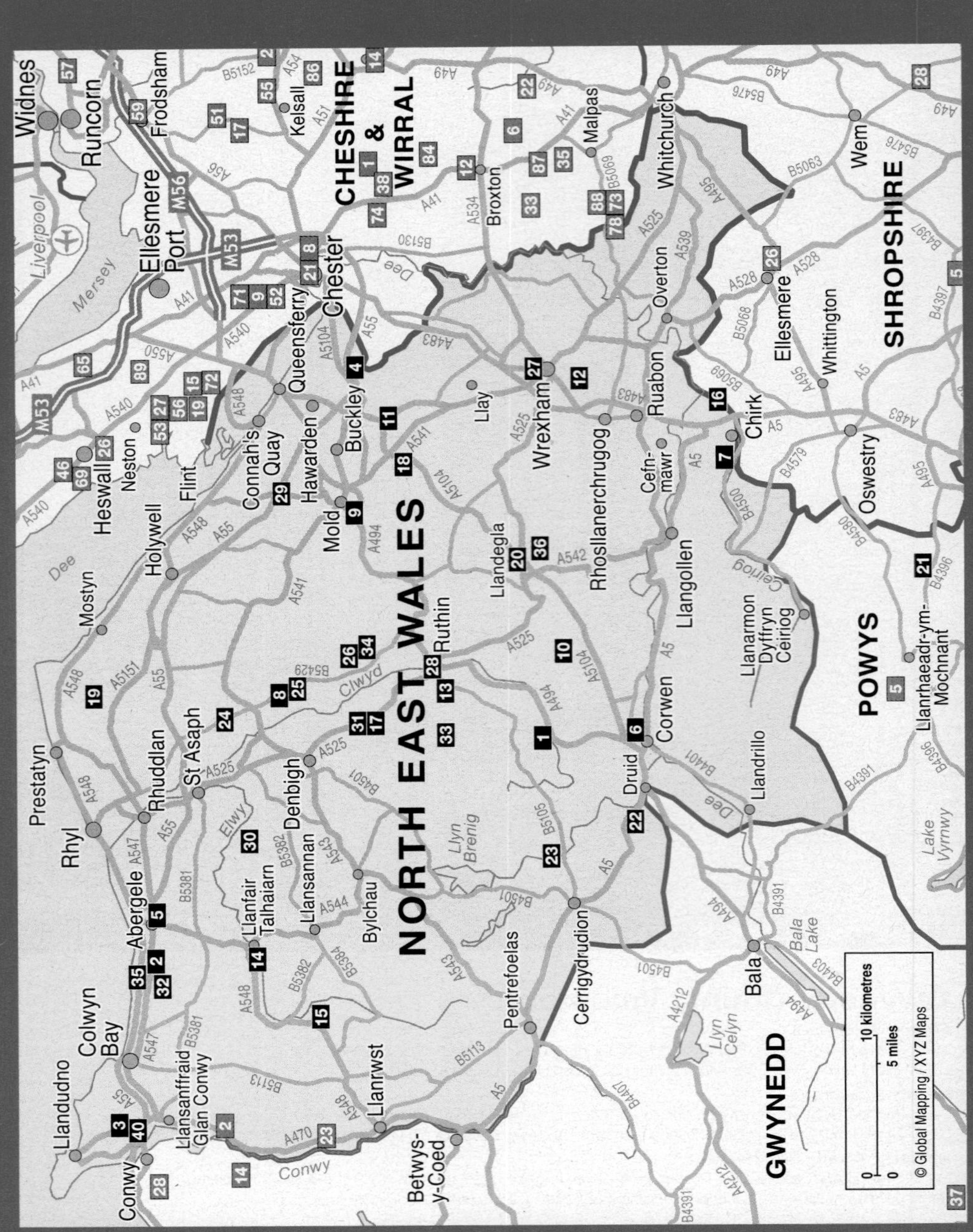

Opening Dates

All entries subject to change. For latest information check www.ngs.org.uk

February

Wednesday 12
8 Clwydfryn

Thursday 20
15 Glog Ddu

Thursday 27
15 Glog Ddu

March

Wednesday 12
8 Clwydfryn

Sunday 23
23 The Old Rectory, Llanfihangel Glyn Myfyr

April

1 **Aberclwyd Manor (Every Wednesday)**

Wednesday 9
8 Clwydfryn

Sunday 20
32 Tudor Cottage

May

1 **Aberclwyd Manor (Every Wednesday)**

Saturday 3
10 Dibleys Nurseries
12 Erddig Hall

Sunday 4
10 Dibleys Nurseries

Monday 5
10 Dibleys Nurseries

Wednesday 14
8 Clwydfryn

Sunday 25
5 33 Bryn Twr and Lynton

June

1 **Aberclwyd Manor (Every Wednesday)**

Sunday 1
22 Maesmor Hall

Festival Weekend

Saturday 7
17 NEW The Laundry
29 90 St Peters Park
31 Tan-y-Parc

Sunday 8
17 NEW The Laundry
31 Tan-y-Parc

Wednesday 11
8 Clwydfryn

Saturday 14
7 Chirk Castle
16 Hillside

Sunday 15
16 Hillside
19 Llanasa Village Gardens

Sunday 22
5 33 Bryn Twr and Lynton
21 Llangedwyn Hall
23 The Old Rectory, Llanfihangel Glyn Myfyr

Tuesday 24
3 Bodysgallen Hall & Spa

Saturday 28
18 Leeswood Green Farm
30 Tal-y-Bryn Farm
32 Tudor Cottage

Sunday 29
18 Leeswood Green Farm
26 Plas yn Llan
30 Tal-y-Bryn Farm
32 Tudor Cottage

July

1 **Aberclwyd Manor (Every Wednesday)**

Saturday 5
35 Y Bwthyn

Wednesday 9
8 Clwydfryn

Sunday 13
4 Broughton & Bretton Allotments
9 The Cottage Nursing Home
25 Plas Ashpool
27 Prices Lane Allotments
34 Wylan

Sunday 20
2 NEW Ael y Grug
5 33 Bryn Twr and Lynton
28 Ruthin Town Gardens

Sunday 27
20 Llandegla Village Gardens

August

1 **Aberclwyd Manor (Every Wednesday)**

Sunday 3
11 Dove Cottage
12 Erddig Hall

Wednesday 13
8 Clwydfryn

Sunday 24
6 Caereuni

Monday 25
6 Caereuni

Sunday 31
25 Plas Ashpool

September

1 **Aberclwyd Manor (Every Wednesday)**

Thursday 4
15 Glog Ddu

Wednesday 10
8 Clwydfryn

Thursday 18
15 Glog Ddu

February 2015

Wednesday 11
8 Clwydfryn

Gardens open to the public

7 Chirk Castle
12 Erddig Hall

By appointment only

13 Firgrove
14 Garthewin
24 Pen Y Graig Bach
33 Tyddyn Bach
36 Y Graig

Also open by appointment

1 Aberclwyd Manor
5 33 Bryn Twr and Lynton
8 Clwydfryn
11 Dove Cottage
15 Glog Ddu
17 The Laundry
18 Leeswood Green Farm
20 Glan-yr-Afon, Llandegla Village Gardens
20 Swn y Gwynt, Llandegla Village Gardens
28 46 Mwrog Street, Ruthin Town Gardens
29 90 St Peters Park
30 Tal-y-Bryn Farm
32 Tudor Cottage

You are always welcome at an NGS garden!

33 Bryn Twr and Lynton

Visit a garden on National Gardens Weekend 7 & 8 June

The Gardens

1 ABERCLWYD MANOR
Derwen, Corwen LL21 9SF. Miss Irene Brown & Mr G Sparvoli, 01824 750431, irene662010@live.com. *7m from Ruthin. Travelling on A494 from Ruthin to Corwen. At Bryn S.M service station turn R, follow sign to Derwen. Aberclwyd gates will be seen on L before Derwen.* **Adm £3, chd free. Every Wed 1 Apr to 30 Sept (11-4). Visitors also welcome by appt Feb to Sept. Groups 10+ daytime or evenings.**
A 4 acre garden on a sloping hillside overlooking the Upper Clwyd Valley. The garden has many mature trees underplanted with snowdrops, fritillaries and cyclamen. An Italianate garden of box hedging lies below the house and shrubs, ponds, perennials, roses and an orchard are also to be enjoyed within this cleverly structured area. Mostly flat with some steps and slopes.

2 NEW AEL Y GRUG
Rhyd y Foel Road, Llanddulas, Abergele LL22 8EG. Mr Neville McClellan. *From Abergele, go W on Market St (A547) towards Llanddulas. After 2m turn L at Rhydyfoel Rd. Turn R into New Rd & park here.* Light refreshments. **Combined adm £5, chd free. Sun 20 July (1-5). Combined with 33 Bryn Twr and Lynton.**
A hillside garden, on several levels, with steep entry, set in ½ acre. Mixed herbaceous borders, connected by paths taking you through areas of mature shrubs and perennial flower beds. Beautiful valley views to the Irish sea in the distance.

3 BODYSGALLEN HALL & SPA
The Royal Welsh Way, nr Llandudno LL30 1RS. The National Trust, 01492 584466, www.bodysgallen.com. *2m from Llandudno. Take A55 to its intersection with A470 (The Royal Welsh Way) towards Llandudno. Proceed 1m, hotel is 1m on R.* Home-made teas in The Upper Wynn Room. **Adm £4, chd free. Tue 24 June (1-5).**
Garden is well known for C17 box-hedged parterre. Stone walls surround lower gardens with rose gardens and herbaceous borders. Outside walled garden is cascade over rocks. Enclosed working fruit and vegetable garden with espalier-trained fruit trees, hedging area for cut flowers with walls covered in wineberry and Chinese gooseberry. Restored Victorian woodland, walks with stunning views of Conwy and Snowdonia. Gravel paths in places and steep slopes.

ALLOTMENTS

4 BROUGHTON & BRETTON ALLOTMENTS
Main Road, Broughton CH4 0NT. Broughton & Bretton Allotments Association, www.broughtonandbretton allotments.co.uk. *5m W of Chester. On A5104 (signed Penyffordd) in village of Broughton.* Home-made teas at War Memorial Institute. **Adm £3, chd free. Sun 13 July (12-5).**
56 half sized allotment plots used by the local community to grow a mix of vegetables, flowers and soft fruit. Seasonal produce for sale.

Beautiful valley views to the Irish sea in the distance . . .

5 33 BRYN TWR AND LYNTON
Lynton, Highfield Park, Abergele LL22 7AU. Mr & Mrs Colin Knowlson, 01745 832002, apk@slaters.com. *Abergele. From A55 head W take slip rd into Abergele town centre. Turn L at 2nd set of T-lights signed Llanfair TH, 3rd rd on L Sat Nav - please use LL22 8DD.* Home-made teas. **Adm £3.50, chd free (share to Ty Croesco (Dawn Elizabeth House & Glan Clwyd Hospital)). Sun 25 May; Sun 22 June; Sun 20 July (1-5). Combined with Ael Y Grug, Sun 20 July, combined adm £5, chd free. Visitors also welcome by appt Mar to Aug, any size group, coaches welcome by appointment.**
More changes have been made to the gardens for 2014, mixed herbaceous and shrub borders, some trees plus many unusual plants. Lawn at Lynton replaced with slate chips and more planting. Garage with interesting fire engine, cars and memorabilia, greenhouse over water capture system, the surrounding planting coming along nicely. Limited wheelchair access.

6 CAEREUNI
Ffordd Ty Cerrig, Godre'r Gaer, nr Corwen LL21 9YA. Mr S Williams, www.plantationcaereunigarden.co.uk. *1m N of Corwen. A5 Corwen to Bala rd, turn R at T-lights onto A494 to Chester. 1st R after lay-by. House ¼ m on L.* **Adm £3.50, chd free. Sun 24, Mon 25 Aug (2-5).**
Plantsman's collection of rare trees, shrubs, plants, containers of tender plants and topiary set in a quirky themed garden. This 0.3 acre garden incls Japanese smoke water garden, old ruin, Spanish courtyard, Welsh gold mine, Chinese peace garden, Mexican chapel, 1950s petrol garage, woodman's lodge and jungle.

7 ◆ CHIRK CASTLE
Chirk, nr Wrexham LL14 5AF. National Trust, 01691 777701, www.nationaltrust.org.uk. *7m S of Wrexham, 2m W of Chirk Village. Follow brown signs from A483 to Chirk Village. 2m W on minor rds.* **Adm £11.44, chd £5.72. For NGS: Sat 14 June (10-6). For other opening times and information, please phone or see garden website.**
5½ -acre hilltop garden with good views over Shropshire and Cheshire. Often thought to be at its peak at this time of yr. Formal garden with outstanding yew topiary, rose garden, herbaceous borders, rare trees and shrubs, pond, thatched Hawk House, Ha-Ha with Terrace and Pavilion. Newly opened vegetable garden. Most of garden accessible for wheelchairs.

8 CLWYDFRYN

Bodfari LL16 4HU. Keith & Susan Watson, 01745 710232, clwydfryn@btinternet.com. *5m outside Denbigh. Halfway between Bodfari & Llandyrnog on B5429.* Home-made teas. **Adm £3.50, chd free. Weds 12 Feb, 12 Mar, 9 Apr, 14 May, 11 June, 9 July, 13 Aug, 10 Sept (11-4); Wed 11 Feb 2015. Visitors also welcome by appt Feb to Sept, groups 10+.**

¾ -acre plantswoman's garden, well worth a visit any time of the yr. Collection of epimediums, hellebores and daffodils in spring. Many unusual spring shade loving plants and perennial borders in summer. Grass border, orchard and colourful cottage garden potager. Garden access up a slope from parking area to main garden.

9 THE COTTAGE NURSING HOME

54 Hendy Road, Mold CH7 1QS. Mr & Mrs A G & L I Lanini. *10m W of Chester. From Mold town centre take A494 towards Ruthin then follow yellow NGS signs.* Cream teas. **Adm £2, chd £1 (share to British Heart Foundation). Sun 13 July (2-5).**

Beautiful garden set in approx 1 acre. Well-established shrubs, herbaceous plants and abundance of colourful window boxes and tubs. Heart-shaped patio, incl water feature and pergola, with natural reclaimed stone walling.

10 DIBLEYS NURSERIES

Llanelidan, Cefn Rhydd LL15 2LG. Mr & Mrs R Dibley, 01978 790677, info@dibleys.com, www.dibleys.com. *7m S of Ruthin. Follow brown signs off A525 nr Llysfasi College.* **Adm £4, chd free. Sat 3, Sun 4, Mon 5 May (10-5).**

8-acre arboretum with wide selection of rare and unusual trees. There will be a lovely display of rhododendrons, magnolias, cherries and camellias. Ride through the garden on a miniature railway. ¾ acre of glasshouses are open to show a spectacular display of streptocarpus and other house plants. National Collection of *Streptocarpus*. Awarded our 24th Chelsea Gold Medal and our streptocarpus 'Harlequin Blue' named RHS plant of the Decade (2003-2012). Limited wheelchair access to glasshouses, uneven ground in arboretum and elsewhere.

NCH

11 DOVE COTTAGE

Rhos Road, Penyffordd, nr Chester CH4 0JR. Chris & Denise Wallis, 01244 547539, dovecottage@supanet.com. *6m SW of Chester. Leave A55 at J35 take A550 to Wrexham. Drive 2m, turn R onto A5104. From A541 Wrexham/Mold Rd in Pontblyddyn take A5104 to Chester. Garden opp rail station.* Home-made teas. **Adm £3.50, chd free. Sun 3 Aug (2-5). Visitors also welcome by appt June to Sept.**

Approx 1½ -acre garden, shrubs and herbaceous plants set informally around lawns. Established vegetable area, 2 ponds (1 wildlife), summerhouse and woodland planted area. Gravel paths.

12 ◆ ERDDIG HALL

nr Wrexham LL13 0YT. National Trust, 01978 315150, www.nationaltrust.org.uk. *2m S of Wrexham. Signed from A483/A5125 Oswestry rd; also from A525 Whitchurch rd.* **Adm £6.60, chd £3.30. For NGS: Sat 3 May, Sun 3 Aug (11-5). For other opening times and information, please phone or see garden website.**

Important, listed Grade I, historic garden. Formal C18 and later Victorian design elements incl pleached lime tree avenues, trained fruit trees, wall plants and climbers, herbaceous borders, roses, herb border, annual bedding, restored glasshouse and vine house. National Collection of Hedera. Free garden tours at set times during the day. Guide dogs permitted. Light refreshments in Restaurant, Parlour or Tea-Garden. All areas of the garden accessible to wheelchairs. Gravelled paths, two steps which can be avoided and some short sloping sections.

13 FIRGROVE

Llanfwrog, Ruthin LL15 2LL. Philip & Anna Meadway, 01824 702677, meadway@firgrovecountryhouse.co.uk, www.firgrovecountryhouse.co.uk. *1½ m SW of Ruthin. Exit Ruthin on B5105 towards Cerrigydrudion. After church & inn, garden is ½ m on the R.* Home-made teas. **Adm £3.50, chd £2. Visitors welcome by appt May to Sept between 11.30am and 3.30pm.**

1½ acre mature plantsman's garden that is still developing. A garden for all seasons whose microclimate allows tender and unusual shrubs to thrive. Under planting with streptocarpus for the summer. Containers of large exotica for summer. Many varieties of camellias, magnolias,clematis and brugmansias. For 2014 by appointment only to allow revitalisation! Please telephone to review progress.

14 GARTHEWIN

Llanfair T.H LL22 8YR. Mr Michael Grime, 01745 720288. *6m S of Abergele & A55. From Abergele take A548 to Llanfair TH & Llanrwst. Entrance to Garthewin 300yds W of Llanfair TH on A548 to Llanrwst. Sat nav misleading.* **Adm £3.50, chd free. Visitors welcome by appt Apr to Oct, max 40 visitors. Sorry, no coaches.**

Valley garden with ponds and woodland areas. Much of the 8 acres have been reclaimed and redesigned providing a younger garden with a great variety of azaleas, rhododendrons and young trees, all within a framework of mature shrubs and trees.

15 GLOG DDU

Llangernyw, Abergele LL22 8PS. Pamela & Anthony Harris, 01745 860611. *1m S of Llangernyw. Llangernyw is half-way between Abergele & Llanrwst on A548. Do not use SAT NAV. Turn up Uwch Afon Rd on Llanrwst side of village.* **Adm £3.50, chd free. Thur 20, Thur 27 Feb (12-3); Thur 4, Thur 18 Sept (2-5). Visitors also welcome by appt June to Oct.**

Approx 2-acres consisting of snowdrops, rhododendrons, herbaceous borders, rare trees and shrubs, many grown from seed. Planted for yr-round interest with an emphasis on autumn colour. New prairie border. Over 300 different varieties of snowdrops with many hard-to-find available for sale.

16 HILLSIDE

Pont-y-Blew, Wrexham, Chirk LL14 5BH. Ferelith & Robert Smith, fereliths@btinternet.com. *2m E of Chirk. Follow B5070 to Chirk. Turn into Collery Rd & follow NGS signs to Pont-y-Blew or follow NGS signs from Halton r'about A483 (McDonalds).* Home-made teas. **Adm £3, chd free. Sat 14, Sun 15 June (1-5).**

Country cottage garden in fabulous setting, looking across the lower Ceiriog Valley. C17 half-timbered cottage (not open) in middle of 3/4 - acre lawned garden with mixed borders, woodland stream, roses, fruit and vegetable gardens. Wild flower bank. Stream and lower garden accessible by steep paths. Limited wheelchair access.

17 NEW THE LAUNDRY

Llanrhaeadr, Denbigh LL16 4NL. Mr & Mrs T Williams, 01745 890515, tomjenny@btinternet.com. *3m SE of Denbigh. Entrance off A525 Denbigh to Ruthin Rd.* Home-made teas. **Combined adm £5, chd free. Sat 7, Sun 8 June (11.30-5.30). Combined with Tan y Parc. Visitors also welcome by appt Jan to Oct, groups 10+.**

Terraced courtyard garden developed since 2009 surrounded by old stone walls enclosing cottage style planting and formal hedging. One year ago work started on the old kitchen walled garden with a view to incorporating it within the whole garden plan. A chance to see a new garden evolving within an old setting. Woodland walk, roses, pleached limes, peonies and herbaceous planting. Featured in House Beautiful and awarded Best Kept Garden in Llanrhaeadr. Some gravel areas.

18 LEESWOOD GREEN FARM

Leeswood CH7 4SQ. Anne Saxon & John Glenn, 01352 771222, annemsaxon@yahoo.co.uk. *3m SE of Mold. 9m NW of Wrexham. From Wrexham turn L after garage into Dingle rd, at T junc turn L, after 50 yds turn R down country track.*

Ruthin Castle, Ruthin Town Gardens

© Jessie Williams

Home-made teas. **Adm £3.50, chd free. Sat 28, Sun 29 June (1-5). Visitors also welcome by appt Apr to Sept. Limited parking, no space for coaches.**

Plantswoman's garden surrounding C15 farmhouse in lovely rural location. Many unusual trees, shrubs, perennials and bulbs set around lawns. Ornamental vegetable garden, orchard and paved areas with some unusual features. Meadow with wild flowers and seating to enjoy the vistas. Large plant stall. Gravel area near house. Lawned areas, slight incline.

GROUP OPENING

19 LLANASA VILLAGE GARDENS

Nr Holywell CH8 9NE. *3m SE of Prestatyn. Llanasa is situated between Holywell & Prestayn, signed off A5151 by village of Trelawnyd.* Home-made teas in village hall and Tree Tops Caravan Park. **Combined adm £5, chd free. Sun 15 June (11-5).**

GLANABER
Mr & Mrs Roberts

GOLDEN GROVE HOUSE
N R & M M J Steele-Mortimer
01745 854452
golden.grove@lineone.net

GROVE VILLA
John Law

THE OLD COACH HOUSE
Mr & Mrs Robert Edwards

THE OLD MANSE
Jill Espley

THE OLD POST OFFICE
Mrs Jean Jones

TAN Y COED
Bill & Dawn Jones

NEW TREE TOP CARAVAN PARK
Andrew Walker
www.treetopscaravanpark.co.uk

Llanasa village gardens are situated in a conservation village clustered around a C15 church. Approx 1m above the village is the Golden Grove Estate with its terraced gardens designed by Lady Aberconwy and featuring a nuttery. Within the boundaries of the village is The Old Manse with lovely roses and lavenders, lawns and herbaceous borders. Glan Aber features two ponds and a good collection of mature trees and shrubs. The Old Coach House always has a great show of hanging baskets, a lawn and perennials. The Old Post Office has a beautiful cottage garden with its pathway alongside the church. Grove Villa is an old cottage with a new garden under development. Tan y Coed has three colourful borders, many raised vegetable beds, two greenhouses and polytunnel. There is a new garden this yr about 2m in the coastal direction - Tree Tops Caravan Park - many times winner of Wales in Bloom. The abundance of annuals presented in baskets, mangers, beds and borders are a picture.

Y Bwthyn

GROUP OPENING

20 LLANDEGLA VILLAGE GARDENS

Llandegla LL11 3AP. *10m W of Wrexham. Off A525 at Llandegla Memorial Hall. Parking & minibus from hall. Please park in centre of village as parking is difficult for some gardens.* Home-made teas in Llandegla Memorial Hall. **Combined adm £5, chd free. Sun 27 July (2-6).**

ERW LLAN
Mr & Mrs Keith Jackson

GLAN-YR-AFON
Mr & Mrs D C Ion
Visitors also welcome by appt June to Sept.
01978 790286

ISIS
Janet & David Rose

13 MAES TEG
Phil & Joan Crawshaw

11 MAES TEG
Mr & Mrs L Evans

SWN Y GWYNT
Phil Clark
Visitors also welcome by appt June to Aug.
01978 790344

Selection of 7 widely varied gardens in the picturesque village of Llandegla. The garden at the Gate House has a wide variety of interesting features, incl colourful shrubs and borders, water features, orchard areas and native trees. You will find Swn y Gwynt a real plantsman's garden. This garden demonstrates the interest which can be developed in a shady garden with a wide variety of plants and shrubs. Isis offers a colourful display of a variety of herbaceous plants, as well as a vegetable garden and shrubs designed for yr-round interest. 11 and 13 Maes Teg demonstrate how much interest can be achieved in a compact space, with colourful herbaceous plants, and shrubs for all-yr colour, water features, yet low maintenance. Erw Llan is a ¼-acre garden made to attract wildlife. Habitats are provided and plants are grown for birds, butterflies and insects. There is also a well maintained pond to encourage other wildlife. Glan yr Afon has a 1-acre informal country garden with a variety of features incl stream, ponds, herbaceous borders, trees and vegetable patch. Some gardens may be difficult for wheelchair users.

21 LLANGEDWYN HALL

Llangedwyn, Oswestry SY10 9JW. Mr & Mrs T M Bell. *8m W of Oswestry. On B4396 to Llanrhaeadr-ym-Mochnant about 5m W of Llynclys Xrds.* Home-made teas. **Adm £4, chd free. Sun 22 June (12-5).**

Approx 4-acre formal terraced garden on 3 levels, designed and laid out in late C17 and early C18. Unusual herbaceous plants, sunken rose garden, small water garden, walled kitchen garden and woodland walk.

22 MAESMOR HALL

Maerdy, Corwen LL21 0NS. Dr & Mrs G M Jackson, 01490 460411, www.maesmor.com. *5m W of Corwen. Take A5 from Corwen, through 2 sets of T-lights. In Maerdy take 1st L after church & opp The Goat PH.* Home-made teas. **Adm £4, chd free (share to St Dunstans (charity for injured soldiers)). Sun 1 June (10-6).**

Garden with riverside and estate walks featuring a water and white plant garden. The rhododendrons are extensive and provide a fitting backdrop to the parkland. Large azalea beds are a mixture of colour. Wooded walks around the hall go towards a new folly amongst the bluebells in the arboretum. A 100yr old Fig and Vine House has been restored and incl exotic plants, flowers, pomegranates, lemons, oranges, and bananas. Also many patios and front of hall rose displays. Enormous stone table has been brought down from the surrounding mountain - it could have been King Arthur's. Gravel paths.

23 THE OLD RECTORY, LLANFIHANGEL GLYN MYFYR

Corwen LL21 9UN. Mr & Mrs E T Hughes. *2½ m NE of Cerrigydrudion. From Ruthin take B5105 SW for 12m to Llanfihangel Glyn Myfyr. Turn R just after Crown PH (follow signs). Proceed for ⅓ m, garden on L.* Home-made teas. **Adm £3.50, chd free (share to Cancer Research U.K). Sun 23 Mar, Sun 22 June (2-5).**

Garden of approx 1 acre set in beautiful, tranquil, sheltered valley. A garden for all seasons; hellebores; abundance of spring flowers; mixed borders; water, bog, and gravel gardens; walled garden with old roses, pergola, bower and garden of meditation. Also hardy orchids, gentians, daffodils, rhododendrons and acers. Limited wheelchair access in places.

24 PEN Y GRAIG BACH

Tremeirchion, St Asaph LL17 0UR. Roger Pawling and Christine Hoyle, 07875 642270, rogerpawling@gmail.com. *4m SE of St Asaph. A55 take J 28/29/30 to Tremeirchion, take B5429 to Bodfari, go 0.7m, turn L up steep hill, L at fork continue to rd end. From Bodfari go R after 1¼ m.* **Adm £3, chd free. Visitors welcome by appt Apr to Oct.**

Half-acre wildlife-friendly rural cottage garden. Box hedges and fruit trees enclose 5 plots of herbaceous perennials, unusual climbers, flowering shrubs, soft fruit and vegetables. Collection of native and ornamental trees. Colour throughout the yr, best in June/July. 4 ponds and 2 acres of paddocks which are managed organically for wild flowers. Beehives. Stunning views from sea to mountains. Partial wheelchair access, gravel paths between box hedges and grass paths.

The rhododendrons are extensive and provide a fitting backdrop to the parkland . . .

25 PLAS ASHPOOL

Llandyrnog LL16 4HP. Fiona Bell. *5m outside Denbigh. Half way between Bodfari & Llandyrnog on B5429.* Home-made teas. **Adm £3.50, chd free. Sun 13 July, Sun 31 Aug (1.30-6).**

This country house garden with views of the Clwydian hills and Vale of Clwyd was developed over 40 yrs ago by present owner's family and is now undergoing restoration. The herbaceous and shrub borders, orchard, vegetable garden and sunken rose garden are surrounded by historic farm buildings which are also being rescued from disrepair. Pigs, hens and bees help complete this rural picture. Limited wheelchair access.

26 PLAS YN LLAN

Llangynhafal LL16 4LN. Richard & Jenni Wykes. *4m N of Ruthin. From Ruthin take A494 towards Mold. After 1½ m turn L at Griffin PH onto B5429. ½ m turn R at Llangynhafal signpost. After 2½ m turn R to church.* Home-made teas. **Adm £3.50, chd free. Sun 29 June (2-6).**

Garden is divided into a number of 'rooms' incl cottage garden, parterre, fountain garden, rose garden, stream and pond garden and secret garden. Many unusual plants and wide variety of roses, peonies and tree peonies.

ALLOTMENTS

27 PRICES LANE ALLOTMENTS

Prices Lane, Wrexham LL11 2NB. Wrexham Allotment & Leisure Gardeners Association. *1m N of Wrexham town centre. Between A5152 Chester Rd & B5425 Rhosddu Rd. From J6 on A483 take A5152. From J5 take A541 to Wrexham, 1st exit B5101, continue 0.7m & at junction turn L onto B5425 then R into Prices Lane.* **Adm £3, chd free. Sun 13 July (12-5).**

120 plus plots, growing a good variety of flowers, fruit and vegetables. Plots for the disabled and school children. Association shop, selling a wide range of garden requisites and seeds.

GROUP OPENING

28 RUTHIN TOWN GARDENS

Ruthin LL16 4HP. *Tickets & maps available at 46 Mwrog St on A494 & Ruthin Castle in centre of town. Park at one of the many car parks around town.* Refreshments available at various Inns and cafes in town. **Combined adm £5, chd free. Sun 20 July (11-5).**

NEW **24 BORTHYN**
Paul & Suzanne Simm

NEW **14 CAE SEREN**
Mrs Angela Carrington-Roberts

GWYNFA
Mr & Mrs R G Jones

NEW **153 MWROG ST**
Mrs Hazel Moseley

46 MWROG STREET
Glenna & David Toyne
Visitors also welcome by appt July.
01824 707470

RUTHIN CASTLE
Ruthin Castle Ltd
01824 702664
reservations@ruthincastle.co.uk

On the Craft Centre side of town is Gwynfa, a small graveled town garden with raised beds, pots and colourful baskets covering the walls, and a new garden 14 Cae Seren which is packed with a good variety of plants. The large garden of Ruthin Castle Hotel is surrounded by picturesque grounds and ancient walls. Three gardens to the west of St Peters Square all have interesting gardens to the rear of the properties. 24 Borthyn is new and so colourful it is hard to be believe it has only been created over the last 3 years, 153 Mwrog St is a mature cottage garden with good views over Ruthin Town whose owner loves propagating new plants, and 46 Mwrog St is a plantswomens oasis hidden behind her terraced cottage.

29 90 ST PETERS PARK

Northop CH7 6YU. Mr P Hunt, 01352 840758, philipbhunt@hotmail.co.uk. *3m N of Mold, 3m S of Flint. Leave A55 at Northop exit J33. Opp cricket ground, turn R. Take 5th turning on R. Garden on R.* Home-made teas. **Adm £3, chd free. Sat 7 June (2-5.30). Visitors also welcome by appt all yr.**

Garden planted by professional botanist and horticulturalist, Custos Hortorum at Chester Cathedral and creator of Cloister Garth, Cheshire Garden of Distinction. A plantsman's garden with exotic and rare species of trees and ornamental plants. Unique garden cruck house with sedum roof, beamed ceilings, stained glass windows and inglenook fireplace. Other interesting timber framed structures.

30 TAL-Y-BRYN FARM

Llannefydd, Denbigh LL16 5DR. Mr & Mrs Gareth Roberts, 01745 540256, llaeth@villagedairy.co.uk, www.villagedairy.co.uk. *3m W of Henllan. From Henllan take rd signed Llannefydd. After 2½ m turn R signed Bont Newydd. Garden ½ m on L.* Home-made teas. **Adm £3.50, chd free (share to Elderly Committee of Llannefydd). Sat 28, Sun 29 June (2-5). Visitors also welcome by appt June. Tours of the yoghurt dairy may also be booked.**
Medium-sized working farmhouse cottage garden. Ancient farm machinery. Incorporating ancient privy festooned with honeysuckle, clematis and roses. Terraced arches, sunken garden pool and bog garden, fountains and old water pumps. Herb wheels, shrubs and other interesting features. Lovely views of the Clwydian range. Water feature, new rose tunnel, vegetable tunnel and small garden summer house. Featured in local paper Welsh Gardening Programme.

31 TAN-Y-PARC

Llanrhaeadr, Denbigh LL16 4NL. Mrs Sandra Edwards. *3m S of Denbigh. 5m N of Ruthin. Take A525 from Denbigh or Ruthin. Follow signs at Llanrhaeadr.* Cream teas. **Combined adm £5, chd free. Sat 7, Sun 8 June (11.30-5.30). Combined with The Laundry.**
Small cottage garden, new planted borders in paddock area, greenhouse and raised vegetable plots, fruit bushes. Rear garden enclosed with beech hedges, 2 large raised beds. Pergola with grape vine. New features in paddock, pond and wild flower area, new planted beds in front areas. Level grass areas suitable for wheelchairs.

32 TUDOR COTTAGE

Isallt Road, Llysfaen, Colwyn Bay LL29 8LJ. Mr & Mrs C Manifold, 01492 518510. *1½ m SE of Old Colwyn. Turn S off A547 bt Llandulas & Old Colwyn. Up Highlands Rd for ½ m, R onto Tan-y-Graig, ignore sat nav, ¾ m to swings. Take Isallt Rd on far R.* Home-made teas. **Adm £4, (incl hot drink April only), chd free. Sun 20 Apr (2-4); Sat 28, Sun 29 June (1-5). Visitors also welcome by appt Apr to Aug. Refreshments by prior arrangement.**
¾ -acre garden on different levels set amongst natural rock faces. Unusual and varied planting featuring cottage, scree, Japanese, shade and bog gardens. Display bedding, an abundance of colourful pots and baskets, together with quirky statues, ponds, bridges and a folly. Lovely views from upper level. Some uneven paths and steep steps. Care required. Children to be under adult control at all times.

33 TYDDYN BACH

Bontuchel, Ruthin LL15 2DG. Mr & Mrs L G Starling, 01824 710248, les.starling@boyns.net. *4m W of Ruthin. B5105 from Ruthin. R at Cross Keys PH to Cyffilliog. Through Bontuchel, 400yds, L up hill before chevron signs. White house on L. Limited parking.* Light refreshments. **Adm £3, chd free. Visitors welcome by appt July to Aug. Groups and visitors 1 to 25 max.**
Mainly organic, very pretty cottage garden with prolific vegetable garden. Wildlife friendly with hedges and wood pile. Greenhouse packed with plants for both pots and the garden. Small wildlife pond completed in May 2010 and small stumpery completed 2012. Excellent views of surrounding countryside.

34 WYLAN

Llangynhafal, Ruthin LL15 1RU. John & Carol Perkins. *3m N of Ruthin. Take A494 from Ruthin to Llanbedr then B5429. After ½ m turn R signed 'Llangynhafal 1½ m'. Entrance on R.* Light refreshments. **Adm £3, chd free. Sun 13 July (1-5).**
1-acre garden designed by owners for all parts to be easily accessible. Magnificent panoramic views. Mature shrubs, mixed borders and water features. Pergola leading into sunken patio with colourful containers. 4th time Winner of Best Kept Country Garden, Ruthin Flower Show. Gradual grass slope at end of front garden to access back garden.

35 Y BWTHYN

New Road, Llanddulas, Abergele LL22 8EL. Mr David Roberts & Mr Mark Cooke. *J23 on A55. Through village pass Valentine Inn (R) then take 1st R (Beaula Av), 2nd L (New Rd).Y Bwthyn, last bungalow on L at top of hill.* Home-made teas. **Adm £3.50, chd free. Sat 5 July (12-5).**
A garden with meandering paths that leads the eye to explore the varied themes created within the different 'rooms'. From a cottage garden (busy and lush) to a lawned area of tranquility and space. From a shady grove to a watery nook, all within the back drop of the beautiful Llanddulas mountain. An artist's garden with roses, clematis, hostas and ferns featured as some of the favourites.

36 Y GRAIG

Llandegla, Wrexham LL11 3BG. Janet Strivens & Phillip Tidey, 01978 790657, janet@ygraig.org.uk. *8m SE of Ruthin. From Wrexham take A525 towards Ruthin. After approx 7m turn L immed before The Plough PH on L, garden is 1m up narrow winding rd.* **Adm £3.50, chd free. Visitors welcome by appt Apr to Sept.**
½ acre of enchanting informal hillside garden at over 1000ft beneath a limestone outcrop. Herbaceous beds full of colour, rockeries, many clematis and old roses, small ponds and water lilies. 3 acres of field with recently established woodland incl specimen trees. Vegetable garden and wonderful views over the Clwydians. Limited wheelchair access due to gravel areas, some steps and steep slopes especially in woodland walk.

Tudor Cottage

North East Wales

County Organiser
Jane Moore, Stella Maris, Mynydd Llech, Llanrhaedr, Denbigh LL16 4PW, 01745 890475/07769 046317, jemoore01@live.com

Booklet Coordinator
Roy Hambleton, Greenheys, Cefn Bychan Road, Pantymwyn, Mold GH7 5EN, 01352 740206, royhambleton@btinternet.com

County Treasurers
Elizabeth Sasse, Ty'r Ardd, High Street, Caerwys, Mold CH7 5BB, 01352 720220, Elizabeth.sasse246@btinternet.com
Wendy Sime, Park Cottage, Penley, Wrexham LL13 0LS, 01948 830126, sjsime@hotmail.com

Press & Publicity Officer
Ann Rathbone, Woodfirld House, Station Lane, Hawarden CH5 3EG, 01244 532948, rathbone.ann@gmail.com

Assistant County Organisers
Fiona Bell, Plas Ashpool, Llandyrnog, Denbigh LL16 4HP, 01824 790612, bell_fab@hotmail.com
Ruth Davies, Arfryn, Pentrecelyn, nr Ruthin LL15 2HR, 01978 790475, arfrynpentrecelyn@btinternet.com
Bill & Dawn Jones, Tan y Coed, Llanasa, nr Holywell CH8 9NE, 01745 889919, w.jones844@btinternet.com
Mrs Ann Knowlson, Lynton, Highfield Park, Abergele LL22 7AU, 01745 832002, apk@slaters.com
Ann Rathbone, Woodfield House, Station Lane Hawarden CH5 3EG, 01244 532948, rathbone.ann@gmail.com
Anne Saxon, Leeswood Green Farm, Leeswood, Mold CH7 4SQ, 01352 771222, annemsaxon@yahoo.com
Susan Watson, Clwydfryn, Bodfari, Denbigh LL16 4HU, 01745 710232, clwydfryn@btinternet.com

POWYS

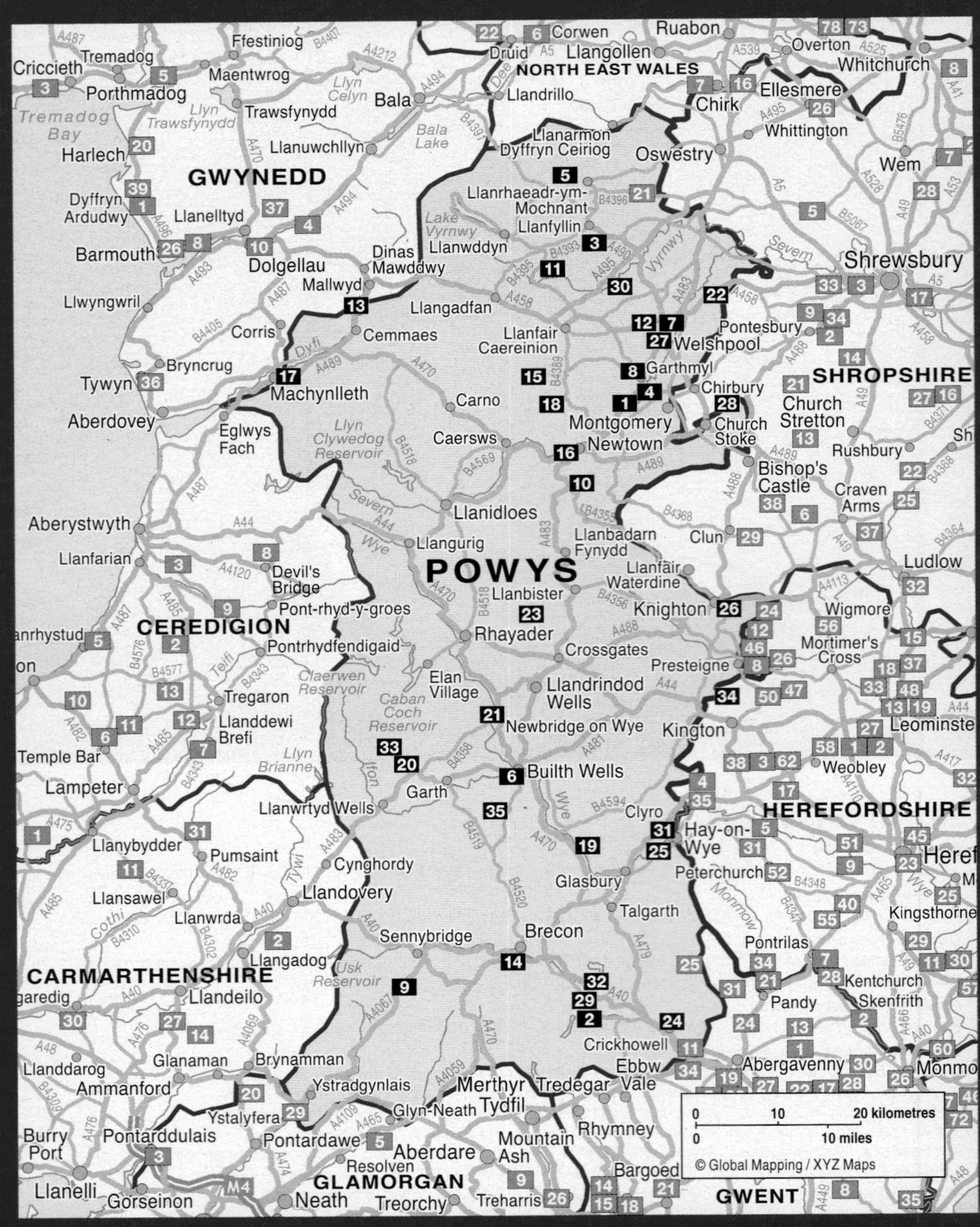

POWYS
GWYNEDD
NORTH EAST WALES
SHROPSHIRE
CEREDIGION
HEREFORDSHIRE
CARMARTHENSHIRE
GLAMORGAN
GWENT
Machynlleth
Llanidloes
Newtown
Montgomery
Welshpool
Rhayader
Llandrindod Wells
Builth Wells
Brecon
Crickhowell
Hay-on-Wye
Knighton
Presteigne
Kington
Shrewsbury
Oswestry
Aberystwyth
Merthyr Tydfil
Abergavenny
0 10 20 kilometres
0 10 miles
© Global Mapping / XYZ Maps

Opening Dates

All entries subject to change. For latest information check www.ngs.org.uk

April

2 **Ashford House (Every Tuesday)**

Monday 21
34 The Walled Garden

Saturday 26
7 1 Church Bank

Sunday 27
7 1 Church Bank

May

2 **Ashford House (Every Tuesday)**

Saturday 3
30 Tan-y-Llyn

Sunday 4
30 Tan-y-Llyn

Friday 9
12 Dingle Nurseries & Garden

Saturday 10
12 Dingle Nurseries & Garden

Saturday 17
28 Priest Weston Gardens

Sunday 18
15 Fraithwen
28 Priest Weston Gardens

Sunday 25
20 Llwyn Madoc
33 Tyn y Cwm

Monday 26
6 Caer Beris Manor Hotel
19 Llanstephan House
21 Llysdinam

Wednesday 28
17 Grandma's Garden

June

2 **Ashford House (Every Tuesday)**
10 **Cwm-Wegg (Every Sunday)**

Festival Weekend

Saturday 7
8 Cil y Wennol
30 Tan-y-Llyn

Sunday 8
8 Cil y Wennol
14 Ffrwdgrech House
18 Gregynog Hall & Garden
24 The Neuadd
30 Tan-y-Llyn

Saturday 14
5 NEW Bryn y Llidiart
28 Priest Weston Gardens

Sunday 15
5 NEW Bryn y Llidiart
28 Priest Weston Gardens

Saturday 21
26 Pont Faen House
27 Powis Castle Garden

Sunday 22
3 Bachie Uchaf
26 Pont Faen House
34 The Walled Garden

Saturday 28
7 1 Church Bank

Sunday 29
7 1 Church Bank

July

2 **Ashford House (Every Tuesday)**

Wednesday 2
7 1 Church Bank

Saturday 5
30 Tan-y-Llyn

Sunday 6
13 Esgair Angell
25 Pen-y-Maes
30 Tan-y-Llyn

Saturday 12
28 Priest Weston Gardens

Sunday 13
9 Crai Gardens
28 Priest Weston Gardens
29 Talybont Gardens

Sunday 20
16 Glynderyn
32 Treberfydd

Saturday 26
35 Welsh Lavender

Sunday 27
15 Fraithwen
35 Welsh Lavender

August

2 **Ashford House (Every Tuesday)**
10 **Cwm-Wegg (Every Sunday)**

Sunday 10
22 Maesfron Hall and Gardens
33 Tyn y Cwm

September

2 **Ashford House (Every Tuesday)**

October

Saturday 11
12 Dingle Nurseries & Garden

Sunday 12
12 Dingle Nurseries & Garden

Gardens open to the public

2 Ashford House
12 Dingle Nurseries & Garden
17 Grandma's Garden
18 Gregynog Hall & Garden
27 Powis Castle Garden
35 Welsh Lavender

By appointment only

1 Abernant
4 Bron Hafren
11 Cyfie Farm
23 Mill Cottage
31 Tawryn

Also open by appointment

5 Bryn y Llidiart
7 1 Church Bank
14 Ffrwdgrech House
15 Fraithwen
16 Glynderyn
21 Llysdinam
26 Pont Faen House
28 Chapel House, Priest Weston Gardens
28 Priest Weston Gardens
28 Quarry House, Priest Weston Gardens
30 Tan-y-Llyn
32 Treberfydd
33 Tyn y Cwm
34 The Walled Garden

Weekly openings mean visitors may enjoy a peaceful garden in its everyday state . . .

The Gardens

1 ABERNANT

Garthmyl SY15 6RZ. J A & B M Gleave, 01686 640494, john.gleave@mac.com. *On A483 mid-way between Welshpool & Newtown (both 8m). 1½ m S of Garthmyl. Approached over steep humpback bridge, then straight ahead through gate. No parking for coaches.* Home-made teas. **Adm £3.50, chd free. Visitors welcome by appt Apr to July.**

Approx 3 acres incl cherry orchard, roses, knot garden, lavender, box hedging, rockery, pond, shrubs, ornamental trees, raised specimen fern beds in natural setting. Examples of archaic sundials, fossilised wood and stone heads. Additional woodland of 9 acres, pond and stream with borrowed views of the Severn Valley. Late April - 90 cherry trees blossom: late June - roses. Picnics welcome.

Sounds of water fill the air and interesting plants fill the space . . .

2 ◆ ASHFORD HOUSE

Talybont-on-Usk LD3 7YR. Mrs E Anderson, 01874 676271. *6½ m SE of Brecon. Off A40 on B4558. 1m SE of Talybont-on-Usk.* **Adm £3, chd free. For NGS: Every Tue 1 Apr to 30 Sept (2-3). For other opening times and information, please phone.**

1-acre walled garden surrounded by woodland and wild garden approx 4 acres altogether. Mixed shrub and herbaceous borders; meadow garden and pond; alpine house and beds; vegetables. A relaxed plantsman's garden. Weekly openings mean visitors may enjoy a peaceful garden in its everyday state. Wheelchair access to main garden only.

3 BACHIE UCHAF

Bachie Road, Llanfyllin SY22 5NF. Glyn & Glenys Lloyd. *S of Llanfyllin. Going towards Welshpool on A490 turn R onto Bachie Rd after Llanfyllin primary school. Keep straight for 0.8m. Take drive R uphill at cottage on L.* Home-made teas. **Adm £4, chd free. Sun 22 June (2-5).**

Inspiring, colourful hillside country garden. Gravel paths meander around extensive planting and over streams cascading down into ponds. Specimen trees, shrubs and vegetable garden. Enjoy the wonderful views from one of the many seats; your senses will be rewarded.

4 NEW BRON HAFREN

Garthmyl, Montgomery SY15 6RT. John & Marilyn, 01686 640106, mbedworth@googlemail.com. *By Caerhowel bridge over R Severn, A483 between Welshpool & Newtown. Opp Nags Head turn onto B4835 to Montgomery. 700 metres park in paddock opp turn to Argae Hall Caravan Park. Enter garden through paddock gate.* Home-made teas served in timber barn with plenty of seating in bad weather. **Adm £3.50, chd free. Visitors welcome by appt Apr to Sept.**

1½ acre mature garden on banks of R Severn. Access from the lawn to further ¾ acre riverside woodland area (uneven) with view of ornate bridge. Surrounding the Victorian house is an orchard, mixed borders, shrubbery, spinney and large redwood. Gravelled area with chicken enclosure, raised vegetable beds, fruit cage, polytunnel, greenhouse, potting shed and outbuildings incl original Ty Bach. Uneven surface in paddock parking area. Wheelchair access to refreshments over gravel.

5 NEW BRYN Y LLIDIART

Cefn Coch, Llanrhaeadr ym Mochnant, Oswestry SY10 0BP. Dr John & Mrs Christine Scott, 01691 780080, christinemargaretscott@yahoo.com. *2m W of Llanrhaeadr. From Llanrhaeadr take rd W up hill towards Penybontfawr, ½ m turn R at Bitfel, onto SINGLE TRACK RD, follow yellow NGS signs for 1m.* Home-made teas. **Adm £4, chd free. Sat 14, Sun 15 June (2-5). Visitors also welcome by appt May to Sept.**

Exposed hillside garden in S facing lee of the Berwyns with breathtaking views. Lush planting around the longhouse and contemporary extension merges into the wildflower meadows with dry stone walls, slate, shale and large erratic boulders to reflect the landscape beyond. Meander mown paths to view a biodiverse roof, 'sitouterie', bog garden, pond and vegetable garden in unique surroundings. Limited wheelchair access, shale and rough grass paths, some steps.

6 CAER BERIS MANOR HOTEL

Builth Wells LD2 3NP. Mr Peter & Mrs Katharine Smith, www.caerberis.com. *W edge Builth Wells. From Builth Wells town centre take A483 signed Llandovery. Caer Beris Manor is on L as you leave Builth.* Cream teas. **Adm £3.50, chd free. Mon 26 May (11-6).**

An original 1927 NGS pioneer garden. 27 acres of mature parklands planted early C20 by Lord Swansea. Many varied specimen trees forming Arboretum. Large displays of rhododendrons at time of opening. Rose trestle archways. 3 sites of Special Scientific Interest. Concert by Builth Wells Ladies Voice Choir. Sunday lunches. Afternoon teas. Lower parkland can be accessed by car or wheelchair.

7 1 CHURCH BANK

Welshpool SY21 7DR. Mel & Heather Parkes, 01938 559112, melandheather@live.co.uk. *Centre of Welshpool. Church Bank leads onto Salop Rd from Church St. Follow one way system & use Main Car Park then short walk - follow yellow NGS signs.* Home-made teas. **Adm £3, chd free. Sat 26, Sun 27 Apr, Sat 28, Sun 29 June, Wed 2 July (12-5). Visitors also welcome by appt May to Sept.**

A jewel in the town, Gothic arch over a zig zag path leads to exotic arbours in the intimate rear garden of an old town house. Sounds of water fill the air and interesting plants fill the space. After exciting enlargement and alteration last yr, new features have been added for this yr. Children's garden quiz. Featured in Shropshire Star County Times.

8 CIL Y WENNOL

Berriew, Welshpool SY21 8AZ. Mr & Mrs Bowen. *5m SW of Welshpool. Berriew off A483 Welshpool to Newtown rd. By Berriew School take B4385 towards Castle Caereinion. Cil y Wennol is ¾ m along B4385.* Tea and cake. **Adm £4, chd free. Sat 7, Sun 8 June (2-5).**
3½ -acre established garden set around Tudor cottage (not open). Long curving drive, through terraced landforms leads to front garden of traditional formal cottage design with more recent influences. Rear gardens: sweeping array of new-style prairie planting, spectacular views, enclosed vegetable garden, croquet lawn. Crescent-shaped hedges, slate walls, amphitheatre steps.

9 CRAI GARDENS

Crai LD3 8YP. *13m SW of Brecon. Turn W off A4067 signed Crai. Village hall is 50yds straight ahead; park here for admission & information about gardens.* Home-made teas in village hall. **Combined adm £5, chd free. Sun 13 July (2-6).**
Set against the backdrop of Fan Gyhirych and Fan Brycheiniog, at 1000ft above sea level the Crai valley is a hidden gem, off the beaten track between Brecon and Swansea. Those in the know have long enjoyed visiting our serene valley, with its easy access to the hills and its fabulous views. In difficult climatic conditions, the Crai Gardens reflect a true passion for gardening. The gardens come in a wide variety of size, purpose and design, and range from well-established to very recent, from cottage-style to several acres with ponds and orchard. Our gardens incl: a range of shrubs, perennials and annuals; organically grown vegetables; raised beds; a polytunnel; a bog garden; water features; prolific hanging baskets, patio containers and window boxes. Not to forget the chickens, ducks and donkeys. And to complete your Sunday afternoon, come and enjoy the renowned hospitality of the Crai ladies by sampling their delicious homemade cakes in the village hall.

10 CWM-WEEG

Dolfor, Newtown SY16 4AT. Dr W Schaefer & Mr K D George, 01686 628992, wolfgang.schaefer@virgin.net.

Cil y Wennol

4½ m SE of Newtown. Take A489 E from Newtown for 1½ m, turn R towards Dolfor. After 2m turn L down farm track, signed at entrance. Home-made teas. Conservatory available for refreshments in bad weather. **Adm £4, chd free. Every Sun 1 June to 31 Aug (2-5).**
2½ -acre garden set within 24 acres of wild flower meadows and bluebell woodland with stream centred around C15 farmhouse (open by prior arrangement). Formal garden in English landscape tradition with vistas, grottos, lawns and extensive borders terraced with stone walls, translates older garden vocabulary into an innovative C21 concept. Limited wheelchair access.

11 CYFIE FARM

Llanfihangel, Llanfyllin SY22 5JE. Group Captain Neil & Mrs Claire Bale, 01691 648451, info@cyfiefarm.co.uk, www.cyfiefarm.co.uk. *6m SE of Lake Vyrnwy. ½ m N Llanfyllin on B490 turn L B4393 towards L Vrynwy. 4m turn L B4382 signed Llanfihangel go straight through, 1½ m, 1st L, 3rd on L.* Light refreshments. Undercover area available in the event of bad weather. **Adm £4, chd free. Visitors welcome by appt Mar to Oct. 2 days notice required, refreshments by prior arrangement.**
Beautiful 1-acre hillside garden with spectacular views of Vyrnwy valley and Welsh hills. Linger over the roses or wander through the woodland garden with rhododendrons and bluebell banks. Many places to sit and contemplate the stunning views. Wild flower meadow and garden sculptures. Unusual garden statues. Spectacular Views, Peaceful setting. Featured in BBC Countryfile Magazine, The Guardian and The Independent Newspaper Food and Travel Magazine. Limited wheelchair access.

12 ◆ DINGLE NURSERIES & GARDEN

Welshpool SY21 9JD. Mr & Mrs D Hamer, 01938 555145, www.dinglenurseries.co.uk. *2m NW of Welshpool. Take A490 towards Llanfyllin & Guilsfield. After 1m turn L at sign for Dingle Nurseries & Garden.* **Adm £3.50, chd free. For NGS: Fri 9, Sat 10 May, Sat 11, Sun 12 Oct (9-5). For other opening times and information, please phone or see garden website.**
RHS recommended 4½ -acre garden on S-facing site, sloping down to lakes surrounded by yr-round interest. Beds mostly colour themed with a huge variety of rare and unusual trees, ornamental shrubs and herbaceous plants. Set in hills of mid Wales this beautiful and well known garden attracts visitors from Britain and abroad. Open all yr except 24 Dec - 2 Jan.

Esgair Angell

13 ESGAIR ANGELL

Aberangell, Machynlleth SY20 9QJ. Carole Jones, jonesey200@gmail.com. *Midway between Dogellau & Machynlleth. Turn off A470 towards village of Aberangell, then signed*. Home-made teas. **Adm £4, chd free. Sun 6 July (12-5).**

The garden of about 2 acres, sits above the R Angell, within the Dovey Forest and Snowdonia National Park. A crystal-clear lake, which supports an abundance of plant and animal life is surrounded by a small wood, a wildlife meadow, our grand giant oak, vegetable garden and the aviaries that house our families of eagle owls and barn owls. Limited wheelchair access, mainly laid to lawn. Access on gravelled area above the lake, offering extensive views of the garden.

14 FFRWDGRECH HOUSE

Ffrwdgrech, Brecon LD3 8LB. Mr & Mrs Michael Evans, 01874 622519, ffrwdgrech@btinternet.com. *1/2 m W of Brecon. Enter Brecon from A40 bypass. Take 3rd turning on R, Ffrwdgrech Rd. In 3/4 m at oak gate, Lodge on L*. Home-made teas. **Adm £4, chd free. Sun 8 June (2-5). Visitors also welcome by appt May to Sept.**

7-acre Victorian pleasure garden, lake, specimen trees incl fine examples of ginkgo, swamp cyprus, davidia involucrata, subtropical shrubs, rhododendrons and azaleas. Beautiful stream and waterfall, woodland walks. Views of Brecon Beacons. Robert Lugar designed garden, landscape and water features. Award winning woodland. Listed lawns for rare fungi specimens. Lesser Horseshoe Bat sanctuary.

15 FRAITHWEN

Tregynon SY16 3EW. Sydney Thomas, 01686 650307. *6m N of Newtown. On B4389 mid-way between villages of Bettws Cedewain & Tregynon*. **Adm £3, chd free. Sun 18 May, Sun 27 July (2-6). Visitors also welcome by appt Feb to Oct.**

1 1/2 -acre established garden with herbaceous borders, rockeries and ponds. Planted with rare plants for yr-round interest. Plants in flower every day of the year. Partial wheelchair access. Some steps, gravel and slopes.

16 GLYNDERYN

Milford Road, Newtown SY16 3HD. Janet & Frank Podmore, 01686 626745. *1/2 m W of Newtown. On B4568 Newtown to Aberhafesp rd. Glynderyn, 1st gate past Dolerw Park Drive*. Home-made teas. **Adm £2, chd free. Sun 20 July (2-5). Visitors also welcome by appt Apr to Sept max group 20. Refreshments by request.**

Lovingly restored by plant enthusiast, this 1/4 -acre garden with geometric beds complements the 1965 bungalow. Oblong rose and raised alpine beds, curved pergola for wisterias begin the journey around the garden with views across the valley. Trees, shrubs, small pond, wild flower and vegetable patch create diverse interest.

17 ◆ GRANDMA'S GARDEN

Dolguog Estates, Felingerrig, Machynlleth SY20 8UJ. Diana & Richard Rhodes, 01654 702244, www.plasdolguog.co.uk/grandmasgarden.htm. *1 1/2 m E of Machynlleth. Turn L off A489 Machynlleth to Newtown rd. Follow brown tourist signs to Plas Dolguog Hotel*. **Adm £4, chd £1.50. For NGS: Wed 28 May (10.30-4.30). For other opening times and information, please phone or see garden website.**

Inspiration for the senses, unique, fascinating, educational and fun. Strategic seating, continuous new attractions, wildlife abundant, 9 acres of peace. Sculptures, poetry arboretum. Seven sensory gardens, wildlife pond, riverside boardwalk, stone circle, labyrinth. Azaleas and bluebells in May. Children welcome. Open every Sun & Wed (10.30-4.30). Cream teas Plas Dolguog Hotel open their café in the conservatory - the hotel is the admission point - serving inside, and outside on patio overlooking gardens.

18 ◆ GREGYNOG HALL & GARDEN

Tregynon, Newtown SY16 3PW. Gregynog, 01686 650224, www.gregynog.org. *5m N of Newtown. From main A483, take turning for Berriew. In Berriew follow sign for Bettws then for Tregynon (£2.50 car parking charge applies)*. Home-made teas at Courtyard Cafe. **Adm £3, chd £1. For NGS: Sun 8 June (11-4.30). For other opening times and information, please phone or see garden website.**

Grade I listed garden set within 750 acres of Gregynog Estate which was designated a National Nature Reserve in 2013. Fountains, lily lake and water garden. A mass display of rhododendrons and yew hedge create a spectacular backdrop to the sunken lawns. Free welcome talks available at 11.30am, 12.30 and 1.30pm. Book a place on 01686 650224. Shop and Courtyard Cafe open for lunches and Welsh afternoon teas. Some gravel paths.

19 LLANSTEPHAN HOUSE

nr Llyswen, Powys LD3 0YR. Lord & Lady Milford. *10m SW of Builth Wells. Leave A470 at Llyswen onto B4350. 1st L after crossing river in Boughrood. From Builth Wells leave A470, Erwood Bridge, 1st L. Follow signs*. Home-made teas. **Adm £3, chd free. Mon 26 May (1-5).**

Large garden with rhododendrons, azaleas, shrubs, water garden, shrub roses, walled kitchen garden, greenhouses and very fine specimen trees. Beautiful views of Wye Valley and Black Mountains.

20 LLWYN MADOC

Beulah, Llanwrtyd Wells LD5 4TU. Patrick & Miranda Bourdillon, 01591 620564, miranda.bourdillon@gmail.com. *8m W of Builth Wells. On A483 at Beulah take rd towards Abergwesyn for 1m. Drive on R*. Cream teas. **Adm £3, chd free. Sun 25 May (2-5.30). Also open Tyn y Cwm.**

Terraced garden in attractive wooded valley overlooking newly restored lake; yew hedges; rose garden with pergola; kitchen garden and small orchard; azaleas and rhododendrons.

21 LLYSDINAM

Newbridge-on-Wye LD1 6NB. Sir John & Lady Venables-Llewelyn & Llysdinam Charitable Trust, 01597 861190, elster@f2s.com. *5m SW of Llandrindod Wells. Turn W off A470 at Newbridge-on-Wye; turn R immed after crossing R Wye; entrance up hill*. Cream teas. **Adm £3, chd free. Mon 26 May (2-5). Visitors also welcome by appt Mar to Oct.**

Llysdinam Gardens are among the loveliest in Mid Wales, especially noted for a magnificent display of rhododendrons and azaleas in May. Covering some 6 acres in all, they command sweeping views down the Wye Valley. Successive family members have developed the gardens over the last 150yrs to incl woodland with specimen trees, large herbaceous and shrub borders and a water garden, all of which provide varied and colourful planting throughout the year. The Victorian walled kitchen garden and extensive greenhouses grow a wide variety of vegetables, hothouse fruit, and exotic plants. Gravel paths.

22 MAESFRON HALL AND GARDENS

Trewern, Welshpool SY21 8EA. Dr & Mrs TD Owen, www.maesfron.co.uk. *4m E of Welshpool. On N side of A458 Welshpool to Shrewsbury Rd*. Home-made teas. **Adm £4, chd £1. Sun 10 Aug (12-5).**

Georgian house (partly open) built in Italian villa style set in 4 acres of S-facing gardens on lower slopes of Moel-y-Golfa with panoramic views of The Long Mountain. Terraces, walled kitchen garden, tropical garden, restored Victorian conservatories, tower and shell grotto. Woodland and parkland walks with wide variety of trees. Enjoy a lazy Summer's afternoon in gorgeous surroundings with a free glass of Pimms and a full Afternoon Tea for only £2.50. Gardens open from 12 noon bring your own lunchtime picnic to enjoy in the grounds. Some gravel, steps and slopes.

23 MILL COTTAGE

Abbeycwmhir LD1 6PH. Mr & Mrs B D Parfitt, 01597 851935, nkmillcottage@yahoo.co.uk, www.abbeycwmhir.co.uk. *8m N of Llandrindod Wells. Turn L off A483 1m N of Crossgates r'about, then 3½ m on L, signed Abbeycwmhir. Limited parking*. **Adm by donation. Visitors welcome by appt May to Sept, please phone first.**

⅓ -acre streamside garden in spectacular valley setting on the Glyndwr Way, consisting mainly of mature, rare and unusual trees and shrubs, particularly interesting to the plantsman. Rockery with numerous ericaceous plants and interesting water feature. Beautiful church and Abbey ruins nearby on a national trail - Glydr's Way.

24 THE NEUADD

Llanbedr, Nr Crickhowell NP8 1SP. Robin & Philippa Herbert. *1m NE of Crickhowell. Leave Crickhowell by Llanbedr Rd. At junction with Great Oak Rd bear L, continue up hill for approx 1m, garden on L. Ample parking*. Home-made teas. **Adm £4.50, chd free. Sun 8 June (2-6).**

Robin and Philippa Herbert have worked on the restoration of the garden at The Neuadd since 1999 and have planted a wide range of unusual trees and shrubs in the dramatic setting of the Brecon Beacons National Park. One of the major features is the walled garden, which has both traditional and decorative planting of fruit, vegetables and flowers. There is also a woodland walk with ponds, streams and a formal garden with flowering terraces.

25 PEN-Y-MAES

Hay-on-Wye HR3 5PP. Shân Egerton. *1m SW of Hay-on-Wye. On B4350 towards Hay from Brecon. 2½ m from Glasbury*. Cream teas. **Adm £4, chd free. Sun 6 July (2-3).**

2-acre garden incl mixed and herbaceous borders; topiary; walled formal kitchen garden; shrub, modern and climbing roses, peony borders, espaliered pears. Fine mulberry. Beautiful dry stone walling and mature trees. Great double view of Black Mountains and the Brecon Beacons. Emphasis on foliage and shape. Artist's garden.

Enjoy a Summer's afternoon in gorgeous surroundings . . .

26 PONT FAEN HOUSE

Farrington Lane, Knighton LD7 1LA. Mr John & Mrs Brenda Morgan, 01547 520847. *S of Knighton off Ludlow Rd. W from Ludlow on A4113 into Knighton. 1st L after 20mph sign before school*. Home-made teas. **Adm £3.50, chd free. Sat 21, Sun 22 June (2-5). Visitors also welcome by appt Apr to Sept, adm £5 incl tea and cake.**

Colourful ½ -acre garden, full of flowers, surrounds house on edge of town. Paths through floriferous arches and gazebos lead from shady, ferny corners to deep borders around lawns. Trees incl specimen beech, shrubs, perennials and annuals, fish pond and small vegetable plot. Seats with vistas through garden to hills beyond.

27 ◆ **POWIS CASTLE GARDEN**
Welshpool SY21 8RF. National Trust, 01938 551929, www.nationaltrust.org.uk. *1m S of Welshpool. From Welshpool take A490 S towards Newtown. After 3/4 m turn R into Red Lane. Continue up lane for 1/4 m & turn R into property.* Light refreshments. **Adm £8.70, chd £4.30. For NGS: Sat 21 June (10-6). For other opening times and information, please phone or see garden website.**
Laid out in early C18 the garden features the finest remaining examples of Italian terraces in Britain. Richly planted herbaceous borders; enormous yew hedges; lead statuary, Orangery and large wild flower areas. One of the NT's finest gardens. National Collection of *Laburnum*. Short introduction talks run throughout the day. Step free route around the garden, gravel paths, due to steep slopes only 4-wheeled PMV's permitted.

GROUP OPENING

28 **PRIEST WESTON GARDENS**
Priest Weston, Montgomery SY15 6DF, 01938 561397, chris.rog.dixon@hotmail.co.uk. *Approx 4m E Montgomery. Follow signs to Priestweston out of Churchstoke or Chirbury.* Home-made teas at Quarry House. **Combined adm £4.50, chd free. Sat 17, Sun 18 May, Sat 14, Sun 15 June, Sat 12, Sun 13 July (11-4.30). Visitors also welcome by appt May to Sept.**

NEW **CHAPEL HOUSE**
Mr & Mrs Andrew Craig
Visitors also welcome by appt May to Sept for groups max 10.
01938 561336
jaycraig@priestweston.com

QUARRY HOUSE
Roger & Christine Dixon
Visitors also welcome by appt May to Aug for groups max 10, evenings preferred.
01938 561397
chris.rog.dixon@hotmail.co.uk

Quarry House stands in an elevated position with stunning views south towards the Kerry Ridgeway and west towards Snowdonia. The garden has evolved over 18yrs into a series of herbaceous borders, accessed by steep zig-zagged grass paths and steps. A lower lawn is bordered by lilac trees Higher up there is a wild flower meadow (harebells, lady's bedstraw) where you may picnic. Chapel House - approx 1 acre slightly wild cottage garden on a steep hillside. Several different terraces each with its own character including: kitchen garden, orchard, gravel garden, woodland area and meadow, borders and lawns. Spectacular views across valley to Montgomery and beyond. These gardens are not suitable for people who are unsure of foot.

GROUP OPENING

29 **TALYBONT GARDENS**
Talybont-on-Usk LD3 7JE. *6m SE of Brecon. Off A40 signed Talybont-on-Usk. Follow yellow NGS signs to gardens.* Teas at the Usk Inn. **Combined adm £5, chd free. Sun 13 July (2-6).**

BRODAWEL
Miss Brenda Powell

LONICERA
Gareth & Eirona Davies

TY CAM
Harry & Ceri Chapman

Three garden gems offering something of interest to all. Brodawel - a very pretty small cottage garden; herbaceous and perennials, wisteria climbing roses, clematis and honeysuckle. Pond surrounded by bamboos. HT and Floribunda roses, summerhouse and vegetable and fruit area. Lonicera - 1/2 -acre garden of varied interest incorporating several small feature gardens. Rose garden; heather garden with conifers; herbaceous and woody perennials; colourful summer bedding displays; hanging baskets and patio tubs forming extensive frontage display; greenhouses. Small water features. Ty Cam - a small garden of secret surprises imaginatively created on three levels with steps built into an old railway embankment. Attractive features incl patios, decks, pergola, pond and waterfalls. Many choice herbaceous plants, trees and shrubs. A small 'menagerie' of chickens and aviary birds. Woodturning workshop and craft gallery.

30 **TAN-Y-LLYN**
Meifod SY22 6YB. Callum Johnston & Brenda Moor, 01938 500370, admin@tanyllyn-nurseries.co.uk, http://www.tanyllyn-nurseries.co.uk. *1m SE of Meifod. From Oswestry on A495 turn L in village, cross R Vyrnwy & climb hill for 1/2 m. From Welshpool on A490 look for Meifod sign on L just past Groesllwyd.* Home-made teas. **Adm £3.50, chd free (share to Ponthafren Association). Sat 3, Sun 4 May, Sat 7, Sun 8 June, Sat 5, Sun 6 July (2-5). Visitors also welcome by appt Apr to Nov.**
Surrounded by woodland and pasture, Tanyllyn sits in a quiet valley above the Dyffryn Meifod in the old county of Montgomeryshire. The garden grows out of the landscape and the surroundings are seen though portholes, sculpted hedges and openings in the trees. Exhibitions and Music. May: Judith Harrison, July: Bob Guy & Iris Gordijn, July: 'Visit the Emporium'.

31 **TAWRYN**
6 Baskerville Court, Clyro HR3 5SS. Chris & Clive Young, 01497 821939. *1m NW of Hay-on-Wye. Leave A438 Hereford to Brecon rd at Clyro. Baskerville Court is behind church & Baskerville Arms Hotel. Please park in village.* **Adm £3, chd free. Visitors welcome by appt Apr to Sept.**
1-acre steeply-terraced garden on an oriental theme. Come and see the Ghost Dragon and the River of Slate. Lots of new crooked paths and planting. Stunning views of the Black Mountains and Kilvert's Church.

Colour all yr. Bring a picnic. Talks by Chris on NGS and its charities to garden groups, WI etc. Please call for more information.

32 TREBERFYDD

Llangasty, Bwlch, Brecon LD3 7PX. David Raikes, 01874 730205, info@treberfydd.com, www.treberfydd.com. *6 1/2 m E of Brecon. From Abergavenny on A40, turn R in Blwch on B5460. Take 1st turning L towards Pennorth & continue 2m down lane.* Light refreshments. **Adm £5.50, chd free. Sun 20 July (12-6). Visitors also welcome by appt.**

Grade 1-listed Victorian Gothic house with 10 acres of grounds designed by W A Nesfield. Magnificent Cedar of Lebanon, avenue of mature Beech, towering Atlantic Cedars, Victorian rockery, herbaceous border and manicured lawns ideal for a picnic. Wonderful views of the Black Mountains. Beacons Nurseries in walled garden. House tours every half hour, Contemporary Art Exhibition, Commercial Nursery on the grounds.

33 TYN Y CWM

Beulah, Llanwrtyd Wells LD5 4TS. Steve & Christine Carrow, 01591 620461, stevetynycwm@hotmail.co.uk. *10m W of Builth Wells. On A483 at Beulah take rd towards Abergwesyn for 2m. Drive drops down to L.* Home-made teas. **Adm £3, chd free. Sun 25 May, Sun 10 Aug (2-5.30). Also opening Llwyn Madoc (Sun 25 May). Visitors also welcome by appt Mar to Sept.**

Garden mainly started 12yrs ago, lower garden has spring/woodland area, raised beds mixed with vegetables, fruit trees, fruit and flowers. Perennial borders, summer house gravel paths through rose and clematis pergola. Upper garden, partly sloped, incl bog, winter, water gardens and perennial beds with unusual slate steps. Beautiful views. Property bounded by small river. Craft Stall. Lower garden has wide gravel mainly level paths. Upper garden is grassed with slopes and not suitable for wheelchairs.

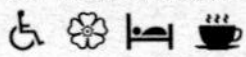

Wonderful views of the Black Mountains . . .

34 THE WALLED GARDEN

Knill, nr Presteigne LD8 2PR. Dame Margaret Anstee, 01544 267411, agapanthus1@btinternet.com. *3m SW of Presteigne. B4362 Walton-Presteigne rd. In Knill village turn R over cattle grid, keep R down drive. SatNav stops short of property. Coaches park up hill by church.* Teas available in neighboring garden, The Rose Garden. **Adm £4, chd free. Mon 21 Apr, Sun 22 June (2-5). Visitors also welcome by appt Jan to Oct, refreshments by prior arrangement only.**

4 acres: walled garden; river, bog garden and small grotto; primulas; over 100 varieties of roses, shrub, modern and climbing; peonies; mixed and herbaceous borders; many varieties of shrubs and mature trees; lovely spring garden. Nr C13 church in beautiful valley. Most of main garden accessible to wheelchairs.

35 ◆ WELSH LAVENDER

Maesmynis, Builth Wells LD2 3HU. Nancy Durham & Bill Newton-Smith, 01982 552467, www.welshlavender.com. *Approx 4 1/2 m S of Builth Wells off B4520. Alternatively our turn is approx 12m from Brecon Cathedral off B4520.* **Adm £3.50, chd free. For NGS: Sat 26, Sun 27 July (10-7). For other opening times and information, please phone or see garden website.**

Our 10,000 lavender plants grow on a steep mid Wales hillside. 2 varieties are purely decorative. 3 others produce oil which we distil on site. Our fields are surrounded by a riot of wild flowers. At 1100ft our growing season is short and challenging. Flower beds around the house are colourful and unpredictable. A pond high in the hills was added in late summer 2012. Visitors welcome to tour the distillation room. Products produced from our lavender oil are on sale with 10% of proceeds going to the NGS. Coffee, home-made teas and light refreshments available. Featured in Country Living and on ITV's Countrywise. Limited wheelchair access but large paved area around and inside tea and sales area easy to negotiate.

Powys County Volunteers

County Organisers

South Position Vacant. Please contact Linda Ellis 01483 213911, lellis@ngs.org.uk for details

North Christine Scott, Bryn-y-Llidiart, Cefn Coch, Llanrhaeadr ym Mochnant, Oswestry SY10 0BP, 01691 780080, christinemargaretscott@yahoo.com

County Treasurer

North Gwyneth Jackson-Jones, Bryn yr Aur, Delwyn Lane, Llanfyllin SY22 5LB, 01691 648578, g.jackson-jones@tiscali.co.uk

South Position Vacant. Please contact Linda Ellis 01483 213911, lellis@ngs.org.uk for details

Publicity

North Group Captain Neil Bale, Cyfie Farm, Llanfihangel, Llanfyllin SY22 5JE, 01691 648451, info@cyfiefarm.co.uk

Assistant County Organisers

North Penny Davies, Plas Derwen, Llansantffraid, Powys SY22 6SX, 01691 828373, digbydavies@aol.com

South Shân Egerton, Pen-y-Maes, Hay-on-Wye HR3 5PP, 01497 820423, sre@waitrose.com

North Susan See-Paynton, Oerle Hall, Berriew SY21 8QX, 01686 650531, susanakeen@aol.co.uk

South Katherine Smith, Caer Beris Manor, Builth Wells, Powys LD2 3NP, 01982 552601, katherinejsmith@hotmail.com

Early Openings 2015

Plan your garden visiting well ahead – put these dates in your 2015 diary!

Gardens across the country open from early January onwards – before the new Yellow Book is published – with glorious displays of colour including hellebores, aconites, snowdrops and carpets of spring bulbs.

Bedfordshire

Sun 25 January (2-4)
King's Arms Garden

Buckinghamshire

Sun 22 February (12-4)
Quainton Gardens

Cheshire & Wirral

Sun 15 February (11-4)
Dunham Massey

Cumbria

Sun 15 February (11-4.30)
Summerdale House

Devon

Sun 1, Fri 20 February (2-5)
Cherubeer Gardens

Suns 8, 15 February (12-3.30)
Littleham House Cottage

Gloucestershire

Suns 1, 15 February (11-4)
Home Farm

Suns 15, 22 February (11-5)
Trench Hill

Sun 22 February (11-4)
Dr Jenner's House & Garden

Gwynedd

Sun 8 February (11-3)
Plas Yn Rhiw

Sat 14 February (12-3)
Penrhyn Castle

Hampshire

Fri 20, Sun 22, Tue 24 February (2-5)
Little Court

Herefordshire

Wed 21 January (11-4)
The Weir

Thurs 5, 12, 19, 26 February (9-4)
Ivy Croft

Kent

Sat 7, Sun 8 February (11-3)
Spring Platt

Suns 8, 22 February (11-3)
Knowle Hill Farm

Sun 15 February (12-4)
Copton Ash

Sun 22 February (2-5)
Mere House

Lancashire, Merseyside & Greater Manchester

Suns 1, 8, 15, 22 February (11-4)
Weeping Ash

Lincolnshire

Sat 14, Sun 15 February (11-4)
Little Ponton Hall

Sat 21, Sun 22 February (11-5)
21 Chapel Street

North East Wales

Wed 11 February (11-4)
Clwydfryn

Northamptonshire

Sun 22 February (12-5)
Jericho

Oxfordshire

Sun 22 February (1.30-4)
14 Chawley Lane

Somerset, Bristol & South Gloucestershire

Suns 1, 8 February (11-4)
Rock House

Sun 8 February (10-5)
East Lambrook Manor Gardens

Sun 15, Mon 16 February (11-4)
Sherborne Garden

Suffolk

Sun 15 February (11-4)
Gable House

Surrey

Sun 15 February (11-4)
Gatton Park

Sussex

Tues, Weds, Thurs 10, 11, 12, 17, 18, 19 February (11-4)
Pembury House

Sun 15 February (2-4.30)
Manor of Dean

Wiltshire

Wed 25, Sat 28 February (10.30-5.30)
Lacock Abbey Gardens

Yorkshire

By appt 16 to 23 February
3 Bainton Close

Wed 25 February (12-4)
Austwick Hall

Garden Index

This index lists gardens alphabetically and gives the page number on which they are to be found.

A

B

Marie Curie
Cancer Care

Help the
Hospices

D

E

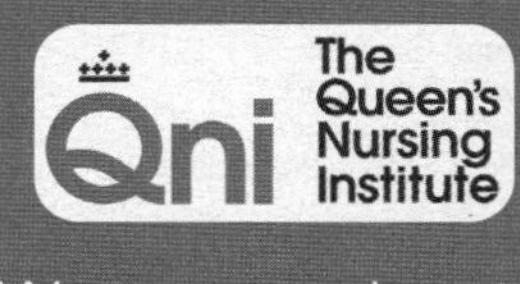
Qni
The Queen's Nursing Institute

From tiny back plots to country estates

carerstrust
action · help · advice

I

J

K

M

N

O

P

Q

R

Qni
The Queen's Nursing Institute
NGS directly supports 500 Queen's Nurses working in the community

S

T

U

V

W

PERENNIAL
Gardeners' Royal Benevolent Society
Helping Horticulturists In Need Since 1839

Accommodation available at NGS Gardens

We feature here a list of NGS gardens offering accommodation, listed by Yellow Book county. You will find contact details in the garden listing.

We are happy to provide this list to help you find accommodation, however please note:

The NGS has no statutory control over the establishments or their methods of operating. The NGS cannot become involved in legal or contractual matters and cannot get involved in seeking financial recompense. All liability for loss, disappointment, negligence or other damage is hereby excluded.

Bedfordshire

Luton Hoo Hotel Golf & Spa

Berkshire

Field Farm Cottage
Littlecote House Hotel
Rookwood Farm House
Sunningdale Park
Whitehouse Farm Cottage

Buckinghamshire

Danesfield House
Kayalami
Magnolia House, Grange Drive Wooburn
Nether Winchendon House
Westend House, Cheddington Gardens

Cambridgeshire

Chequer Cottage, Streetly End Gardens
39 Foster Road
Kenilworth Smallholding
Madingley Hall
Pavilion House

Carmarthenshire & Pembrokeshire

Blaenfforest
The Cors
Dyffryn Fernant
The Old Vicarage
Pant-y-Fedwen
Picton Castle & Gardens
Rhosygilwen Mansion
Swan Cottage
Talardd
Ty Castell
Upton Castle Gardens

Cheshire & Wirral

Tatton Park

Cornwall

The Barn House
Benallack Barn
Boconnoc
Bonython Manor
Carminowe Valley Garden
Cosawes Barton
Glendurgan
Hidden Valley Gardens
The Homestead
Trelissick
Trevoole Farm

Cumbria

Askham Hall
Eller How House
Lakeside Hotel & Rocky Bank
Langholme Mill
Matson Ground
Rydal Hall
Swarthmoor Hall
Windy Hall

Derbyshire

Tissington Hall

Devon

Avenue Cottage
Cliffe
Coombe Trenchard
The Downes
Durcombe Water
East Woodlands Farmhouse
Fursdon
Goren Farm
Hotel Endsleigh
Langtrees
Regency House
South Worden
Whitstone Bluebells
Whitstone Farm

Dorset

Deans Court
Domineys
Farrs
Holworth Farmhouse
Marren
Old Down House
Queen Ann House
The Secret Garden

Essex

Rookwoods

Glamorgan

Bryn-y-Ddafad
Gileston Manor
Slade

Gloucestershire

Barnsley House
Berrys Place Farm
Kempsford Manor
Matara Gardens of Wellbeing
The Old Coach House, Eastcombe, Bussage and Brownshill Gardens
Wells Cottage

Gwent

The Bell at Skenfrith
Brynderi
Castle House
Glangrwyney Court
Middle Ninfa Farm & Bunkhouse
Penpergwm Lodge
Usk Open Gardens

Gwynedd

Coedmor
Plas Cadnant Hidden Gardens

Hampshire

Ashen Bank, Sway Village Gardens
12 Christchurch Road
Durmast House
Four Seasons Hotel
The Mill at Gordleton
Tylney Hall Hotel

Herefordshire

Brobury House Gardens
Caves Folly Nurseries
Holme Lacy House Hotel
Kentchurch Court, Kentchurch Gardens
Lawless Hill
Little Llanavon
Montpelier Cottage
The Old Rectory, Thruxton
Wellbrook Manor
Wolferlow House

Isle of Wight

Northcourt Manor Gardens

Kent

Boldshaves
Canterbury Cathedral Gardens
Mistral, Wye Gardens
Port Lympne, The Aspinall Foundation
Rock Farm
The Secret Gardens of Sandwich at The Salutation
Sissinghurst Castle
Wickham Lodge

Lancashire, Merseyside & Greater Manchester

Mill Barn
The Ridges
Sefton Villa, Sefton Park Gardens

Leicestershire & Rutland

The Grange
Hedgehog Hall
Tresillian House

Lincolnshire

Goltho House
Gunby Hall & Gardens
Hall Farm
Hope House
Manor House
Marigold Cottage
Stoke Rochford Hall
Willow Holt

London

6 Cornford Grove
58A Teignmouth Road
West Lodge Park

Norfolk

Bagthorpe Hall
Chaucer Barn
Hindringham Hall
The Old Rectory, Ridlington
Severals Grange

North East

Broaches Farm
Gibside
Loughbrow House
Thornley House
Whalton Manor Gardens

North East Wales

Aberclwyd Manor
Bodysgallen Hall & Spa
33 Bryn Twr and Lynton
Dove Cottage
Firgrove
Golden Grove House, Llanasa Village Gardens
Maesmor Hall
Ruthin Castle, Ruthin Town Gardens
Tal-y-Bryn Farm

Northamptonshire

Dale House, Spratton Gardens

Nottinghamshire

Hodsock Priory Gardens
The Summer House, Gringley Gardens

Oxfordshire

Buttslade House, Sibford Gower Gardens
Gowers Close, Sibford Gower Gardens
Ruskin College, Headington Gardens
South Newington House
Trinity College

Powys

Caer Beris Manor Hotel
Cyfie Farm
Esgair Angell
Grandma's Garden
Gregynog Hall & Garden
Llwyn Madoc
Mill Cottage
Quarry House, Priest Weston Gardens
Treberfydd
Tyn y Cwm

Shropshire

Brownhill House
The Citadel
Edge Villa
Goldstone Hall Gardens
Marehay Farm
Sambrook Manor

Somerset, Bristol & South Gloucestershire

Binham Grange Gardens
Cherry Bolberry Farm
Church Farm House
Farndon Thatch
Hangeridge Farmhouse
Hartwood House
Honeyhurst Farm
Jacob's Loft, Glastonbury Secret Gardens
Self Realization Meditation Healing Centre Garden
Stoberry Garden
Ston Easton Park
Westbrook House

Staffordshire, Birmingham & West Midlands

Badger Hill
Colour Mill
The Trentham Estate

Suffolk

Bays Farm
Drinkstone Park
Rosemary

Surrey

Coverwood Lakes
7 Rose Lane

Sussex

Ashdown Park Hotel
Butlers Farmhouse
Follers Manor
Holly House
King John's Lodge
Lordington House
The Middle House, Mayfield Gardens
Netherwood Lodge, Chiddingly Laughton Duo
Newtimber Place
Ocklynge Manor
The Old Farmhouse
South Grange
Stane House
West Dean Gardens

Warwickshire

The Granary
Springfield House, Warmington Village Gardens

Wiltshire

Dauntsey Park, Dauntsey Gardens
The Mill House
The Pound House
Ridleys Cheer
Stourhead Garden
Whatley Manor

Worcestershire

Brook Farm
Nafford House, Eckington Gardens
Rectory Cottage, Alvechurch Gardens

Yorkshire

Austwick Hall
Basin Howe Farm
Cold Cotes
Daneswell House, Stamford Bridge Gardens
Devonshire Mill
Dowthorpe Hall & Horse Pasture Cottage
Fawley House
Four Gables
Goldsborough Hall
Holly Croft
Low Hall, Dacre Banks & Summerbridge Gardens
Low Sutton
Lower Heugh Cottage Garden
Manor Farm
Manor House
Millgate House
Rudding Park
Shandy Hall Gardens

Kentchurch Court, Kentchurch Gardens, Herefordshire

Garden Visiting Around the World

The National Gardens Scheme is without doubt the largest and oldest of its type in the world but there are others in existence. So if you are heading off on holiday and a passionate garden visitor here are the details of other schemes that you can support.

America

GARDEN CONSERVANCY

Publication Open Days Directory
W www.gardenconservancy.org
Visit America's very best rarely seen private gardens. Open Days is a national program of The Garden Conservancy, a non-profit organisation dedicated to preserving America's gardening heritage.

VIRGINIA'S HISTORIC GARDEN WEEK

April 26-May 3, 2014
Tour proceeds fund the restoration and preservation of Virginia's historic gardens.
Each spring visitors are welcomed to more than 250 of Virginia's most beautiful gardens, homes and historic landmarks during "America's Largest Open House." This 8-day statewide event provides visitors a unique opportunity to see unforgettable gardens at the peak of Virginia's springtime colour, as well as beautiful houses sparkling with over 2,000 fabulous flower arrangements created by Garden Club of Virginia members.

Australia

OPEN GARDENS AUSTRALIA

Publication Open Gardens Australia
Contact National Office
E national@opengarden.org.au
W www.opengarden.org.au
Around 500 inspiring gardens drawn from every Australian state and territory including tropical gardens, arid-zone gardens and gardens featuring Australia's unique flora.

Belgium

JARDINS OUVERTS DE BELGIQUE – OPEN TUINEN VAN BELGIË

Publication Catalogue of private Belgian Open Gardens, published annually in March
Contact Dominique Petit-Heymans
E info@jardinsouverts.be
W www.jardinsouverts.be
A non-profit organization founded in 1994. Over 200 remarkable private gardens throughout Belgium open to members. Membership (for two people) of €25 entitles you to the full-colour yearly agenda, comprising photographs, descriptions, opening dates and access plans of the gardens. Most of the proceeds from entry fees support charities chosen by garden owners.

France

JARDINS ET SANTE

E contact@jardins-sante.org
W www.jardins-sante.org
Founded in 2004, Jardins et Santé is a charitable voluntary association with humanitarian aims. Increasing numbers of gardens open each year across many regions of France. Entry often includes guided tours, exhibitions and concerts. Funds raised from visitor entry fees help finance scientific research in the field of mental illness and also contribute to developing the therapeutic role of the garden, particularly in hospitals and care centres. Every two years the Charity receives appeals from over 140 establishments seeking assistance for the creation of healing gardens. We are happy to be able to contribute towards many of these projects. Our role as information hub for the growing interest, research and activities in the field of hortitherapy is rapidly gaining momentum. Our next and 4th Symposium held under the patronage of the French Ministry of Health, will take place in Paris in November 2014. Further details can be found on our website.

Japan

THE N.G.S. JAPAN

Contact Tamie Taniguchi
E tamieta@syd.odn.ne.jp
W www.ngs-jp.org
The N.G.S. Japan was founded in 2001. Most of the proceeds from the entry fees support children's and welfare charities as nominated by owners and Japanese garden conservation. It has run a series of lectures entitled 'Lifestyle & Gardening with Charity' since 2004.

Netherlands

NEDERLANDSE TUINENSTICHTING (DUTCH GARDEN SOCIETY, NTS)

Publication Open Tuinengids, published annually in March.
E info@tuinenstichting.nl
W www.tuinenstichting.nl
Nearly 300 selected private gardens from all over Holland open on behalf of the Dutch Garden Society. This is a not-for profit organisation which was founded in 1980 to protect and restore Dutch gardening heritage consisting of gardens, public parks, urban spaces and cemeteries.

New Zealand

PRIVATE GARDENS OF NEW ZEALAND/ GARDENS TO VISIT

W www.gardenstovisit.co.nz
W www.ruralattractions.co.nz
W www.wineriestovisit.co.nz
The New Zealand websites showcase private gardens of New Zealand which also operate B&Bs and farm stays. In addition some properties can also provide venues for private and corporate hospitality and weddings. Properties may also feature plant, art and sculpture sales, picnics and fishing. Please also check the websites for details of guided, multiday garden tours. To list your event. Email: valeside@xtra.co.nz

Scotland

SCOTLAND'S GARDENS

Publication Scotland's Gardens Guide
Contact Paddy Scott
T 0131 226 3714
E info@scotlandsgardens.org
W www.scotlandsgardens.org
Founded in 1931 Scotland's Gardens facilitates the opening of Scotland's finest gardens of all sizes and kinds to the public as a means of raising money for charity. 40% of the funds raised goes to charities nominated by each garden owner whilst 60% net goes to the Scotland's Gardens beneficiaries: Maggie's Cancer Caring Centres, The Queen's Nursing Institute Scotland, The Gardens Fund of The National Trust for Scotland and Perennial.

National Plant Collections

Over 70 gardens that open for The National Gardens Scheme are guardians of a National Plant Collection, although this may not always be noted in the garden description. These gardens carry the **NCH** (National Collection Holder) symbol.
The county that appears after the garden name indicates the section of The Yellow Book where the entry can be found.

Plant Heritage 12 Home Farm, Loseley Park, Guildford, Surrey GU3 1HS. Tel: 01483 447540 Website: www.plantheritage.com

ACER (EXCL PALMATUM CVS)
Blagdon
North East

AKEBIA
190 Barnet Road
London

ALNUS
Blagdon
North East

ANEMONE (JAPANESE)
Broadview Gardens
Kent

ANEMONE NEMOROSA
Avondale Nursery
Warwickshire

ANEMONE NEMOROSA CVS
Kingston Lacy
Dorset

ARALIACEAE
Meon Orchard
Hampshire

ARUNCUS
Windy Hall
Cumbria

ASPLENIUM SCOLOPENDRIUM
Sizergh Castle
Cumbria

ASTER (AUTUMN FLOWERING)
The Picton Garden
Herefordshire

ASTER NOVAE-ANGLIAE
Avondale Nursery
Warwickshire

ASTILBE
Holehird Gardens
Cumbria
Marwood Hill
Devon

BRUNNERA
Hearns House
Oxfordshire

BUDDEJA DAVIDII CVS & HYBRIDS
Shapcott Barton Estate
Devon

BUDDLEJA
Longstock Park
Hampshire

CAMELLIAS & RHODODENDRONS INTRODUCED TO HELIGAN PRE-1920
The Lost Gardens of Heligan
Cornwall

CARPINUS BETULUS CVS.
West Lodge Park
London

CATALPA
Barton House
Warwickshire

CEANOTHUS
Eccleston Square
London

CENTAUREA
Bide-a-Wee Cottage
North East
Yew Tree House Garden & Special Perennials Nursery
Cheshire

CLEMATIS VITICELLA
Longstock Park
Hampshire

CONVALLARIA
Kingston Lacy
Dorset

CORIARIA
Crûg Farm
Gwynedd & Anglesey

CORNUS (EXCL C FLORIDA CVS)
Newby Hall & Gardens
Yorkshire

COTINUS
Bath Priory Hotel
Somerset, Bristol & South Gloucestershire

CYCLAMEN (EXCL PERSICUM CVS)
Higher Cherubeer, Cherubeer Gardens
Devon

CYDONIA OBLONGA
Norton Priory Museum & Gardens
Cheshire

CYSTOPTERIS
Sizergh Castle
Cumbria

DICENTRA
Boundary Cottage
Yorkshire

DIGITALIS
The Harris Garden
Berkshire

DRYOPTERIS
Sizergh Castle
Cumbria

EMBOTHRIUM
Bodnant Garden
Gwynedd & Anglesey

EUCALYPTUS
Meon Orchard
Hampshire

EUCALYPTUS SPP
The World Garden at Lullingstone Castle
Kent

EUCRYPHIA
Bodnant Garden
Gwynedd & Anglesey
Whitstone Farm
Devon

EUONYMUS (DECIDUOUS)
East Bergholt Place - The Place for Plants
Suffolk

EUPHORBIA
University of Oxford Botanic Garden
Oxfordshire

EUPHORBIA (HARDY)
Firvale Allotment Garden
Yorkshire

FILIPENDULA
Windy Hall
Cumbria

FRAXINUS
The Quinta Arboretum
Cheshire

GALANTHUS
Byndes Cottage
Essex

GEUM
1 Brickwall Cottages
Kent

GUNNERA
The Mowle
Norfolk

HEDERA
Erddig Hall
North East Wales

HEDERA
Ivybank, Broad Marston & Pebworth Gardens
Warwickshire

HELENIUM CVS
Yew Tree House Garden & Special Perennials Nursery
Cheshire

HELIOTROPIUM
Hampton Court Palace
London

HELIOTROPIUM ARBORESCENS CVS
The Homestead
Leicestershire

HELLEBORUS
Broadview Gardens
Kent

HEPATICA SPP & CVS (EXCL H NOBILIS VAR JAPONICA CVS)
Hazelwood Farm
Cumbria

HOHERIA
Abbotsbury Gardens
Dorset

IRIS ENSATA
Marwood Hill
Devon

JUGLANS
Upton Wold
Gloucestershire

JUGLANS (INCL REGIA CVS)
Wimpole Estate
Cambridgeshire

LABURNUM
Powis Castle Garden
Powys

LANTANA
Hampton Court Palace
London

LAPAGERIA ROSEA (& NAMED CVS)
Roseland House
Cornwall

LATHYRUS (EXCL ODORATUS CVS)
Weaver's Cottage, Streetly End Gardens
Cambridgeshire

LEUCANTHEMUM X SUPERBUM (CHRYSANTHEMUM MAXIMUM)
Shapcott Barton Estate
Devon

MAGNOLIA SPP
Bodnant Garden
Gwynedd & Anglesey

MALUS (ORNAMENTAL)
Barnards Farm
Essex

MECONOPSIS (LARGE PERENNIAL SPP & HYBRIDS)
Holehird Gardens
Cumbria

MUSCARI
16 Witton Lane
Norfolk

NERINE SARNIENSIS CVS
Bickham Cottage, Bickham Gardens
Devon

OENOTHERA SPP
The Old Vicarage, Edington Gardens
Wiltshire

OMPHALODES
Hearns House
Oxfordshire

OSMUNDA
Sizergh Castle
Cumbria

PARIS
Crûg Farm
Gwynedd & Anglesey

PATRINIA
The Hyde
Hampshire

PELARGONIUM
Ivybank, Broad Marston & Pebworth Gardens
Warwickshire

PENNISETUM
Knoll Gardens
Dorset

PENSTEMON
Froggery Cottage
Northamptonshire
Mews Cottage
Dorset

PENSTEMON CVS
Kingston Maurward Gardens and Animal Park
Dorset

PHLOMIS
Foamlea
Devon

PINUS SPP
The Quinta Arboretum
Cheshire

PODOCARPACEAE
Meon Orchard
Hampshire

POLEMONIUM, COLLOMIA, GILIA & LEPTODACTYLON (POLEMONIACEAE)
Polemonium Plantery
North East

POLYGONATUM
Crûg Farm
Gwynedd & Anglesey

POLYSTICHUM
Holehird Gardens
Cumbria

PRUNUS SATO-SAKURA GROUP
Batsford Arboretum and Garden Centre
Gloucestershire

PTEROCARYA
Upton Wold
Gloucestershire

QUEEN MARY II EXOTICKS COLLECTION
Hampton Court Palace
London

QUERCUS
Chevithorne Barton
Devon

RHAPIS SPP & CVS
Gwyndy Bach
Gwynedd & Anglesey

RHODODENDRON (GHENT AZALEAS)
Sheffield Park and Garden
Sussex

RHODODENDRON FORRESTII
Bodnant Garden
Gwynedd & Anglesey

ROSA (PRE 1900 SHRUB ROSES)
Mottisfont Abbey & Garden
Hampshire

ROSA (RAMBLING)
Moor Wood
Gloucestershire

SALVIA (TENDER)
Kingston Maurward Gardens and Animal Park
Dorset

SALVIA SPP
2 Hillside Cottages
Hampshire

SANGUISORBA
Avondale Nursery
Warwickshire

SAXIFRAGA SECT LIGULATAE SPP & CVS
Waterperry Gardens
Oxfordshire

SAXIFRAGA SUBSECT KABSCHIA & ENGLERIA
Waterperry Gardens
Oxfordshire

SIBERIAN IRIS CVS: BRITISH, AWARD WINNERS & HISTORICALLY SIGNIFICANT
Aulden Farm, Aulden Arts and Gardens
Herefordshire

SORBUS
Ness Botanic Gardens
Cheshire

SORBUS (BRITISH ENDEMIC SPP)
Blagdon
North East

STERN, SIR F (PLANTS SELECTED BY)
Highdown Gardens
Sussex

STREPTOCARPUS
Dibleys Nurseries
North East Wales

STYRACACEAE (INCL HALESIA, PTEROSTYRAX, STYRAX, SINOJACKIA)
Holker Hall Gardens
Cumbria

TULBAGHIA SPP & SUBSP
Marwood Hill
Devon

Frith Old Farmhouse, Kent

The Society of Garden Designers

Members of The Society of Garden Designers participating in the NGS in 2014.

Fellow of the Society of Garden Designers (FSGD) is awarded to Members for exceptional contributions to the Society or to the profession

Rosemary Alexander FSGD
John Brookes MBE FSGD
Denise Cadwallader FSGD
Sally Court FSGD
Roderick Griffin FSGD
Lucy Huntington FSGD
Ian Kitson FSGD
Robin Templar-Williams FSGD
Julie Toll FSGD

Member of the Society of Garden Designers (MSGD) is awarded after passing adjudication

Timothy Carless MSGD
Mhairi Clutson MSGD
Rosemary Coldstream MSGD
Chris Eves MSGD
Jill Fenwick MSGD
Jane Follis MSGD
Dawn Isaac MSGD
Arabella Lennox-Boyd MSGD
Dan Pearson MSGD
Emma Plunket MSGD
Charles Rutherfoord MSGD
Ana Sanchez-Martin MSGD
Ian Smith MSGD
Tom Stuart-Smith MSGD
Cleve West MSGD
Carol Whitehead MSGD
Barbara Hunt MSGD (retired)

Pre-Registered Member is a member working towards gaining Registered Membership

Joanne Bernstein
Selina Botham
Fiona Cadwallader
Wendy Cartwright
Louise Hardwick
Lorraine Johnson-Rosner
Jane Jordan
Sue McLaughlin
Deborah Nagan
Sue Neave
Jessica Patton
Sean Swallow
Virginia von Celsing
Pauline Weeks
Julia Whiteaway
Joanne Winn
Sue Yerburgh

Wickham House, Berkshire

Acknowledgements

Each year the NGS receives fantastic support from the community of garden photographers who donate and make available images of gardens for use in The Yellow Book and NGS publicity material. The NGS would like to thank them for their generous donations.

We also thank the garden owners who have kindly submitted images of their gardens.

Unless otherwise stated, photographs are kindly supplied by permission of the garden owner.

The Yellow Book 2014 Production Team: Elna Broe, Linda Ellis, Louise Grainger, Rachel Hick, Kali Masure, Chris Morley, Azam Parkar, George Plumptre, Jane Sennett, Georgina Waters. With special thanks to our NGS County Volunteers.

Designed by Level Partnership Ltd · Maps designed and produced by Global Mapping © The XYZ Digital Map Co · Data manipulation and image setting by Chat Noir Design, France · Printed in Italy

Published by Constable, an imprint of Constable & Robinson Ltd, 55-56 Russell Square, London WC1B 4HP
www.constablerobinson.com

A catalogue record of this book is available from the British Library

Typeset in Helvetica Neue font family

The papers used by the NGS are natural recyclable products made from wood grown in sustainable forests

ISBN 978-1-472114-42-6
ISSN 1365-0572
EAN 9 781905 942008

First published February 2014

If you require this information in alternative formats, please telephone 01483 211535 or email ngs@ngs.org.uk

South Wood Farm, Devon

COBRA
www.cobragarden.co.uk
New range of garden machinery
Available early 2014
Powered by
Kawasaki
HONDA
BRIGGS&STRATTON

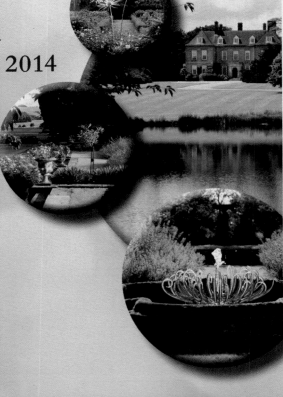